24th EUROPEAN SYMPOSIUM ON COMPUTER AIDED PROCESS ENGINEERING

COMPUTER-AIDED CHEMICAL ENGINEERING, 33

24th EUROPEAN SYMPOSIUM ON COMPUTER AIDED PROCESS ENGINEERING

PART – A

Edited by

Jiří Jaromír Klemeš
University of Pannonia, HU

Petar Sabev Varbanov
University of Pannonia, HU

Peng Yen Liew
University of Pannonia, HU

ELSEVIER

Amsterdam – Boston – Heidelberg – London – New York – Oxford
Paris – San Diego – San Francisco – Singapore – Sydney – Tokyo

Elsevier
Radarweg 29, PO Box 211, 1000 AE Amsterdam, The Netherlands
The Boulevard, Langford Lane, Kidlington, Oxford OX5 1GB, UK

First edition 2014

British Library Cataloguing in Publication Data
A catalogue record for this book is available from the British Library

Library of Congress Cataloging-in-Publication Data
A catalog record for this book is available from the Library of Congress

ISBN (Part A):   978-0-444-63456-6
ISBN (Set):   978-0-444-63434-4
ISSN: 1570-7946

For information on all Elsevier publications
visit our web site at store.elsevier.com

Contents

Synthesis and Design

Numerical and Optimisation Methodology

Dynamics and Control

Novel Computational & Numerical Methods

Design and Optimisation

Contents

Efficient Energy Integrated Solutions for Manufacturing Industries (EFENIS)

Preface

This book contains papers presented at the 24th European Symposium on Computer Aided Process Engineering, ESCAPE-24, held in Budapest, Hungary, from 15 to 18 June 2014.

The ESCAPE series constitute the major European annual event serving as global forum for academia, industry and business to present and discuss progress made in the field of Process Systems Engineering. Previous events took place in Greece (ESCAPE 21), United Kingdom (ESCAPE 22) and Finland (ESCAPE 23).

The symposia on Computer Aided Process Engineering (CAPE) have been supported by the Working Party on CAPE of the European Federation of Chemical Engineering (EFCE) since 1968. The series of ESCAPE symposia assist in bringing together scientists, students and engineers from academia and industry, which are active in research and application of CAPE.

ESCAPE 24 aims to bring together researchers and practitioners of computer aided process engineering (CAPE) community interested in advances in:
1. Synthesis and design
2. Numerical and optimisation methodology
3. Process and enterprise operations
4. Dynamics and control
5. Informatics and knowledge management

A challenging task is to broaden the boundaries of Process Systems Engineering by inviting contributions at different scales of modelling and demonstrating vertical and horizontal integration. Invited contributions range from fundamental developments at the molecular level to applications at the strategic level of the supply chain and sustainable development. The conference covered major classical themes, exploring, at the same time, a new range of applications that address the production of renewable forms of energy, environmental footprints and sustainable use of resources and water, presenting CAPE contribution to:
- Novel Computational and Numerical Methods
- Sustainability and LCA
- Efficiency in Resources and Production
- Design and Optimisation
- Process Integration

ESCAPE 24 has provided a forum for researchers and practitioners to present and evaluate emerging as well as established research methods and concepts, and to learn from industrial case studies.

This book includes 317 papers selected from 494 submitted abstracts. All papers have been reviewed by 51 members of the International Scientific Committee. The selection process involved review of abstracts, manuscripts and final acceptance of the revised manuscripts. We are very grateful to the members of International Programme Committee for their comments and recommendations. We appreciate the advice from Advisory Editors Prof Rafiqul Gani and Prof Efstratios N. Pistikopoulos. The Hungarian Chemical Society organiser, namely Dr Beáta Androsits and Ms Mónika Bondár have been praised for their logistical support. We would like to thank the ELSEVIER editorial team as well as the members of local editorial group for their support.

We believe that book will serve as a valuable reference document to the scientific and industrial community and will contribute to the progress in computer aided process and product engineering.

ESCAPE 24 Co-Chairs:
Ferenc Friedler
University of Pannonia
Jiří Jaromír Klemeš
University of Pannonia
Péter Mizsey
Budapest University of Technology and Economics

International Scientific Committee

Local Organising Committee

Chairs:

Dr Beáta Androsits, Hungarian Chemical Society
Prof Ferenc Friedler, University of Pannonia
Prof Jiří Jaromír Klemeš, University of Pannonia
Prof Péter Mizsey, Budapest University of Technology and Economics

Members:

Prof János Abonyi, University of Pannonia
Ms Mónika Bondár, Hungarian Chemical Society
Dr Tibor Chován, University of Pannonia
Dr Rozália Lakner, University of Pannonia
Mr Peng Yen Liew, University of Pannonia
Dr László Mika, Budapest University of Technology and Economics
Dr György Pátzay, Budapest University of Technology and Economics
Dr Beatrix Schenker, Hungarian Chemical Society
Dr Petar Varbanov, University of Pannonia

Jiří Jaromír Klemeš, Petar Sabev Varbanov and Peng Yen Liew (Editors)
Proceedings of the 24th European Symposium on Computer Aided Process Engineering – ESCAPE 24
June 15-18, 2014, Budapest, Hungary.

Financial Risk Analysis in the Synthesis and Design of Processing Networks: Balancing Risk and Return

Alberto Quaglia, Gürkan Sin*, Rafiqul Gani

CAPEC, Department of Chemical and Biochemical Engineering, Technical University of Denmark, DK-2800 Kgs. Lyngby, Denmark
gsi@kt.dtu.dk

Abstract

The construction of a processing network is a corporate investment, that processing companies make with the goal of creating the conditions to increase their value. In a previous work, a computer-aided framework supporting the design of processing network under uncertainty has been presented (Quaglia et al. 2013). In this contribution, we study the implications of corporate finance concepts such as funding strategies and cost of the capital on the selection of an optimal processing network. To this end, the process synthesis framework is extended to include various project funding and financial risk models. Through the solution of a small benchmark problem, the impact of financial factors on the optimal network configuration is presented and discussed.

Keywords: Synthesis and design of processing network; Capital budgeting; Mixed Integer Non Linear Programming; Financial optimization.

1. Introduction

The design of a processing network is a decision-making task consisting of the selection of raw materials, process technologies and product portfolio which maximize an optimality indicator. The results define a potential investment, which a corporation may undertake by committing resources to design, build, commission and start-up new processing plants, whose future operation is supposed to payback the investment and generate value for the company. Process Systems Engineering has developed methods and tools to support this activity, under the general framework of enterprise-wide optimization. Through these methods (based on superstructure optimization) data uncertainty (e.g. with respect to price forecasts, market volumes, etc.) is consider within the problem formulation. Most of these approaches employ the maximization of the expected value of some financial indicators (e.g. NPV, EBIT, etc.) as the main criteria for the selection/ design of the optimal investment. Other financial considerations such as investment risk, cost of capital etc. are in general not explicitly included within the design problem formulation which sets the scope for this contribution.

In this contribution, we expand a previously developed framework for synthesis and design of processing network under uncertainty (Quaglia et al. 2013), including corporate finance methods and concepts needed to fund an engineering project. In particular, the expanded framework integrates financial models to calculate the cost of project funding (generally referred to as "cost of capital"), as a function of funding strategy (debt or equity capital), financial landscape and estimated investment risk. Through this expansion, the framework is able to capture the financial aspects of the problem (such as the balance between investment risk and expected revenue) in a more realistic manner. The features of the expanded framework are highlighted through the solution of a simple example under different financial scenarios, and the impact of financial factors on the optimal solution is briefly discussed.

2. The framework for synthesis and design of processing networks

The integrated business and engineering framework for synthesis and design of processing network is a computer-aided decision-making support tool developed in an earlier work (Quaglia et al. 2013). Through the framework, the design space is represented by means of a superstructure, and the design problem is cast as a discrete optimization problem (under data uncertainty), which is solved to identify the network configuration which is feasible for every realization of the uncertain data, and whose expected objective function value is optimal.

3. Cost of capital

Corporations fund their operations through loans from banks and financial institutions (debt capital) or through investments of their shareholders (equity capital). The cost of capital is the cost associated with obtaining such a funding. In corporate finance, different models can be employed for the calculation of the cost of debt and equity capital. In general, this depends on the amount of the funding, and on a set of company specific parameters (company size and perceived financial robustness, history, etc.), market specific conditions (market liquidity, stock market volatility and average return, etc.) and expected risk/ return of the investment for which the funding is required (Patterson 1995). From a corporate finance perspective, the cost of capital represents a hurdle rate that an investment has to overcome, in order to generate value for the enterprise. Therefore, it is an important factor to consider when taking investment decisions. In the next sections, simple corporate finance models which can be used for the calculation of cost of capital will be presented, both for debt and equity capital.

3.1. Cost of debt capital
The cost of debt capital corresponds to the interest paid for the corresponding loan. Consequently, the cost of debt capital $C_{CAPITAL}$ can be calculated as:

$$C_{CAPITAL} = C(1 + r_D)^{t_L} \tag{1}$$

where C is the capital, r_D is the yearly interest rate, and t_L is the duration of the loan.

3.2 Cost of equity capital
The cost of equity capital is the return that shareholders require in order to participate in an investment, as a compensation of the risk they are exposed to (Bodie, 2008). Different theories and models have been proposed for its quantification. Among these, the Capital Market Line (CML) first proposed by Sharpe (1964) is the model which still is most commonly used among finance practitioners and actuaries. In the CML model, investment opportunities existing in the market are statistically analyzed to identify the most convenient performances (in terms of risk/ return combinations) which can be achieved for the current market conditions. The cost of equity capital is then calculated as the opportunity cost of not investing in such a market, hence ensuring that a shareholder funding the company investment will receive a return equal or greater to what could be achieved investing in the market. The CML is built as follows (Figure 2): for a market characterized by a series of risky investment i, whose return r_i is described by an elliptical distribution with expected value $E(r_i)$ and standard deviation σ_i,

different market portfolios M can be obtained as a function of investment weights w_i. Expected return and standard deviation for these portfolios M can be calculated as a function of investment weights as:

$$E(r_M) = \sum_i w_i E(r_i) \tag{2}$$

$$\sigma_M = \left(\sum_i w_i^2 \sigma_i^2 + \sum_i \sum_{i \neq j} w_i w_j \sigma_i \sigma_j \rho_{ij}\right)^{1/2} \tag{3}$$

The relation between expected return and standard deviation parametrically defined by Eqs.(2)-(3) represents the possible risk/ return performances which can be obtained from a portfolio of risky assets i, and it is called Efficiency Frontier (EF). According to modern portfolio theory (Markowitz, 1952), for rational risk-neutral investors accepting standard deviation as a definition of investment risk, the optimal market portfolio P corresponds (in the Expected return – standard deviation space) as the tangent point between the EF and a straight line passing through a risk-free investment. Such a tangent line is defined Capital Market Line (CML) and it is defined as follows (Sharpe, 1964):

$$E(r) = r_f + \sigma \frac{E(r_P) - r_f}{\sigma_P} \tag{4}$$

Where r_f is the return of a risk-free investment (e.g. government bonds from financially solid country); by definition, the standard deviation of risk-free investments equals zero. According to modern portfolio theory, the CML represents the most efficient combination between risk and revenues which can be obtained in the market (Sharpe, 1964). Therefore, all points below the CML represent non-optimal investments in the current market conditions. Hence, the CML can be used to calculate, for a given market condition, the cost of equity capital as the opportunity cost of not investing in an efficient market portfolio, as a function of investment risk (Bodie, 2008).

4. Demonstration example: the Network Benchmarking Problem

The Network Benchmarking Problem (NBP) is a small network example proposed for benchmarking and testing purposes (Quaglia et al. 2013). In Figure 1, the superstructure associated to the NBP problem is reported. The mathematical formulation of the NBP problem under data uncertainty is summarized in Table 1 (where i is the index of chemical components, kk represents the different element of the superstructure; ss is the index of Monte Carlo samples representing different future scenarios with respect to the realization of the uncertain data, and $C_{Capital}$ (Eq. 5) represents the cost of capital). For a more detailed explanation of the problem formulation, the reader is invited to refer to the above mentioned reference.

In this section, the NBP problem will be formulated and solved under market price and raw material composition uncertainty for 3 different scenarios with respect to capital funding: 1) funding through debt capital at low interest rate, 2) funding through debt capital at high interest rate and 3) funding through equity capital for current market conditions.

4.1. Scenario 1&2: Debt capital

The NBP problem is formulated for the maximization of Earning Before Interest and Taxes (EBIT) over an investment horizon of 10 years. A yearly interest of 5 % for scenario 1 (representing the conditions for a large corporation in Western Europe) and

Table 1. The mathematical formulation of the NBP problem (Quaglia et al. 2013)

Objective function

$$\max EBIT = \frac{1}{NS}\left(\sum_{i,kk,ss}\left(P3_{i,kk,ss} \cdot F_{i,kk,ss}^{out}\right) - \sum_{i,kk,ss}\left(P2_{i,kk,ss} \cdot R_{i,kk,ss}\right)\right.$$
$$- \sum_{i,kk,ss}\left(P1_{i,kk,ss} \cdot F_{i,kk,ss}^{out}\right) - W^{Price}$$
$$\left. \cdot \sum_{i,kk,ss}\left(F_{i,kk,ss}^{R} \cdot SW_{i,kk,ss}\right)\right) - \frac{CAPEX}{t} - C_{Capital} \quad (5)$$

Raw material assignment

$$F_{i,kk,ss}^{out} = \phi_{i,kk,ss} \quad \forall \, kk \in RAW \quad (6)$$

Utility consumption

$$F_{i,kk,ss}^{M} = \sum_{k}\left(F_{i,k,kk,ss}\right) + \alpha_{i,kk,ss} \cdot \mu_{i,kk,ss} \cdot \sum_{i,k}\left(F_{i,k,kk,ss}\right) \quad (7)$$

Reaction

$$F_{i,kk,ss}^{R} = F_{i,kk,ss}^{M} + \sum_{rr,react}\left(\gamma_{i,kk,rr} \cdot \theta_{react,kk,rr,ss} \cdot F_{react,kk,ss}^{M}\right) \quad (8)$$

Wastes separation

$$F_{i,kk,ss}^{out} = F_{i,kk,ss}^{R} \cdot \left(1 - SW_{i,kk,ss}\right) \quad \forall \, kk \in PROCESS \quad (9)$$

Product-product separation

$$F_{i,kk,ss}^{out1} = F_{i,kk,ss}^{out} \cdot SF_{i,kk} \,;\, F_{i,kk,ss}^{out2} = F_{i,kk,ss}^{out} \cdot \left(1 - SF_{i,kk}\right) \quad (10)$$

Superstructure flow model

$$F_{i,k,kk,ss}^{1} \le F_{i,kk,ss}^{out1} \cdot S_p \,;\, F_{i,k,kk,ss}^{2} \le F_{i,kk,ss}^{out2} \cdot \left(S - S_p\right) \quad (11)$$

$$\sum_{k}F_{i,k,kk,ss}^{1} = F_{i,kk,ss}^{out1} \,;\, \sum_{k}F_{i,k,kk,ss}^{2} = F_{i,kk,ss}^{out2} \quad (12)$$

Superstructure logic model

$$F_{i,kk,ss}^{R} \le M \cdot y_{kk} \quad (13)$$

Throughput limitations

$$\sum_{i}F_{i,kk,ss}^{R} \le F_{kk}^{MAX} \quad (14)$$

Capital cost model

$$CAPEX = \sum_{kk}\left[\sum_{j}\left(\alpha_{j,kk} \cdot w_{j,kk} + \beta_{j,kk} \cdot Q_{j,kk}\right)\right] \quad (15)$$

$$F_{kk}^{Thr} = \sum_{j}Q_{j,kk} \,;\, \sum_{j}w_{j,kk} = 1 \,;\, Q_{j,kk}^{o} \cdot w_{j,kk} \le Q_{j,kk} \le Q_{j+1,kk}^{o} \cdot w_{j,kk} \quad (16)$$

of 10 % for scenario 2 (as for a start-up company in developing countries) is considered for the calculation. The MINLP problem under uncertainty constituted by Eq. 1 and 5-16 is formulated and solved in GAMS for the 2 scenarios. The results (reported in Figure 1) show that different optimal network topologies are obtained for the 2 scenarios. In particular, the comparison among the 2 scenarios shows that, when the interest rate is increased from 5 % to 10 %, the increased interest cost leads to the selection of a network characterized by a lower capital cost, even though its operating performances (measured in terms of operating margin) are lower.

4.2. Scenario 3: Equity capital – capital market line

In scenario 3 the problem is solved for equity capital funding. In order to obtain the parameters for the cost of equity capital model (Eq. 4) the CML equation is calculated for the current market conditions. For the sake of simplicity the Standard&Poor's 500 and BRIC index have been considered as representative of the entire market, and 5 years Swiss Bonds are assumed to represent risk-free investments (see Table 2). The CML parameters are calculated according to the method described in section 3.2 for the market conditions reported in Table 2, and the corresponding CML model is:

$$E(r) = (0.904 \, \sigma + 0.0115) \quad (17)$$

Consequently, the cost of equity capital is calculated as:

$$C_{EQUITY} = CAPEX \left(1 + (0.904\,\sigma + 0.0115)\right) \tag{18}$$

The MINLP problem constituted by Eqs.(5)-(16), (18) is solved, and the optimal solution is identified (reported in Table 3 as solution #1). From a risk/ return perspective, this solution is competitive with the investment market (see Figure 2). Solution #1 is eliminated from the search space and the problem is solved again to obtain the second best solution. The procedure is repeated to identify all solutions

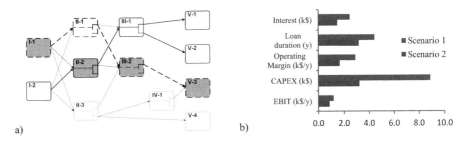

a)   b)

Figure 1. Results scenarios 1&2: a) topology (color: Scen. 1, dashed: Scen. 2); b) cost structure

Table 2. Securities data (Source: Standard and Poor Dow Jones Indices, 2013)

	Risky assets			Risk-free asset
	SP500TR	SPBRIC	Correlation	
Expected Annual return	17.54 %	19.61 %	0.639	1.15 %
Standard Deviation	22.68 %	27.80 %		0.00 %

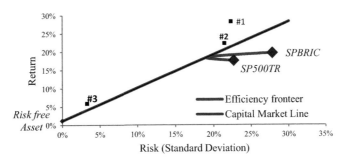

Figure 2. Capital Market Line and network solutions

Table 3. Summary of solutions - scenario 3

Solution	Results
#1 (optimal)	I-1, II-2, III-2, V-3 EBIT=1.2M$/y Risk=22%
#2	I-1, II-1, III-2, V-3 EBIT=0.9M$/y Risk=21%
#3	I-1, II-1, III-1, V-1, V-2 EBIT=0.5M$/y Risk=9%

whose performances are better than the market. As a result, 3 solutions (reported in Table 3 and Figure 1 as #1, #2 and #3) characterized by different balances between investment risk and expected return are obtained. In particular, solutions #1 and #2 are characterized by relatively high investment risk, balanced by high expected return. On the contrary, solution #3 exhibits a low risk and a low expected return.

5. Conclusions and Future Works

In this contribution, the significance of corporate finance considerations on the *optimal* design of processing networks is studied and demonstrated through the solution of a simple numerical problem under different scenarios with respect to financial conditions. The results show that for project funded through debt capital, the interest rate may influence the optimal network design. In particular for the NBP, 2 different optimal solutions are identified as a function of a 5% increase in interest rate. In the former case, the relatively low cost of capital (5%) leads to the selection of a solution with high capital cost and high operating margin. In the latter case (10% interest rate), a solution with lower capital cost and lower operating margin is selected. On the other hand, when equity capital is employed, the CML model allows quantifying the minimum return required (as function of its risk) for the designed investment in order to be competitive with the current market conditions. For the NBP problem, this approach allows to identify 3 solutions: two high-risk/ high-return networks (solution #1 and #2, with EBIT=1.2 and 0.9 M$/yr respectively) and a low-risk/ low-revenues one (#3, EBIT=0.5 M$/yr). The analysis shows that these 3 solutions represent good investments, which overperform the market (Figure 2). Therefore, the implementation of one of these 3 solutions (selected based on the attitude toward risk of the decision-maker) is suggested. The results obtained showed that different processing network topology becomes *optimal* depending on financial conditions, funding strategies, and corporate attitude toward risk, therefore highlighting the importance of including financial considerations within the processing network synthesis and design problem. Future works will focus on the application of the extended framework to industrial problems, as well as on the integration of different financial models (e.g behavioural economics) within the framework structure, in order to further extend its scope of applicability.

The authors wish to acknowledge Mr. Filippo Maggi (Interest Rate Structuring VP at Nomura) for his important contribution to the formulation of the financial problem.

References

A. Quaglia, B. Sarup, G. Sin, R. Gani, 2013, A systematic framework for enterprise-wide optimization: Synthesis and design of processing networks, Computers and Chemical Engineering, 59, 47-62.
C. Patterson, 1995, The Cost of Capital, Greenwood, Westerport.
W. Sharpe, 1964, Capital asset prices: A theory of market equilibrium under conditions of risk, Journal of Finance, 19, 425-442.
Z. Bodie, A. Marcus, A. Kane, 2008, Essential of Investments, McGraw-Hill, New York.
H.M. Markowitz, 1952, Portfolio selection, Journal of Finance, 7, 1, 77–91.
S&P Dow Jones Indeces, 2013, < eu.spindices.com>, accessed on 08-10-2013.

Jiří Jaromír Klemeš, Petar Sabev Varbanov and Peng Yen Liew (Editors)
Proceedings of the 24th European Symposium on Computer Aided Process Engineering – ESCAPE 24
June 15-18, 2014, Budapest, Hungary.

De Novo Molecular Design using a Graph-Based Genetic Algorithm Approach

Robert H. Herring III, Mario R. Eden*

Department of Chemical Engineering, Auburn University, AL 36849, USA
edenmar@auburn.edu

Abstract

The area of computer-aided molecular design has greatly influenced the rate and cost at which novel chemicals with desired attributes have been identified. As such, great effort has been invested in new methodologies which allow for the solution of larger and more complex problems of this nature. The application of genetic algorithms (GAs) is one such technique which has shown promise in the solution of large combinatorial, and highly non-linear molecular design problems. In addition, it has been shown that many molecular properties or attributes are often best characterized by a combination of descriptors with varying dimensionality. The inverse solution to property models of this nature, which entails identifying candidate molecular structures with the desired properties as defined by the given model, is often highly non-linear in nature. In addition, the use of molecular fragments, as often practiced in the de novo design of novel structures, can lead to a combinatorially large search space which becomes intractable for exhaustive solution techniques. The application of GAs provides a powerful method for the solution of these types of molecular design problems in which there are often multiple objective constraints with high computational complexity and a large search space. This approach utilizes a fragment based descriptor known as the signature descriptor, which is represented as a molecular graph, as building blocks to generate candidate solutions. The graph-based genetic operators necessary for such an approach will be outlined as well as exemplified through a case study which will highlight the advantages of this algorithm.

Keywords: Molecular Design, Genetic Algorithm, Descriptors

1. Background

1.1. Signature Descriptor

The signature descriptor is a fragment based descriptor which encodes the environment around a central atom up to a pre-defined height, *h*. An example of this is shown below:

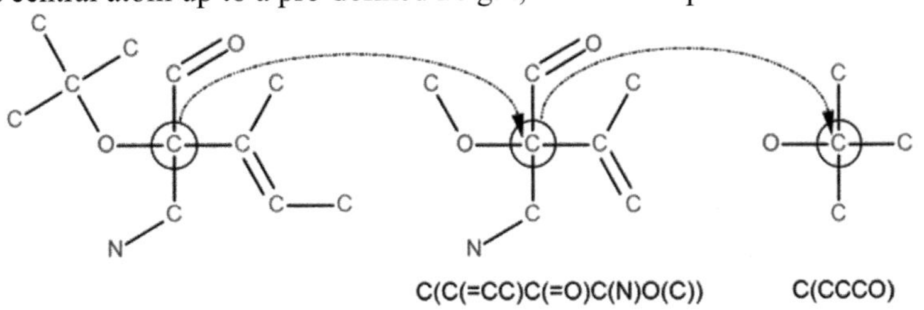

C(C(=CC)C(=O)C(N)O(C))   C(CCCO)

Figure 1. Example of height one and two atomic signatures

For the structure in Fig.(1), the height two atomic signature for the circled carbon atom includes all atoms at a distance of two bonds from this central atom. In addition, the atoms included in the height one atomic signature are shown on the right. The respective atomic signatures are also expressed below both height representations. Each atom in the molecule would have its own atomic signature and the summation of these would represent the respective molecular signature. The signature descriptor was originally developed by Visco et al. (2002) and has since proven quite useful in a variety of molecular design applications (Chemmangattuvalappil and Eden 2013; Churchwell et al., 2004; Weis et al., 2005) ranging from the design of HIV-1 protease inhibitors to hydrofluoroether foam blowing agents. This diversity of studies exemplifies the applicability of signature descriptors in a multitude of areas.

1.1.1. Spatial Signature Descriptor

Most molecular descriptors, from simple constitutional types to more complex topochemical indices, can be derived from molecular signatures. This allows one to solve existing SAR's (structure-activity relationships) in signature space, while maintaining the predictability of the original SAR along with the low degeneracy attributed to signature descriptors in enumerating potential solutions. However, the original signature representation is limited to capturing only two-dimensional information. Extension of the signature descriptor to include spatial information benefits from the efficiencies seen in previous applications while offering the discriminatory power of including descriptors of higher dimensionality in the property models utilized (Herring et al., 2012). This information is developed through molecular mechanical simulations utilized to obtain conformational geometry information about the chemical space under consideration.

1.2. Genetic Algorithm

Genetic algorithms (Holland, 1975) are a subclass of evolutionary algorithms, which mimic the process of natural selection, that encode the characteristics of an individual, in this case a potential candidate molecule, within a chromosome. The typical approach begins with a population of randomly generated individuals and the more fit members are stochastically selected to undergo computational analogues of natural recombination and mutation. This process is iterative until the resultant population possesses the desired attributes, which could be evaluated with existing quantitative structure property (activity) relationships (QSPR's) or other types of property models. One such application of an evolutionary algorithm for the fragment-based design of drug-like molecules was conducted by Kawai et al. (2013). In this study, novel inhibitors were designed based on structural similarity to an established inhibitor, which was measured with Tanimoto coefficients calculated as a function of a topological fragment based descriptor. Another study (Nicolaou et al., 2009), which has applied the technique of graph-based multi-objective evolutionary optimization, allows for the consideration of molecular similarity as well as other important properties (e.g. ADMET properties). Both of these approaches take advantage of the efficiency seen in fragment-based evolutionary algorithms; however, they do not consider three-dimensional characteristics known to be important in the design of inhibitor molecules.

2. Methodology

2.1. Spatial Signature Development

A set of molecules is chosen for an initial conformational analysis. This set can be selected such that it falls within the applicability domain for the various property models utilized. In addition, the candidate molecules generated will be within the same space since they are recombinations of the original atomic signatures. The conformational analysis captures the spatial capabilities of the subsequently generated molecular signatures and allows for a quick estimation of their three-dimensional characteristics. The Signature Translator Program (v. 3.0), developed by J.-L. Faulon, is implemented in Unix to calculate the set of canonical atomic signatures found in each conformer. The program accepts as input a .mol formatted file and the desired signature height and returns an output text file containing the respective atomic signatures. NetworkX is a Python language software package containing many modules and functions useful for the graph theoretical analysis of molecules, as well as countless other applications. This software is used to turn each atomic signature into a graph object, which represents the molecular fragment encoded within the signature. Structural isomers are quickly identified, through matching atomic signature strings, and grouped together along with the Cartesian coordinates of each atom found within the structure.

2.2. Bonding Network

NetworkX is also utilized to create a graph which stores the bonding capabilities of each atomic signature with respect to other signatures generated. Each unique atomic signature is initiated as a node within this bonding network, which initially contains no edges. The spatial information within the network is compressed by comparing all signatures stored within a node, which represents a unique structural isomer. The technique chosen for this task is to compare all pairwise distances between atoms for the given structural isomers. The absolute difference between pairwise distance values is analyzed subject to a given cutoff value. An isomorphism mapping between each pair of conformers is generated to facilitate such a comparison. Once the network has been compressed to contain a minimal amount of conformers capturing the original spatial diversity, nodes are analyzed pairwise to establish possible bonds. A bond between two atomic signatures, $^h\sigma_M(x)$ and $^h\sigma_M(y)$, is possible when the $^{h-1}\sigma_M(z)$ signature of atom z, neighboring atom x, matches the $^{h-1}\sigma_M(y)$ signature. This can also be stated, from a graph theoretical viewpoint, as a subgraph, with radius h-1 centered at an atom neighboring the x-signature center atom, being isomorphic to the radius h-1 subgraph centered at the y-signature center atom. To facilitate subsequent docking operations, used to establish a global geometry between the potentially discrepant fragment geometries, a mapping is stored within each edge. This mapping links the overlapping atoms from their respective atomic signature labeling.

2.3. Genetic Design Algorithm

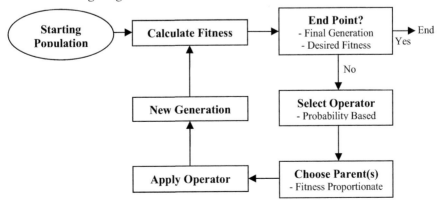

Figure 2. Algorithm Flowchart

2.3.1. Starting Population

An initial generation of molecules is selected at random to develop a population, which encompasses a variety of structural features spanning the chosen chemical space, on which to begin reproduction. The input required for this step consists of an upper and lower limit on atom count as well as a population size. For each member of the chosen population size, a target atom count is selected at random from the acceptable size range. Then a node is selected at random from the bonding network and the possible neighbor list is developed, from which the subsequent signature fragment is chosen. This process continues for a growing graph while the selection of signature fragments is a function of the current graph size. The following equation is utilized as a probability function for the selection of a signature which would either maintain graph unsaturation or effectively cap the growing molecule when nearing the desired size. In Eq.(1) P_{cap} is the probably of selecting a signature fragment which would saturate the growing graph, N_T is the target number of atoms and N_C is the current number of atoms.

$$P_{cap} = 1 - \left[\frac{(N_T - N_C)}{N_T} \right] \qquad (1)$$

This constraint helps provide a range of graph sizes for the starting population. It is possible for the probability to exceed a value of one, in which case graph growth would be immediately terminated.

2.3.2. Genetic Operators

Various genetic operators are applied to maintain diversity within the population and effectively explore the available chemical space. New techniques were developed to tackle the unique format of the problem addressed here, namely the stochastic graph based approach to a multi-dimensional molecular design problem. The two main types of operators are mutation and crossover. Within the category of mutation operators, three types were created: reduction, insertion, and fragment mutation. The probability based decision of which mutation operator to utilize is a function of the current graph size, in addition to a parameter, N_{opt}, which represents the current optimal graph size derived from previous data. N_{opt} is continuously updated as generations are analyzed and is calculated as shown in Eq.(2).

$$N_{opt} = \frac{\Sigma_i (f_i \cdot N_i)}{\Sigma_i f_i} \qquad (2)$$

Eq.(2) represents the optimal size as a function of fitness (f_i) and atom count (N_i) for all molecular graphs (i) analyzed up to that point. The fitness of each molecular graph is calculated with a Gaussian-like function over the range of desired property constraints as shown in Eq.(3).

$$f_i = exp \left(-\alpha \left[\sum_i^n \frac{(P_i - \bar{P}_i)^2}{(P_{imax} - P_{imin})^2} \right] \right) \qquad (3)$$

The selection of a mutation or crossover operation is a probabilistic event. Once this decision has been made, the parent(s) for the given operation must be chosen. This step is performed using a standard fitness proportionate selection technique where the probability of being selected is based on the relative fitness of the individual molecular graphs. Mutation operations require only one selection whereas crossover operations need two members to be chosen from the population.

Once a mutation type operation has been decided upon, the operator selection is a function of the current graph size and the optimal graph size N_{opt}, referenced in Eq.(2). Graphs within a certain percentage β of the optimal size undergo a signature mutation such that the size of the graph is preserved, while graphs above and below this range undergo reduction and insertion, respectively. Signature mutation involves the selection of a random node, which is then exchanged based on bond compatibility information available in the bonding network. Graph reduction involves the random selection of two or more bonded signatures, which is then replaced by a shorter path identified within the bonding network. Similarly, graph insertion involves the selection of a random bond between two signatures, in which a compatible signature is inserted to increase the size of the resultant molecular graph. Upon selection of the crossover operator, two parent graphs are selected from the population and are cut/recombined at compatible points just as in conventional crossover operations. For this study, only single-point crossovers were utilized. Each of these operators rely heavily on information stored within the bonding network, which is why this information is pre-calculated for the signature space developed from the initial data set.

2.3.3. Conformational Analysis
Once the graphs for each member of the population are developed, their underlying geometry is developed through conformational analysis. Each atomic signature within the graph has a set of accessible conformations, which are utilized in an iterative manner to develop a conformational ensemble for each molecular graph considered. The topographic descriptors are averaged over this ensemble to account for variations seen in geometries throughout the conformational space.

3. Case Study

The case study chosen to exemplify this approach involves the design of a molecule with a specified boiling point temperature. Basak et al. (1996) developed a structure activity relationship correlating various 2D and 3D molecular descriptors to the normal boiling point for a data set of 1023 chemicals from the Toxic Substances Control Act (TSCA) Inventory. The best fit model, shown in Eq.(4), resulted from a combination of 2D topological, 2D topochemical, and 3D descriptors with an R^2 of 0.967.

$$BP = -285.7 + 125.3(^6\chi) + 10.9(P_{10}) + 74.5(IC_0) - 125.0(^6\chi^b) - 86.3(^3\chi_C^b) + 175.3(^0\chi^v) + 49.1(^2\chi^v) + 18.7(^5\chi_{PC}^v) - 9.1(^{3D}W_H) + 8.1(^{3D}W) \tag{4}$$

3.1. Spatial Signatures from Data Set
A subset of 245 molecules was chosen from the initial 1023 utilized to develop the boiling point property model with the aim of maintaining the original variance in structural features. A conformational analysis was performed for these molecules with an acceptance criterion of each conformer being within 15 kcal/mol of the identified conformational minimum. These conformers were dissected into 194 unique height-2 atomic signatures, or structural isomers. The conformational information for each signature was further compressed by removing conformers exhibiting a similarity limited to 0.2 angstrom for each pairwise inter-atomic distance comparison.

3.2. Parameters

The parameters necessary for this design problem include a lower (10) and upper (25) bound placed on the number of atoms allowed in candidate molecular graphs. In addition the lower and upper limits on acceptable boiling points were placed at 75 and 80°C, respectively. The steady state population size was chosen to be 100 graphs and each run, of which there were 10, continued for 100 generations. The probability of mutation and crossover operators were both set to 0.5. The β variable discussed in section 2.3.2 was set to 0.15 and the Gaussian fitness decay rate, α, was set to 0.001.

4. Results and Conclusions

Each run was able to identify several solutions to the problem at hand. The average generation number after which the first solution molecular graph was identified was 12.8 and the average number of total solutions identified was 34.9. The exhaustive combinatorial search for solutions in a chemical space of this size would have been much more time consuming, whereas the genetic algorithm applied here was able to identify satisfactory solutions much more quickly. This approach could benefit from inclusion of new types of mutation operators; however, the techniques utilized here were effective in controlling the size and diversity of solutions generated. There is much work to be conducted in order to analyze the sensitivity of this approach with respect to the various parameters utilized. Future work will likely include a thorough analysis of these parameters and their effect on the run time as well as diversity and magnitude of solutions generated. In addition, studies with a more justifiable inclusion of conformational data, such as the design of inhibitors satisfying a pharmacophore model, will be considered. In conclusion, this algorithm represents a novel technique useful for the quick estimation and inclusion of conformational space data from molecular graphs within a genetic algorithm based approach.

References

S. Basak, B. Gute, G. Grunwald, 1996, A Comparative Study of Topological and Geometrical Parameters in Estimating Normal Boiling Point and Octanol/Water Partition Coefficient, J. Chem. Inf. Comput. Sci., 36, 1054-1060.

N. Chemmangattuvalappil, M. Eden, 2013, A Novel Methodology for Property Based Molecular Design using Multiple Topological Indices, Ind. Eng. Chem. Res., 52,22, 7090-7103.

C. Churchwell, M. Rintoul, S. Martin, D. Visco Jr., A. Kotu, R. Larson, L. Sillerud, D. Brown, J.-L. Faulon, 2004, The Signature Molecular Descriptor. 3. Inverse-quantitative structure-activity relationship of ICAM-1 inhibitory peptides, J. of Mol. Graphics and Modelling, 22, 4, 263-73.

R. Herring, R. Namikis, N. Chemmangattuvalappil, C. Roberts, M. Eden, 2012, Molecular Design Using Three-Dimensional Signature Descriptors, Computer Aided Chemical Engineering, 31, 225-229.

J. Holland, 1975, Adaptation in Natural and Artificial Systems, The University of Michigan Press, Ann Arbor, USA.

K. Kawai, N. Nagata, Y. Takahashi, 2014, De Novo Design of Drug-Like Molecules by a Fragment-Based Molecular Evolutionary Approach, J. Chem. Inf. Model, 54, 49-56.

C. Nicolaou, J. Apostolakis, C. Pattichis, 2009, De Novo Drug Design Using Multiobjective Evolutionary Graphs, J. Chem. Inf. Model., 49, 295-307.

D. Visco Jr., R. Pophale, M. Rintoul, J.-L. Faulon, 2002, Developing a methodology for an inverse quantitative structure-activity relationship using the signature molecular descriptor, J. of Mol. Graphics and Modelling, 20, 429-438.

D. Weis, J.-L. Faulon, R. LeBorne, D. Visco Jr., 2005, The Signature Molecular Desciptor. 5. The Design of Hydrofluoroether Foam Blowing Agents Using Inverse-QSAR, Ind. Eng. Chem. Res., 44, 8883-8891.

Jiří Jaromír Klemeš, Petar Sabev Varbanov and Peng Yen Liew (Editors)
Proceedings of the 24th European Symposium on Computer Aided Process Engineering – ESCAPE 24
June 15-18, 2014, Budapest, Hungary. Copyright © 2014 Elsevier B.V. All rights reserved.

Assessment of Solvent Degradation within a Global Process Model of Post-Combustion CO$_2$ Capture

Grégoire Léonard*, Dominique Toye, Georges Heyen

Department of Chemical Engineering, B6a Allée de la chimie, 4000 Liège Sart-Tilman, Belgium
g.leonard@ulg.ac.be

Abstract

Solvent degradation may be a major drawback for the large-scale implementation of post-combustion CO$_2$ capture due to amine consumption and emission of degradation products. However, its influence on the process operations has rarely been studied. In the present work, a kinetics model describing solvent oxidative and thermal degradation has been developed based on own experimental results for the benchmark solvent, i.e. 30 wt% monoethanolamine (MEA) in water. This model has been included into a global Aspen Plus model of the CO$_2$ capture process. The selected process modelling approaches are described in the present work. Using the resulting simulation model, optimal operating conditions can be identified to minimize both the energy requirement and the solvent degradation in the process. This kind of process model assessing solvent degradation may contribute to the design of large-scale CO$_2$ capture plants to consider not only the process energy penalty, but also its environmental penalty. Indeed, both aspects are relevant for the large-scale deployment of the CO$_2$ capture technology.

Keywords: Post-combustion CO$_2$ capture, Solvent degradation, Process modelling.

1. Introduction

In a context of growing world energy demand and environmental concerns, CO$_2$ capture, re-use and storage is one of the most promising technologies to significantly and rapidly reduce greenhouse gas emissions. Among the different CO$_2$ capture methods, the post-combustion capture is the most mature one for a large-scale deployment. It consists in an absorption – regeneration loop in which CO$_2$ from the flue gas is absorbed in an amine solvent at temperatures varying between 40 and 60 °C. The process is usually designed so that the flue gas vented to the atmosphere after absorption contains 90 % less CO$_2$. The CO$_2$-loaded solvent is regenerated in a stripper at a higher temperature (between 100 and 140 °C, depending on the solvent). The produced CO$_2$ stream is almost pure and may be valorized (applications in food industry, enhanced oil recovery…) or stored underground. The present work studies the CO$_2$ capture in coal and natural gas fired power plants.

At the operational level, Svendsen et al. (2011) have identified two main drawbacks regarding post-combustion CO$_2$ capture. First, the high energy requirement for regenerating the amine solvent leads to a decrease by about 30 % of the plant efficiency. Then, the environmental impact of the CO$_2$ capture is affected by the emissions of amine solvent and solvent degradation products. Besides the emission of potentially harmful products, solvent degradation also impacts the process operating and capital costs. Indeed, the solvent absorption capacity decreases, its viscosity and its corrosivity increase, the vapour-liquid equilibrium is modified and foaming and fouling may appear in the columns (Bedell, 2009). So far, the process energy penalty and the degradation of amine solvents have been studied separately and previously published models of the CO_2 capture process did not consider solvent degradation at all (e.g. Léonard and Heyen, 2011). Thus, the objective of the present work is to develop a model of the CO_2 capture process that assesses solvent degradation based on own experimental work, so that the influence of process operating conditions on solvent degradation may be better understood. As a result, solvent degradation could be considered more accurately during the design of CO_2 capture units, which is especially relevant for large-scale plants.

2. Experimental study

Two main solvent degradation mechanisms take place in the CO_2 capture process: oxidative degradation and thermal degradation with CO_2. However, few data were available to describe the influence of process operating conditions on solvent degradation. Because solvent degradation is a slow phenomenon, accelerated conditions are necessary to study it within a reasonable timeframe. Thus, an experimental test rig consisting in an agitated pressurized reactor with continuous gas feed has been designed for accelerating solvent degradation. Figure 1 shows this test rig which allows the degradation of solvents at temperatures up to 140 °C and pressures up to 20 bar, with flexible gas composition. Liquid degradation products are quantified using gas chromatography while the MEA content is determined by high performance liquid chromatography. Gaseous degradation products are quantified by Fourier transformed infra-red spectroscopy. The nitrogen mass balance of degradation experiments could be closed within 10 % and repeatability is demonstrated with a deviation lower than 5 %.

Various degradation experiments have been performed to study the influence of process operating variables on the degradation of 30 wt% MEA in water (benchmark solvent for CO_2 capture). Among other, the influence of the agitation rate, the temperature and the composition of the flue gas feed (varying concentrations in N_2, O_2 and CO_2) have been tested. Identified degradation pathways at lab-scale are observed to be similar to pathways observed in CO_2 capture pilot plants as evidenced in Figure 2 by the comparison of lab and industrial degraded solvent samples. The main products identified in Figure 2 have been listed in Table 1. Moreover, ammonia is the main degradation product identified in the gas phase. More details and results of the experimental degradation study are given in a previous work (Léonard, 2013).

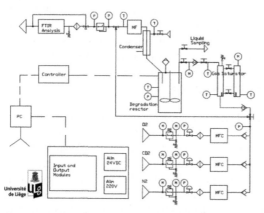

Figure 1. Degradation test rig designed and built at the University of Liège

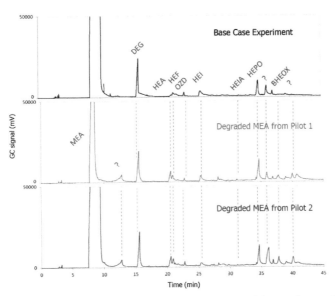

Figure 2. Comparison of the gas chromatography spectra between lab experiments (base case experiment) and degraded MEA samples from industrial pilot plants

Table 1. Main identified products by gas chromatography of degraded MEA solutions

	Compound	Formula	Structure
MEA	Monoethanolamine	C_2H_7NO	
DEG	Diethylene glycol (internal standard)	$C_4H_{10}O_3$	
HEA	*N*-(2-hydroxyethyl)acetamide	$C_4H_9NO_2$	
HEF	*N*-(2-hydroxyethyl)formamide	$C_3H_7NO_2$	
OZD	2-oxazolidinone	$C_3H_5NO_2$	
HEI	*N*-(2-hydroxyethyl)imidazole	$C_5H_8N_2O$	
HEIA	*N*-(2-hydroxyethyl)imidazolidinone	$C_5H_{10}N_2O_2$	
HEPO	4-(2-hydroxyethyl)piperazine-2-one	$C_6H_{12}N_2O_2$	
BHEOX	N,N'-Bis(2-hydroxyethyl)oxamide	$C_6H_{12}N_2O_4$	

3. Model construction

Based on the results of the degradation study, a kinetics model of MEA degradation is proposed, assuming one empirical degradation reaction for each studied degradation pathway. Since the exact reaction mechanisms of MEA oxidative degradation are still unknown, the stoichiometric coefficients of degradation products are determined from the product distribution observed in the experimental study and normalized to the degradation of one mol MEA. Although not measured in the present work, formic acid has been included to take the formation of heat stable salts into account since they have been identified in previous experimental studies (Sexton and Rochelle, 2009). The resulting apparent reaction of MEA with oxygen is represented in Equation (1) while its kinetics is given in Equation (2) according Arrhenius' equation. Regarding the thermal degradation of MEA with CO_2, degradation mechanisms are known and lead to Equation (3) with the associated kinetics from Equation (4). R is the universal gas constant (8.314 J/mol.K), T the temperature (K), and the MEA, O_2 and CO_2 concentrations are in mol/L. The values for the activation energy are given in J/mol.

$$MEA + 1.3\ O_2$$
$$=> 0.6\ NH_3 + 0.1\ C_5H_8N_2O + 0.1\ C_6H_{12}N_2O_2 + 0.1\ HCOOH + 0.8\ CO_2 + 1.5\ H_2O \tag{1}$$

$$-r_{MEA,\ Oxidative} = 5.35\ 10^5 \cdot e^{-41,730/RT} \cdot [O_2]^{1.46} \tag{2}$$

$$MEA + 0.5\ CO_2 => 0.5\ C_5H_{10}N_2O_2 + H_2O \tag{3}$$

$$-r_{MEA,\ Thermal} = 6.27\ 10^{11} \cdot e^{-143,106/RT} \cdot [CO_2]^{0.9} \tag{4}$$

This kinetics model for MEA oxidative and thermal degradation with CO_2 has been included into a global rate-based process model developed in Aspen Plus (Léonard and Heyen, 2013). This model represents the pilot plant described by Knudsen et al. (2011), treating a flue gas flow rate of 5000 Nm³/h. In order to integrate the degradation into the CO_2 capture process, different process modelling assumptions have been considered. First, the degradation reactions have been included into a steady-state model since dynamic simulations are not adapted to describe small modifications over long time scales (several months). Then, the degradation reactions have been considered to take place in the absorption and stripping columns, which better reflects the actual process operating conditions. Degradation in other process equipment has been neglected. Moreover, the degradation model has been designed without any purge or MEA make-up stream. These streams were initially present in the model, but since the degradation rates are very low, accumulating degradation products did not prevent the simulation from converging even in the absence of purge and make-up streams. This implies that the calculation converges although the tear streams of the solvent loop are not rigorously in mass balance. As a consequence, degradation rates are quantified by the formation of degradation products in the mass transfer columns since column reactions are precisely calculated by Aspen Plus at the contrary of solvent loop concentrations. Finally, the degradation products appearing in the degradation reactions had to be specified in Aspen Plus. Component data for NH_3 and HCOOH have been retrieved from Aspen Plus databases. However, no data were available for the other organic degradation products, but they could be estimated by Aspen Plus based on their molecular structure. In a first approach, these components have been defined as non-volatile to facilitate the liquid-vapor equilibria calculations. Considering the high molecular weights of these components, this non-volatility assumption appears relevant.

4. Simulation results

The main observations reported for the base case configuration of the degradation model are listed in Table 2. Ammonia and HEIA production rates have been reported, since ammonia is the main product of MEA oxidative degradation and HEIA the main product of the MEA thermal degradation with CO_2. The model confirms that oxidative degradation in the absorber is the main cause for solvent loss in CO_2 capture plants. It also confirms that ammonia emissions at the absorber outlet are one of the major environmental issues of this technology (Mertens et al., 2013). The amount of degraded

MEA observed in the model is in the same order of magnitude compared with CO_2 capture plant results, although the predicted values are lower. Indeed, the total MEA loss equals 0.082 kg MEA/t CO_2 and recent pilot plant results (Moser et al., 2011) report a degradation rate of 0.284 kg MEA/t CO_2 in the absence of degradation inhibitors. This difference may be due to two assumptions done in first-approach, which are to neglect the presence of SO_X and NO_X contaminants in the flue gas, and to neglect the presence of dissolved metals in the solvent solution as well. Since all these components are known to increase the degradation rate (Sexton and Rochelle, 2009), they should be considered in further model developments.

Using the developed model, the influence of process operating variables on the energy and the environmental penalties of the CO_2 capture process can be quantified. The solvent flow rate and concentration, the stripper pressure and the oxygen concentration in the flue gas are varied. The largest energy savings are observed when increasing the stripper pressure and the solvent concentration, while the most significant increases of the MEA consumption are due to the increased oxygen concentration in the flue gas and to the higher solvent concentration. An example of such result is represented in Figure 3. It appears that increasing the MEA concentration from 30 wt% to 40 wt% reduces the reboiler heat duty by 4 % from 3.64 to 3.49 GJ/t CO_2. However, it also doubles the MEA loss from 0.082 up to 0.175 kg/t CO_2, so that concentrated MEA is not an advantageous solvent except if degradation inhibitors are added to the solvent solution. Finally, two process improvements are tested (absorber intercooling and lean vapour compression) that both reduce the total process energy requirement with no significant influence on solvent degradation. Combining these two improvements with optimal operating conditions leads to a reduction of the process energy requirement by 12 % at equivalent solvent consumption rate. The corresponding energy requirement of the CO_2 capture process is evaluated to 3.1 GJ/t CO_2, with a resulting MEA consumption of 78 g MEA/t CO_2.

Table 2. Degradation and emission results for the degradation model

Parameter	Unit	Absorber	Stripper	Total
MEA degradation	kg/t CO_2	8.2e-2	1.4e-5	8.2e-2
NH_3 formation	kg/t CO_2	1.4e-2	8.4e-7	1.4e-2
HEIA formation	kg/t CO_2	1.1e-5	1.1e-5	2.2e-5
MEA emission	kg/t CO_2	8.7e-4	9.4e-9	8.7e-4
NH_3 emission	kg/t CO_2	9.5e-3	3.0e-3	1.3e-2
Top stage liquid temperature	°C	57.4	96.6	-
Bottom stage liquid temperature	°C	51.1	115.6	-
Top stage vapor O_2 content	mol%	6.3	9.6e-3	-
Bottom stage vapor O_2 content	mol%	6.1	7.0e-14	-

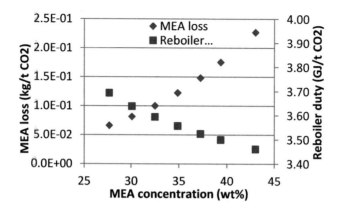

Figure 3. Influence of the MEA concentration on the process energy and environmental penalties

5. Conclusions

The present work may be considered as a first step for assessing both solvent degradation and energy requirement in CO_2 capture plants. This methodology that has been developed for the case of MEA in CO_2 capture conditions may be extended to alternative promising solvents, like piperazine for instance. This kind of model could and should be used for the capture plant design to consider not only the process energy penalty, but also its environmental penalty. Indeed, both aspects are particularly relevant in case of large-scale deployment of the CO_2 capture technology. Further modelling perspectives may consider the catalytic effect of dissolved metals on solvent oxidative degradation and the presence of SO_x and NO_x contaminants in the power plant flue gas.

Acknowledgements

The authors would like to thank the Belgian Fund for Scientific Research (FRIA-FNRS) and the company Laborelec (GDF SUEZ group) for the financial and technical support.

References

S. Bedell, 2009, Oxidative degradation mechanisms for amine in flue gas capture, Energy Procedia, 1, 771-778.

J. Knudsen, J. Andersen, J. Jensen, O. Biede, 2011, Evaluation of process upgrades and novel solvents for the post combustion CO_2 capture in pilot-scale, Energy Procedia, 4, 1558-1565.

G. Léonard, G. Heyen, 2011, Modeling post-combustion CO_2 capture with amine solvents, Computer Aided Chemical Engineering, 29, 1768-1772.

G. Léonard, C. B. Mogador, S. Belletante, G. Heyen, 2013, Dynamic modelling and control of a pilot plant for post-combustion capture, Computer Aided Chemical Engineering, 31, 451-456.

G. Léonard, 2013, Optimal design of a CO_2 capture unit with assessment of solvent degradation, PhD Thesis, University of Liège, Belgium.

J. Mertens, H. Lepaumier, D. Desagher, M.-L. Thielens, 2013, Understanding ethanolamine (MEA) and ammonia emissions from amine based post combustion carbon capture: Lessons learned from field tests, International Journal of Greenhouse Gas Control, 13, 72-77.

P. Moser, S. Schmidt, K. Stahl, 2011, Investigation of trace elements in the inlet and outlet streams of a MEA-based post-combustion capture process - Results from the test programme at the Niederaussem pilot plant, Energy Procedia, 4, 473-479.

A. Sexton, G. Rochelle, 2009, Catalysts and inhibitors for oxidative degradation of monoethanolamine, International Journal of Greenhouse Gas Control, 3, 704-711.

H. Svendsen, E. Essen, T. Mejdell, 2011, Carbon dioxide capture by absorption, challenges and possibilities, Chemical Engineering Journal, 171, 718-724.

Jiří Jaromír Klemeš, Petar Sabev Varbanov and Peng Yen Liew (Editors)
Proceedings of the 24th European Symposium on Computer Aided Process Engineering – ESCAPE 24
June 15-18, 2014, Budapest, Hungary.

A Cyclin Distributed Cell Cycle Model in GS-NS0

David G. García Münzer,[a*] Margaritis Kostoglou,[b] Michael C. Georgiadis,[c]
Efstratios N. Pistikopoulos,[a] Athanasios Mantalaris[a]

[a]*Biological Systems Engineering Laboratory, Centre for Process Systems Engineering,
Department of Chemical Engineering, Imperial College London, London SW7 2AZ, UK*
[b]*Department of Chemistry, Aristotle University of Thessaloniki, Thessaloniki 54124
Greece*
[c]*Department of Chemical Engineering, Aristotle University of Thessaloniki,
Thessaloniki 54124 Greece*
dgarciam@ic.ac.uk

Abstract

Mammalian cell factories are typically complex production systems as productivity and
product quality are controlled by a large number of coordinated metabolic reactions
influenced by culture parameters. The cell cycle is at the centre of cellular growth,
death, and productivity, which varies during the different cell cycle phases. In order to
rigorously capture the cell cycle heterogeneity, utilization of biomarkers is required.

Herein, we present, for the first time, a biologically accurate and experimentally
supported cell cycle model for the GS-NS0 cell line. In order to develop the model, the
cell line's cell cycle blueprint was elucidated by studying the timing of expression of
two cyclins (E and B) and cell cycle proliferation times by flow cytometry. The
formulated model is hybrid consisting both on unstructured and structured elements.
The cell cycle is segregated/structured by using a multistaged (G_1/G_0, S, G_2/M) and
multivariable (cyclin E, DNA and cyclin B) PBE, and it is coupled to an unstructured
metabolic model. A model approximation and discretization solution is implemented
making it unconditionally stable, fully conservative and computationally tractable
(solution time ~ 4 s).

Keywords: mammalian cell modelling, cell cycle, monoclonal antibodies.

1. Introduction

Monoclonal antibodies (mAb) are a key growing section of the high value biopharmaceuticals (biologics) market. The cells are complex mAb production facilities,
which are structured from its physical compartmentalization and chemical structure, up
to the regulatory pathways - including its cyclic proliferation. The cell productivity has
been reported to be cell cycle, cell line and promoter dependent (Alrubeai and Emery,
1990). The cell cycle is divided in sequentially distinctive phases: G_1 (first gap), S
(synthesis), G_2 (second gap) and M (mitosis). Progression between the G_1/S checkpoint
has been reported to be regulated by two cyclins, cyclins D and E. Similarly, cyclin B is
reported to regulate the cell's entrance into mitosis (Darzynkiewicz et al., 1996).

Despite the plethora of models and advancement on modelling techniques, the inclusion
of segregation still remains a challenge. Two main challenges have limited the inclusion
of segregation (both at the biophase and cell level) in cell culture mathematical models:
1) experimental validation and 2) computational tractability. In the past two decades, the

advancement of analytical techniques, have allowed to discriminate the cell culture to the population level. Particularly, techniques such as flow cytometry allow studying the physiological state of individual cells and distribution of populations on the different phases of the cell cycle.

A major shortcoming of segregated cell cycle models is the use of mass (Karra et al, 2010), volume or age - weakly biologically supported - as the distributed variable for the cell cycle transition in mammalian cells. More structured models have introduced additional biological detail, but have failed to provide experimental validation. Although relevant studies have helped to address numerical difficulties and have highlighted its potential use as an optimization tool; others have shown the computational intensive issues of attempting to capture mammalian cell complexity by coupling a population balance equation (PBE) to a single cell model. Consequently, inclusion of segregation still remains a challenge.

An experimentally supported GS-NS0 cell cycle blueprint was derived by studying the timing of expression of two cyclins (E and B) and the cell cycle in the GS-NS0 cell line by flow cytometry. Herein, we present for the first time, the development of a cyclin distributed cell cycle model based on the experimental blueprint.

2. Experimental set-up and Mathematical model

2.1. Experimental Setup

2.1.1. Batch Cell Culture

GS-NS0 cells (kindly provided by Lonza) were cultured in triplicate in 1L Erlenmeyer flasks (Corning) with 200 mL working volume. Cultures were carried out in a NU-5500E (Triple Red, UK) CO_2 incubator with a temperature set of 37 °C and controlled CO_2 concentration in the air at 5 % (V/V). The media contained: Glutamine Free Advanced-DMEM (Invitrogen Ltd.), MEM-Vitamins (Gibco) X2, Non-Essential Amino Acids (Sigma Aldrich, UK) X1, MEM-Amino Acids (Gibco) X2, GS-Supplement (SAFC) X2, Penicillin/Streptomycin (Gibco) X1, 4.5 g/L MSX (Sigma-Aldrich Ltd., UK) and 10 % (V/V) Fetal bovine serum (Gibco). The culture flasks were set on a Stuart SSL1 orbital shaker (Bibby Scientific, UK) operating continuously at 125 rpm.

2.1.2. Cell Cycle Arrest Experiment

Two arrest experiments were performed: Thymidine and dimethyl sulfoxide (DMSO). Details of the experimental setup, sampling, cyclins' sample preparation/quantification, metabolites and antibody quantification have been reported (García Münzer et al., 2013).

2.1.3. Proliferation Assay

Cells in mid-exponential growth were exposed for 3 h to 30 uM of 5-ethynyl-2´-deoxyuridine (EdU, Invitrogen C10419). After the exposure, the cells were washed twice with PBS and re-suspended in the standard growth media (in the absence of EdU) and culture in batch mode for 5 days. In parallel a control experiment took place, including all the centrifugation and washing steps but without exposing the cells to EdU. Samples were taken every 2 h for the first 28 h and every 24 h afterwards. Sample preparation for EdU detection is the same as for the cyclins. Before staining for the cyclins, the incorporated EdU was detected by preparing the reaction cocktail following the vendor directions. Then the cells were washed twice with PBS and the cyclin staining was performed as reported (García Münzer et al., 2013). In addition, unexposed cell samples were used as negative controls, as well as single stained samples for colour compensation. A BD LSRFortessa flow cytometer was used. Flow cytometry data was acquired as reported and the EdU was detected with an excitation wavelength laser 633nm laser for Alexa647 collected with a 670/14 filter.

2.2. Mathematical Model

The proposed model is cyclin distributed for the lumped phases (G_1/G_0) and G_2/M, and is DNA distributed for the S phase as presented in Eq.(1).

G_1/G_0 phase:

$$\frac{\partial N_{G1}(cycE,\,t)}{\partial t} + \frac{\partial r_{G1}(cycE,S)N_{G1}(cycE,t)}{\partial cycE} = -\Gamma_{G1}(cycE)N_{G1}(cycE,t)$$

$$-k_d(S)N_{G1}(cycE,t) + 2\delta(cycE)\int_{cycB_{min}}^{cycB_{max}} \Gamma_{G2}(cycB,S)N_{G2}(cycB,t)\,dcycB \qquad (1)$$

S phase:

$$\frac{\partial N_S(DNA,t)}{\partial t} + \frac{\partial r_S(DNA,S)N_S(DNA,t)}{\partial DNA} = \Gamma_{G1}(cycE)N_{G1}(cycE,t) - k_d(S)N_S(DNA,t)$$

G_2/M phase:

$$\frac{\partial N_{G2}(cycB,t)}{\partial t} + \frac{\partial r_{G2}(cycB,S)N_{G2}(cycB,t)}{\partial cycB}$$
$$= -\Gamma_{G2}(cycB)N_{G2}(cycB,t) - k_d(S)N_{G2}(cycB,t) + \delta(cycB)r_S(DNA,S)N_S(2,t)$$

The number distribution ($N_{i=G1,S,G2}$) is the number of cells distributed on a variable for each phase. The PBM make use of the experimentally derived cyclin transition intensity functions, see Eq.(2). Cyclin E (key for the transition from G_0/G_1 to S phase), DNA (key for the transition between S phase and G_2/M) and cyclin B (key for the transition between G_2/M phase to G_0/G_1). The cyclins and DNA growth functions are glucose dependant, where Glc represents the extracellular glucose and K_{Glc} the glucose affinity.

Cyclin/DNA growth functions:
$$r_{i=G1,S,G2}(i,S) = Cte\frac{Glc^n}{K_{Glc}{}^n + Glc^n} \qquad (2)$$

Cyclin transition functions:
$$\Gamma_{i=G1,G2}(i,S) = \begin{cases} 0, & below\ threshold \\ Constant, & above\ threshold \end{cases}$$

The different populations are calculated as follows, see Eq.(3).The PBM is coupled to a metabolic model in order to fully represent the system. The model works under the standard operating assumption of perfect mixing within the flasks and is presented in batch operation mode. The total balances on viable (X_V) and dead (X_D) cells are given by Eq.(4).

Phase populations:
$$Phase_{i=G1,S,G2} = \sum_{i=0}^{Phasemax} N_{Phase} \qquad (3)$$

Total:
$$Total = G_1 + S + G_2$$

Viable cells:
$$X_V = \frac{Total}{V} \qquad (4)$$

Dead cells:
$$\frac{d(VX_D)}{dt} = X_V k_d V - X_D k_{lys} V$$

Respectively, the specific death rate (k_d) is linked to the toxic extracellular presence of lactate (Lac) with an inhibition constant (K_{lac}) and the lysis specific rate (k_{lys}) which is assumed to be constant. The specific growth rate (μ) is composed of two terms: 1) glutamate (Glu) component (μ_{Glu}) –for ATP synthesis and 2) cyclin times component (μ_{Glc}) – for biosynthesis, see Eq.(5).

Specific growth rate: $\mu = \mu_{Glu} + \mu_{Glc}$ (5)

$$\mu_{Glu} = \mu_{GluMAX} \frac{Glu^p}{K_{Glu}{}^p + Glu^p}$$

$$\mu_{Glc} = (1 - Q_{met}) \frac{\ln(2)}{t_{G1} + t_S + t_{G2}}$$

Specific death rate: $k_d = \dfrac{k_{dMAX}}{1 + \left(\dfrac{K_{lac}}{Lac}\right)^m}$

The average cyclin times ($t_{i=G1,S,G2}$) are calculated from the PBM based on the cyclin E, DNA and cyclin B growth functions (which are glucose dependant as shown Eq.(2). The nutrient, metabolite and antibody balances are shown in Eq.(6).

Nutrient/Metabolite: $\dfrac{dS}{dt} = -\dfrac{\mu}{Y_S} X_V V$ (6)

Antibody: $\dfrac{dmAb}{dt} = \left(\dfrac{\mu}{Y_{mAb}} + m_{mAb}\right) X_V V$

Where S represents glucose, glutamate, and lactate; $Y_{S,mAb}$ is the yield on biomass of a component and m_{mAb} is the non-growth associated antibody production.

3. Results and Discussion

From the arrest experiments the average cyclin expression profiles, timings, and thresholds were elucidated (García Münzer et al., 2013). Cyclin E showed a clear pattern being expressed approximately 10 % higher in G_1 compared to G_2 phase and decreased through S phase. Similarly, cyclin B showed a clear cell cycle phase-specific expression starting in the S phase and increasing during G_2 phase where it was approximately 40 % higher when compared to G_1 phase.

Further, from the proliferation assay the cell cycle average timings can be estimated (cell cycle doubling time: 19±3 h, average traversing time for G_1/G_0 and G_2/M lumped phases: 5±1 h, and S phase :9±1 h). By combining the cyclin thresholds with the cycle phases average times is possible to formulate piece-wise linear functions representative of the cyclin and DNA growth. The transition threshold is captured by assigning a step transition probability function. The cyclins' patterns and cell cycle timings combined allow establishing the cell line's cell cycle blueprint.

All model simulations were implemented in the advanced process modelling environment gPROMS®. Based on the form of the cyclin growth and DNA growth (i.e. constant) an approximation on the S phase is performed. The approximation relies on rather than distributing the S phase in two domains (cyclin B and DNA -biologically accurate), it is only distributed on DNA (as herein presented). Then, the system of integrodifferential Eqs.(1-3) is replaced by a system of ordinary differential equations by applying a first order discretization in the cell content space. Low order discretization is the best approach since it can trivially accommodate discontinuities in growth and transition functions. The larger number of resulting ordinary differential equations compared to higher order discretization techniques is not really a problem given the low total computational effort needed for the implementation of the model. The model approximation and discretization solution proposed makes it unconditionally stable, fully conservative, and computationally tractable (solution time ~4 s). The model predictive capabilities, prior to parameter estimation are presented in Figure 1 for two experiments. The model satisfactorily predicts the cell growth, including the lag phase, cell peak and the mAb productivity (Figure 1a/d). Similarly, both substrates (glucose, glutamate) consumption trends are predicted (Figure 1b/e), whereas the lactate production (not shown) was underpredicted at early stages. The cell cycle distributions trends were captured in both cases as presented in Figure 1c/f.

The results of our model indicate that the cyclin initial distribution play an important role on the cell cycle distributions attainable, confirming the biological relevance for the transitions. Moreover, the ability to capture the lag phase is linked to the initial cyclin distribution, as it does play a role directly on the time required for the cells to resume proliferation. The cyclin simulated distributions (not shown) fitted the experimental derived blueprint. The cell distribution in each respective cyclins domains correlates with the experimental data without the need of establishing a deterministic transition between G_1/G_0 and S phases (for cyclin E) or G_2/M to G_1/G_0 (for cyclin B). In order to identify significant model parameters, Global Sensitivity Analysis (GSA) was performed as proposed on the model development framework (Kiparissides et al., 2011).

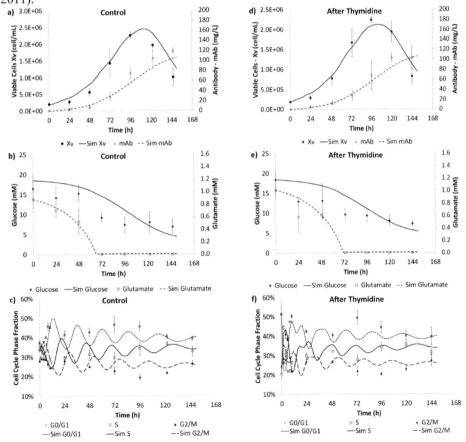

Figure 1. Batch culture profiles. Viable cells and mAb: a), d). Glucose/Glutamate: b), e). Cell cycle phases: c), f).

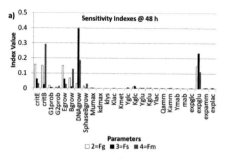 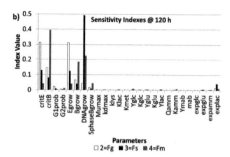

Figure 2. GSA for the cell cycle phases: G_1/G_0 (Fg), S (Fs), G_2/M (Fm). a) At 48 h, b) At 120 h.

The Sobol method was employed for the GSA and varying the 26 parameters ±20 % at 4 time points (12, 48, 84, 120 h). Such analysis facilitates the identification of significant parameters that should be re-estimated to minimize the output (e.g. viable cells, cell cycle fractions -Figure 2- and antibody titre) uncertainty. The significant threshold is an empirical choice (usually between 0.1-0.3). If a threshold of 0.1 is selected, only 9 of the 26 parameters are significant throughout the culture. The subset of significant parameters should be re-estimated to improve the model predictive capabilities. Moreover, the GSA did not find significant the transition probability parameters throughout the culture for all the outputs. Nonetheless, it did consistently identify as significant the cyclins' thresholds and the cyclin/DNA growth rates.

4. Conclusions and Future work

The model captures the complexity of the system – based on biologically relevant markers that are experimentally validated – and allows including significant cell structured features such as apoptosis, energy utilization, and metabolic requirements, among others. The next step is to include cell cycle dependant production profiles – providing a platform for a quantitative study between the cell cycle and productivity. Ultimately, the development of these models will allow the development of optimal operating policies for the improvement of productivity and potentially product quality.

Acknowledgements

The authors are thankful for the financial support from the MULTIMOD Training Network, European Commission, FP7/2007-2013, under the grant agreement No 238013 and to Lonza for generously supplying us the GS-NS0 cell line.

References

M. Alrubeai, A. N. Emery, 1990, Mechanisms and Kinetics of Monoclonal-Antibody Synthesis and Secretion in Synchronous and Asynchronous Hybridoma Cell-Cultures, Journal of Biotechnology, 16, 1-2, 67-86.

Z. Darzynkiewicz, J. Gong, G. Juan, B. Ardelt, F. Traganos, 1996, Cytometry of Cyclin Proteins, Cytometry, 25, 1-13.

S. Karra, B. Sager, M.N. Karim, 2010, Multi-Scale Modeling of Heterogeneities in Mammalian Cell Culture Processes, Industrial & Engineering Chemistry Research, 49, 17, 7990-8006.

D.G. García Münzer, M. Kostoglou, M.C. Georgiadis, E.N. Pistikopoulos, A. Mantalaris, 2013, Developing a Cyclin Blueprint as a Tool for Mapping the Cell Cycle in GS-NS0, Biochemical Engineering Journal, DOI: 10.1016/j.bej.2013.10.008.

A. Kiparissides, M. Koutinas, C. Kontoravdi, A. Mantalaris, E.N. Pistikopoulos, 2011, 'Closing the loop' in biological systems modeling - From the in silico to the in vitro, Automatica, 47, 1147-1155.

Jiří Jaromír Klemeš, Petar Sabev Varbanov and Peng Yen Liew (Editors)
Proceedings of the 24th European Symposium on Computer Aided Process Engineering – ESCAPE 24
June 15-18, 2014, Budapest, Hungary.

The Good, the Bad, and Your Real Choices – Decision Support for Energy Systems Synthesis through Near-Optimal Solutions Analysis

Philip Voll,[a] Mark Jennings,[b] Maike Hennen,[a] Nilay Shah,[b] André Bardow,[a*]

[a]*Institute of Technical Thermodynamics, RWTH Aachen University, Schinkelstr. 8, 52062 Aachen, Germany*
[b]*Centre for Process Systems Engineering, Department of Chemical Engineering, Imperial College London, South Kensington Campus, London SW7 2AZ, United Kingdom*
andre.bardow@ltt.rwth-aachen.de

Abstract

An optimisation-based decision support methodology is proposed for the synthesis of energy supply systems. Given that mathematical models never perfectly represent the real world and that decision makers are often not aware of all practical constraints, the mathematically optimal solution is usually only an approximation of the real-world optimum. Therefore, in this paper, a synthesis approach is proposed that supports the decision maker through the generation of a set of near-optimal solution alternatives, which can be evaluated in more detail a posteriori. We study two very different synthesis problems at the district and the industrial scale. In both test cases, rich near-optimal solution spaces are identified that exhibit practically identical objective function values. Considering the many uncertainties and constraints arising in practice, a ranking of the generated solutions based on a single objective function value is not significant. Instead, the near-optimal solutions are analysed to support the synthesis process by extracting common features and differences. The obtained information provides deeper understanding of the synthesis problem enabling engineers to reach more rational synthesis decisions.

Keywords: distributed energy systems, synthesis, optimisation, near-optimal solutions.

1. Introduction

The synthesis of energy supply systems is a complex task that needs to be addressed on three levels (Frangopoulos et al., 2002): At the synthesis level, the equipment configuration and the network layout is specified; at the design level, the technical specifications of the employed equipment are determined; finally, at the operational level, the operating strategies are defined. Optimisation-based synthesis methods enable practitioners to consider all three levels simultaneously by searching for the one solution minimising (or maximising) the objective function (Liu et al., 2011). For nonlinear problems, the optimization problem might suffer from many local minima (Urselmann et al., 2011). However, even a global optimum has only limited significance considering that:

1. optimisation models generally only approximate the real-world situation,
2. the constraints (e.g., energy tariffs and demands) usually change in the future, and

3. the analysis of a single solution does not provide any information on its robustness, i.e., on the "must haves" of good solutions and the rational decision options (the "real choices") of possible alternatives.

For these reasons, in this paper, we propose to generate and analyse a set of promising solution alternatives rather than focusing on the single optimal solution only.

2. Decision support through near-optimal solutions analysis

We aim at supporting the design process by exploring the near-optimal solution space in order to identify structurally different solution alternatives. For this purpose, we employ integer-cut constraints (Raman and Grossmann, 1991).

The basic concept of this approach is to solve a series of optimisation models in order to systematically generate a ranked set of solutions; for each optimisation, a constraint is added on the integer variables excluding already known solutions from consideration. The generated solutions are then compared to identify common features and differences among the solutions. The common features can be interpreted as "must haves" of good solutions; the differences represent rational decision options (the "real choices") between which the designer can choose to respond to practical constraints not reflected in the model. The basic concept has been introduced in a conference paper by Voll et al. (2013a), however, for one specific model only. In this paper, we analyse very different energy systems synthesis problems from the field of industrial (section 2) and district energy systems (section 3). We find that the near-optimal solutions behaviour is not unique for the one problem analysed before; instead, the analysis enriches the design procedure for very different synthesis problems. In section 4, the paper is summarised and conclusions are drawn.

3. Industrial synthesis problem

The industrial case study is an energy systems retrofit problem taken from the pharmaceutical industry. The considered site spans an estimated total floor area of 0.04 km^2 comprising twenty-one buildings. The site is separated by a public road into sites A and B. The existing heating network transfers hot water between both sites. In contrast, the cooling network is located on site A only and it cannot be extended to site B due to the public road. The base case system incorporates three boilers, one CHP engine, and three compression chillers. For retrofit synthesis, the optimisation framework TOP-Energy/eSynthesis is employed that features algorithms for automated model generation and optimisation (Voll et al., 2013b). For optimisation, the net present value is maximised assuming a cash flow time of 10 years and a discount rate of 8 %. For this case study, rather detailed equipment models are employed reflecting economy of scale of equipment investments, continuous equipment sizing, part-load dependent operating efficiencies, and minimum operation loads. The equipment available for retrofit constitutes modern boilers, CHP engines, compression and absorption chillers. The underlying demands for heating and cooling are modelled by monthly-averaged demand time series plus two further time steps representing the minimum and maximum demands. The layout of the heating and cooling networks is neglected. A detailed description of the equipment and system model is given by Voll et al. (2013b).

3.1. Optimal solution
The optimal solution includes already existing and newly installed equipment (Figure 1). The net present value is improved by 39 % compared to the base case. In the

optimal solution, one of the base case boilers is kept and two new CHP engines are installed. The boiler is reserved to meet heating peak-loads in winter. Cooling on site A is generated by one base case turbo-chiller, two new compression chillers, and one new absorption chiller. Cooling on site B is provided by two new compression and one new absorption chillers.

3.2. Near-optimal solution alternatives

By sequentially introducing integer-cut constraints, a rich near-optimal solution space is observed for the industrial case study. The ten best solutions differ with regard to their objective function values by less than 0.2 %. For illustration, the 5th and 10th best solutions are discussed in more detail focusing on their structural characteristics (Figure 2): Both solutions are similar with respect to the heating systems, however they differ with regard to the cooling systems: In comparison to the optimal solution, the 5th best solution installs a larger number of smaller chiller units on site A, but fewer chiller units with correspondingly larger sizing on site B. The 10th best solution is special in the way that it does not implement any absorption chillers on site B.

3.3. Rational decision options

Analysis of the obtained solutions shows that many practically equally good, but structurally different alternatives can be identified. As "must haves", all generated solutions implement one of the base-case boilers and one of the base-case turbo-chillers for peak-load requirements. Besides, all solutions include two new CHP engines. Thus, keeping any other equipment from the base case or installing other heating equipment can be understood as "must avoids". The "real choices" mainly concern the trade-offs between the number and sizing of the chiller units. Within this class of choices the designer can balance the required effort for equipment installation, operation and control, and the system's flexibility towards changing energy demands:

- Solutions that incorporate fewer chillers represent promising options because they minimise the complexity of equipment installation and control.
- In contrast, solutions with many chillers provide greater flexibility with regard to decentralization options, operation strategies, system up- and down-scaling, etc.
- Finally, avoiding absorption chillers removes any costs related to the heating network installation and operation to transfer the driving heat from site A to B.

The analysis procedure thus identifies the rational decision options for the decision maker that can be assessed with practical criteria beyond the optimisation model.

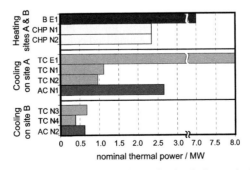

Figure 1. Equipment configuration and sizing of the optimal solution to the industrial case study (bars represent the sizing of the different technologies). B: boiler, CHP: CHP engine, TC: turbo-driven compression chiller, AC: absorption chiller, E: existing units from base case, N: newly installed units.

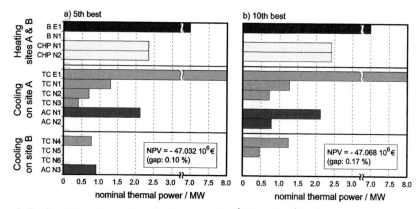

Figure 2. Equipment configuration and sizing for the 5th (a) and 10th best solution (b) to the industrial case study. The bars represent the units' sizing and are filled with different shades of gray for each type of technology.

4. District synthesis problem

The district case study represents a grassroots synthesis problem for an eco-town in the south of England. This case study has already been presented in detail by Weber and Shah (2011), however, focusing on the single optimal solution only. The synthesis problem is solved employing the tool DESDOP by Maréchal et al. (2008). Compared to the industrial case study, a 12 times larger estimated total floor area (0.48 km^2) and much more energy users (6,500 inhabitants, 39 districts) are considered. For this reason, the modelling details are somewhat shifted such that the optimal layout of the district heating system is a key subject of the synthesis while quite simple equipment models are assumed with constant efficiencies only. The set of available energy conversion technologies includes gas engines for the central district heat station and a range of distributed units (boilers, heat pumps, pumps, photovoltaic cells, wind turbines, and district heating pipes). The designers are mainly concerned with the network layout and the gas engines in the district heat station. As a constraint, the number of district heat stations is limited to one, i.e., all gas engines have to be installed at a single node of the district network. The gas engines and the single pipes are modelled by integer variables, while the distributed equipment is represented by real-valued sizing variables. The energy demands are modelled by time series reflecting three representative seasons (winter, mid-season, and summer) and six periods per day. Optimisation is performed over the course of one year employing annualised equipment costs.

4.1. Optimal solution

The total annualised costs of the optimal solution amount to £2.96 M/y. In this solution, the district heat station (plant node) is located in the north-east of the town, housing three gas engines. The total design size of the installed gas engines amounts to 3.5 MW with varying sizes of the single units (0.5 MW, 1 MW and 2 MW). The heating network (Figure 3) spreads out from the plant node in the north-east of the town to the town centre. The neighbourhoods in the south-west of the town are not connected to the heating network, and thus rely on decentralised units for energy supply.

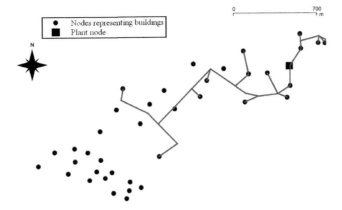

Figure 3. District heating network of the eco-town's optimal district energy system.

4.2. Near-optimal solutions

The ten best solution structures have objective function values within a range of 1.2 %. For illustration, in the following, the layouts of the 1st and the 6th best solutions are compared: In the 6th best solution (Figure 4), the location of the centralised heat station (plant node) is shifted from the north-east to the mid-west of the town. Regardless of the heat station's location, the heating networks of both solutions resemble each other aside from some feeder pipes. This behaviour suggests that the siting of the heat station does not significantly impact the total costs of the energy system. In both solutions, three gas engines are installed in the heat station with a total design size of 3.5 MW. This provides flexibility for meeting seasonally and daily varying demands. The layout of the heating network is similarly spanning from the north-east to the mid-west of the town.

4.3. Rational decision options

Analysing the near-optimal solutions, we observe as "must have" that all generated solutions install three or more gas engines with a total design size of 3.5 MW (+/- 0.25 MW). Moreover, in all solutions, the central heating network spans from the north-east to the mid-west of the town. In contrast, the south-west is never connected to the network ("must avoid"), but is supplied by decentralised units. The analysis shows

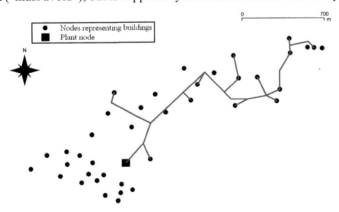

Figure 4. District heating network of the 6th best solution.

that there is no technical reason based upon which the location of the central heat station can be decided. Instead, to reach a final decision on the siting of the heat station, the designers should consider soft urban planning constraints such as civil matters like isolating industrial from recreational areas. Without the near-optimal solutions analysis, these insights were not available, but the heat station would have been installed in the north-east regardless of further urban planning constraints.

5. Conclusions

In this paper, we carry out optimisation for the synthesis of two energy systems on the district and industrial scale. The results suggest that analysing the near-optimal solution spaces of such problems rather than focusing on the single optimal solution only provides much more value from the modeling activity. For the discussed case studies, we generate the ten best solution structures and find a rich near-optimal solution space with practically equally good solutions. While a significant comparison of the generated solutions is thus hardly possible strictly based on a single optimisation criterion, the solutions are analysed to obtain valuable information on common features and differences among the solutions. With this information, designers can identify the rational decision options among all possible synthesis decisions. This allows designers to account for practical considerations that have not been explicitly accounted for in the optimisation model or that can change with time (e.g., effort for equipment installation, operation and control, flexibility towards changing energy demands). Based on our experience, we assume that the observation made in this paper can be generalised for most problems in the field of energy systems synthesis. Thus, we strongly advise practitioners to analyse the near-optimal solution space of a synthesis problem as presented in this paper rather than relying on the single optimal solution only.

Acknowledgements

The authors from Imperial College London are thankful for the funding of BP via the Urban Energy Systems Project. The authors from RWTH Aachen University gratefully acknowledge the funding by the German Federal Ministry of Economics and Technology (ref. no.: 0327885A).

References

C.A. Frangopoulos, M.R. von Spakovsky, E. Sciubba, 2002, A brief review of methods for the design and synthesis optimization of energy systems, Int. J. Appl. Therm., 5, 151-160.

P. Liu, M.C. Georgiadis, E.N. Pistikopoulos, 2011, Advances in energy systems engineering, Ind. Eng. Chem. Res., 50, 4915-4926.

F. Maréchal, C. Weber, D. Favrat, 2008, Multiobjective design and optimization of urban energy systems, Energy systems engineering, 5, Wiley-VCH, Weinheim, Germany.

R. Raman, I. E. Grossmann, 1991, Relation between MILP modelling and logical inference for chemical process synthesis, Comput. Chem. Eng., 15, 73-84.

M. Urselmann, S. Barkmann, G. Sand, S. Engell, 2011, Optimization-based design of reactive distillation columns using a memetic algorithm, Comput. Chem. Eng., 35, 787-805.

P. Voll, M. Hennen, C. Klaffke, M. Lampe, A. Bardow, 2013a, Exploring the near-optimal solution space for the synthesis of distributed energy supply systems, Chem. Eng. Trans., 35, 277-282.

P. Voll, C. Klaffke, M. Hennen, A. Bardow, 2013b, Automated superstructure-based synthesis and optimization of distributed energy supply systems, Energy, 50, 374-388.

C. Weber, N. Shah, 2011, Optimisation based design of a district energy system for an eco-town in the United Kingdom, Energy, 36, 1292-1308.

Jiří Jaromír Klemeš, Petar Sabev Varbanov and Peng Yen Liew (Editors)
Proceedings of the 24th European Symposium on Computer Aided Process Engineering – ESCAPE 24
June 15-18, 2014, Budapest, Hungary.

Achieving More Sustainable Designs through a Process Synthesis-Intensification Framework

Deenesh K. Babi, John M. Woodley, Rafiqul Gani[*]

CAPEC-Department of Chemical and Bio-chemical Engineering, Technical University of Denmark, Søltofts Plads, Building 229, DK-2800, Kgs. Lyngby Denmark.
rag@kt.dtu.dk

Abstract

More sustainable process designs refer to design alternatives that correspond to lower values of a set of targeted performance criteria. In this paper, a multi-level framework for process synthesis-intensification that leads to more sustainable process designs is presented. At the highest level of aggregation, process flowsheets are synthesized in terms of a sequence of unit operations that correspond to acceptable values for a set of targeted performance criteria. This defines the upper-bound of the performance criteria and the design is called the base-case design. At the next lower level, tasks representing unit operations are identified and analysed in terms of means-ends to find more flowsheet alternatives that improve the base-case design and correspond to lower values of the set of targeted performance criteria. At the lowest level, phenomena employed to perform the specific tasks are identified and manipulated to find intensified operations, leading to more flowsheets that further improve the base-case design and correspond to even lower values of the set of target performance criteria. An overview of the framework is presented together with a case study that highlights the key concepts and application work-flow.

Keywords: Process Synthesis, Process Intensification, Sustainable Design, LCA

1. Introduction

The objective of process synthesis is to find the best processing route, among numerous alternatives for converting given raw materials to specific desired products subject to predefined performance criteria. A flowsheet can be represented in terms of, unit operations (Unit-Ops) (Jaksland et al., 1995), tasks (Siirola, 1996) and phenomena as defined originally (Papalexandri et al., 1996) and more recently (Lutze et al., 2013). Therefore it is possible to perform process synthesis at different levels of aggregation. At Unit-Ops level, operations (equipment) are connected to define a processing routes (flowsheets) that satisfy a specified set of process constraints and minimizes (or maximizes) an objective function. The objective function includes terms related to economics, sustainability metrics and/or life cycle assessment factors. At this level, only known technologies and corresponding unit operations are applied. The number of alternative process designs is limited by the number and types of unit operations considered and the optimal process flowsheet corresponds to a more sustainable process option. However, can this design be further improved? Yes, it can, if new unit operations not considered before are employed, thus giving the opportunity to generate more processing routes, some of which may lead to a better (lower) objective function while satisfying all other constraints. At the task level, the need for specific unit operations are verified through a means-ends analysis (Siirola, 1996) and new hybrid (intensified) unit operations are employed. This leads to the generation of more process alternatives some of which most likely would correspond to lower (or higher) values of the objective function. However, can this design be further improved? Yes, it can, if new unit operations are generated. At the phenomena-level, the phenomena employed by the different tasks are identified and manipulated-combined in different ways to perform the same tasks as above but in a more sustainable way, resulting in even lower (or higher) values of the objective function.

The objective of this work is to develop a framework that allows the application of the above multi-level scheme for process synthesis-intensification. The paper gives a brief overview of the synthesis-intensification framework, highlighting the main concepts and the main steps of the work-flow. The well-known methyl-acetate esterification process is used as a case study to highlight the application of the framework.

2. Process Synthesis-Intensification Framework

The framework offers process synthesis-intensification options at Unit-Ops (Jaksland et al., 1995) level, at task level (Siirola, 1996) and at the phenomena level as defined recently (Lutze et al., 2013). In this paper, only the phenomena-based process synthesis-intensification method is highlighted.

2.1. Concept of Phenomena-based Synthesis

Consider as analogy, the design of chemicals based products, where a set of target property attributes of the product are matched by considering a set of molecules available in the database; and/or by considering functional groups (of atoms) that can be combined to form existing as well as new molecules that match the specified targets; and/or by considering a set of atoms that can be combined to generate even more existing as well as new molecules that match the specified targets. The key concepts in phenomena-based synthesis are presented below.

Phenomena-based process flowsheet structure representation: First, the involved PBB in the process need to be identified. This is done through a knowledge-base of unit operations, the tasks that they perform, and the phenomena that they employ. Based on a study of chemical processes, it was found that most chemical processes can represented through the following 8 phenomena building blocks (PBBs): mixing (M) (including the mixing of two phases that is two-phase-mixing (2phM)), heating (H), cooling (C), reaction (R), phase contact (PC), phase transition (PT), phase separation (PS), dividing(D).

Combination of phenomena to represent tasks and unit operations: One or more phenomena can be combined according to a set of rules to fulfil the objectives of any task. First, PBBs are identified and these are combined to form simultaneous phenomena building blocks (SPBs). For example, by combining mixing, two-phase-mixing, reaction, phase-contact and phase transition PBBs, a reaction-separation SPB [M=2phM=R=PC(VL)=PT(VL)=PS(VL)] is generated, where PT(VL) is a PBB representing a VL-separation task. Combination of SPBs leads to operations that can be translated to known or totally new unit operations. An example of the representation of a distillation column through the combination of 3 SPBs is shown in Figure 1.

2.2. The Framework

An overview of the framework, which is a special version of the phenomena-based methodology developed earlier (Lutze et al., 2013), is presented in Figure 2, where the computer-aided tools used in the different stages of the framework are highlighted. These tools are available in the updated version of ICAS (Gani et al., 1997), except for process simulators (PROII and ASPEN). The first stage of the framework determines a base case design at the Unit-Ops level considering a superstructure of all possible alternatives based on known technologies. The second stage performs a sustainability analysis (Carvalho et al., 2013) to systematically and logically identify process bottlenecks, which sets the targets for process improvement. The inputs to the analysis are detailed mass and energy balance data and the base case process flowsheet information. The third stage performs phenomena-based synthesis subject to the following conditions: the new flowsheet should have a smaller number of Unit-Ops for all synthesized alternatives compared to the base case. Analysis of the chemical system is performed using ICAS tools (Gani et al., 1997).

The unit operation based flowsheet is translated to a task-based flowsheet that is further translated to a phenomena-based flowsheet. Then all the PBBs that are found in the flowsheet are listed and using combination rules, SPBs are generated and screened. Next, SPBs are combined to form operations (tasks), which are combined to form unit operations. Only those operations and their combination to flowsheets are retained if they satisfy all constraints and move the objective function in the desired direction.

3. Case Study

The key steps of the framework are highlighted through this case study involved with the production of methyl-acetate (MeOAc) from an equilibrium-limited reaction between methanol (MeOH) and acetic acid (HOAc) with water (H_2O) as a by-product. The reaction is a liquid phase reaction catalysed by Amberlyst 15. A molar feed ratio of 2:1 for the base case design for MeOH and HOAc are used respectively with a total production of 122×10^6 t/y (Agreda et al., 1986).

3.1. Stage 1

The synthesis problem is defined as: Find intensified process design options for the production of MeOAc having a conversion of HOAc≥92% by maximising the objective function (Eq. 1) subject to:

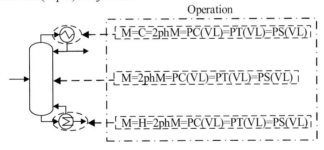

Figure 1. Combination of tasks (operations) represented by SPBs to represent a distillation column

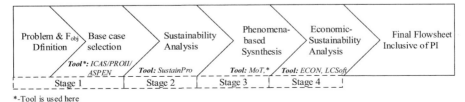

Figure 2. Overview of process synthesis-intensification framework. Tools, ICAS/PROII/ASPEN-Compound analysis/Rigorous Simulation, SustainPro-Sustainability analysis, MoT-Model based analysis, ECON-Economic analysis, LCSoft-Life cycle analysis

$$F_{obj}(C_{\text{Prod}}, C_{RM}, C_{Ut}) = Opt\left\{ \left(\sum m_j C_{\text{Prod},j} - \sum m_j C_{RM,j} - \sum E_j C_{Ut,j} \right) \Big/ _{\text{kg Prod}} \right\} \qquad (1)$$

C, m and E represent cost, mass and energy flows, respectively. Also, the following additional constraints are specified: compared to the base-case, use of solvents should be less; the number of Unit-Ops for the intensified alternatives must be less; sustainability metrics and LCA factors must be the same or better. From a literature survey a base-case design is available (Agreda et al., 1986) and it consists of ten unit operations (one reactor, five distillation columns, one liquid-liquid extractor and decanter). It should be noted that if a base-case design does not exist, the framework has the option to generate one. The base case design is then simulated to obtain detailed mass and energy balance data.

3.2. Stage 2
Sustainability analysis is performed and two potential process hot-spots are identified: the reaction does not go to full completion (limited-equilibrium) therefore high amount of raw material in the reactor outlet is found and high energy consumption for solvent recovery. These process hot-spots are then used as the targets that must be overcome through the design of a more sustainable intensified process.

3.3. Stage 3
Identification of tasks and phenomena: Using the appropriate tools the chemical system pure component and mixture properties are analyzed and the following minimum boiling binary azeotropes are found: HOAc/H_2O, MeOH/MeOAc and MeOAc/H_2O. Next, the base-case flowsheet is represented in terms of tasks and then in terms of phenomena, resulting in the following 15 PBBs: R, M (assuming four types, ideal, flow, rectangular, vapor), 2phM, PC(VL), PS(VL), PS(VV), PT(VL), PT(P:VL), PT(V:V) (key PBB for a vapour permeation membrane), H, C and dividing (D) PBB. Considering all possible combinations of the identified PBBs resulted in 16278 SPBs, out of which 64 were found to be feasible.

Generation of more sustainable alternatives: Only a brief overview of the flowsheet generation procedure is highlighted here. Starting with the first task of reaction, a second task, *in situ* removal of H_2O, could be added to obtain a SPB that translates into a membrane reactor at the Unit-Ops level. From the top product of the membrane reactor (see Figure 3), according to thermodynamic insights (Jaksland et al. 1995) HOAc should be removed first before handling the pressure-sensitive azeotrope of MeOH/MeOAc. The first separation task is easily accomplished by a VL-separation, that is, using a PT(VL) PBB. Two VL-separation tasks operating at different pressures are employed to first separate MeOH and then MeOAc, thereby avoiding the use of solvents. The final flowsheet (alternative 1 - satisfies the specified constraints) is shown in Figure 3. Using the presented concepts of flowsheet generation, 3 other feasible flowsheet alternatives were generated, including the well-known reactive distillation (Agreda et al., 1986), also shown in Figure 3 (as alternative 4).

Alternatives 2 and 3 are generated by further reducing the flowsheet of alternative 1 by changing the MeOH-HOAc feed ratio resulting in easier and lesser separation tasks after the membrane reactor. Among the different SPBs that can be generated, only those that have the potential to overcome the process hot-spots are considered. Figure 4 shows how a SPB that represents an intensified operation is formed. As seen in Figure 4a, the objective is to increase the conversion of MeOH and HOAc to MeOAc and remove

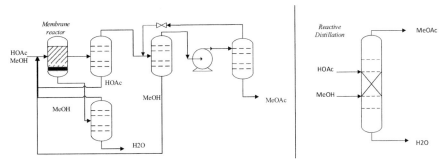

Figure 3. Intensified flowsheet alternative 1 and alternative 4 for the production of MeOAc

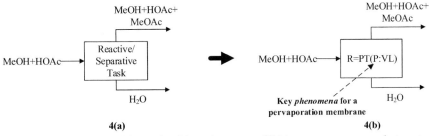

Figure 4. Identified task (4a) translated into phenomena (4b) to overcome process hot-spot

them from water. Figure 3b shows that this would be feasible if a pervaporation membrane (P:VL) is employed to remove water from the 2-phase reacting system (R=PT), thereby avoiding solvent-based separation for the azeotropes $HOAc/H_2O$ and $MeOAc/H_2O$. The resulting SPB is R=PT(P:VL). Note that additional mixing, heating or cooling PBB could also be added to this SPB.

3.4. Stage 4

Selection of the best alternative is dependent on economic factors, sustainability metrics and LCA factors in addition to the objective function value. Table 1 gives values of a selected set of performance criteria for the base-case design and the four alternative (intensified) designs. For each alternative the conversion of HOAc $\geq$ 92 % has been achieved, no solvents have been used and the number of unit operations have been reduced from 10 (the base case) to 1 (alternative 4). The concept of generation of more sustainable process designs by matching a set of targeted performance criteria is illustrated in Figure 5, where, the ratios of different performance criteria with respect to the base-case multiplied by 100 have been plotted (for profit, the inverse has been taken). The base-case design is at the boundary while the more sustainable alternatives are all within the boundary, indicating quite clearly that these alternatives are more sustainable than the base-case. Alternatives 3 and 4 give the best results.

4. Conclusions

A framework incorporating process intensification into process synthesis has been developed. The framework operates at different levels of aggregation and the benefit of such a framework is that it provides the opportunity to generate more sustainable alternatives by employing hybrid/intensified unit operations. The framework has been applied to several case studies and the results for one of them, production of methyl acetate, have been highlighted. The results show that better alternatives than reactive distillation are possible.

D. K. Babi et al.

Table 1. Selected performance criteria for base-case and 4 more sustainable alternatives

Performance Metrics	Base case	Alternatives			
		1	2	3	4
Feed Ratio	2:1	2:1	2:1	1:1	1:1
Energy Usage (MJ/kg MeOAc)	21.9	20.6	19.1	3.6	2.2
Raw material (kg/kg MeOAc)	0.88	0.87	0.87	0.87	0.88
Utility cost ($/kg MeOAc)	0.1	0.09	0.08	0.01	0.01
Carbon Footprint (eq. kg of CO_2)	0.92	0.56	0.52.	0.09	0.05
Fobj (Eq. 1)	2.06	2.08	2.09	2.16	2.16

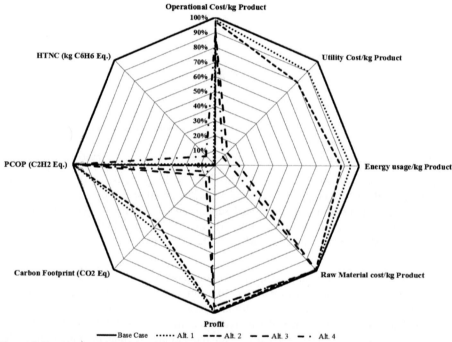

Figure 5. Economic and LCA improvements relative to the base case design. HTNC-human toxicity (carcinogenic effects); PCOP-Photochemical Oxidation Potential

References

A. Carvalho, H. M. Matos, R. Gani, 2013, SustainPro-A tool for systematic process analysis, generation and evaluation of sustainable design alternatives, Comput. Chem. Eng, 50, 8-27.

C. Jaksland, R. Gani, K. M. Lien, 1995, Separation process design and synthesis based on thermodynamic insights, Chem Eng Sci., 50, 511-530.

J. Siirola, 1996, Strategic process Synthesis: Advances in the Hierarchical Approach, Comput. Chem. Eng., Supplement 2, 20, S1637-S1643.

K.P. Papalexandri, E.N. Pistikopoulos, 1996, Generalized modular representation framework for process synthesis, AIChE J, 42, 1010-1032

P. Lutze, D. K. Babi, J. M. Woodley, R. Gani, 2013, Phenomena Based Methodology for Process Synthesis Incorporating Process Intensification, Ind. Eng. Chem. Res., 52, 7127-7144.

R. Gani, G. Hytoft, C. Jaksland, A. K. Jensen, 1997, An integrated computer aided system for integrated design of chemical processes, Comput. Chem. Eng., 21, 1135-1146.

V. H. Agreda, L. R. Partin, W. H. Heise, 1986, High Purity Methyl-Acetate via reactive Distillation, Chem. Eng. Prog., 2, 40–46.

Jiří Jaromír Klemeš, Petar Sabev Varbanov and Peng Yen Liew (Editors)
Proceedings of the 24th European Symposium on Computer Aided Process Engineering – ESCAPE 24
June 15-18, 2014, Budapest, Hungary. Copyright © 2014 Elsevier B.V. All rights reserved.

Superstructure Development and Optimization under Uncertainty for Design and Retrofit of Municipal Wastewater Treatment Plants

Hande Bozkurt[a], Alberto Quaglia[a], Krist V. Gernaey[b], Gürkan Sin[a*]

*[a]CAPEC/[b]PROCESS, Department of Chemical and Biochemical Engineering, Technical University of Denmark, DK-2800 Lyngby, Denmark.
gsi@kt.dtu.dk*

Abstract

In this contribution, an optimization-based approach is presented for optimal process selection and design for domestic wastewater treatment plants (WWTPs). In particular, we address the issue of uncertainties by formulating the WWTP design problem as a Stochastic Mixed Integer (Non)Linear Programming (sMI(N)LP) problem and solve it to determine the optimal process selection and flow diagram that meets a set of performance criteria including effluent quality requirements, cost and technical requirements. The application of the framework is highlighted using a case study aiming at designing a new WWTP under different objective function scenarios. For the uncertainty analysis, sources related to influent wastewater composition, operational cost and effluent permit requirements are studied and robust design candidates are generated and discussed.

Keywords: Design, modelling, superstructure optimization, uncertainty analysis, wastewater treatment

1. Introduction

The WWTP process selection and design problem needs to factor in many criteria especially in the early stage decision making such as nutrient recovery capacity, energy efficiency, water and sludge reuse in addition to typical design issues like cost and effluent quality (Hamouda, 2009). Moreover the design space that includes the number of available wastewater treatment technologies has increased noticeably in response to a number of drivers, most importantly the stricter regulations. Another consideration in design studies is that the plant design should be robust and feasible over the lifetime of the project; therefore, data and model uncertainties need to be considered in the design phase. As a result, early stage decision making in WWTP design and retrofitting studies became a complex engineering task. Currently, the early stage decision making for process selection for WWTP design is mainly based on expert decisions and previous experiences (Daigger, 2005); however, this approach is arguably not fit to handle such complex multi-criteria based problems and hence is expected to provide sub-optimal solutions. This contribution proposes an alternative approach to cast the decision problem using mathematical programming techniques for process synthesis and design for a domestic WWTP under uncertainty.

2. Framework for synthesis and design of WWTP networks under uncertainty

The mathematical programming based optimization methodology developed for chemical process synthesis and design by Quaglia et al. (2013) was modified and adapted to the context of a WWTP design problem. A schematic representation of the framework structure is shown in Figure 1 on the right. The details of the steps are discussed below.

2.1. Step 1: Problem definition and formulation.

In this step the problem is defined and its mathematical formulation is developed. The objective function is defined, together with the characteristics of the incoming wastewater and the emission limits. The superstructure containing all relevant treatment technologies and their interconnections is developed. For each treatment technology, data are collected and systematized in a predefined knowledge structure, and common design procedures of German ATV standards (ATV DVWK, 2000) and several biological wastewater treatment (Henze et al., 2008; Tchobanoglous et al., 2003) and municipal WWTP design handbooks (WEF, 2010) are employed to calculate design parameters (volumes, utility consumption, etc.), as well as performances (contaminant removal, sludge production, etc.).

2.2. Step 2: Uncertainty characterization.

In WWTP design, individual uncertainty sources, i.e. different flow and load scenarios, effluent standards etc. are in general lumped into safety factors, often resulting in overly conservative designs (Belia et al., 2009). In order to maximize the efficiency and avoid excessively sized plant designs, different individual sources of uncertainty are evaluated in this study, moving away from lumped uncertainty safety factors. In this step, the domain of uncertainty is defined with respect to the selected uncertain parameters. By means of sampling the uncertain domain, future scenarios are generated assuming different realizations of uncertain parameters. Latin hypercube sampling (LHS) was used to sample the uncertain space uniformly.

2.3. Step 3: MI(N)LP formulation and deterministic solution.

The formulation of the optimization problem and deterministic solution is performed in this step. With respect to the nature of the design task, the optimization problem can result in either a linear or a non-linear problem.

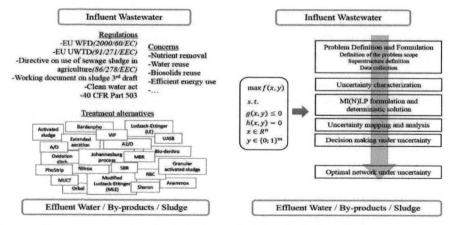

Figure 1. The superstructure based optimization methodology for design of WWTP systems: (left) increasing alternatives for process selection, (right) optimization framework for WWTP design

The models represent the mass input-output model for each process interval in the superstructure, process constraints, structural constraints, effluent limit constraints, cost models together with the objective function (Eq.(1)). Each process interval is structured using a generic model and composed of several phenomena namely: mixing (Eq.(2)), utility addition (Eq.(3)), reaction (Eq.(4)), waste separation (Eq.(5)) and flow separation (Eq.(6)). Eq.(7) defines the effluent limitations for the constraints. Eq.(8) is the activation constraint whereas Eq.(9) enables to establish logical cuts to ensure the selection of only one process interval from a processing task. When the deterministic problem is solved, it results in the optimal network, fate of pollutants throughout the treatment network and the value of the objective function.

$$\text{Min OBJ} = \sum_{kk} \text{OPEX}_{kk} + \frac{\text{CAPEX}_{kk}}{t} \qquad (1)$$

subject to;

$$F_{i,kk}^{mix} = F_{i,kk}^{in} + \alpha_{i,kk} * R_{i,kk} \qquad (2)$$

$$R_{i,kk} = \sum_{ii} \left(\mu_{i,ii,kk} * F_{i,kk}^{in} \right) \qquad (3)$$

$$F_{i,kk}^{reac} = F_{i,kk}^{mix} + \qquad (4)$$

$$\sum_{rr,react} \left(\gamma_{i,kk,rr} * \theta_{react,kk,rr} * F_{react,kk} \right)$$

$$F_{i,kk}^{w} = F_{i,kk}^{reac} * \left(1 - W_{i,kk} \right) \qquad (5)$$

$$FX_{i,k,kk} \le F_{i,kk}^{w} * Split_{i,kk} * S_{k,kk} \qquad (6)$$

$$F_{i,kk}^{in} \le F_{i,kk}^{max} \qquad (7)$$

$$y_{kk} * x_k^{LO} \le x_k \le y_{kk} * x_k^{UP} \qquad (8)$$

$$\sum_{kk} y_{kk} \le 1 \qquad (9)$$

i,ii: component index
k,kk: process interval index
$Fmix_{i,kk}$: flow of after mixing
$Fin_{k,kk}$: inflow of component i to process kk
$R_{i,kk}$: utility flow
$\alpha_{i,kk}$: fraction of utility consumed
$\mu_{i,ii,kk}$: specific consumption of utility
$Freac_{i,kk}$: flow after reaction
$\gamma_{i,kk,rr}$: matrix representing reaction stoichiometry
$\theta_{react,kk,rr}$: conversion efficiency of the key reactant *react*
$Fw_{i,kk}$: flow after waste separation
$W_{i,kk}$: waste split factor
$FX_{i,k,kk}$: Outlet streams from interval
X: 1,2,3 (representing three different outlet flow streams)
$Split_{i,kk}$: flow split factor
$S_{k,kk}$: binary variables containing superstructure information
y_{kk}: binary variable describing the process interval
x_k: variable bounded by x_k^{LO} and x_k^{UP}
$Fmax_{i,kk}$: Effluent limit for component i

2.4. Step 4:Uncertainty mapping and analysis.
The optimization problem is solved for the defined number of scenarios which are generated with regard to the uncertain data defined in step 2. The solution results in a distribution of optimal networks and objective function values which are then analyzed to understand the effect of uncertainty on the decision making procedure.

2.5. Step 5: Decision making under uncertainty.
The last step of the framework is where the stochastic problem is formulated and solved to find the optimal treatment network under uncertainty. For this purpose, the MI(N)LP problem is reformulated and solved by sample average approximation (Birge & Louveaux, 1997).

3. Case Study: Benchmark Wastewater Treatment Plant

3.1. Step 1: Problem definition and formulation
The problem is defined as the design of a WWTP for the treatment of an average dry weather wastewater composition (Copp, 2002) in compliance with the emission limits defined by the EU Urban Wastewater Treatment Directive. The objective of the design

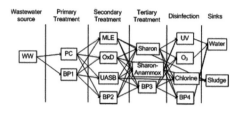

Figure 2. Case study superstructure

Table 1. Process interval descriptions

Interval	Description
PC	Primary Clarifier
MLE	Pre-denitrification (low SRT)
OxD	Pre-denitrification (high SRT)
Sharon	Single reactor system for High activity Ammonium Removal Over Nitrite
UASB	Upflow Anaerobic Sludge Blanket
Sharon-Anammox	Combination of Sharon and Anaerobic Ammonia Oxidation
UV, O_3, Chlorine	Disinfection by means of UV, O_3 and chlorine
BP	By-pass intervals

is the minimization of the total annualized cost (TAC) (Eq.1). The superstructure developed for the case study problem is presented in Figure 2 and the treatment alternatives placed in between the source (WW) and sink intervals (Water and Sludge) are defined in Table 1. The systematic data collection procedure is followed to design the treatment technologies prior to placing them in the process intervals.

3.2. Step 2: Uncertainty characterization

The uncertainty characterization is done under two scenarios: The first scenario deals with uncertainty with respect to cost parameters and effluent total nitrogen limitation; the second scenario deals with the effect of uncertainty in influent wastewater characterization. The parameters that are considered uncertain for the first and second scenarios and their probability distributions together with mean, minimum and maximum values are given in Table 2. The alpha, beta and fouling factor parameters in Table 2 are correction factors when the standard oxygen transfer rate in tap water (SOTR) is converted to actual oxygen transfer rate (AOTR) by taking into account the effects of salinity-surface tension, temperature, elevation etc. The relation between AOTR and SOTR is given in Eq. (10) (Tchobanoglous et al., 2003). This affects the electricity consumption needed to supply the oxygen demand to the WWTP. The electricity price is taken as the end-user energy price for industrial consumers in Denmark and a variation of 20 % is assumed over the average price given. Landfill cost, given for Denmark by the Confederation of European Waste-to-energy Plants as a range, is used in the study. Lastly, the effluent total nitrogen limitation is assumed to change between its current value 15 and 10 mg N/L. For the second scenario on the other hand, the possible change in the COD fractionation is taken into account together with the change in influent ammonium nitrogen (S_{NH}) concentration. Four different COD fractions (S_I, S_S, X_I and X_{BH}) were sampled and the resulting X_S concentration was calculated assuming that the total COD in the influent wastewater is constant.

$$AOTR = SOTR \left(\frac{\beta * C_{s,T,H} - C_L}{C_{s,20}} \right) (1.024^{T-20})(\alpha)(F) \tag{10}$$

3.3. Step 3: MI(N)LP formulation and deterministic solution

The deterministic problem was formulated as an MILP problem and solved by using GAMS using CPLEX as the solver. The resulting process flow diagram and cost summary and performance evaluation are shown in Figure 3 and Table 3 (all values given in unit cost), respectively.

Table 2. Probability distribution of uncertain data

Scenario	Data	Probability distribution	Mean	Min	Max	Unit
1	Alpha (α)	Uniform	0.75	0.30	1.20	dimensionless
	Beta (β)	Uniform	0.965	0.95	0.98	dimensionless
	Fouling factor (F)	Uniform	0.775	0.65	0.9	dimensionless
	Std. aeration efficiency	Uniform	4.85	3.6	6.1	kg O_2/kWh
	Price of electricity	Uniform	0.0977	0.08	0.12	Euro/kWh
	Landfill cost	Uniform	127	75	179	Euro/t of sludge
	Limit – Total N	Uniform	12.5	10	15	g N/m^3
2	S_I	Uniform	30	27	33	g COD/m^3
	S_S	Uniform	63.18	56.86	69.5	g COD/ m^3
	X_I	Uniform	51.2	46.08	56.32	g COD/ m^3
	$X_{B,H}$	Uniform	28.17	25.35	30.99	g COD/ m^3
	S_{NH}	Uniform	31.56	28.4	34.72	g N/ m^3

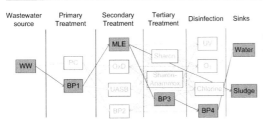

Figure 3. Resulting WWTP process flow diagram shown by bold line and units with grey shading

Table 3. Cost summary and performance evaluation

	Value
Aeration cost	111.421
Landfill cost	237.972
Biogas price	-
Electricity price	-
Capital cost	621.363
Objective function	970.756
Effluent COD	43.15
Effluent Total N	13.62
Sludge Production	2,224.03

3.4. Step 4:Uncertainty mapping and analysis

LHS was used to generate 100 samples, and for each of them the optimization problem was solved resulting in 100 different solutions. The results are presented in Table 4 and Figure 4. The value of the objective function changes from 818 to 1,530 (unit cost) for scenario 1 with the realization of 3 different selected configurations; whereas in scenario 2 the objective function value differs between 978 and 1,402 (unit cost) with 2 possible process flow diagram configurations. Figure 4 shows the probability (y-axis) that the value of TAC will be lower than or equal to the value represented in the x-axis. It can be inferred that the value of TAC changes with the changing network configuration (3 main parts in the graph on the left and 2 main parts in the graph on the right) and also a large variability can be observed within the selected network for different future scenarios.

3.5. Step 5: Decision making under uncertainty

In this step, the optimization problem is formulated and solved using sample average

Table 4. Uncertainty mapping results

Scenario	Network	Frequency of realization	Selected intervals
1	1	41 %	WW-BP1-MLE-BP3-BP4-Water-Sludge
	2	9 %	WW-BP1-MLE-Shar/An-BP4-Water-Sludge
	3	50 %	WW-BP1-OxD-BP3-BP4-Water-Sludge
2	1	98 %	WW-BP1-MLE-BP3-BP4-Water-Sludge
	2	2 %	WW-BP1-MLE-Shar/An-BP4-Water-Sludge

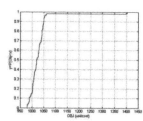 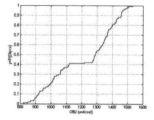

Figure 4. Uncertainty mapping results for scenario 1 (left) and scenario 2 (right)

Table 5. Summary of SAA results

	Scenario 1	Scenario 2
Network	WW-BP1-MLE-BP3-BP4-Water-Sludge	WW-BP1-MLE-Shar/An-BP4-Water-Sludge
Utility cost	71.391	119.933
Landfill cost	263.676	286.187
Capital cost	1044.944	957.271
Obj. function	1,380.1	1,363.391

approximation (SAA), and the results presented in Table 5 are obtained.

4. Conclusions and Future Works

A superstructure based optimization methodology is presented in this paper which is used to deal with the early stage WWTP design/retrofit problem under uncertainty. The uncertainty analysis resulted in different possible network configurations and objective function values which proved the importance of considering the sources of uncertainty in the early design studies. The presented framework with its models and database comprises a tool which is expected to assist the decision making by generating novel ideas for the WWTP process selection problem. The future work will focus on further expansion of the superstructure and its database and applying it to real case studies.

References

ATV-DVWK, 2000, Standard - A131E Dimensioning of single-stage activated sludge plants.

E. Belia, Y. Amerlinck, L. Benedetti, B. Johnson, G. Sin, P.A. Vanrolleghem, K.V. Gernaey, S. Gillot, M.B. Neumann, L. Rieger, A. Shaw, K. Villez, 2009, Wastewater treatment modelling: dealing with uncertainties, Water Sci Technol, 60, 8, 1929-1941.

J.K. Birge, F. Louveaux, 1999, Introduction to stochastic programming, Springer, NY, U.S.A.

J.B. Copp, 2002, The COST Simulation Benchmark: Description and Simulator Manual, Luxembourg.

G.T. Daigger, 2005, Wastewater treatment plant of the future: Decision analysis approach for increased sustainability, Water Security: Policies and Investments Water Week 2005, Washington DC, U.S.A.

M.A.Hamouda, W.B. Anderson, P.M. Huck, 2009, Decision support systems in water and wastewater treatment process selection and design: a review, Water Sci Technol, 60, 7, 1757-1770.

M. Henze, M.C.M. van Loosdrecht, G.A. Ekama, D. Brdjanovic, 2008, Biological Wastewater Treatment Principles, Modelling and Design, IWA, Glasgow, UK.

A. Quaglia, B. Sarup, G. Sin, R. Gani, 2013, A systematic framework for enterprise-wide optimization: Synthesis and design of processing networks under uncertainty, Comput Chem Eng, 59, 47-62.

G. Tchobanoglous, F. L. Burton, H. D. Stensel, 2003, Wastewater engineering: Treatment and Reuse, McGraw-Hill, NY, U.S.A.

WEF and ASCE/EWRI, 2010, Design of Municipal Wastewater Treatment Plants, WEF Press, Virginia, U.S.A.

Jiří Jaromír Klemeš, Petar Sabev Varbanov and Peng Yen Liew (Editors)
Proceedings of the 24th European Symposium on Computer Aided Process Engineering – ESCAPE 24
June 15-18, 2014, Budapest, Hungary. Copyright © 2014 Elsevier B.V. All rights reserved.

Scale-up and Techno-economical Study for the Production of Polyesters from Glycerol

Laura Bueno[a,*], Claudio A. Toro[b], Mariano Martín[a],

[a]*Department of Chemical Engineering, University of Salamanca, 37008, Salamanca, Spain*
[b]*Centro de Investigación de Polímeros Avanzados, CIPA. Beltrán Mathieu, 224, CP 4030000, Concepción, Chile*
LXB269@bham.ac.uk

Abstract

In this paper we conceptually design and scale up a process for the production of polyesters out of glycerol to be integrated within biodiesel production facilities. Experimental data for the polycondensation reaction and process simulation tools (CHEMCAD and gPROMS) are used to perform a techno-economical analysis of the scaled up production of polyesters from glycerol and adipic acid. The plant is flexible for the production of two grades of polyesters, solid and liquid types. The process consists of glycerol purification, polycondensation reaction, and, for the solid polymer, monomers recovery. The solid polymer is also used as adsorbent to purify the biodiesel obtained in the adjacent plant that serves the glycerol. The analysis reveals that the production is economically feasible, with a production cost for the polyester of 1.7 €/kg, providing good asset out of the glycerol based on current market prices for these resins.

Keywords: Biorefinery Glycerol, Resins, Polymerization

1. Introduction

The economy of biofuels has traditionally been highly dependent on the by-products. In the transesterification of oil we do not only produce biodiesel, FAME or FAEE depending on the use of methanol or ethanol as transesterifying agent, but we also obtain 10 % by weight of glycerol. Glycerol has been an expensive by-product with a wide range of applications in the food and cosmetic industries (Pagliaro and Rossi, 2010) leading to a high price, $0.6/kg, and representing a credit for the production of biodiesel (Fan et al 2010). However, the increase in the production of biodiesel is saturating the glycerol market and its price is expected to decrease down to $0.2 /kg. As a result, the production cost of biodiesel may increase $0.15 /gal (Martín and Grossmann, 2012). Glycerol can be used either for the production of biofuels, methanol, ethanol or hydrogen or to produced added value products such as polymers, polyesters, with adipic acid (Toro et al 2011), with 2,5-furandicarboxylic acid (Amaresekara et al., 2013) or others such as succinic glutaric or azelaic acid (Wyatt, 2012).In this paper we focus on this second option. We use experimental data for evaluation the performance of the polymerization process to produce polyesters from glycerol and adipic acid and process simulators for scaling up and building the production process.

2. Methodology

2.1. Process description

The process consists of four stages, see Figure 1. The incoming glycerol is purified to remove water and methanol from the biodiesel production using a distillation column (T01). Next glycerol reacts with adipic acid following a polycondensation reaction at 421 K. The experimental data for the reaction were obtained using the set up presented in Figure 2. In the lab scale reactor, glycerol and adipic acid are mixed in a four-neck round-bottomed jacketed glass reactor fitted with a mechanical stirrer, a Claisen condenser with vacuum adapter and nitrogen inlet. The experimental data show that the molar ratio 1:1 is the most suitable for biodiesel purification. The temperature of the reaction was controlled by the thermostatic bath beside. In the lab, the mixture was first heated up to 373 K under constant agitation. Once the mixture was homogenized, 0.15 %wt of dibutyltin dilaurate, the catalyst, based on the total mass of monomers is added to the flask, while the temperature was quickly increased to 421 K, promoting polycondensation start-up. Water formed during the reaction was distilled off to obtain a higher conversion yield. The reaction is stopped at the proper time depending on the product desired (liquid or solid polymer).We consider two possible products, a liquid type polymer (R01) and a solid type (R02), (Toro et al., 2011), which differ in the degree of polymerization.

Liquid state polymer: $C_3H_8O_3 + C_6H_{10}O_4 \rightarrow 2\,H_2O + 0.12\,C_{75}H_{117}O_{42}$ (1)

Solid state polymer: $C_3H_8O_3 + C_6H_{10}O_4 \rightarrow 2\,H_2O + 0.06C_{136}H_{212}O_{76}$ (2)

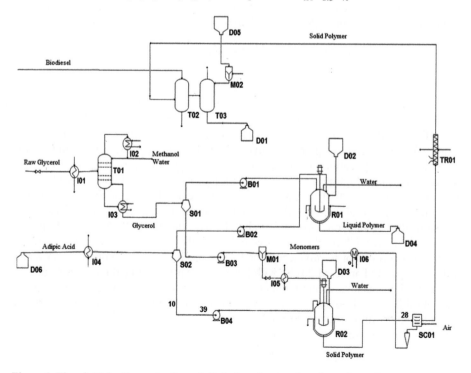

Figure 1. Flowsheet for the production of aliphatic polyesters based on glycerol.

Figure 2. Experimental set up

While the liquid polymer retains the unreacted monomers within and is used as precursor for the synthesis of polyurethanes and plasticisers, the solid one is intended to be adsorbent material. This last one is further purified to eliminate the unreacted monomers (SC01), glycerol and adipic acid, to be recycled to the reactor. Polyesters from glycerol are able to remove Na from biodiesel with a removal capacity of 2.1 mg Na/kg dry adsorbent. It is important to notice that the steam generated at the reaction is used to provide heat to the biodiesel production process while the bottoms of the distillation column heat up the adipic providing certain heat integration.

2.2. Process modeling
In this process we are dealing with particular species such as polyesters that in some cases retain part of the monomers. In order to better capture such features we use a hybrid simulation approach. For the rigorous modeling of the glycerol purification we use CHEMCAD® 6.3. However, for the reactors, driers, mixers and splitters we use an equation based approach using gPROMS® 3.6.0, linked to CHEMCAD® 6.3 through EXCEL®.

3. Results

3.1. Process results
Tables 1-3 present the operating values of the scaled up plant. The production capacity is based on the glycerol availability, 25,600 t/y within a particular region, see Table 1. 1/3 of the solid polymer produced is used to purify the biodiesel. Considering that we have to replace it every year. The energy and cooling needs are reported in Table 2 per kg of product. The energy needs represent only 10 % compared to biodiesel production (Martín and Grossmann, 2012) so that the integrated plant biodiesel-polyester production does not add up high energy consumption. 28 % of the final product is solid and 72 % is liquid, see Table 3.

Table 1. Requirements of raw materials

Raw Material	Quantity (t/year)
Glycerol	25,600
Adipic Acid	33,378
Dibutylin Dilaurate	94

Table 2. Auxiliary Utilities requirements

Auxiliary Utility	
Cooling (kJ/kg$_{total\ polymer}$)	621.097
Steam (1,034 Mpa, 458,71 K)	11,858 (t/year)
Energy (kJ/kg$_{total\ polymer}$)	68.146

Table 3. Synthesized products.

Product	Quantity (t/year)	Purity (%)
Liquid polymer	30,620	72.5
Solid polymer	18,359	100

3.2. Economic evaluation

We used Sinnot's method (Sinnot and Towler, 2009) to estimate the investment cost. The equipment cost is estimated using www.matche.com and Peters and Timmerhaus' 2003 web page. The total investment cost adds up to 66 M€. The fixed capital is 40 M€. More than 60 % of it is due to the direct capital corresponds to the physical capital and fees. The working capital adds up to 26 M€ being outstanding sales the main contribution representing 36 %. See Figure 3 for the breakdown on the investment cost.

In terms of production costs, we consider financial and manufacturing costs. This last one accounts for raw material, insurance, taxes amortization, man power, maintenance, taxes, and general services. For the average annual cost, we consider general services (10 % of manufacturing costs), supplies (15 % of fix costs), equipment maintenance (7 % of fix costs), amortization (linear with time in 20 years), laboratory costs (30 % of direct manpower), taxes and insurance (1 % of fix costs respectively). The distribution of the costs is shown in Figure 7. The total production cost of the aliphatic polyester is 1.71 €/kg at 0.060 €/kg cost of glycerol (Martín & Grossman, 2012) and 1.57 €/kg cost of adipic acid (icis pricing, 2012).

The cost of glycerol is an uncertain parameter in the process since the increase in its production as by-product of the biodiesel industry promotes a decrease in its price. However, within the range of costs for the raw material, we can maintain a production cost below 2 €/kg, see Figure 5.

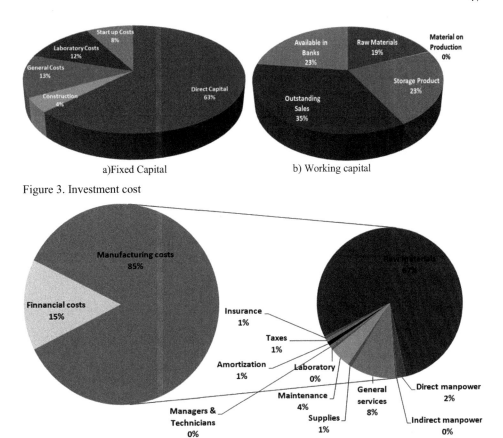

a)Fixed Capital

b) Working capital

Figure 3. Investment cost

Figure 4. Breakdwon of production cost

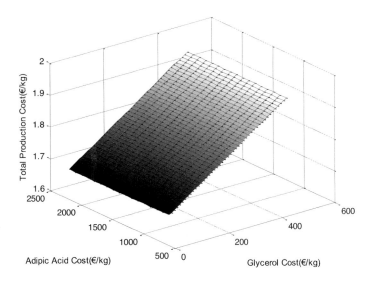

Figure 5. Effect of the raw materials price on the production costs

4. Conclusions

In this paper we have designed and scaled up a production process to obtain high added value products out of glycerol, a byproduct in the biodiesel industry. The facility is flexible allowing for the production of two grades of polymers, liquid and solid.

We use a hybrid approach based on experimental results obtained in the lab and simulation tools, either modular process simulators (CHEMCAD) or equation oriented ones (gPROMS), do perform a techno-economical analysis for a process that consists of four stages, glycerol purification, polycondensation with adipic acid, product purification and the use of the solid polymer to purify the biodiesel obtained in the adjacent plant that serves the glycerol. The process is not only technically feasible but also economically promising resulting in production costs for the polymer of 1.7 €/kg when typically in the market values of 5 €/kg can be found.

Acknowledgments

The authors would like to thank Salamanca Research for software licenses, CIPA and CONICYT regional R08C1002

References

A.S. Amarasekara, A. Razzaq, P. Bonham, 2013, Synthesis and Characterization of All Renewable Resources Based Branched Polyester: Poly(2,5-furandicarboxylic acid-co-glycerol), ISRN Polymer Science, doi:10.1155/2013/645169.

M. Martín, I.E. Grossmann, 2012, Simultaneous optimization and heat integration for biodiesel production from cooking oil and algae, Ind. Eng. Chem. Res., 51, 23, 7998–8014.

MATCHE, 2007, <www.matche.com/EquipCost/index.htm>, Accesed on 01/01/2014.

ISICPricing, 2012, Adipic acid, <www.icispricing.com/il_shared/Samples/SubPage121.asp>, Accessed on 01/05/2013.

M. Pagliaro, M. Rossi, 2010, Future of Glycerol, 2nd Edition, The royal society of Chemistry, Cambridge, UK.

M.S., Peters, K.D. Timmerhaus, 2003, Plant design and economics for chemical engineers, 5th Edición, McGrawHill, New York, US.

R. Sinnott, G. Towler, 2009 Chemical Engineering Design. Elsevier Ltd Oxford, UK,

S. Trinder, 2013, Crudeglycerol, <www.icispricing.com/il_shared/Samples/SubPage170.asp>, Accesed on 01/05/2013.

C.A. Toro, P. Hidalgo, R. Navia, 2011,. Development of Polyesters from Glycerol for Na Removal in Biodiesel Refining, J. Biobased Mater. Bio., 5, 1–8.

V.T. Wyatt, 2012, Lewis Acid-Catalyzed Synthesis of Hyperbranched Polymers Based on Glycerol and Diacids in Toluene, Journal of the American Oil Chemists' Society, 89, 313-319.

Jiří Jaromír Klemeš, Petar Sabev Varbanov and Peng Yen Liew (Editors)
Proceedings of the 24th European Symposium on Computer Aided Process Engineering – ESCAPE 24
June 15-18, 2014, Budapest, Hungary.

Uncertainty Analysis in Raw Material and Utility Cost of Biorefinery Synthesis and Design

Peam Cheali, Alberto Quaglia, Krist V. Gernaey, Gürkan Sin*

Department of Chemical and Biochemical Engineering, Technical University of Denmark (DTU), Building 229, DK-2800 Lyngby, Denmark
gsi@kt.dtu.dk

Abstract

This study presents the impact of uncertain data on the solution obtained by using a superstructure-based optimization approach in synthesis and design of biorefinery processing networks. In the early stages of biorefinery design, many of the data required for the formulation of the design problem are characterized by considerable uncertainty. These uncertainties might have significant impact on the results of the design problem, and therefore need to be carefully evaluated and managed, in order to generate candidates for robust design. In this contribution, we study the effect of data uncertainty (raw material price and utility cost) on the design of a biorefinery process network.

Keywords: Uncertainty analysis, process synthesis, MIP/MINLP, biorefinery.

1. Introduction

In a typical biorefinery, a bio-based feedstock is processed to produce various products such as fuel, chemicals, feed or power/heat. As there are several feedstock sources and many alternative conversion technologies to choose from to match a range of products, this creates a number of potential processing paths for biorefinery development. Therefore, during the early stage of planning and design, it is important to identify the optimal biorefinery processing path with respect to techno-economic performance criteria. Moreover, during the early design stage, accurate input data are usually scarce, and some design decisions are taken based on premises characterized by considerable uncertainties. Consequently, the biorefinery design which is obtained can be sub-optimal or incorrect. The effect of uncertainties on mathematical programming in particular stochastic optimisation problems and their solution methods have been addressed in detail by Birge and Louveaux (1999). Optimization under uncertainty has also been widely-used in synthesis and design of biorefinery in different fields to investigate the effect of uncertain input data on simulated system performance i.e. (i) an identification of an optimal inventory level and processing network under uncertainty (Yue and You, 2013); or (ii) an identification of an optimal sustainable supply chains under uncertainty (Gosálbez and Grossmann, 2009).

A framework to generate and identify optimal processing networks under uncertainty has been developed earlier (Quaglia et al., 2013), and is used here for supporting biorefinery synthesis and design. The framework, based on superstructure-based optimization coupled with a generic modeling approach and Monte Carlo simulation, consists of tools, databases, models, and solution strategies to represent and identify the optimal processing network among the potential processing network alternatives. In this paper, first the framework is first explained briefly and is then followed step-by-step to identify the optimal processing path for a given optimization scenario (minimize total annualized cost) and the quantified risks under uncertainties (raw material and utility cost) on the optimal solution(s).Combining the extended biorefinery database with uncertainty analysis thus results in a promising and powerful process synthesis toolbox for the early stage design of future biorefineries. In the paper, we highlight the application of the framework for designing an optimal lignocellulosic biorefinery network.

2. Framework

2.1. Step 1: Problem formulation: (i) problem definition; (ii) superstructure definition and data collection; (iii) model selection and validation.
The first step consists of defining the problem scope by selecting objective function and optimization scenarios with respect to economic/business metrics, engineering performance, or sustainability criteria. The superstructure (processing network) is also defined and the necessary data are collected. The model selection and validation task is then performed, i.e. a consistency check. Each processing technology is simulated in GAMS to reproduce the collected results to verify the input parameters and models used prior to the optimization problem.

2.2. Step 2: Uncertainty characterization.
In this step, the domain of uncertainty is defined and characterized. Monte Carlo simulation and Latin Hypercube Sampling with correlation control are then used to sample uncertain data. The sampling of uncertain data yields the potential scenarios that are to be analyzed in the next step.

2.3. Step 3: Deterministic formulation and solution.
The optimization problem which is formulated in step 1 is performed and solved in this step using the nominal values for the parameters – in case a parameter is characterized by a certain statistical distribution (hence uncertain input) then its mean value is used here. The result in this step is the deterministic optimal processing path, i.e. yielding one optimization scenario on the basis of mean value of the input data.

2.4. Step 4: Uncertainty mapping and analysis.
In this step, the deterministic optimization problem is performed separately for each sample generated from the uncertainty domain (in Step 2). The results are the probability distribution of the objective function value and the frequency of occurrence of the optimal processing path candidates that are selected for given uncertain inputs.

2.5. Step 5: Decision making under uncertainty
In this step, the optimization problem is modified as a stochastic programming problem by including uncertainty domain (inputs, parameters, etc). To this end, the objective function is reformulated as to minimize or maximize the expected value of the objective function over the uncertain domain.

2.6. Step 6: Flexible network
In this step, the optimal trade-off between the investment cost and the ability of the network to adapt its structure in order to mitigate the negative consequences of the uncertainty is identified. The problem is reformulated as a two-stage stochastic programming problem. This step is beyond the scope of this study.

2.7. Step 7: Report generation
This section presents the results regarding the optimal solutions under uncertainty. There are a number of suggested indicators (Birge and Louveaux, 1999) in order to

analyze the solution under uncertainties such as Expected Value of Perfect Information (EVPI), Value of Stochastic Solution (VSS) and Uncertainty Penalty (UP), see Eqs. 1-3.

$$EVPI = E_\theta(\max(f(x,y,\theta))) - \max\left(E_\theta(f(x,y,\theta))\right) \tag{1}$$

$$VSS = max(E_\theta(f(x,y,\theta))) - (E_\theta(f(x_{det}^*, y_{det}^*, \theta))) \tag{2}$$

$$UP = max(f(x,y)) - \max(E_\theta(f(x,y,\theta))) \tag{3}$$

EVPI indicates the cost relevant to the lack of knowing the exact data during the decision making process. VSS indicates the cost relevant to the performance of stochastic and deterministic solutions. UP indicates the cost relevant to the impact of uncertainty.

3. Uncertainty analysis of a superstructure-based optimization

In this section, the superstructure of an extended biorefinery network (combination of biochemical and thermochemical conversion platforms) developed in a previous work (Cheali et al., 2013) was used within the framework under uncertainty.

3.1. Step 1: Problem formulation: (i) problem definition; (ii) superstructure definition and data collection; (iii) model selection and validation

The problem statement was formulated as the identification of optimal biorefinery concepts with respect to techno-economic specifications under a specific objective function aiming at minimizing the total annualized cost (operating and capital cost). The superstructure (Figure 1) of the biorefinery processing network is to convert corn stover and wood to bioethanol (Cheali et al., 2013). The data management and model verification performed in the previous study also formed the basis for this study and was thus not repeated again.

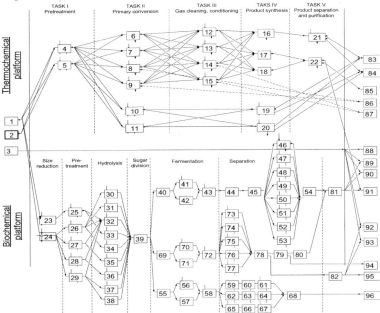

Figure 1. Combined superstructure (Cheali et al., 2013) of two biorefinery conversion platforms: thermochemical (top) and biochemical platform (bottom)

Table 1. Input uncertainty and correlation matrix criteria

Input uncertainty	Min.	Max.	References
Corn stover cost ($/t)	60	100	NREL
Wood cost ($/t)	60	100	NREL
	Mean	Min./Max.	References
Steam cost ($/t)	77	65/90	U.S. EIA
Correlation matrix	Stover cost	Wood cost	Steam cost
Corn stover cost	1	0	0
Wood cost	0	1	0
Steam cost	0	0	1

3.2. Step 2: Uncertainty characterization

In this study, the uncertainties of market prices (raw material and utility cost) were identified as the important sources of uncertainty affecting the decision concerning the biorefinery design. Other potential sources of uncertainties (such as yields, reaction conversions, efficiencies etc) were not considered. A summary of the input uncertainties and the correlation control information used here is presented in Table 1. These data were then used to generate 200 samples of the uncertain inputs using Latin Hypercube Sampling (LHS) technique.

3.3. Deterministic formulation and solution

In this study, the objective function was defined as minimizing the total annualized cost (TAC) for the ethanol scenario (Eq. 4) in order to compare the expenses between both platforms. The formulated MIP/MINLP was solved in this step for the deterministic case (mean input values). The optimization results are presented in Table 3.

Objective function:
$$\min. TAC = \sum_{kk^*} CAPEX_{kk^*} + \sum_{kk^*} OPEX_{kk^*}; \ kk^* \equiv the\ seleacted\ process\ intervals; \quad (4)$$

3.4. Step 4: Uncertainty mapping and analysis

In this step the 200 samples generated from the LHS sampling were used as the input data for the MIP/MINLP problem, resulting in 200 optimal solutions. The full results were then analysed to identify the optimal solution under uncertainty. The different processing paths resulting from this procedure, their frequency of selection and their corresponding objective value are presented in Table 2 and Figure 2.From the 200 considered scenarios under uncertainty, there were 4 processing paths selected (Figure 2, left), and of these 4 paths network 1 is the best candidate. From Figure 2 (middle) and Figure 2 (right), it is clear that there were no results below 50 (M$/y) and no results higher than 80 (M$/y) indicating the range for the expected TAC. In addition, when a network decision is fixed, the CDF function appears to be linear which indicates that the TAC (a random variable due to uncertainties) is distributed uniformly).

Table 2. The frequency of selection of the optimal processing paths for 200 scenarios

Network no.	Processing path	Frequency of selection	TAC (M$/y)	Mean	Std.
1	1 24 29 37 39 40 41 42 43 44 45 53 54 81 91	140/200	50-80	62	7.5
2	1 24 29 38 39 40 41 42 43 44 45 53 54 81 91	38/200	56-76	65	5.8
3	2 5 8 14 17 22 85 91	21/200	56-77	63	5
4	2 5 9 14 17 22 85 91	1/200	65	-	-

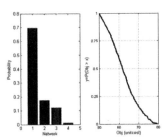 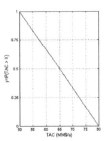

Figure 2. Uncertainty mapping and analysis: the frequency of selection (left), the cumulative distribution function (CDF) of all solutions under uncertainties (middle), and the CDF of network 1 under uncertainties (right).

3.5. Decision making under uncertainty(Stochastic problem)

In this step, a stochastic programming problem was formulated. The uncertain domain was thus incorporated into the optimization problem. In this problem, the uncertain data are raw material costs and utility cost (Table 1). The result of this step is 65.09 (M$/y) which is lower than the result of step 3 due to the effect of uncertainties. The result of the optimal solution under uncertainties is presented in Table 3.

3.6. Report generation

As explained in the previous section, the results of the indicators representing the effect of uncertainties are summarized here (Table 3). All results obtained from each step (step 3-5), were used to determine the value of each indicator.

Table 2 and 3 present the optimal processing paths under uncertainty. The biochemical conversion platform requires less operating cost and a lower capital cost. Corn stover is the favorable feedstock for the biochemical platform. Lime pretreatment and enzymatic hydrolysis need the minimum capital and operating cost for the pretreatment and hydrolysis section, and the same goes for the use of a molecular sieve for the separation section. As regards the optimal network solution under uncertainty, the same process topology was selected (Table 3) as for the deterministic case, thus confirming the robustness of the deterministic solution. This is also shown by uncertainty indicators VSS and UP, which were zero and close to zero respectively.

The reason optimal network solution remains the same indicates that the problem is linear with respect to constraints (which is true for the problem formulation presented here) and the effect of uncertainty scales linearly to the performance metrics as well. Overall, these confirm that biochemical platform using corn stover, lime pretreatment, enzymatic hydrolysis and molecular sieve requires the lowest total annualized cost with and without considering uncertainty.

Table 3. Report generation (Processing paths referred to Figure 1)

Solution	Network		TAC (M$/y)
Optimal network (step3)	1 24 29 37 39 40 41 42 43 44 45 53 54 81 91		65.16
Network under uncertainty (Step 5)			65.09
Scenarios	EVPI (M$/y)	VSS ((M$/y)	UP (M$/y)
Network under the effect of uncertainty (Step 3-5)	2.1	0	0.07

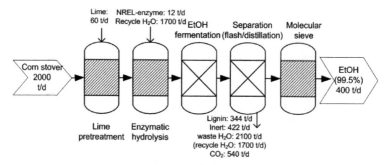

Figure 3. The optimal processing network (simplified flowsheet)

To sum up, based on the techno-economic analysis of optimal biorefinery network presented in the previous steps of the methodology, the network presented in Figure 3 is found as the optimal solution both under deterministic case and under uncertainty against market uncertainties. Hence network 3 is the recommended as the best alternative among the design space considered in this study.

4. Conclusion

In this study, the impact of data uncertainties on design of optimal biorefinery networks using superstructure-based approach is discussed. The combination of the deterministic problem, the deterministic problem under uncertainty and the stochastic problem was used to effectively identify the impact of uncertainty on the optimal solution. Biochemical platform using corn stover, lime pretreatment, enzymatic hydrolysis and molecular sieve was found optimal with respect to total annualized cost. Moreover on the effect of uncertainty, the indicators show that the uncertainty of raw material and utility cost has an impact on the expected performance of optimal biorefinery design, however, the optimal process topology did not change under the given/defined domain of market uncertainty. This confirms the robustness of the deterministic solution.

References

J. K. Birge, F. Louveaux, 1999, Introduction to stochastic programming (springer series in operations research and financial engineering), Springer, New York, U.S.
P. Cheali, K. V. Gernaey, G. Sin, 2014, Toward a Computer-Aided Synthesis and Design of Biorefinery Networks: Data Collection and Management Using a Generic Modeling Approach, ACS Sustainable Chem. Eng., 2, 19-29.
G. G. Gosálbez, I. E. Grossmann, 2009, Optimal design and planning of sustainable chemical supply chains under uncertainty, AIChE Journal, 55, 99-121.
A. Quaglia, B. Sarup, G. Sin, R. Gani, 2013, A systematic framework for enterprise-wide optimization: Synthesis and design of processing networks under uncertainty, Computers and Chemical Engineering, 59, 47-62.
D. Yue, F. You, 2013, Planning and scheduling of flexible process networks under uncertainty with stochastic inventory: MINLP models and algorithm, AIChE Journal, doi: 10.1002/aic.13924.

Jiří Jaromír Klemeš, Petar Sabev Varbanov and Peng Yen Liew (Editors)
Proceedings of the 24th European Symposium on Computer Aided Process Engineering – ESCAPE 24
June 15-18, 2014, Budapest, Hungary. Copyright © 2014 Elsevier B.V. All rights reserved.

Rigorous Optimization-based Synthesis of Distillation Cascades without Integer Variables

Alexander W. Dowling, Lorenz T. Biegler[*]

Carnegie Mellon University, 5000 Forbes Ave, Pittsburgh, PA (USA), 15213
lb01@andrew.cmu.edu

Abstract

In this paper we present a novel alternate model for distillation cascades without integer variables. This allows for optimization of highly nonlinear process flowsheets with embedded distillation columns, modeled with rigorous mass, equilibrium, summation and heat (MESH) equations. Instead of reformulating the famous MINLP distillation column model as an MPCC (mathematical program with complementarity constraints), bypass streams are added to the distillation cascade superstructure. If a tray is fully active the bypass streams are inactive (zero flow) and the standard MESH results are obtained. If a tray is completely inactive all of the flow bypasses the tray, resulting in no separation. As a result the interior of the bypass fraction (analogous to integer variables in the MINLP model) is well defined. In fact a partially bypassed stream is physically realizable (although inefficient). For this reason we postulate that this alternate model with bypass leads to well-behaved solution strategies.

Keywords: distillation synthesis, optimization, air separation units, heat integration

1. Introduction

Flowsheet optimization provides a systematic methodology for improving process profitability, reducing environmental impact and increasing reliability. Improvements in optimization algorithms and problem formulations continue to increase the effectiveness of equation based process optimization methods and allow for larger, more challenging design problems to be considered.

Distillation is central to many chemical processes, which has motivated extensive development of mathematical models for distillation sequence and column optimization. Andrecovich and Westerberg (1985) developed a mixed integer linear programming (MILP) formulation to optimize heat integrated distillation sequences using approximate models. This approach includes several assumptions to avoid nonlinearities. Viswanathan and Grossmann (1990) developed a rigorous mixed integer nonlinear programming (MINLP) model for distillation column optimization. Detailed (nonlinear) equilibrium calculations are included. Integer variables are used to select the optimal feed tray location and activate/deactivate trays. Unfortunately in many cases these models are too complex to embed with several other units for chemical process flowsheet optimization. For example Baliban et al. (2013) use simplified split fraction models for distillation units in synthesis studies of natural gas to liquid fuels processes.

Recent work has focused on reformulation of the MINLP distillation column model to remove the integer variables and thus combinatorial aspects of the problem. Because rigorous thermodynamics models add significant nonconvex constraints, they remain computationally expensive to solve in mixed integer problems. This motivated Lang and Biegler (2002) to propose the distributed stream-tray optimization method that uses differentiable density functions for feed placement along with simple smoothing of complementarity conditions, resulting in a conventional, but highly nonlinear, NLP. The method has been demonstrated in several industrial examples and extended by Neves et al (2005) and others. Similarly Kamath et al. (2010) proposed a revised group method as an approximate distillation model. Unfortunately there can be significant mismatch between this model and more rigorous MESH equations for certain distillation systems. Kraemer et al. (2009) investigated relaxing the integer variables to continuous and including Fischer-Burmeister function constraints to drive these variables to 0 or 1 values. However, their approach has some drawbacks, especially since this relaxation of integer variables (non-binary values) can lead to local solutions and infeasibilities when the problem is not carefully initialized. This drawback inspired the proposed model.

2. A New Distillation Model

The new distillation model is built upon the standard Mass, Equilibrium, Summation and Heat equations, shown in Eqs.(1) – (4). Variables include mole fractions (x, y), liquid molar flowrate (L) and vapour molar flowrate (V). Specific enthalpies (H) and the phase equilibrium coefficients (K) are determined from a thermodynamic model, such as Raoult's Law or a Cubic Equation of State. Optionally slack variables are added to relax (2) to accommodate disappearing phases (Kamath et al., 2010).

$$x_{i+1}^c L_{i+1} + y_{i-1}^c V_{i-1} = x_i^c L_i + y_i^c V_i, \quad \forall i \in \{Trays\}, \forall c \in \{Comps.\} \tag{1}$$

$$y_i^c = K_i^c x_i^c, \quad \forall i,c \tag{2}$$

$$\sum_c y_c^i - x_c^i = 0, \quad \forall i \tag{3}$$

$$H_{i+1}^l L_{i+1} + H_{i-1}^v V_{i-1} = H_i^l L_i + H_i^v V_i \tag{4}$$

The MESH model is modified with the addition of bypass streams, denoted by L_i^* and V_i^* in Figure 1. These bypass streams duplicate the pressure, temperature and compositions of their parent streams (L_{i+1} and V_{i-1}). Bypass streams were initially introduced by Yeomans and Grossmann (2000) using disjunctive programming techniques for distillation synthesis. Solution of their model required a logic-based algorithm with the outer loop solving an MILP to determine the existence of trays (integer/logic variables) and an inner loop to solve the nonlinear MESH model. This allowed deactivated trays to be removed from the inner NLP, and degeneracies due to zero flowrates to be avoided.

In this work tray bypass is carefully defined to avoid these degeneracies. As shown in Figure 1, the bypass efficiency (ε_i) is the ratio of non-bypassed flow to total flow for tray i. The number of trays in a cascade is approximated by summing the bypass efficiencies, as shown in Eq.(5). Calculation of the equilibrium streams' properties is done with the main tray inlet streams (L_{i+1} and V_{i-1}) as if there were no bypass. This leads to $\hat{L}_i$ and $\hat{V}_i$, with compositions $\widehat{x_i^c}$ and $\widehat{y_i^c}$, respectively, which replace the outlet streams (L_i, V_i) in the MESH equations, shown in Eqs.(1) – (4). The bypass efficiency is applied to $\hat{L}_i$ and $\hat{V}_i$, as shown in Figure 1, resulting in the actual flowrates leaving the tray, which are used in mass and energy balances for stream mixing, as shown in Eqs.(6) – (9). Note that bypass efficiency must be the same for both vapour and liquid streams in a particular tray.

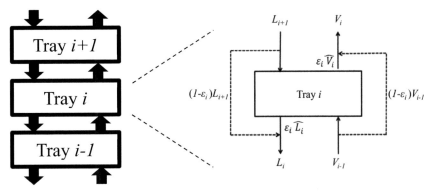

Figure 1. (Left) Distillation cascade with multiple trays. (Right) Single distillation tray with bypass streams

$$Number\ of\ Trays\ \approx \sum_i \varepsilon_i \tag{5}$$

$$x_i^c L_i = (1 - \varepsilon_i)\, x_{i+1}^c L_{i+1} + \varepsilon_i\, \widehat{x_i^c}\widehat{L}_i \tag{6}$$

$$y_i^c V_i = (1 - \varepsilon_i)\, y_{i-1}^c V_{i-1} + \varepsilon_i\, \widehat{y_i^c}\widehat{V}_i \tag{7}$$

$$H_i^l L_i = (1 - \varepsilon_i)\, H_{i+1}^l L_{i+1} + \varepsilon_i\, \widehat{H_i^l}\widehat{L}_i \tag{8}$$

$$H_i^v V_i = (1 - \varepsilon_i)\, H_{i-1}^v V_{i-1} + \varepsilon_i\, \widehat{H_i^v}\widehat{V}_i \tag{9}$$

Calculating vapour-liquid equilibrium with the main tray inlet streams (L_{i+1} and V_{i-1}) is the most important part of the model. This reformulation prevents degeneracies of the equilibrium calculation because the flow rates of L_i, L_{i+1}, ..., V_{i-1}, V_i, etc are bounded away from zero. Mitigating zero flowrate degeneracy problems allows for a nonlinear programming problem to be solved more effectively, providing an alternative to complex disjunctive or mixed integer programming approaches. Thus the new distillation model is well suited for complex process synthesis problems, such as design of large flowsheets or heat integrated multi-effect distillation systems, which typically include many higher nonlinear and nonconvex equations.

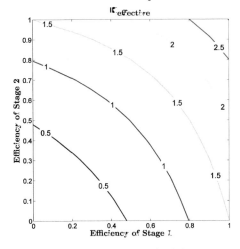

Figure 2. Separation efficiency contours ($K_{effective} = y_{out}/x_{out}$) for two tray cascade with bypass

3. Example 1 – A Single Idealized Cascade

In the first example a cascade with two equilibrium trays is simulated to demonstrate a preference for binary values for bypass efficiencies. Equal molar flowrates and a constant equilibrium coefficient are assumed for simplicity. As shown in the Figure 2 the largest $K_{effective}$ (y_{out}/x_{out}) is seen when both trays are active ($\varepsilon_1 = \varepsilon_2 = 1$). If the problem is constrained such that $\varepsilon_1 + \varepsilon_2 = 1$ the sharpest separation (largest $K_{effective}$) is observed when one tray is completely active and the other is completely bypassed. These results make physical sense, as partial bypass results in inefficient mixing between stages. These results also explain why optimization with the new model typically results in binary values for bypass fractions. Finally this example shows that non-unique solutions exist (either $\varepsilon_1 = 1$ or $\varepsilon_2 = 1$) and can be prevented with an optional ordering constraint: $\varepsilon_i \geq \varepsilon_{i+1}$.

4. Example 2 – Cryogenic Air Separation Unit Synthesis

The effectiveness of the new MESH distillation model with bypass is demonstrated in a cryogenic air separation unit (ASU) synthesis case study. ASU systems are especially difficult to optimize due to their tight heat integration requirements. Approach temperatures in these systems are typically $1 - 2$ K with multiple pinch points. ASU systems commonly include two to three columns operating at different pressures that are thermally coupled. The solution methodology and models for this case study contain several notable features. See Dowling and Biegler (2014) for additional details.

1. Double column superstructure (shown in Figure 3) with several possible feed and recycle configurations
2. Mass, equilibrium, summation and heat (MESH) equations to model distillation trays with pressure drop
3. Detailed Peng-Robinson thermodynamics with vanishing/reappearing phases
4. Large-scale nonlinear programming algorithms that exploit sparsity and exact 1st and 2nd derivatives
5. Pinch based heat integration using Duran and Grossmann (1986) formulation
6. Automated initialization procedure based on model refinements that uses the approximate cascade models developed by Kamath et al. (2010)
7. Custom multistart procedure to mitigate the impacts of nonconvex models and local optima.

The ASU superstructure (Figure 3) contains four distillation cascade sections, each with a variable number of trays. This allows for the feed location and number of trays to be optimized. Initial values for each cascade in the ASU superstructure (Figure 3) are obtained by optimizing the ASU system with an Edmister inspired compartment cascade model (Kamath et al., 2010). Rounding, fixing and re-optimization are used to obtain an integer number of trays with this approximate model. Next each cascade is initialized with as many non-bypassed trays as suggested by the approximate results. Intermediate stream temperatures, pressures, compositions and flowrates for the MESH model are calculated using interpolation. For each cascade 10 initially bypassed trays are also considered in the optimization problem, which allows for the number of active (non-bypassed) trays to increase. The MESH with bypass model is optimized several times in an iterative fashion. Between each optimization run the number of trays available in each cascade is adjusted such that there are 10 additional, initially inactive trays compared to the previous iteration results. This allows the number of trays to

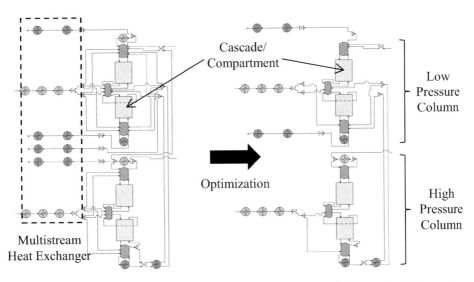

Figure 3. The optimizer starts with the double column superstructure (left image) and selects the best configuration and recycle strategy, as shown for the 95 mol% O_2 case study (right image).

significantly increase compared to the initial approximate model results. The initialization and cascade superstructure resizing procedures are completely automated in GAMS and require no user interaction between optimization runs.

Energy usage for a cryogenic air separation unit was minimized using the new MESH bypass model and initialization procedure. Optimization led to a specific energy of 0.185 kWh/kg O_2 assuming 95 mol% O_2 product, $\Delta T_{min} = 1.5$ K in the multistream heat exchanger and 86% efficient compressors, which is competitive with other studies. Detailed results and comparisons with literature are presented in Dowling and Biegler (submitted).

A custom multistart procedure, with many initial points considered in parallel, revealed several clusters of locally optimal ASU designs, each with different double column configurations (Figure 3). Optimization was performed in GAMS using CONOPT3. The entire initialization and validation procedure took 5 – 20 CPU minutes for each initial point considered. The final NLPs contained approximately 16,000 equations and constraints. As expected bypass efficiency (ε) was selected as either 0 or 1 by the NLP optimization for most of the solutions.

5. Conclusions

Reformulation of the disjunctive programming model of Yeomans and Grossmann (2000) led us to develop a new distillation model with bypass streams, which allows for a purely nonlinear model without integer variables. Most notably this model avoids degenerate equations through careful definition of bypass efficiency. Unburdened by the computational complexity of integer variables the new bypass model is well suited for optimization of large flowsheets or tightly heat integrated distillation systems. The efficacy of the model is demonstrated in an air separation unit (ASU) synthesis example that involves (a) selection of the best topology, (b) design of the multistream heat exchanger, (c) very nonlinear, nonconvex thermodynamics and (d) optimization of two thermally coupled distillation columns; this large-scale model includes approximately 16,000 equations. Furthermore the ASU case study is solved using a generic NLP solver, in contrast to the decomposition method required by Yeomans and Grossmann (2000). We plan on further demonstrating the economic benefit and efficacy of this model by optimization of an entire oxycombustion power plant, which consists of an ASU, boiler, steam turbines, pollution controls and CO_2 purification system. In this application the new distillation models enable rigorous heat integration of the air separation unit and other cryogenic systems. As future work we also plan to compare the new bypass model with the existing MINLP and NLP formulations.

Acknowledgments

This article was prepared as an account of work sponsored by an agency of the United States Government. Neither the United States Government nor any agency thereof, nor any of their employees, makes any warranty, express or implied, or assumes any legal liability or responsibility for the accuracy, completeness, or usefulness of any information, apparatus, product, or process disclosed, or represents that its use would not infringe privately owned rights. Reference herein to any specific commercial product, process, or service by trade name, trademark, manufacturer, or otherwise does not necessarily constitute or imply its endorsement, recommendation, or favoring by the United States Government or any agency thereof. The views and opinions of authors expressed herein do not necessarily state or reflect those of the United States Government or any agency thereof.

References

M. J. Andrecovich, A. W. Westerberg, 1985, An MILP formulation for heat-integrated distillation sequence synthesis, AIChE Journal, 31, 9, 1461–1474.

R. C. Baliban, J. A. Elia, C. A. Floudas, 2013, Novel Natural Gas to Liquids Processes: Process Synthesis and Global Optimization Strategies, AIChE Journal, 59, 2, 505 – 531.

A. W. Dowling, L.T. Biegler, 2014, A Framework for Efficient Large Scale Equation-Oriented Flowsheet Optimization, Computers and Chemical Engineering, http://dx.doi.org/10.1016/j.compchemeng.2014.05.013.

M. A. Duran, I. E. Grossmann, 1986, Simultaneous optimization and heat integration of chemical processes, AIChE Journal, 32, 1, 123–138.

R. S. Kamath, L. T. Biegler, I. E. Grossmann, 2010, An equation-oriented approach for handling thermodynamics based on cubic equation of state in process optimization, Computers and Chemical Engineering, 34, 12, 2085–2096.

R. S. Kamath, I. E. Grossmann, L. T. Biegler, 2010, Aggregate models based on improved group methods for simulation and optimization of distillation systems, Computers and Chemical Engineering, 34, 8, 1312–1319.

K. Kraemer, S. Kossack, W. Marquardt, 2009, Efficient Optimization-Based Design of Distillation Processes for Homogeneous Azeotropic Mixtures, Industrial and Engineering Chemistry Research, 48, 14, 6749–6764.

Y. D. Yang, L. T. Biegler, 2002, Distributed Stream Model for Tray Optimization, AIChE Journal, 48, 3, 582–59.

F. J. M. Neves, D. C. M. Silva, N. M. C. Oliveira, 2005, A robust strategy for optimization complex distillation columns, Computers and Chemical Engineering, 29, 6, 1457–1471.

J. Viswanathan, I. E. Grossmann, 1990, A Combined Penalty Function and Outer-Approximation Method for MINLP Optimization, Computers and Chemical Engineering, 14, 7, 769–782.

H. Yeomans, I. E. Grossmann, 2000, Disjunctive Programming Models for the Optimal Design of Distillation Columns and Separation Sequences, Industrial and Engineering Chemistry Research, 39, 6, 1637–1648.

Jiří Jaromír Klemeš, Petar Sabev Varbanov and Peng Yen Liew (Editors)
Proceedings of the 24th European Symposium on Computer Aided Process Engineering – ESCAPE 24
June 15-18, 2014, Budapest, Hungary. Copyright © 2014 Elsevier B.V. All rights reserved.

The Virtual Product-Process Design Laboratory for Structured Chemical Product Design and Analysis

Michele Mattei, Nor A. Yunus, Sawitree Kalakul, Georgios M. Kontogeorgis, John M. Woodley, Krist V. Gernaey, Rafiqul Gani[*]

Department of Chemical and Biochemical Engineering, Technical University of Denmark, Søltofts Plads, Building 229, Kgs. Lyngby, 2800, Denmark
rag@kt.dtu.dk

Abstract

The objective of this paper is to present new methods for design of chemicals based formulated products and their implementation in the software, the Virtual Product-Process Design Laboratory. The new products are tailor-made blended liquid products and emulsion-based products. The new software employs a template approach, where each template follows the same common steps in the workflow for design of formulated products, but has the option to employ different product specific property models, data and calculation routines, when necessary. With the new additions, the software is able to support the design and analysis of a wide range of homogeneous formulated products: tailor-made blends, single phase liquid formulations and emulsion-based products. The decision making process is supported by dedicated property models and structured databases, specifically developed for each design problem scenario. Output from the software is a small set of most promising product candidates and a short list of recommended experiments that can validate and further fine-tune the product composition. The application of the new features is highlighted through two case studies relative to an emulsion-based product and a tailor-made blend.

Keywords: Blend Design, Emulsion Design, Formulation Design, Product Design

1. Chemical Product Design

Chemical engineering is changing, gradually moving beyond the production of commodity chemicals, towards higher value added chemicals (Cussler and Moggridge, 2011). Since, however, many of the chemicals based products use these higher value chemicals, there is a rising interest in the development of systematic methodologies and related tools for the formulation and solution of chemical product design problems, reducing thereby valuable time and resources in the design stage of product development. Such systematic methods should allow these products to reach the market earlier and at a reduced cost (Gani, 2004). Recent efforts have been going towards the integration of product and process design (Chemmangattuvalappil and Ng, 2013), the improvement of experimental design (Duarte and Oliveira, 2013), but also on the development of a systematic model-based methodology applied to the design of homogeneous formulated products (Conte et al., 2011) and later adopted by Yunus et al. (2014) for the design of blended products and by Mattei et al. (2013a) for the design of emulsified products. Such approaches require the use and management of a wide range of property models, calculation procedures and a very large amount of data. To simplify the use of these procedures, they are integrated into a computer-aided framework for a class of formulated products (blends, single phase liquid formulations and emulsions).

The framework consists of a generic design workflow within which a number of problem specific templates are available for different types of product design problems. Implementation of this framework as a software has resulted in the development of the Virtual Process-Product Design Laboratory (VPPD-Lab), originally developed for the design/analysis of homogeneous formulated products (Conte et al., 2010) and now extended to tailor-made liquid blends and emulsions. A unique feature of the framework is the use of the problem specific templates employed through the generic design workflow. VPPD-Lab allows the product designer to perform virtual experiments while searching for the most promising candidates. When these are found, VPPD-Lab recommends experiments to verify the product formulations. That is, computer-aided techniques are used to search through a wide range of alternatives while precious experimental resources are reserved for focused experiments to verify the best candidates. That is, just as a process simulator is able to simulate and analyse a wide range of chemicals based processes, the VPPD-Lab is able to design and analyse a wide range of chemicals based products.

2. The Generic Workflow

The framework and its implementation as VPPD-lab are based on a generic workflow (as shown in Fig. 1) that allows different problem specific design templates to be used for different product design scenarios. The workflow consists of a set of hierarchical steps and is supported by a collection of tools (model libraries, calculation routines and databases). The workflow is based on a specifically developed ontology for knowledge representation covered by associated product attributes, their translation into properties, the corresponding property prediction models, and a wide range of data from different sources. In the first step, the product type is selected from a list of products available in the database: homogeneous formulations, gasoline blends, lubricant blends, jet fuel blends and emulsion-based formulations. In the second step, a set of product needs is retrieved from the knowledge-base and augmented, if necessary. In the third step, the product needs are translated to product attributes (properties) by the knowledgebase, which also helps to define the property target values. The fourth step employs the problem specific formulation design in terms of selecting the ingredients (chemicals) and their amounts such that the property targets are satisfied. The ingredients are classified in terms of active

Figure 1. Generic workflow

ingredients (performs the main function or activity of the product), solvents (to dissolve the active ingredient and/or to deliver the product) and additives (to enhance the product quality). In the final fifth step, each feasible product formulation is verified through model-based tests to check for stability, performance enhancement, etc. A large number of properties is needed, as well as a large number of property models to generate these values, when experimental data are missing- These are both implemented in VPPD-Lab, in terms of structured databases and property models, some of which are common to all the product types, while others are product specific. Properties like the cost, the density and the Hansen solubility parameters are necessary for all the different product design scenarios, and the property models employed are the same. Examples of product specific properties, instead, are the octane number and the Reid vapour pressure for the gasoline blends; the pour point, the vapour loss and the viscosity index for the lubricant blends; the freezing point, the net heat of combustion and the smoke point for the jet-fuel blends; and the cloud point, the Krafft temperature and the critical micelle concentration for the emulsified formulations. Additional details on the models employed for the prediction of the property values are given by Mattei et al. (2013b) in relation to emulsified formulations and by Yunus et al. (2014) in relation to gasoline and lubricant blends. Also, the product specific algorithms employed in the fourth step for individual product design can be found in Conte et al. (2011) for homogeneous formulated products, Mattei et al. (2013a) for emulsified formulations and Yunus et al. (2014) for tailor-made blends. The common elements are, for example, test for mixture stability, colouring agents, selection of aroma compounds, while, problem specific elements are, for example, selection of the main ingredients, product specific properties and their prediction models.

3. The Templates

The generic workflow employs different templates corresponding to different product design scenarios.

3.1. Tailor-made Blended Products

The design of blended liquid products (gasoline, lubricant and jet fuel) follows a systematic procedure defined in terms of four tasks.

- o   Task 1, the problem definition, is responsible for the identification of the product needs, their translation into target properties and the specification of a set of appropriate target values for the identified target properties. These data are passed from steps 1-3 of the generic workflow.
- o   Task 2collects the necessary property models from the model library. Note that different blend problems need different sets of property models. At this early design stage, simple models, even though less accurate, are preferred in order to efficiently screen the number of alternatives.
- o   Task 3 retrieves the relevant ingredient databases, then generates and screens all blend alternatives to identify the feasible set. The feasible candidates are ranked according to any desired criterion, for example, the main ingredient composition limit, a target property value, or cost. This is the fourth step in the generic workflow.
- o   Task 4 performs a model-based verification that the chosen blend satisfies the target properties. If the target values are not matched with these models, Task 3 is repeated assigning a new composition as input until a matched blend is found. This corresponds to the fifth step of the generic workflow.

3.2. Emulsion-based Products

The template for emulsion-based formulation design also follows a four tasks procedure.

- o   Task 1 is similar to the corresponding task 1 in blend design.
- o   Task 2 selects the active ingredients of the formulation from the available database. The necessary property models and data are retrieved from the libraries and a rule-based procedure is employed to make the selections.
- o   Task 3 determines the solvent mixture. For emulsion-based products, a choice needs to be made of two pure liquids required to form two distinct phases (the oil phase and the water phase). Also, a selection of an appropriate surfactant, needed to keep the above mentioned liquids in the emulsified form, is made.
- o   Task 4 is responsible for the selection of additives. When all the ingredients are chosen, a knowledgebase composition calculator determines the composition

of the formulation, decided on the basis of the cost, the product performances, and/or a combination of the two. Finally the stability of the product is assessed by means of an in-house algorithm.

4. Case Study – Tank Cleaning Detergent

The application of the new features is highlighted through the design of an emulsion-based product: a tank cleaning detergent for palm oil removal and for a tailor-made gasoline blend.

4.1. Case Study: Design of tank cleaning detergent

Step-1: Select Product Type – The product type is an emulsion based oil-in-water type of liquid product.

Step-2: Identify Product Needs -The main needs of this product are satisfactory cleaning performances and low foaming ability. As secondary needs, the product is desired to be stable in its physical form before and after the application, to have a low impact on the surface, to be easily applicable and to have a determined color, so that possible leftovers of detergent on the tank surface can be easily spotted and removed before a new loading of the tank takes place.

Step-3: Translate Product Needs - The above mentioned consumer assessments are translated into target properties and target values through the knowledgebase, as given in Table 1. Also, In relation to the water phase, non-miscibility with palm oil, physical stability (vapor pressure higher than 1 bar), safety (flash point above 100 °C) and low toxicity (lethal concentration above 3.15 mol/m^3) are needs that must be satisfied by the product to be designed.

Step-4: Select Ingredients – The emulsion-based product design algorithm outlined in section 3.2 is applied. Only tasks 2-4 are described below since task 1 has already been considered above through steps 1-3.

> Task 2: Active Ingredients Identification - The active ingredients needed for detergents are surfactants. The presence of surfactants in a water solution above their critical micelle concentration, in fact, allows the formation of micelles, which accomplish the cleaning function. Among the surfactants, non-ionic surfactants are

Table 1. List of consumer assessments and target properties for a tank cleaning detergent

	Consumer Assessment	Target Properties	Target Values
Main Needs	Cleaning performances	Surface tension	σ<40 mN/m
		Hansen solubility parameters	δ_D=17.7, δ_P=3.5, δ_H=3.7 MPa$^{0.5}$
		Hydrophilic-lipophilic balance	HLB>12
	Low foaming ability	Surface tension	σ<25 mN/m
		Critical micelle concentration	CMC>0.01 mol/L
Secondary Needs	Stability	Cloud point,	T_C>80°C
		Hydrophilic lipophilic deviation	HLD≠0
		Presence of a preservative	-
	Easy application	Kinematic viscosity	ν<75cS
	Improved dissolution	Presence of a bleaching agent	-
	Defined color	Presence of a pigment	-
	Low impact on the surface	Presence of a builder	-

usually preferred in industrial operations because of their lower foaming ability. Moreover, non-ionic surfactants are not very sensitive to changes in salinity of the solution, making the product more flexible. Employing the non-ionic surfactant database and the target values of Table 1, the final selection is made by simultaneously minimizing the cost and maximizing the performance in terms of palm oil dissolution, qualitatively modeled through Hansen solubility parameters. The most advantageous candidate obtained is a linear alkyl ethoxylate: decyl esaethylene oxide.

Task 3: Solvent Mixture Design - The oil phase in this problem is palm oil. The database relative to water phase ingredients is then screened for candidates and the decision, realized by minimizing the cost, gives water as the most advantageous water phase ingredient. Also, a surfactant must be added to the formulation in order to improve the stability of it in the emulsified form. However, an ingredient has already been chosen from the surfactant database (the active ingredient), so the co-surfactant database is considered instead. Boundaries for low foaming ability (as from Table 1) safety and toxicity are set. Moreover, it is necessary that the designed co-surfactant is compatible with the surfactant identified as active ingredient (HLB>12). Based on the above criteria, the selection of the optimal ingredient is made by minimizing the cost and butyl glycol is identified.

Task 4: Additives Identification - To match the secondary needs (see Table 1), a suitable preservative, a suitable builder, a suitable bleaching agent and a suitable pigment are needed. The selection is made through a rule-based search, where boundaries on safety and toxicity are applied again together with cost. Sodium silicate, sodium triphosphate, potassium hydroxide and titanium oxide are selected as preservative, builder, bleaching agent and pigment, respectively.

Step-5: Verify Product - In order to estimate the optimal composition, boundaries on the overall kinematic viscosity (v<75cS), and on the emulsion stability (HLD$\neq$0) are set, while the solubility of the active ingredients and additives in the two liquid phases are calculated through the UNIFAC model. Table 2 summarizes the results.

Finally, hints on experiments to be performed to validate the optimal formulation of Table 2 are given. These are the verification of the main needs (cleaning performances and low foaming ability) and of the secondary needs (mainly easy application and low impact on the surface). Moreover, stability issues such as the verification of the solubility of the ingredients in the solvent mixture and the verification of the stability of the formulation as an emulsion are needed.

4.2. Case Study – Tailor-made gasoline design
The objective here is to find renewable additives to a base gasoline that will enhance its properties while at the same time reduce the amount of non-renewable fuel. The gasoline should be able to burn and run the engine efficiently, can flow continuously

Table 2. Optimal formulation for a tank cleaning detergent for the removal of palm oil from stainless steel tanks

Ingredient	Mole %	Ingredient	Mole %
Decyl esaethylene oxide	12.3	Sodium triphosphate	2.5
Water	67.9	Potassium hydroxide	8.4
Butyl glycol	3.6	Titanium oxide	3.4
Sodium silicate	1.9		

from the fuel tank to the combustion chamber, have a suitable flammability limit, have low toxicity, be environmentally friendly and stable and does not oxidize easily. These needs are translated into the following properties and target values: heating value (HHV>40 MJ/kg), octane number (RON>92), viscosity ($0.3<\eta<0.6$ cP), density ($0.72<\rho<0.775$ g/cm^3), flash point ($T_f<300$ K), lethal concentration ($-logLC_{50}<3.08$ mol/L), oxygen content ($2<W_{tO2}<20$), Gibbs energy of mixing ($\Delta G^{mix}<0$) and suitable choice of additives, respectively. Applying the algorithm outlined in section 3.1 and the generic workflow of Fig. 1, one of the feasible blends found is the following: 69 % gasoline, 11 % tetrahydrofuran and 20 % tetrahydro-2-methyl furan, given as volumetric percentages. A more detailed case study can be found in Yunus et al. (2014).

5. Conclusion

A computer-aided framework for design of liquid formulated products of various types has been developed and implemented into the Virtual Process-Product Design Laboratory software. New templates that are employed through a generic workflow have been added to the software, making it more flexible and capable of solving a wide range of product design problems. The model libraries, the structured databases and the generic workflow are integrated through a product design ontology developed to represent the associated knowledge. The use of the framework has been highlighted through two representative case studies involving an emulsion-based detergent and a tailor-made gasoline blend.

References

N.G. Chemmangattuvalappil, D.K.S. Ng, 2013, A systematic methodology for optimal product design in an integrated biorefinery, Computer Aided Chemical Engineering, 32, 91-96.

E. Conte, R. Gani, T.I. Malik, 2010, The Virtual Process-Product Laboratory Applied to Personal Care Formulations, Computer Aided Chemical Engineering, 28, 1297-1302.

E. Conte, R. Gani, K.M. Ng, 2011, Design of Formulated Products: A Systematic Methodology, AIChE Journal, 57, 2431-2449.

E.L. Cussler, G.D. Moggridge, 2011,Chemical Product Design, Second Edition, Cambridge University Press, Cambridge, UK.

B.P.M. Duarte, N.M.C. Oliveira, 2013, Model based optimal experimental design – A semi-definite programming approach applied to a solvent design problem, Computer Aided Chemical Engineering, 32, 781-786.

R. Gani, 2004, Chemical Product Design: Challenges & Opportunities, Computers and Chemical Engineering, 28, 2441-2457.

M. Mattei, M. Hill, G.M. Kontogeorgis, R. Gani, 2013a, Design of an Emulsion Based Personal Detergent Through a Model Based Chemical Product Design Methodology, Computer Aided Chemical Engineering, 32, 817-822.

M. Mattei, E. Conte, G.M. Kontogeorgis, R. Gani, 2013b, Prediction of Thermophysical Properties of Liquid Formulated Products - U. Brockel, W. Meier, G. Wagner, Product Design and Engineering - Formulation of Gels and Pastes, WILEY-VCH, Weinheim, Germany.

N.A. Yunus, K.V. Gernaey, J.M. Woodley, R. Gani, 2014, A Systematic Methodology for Design of Tailor-made Blended Products, Computers and Chemical Engineering, DOI:10.1016/j.compchemeng.2013.12.011.

Jiří Jaromír Klemeš, Petar Sabev Varbanov and Peng Yen Liew (Editors)
Proceedings of the 24th European Symposium on Computer Aided Process Engineering – ESCAPE 24
June 15-18, 2014, Budapest, Hungary. Copyright © 2014 Elsevier B.V. All rights reserved.

Physically-based Thermodynamic Models in Integrated Process and Molecular Design

Marina Stavrou[a,c], Matthias Lampe[b], André Bardow[b], Joachim Gross[a,*]

[a] *Institute of Thermodynamics and Thermal Process Engineering, Pfaffenwaldring 9, Stuttgart University, Germany*
[b] *Institute of Technical Thermodynamics, Schinkelstrasse 8, RWTH Aachen University, Germany*
[c] *Process and Energy Laboratory, Leeghwaterstraat 44, Delft University of Technology, The Netherlands*
gross@itt.uni-stuttgart.de

Abstract

We illustrate how a physically-based thermodynamic model can be used to solve the integrated process and solvent design problem. In particular, the usually required decomposition of the integrated problem into two subproblems, a solvent design and a process optimization, is largely avoided. Our Continuous Molecular Targeting (CoMT-CAMD) method is applied to select a solvent for carbon dioxide pre-combustion capture. Molecular optimization is carried-out using a single objective function on the process costs. Physical properties of the proposed solvent are here predicted from the PC-SAFT model (Perturbed-Chain Statistical Associating Fluid Theory).

Keywords: CoMT-CAMD, PC-SAFT, solvent design, process optimization

1. Introduction

The integrated optimization of solvents and processes problem can for most practical applications not be solved directly due to the large integer search-space defined by all conceivable candidate solvents (Gani, 2004). In order to reduce the dimensionality of the design problem, a set of suitable candidate components is therefore typically pre-selected by Computer-Aided Molecular Design (CAMD). Samudra et al. (2013) reduce the initial search-space using approximate property models to allow for mixed integer linear optimization reducing the computational effort. In a subsequent step, the suitable candidates are evaluated by means of process optimization (Gani, 2007). The preliminary short-listing of components is based on auxiliary objective functions, targeting certain properties (or certain combination of properties) and on heuristics, which requires a fair knowledge and practical experience on the examined process and may lead to exclusion of the true optimal solvent.

Papadopoulos et al. (2009) proposed a multi-objective optimization strategy based on a group contribution method for modelling molecular properties. A sub-set of functional groups is pre-selected according to a certain process-related rationale and the optimal solvent is comprised of these functional groups. Pereira et al. (2011) demonstrated a CAMPD (Computer Aided Molecular and Process Design) approach to design optimal alkane blends using the SAFT-VR EoS and a cost objective function. In both cases, preliminary decisions concerning the molecular structure are introduced in order to limit the numerical complexity of the problem.

In this work, we illustrate the so-called CoMT (Continuous Molecular Targeting) -
CAMD method (Bardow et al., 2010), which utilizes a physically-based thermodynamic
model (PC-SAFT) and circumvents the mixed-integer problem formulation. Lampe et
al. (2012) recently illustrated the CoMT-CAMD method for the selection of Organic
Rankine Cycle working fluids.

2. Continuous Molecular Targeting (CoMT)-CAMD for solvent selection

Within the PC-SAFT model, each solvent is uniquely represented by a vector of pure
component molecular parameters, here referred to as 'solvent parameters', defining its
thermodynamic properties. The integrated solvent and process optimization can readily
be formulated as a regular non-linear programming (NLP) problem, when the solvent
parameters are introduced as continuous variables and treated as degrees of freedom in
the optimization (on equal footing as other process variables). Thereby, we circumvent
the mixed-integer problem and simultaneously optimize process variables and the
solvent on the basis of a single objective function defined on the process-level ("CoMT-
step"). The objective function captures the full costs of the process and thus describes
the real trade-offs that determine the optimal solvent.

The resulting optimal solvent parameters do, in general, not correspond to a real
substance. The optimization thus leads to a hypothetical substance and to process
variables optimized for this hypothetical optimal fluid. Real components with parameter
vectors in the vicinity of the optimal solvent parameters are expected to give the best
overall performance and they are identified in the final CAMD step, referred to as the
mapping step. For each real component from a parameter database, the value of the
objective function is approximated using a second order Taylor-series expansion around
the optimum, as

$$F_i^{appr} = F^{opt} + J\left(\bar{y}_{opt}\right) \cdot \left(\bar{y}_i - \bar{y}_{opt}\right)^T + \frac{1}{2} \cdot \left(\bar{y}_i - \bar{y}_{opt}\right)^T \cdot H\left(\bar{y}_{opt}\right) \cdot \left(\bar{y}_i - \bar{y}_{opt}\right). \tag{1}$$

The Jacobian (J) and the Hessian (H) of the objective at the optimum are used for this
quadratic approximation. Both, the Jacobian and the Hessian are calculated numerically
on the surface of optimal process parameters. The expansion thus accounts to second
order for shifts of the process variables for real solvents.

The result of the CoMT-CAMD approach is a list of most promising solvents that has to
be finally evaluated for other operational aspects, such as corrosiveness, hazardousness
and alike.

3. Prediction of physical properties with PC-SAFT

The PC-SAFT equation of state (Gross and Sadowski, 2001) is based on a coarse-
grained molecular model representing each molecule as a chain of spherical segments
interacting with other chain molecules. Various types of attractive interactions are taken
into account, such as van der Waals (dispersive) attraction, hydrogen-bonding
(associating) attraction, and polar interactions.

The pure component parameters that define the model for any fluid are the segment
number (m) and size (σ), the dispersive energy parameter (ε/k) and the association
energy parameter (ε^{AB}/k). Further parameters define the dipole (μ) and quadrupole
moment (Q). In this study, the association volume (κ^{AB}) is held constant to a value of

0.03. The PC-SAFT molecular parameters are available for about 1000 components in our database.

3.1. Correlation of physical properties using QSPR

To allow for a full process optimization within the proposed CoMT-CAMD method, physical properties beyond the standard properties accessible from the PC-SAFT model are required. Examples are the molar mass, the ideal gas heat capacity or transport properties. Since the CoMT-step optimizes a hypothetical molecule entirely characterized by solvent parameters of the PC-SAFT model, it is necessary to estimate these properties based on the solvent parameters. We use Quantitative Structure Property Relationship (QSPR) methods for this purpose.

Correlating transport properties, such as shear viscosity, is subject of our current development with very satisfying results. Transport properties do not enter the case study presented below and the inclusion of transport properties into the CoMT-CAMD methodology is therefore not detailed here. For problems such as the simultaneous process and working fluid design of Organic Rankine Cycles, however, these transport properties act strongly on the objective function (Lampe et al., 2012).

3.1.1. Molar mass (M) and ideal gas specific heat capacity

Molar mass can be correlated well with the PC-SAFT molecular parameters as Gross and Sadowski (2001) showed for alkanes and Grenner et al. (2007) for glycols. In this work, we present molar mass correlations for a much wider range of substances. Combinations of the PC-SAFT molecular parameters, like $m \cdot \sigma^3$ or $m \cdot \varepsilon/(kT)$, are used as descriptors (d_i) in a QSPR method with a multilinear regression model

$$M^{calc} = a_0 + \sum_{i=1}^{n} a_i \cdot d_i \cdot \tag{2}$$

The ideal gas specific heat capacity (c_p^{IG}) can be correlated with the PC-SAFT molecular parameters using also parameter combinations as descriptors, according to

$$\left(c_p^{IG}\right)^{calc} = b_0 + \sum_{i=1}^{k} b_i \cdot d_i \cdot \tag{3}$$

In the current study, we have divided the components' database into three sub-groups. The first includes all non-polar, non-associating molecules, the second all polar, non-associating molecules and the third for polar and associating molecules. The QSPR regression coefficients are calculated for each one of those subgroups.

4. Case Study: Solvent selection for a CO_2 physical absorption process

In this section, we consider the problem of solvent selection for carbon dioxide (CO_2) pre-combustion capture from a syn-gas stream of a coal-fired energy production plant. Physical absorption of CO_2 is a well-established process and allows evaluating the results of CoMT-CAMD for a sufficiently complex process flowsheet.

The considered process topology of the CO_2-absorption and desorption cycle is given in Figure 1. In the absorber, we define a constant pressure ($P_{abs} = 2$ MPa), a constant capture rate of CO_2 ($\alpha_{CO2} = 90$ %) and fixed numbers of equilibrium stages ($N_{abs} = 7$).

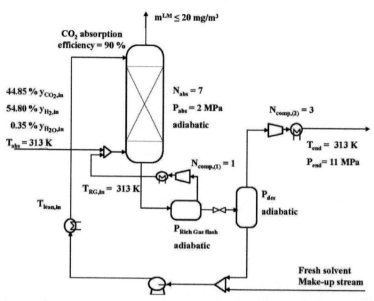

Figure 1. Process flowsheet for CO_2 capture with physical absorption and specifications

For the desorption we consider a rich-gas flash and an additional flash desorption stage. The objective function $C_{tot}(x,y,z)$ of the minimization problem defines the operating costs per ton of captured CO_2. There are two sets of optimization variables: y for the PC-SAFT molecular parameters m, σ and ε/k and x for the process variables. In this case study, we consider only non-polar, non-associating candidate solvents. The vector x, in our case, contains the desorption-flash pressure, the rich-gas flash pressure and the temperature of the lean solvent as degrees of freedom for the integrated optimization problem. The vector z includes the variables of the process streams and phase equilibria.

An emission limit m_S for the solvent in the gas stream exiting the absorber is taken into account as non-linear inequality constraint. Further, a set of linear inequality constraints is used to limit the search space to the convex hull of the molecular parameters in our database. The optimization problem is thus given by

$$\min_{\overline{x},\overline{y}} C_{tot}\left(\overline{x},\overline{y},\overline{z}\right) = \min_{\overline{x},\overline{y}}\left(\sum_{i=1} C_i\left(\overline{x},\overline{y},\overline{z}\right)\right)$$

s.t. $g\left(\overline{x},\overline{y},\overline{z}\right)=0$ \qquad (MESH flowsheet model)

$m_S\left(\overline{x},\overline{y},\overline{z}\right) \leq 20\ \frac{mg}{m^3}$ \qquad (solvent emission) \hfill (4)

$\overline{\overline{A}}\cdot\overline{y} \leq \overline{b}$ \qquad (convex hull)

$\overline{x}_{lb} \leq \overline{x} \leq \overline{x}_{ub}, \quad \overline{y}_{lb} \leq \overline{y} \leq \overline{y}_{ub}, \quad \overline{z}_{lb} \leq \overline{z} \leq \overline{z}_{ub}$

The objective function C_{tot} accounts for the following cost contributions: the costs for the overall energy demand (compressors, pump), the cost of hydrogen loss, the cost of fresh solvent (make-up) and the cost of utilities. All terms are expressed as costs [€] per ton of captured CO_2.

The binary interaction parameter, k_{ij}, for the system (CO_2 - iterated solvent) is set equal to zero for the non-associating non-polar solvents handled in this case study. For the binary systems (H_2-H_2O) and (CO_2-H_2), kij values are taken from literature. For the system (CO_2-H_2O), the temperature dependence of k_{ij} is taken into account and is based on the work of Valtz et al. (2004).

5. Results

5.1. QSPR method for c_p^{IG} and molar mass

The quality of the QSPR correlations for molar mass and for c_p^{IG} (T = 300 K) are measured with the regression coefficient R^2. We find values of R^2 = 0.9644 and R^2 = 0.9897 for molar mass and c_p^{IG} respectively. The high values of the regression coefficients show that the PC-SAFT molecular parameters are meaningful for correlating the molar mass and c_p^{IG} of the optimized molecule.

5.2. CoMT-CAMD Results

The hypothetical (non-polar, non-associating) molecule from the CoMT step is mapped onto our database of non-associating, non-polar components. The 194 entries of this subgroup are ranked according to the approximated value of the objective function using the Taylor expansion in Eq. (1). Table 1 summarizes the 10 first components of this rank list ("mapping ranking"). In order to assess the accuracy of the proposed ranked list, we performed a process optimization for each component in the database. The result of this brute-force optimization of each substances in our database ("real ranking") is compared to the performance predicted from CoMT-CAMD in Table 1.

The excellent agreement between the ranking of the CoMT-CAMD approach and the "real" ranking of processes individually optimized for the 194 database entries is an important result.

Table 1. Top solvents identified by CoMT-CAMD: "mapping ranking" denotes the rank of a substance from the mapping step according to Eq. (1). "Real ranking" gives the rank of a substance from individual process optimizations.

Component name	#mapping Ranking	#real Ranking	C_{tot} (€/$t_{capt.CO2}$)
1,5,9-CYCLODODECATRIENE	1	1	9.20
BIS(alpha-METHYLBENZYL)ETHER	2	2	9.37
2-ETHYLNAPHTHALENE	3	4	9.89
n-HEPTYLBENZENE	4	3	9.88
1-n-PROPYLNAPHTHALENE	5	5	10.00
n-HEXYLBENZENE	6	6	10.01
1,2,4-TRIETHYLBENZENE	7	7	10.04
n-OCTYLBENZENE	8	8	10.05
n-TRIDECANE	9	9	10.14
n-NONYLBENZENE	10	10	10.17

The result confirms that the CoMT step identifies the best solvent that captures all process trade-offs and that the subsequent CAMD step using a Taylor expansion is able to identify the most promising real solvents.

The rank list can be further examined concerning properties that are not captured by our model, such as toxicity or corrosivity. Higher reliability in our results concerning the real performance of the key-candidates can be gained when binary interaction parameters k_{ij} are estimated. This is subject of our future work.

6. Conclusions

In this work, we have applied the Continuous Molecular-Targeting (CoMT-CAMD) approach to solve the integrated solvent and process optimization problem of a pre-combustion carbon dioxide capture process. A sufficiently representative process topology is considered for the physical CO_2-absorption and desorption cycle. We have extended the CoMT-CAMD approach to include physical properties beyond the properties accessible from the PC-SAFT model, like the molar mass, the ideal gas specific heat capacity. With CoMT-CAMD, we successfully identified the components with the best overall performance using a single cost objective.

Acknowledgement

This study has been performed within the CO_2 Catch-up R&D program aimed at demonstrating and optimizing pre-combustion CO_2 capture technology for the energy sector. This program is executed in a consortium of Nuon (part of Vattenfall), TU Delft and ECN.

References

A. Bardow, K. Steur, J. Gross, 2009, A Continuous Targeting Approach for integrated Solvent and Process Design Based on Molecular Thermodynamic Models, Comput. Aided Chem. Eng., 27, 813-818.

R. Gani, 2004, Computer Aided Methods and Tools for Chemical Product Design, Chem. Eng. Res. Des., 82, 1494-1504.

R. Gani, 2007, Chapter 14 Case studies in chemical product design – use of CAMD techniques, Comput. Aided Chem. Eng., 23, 435-458.

A. Grenner, G. Kontogeorgis, N. von Solms, M. Michelsen, 2007, Application of PC-SAFT to glycol containing systems-PC-SAFT towards a predictive approach, Fluid Phase Equil., 261, 248-257.

J. Gross, G.Sadowski, 2001, Perturbed-chain SAFT: An equation of state based on a perturbation theory for chain molecules. Ind. Eng. Chem. Res., 40, 1244-1260.

M. Lampe, J. Gross, A. Bardow, 2012, Simultaneous process and working fluid optimization for Organic Rankine Cycles (ORC) using PC-SAFT, Comput. Aided Chem. Eng., 30, 572-576.

A. I. Papadopoulos, P. Linke, 2009, Integrated solvent and process selection for separation and reactive separation systems. Chem. Eng. Process., 48, 1047–1060.

F.E. Pereira, E. Keskes, A. Galindo, G. Jackson, C.S. Adjiman, 2011, Integrated solvent and Process design using a SAFT-VR thermodynamicdescription: High-pressure separation of carbon dioxide and methane, Comput. Chem. Eng., 35, 474-491.

A.P. Samudra, N.V. Sahinidis, 2013, Optimization-Based Framework for Computer-Aided Molecular Design, AIChE J, 59, 3686–3701.

A. Valtz, A. Chapoy, C. Coquelet, P. Paricaud, D. Richon, 2004, Vapour-liquid equilibria in the carbon dioxide-water system measurement and modeling from 278.2 to 318.2K, Fluid Phase Equil., 226, 333-344.

Jiří Jaromír Klemeš, Petar Sabev Varbanov and Peng Yen Liew (Editors)
Proceedings of the 24th European Symposium on Computer Aided Process Engineering – ESCAPE 24
June 15-18, 2014, Budapest, Hungary. Copyright © 2014 Elsevier B.V. All rights reserved.

Synthesis and Design of Interplant Water Networks using Direct Recycling Techniques within Industrial Cities

Sabla Y. Alnouri [a,b], Patrick Linke [a,*], Mahmoud M. El-Halwagi [b]

[a]*Department of Chemical Engineering, Texas A&M University at Qatar, P.O Box 23874, Education City, Doha, Qatar*
[b]*The Artie McFerrin Department of Chemical Engineering, Texas A&M University, College Station, Texas, USA*
patrick.linke@qatar.tamu.edu

Abstract

An optimization framework that considers direct recycling strategies for wastewater re-use amongst multiple processing facilities is utilized in this work. The approach considers industrial city arrangements, by capturing water source and sink locations, available service corridors for water transport, as well as any barriers that exist in between. Shortest source-to-sink routings were determined according to Dijkstra's Algorithm, which is a path search algorithm that produces a shortest path tree for determining the best route. This greatly facilitates finding optimum distances for the planning of cost-effective water piping layouts. Moreover, a systems water integration approach in the form of direct recycling was utilized to make decisions on optimal stream allocation for source-to-sink options within the plot. In order to illustrate the proposed methodology, a case study has been carried out that involves an industrial city layout consisting of five water sources, five water sinks, and a total of three plants. Efficient water allocation strategies that employ shortest source-to-sink routes were obtained, thus allowing cost-effective water network designs to be achieved. Moreover, pressure drops within the pipe segments of the water network were also accounted for.

Keywords: Water Integration, Network Design, Industrial Cities

1. Introduction

The development of effective wastewater management strategies is a major challenge faced by industries today. Many recent studies are focused on the efficient sharing of water resources that can bring considerable economic and environmental benefits to industrial cities, and hence promote sustainable development. Based on the concept of industrial symbiosis that has been introduced in the field of industrial ecology (Gibbs and Deutz, 2007), resource consumption and waste generation can be minimized by allowing industrial wastewater to be recycled amongst several co-locating firms, according to their geographical proximity. The interaction of multiple processing facilities within an industrial city often makes it easier to achieve attractive water conservation strategies, and hence would be more economically attractive than having separate wastewater handling schemes for each plant. Identifying effective opportunities for wastewater reuse and recycle amongst processing facilities can be achieved by applying water integration techniques, which in turn can significantly decrease wastewater disposal, as well as freshwater utility usage.

2. Previous Work

Wang and Smith (1994) proposed a conceptual methodology that is aimed towards maximizing water reuse (MWR) in process industries, in which wastewater minimization can be achieved via a targeting stage. Attempts to take water integration methodologies from a local level to a global one were then tackled. A number of problems that involve water integration within Eco-Industrial Parks (Côté and Cohen-Rosenthal, 1998) were studied, using a variety of mathematical programming techniques, to establish interplant water network designs that are capable of maximizing industrial wastewater reuse. Chew et al. (2008) studied the various opportunities for Interplant Water Integration (IPWI) problems by formulating both MILP and MINLP models that obtain global solutions for optimum water integration. Lovelady and El-Halwagi (2009) employed a source-interception-sink representation that accounts for direct recycling options, as well as the utilization of water treatment interception units, and achieves solutions for water allocation scenarios amongst multiple processing systems that have a common Eco-Industrial Park (EIP) facility. More recent studies by Biox et al. (2012) involve the development of a methodology to design industrial water networks in a multi-objective optimization strategy.

3. Research Problem

Despite all research efforts that have been made for the design of interplant water integration networks, capturing industrial city spatial layouts within the problem is frequently disregarded. As a result, plant arrangements are often not accounted for, and this certainly affects information needed in terms of distances between water sources and sinks within the different processing facilities. Moreover, even though corridor availability in between plants must also be one of the factors that should determine the feasibility of a particular water allocation strategy, no attempts have yet been made in this regard. Thus, the ability to efficiently capture plant locations using an industrial city spatial representation is inevitably important when designing interplant water networks. Effective routing opportunities often need to be achieved between water sources and sinks, by taking into consideration industrial city corridor boundaries that define available regions for water transport. Therefore, this work attempts to demonstrate the design of interplant networks using conventional direct recycling techniques for water integration, whilst accounting for industrial city layouts, and providing optimum water allocation routes.

4. Methodology

This work adopts a flexible approach that helps identify plausible interplant water allocation strategies within any defined industrial city layout, whilst taking into consideration existing boundaries and barriers when extracting the optimum source-sink paths. Once all routing and connectivity between the respective plants has been determined according to the defined layout, feasible water source-sink allocations that satisfy composition and flowrate requirements can be obtained, allowing optimum designs to be extracted. Hence, this work involves the following main aspects: (1) defining the industrial city or (EIP) layout, (2) obtaining routing and connectivity for interplant piping, and (3) determining optimum source-sink water allocations.

4.1. Defining the Industrial City layout

An industrial city is a zone or area that consists of a cluster of stand-alone industrial facilities, all operating simultaneously. It is usually located on the outskirts of a city, and is normally provided with good transportation access, including road and rail. Industrial cities offer integrated infrastructure for the various plants in one location, which would regulate the operation of all existing processes. Specifying the locations of all processing plants, and their respective water consuming and producing operations is essential when defining the area/zone. Moreover, all available service corridors that can accommodate water transport, access ports that allow corridors to be reached from within a plant facility, and any barriers that exist in between plants and corridor facilities need to be identified. Figure 1 demonstrates an example consisting of a total of 3 plants, with 5 water sources and 5 water sinks.

4.2. Obtaining routing and connectivity for interplant piping

Having defined the layout of the industrial city, obtaining information for optimum routes between the respective water source & sink locations, is required for water network design. The optimum distance was always assumed to be the shortest one; therefore, Dijkstra's Algorithm (Dijkstra, 1959), which is a path search algorithm that produces the shortest path tree between a source node and a destination node, was used to determine all shortest source-to-sink routes. The industrial city was classified into two different regions: (1) active regions which include areas that are available for water transport, (2) inactive regions that involve obstructed areas that must to be excluded when determining pathways for water transport.

This greatly facilitates finding all optimum distance information for planning cost-effective interplant water piping.

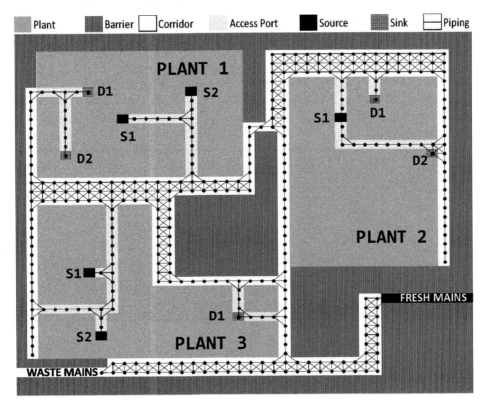

Figure 1. Industrial city layout example

4.3. Determining optimum source-sink water allocation

Conventional water integration methods for direct recycling were utilized for finding optimum source-sink mappings (Wang and Smith, 1994). Flow and contaminant concentrations for available water users (sources) were used to determine plausible recycling strategies, by making sure that maximum contamination levels that are allowed in each water sink are not exceeded, while satisfying the required sink flowrates. The problem was formulated as a NLP, for which optimum solutions that identify cost effective source-sink allocation strategies can be obtained, whilst considering the target limits for minimum use of freshwater across all plants, as well as minimum water discharge.

5. Case Study

This case study illustrates the methodology that has been proposed in this work, using the layout in Figure 1. A total area of 36 km^2, spread over 1600 equally-spaced regions, was assumed for the plot. All shortest source-to-sink distances were obtained by executing Dijkstra's Algorthim. Table 1 summarizes all the distance information, together with the number of elbow's/bends within each optimum route that has been extracted, which in turn was used for computing the respective pressure drops within the pipes. It should be noted that this work utilizes a separate pipe for each source-sink allocation, and no merging scenarios for common regions amongst the pipelines were considered.

Table 2 provides the flowrate and contaminant composition data used in this case study. In order to determine the optimum water allocation strategies using the routing information that has been extracted, the nonlinear optimization problem for direct recycling was solved using "what'sBest9.0.5.0" LINDO Global Solver for Microsoft Excel 2010, using a desktop PC with Intel® Core ™ i7-2620M, 2.7 GHz, 8.00 GB RAM, and a 64-bit Operating System. Minimizing the global freshwater consumption yields a total of 416.5 t/h and 291.5 t/h of minimum fresh and wastewater as targets.

Table 1.Shortest distances for source-to sink routes extracted, and number of elbows/bends associated (in brackets)

Distances (km)	P1D1	P1D2	P2D1	P2D2	P3D1	Waste
P1S1	5.94 (8)	6.6 (10)	5.88 (12)	7.3 5(15)	4.95 (8)	8.49 (15)
P1S2	5.58 (6)	6.24 (8)	5.52 (10)	6.99 (13)	4.59 (6)	8.13 (13)
P2S1	8.13 (12)	8.79 (14)	1.47 (4)	1.62 (3)	5.79 (8)	8.49 (7)
P3S1	4.56 (8)	5.22 (10)	6.6 (14)	8.07 (17)	4.56 (10)	8.1 (17)
P3S2	5.43 (6)	6.09 (8)	7.5 (14)	8.97 (17)	5.46 (10)	9.0 (17)
Fresh	9.69 (21)	10.35 (23)	8.31 (11)	9.78 (14)	3.3 (9)	4.59 (6)

Table 2.Flowrate and composition data for respective water sources and sinks

Source	Flow (ton/h)	Conc. (ppm)	Sink	Flow(ton/h)	Max. Conc. (ppm)
P1S1	160	200	P1D1	210	140
P1S2	180	350	P1D2	160	180
P2S1	70	470	P2D1	200	90
P3S1	105	320	P2D2	150	150
P3S2	230	280	P3D1	150	120

Table 3. Optimum water allocation strategy & calculated pressure drop values for each allocation

	P1D1	P1D2	P2D1	P2D2	P3D1	Waste
P1S1 (ton/h)	0	0	0	70.0	90.0	0
(bar)	0	0	0	5.62	5.99	0
P1S2 (ton/h)	0	0	0	0	0	180.0
(bar)	0	0	0	0	0	6.17
P2S1 (ton/h)	0	0	0	0	0	70.0
(bar)	0	0	0	0	0	6.3
P3S1 (ton/h)	63.43	0	0	0	0	41.56
(bar)	2.91	0	0	0	0	2.89
P3S2 (ton/h)	32.5	102.8	64.28	30.35	0	0
(bar)	1.03	9.43	4.91	1.51	0	0
Fresh (ton/h)	114.06	57.14	135.7	49.64	60.0	0
(bar)	15.9	4.28	3.01	3.31	5.19	0

The optimum interplant water network design was found to achieve the same water targets, for a minimum total annualized cost of 1.073×10^6 \$/yr (5.98×10^5 \$/yr of which correspond to annualized piping expenses, and 4.74×10^5 \$/yr are for freshwater costs). Carbon steel Schedule 80 welded pipes were assumed (having cost parameters a=696.58 and b=1.215). Moreover, freshwater cost =0.13 \$/t, operating hours =8,760 hr/yr, and piping costs were annualized over 20 years Table 3 summarizes the optimum water allocation strategy, and provides the pressure drops obtained, corresponding to a range of values between 1~16 bars. Figure 2 illustrates the solution obtained. Performing water integration in between plants was found to yield significant savings in fresh consumption and waste discharge (52.19 % and 50.16 % respectively).

6. Conclusions

A flexible representation for industrial city layouts has been captured, which assisted in the exploration of infrastructure settings whilst designing interplant water networks. The representation considers industrial city corridors, access ports, as well as barriers in between. A case study has been carried out as a demonstrative example, showing an effective water allocation strategy for the network.

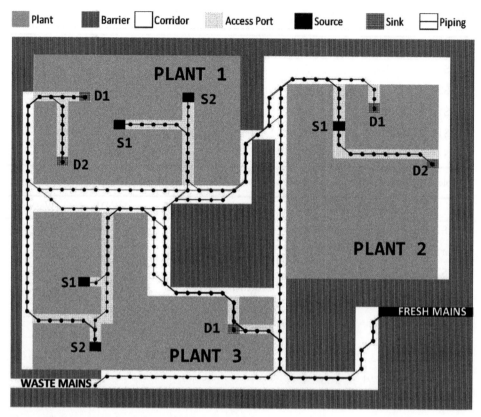

Figure 2.Solution extracted for interplant water network

Acknowledgment

This publication was made possible by NPRP grant no. 4-1191-2-468 from the Qatar National Research Fund (a member of Qatar Foundation). The statements made herein are solely the responsibility of the authors.

References

D. Gibbs, P. Deutz, 2007, Reflections on implementing industrial ecology through ecoindustrial park development, J. Clean. Prod., 15, 1685–1695.

E.M. Lovelady, M.M. El-Halwagi, 2009, Design and integration of eco-industrial parks for managing water resources, Environ. Prog. Sustain. Energy, 28, 265-272.

E.W. Dijkstra, 1959, A note on two problems in connexion with graphs, Numerische Mathematik, 1, 269–271.

I.M.L. Chew, R.R. Tan, D.K.S. Ng, D.C.Y. Foo, T. Majozi, J. Gouws, 2008, Synthesis of direct and indirect interplant water network, Ind. Eng. Chem. Res., 47, 9485-9496.

Lindo Systems, What'sBest! 9.0 - Excel Add-In for Linear, Nonlinear Optimization <www.lindo. com/index.php?option=com_content&view=article&id=3&Itemid=11> accessed on 18/07/2013

M. Boix, L. Montastruc, L. Pibouleau, C. Azzaro-Pantel, S. Domenech, 2012, Industrial water management by multi-objective optimization, J.Clean. Prod., 22, 85-97.

R. P. Côté, E. Cohen-Rosenthal, 1998, Designing eco-industrial parks: a synthesis of some experience, J. of Clean. Prod., 6, 3-4, 181-188.

Y. P. Wang, R. Smith, 1994, Wastewater minimization, Chem. Eng. Sci., 49, 7, 981.

Jiří Jaromír Klemeš, Petar Sabev Varbanov and Peng Yen Liew (Editors)
Proceedings of the 24th European Symposium on Computer Aided Process Engineering – ESCAPE 24
June 15-18, 2014, Budapest, Hungary.

Reliability Integration to Process Synthesis applied to GTL Processes

Herib Blanco,[a,b*] Johan Grievink,[a] Nort Thijssen,[b] Paulien Herder[c]

[a] *Department of ChemE, Delft University of Technology, Julianalaan 136, 2628 BL Delft, The Netherlands*
[b] *Shell Global Solutions International BV, 1030 BN Amsterdam, The Netherlands*
[c] *Faculty of Technology, Policy and Management, Delft University of Technology, 2600 GA Delft, The Netherlands*
herib.blanco@shell.com

Abstract

This work presents a simplified steady state reliability model to estimate the variation in stream days due to structural changes in a process and makes a trade-off with process efficiency and cost. The model does not consider simultaneous failures in different parts of the process, leading to an error of less than 1 % point in the plant reliability. The main variables to manipulate are number of equipment in parallel and individual capacity. The model has been implemented in Excel for developing understanding and validation as well as in AIMMS for integration with the existing superstructure for GTL process synthesis. The model setup and approach can be applied to any process: an application is defined by the data used and configuration. An application to GTL yields a reduced cost at the expense of slight decrease in number of stream days.

Keywords: Reliability modeling, process synthesis, optimization, GTL.

1. Introduction

Gas-to-Liquid (GTL) processes can play a pivotal role in turning an abundance of natural gas into a secure long term and clean supply of energy. GTL processes are capital intensive and have a complicated structure, justifying a study into reliability integration in process synthesis. The process design is determined by three features: (a) Conversion efficiency of feed into products (GTL: Natural Gas => Liquid fuels); (b) Availability (stream days or fraction of time available for production per year); (c) Annual profit (before taxes) defined as revenues minus CAPEX and OPEX. Finding an optimal design requires looking broad enough, both in terms of processing structure and in terms of operating conditions. Creating a process superstructure and applying optimization is one solution for such a problem. This has been successfully solved with Mixed Integer Non Linear Programming (MINLP) for new GTL processes (Baliban et al., 2013). A superstructure with process model for GTL process synthesis is available (Ellepola et al., 2012). The reliability consideration early in the design process has been recognized before (Sriramdas et al., 2014), the difference being the focus on reliability allocation for the uncertainty in the structure rather than optimization.

The objective of this work is to present a simplified reliability model to determine intrinsic availability to use in combination with the process superstructure. Model complexity has to be low enough to consider the simultaneous use of different criteria and still have a manageable and comprehensive enough problem. In agreement with this objective, the values considered for reliability are the corresponding steady state values.

For some units, the planned downtime dominates the availability. Thus, to obtain the total on-stream days, the major planned activities (requiring equipment shutdown) have to be considered. Shutdown and startup time is considered additional to the repair time. The planned downtime is considered as fixed input and maintenance optimization is not done. The balance between reliability and cost has been studied before in a more complex way (Sharma et al., 2012). This work considers a simple approach, with annual profit as objective function, with reliability being a system of algebraic equations representing a behavioral model, including design decision variables.

2. Reliability Model

The starting point for the model is the process flow sheet. From this, the consequences upon failure for each unit are assessed, in terms of production loss. One way of representing the failure-effect behavior for the system is a Reliability Block Diagram (RBD), see Hoyland and Rausand (1994). The RBD has been used before (Goel, 2004), as representation for the reliability when integrating it with process synthesis. The model comprises a structure given by failure-consequence relations and a behavioral part given by the representative equation depending on the configuration. The RBD segregation is in the process unit level and each sub-system is defined based on the change between parallel equipment and common units.

The first step is to identify the possible configurations in an RBD based on subsystems and sub-divide it in cases. Depending on criticality, the equipment could be arranged in series or in parallel. The approach is to have a set of generic equations to calculate the sub-system reliability and then build up the process reliability from the individual reliabilities of subsystems by using structural information. The key variables to estimate the reliability of each sub-system are inherent equipment reliability, number of equipment items in parallel and capacity of a single item. The individual capacity is the flow that equipment can process in relation to the maximum for the system.

When the n elements in a sub-system are in parallel, the equivalent capacity for the configuration is obtained through the sum of the possible intermediate levels of production (system state). For each state of a subsystem (j) it is needed: 1. Capacity (maximum flow produced); 2. Probability.

$$C_j = \min[\textstyle\sum_{i=1}^n C_i, C_S] \; ; A_j = \prod_{i=1}^n A_i \; C_{T,j} = C_j \cdot A_j \tag{1}$$

Individual availability is estimated as: $A_i = MTTF_i/(MTTF_i + MTTR_i)$; which is equivalent to the uptime divided by the total time span. The capacity for the sub-system state (C_j) is the minimum between the design capacity for the entire plant ($C_S = 100\ \%$) and the sum of the equipment capacity in parallel (C_i). The probability for each state (A_j) of a sub-system is obtained from the multiplication of the inherent availability for each element, considering its operating condition. When all the states are added up and considering the different combinations possible for each production level, a general equation can be deducted for the expected capacity of a subsystem:

$$C_T = \textstyle\sum_{i=w+1}^{n-1}(n-i)C_i \binom{n}{n-i} A^{n-i}(1-A)^i + C_S \cdot \sum_{i=0}^{w}\binom{n}{n-i} A^{n-i}(1-A)^i \tag{2}$$

Where "i" is the number of equipment down, "w" is the number of full spares and "A" and "C" are the availability and capacity for a single element. As an example, for a 4-element sub-system where each element has 30 % capacity, expected capacity will be:

$$C_T = 100\ \%\cdot0.95^4 + 4*90\ \%\cdot0.95^3\cdot0.05 + 6\cdot60\ \%\cdot0.95^2\cdot0.05^2 + 4\cdot30\ \%\cdot0.95\cdot0.05^3 \quad (3)$$

When the elements in the system are in series, the complexity is lower. The system capacity is equal to the element with the lower capacity from the sequence, being this a restricting element. A new variable is introduced, namely a bypass capacity ($C_{R,i}$), this is defined as the partial production upon failure. An example is a reactor operating at lower throughput upon failure of the recycle compressor. The effectiveness of each sub-system is corrected with the bypass capacity.

$$C_T = C_s \cdot \prod_{i=1}^{n} A_i + \sum_{i=1}^{n}\left(C_{R,i} \cdot (1 - A_i) \cdot \prod_{j \neq i}^{n} A_j\right) \quad (4)$$

With these equations, sub-systems are successively combined until a single equivalent availability is obtained. First, parallel equipment is collapsed into one, considering the single capacities and availabilities. Then, parallel blocks are combined. This parallel-series reduction can be carried out a few times. The main outcome is an expected availability and capacity of the entire system obtained by summation over all productive states. The main assumptions are: sub-systems are considered individually, failures in other sub-systems are not considered; failure rates are not dependent on the process operating conditions; an item after each repair is considered to be "as good as new".

3. Reliability Superstructure

In spite of the process complexity, the reliability representation is much simpler than the process superstructure. All the elements can be in a series arrangement and additional inequality constraints can be added to determine the reliability of a sub-system according to its presence or not in the superstructure. When the sub-system is being considered ($y_i = 1$), the reliability comes from the expressions in Section 2, whereas when the unit is not there ($y_i = 0$), the unit reliability is assigned as 1, having no effect over the system reliability. The additional constraints are:

$$(1 - y_i) \cdot (1 - A_{i.min}) + A_{i.min} \leq A_i \leq (1 - y_i) \cdot (1 - A_{i.max}) + A_{i.max} \quad (5)$$

In case of recycles and process interactions, the treatment for the superstructure is the same as presented before, where it is an additional block in series with partial or no production (reduced capacity, C_R) upon failure depending on the effect over the process. The level of detail in the superstructure can also be adjusted. The initial consideration is the equipment level, but it can also be broken down to individual elements (valves, transmitters, switches, etc.) for more detailed process engineering.

4. Economic Model and Objective Function

For the case of reliability, the economics serve both as a variable to quantify the improvements and to quantify the additional resource (investment) required. Hence, the variables can be related to the objective function (on annual basis):

Profit = Revenues-Investment (Annual)-Maintenance-Operation-Feed (6)
Revenues = Liquid Production (t/d) $\cdot C_T/C_S\cdot$365.25$\cdot$Product price ($/t) (7)

The revenues are related to the production rate, which comes from the process simplified (mass balance) equations and superstructure. At the same time, the revenues are dependent on the number of operating days, which is a function of the reliability.

Investment is a function of the equipment count and size, which are the two main variables affecting the reliability. Therefore, the investment is expressed as a function of these two variables, through a continuous and differentiable function.

$$TIC_i = \text{f(X)} \cdot TIC_{ref} \quad \text{with} \quad f(1) = 1 \quad \frac{df}{dx} > 0 \quad \text{and} \quad X_{min} < X < X_{max} \tag{8}$$

"X" is the ratio between the capacity being estimated and the reference. It considers number of equipment in parallel (n) and overdesign (f), which is defined as the capacity surplus for individual equipment.

$$X = \frac{c_O}{c_{ref}} = \frac{c_S}{n \cdot c_{ref}} \cdot (1 + f) \tag{9}$$

There are additional constraints to maintain the equipment size within the known range for the investment correlations. All the critical information for the optimization problem is shown in Figure 1a. A new part of this problem is the behavioral model for the reliability, which has to be validated.

5. Model validation: accuracy and limitations

A disadvantage of the proposed model is that through the summation the intermediate states are lost. For example, when there are two sub-systems of 4 elements and one element fails, the other sub-system has a spare, which improves its reliability. When systems are considered individually, advantage is not taken when the bottleneck is somewhere else. To validate the model, the contribution of these intermediate states is quantified. The reliability was estimated by the successive parallel-series reduction presented before. The exact reliability was done with Shell's in-house software (System for Production Availability and Resource Consumption – SPARC). When a single sub-system is considered, there is no difference, as the equations are the same. The difference arises when more sub-systems in parallel are considered. The main effects to evaluate are: lower individual reliability (higher probability of simultaneous failures) and number of equipment in parallel. For doing this, the number of sub-systems of 2-parallel units is successively increased (Figure 1b).

The difference is expressed as the exact reliability minus the approximate value divided by the approximate one (percentage wise). The difference becomes larger with more systems in series, as there are more items which can fail and increases the probability of two being down at the same time. The same effect is seen with lower individual reliability. For a high reliability >99 %, the difference is <0.3 %.

To have the trade-off between both effects (high unit reliability and number of systems in parallel), an example is presented in Table 1. The plant has been divided in 3 main sections and the reliability for each section is presented along with the number of sub-

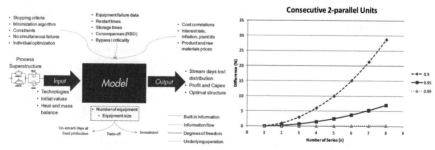

Figure 1. (a) Input-output diagram for the combined process-reliability-economics optimization. (b) Difference between exact and approximate reliability.

systems in series. It can be seen that for each of the sections, the error remains under 0.3 % point and for the entire plant is in the order of 0.8 % point.

6. Implementation and solving

The model implementation is done for GTL, with the capability of all the possible connections (no specific case). For developing understanding of the reliability model and interaction with economics, the model has been built in Excel, using Visual Basic. The Excel solver is used for getting an initial idea of the optimal values. The Excel tool is capable of either optimizing the single systems without considering the interaction or doing the exact reliability estimation (by considering intermediate states) and eliminating the error seen in Figure 1. Each step (exact reliability and optimization) takes some time to solve, which is the reason for not doing the exact reliability for each of the iterations, but only for the final configuration. There are a total of 24 sub-systems, which are arranged all in series and have the constraints (depending on structure) to consider the single reliability.

Profit optimization with the reliability model is a MINLP problem. Integer variables are needed to count the number of parallel units in a sub-system and to ensure that the subsystem capacity percentage does not exceed the maximum capacity percentage of a subsystem (which can occur in case there are spare units). The reliability model has been implemented in AIMMS 3.13 to enable a) integration with the existing Process Synthesis Tool (Ellepola et al. 2012) and b) usage of the state of the art solvers CONOPT 3.14V (Drudd, 1994), for NLP and BARON 11 for MINLP (Sahinidis and Tawarmalani, 2009). As there are no interactions between the subsystems, the problem can be decomposed by subsequently solving the problem for each particular subsystem. As starting point the solution from the EXCEL model is used and a range is given for adapting the initial number of units in a subsystem. The size of the resulting sub-problems can go up to 492 rows, 504 columns (170 integer) and 1310 non-zeros. Solving time on a 64-bit Intel® Core™ i7-2820QM CPU @ 2.30 GHz laptop is less than 2.2 s per subsystem. No changes to the default settings of CONOPT and BARON were needed. For 4 subsystems the solution found by AIMMS was better than the solution provided by EXCEL. When the problem is given to AIMMS/BARON/CONOPT as one integrated problem (3,562 rows, 3,740 columns (1,281 integer) and 9,555 non-zeros) the software does not detect automatically that the problem could be decomposed in independent sub-problems and could not be solved to optimality in an acceptable amount of time.

7. Case study

A desktop conceptual design case is taken and some common initial values are assumed, the representative initial values are presented in

Table 2, in columns 3 - 6, along with the resulting parameters after optimization, in columns 7 - 10.

Table 1. Reliability comparison for an example GTL plant.

	Systems in parallel	Exact	Approximate	Difference
Section 1	4	98.1 %	97.9 %	0.18 %
Section 2	10	97.3 %	97.0 %	0.33 %
Section 3	3	96.0 %	95.9 %	0.09 %
Total	17	91.8 %	91.0 %	0.82 %

Table 2. Difference in variables, reliability and cost for a desktop conceptual design case.

Unit	Bypass	Before optimization				After optimization				Constraint
		n	f	SDL	TIC	n	f	SDL	TIC	
A	0	2	0	3.8	0.12	1	0	3.8	0.11	Cost max size
B	0	1	0	4.4	0.15	1	0	4.4	0.17	Cost max size
C	0	4	0.5	0.1	0.08	4	0.35	0.1	0.07	Cost min size
D	0	7	0.1	1.7	1.00	5	0	4.0	1.00	Cost max size
E	0	7	0.2	1.2	0.34	4	0.33	0.8	0.24	Cost > Benefit
F	0	6	0.2	3.0	0.61	9	1/8	3.0	0.62	Cost > Benefit
G	0.875	2	0	1.1	0.30	3	0	1.5	0.21	Cost > Benefit
H	0	1	0	0.7	0.01	1	0	0.6	0.01	Cost > Benefit
I	0.875	2	0.1	0.1	0.19	2	0	0.1	0.21	Cost > Benefit
J	0.875	2	0.1	0.7	0.11	2	0	0.7	0.13	Cost > Benefit
Total				17	5.81			19	4.96	

The more units in parallel, the larger is the effect of a small overdesign, while smaller equipment leads to a higher cost. The scaled costs (TIC) are expressed relative to the most expensive unit (Unit D) and the total is presented just for comparison with the cost after optimization. Some units (G, I, J) have bypass, reducing the contribution to stream days lost (SDL). A and B, the economies of scale dominate over splitting in two or more and having overdesign. Hence, it is better to lose 8.2 SD for the two units. Unit C had initially spare capacity which was too expensive for the benefit in SD. Unit D is so expensive that it is better to lose SD and avoid any extra investment in spare capacity. Overall, a counter-intuitive result is obtained, the stream days lost increase (from 17 to 19), while the cost reduces.

8. Conclusions

A simplified reliability model has been developed for use in process design. This model is based on algebraic equations by adding up the different production levels at various states of partial failure of process units. The model does not consider simultaneous failures, which introduces an error. This error is below 1 % point for the plant reliability for common values of unit reliabilities. A reliability superstructure was constructed with all the reliabilities being multiplied and additional constraints to avoid the influence of units not present. The model was implemented in Excel for testing and validation and in AIMMS for integration with a GTL process superstructure. An application to a desktop conceptual design case study showed a reduction in cost with a two stream days loss.

References

R. Baliban, J. Elia, C. Floudas, 2013, Novel Natural Gas to Liquids Processes: Process Synthesis and Global Optimization Strategies, AIChE Journal, 59, 505-531.

A. Drudd, 1994, CONOPT – A large-scale GRG code, ORSA J Comput, 6(2), 207–16.

J. Ellepola. N. Thijssen, J. Grievink, G. Baak, A. Avhale, J. Schijndel, 2012, Development of a synthesis tool for Gas-To-Liquid complexes, Computers and Chemical Engineering, 42, 2– 14.

H. Goel, 2004, Integrating Reliability, Availability and Maintainability (RAM) in Conceptual Process Design, PhD Thesis, TU Delft, Netherlands, ISBN 90-4027-2502-0.

N. Sahinidis, M. Tawarmalani, 2009, BARON, <www.gams.com/dd/docs/solvers/baron.pdf> accessed on 01/12/2013

R. Sharma, P. Sharma, 2012, Integrated framework to optimize RAM and cost decisions in a process plant, Journal of Loss Prevention in the Process Industries, 25, 6, 883-904.

V. Sriramdas, S. Chatuverdi, H. Gargama, 2014, Fuzzy arithmetic based reliability allocation approach during early design and development, Expert Syst. Appl., 41, 3444-3449.

Jiří Jaromír Klemeš, Petar Sabev Varbanov and Peng Yen Liew (Editors)
Proceedings of the 24th European Symposium on Computer Aided Process Engineering – ESCAPE 24
June 15-18, 2014, Budapest, Hungary. Copyright © 2014 Elsevier B.V. All rights reserved.

Integrating Glycerol to Methanol vs. Glycerol to Ethanol within the Production of Biodiesel from Algae

Mariano Martín[a] [*], Ignacio Grossmann[b]

[a]*Department of Chemical Engineering, University of Salamanca, 37008, Salamanca, Spain*
[b]*Department of Chemical Engineering. Carnegie Mellon University. 5000 Forbes Ave., Pittsburgh P.A.*
mariano.m3@usal.es

Abstract

In this work, we use a superstrucutre optimization approach for the comparison between traditional biodiesel plants and the integration of glycerol to methanol production or its use to obtain ethanol within the production of biodiesel from algae. In the first case the glycerol is reformed, either autoreforming or steam reforming, the raw syngas purified and whose composition (H_2:CO ratio) is adjusted for the production of methanol. The methanol once purified is used for the transesterification of the oil produced from the algae. In the second case we take advantage of the fact that the algae composition allows the simultaneous production of ethanol and biodiesel. The starch is liquified and saccharified to obtain glucose that is fermented to ethanol. On the other hand, the oil is transesterified with ethanol to produce biodiesel, either using an enzymatic or an homogeneous catalysts. The glycerol is fermented to ethanol. Both water-ethanol, streams from glucose and from glycerol are fed to a multieffect column and later to a molecular sieve. The dehydrated ethanol is used for the transesterification of the oil while the excess is sold as biofuel. Glycerol as byproduct is still interesting as long as its price is over \$0.05 /kg. In terms of integrated facilities, the use of glycerol to produce ethanol requires almost twice the investment, but the production cost is a fourth lower with an increased production of biofuels by 50 %.

Keywords: Biodiesel, bioethanol, methanol, algae.

1. Introduction

The use of biomass as feedstock to obtain liquid fuels has become potentially attractive due to their compatibility with the current automobiles and petrol supply chains. In many cases the profitability of biofuels depends on the economy of the byproducts. For some time glycerol has been a valuable byproduct in the biodiesel industry. However, the increase in the production of biodiesel results in an excess of glycerol with a limited market (Pagliaro and Rossi, 2010) reducing the price of glycerol to values below \$0.10 /lb (Ahmed and Papalias, 2010). Under these expected revenues from glycerol, the production cost of biodiesel increases at least \$0.15 /gal from the values presented by Martín and Grossmann (2012). Glycerol is an interesting raw material that can be used for the production of a number of chemicals from H_2 (Siew et al., 2013), FT-fuels, propanodiol, glycerol ethers (Cheng et al., 2011), but also methanol and ethanol (Jensen et al., 2012). In this work, we use mathematical programming techniques for the optimal conceptual design and operation of integrated facilities that use glycerol for the production of methanol or of ethanol within the production of biodiesel from algae.

2. Modeling Assumptions

Both processes can be divided in steps such as algae growing and harvesting, oil transesterification, either use of biomass to obtain power or starch hydrolysis and glucose fermentation, glycerol fermentation and ethanol dehydration or glycerol reforming, gas treatment and methanol synthesis and purification. Mechanistic models for the reactors involving equilibria (transesterification, glycerol reforming, methanol synthesis), first principles or rules of thumb models are used to formulate a superstructure of alternatives for both cases. We use simultaneous optimization and heat integration for determining the optimal operating conditions of the different reactors and multi-effect columns.

2.1. Algae production

The first stage includes the production of biomass (oil, starch, protein). Algae are grown by injecting CO_2 into the water, which can be saline so that the consumption of freshwater is reduced, together with air and fertilizers. We assume that the dry algae biomass is composed by oil, up to a maximum of 60 %w/w, starch and protein with a minimum of 10 %w/w to be conservative. Together with the algae, oxygen is produced and water is evaporated. Univenture Inc. has presented an innovative technology capable of integrating harvesting and drying the algae with low energy consumption. It is based on the use of capillarity, membrane systems and paint drying to obtain 5 % wet algae with a consumption of 40 W per 500 L/h. The biomass is mixed with cyclo-hexane and pressed so that oil is extracted and the biomass (starch and protein) is separated from the oil (Martín and Grossmann, 2012).

2.2. Glycerol to methanol

In this case, while the biomass is used for energy production, the algae oil is transesterified with methanol, either produced out of the glycerol or from the market, using heterogeneous catalysts. The excess of ethanol used to drive the equilibrium to the products is recovered in a distillation column and mixed with fresh methanol (Martín and Grossmann, 2012), see Figure 1.

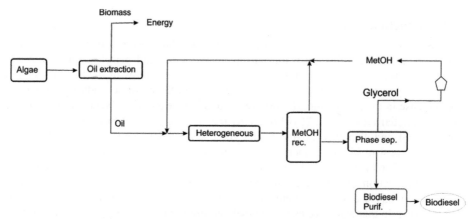

Figure 1. Algae to Biodiesel and Methanol integration

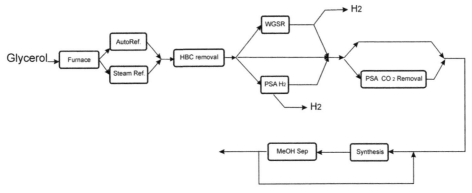

Figure 2. Glycerol to methanol stage

The glycerol is fed to a furnace where it is heated up and gasified. In this paper we consider steam reforming and auto-reforming to obtain raw syngas as seen in Figure 2. Steam reforming is an endothermic process with high yield to hydrogen (Adhikari et al., 2007). On the other hand, autoreforming is a process that combines steam reforming and partial oxidation so that the oxidation of part of the raw material provides energy for the steam reforming (Douette et al., 2007). The traces of hydrocarbons are withdrawn from the gas stream using a PSA system. The typical working conditions for PSA systems are low temperature (25 °C) and moderate pressure (4.5 bar). Once the main contaminants are eliminated, the ratio between CO and H_2 may have to be adjusted so that the feed to the reactor is appropriate for the optimal production of methanol. In order to perform such adjustment, three alternatives are considered. The first one is the use of water gas shift to reduce the amount of CO by producing more H_2. The second is a bypass. Finally, a hybrid membrane/PSA system with a bed of Zeolite 13X is needed to remove the excess of hydrogen. CO_2 must be partially removed from the gas stream to achieve the values recommended in the literature at the reactor from 2 % to 8 % in volume (Lee, 2007). In order to achieve this concentration, we consider a bypass so that only part of the gas stream is treated in a PSA system to absorb the excess of CO_2 using Zeolite 5A. We assume that the removal of CO_2 is up to 95 % of that in stream. Finally, methanol is produced from synthesis gas and the reaction is catalyzed by a catalyst composed of $(CuO - ZnO - AlO)$. The three main reactions that take place are the following:

$$CO + H_2 \leftrightarrow CH_3OH$$
$$CO_2 + H_2 \leftrightarrow CO + H_2O$$
$$CO_2 + 3H_2 \leftrightarrow CH_3OH + H_2O$$

(1)

2.3. Glycerol to ethanol

In the second case, see Figure 3, the starch follows saccharification (85 °C) and liquefaction (65 °C) to break down the polymers into glucose. Next, the glucose is fermented into ethanol at 38 °C. The solid phase, mainly protein, is separated from the liquid phase and can be sold. The liquid phase, mainly ethanol and water but containing other products in small amounts (glycerol, succinic acid, lactic acid), is distilled in a multi-effect distillation column to reduce the consumption of energy and cooling needs in the purification of ethanol. The last stage for the production of ethanol is the final dehydration using molecular sieves. This section is common for the ethanol produced out of the starch, as well as for that obtained from the fermentation of glycerol. Part of this ethanol will be used in the transesterification of the oil and the rest can be sold as biofuel (Martín and Grossmann, 2012)

The production of biodiesel via ethanolysis considers two catalysts (Martín and Grossmann, 2012), enzymes and KOH. Surface response models for the reactors were developed to evaluate the tradeoffs related to the operating variables at the reactor, namely, temperature, excess of ethanol, catalysis load and composition, and its effect on the yield. Next, the mixture of ethanol, glycerol and biodiesel is distilled to recover and recycle the excess of ethanol used. The polar phase containing glycerol is separated from the non polar phase containing the biodiesel and while the biodiesel is purified in a distillation column to remove mainly the oil remaining, the glycerol is sent to fermentation. Recently, it has been reported that the glycerol can be fermented anaerobically to ethanol as main product using different bacteria (Liu et al., 2012; Jensen et al., 2012) as given by eq. (2):

$$C_3H_8O_3 \rightarrow C_2H_6O + H_2 + CO_2 \tag{2}$$

with succinic acid and biomass as sideproducts. The gas phase is recovered separately and the liquid phase containing the ethanol, biomass and traces of other organic chemicals needs to be purified. This liquid phase is similar to the one that is obtained from the fermentation of glucose, and thus we can share the same purification and dehydration scheme. We mix both liquid phases from the fermentors, and after the recovery of the biomass and protein, we dehydrate the ethanol using a three effect multieffect distillation column and molecular sieves.

2.4. Optimization procedure

For the glycerol to methanol, the MINLP problem is decomposed into 2 NLP's subproblems of about 2,100 equations and 2,300 variables each, one for each reforming mode, autoreforming (AR) and steam reforming (SR). In that sense, we evaluate the production of methanol using each of the reforming technologies. Each of the subproblems simultaneously optimizes the operating conditions such as the ratio CO/H_2 to be used at the reactor, the working temperature and the steam added at the WGSR, and the operating pressure and temperature at the methanol reactor, and the operating conditions at the transesterification reactor. Heat integration is performed using the Duran and Grossmann (1986) model.

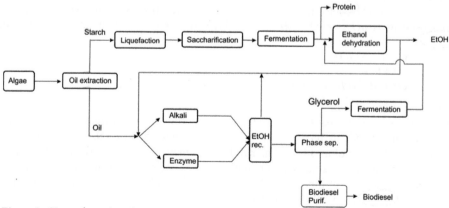

Figure 3. Glycerol to ethanol.

For the glycerol to ethanol, we also decompose the problem into two NLP, one per catalyst and each consisting of 4,000 variables and 3,500 equations. We simultaneously optimize and heat integrate each subproblem, either for enzymatic or alkali catalyzed technologies. The objective functions to be maximized are given by a simplified manufacturing cost.

3. Results

3.1. Individual process optimization

The optimal process for methanol integration involves the use of heterogeneous catalyst in the transesterification reactor followed by autoreforming for the synthesis of methanol from glycerol resulting in a production cost of $ 0.66 /gal, consuming 3.65 MJ/gal and 0.79 gal_{water}/$gal_{biodiesel}$ (vs. $ 0.69 /gal, 3.71 MJ/gal and 0.79 gal_{water}/$gal_{biodiesel}$ when using steam reforming). Hydrogen is obtained as byproduct of the methanol synthesis. The integrated process is capable of decreasing the dependency on fossil fuels reducing the methanol input to the process by more than half. The second optimally integrated process presents an interesting trade-off. The cheapest process in terms of production cost (0.38 $/gal vs 0.45 $/gal) and investment ($ 198 M vs. $ 211 M) uses an alkali catalyst instead of enzymes, but shows far larger energy (7.65 MJ/gal vs 4.2 MJ/gal) and water consumptions (0.84 gal/gal vs 0.59 gal/gal). Thus we focus on the enzymatic based for further comparison.

3.2. Comparison among processes

Two comparisons can be made, as seen in Table 1. On the one hand the comparison between typical processes where glycerol is a byproduct or when it is further used. The further use of glycerol is interesting as long as the glycerol price drops below $ 0.05 /kg. In this regard, the use of glycerol results in higher energy and water consumption per gal of fuel produced and investment, but the production cost is less subject to the expected decrease in the glycerol price. While the production of methanol reduces the dependency on fossil fuels to one half with no increase in biofuel yield, the production of ethanol increases the production of biofuels by 5 % with no need for fossil fuel based raw material.

When we compare the integration of the use of glycerol to methanol or ethanol production, it turns out that the use of bioethanol for the production of biodiesel, traditionally discarded due to its higher price compared to methanol, becomes promising when methanol is to be produced from renewable raw materials, not only in terms of production cost, but also due competitive energy and freshwater needs. The main disadvantage is the larger investment costs derived from the starch conversion into ethanol.

Table 1. Comparison of itegrated processes

	Enzymatic (Ethanol and Glycerol as products)	Hetergenous (MetOH and Glycerol as products)	Enhanced ethanol production	Integrating MetOH (AR)
Fuel price ($/$gal_{biofuel}$)	0.35	0.45	0.45	0.66
Energy (MJ/$gal_{biofuel}$)	4.00	1.94	4.20	3.65
Water (gal/$gal_{biofuel}$)	0.59	0.59	0.59	0.79
Investment(MM$)	180	110	211	118
Capacity (Mgal/yr)	90	69	94 (81biod/13bioet)	69

4. Conclusions

We have compared the use of glycerol for the production of methanol or ethanol within algae based biodiesel production facilities. For the use of glycerol to methanol, the optimal process involves heterogeneous catalyst in the transesterification reactor, followed by auto-reforming of glycerol. For the production of ethanol from glycerol, the enzyme catalyst is selected. The use of glycerol to enhance the production of ethanol results in 5 % increase in biofuel yield, lower production costs and water consumption, but higher investment costs and energy consumption due to the ethanol dehydration compared to its use for methanol production. The advantage when using methanol is the reduction in the need for fossil fuel based raw materials with no increase in the biofuels yield. Therefore, the ethanolysis of oil is competitive if methanol needs to be produced from renewable sources.

Acknowledgments

CAPD industrial consortium, NSF Grant CBET0966524 and Salamanca Research

References

S. Adhikari, S. Fernando, S.R. Gwaltney, S.D. Filip To., R.M. Bricka, P.H. Steele, A. Haryanto, 2007, A thermodynamic analysis of hydrogen production by steam reforming of glycerol, International Journal Hydrogen Energy, 32, 2875-2880.

S. Ahmed, D. Papalias, 2010, Hydrogen from Glycerol: A Feasibility Study, the 2010 Hydrogen Program Annual Merit Review Meeting, Washington DC.

J.K. Cheng, C-L. Lee, Y-T. Jhuang, J.D. Ward, L. Chien, 2011, Design and Control of the Glycerol Tertiary Butyl Ethers Process for the Utilization of a Renewable Resource Industrial Engineering Chemistry Research, 50, 12706–12716.

A.M.D. Douette, S.Q.Turn, W. Wang, V.I. Keffer, 2007, Experimental investigation of hydrogen production from glycerin reforming, Energy and Fuels, 21, 3499-3504.

M.A. Duran, I.E. Grossmann, 1986, Simultaneous optimization and heat integration of chemical processes, AIChE J., 32, 123-138.

T. Ø. Jensen, T. Kvist, M.J. Mikkelsen, P.V. Christensen, P. Westermann, P, 2012, Fermentation of crude glycerol from biodiesel production by Clostridium pasteurianum, Journal of Industrial Microbiology Biotechnology, 39,709–717.

S. Lee, 2007, Methanol Synthesis from Syngas, Chapter 9, Hadbook of alternative Fuel technologies, Taylor and Francis, Boca Raton, USA.

X. Liu, P.R. Jensen, M. Workman, 2012, Bioconversion of crude glycerol feedstocks into ethanol by Pachysolen tannophilus, Bioresource Technology, 104, 579–586

M. Martín, I.E. Grossmann, 2012, Simultaneous optimization and heat integration for biodiesel production from cooking oil and algae, Industrial Engineering Chemistry Research, 51, 23, 7998–8014

M. Martín, I.E. Grossmann, 2013, Optimal engineered algae composition for the integrated simultaneous production of bioethanol and biodiesel, AIChE J., 59, 8, 2872-2883

M. Pagliaro, M. Rossi, 2010, Future of Glycerol, 2nd Edition, The royal society of Chemistry, Cambridge.

K.W. Siew, H.C. Lee, J. Gimbun, C.K. Cheng, 2013, Hydrogen Production via Glycerol Dry Reforming over La-Ni/Al2O3 Catalyst, Bulletin of Chemical Reaction Engineering and Catalysis, 8, 2, 160-166.

Jiří Jaromír Klemeš, Petar Sabev Varbanov and Peng Yen Liew (Editors)
Proceedings of the 24th European Symposium on Computer Aided Process Engineering – ESCAPE 24
June 15-18, 2014, Budapest, Hungary. Copyright © 2014 Elsevier B.V. All rights reserved.

Robust Superstructure Optimisation of a Bioreactor that Produces Red Blood Cells

Ruth Misener[a]*, Jonathan Chin[a], Min Lai[a], María Fuentes Garí[a], Eirini Velliou[a],

Nicki Panoskaltsis[b], Efstratios N. Pistikopoulos[a], Athanasios Mantalaris[a]

[a]*Department of Chemical Engineering, Imperial College London, SW7 2AZ*
[b]*Department of Haematology, Imperial College London, HA1 3UJ*
r.misener@imperial.ac.uk

Abstract

Recent work developed a novel, biomimetic, cost effective 3D hollow fibre bioreactor for growing healthy red blood cells ex vivo (Panoskaltsis et al., 2012). This promising bioreactor recapitulates the architectural and functional properties of erythrocyte formation and thereby reduces the need for expensive growth factors by more than an order of magnitude. The optimal bioreactor configuration has not been defined; design choices include: number of bioreactors run in parallel, number of hollow fibres in each reactor, size and aspect ratio of each bioreactor. Individual experiments on the bioreactor are cost- and labour-intensive, so we propose global, robust, superstructure optimisation for designing and operating the bioreactor. Beyond this individual bioreactor, robust superstructure design has the potential to more generally enable bioprocess optimisation.

Keywords: bioreactor design; bioprocess optimisation; superstructure optimisation; robust optimisation

1. Introduction and Literature Review

Ninety-two million units of whole donor blood are globally collected yearly [WHO, 2011]. Despite the success of coordinated blood collection and utilisation: hospitals still experience blood shortages and patients undergoing regular transfusions may require expensive rare blood donation to mitigate the risk of an immune response (Tahhan et al., 1994; Meny et al., 2013). Ex vivo blood production is an attractive solution for filling shortage gaps and scaling-up rare blood donations. But current blood expansion protocols require \$8,330 per unit of blood when an average hospital in the USA pays only \$225.42 for a typical unit of blood (Timmins and Nielsen, 2009) and \$1,150 to \$3,025 for a unit of rare blood (Meny et al., 2013).

Haematopoiesis, or blood cell production, requires delivering nutrients, oxygen, and signaling proteins called growth factors to cells in a specialised 3D micro-environment called the haematopoietic stem cell niche (Panoskaltsis et al., 2005). Although the 3D niche structure is crucial in vivo, ex vivo blood production is typically performed in 2D liquid suspension; these 2D systems are expensive because they require artificially high levels of the specialised growth factor proteins (Timmins and Nielsen, 2009). The bioreactor described by Panoskaltsis et al. (2012) is extremely promising because it recapitulates the architectural and functional properties of blood formation and thereby reduces the need for expensive growth factors by more than an order of magnitude. The blood-producing bioreactor successfully produces red blood cells (RBC) with correct: oxygen-carrying capacity, surface markers, and shape (Macedo, 2011). Individual experiments on the bioreactor are cost- and labour-intensive, so we propose global, robust, superstructure optimisation for designing and operating the bioreactor. Optimisation approaches have been previously used to improve individual degrees of freedom in hollow fibre bioreactors [Davidson, et al., 2010, Shipley et al., 2011], but our proposed bioreactor design and bioprocess optimisation considers multiple design choices and explicitly incorporates uncertainty into the framework for the first time.

In this blood-producing bioreactor: nutrients, growth factors, and oxygen flow through the hollow fibres via Poiseuille flow and diffuse into the 3D polymeric scaffold. The resulting biological signals and reactions cause the cells to grow, proliferate, and differentiate. Products and by-products are mature cells and waste which diffuse out of the scaffold and exit through the hollow fibres. Known sources of quantifiable uncertainty include cellular growth rates and mass transfer characteristics of the bioreactor. We handle the vector of deterministic uncertain parameters as model-inherent uncertainty (Pistikopoulos, 1995).

In Section 2, the bioreactor is modelled using the Krogh Cylinder Approximation (1919) shown in Figure 1. Five species represent mass exchange: glucose corresponds to cellular nutrients; lactate models waste; oxygen stands in for cellular metabolism; stem cell factor (SCF) represents cellular expansion; erythropoietin (EPO) is mapped to cellular differentiation. Mass transfer parameters and associated uncertainty are derived from work of Panoskaltsis et al. (2012). Cellular growth, differentiation, and proliferation are modelled using the approach of Ma et al. (2012). In Section 3, the resulting robust superstructure optimisation problem is formulated as a mixed-integer nonlinear program and solved to global optimality using the global mixed-integer nonlinear optimization (MINLP) solver ANTIGONE (2013a, 2013b). We conclude in Section 4.

2. Model Development

2.1. Optimisation Model

This model minimises cost in a bioreactor producing one unit of red blood cells while providing sufficient nutrient delivery and waste disposal. Operating choices include: (1) size and aspect ratio R_4 by L of the cylindrical bioreactor; (2) number of hollow fibres N_{HF} for delivering reactants and extracting products and by-products; (3) flow rate of nutritious medium UZ through the bioreactor; (4) medium inlet composition $C_{k,IN}$ for k in {Glucose, SCF, EPO}, (5) ambient oxygen concentration $C_{Oxygen,IN}$.

Objective (Eq. 1): Consistent with the data of Timmins and Nielsen (2009), assume that the contributions to the bioreactor cost are represented by the growth factors (i.e., EPO and SCF) needs and thereby neglect the cost of: (1) nutrients; (2) bioreactor materials and fabrication; (3) product transportation and storage. The costs scale with the price p_k of the material entering the reactor at concentration $C_{k,IN}$ and flowing at rate U_Z through each of the N_{HF} hollow fibres in each of the equivalent N_R reactors.

$$\min_{C_{k,IN},L,R_4,N_{HF},N_R,U_Z} U_Z \times N_R \times N_{HF} \times \sum_k p_k \times C_{k,IN} \tag{1}$$

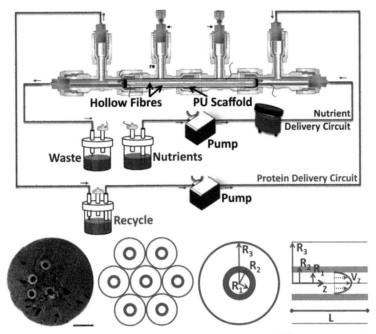

Figure 1. The blood-producing bioreactor (top diagram is of a single bioreactor set-up; left-hand image is a cross section captured using a Scanning Electron Microscope) is modeled using the Krogh Cylinder Approximation (1919); the medium fed to the cells passes through hollow fibers via Poiseuille Flow; exchange in the scaffold is via diffusion

Superstructure Topology (Eqs. 2–5): N_R bioreactors are parallelised to create one unit of red blood cells; each of the N_R bioreactors is a cylinder with aspect ratio R_4 by L and N_{HF} hollow fibres. The N_{HF} hollow fibres define equivalent Krogh Cylinders (1919).

$$Vol_R = \pi R_4^2 L \qquad (2)$$

$$R_3 = \sqrt{\frac{Vol_K}{\pi L}} \qquad (4)$$

$$Vol_K = \frac{Vol_R}{N} \qquad (3)$$

$$Vol_T = N_R(Vol_R - N_{HF}\,\pi R_2^2\,L) \qquad (5)$$

Production Requirements (Eqs. 6-7): We assume that the distribution of cells in the bioreactor is uniform for each of three cell types illustrated in Figure 2(a): dividing cells Q (*e.g.*, haematopoietic stem cells), erythrocytes and maturing erythrocytes E, and other blood cells B (*e.g.*, lymphocytes). The total concentration of cells in the bioreactor may not exceed $C_{Cells,\ MAX}$, the highest cellular density reported by Mortera-Blanco et al. (2011). Eq.(7) constrains the system to produce at least one unit (Unit$_{RBC}$) of red blood cells E in the total volume of reactor Vol_T over the D days; γ_P is the exit rate of E.

$$Q + B + E \leq C_{Cells,MAX} \qquad (6)$$

$$\gamma_P\, D\, E\, Vol_T \geq Unit_{RBC} \qquad (7)$$

Mass Transfer Equations (Eqs.8-9): All species k in {Glucose, Lactate, O_2, SCF, EPO} are bounded by the maximum $C_{k,MAX}$ and minimum $C_{k,MIN}$ concentrations given by Macedo (2011); the governing equations are taken from Jayaraman (1992) and simplified to the original analytical expression of Krogh (1919).

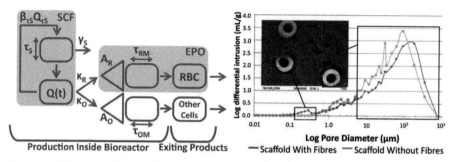

Figure 2. (a) Stem cell factor and erythropoetin represent proliferation and differentiation kinetics (Ma et al., 2012); (b) Variability in mass transfer is modeled using quantifiable uncertainty.

$$C_{k,MIN} \leq C_{k,i}(r,z) \leq C_{k,MAX}; \ \forall \, i,k,r,z \tag{8}$$

$$C_{k,i}(r,z) = \frac{V_k}{D_{k,3}}\left(\frac{R_3^2}{2}\ln\frac{r}{R_2} - \frac{r^2 - R_2^2}{4}\right) + C_{k,i}(0,z); \ \forall \, i,k,r,z \tag{9}$$

Cellular Kinetics (Eqs. 10-15): The model for cellular growth, proliferation, and differentiation is derived from Ma et al. (2012) and Colijn and Mackey (2005). The models of Ma et al. (2012) and Colijn and Mackey (2005) use delay differential equations to model cellular kinetics; we assume for the design problem that the bioreactor is operating at quasi-steady state. The model illustrated in Figure 2(a) therefore assumes that concentrations of cell types Q, B, and E are constant with time. The proliferation rate $\beta(Q)$ is modelled as a Hill Function (Eq. 13) and the entry into the erythroid (υ_E) and other leukocyte (υ_B) lineages is controlled using feedback functions (Eq 14-15). The death rates: γ_Q, γ_B, and γ_E are for each type of cell with respect to the times (τ_Q, τ_{BM}, τ_{BS}, τ_{EM}, τ_{ES}) that the cells require to proliferate and differentiate.

$$-(\vartheta_B + \vartheta_E)\, Q + \left(2\, e^{-\gamma_S \tau_Q} - 1\right)\beta(Q)\, Q = 0 \tag{10}$$

$$-\vartheta_B\, B + A_B \vartheta_B(B)\, Q \left(1 - e^{-\gamma_B(\tau_{BM} + \tau_{BS})}\right) = 0 \tag{11}$$

$$-\vartheta_E\, E + A_E \vartheta_E(E)\, Q \left(1 - e^{-\gamma_E(\tau_{EM} + \tau_{ES})}\right) = 0 \tag{12}$$

$$\beta(Q) = \frac{K_Q \theta^{c_Q}}{\theta^{c_Q} + Q^{c_Q}} \quad (13) \qquad \vartheta_B = \frac{\overline{\vartheta_B}}{1 + K_B B^{c_B}} \quad (14) \qquad \vartheta_E = \frac{\overline{\vartheta_E}}{1 + K_E E^{c_E}} \quad (15)$$

2.2. Model-Inherent Uncertainty

Observe here that *robust optimisation* is, as a conservative method for representing uncertainty, an appropriate choice for optimising a bioreactor where we have to prioritise consistent, effective cellular expansion and require a high degree of certainty that each individual bioreactor will operate.

One important source of uncertainty in the bioreactor is the uncertainty with respect to mass transfer. We assume that there is no convective flow outside the hollow fibre lumen, so effective diffusivity represents the primary source of uncertainty in mass transfer. Full bioreactor characterisation requires quantifying the diffusivity of each species (Glucose, Lactate, pO₂, SCF, EPO) in: (1) the hollow fibre (HF) lumen; (2) the

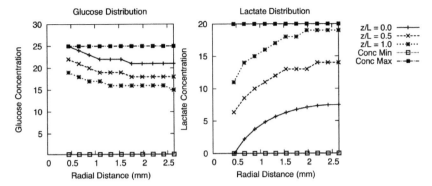

Figure 3. Profile of Glucose and Lactate in the optimised bioreactor.

hollow fibre membranes; (3) the polyurethane (PU) scaffold. This manuscript focusses on diffusivity in the lumen and the PU scaffold and assumes that the membranes pose no barrier to mass transfer.

The diffusivity of each species in the lumen is approximated as the diffusivity of that species in water (Young et al., 1980). Uncertainty in the transfer of EPO and SCF arises from the claim of Young et al. (1980) that their method is accurate within 20 %. The species diffusivities in the PU scaffold are estimated using Maxwell's correlation for transfer within porous medium and the error range is due to the quantifiable uncertainty in the material porosity (see Figure 2(b)). Other sources of model uncertainty not incorporated into the present study include: (1) species reaction rate; (2) cellular proliferation and differentiation rate; (3) exit rate of mature cells from the bioreactor. The bounded uncertainty in this model is incorporated as in Lin et al. (2004); the equality in Eq. 9 is becomes an inequality after reformulation considers that one of $C_{k, MIN}$ or $C_{k, MAX}$ is inactive for each species.

3. Coupling Global Superstructure Optimisation and Robust Optimisation

The model developed in Section 2 was implemented in GAMS 24.1. After discretisation of the axial and radial dimensions using 10 grid points each, it is an MINLP model with 694 continuous variables, 2 binary variables, and 1,069 constraints incorporating: 41 bilinear, 31 signomial, and 10 logarithmic terms. We solved the model to global optimality using the MINLP solver ANTIGONE 1.1 (Misener and Floudas, 2013a; 2013b); ANTIGONE 1.1 consistently solves this problem in less than 60 CPU s. Figure 3 shows a typical output of the model; uncertainty in mass transfer leads us to design a smaller bioreactor with more hollow fibres.

4. Conclusions

This paper incorporates quantifiable uncertainty into the model development framework and conservatively designs a bioreactor that will operate under most circumstances; the resulting bioreactor is competitively priced against rare blood ($USD 1k-3k). This is the first application of superstructure optimisation to a hollow fibre bioreactor; all previous attempts would vary individual parameters rather than using deterministic global optimisation for simultaneously choosing the design and operation. Observe that the potential of robust superstructure design applies not only on this individual bioreactor but also more generally on bioprocess optimisation.

Acknowledgement

R.M. is thankful for a Royal Academy of Engineering Research Fellowship. This work is also supported by ERC-BioBlood, ERC-Mobile Project (no 226462), by the EU 7th Framework Programme [MULTIMOD Project FP7/2007-2013, no 238013] and by the Richard Thomas Leukaemia Research Fund.

References

C. Colijn, M.C. Mackey, 2005, A mathematical model of hematopoiesis—I. Periodic chronic myelogenous leukemia, J. Theor. Bio., 237 2, 117-132.

A.J. Davidson, M.J. Ellis, J.B. Chaudhuri, 2010, A theoretical method to improve and optimize the design of bioartificial livers, Biotech. Bioeng., 106, 6, 980–988.

V.K. Jayaraman, 1992, The solution of hollow fiber bioreactor design equations, Biotechnol. Progr., 8, 5, 462–464.

A. Krogh, 1919, The number and distribution of capillaries in muscles with calculations of the oxygen pressure head necessary for supplying the tissue, J. Physiol., 52, 409–415.

X. Lin, S.L. Janak, C.A. Floudas, 2004, A new robust optimization approach for scheduling under uncertainty: I. Bounded uncertainty, Comput Chem Eng, 28, 1069–1085.

C. Ma, N. Panoskaltsis, R. Kumar, X. Xu, 2012, A Mantalaris. Simulation of ex vivo bone marrow culture: Application to chronic myeloid leukaemia growth model, Biochem. Eng. J., 61, 66–77.

H.M. Macedo, 2011, A Novel 3D Dual Hollow Fibre Bioreactor for the Production of Human Red Blood Cells, PhD thesis, Imperial College London, UK.

G. Meny, C. Flickinger, C. Marcucci, 2013, The American rare donor program, J Crit Care, 28, 1, 110.e9-110.e18.

R. Misener, C.A. Floudas, 2013, GloMIQO: Global Mixed-Integer Quadratic Optimizer, J Glob Optim, 57, 3-50.

R. Misener, C.A. Floudas, 2013, A framework for globally optimizing mixed-integer signomial programs, J. Opt. Theory Appl., DOI:10.1007/s10957-013-0396-3.

T. Mortera-Blanco, A. Mantalaris, A. Bismarck, N. Aqel, N. Panoskaltsis, 2011, Long-term cytokine-free expansion of cord blood mononuclear cells in 3D scaffolds, Biomat., 32, 35, 9263-9270.

N. Panoskaltsis, H.M.M. Macedo, M.T.M. Blanco, A. Mantalaris, A.G. Livingston, 2012, 3D hollow fibre bioreactor systems for the maintenance, expansion, differentiation and harvesting of human stem cells and their progeny, Patent, WO 2012/069841 A1.

N. Panoskaltsis, A. Mantalaris, J.H.D. Wu, 2005, Engineering a mimicry of bone marrow tissue ex vivo, J. Biosci. Bioeng., 100, 1, 28-35.

E.N. Pistikopoulos, 1995, Uncertainty in Process Design and Operations, Comput. Chem. Engin., 19, 553-563.

R.J. Shipley, A.J. Davidson, K. Chan, J.B. Chaudhuri, S.L. Waters, M.J. Ellis, 2011, A strategy to determine operating parameters in tissue engineering hollow fiber bioreactors, Biotech. Bioeng., 108, 6, 1450–1461.

H. Tahhan, C. Holbrook, L. Braddy, L. Brewer, J. Christie, 1994, Antigen-matched donor blood in the transfusion management of patients with sickle cell disease, Transfusion, 34, 562–569.

N.E. Timmins, L.K. Nielsen, 2009, Blood cell manufacture: current methods and future challenges, Trends in Biotechnology, 27, 7, 415–422.

World Health Organization, 2011, Global Database on Blood Safety, <who.int/bloodsafety/global database/GDBS_Summary_Report_2011.pdf>, Accessed on 09/09/2013.

M.E. Young, P.A. Carroad, R.L. Bell, 1980, Estimation of diffusion-coefficients of proteins, Biotech. Bioeng., 22, 5, 947–955,.

Jiří Jaromír Klemeš, Petar Sabev Varbanov and Peng Yen Liew (Editors)
Proceedings of the 24th European Symposium on Computer Aided Process Engineering – ESCAPE 24
June 15-18, 2014, Budapest, Hungary.

New Intensified Distillation Systems for Quaternary Petlyuk Configuration

Ben-Guang Rong,[a*] Massimiliano Errico,[b] Juan Gabriel Segovia-Hernandez[c]

[a]*University of Southern Denmark, Niels Bohrs Alle 1, 5230 Odense,Denmark.*
[b]*Università degli Studi di Cagliari, 09123 Cagliari, Italy.*
[c]*Universidad de Guanajuato, Campus Guanajuato, 36050 Guanajuato, Mexico.*
bgr@kbm.sdu.dk

Abstract

While dividing-wall column for ternary Petlyuk configuration has received wide applications in industries, the dividing-wall column for quaternary Petlyuk configuration has not reached the same applications due to its complexity in both design and control. In this work, the synthesis on the alternative intensified distillation systems than Petlyuk configuration for four-component distillation was investigated. First, the simple column configuration for the separation sequence of Petlyuk configuration is presented. Then four strategies are introduced to change the structure of the simple column configuration in terms of both condensers/reboilers and column sections. These strategies can be used to synthesize the alternative intensified configurations from the simple column configuration of the separation sequence. The objective of this work is to give the synthesis method to generate the new intensified distillation systems for quaternary Petlyuk configuration. In total, five new alternative intensified systems are obtained each with only two columns. The alternative intensified systems are amenable to be easier in both design and control due to the simplicity in the structures. The synthesis method together with the new generated alternative configurations are presented in this work. The numerical design and optimization, as well as dynamics and control of these new alternative configurations are underway.

Keywords: Petlyuk configuration, intensified distillation system, synthesis and design, systematic method, energy saving

1. Introduction

Synthesis of new intensified distillation systems with significant reductions on energy and capital costs is ever being an important research topic for both academics and industries. This is because distillation is the widely used separation technology not only for fossil-based, but also for renewable-based products manufacturing. Among the feasible configurations for multicomponent distillation, the Petlyuk configuration (Petlyuk et al., 1965) has been proved to have the minimum energy requirement than other possible configurations. This is due to that the Petlyuk configuration has the lowest thermodynamic irreversibility with the nonsharp splits and thermal couplings. For an N-component mixture, the Petlyuk configuration needs N-1 columns with one condenser and one reboiler in the product column. The implementation of Petlyuk configuration for ternary distillations has achieved remarkable success in the form of dividing-wall column (DWC). A single shell column with one dividing wall (DWC) can perform a ternary separation with three pure products. Such DWC columns have been successfully used in many industrial separations with remarkable savings on both energy and capital costs (30 % up to 50 %).

Motivated by the ternary Petlyuk column, the Petlyuk configuration has ever been the preferred configuration for four or more component mixtures (Olujic et al., 2012). However, examining the separation sequence of the Petlyuk configuration for four or more component mixtures, it is known that it has the maximum number of individual splits due to the nonsharp splits. Even though the final configuration has only N-1 columns and only one condenser and one reboiler for an N-component mixture, the maximum number of thermal couplings makes the system much more complex for both design and control. When coming to the dividing-wall column for Petlyuk configuration for four or more component mixtures, it is even more difficult for the design and control of a single shell equipment to implement the multiple dividing walls. This is the main reason that the Petlyuk configuration so far is not well implemented in industries for four or more component distillations compared to ternary mixtures.

The objective of this work is to study the synthesis method to generate the new intensified distillation systems for quaternary Petlyuk configuration. The alternative intensified systems are aiming at being easier in both design and control in terms of system's structure. First, the synthesis method is investigated and formulated, then the new generated alternative configurations for quaternary distillation are presented.

2. Petlyuk configuration for quaternary distillation

Petlyuk et al. (1965) summarized four features for the fully thermally coupled configuration for an N-component distillation. 1) the total number of sections required for separating an N-component mixture is equal to N(N-1), instead of 2(N-1) in the conventional scheme; 2) it is sufficient to have only one condenser and one reboiler independent of the number of components to be separated; 3) the key components in each column are the two components with the extreme volatilities; 4) N products of a given purity are obtained in the product column.

In an earlier work to synthesize the heat-integrated configurations for Petlyuk arrangements, we illustrated that the Petlyuk configuration was generated from the unique nonsharp separation sequence in which all of the mixtures with three or more components are separated by the symmetric sloppy splits (Rong et al., 2006). Such unique separation sequence was called fully sloppy separation sequence. For quaternary mixtures, the fully sloppy sequence is: ABCD→ABC→BCD→A/B→B/C→C/D. The quaternary Petlyuk configuration is presented in Figure 1(a).

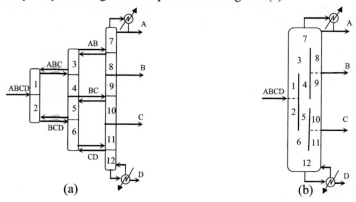

(a)   (b)

Figure 1. (a) Quaternary Petlyuk configuration; (b) Dividing-wall-column of quaternary Petlyuk configuration.

For an N-component mixture, the total number of thermal couplings in the Petlyuk arrangement is (N-2)(N+1)/2. There are N-2 thermal couplings associated with the submixtures involving the most volatile component, which are located at the top ends of the columns. Similarly, there are N-2 thermal couplings associated with the submixtures involving the least volatile component, which are located at the bottom ends of the columns. There are (N-2)(N-3)/2 thermal couplings associated with the submixtures composed of only the middle components, which are located at the intermediate locations in the columns. The two ends of the product column are connected with the only condenser and the only reboiler. The commonly studied dividing-wall-column for quaternary Petlyuk configuration is presented in Figure 1(b) (Christiansen et al., 1997).

3. A method to derive the intensified alternatives for Petlyuk configuration

Starting from the fully sloppy separation sequence with the intended individual splits, it is clear that we need different strategies to deal with the condensers and reboilers, as well as the individual simple columns to achieve a distillation configuration with less number of columns and heat exchangers. To fully explore the possibility to generate the new configurations, we have found that the simple column configuration (SCC) of the sloppy separation sequence is the best representation. This is because that the maximum structural flexibility is kept in the SCC configuration, from which different mechanisms can be explored to change its structure, and from which different intensified distillation systems can be generated. Figure 2 presents the simple column configuration (SCC) for the fully sloppy separation sequence of a quaternary mixture.

To synthesize the new intensified distillation systems with fewer columns and heat exchangers, we have introduced four strategies which are aiming at changing the structure of the SCC configuration, at the same time, also aiming at reducing the number of columns and heat exchangers.

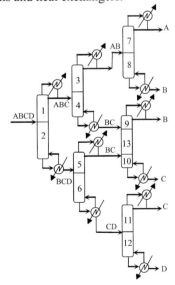

Figure 2. The simple column configuration (SCC) for the fully sloppy separation sequence of a quaternary mixture.

Strategy 1: Heat-Integration strategy to combine the individual columns. This strategy is used to combine two columns by heat integration between a condenser and a reboiler involving only intermediate components. This will reduce the number of columns than the SCC configuration.

Strategy 2: Thermal coupling strategy to eliminate a condenser or a reboiler. This strategy is used to eliminate a condenser or a reboiler which is associated with a mixture of binary or more components. This will reduce the number of heat exchangers than the SCC configuration.

Strategy 3: Rearrangement of column sections strategy to generate thermodynamically equivalent structures. This strategy is used to recombine the column sections in a thermally coupled configuration through movement of the movable column sections. This will generate the thermodynamically equivalent structures which have different columns than the original thermally coupled configuration.

Strategy 4: Elimination of the single-section-side columns strategy to produce the intensified distillation systems. For a thermally coupled configuration, there are thermodynamically equivalent structures in which there are single-section-side columns. This strategy is used to eliminate the single-section-side columns which will generate the intensified distillation systems with fewer columns.

In the following, for the simple column configuration shown in Figure 2, we will illustrate that systematic use of the four strategies will presents a new method to synthesize all of the possible intensified distillation systems with fewer columns and heat exchangers.

4. Systematic synthesis of the new intensified distillation systems for quaternary Petlyuk configuration

The original quaternary Petlyuk configuration shown in Figure 1(a) has three columns, in which five two-way thermal couplings communicate between the columns. It is difficult for practical implementation due to the complexity in design, control and operation. Here, we present the synthesis of new intensified distillation systems which have fewer columns than that of Petlyuk configuration. The synthesis procedure is starting from the SCC configuration shown in Figure 2, then systematically applying the above four strategies to reduce the number of columns and the number of heat exchangers. The key is to generate the thermodynamically equivalent structures in which there are single-section-side columns. A single-section-side column is either serving as transporting an intermediate mixture or as purifying a final product. In certain cases, they can be eliminated to obtain the intensified distillation systems with fewer columns. In total, five distinct new alternative intensified systems are obtained which are shown in parts (a)-(e) of Figure 3. It is seen that each of the new intensified distillation systems has only two columns.

Generation of alternative Figure 3(a): Starting from the SCC in Figure 2, we can use four steps to generate the Figure 3(a). Step 1: combining the columns co-producing the middle products B and C through strategy 1. Step 2: eliminating condenser ABC and reboiler BCD through strategy 2. Step 3: removing the movable sections 3 and 6 to rearrange the column sections through strategy 3. Step 4: eliminating the single-section-side columns 4 and 5 through strategy 4 to generate the Figure 3(a).

Generation of alternative Figure 3(b): Starting from the SCC in Figure 2, we can use four steps to generate the Figure 3(b). Step 1: combining the two columns co-producing the middle product B through strategy 1. Step 2: eliminating condenser ABC, reboiler BCD and reboiler CD through strategy 2. Step 3: removing the movable sections 3, 6and 12 to rearrange the column sections through strategy 3. Step 4: eliminating the single-section-side columns 4, 5 and 11 through strategy 4 to generate the Figure 3(b).

Generation of alternative Figure 3(d): Starting from the SCC in Figure 2, we can use four steps to generate the Figure 3(d). Step 1: combining the two columns co-producing the middle product B through strategy 1. Step 2: eliminating condenser ABC, condenser BC and reboiler CD through strategy 2. Step 3: removing the movable sections 3, 12 and 7+8+9+13 togetherto rearrange the column sections through strategy 3. Step 4: eliminating the single-section-side columns 4, 10 and 11 through strategy 4 to generate the Figure 3(d).

Similarly, alternatives Figure 3(c) and Figure 3(e) can be generated by applying the above four strategies in a systematic manner. Furthermore, the thermally coupled schemes of the intensified systems can be generated by replacing the condensers and reboilers associated with mixtures of binary or more components. For example, Figure 3(f) presents the thermally coupled scheme of the intensified system of Figure 3(a).

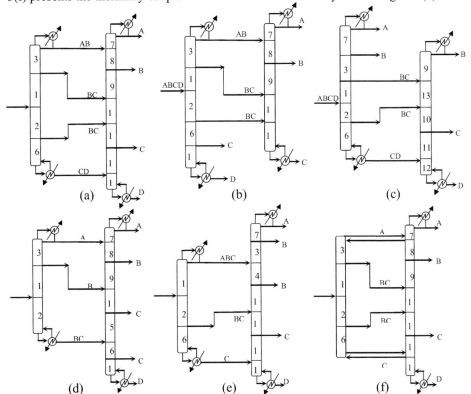

Figure 3. The intensified distillation systems for quaternary Petlyuk configuration

5. Comparison of the intensified distillation systems with the Petlyuk configuration

The intensified distillation systems shown as in Figure 3 have distinct features than the Petlyuk configuration shown as in Figure 1(a). First, instead of three columns, two columns are used in the intensified systems. Second, to facilitate controllability and operability, each column in an intensified system has employed an overhead condenser and a bottom reboiler. Therefore, there are four heat exchangers in the intensified systems. However, the number of heat exchangers can be further reduced by introducing thermal couplings to replace the condensers or reboiler associated with mixtures. For example, Figure 3(f) is obtained from Figure 3(a) by introducing thermal couplings to replace the condenser AB and reboiler CD. As a consequence, the intensified system can also have only one condenser and one reboiler as in the Petlyuk configuration. Also, in Figure 3, the intermediate submixtures are transporting in one-way between the columns, this will also make the control and operation easier than the two-way communications. Finally, in the intensified distillation systems, the products can be obtained from one column as in parts (a), (d) and (e), or obtained from two columns as in parts (b) and (c) in Figure 3. Furthermore, an extra intermediate product B can be obtained in Figures 3(c) and 3(e), and an extra product C can be obtained in Figures 3(b) and 3(d).

6. Conclusions

The Petlyuk configuration is proved to have the minimum energy requirement than other possible configurations for a multicomponent distillation. However, the Petlyuk configuration with the theoretical minimum energy consumption for four or more component mixture is very difficult for practical application due to its complexity. The reason is that the fully thermally coupled Petlyuk configuration has too many thermal couplings between columns, which is difficult for control and operation. On the other hand, its single shell dividing-wall-column needs to implement multiple dividing walls in one column which is even more difficult for equipment design, control and operation. In this paper, the intensified alternative distillation systems for quaternary Petlyuk configuration are presented. The intensified distillation systems use fewer columns than the Petlyuk configuration. Moreover, the fully thermally coupled schemes of the intensified alternatives have less number of two-way thermal couplings between columns than the Petlyuk configuration. These distinct features make the intensified distillation systems not only attractive in terms of economics, but also amenable to systems' design, control and operation.

The method for quaternary Petlyuk configuration presented in this work is applicable to generate the intensified distillation systems for Petlyuk configuration with a feed mixture of any number of components.

References

A.C. Christiansen, S. Skogestad, K. Lien, 1997, Complex distillation arrangements: Extending the Petlyuk ideas, Comput. Chem. Eng., 21, S237-S242.

Z. Olujic, I. Dejanovic, B. Kaibel, H. Jansen, 2012, Dimensioning multipartition dividing wall columns, Chem. Eng. Technol., 35, 1392-1404.

F.B. Petlyuk, V.M. Platonov, V.M. Slavinskii, 1965, Thermodynamically optimal method for separating multicomponent mixture, Inter. Chem. Eng., 5, 555-561.

B.-G. Rong, I. Turunen, 2006, New heat-integrated distillation configurations for Petlyuk arrangements, Chem. Eng. Res. Des., 84, 1117-1133.

Jiří Jaromír Klemeš, Petar Sabev Varbanov and Peng Yen Liew (Editors)
Proceedings of the 24th European Symposium on Computer Aided Process Engineering – ESCAPE 24
June 15-18, 2014, Budapest, Hungary. Copyright © 2014 Elsevier B.V. All rights reserved.

A Numerical Modelling Approach for Dual Reflux PSA Separation of N_2 and CH_4 in LNG Production

Yechun Zhang[a], Thomas L.H. Saleman[b], Eric F. May[b], Brent R. Young[a*]

[a]The University of Auckland, 20 Symonds Street, Auckland 1010, New Zealand
[b]The University of Western Australia, 35 Stirling Highway, Crawley WA 6009, Australia
b.young@auckland.ac.nz

Abstract

In this paper, a novel, full Dual Reflux PSA (PSA) model is proposed for separating methane and nitrogen mixtures. The model is a full, integrated ODE model, in contrast to our former work where stripping PSA and enriching PSA were simulated separately and were combined using the total material balance (referred to as a transfer function model). The full model was built rigorously in a commercial simulator in terms of mass balances, energy balances and pressure-flow relationships, and it was numerically solved by the ODE solver which was integrated in the simulator. The transfer function model which was proven to have a close match with experimental data was compared to the results from the full DR-PSA model using the same key parameters, such as feed composition, total throughput, reflux ratios and cycle time, and resulted in a close match. The impact of feed position, feed temperature, feed composition and cycle time on the system was also studied with the new model.

Keywords: LNG, Separation, Adsorption, Dual Reflux PSA

1. Introduction

Liquefied natural gas (LNG) is gaining more and more attraction these days due to its clean combustion, low carbon emissions and high energy density which allows global transport (Arthur and William, 2006). In 2011, 330.8 Mm^3 of LNG was traded around the world, which is a 10 % increase compared to 2010 (300.6 Mm^3) (BP, 2012). One of the key challenges in the LNG production process is the separation of nitrogen and methane as they both have very low boiling points and nitrogen is an inert gas. The nitrogen concentration in the final LNG product should be limited to 1 mol% in order to prevent stratification and rollover during transport (Arthur and William, 2006). Cryogenic distillation with a 2-stage configuration is the only feasible technology for large scale production (>700 km^3/d), but several alternative separation methodologies such as pressure swing adsorption have the potential to be placed at the nitrogen vent of either the first stage (50 mol% methane) or the second stage (3mol% methane) distillation column, aiming to recover the methane product and to reduce methane emissions into the atmosphere. Conventional PSA units suffer from producing only one relatively pure product. Besides this, the low separation factor of current commercial adsorbents for N_2 and CH_4 separation results in low product purity and unviable numbers of beds required for the separation objective.

Experimental results from an advanced configuration of PSA, Dual Reflux PSA (DR-PSA), (Diagne et al., 1994) reportedly showed in a series of publications that it can achieve high purity for both products in binary gas separations (the latest reference in the series by Ebner, Ritter and co-workers being McIntyre et al., 2010). However due to its complexity, the only model available in literature for describing DR-PSA is the equilibrium model proposed by Ebner and Ritter (Ebner and Ritter, 2004), later enhanced by Kearns and Webley (Kearns and Webley, 2006). The model proved the feasibility of sharp separations and high recoveries by DR-PSA even with low pressure ratios, and the effect of feed concentrations, pressure ratios, total throughput, reflux ratios and feed positions were discussed in detail. The equilibrium model was further enriched by Bhatt et al. lately, in terms of numerically finding an optimal feed position and feed to adsorbent ratio for a specified configuration of DR-PSA (Bhatt et al., 2013). However, the equilibrium model assumes perfect separation so it could not be used to predict product concentrations. Our previous research focused on using a "transfer function" methodology to combine the numerical simulation results of the stripping and enriching PSA parts of DR-PSA in order to estimate the product concentrations when reaching cyclic steady state. The results showed a close match with the experimental data reported by McIntyre et al., as presented elsewhere (Zhang et al., 2013). In this paper a full numerical simulation model of DR-PSA is proposed and the simulation results are presented. The effects of key operational parameters such as temperature, feed location and cycle time were studied with this new model.

2. Methodology

The full numerical model of DR-PSA was built in a commercial simulator: Aspen Adsorption since the simulator is good for modelling dynamic and batched adsorption processes with rigorous pressure flow relationships and mass/energy balances. Furthermore, its interface enables configuration of adsorption systems and the built-in ODE solver can decrease model development time. A feed to high pressure column configuration of DR-PSA was selected mainly due to pressure-flow network stability considerations. The layout of the model is shown in Figure 1.

A four-column configuration was used in order to enable intermediate feed along the column. The feed position can be manipulated by adjusting the height ratio of the two associated columns on each side of the feed. Since the model is based on pressure-flow relationships, the stripping/enriching reflux ratio can be adjusted by the ratio of the valve C_Vs on both product sides and the total throughput was determined by the absolute value of valve C_V for each product stream combined with the pressure ratio of the adsorption and desorption column. The temperature of the DR-PSA system was determined both by the temperature at the feed and the environmental temperature. The thermal conductivity of column walls was set to a high value in order to increase the model stability and meanwhile maintain the temperature inside the column as constant. The integrator was delicately configured, as a large integration step combined with a very stiff equation set will result in integrator break down. On the other hand, a very small integration step will significantly increase the time required for solving the model in dynamics.

A major compromise of the model was to assume an "ideal" compressor at the enriching reflux end in terms of maintaining the output of the compressor at a constant pressure, since the flow and pressure at the outlet of the desorption column dynamically changes with time. The "ideal" compressor only operated during the feed step and a "normal" compressor was used for the pressure equalization/ pressurization/ blow down

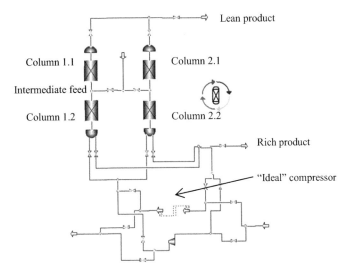

Figure 1. The layout of the full numerical model of DR-PSA in the simulation environment

(EQ/PR/BD) step. How to address this modelling issue in operating a real experimental apparatus needs to be considered further in subsequent experimental studies.

Since the product compositions when the DR-PSA system reached cyclic steady state (CCS) were the key variables observed, the model was run for sufficient time until the compositions in lean and rich products do not change significantly. The empirical criterion used in this work was that the CCS was considered to be reached when the variation of average product compositions during the last feed cycle is less than 0.001mol%.

3. Results and Discussion

3.1. Comparison with the transfer function model

The CH_4/N_2 separation simulation was carried out and the full numerical model of DR-PSA was configured according to the parameters used in the transfer function model. A typical activated carbon, Norit RB3 was used and the isotherm parameters were obtained from our previous work (Rufford et al., 2013). An explicit Euler ODE solver with order of 4 and an integration time step of 0.05s was used. The key parameters for the simulation are shown in Table 1and the comparison results are shown in Table 2.

Table 1. Key parameters used for comparing the full numerical model and the transfer function model

Column Height (m)	Column Diameter (m)	Pressure Ratio	Throughput (km^3/d)	Stripping Reflux Ratio	Enriching Reflux Ratio	Adsorption Time (s)	Feed Position	CH_4mol% in feed
20	3	3	~22	10	~10	250	0.5	3

Table 2. Comparison of predicted data from the transfer function model and the full numerical model

Temperature	302 K		240 K	
	Transfer Function	Full Numerical	Transfer Function	Full Numerical
CH_4 mol% in lean product	0.402	0.456	0.157	0.370
CH_4 mol% in rich product	6.845	5.850	5.713	5.510

It should be noted that even though the full numerical model used an enriching reflux ratio of 10, the same as the transfer function model, the actual flow ratio dynamically changed during the cycle. Nevertheless, the simulation results at 302K and 240K showed a good match. Besides this, both simulation methods illustrated that a lower temperature will simultaneously decrease the CH4 concentration in both products, shifting the DR-PSA towards more being stripping focused.

3.2. Study of key parameters

The full numerical model of DR-PSA was re-configured to act as the second stage cryogenic distillation column which decreases the CH_4 concentration from 50 % to 3 % in a nitrogen rich vent, and meanwhile produces >65 mol% CH_4 in the CH_4 stream in order to be burnt as plant fuel. The column height was adjusted to 10m and the same adsorbent, Norit RB3 was used. Three of the key parameters: temperature, feed position and feed step time was manipulated and their impact on the final product compositions was presented in Figures 2 and 3.

It can be observed from Figure 2 that the maximum separation ability of the system was achieved when the feed position is around 0.3. This indicated that for this separation scenario, 30 % of the column should be used for stripping purpose while 70 % of the column should be used for enriching purpose so that an optimum can be reached. Besides this, the results again confirmed that a lower temperature will shift the DR-PSA system towards being stripping focused, and vice versa, except for the CH_4rich product when the feed position is 0.1. Also it can be observed that different temperatures and feed positions only have a minor effect on the product compositions, indicating that the DR-PSA system appears to be highly self-regulating. Figure 3 illustrated that a larger feed step time can simultaneously decrease the CH_4 concentration in the lean product while holding or slightly increasing the CH_4concentration in the rich product, resulting in better separation ability.

For all the different parameter combinations that have been studied, the maximum separation ability of the DR-PSA system was achieved when the feed step time was 500 s, feed temperature was 240 K and the feed position was at 0.5, where the CH_4 in the lean product reached 7.7 mol% and the CH_4 in the rich product reached 71.4 mol%. This is comparatively close to the first stage cryogenic distillation column, but the total throughput of the DR-PSA system is only around 11 km^3/d. Besides this, it suffers from the same problem that the nitrogen rich product still contains too much methane. Nevertheless, the separation potential of the DR-PSA system can be further studied in terms of manipulating other key parameters such as reflux ratios and pressure ratio to optimise its performance. Also, new adsorbents with higher selectivity can significantly improve the system performance.

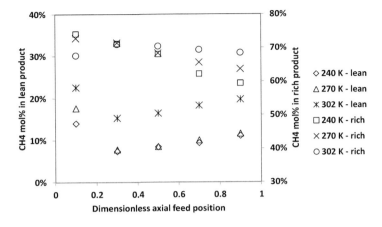

Figure 2. Impact of temperature and feed position on product compositions

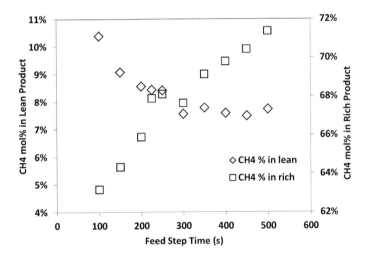

Figure 3. Impact of feed step time on product compositions at 240K and feed position 0.5

4. Conclusions

In this work a novel full numerical simulation methodology for DR-PSA modeling was proposed using commercial simulation software. The model was based on fundamental ODEs for guaranteed rigorous mass and energy balances and pressure-flow networks. The simulation of CH_4/N_2 separation was carried out using the full numerical model and the simulation results showed a good match with the transfer function model previously validated. Three of the key parameters: feed temperature, feed position and feed step time was studied and their impacts on the product compositions were presented. The simulation results showed that the best separation abilities (7.7 mol% CH_4 in lean product and 71.4 mol% CH_4 in rich product) can be obtained at 240 K feed temperature, feed position of 0.5 and a cycle time of 500 s. Though the separation result is comparable to cryogenic distillation, the throughput of the system still needs to be increased. Nevertheless the proposed novel model can serve as a platform for testing other key parameters and configurations for DR-PSA. Future work will focus on further extending the model by studying other key parameters such as pressure ratio and reflux ratios as well as testing other high selectivity adsorbents.

References

K. Arthur, P. R. William, 2006, Fundamental of Natural Gas Processing, Boca Raton, FL, USA, Taylor and Francis, LLC.

T. S. Bhatt, G. Storti, R. Rota, 2013, Optimal design of dual-reflux pressure swing adsorption units via equilibrium theory, Chemical Engineering Science, 102, 11, 42-55.

BP, 2012, Statistical Review of World Energy, <www.bp.com/assets/bp_internet/globalbp/globalbp_uk_english/reports_and_publications/stat istical_energy_review_2011/STAGING/local_assets/pdf/statistical_review_of_world_energy_ full_report_2012.pdf>, Accessed on 15/06/2013,

D. Diagne, M. Goto, T. Hirose, 1994, New PSA Process with Intermediate Feed Inlet Position Operated with Dual Refluxes: Application to Carbon Dioxide Removal and Enrichment, Chem Eng Japan, 27, 1, 85-89.

A. D. Ebner, J. A. Ritter, 2004, Equilibrium Theory Analysis of Dual Reflux PSA for Separation of a Binary Mixture, AIChE Journal, 50, 10, 2418-2429.

D. T. Kearns, P. A. Webley, 2006, Modelling and evaluation of dual-reflux pressure swing adsorption cycles: Part I. Mathematical models, Chemical Engineering Science, 61, 7223-7233.

J. A. McIntyre, A. D. Ebner, J. A. Ritter, 2010, Experimental Study of a Dual Reflux Enriching Pressure Swing Adsorption Process for Concentrating Dilute Feed Streams, Ind. Eng. Chem. Res., 49, 1848-1858.

T. E. Rufford, G. Watson, T. L. H. Saleman, P. S. Hofman, N. K. Jensen, E. F. May, 2013, Adsorption equilibria and kinetics of methane + nitrogen mixtures on the activated carbon Norit RB3, Ind. Eng. Chem. Res., 52, 39, 14270-14281.

Y. Zhang, T. L. H. Saleman, G. Li, E. F. May, B. R. Young, 2013, Modelling Dual Reflux PSA Cycles Using A Transfer Function Methodology for Separating Nitrogen and Methane in LNG Production (Paper ID: L-220), Fundamental of Adsorption 13, Baltimore, USA.

Jiří Jaromír Klemeš, Petar Sabev Varbanov and Peng Yen Liew (Editors)
Proceedings of the 24th European Symposium on Computer Aided Process Engineering – ESCAPE 24
June 15-18, 2014, Budapest, Hungary.

Design of Multi-pressure Organic Rankine Cycles for Waste Heat Recovery in Site Utility Systems

Mirko Z. Stijepovic[a,*], Athanasios I. Papadopoulos[b], Patrick Linke[a], Aleksandar S. Grujic[c], Panos Seferlis[d]

[a]*Department of Chemical Engineering, Texas A&M University at Qatar, PO Box 23874, Education City, Doha, Qatar*
[b]*Chemical and Process Engineering Research Institute, Centre for Research and Technology-Hellas, Thermi 57001, Thessaloniki, Greece*
[c]*Institute of Chemistry, Technology and Metallurgy, University of Belgrade, Njegoševa 12, 11000 Belgrade, Serbia*
[d]*Department of Mechanical Engineering, Aristotle University of Thessaloniki, P.O. Box 484, 54124 Thessaloniki, Greece*
mirko.stijepovic@qatar.tamu.edu

Abstract

This work addresses the design of Organic Rankine Cycle (ORC) processes used for power generation from low-grade heat available in site utility systems. The Exergy Composite Curves approach is used within a systemic optimization framework to explore various complex ORC configurations. The method facilitates interconnectivity at several temperature and pressure levels, considering different types and numbers of turbines as design decision parameters simultaneously with other operating ORC features. It is employed to investigate the performance of two generic ORC configurations, namely one considering independent pressure loops with expansion turbines and the other considering pressure loops contacted through induction turbines. To optimize the number of pressure levels, ORC structural configuration, and operating parameters an inclusive objective function is used considering thermodynamic criteria. The application of the method is demonstrated by a case study on waste heat recovery and reuse in a utility plant.

Keywords: Organic Rankine cycle, Exergy analysis, Utility systems, Process design

1. Introduction

Utility systems are an essential part of process plants, supplying thermal energy in the form of steam which is generated at different pressure levels to satisfy heating demands for a wide range of temperatures. After utilization, the steam results in a saturated condensate often discharged into a lower pressure area where flash steam of low thermal content is generated. Process plants produce large amounts of flash steam often wasted in the environment, while instead it may be recovered for further utilization.

To this end, ORC systems are able to transform heat of low thermal content into useful power hence they have been identified as a very promising technology for waste heat recovery (Kapil et al., 2011). The ORC operation is based on the vaporization (*vap*) of a working fluid to drive a turbine (*turb*), followed by condensation (*cond*) into a liquid which is pumped (*pump*) back to the vaporizer to close the loop. Clearly, the ORC operating and economic performance depends on the way that different ORC equipment components are interconnected and integrated with the heat source. ORCs incorporating conventional heat extraction and expansion configurations are unsuitable for use with sources of varying heat content at different pressure levels; they result in increased entropy generation, leading to waste of thermal energy. More efficient configurations are necessary that are able to extract and transform heat into work at different pressures.

Process integration methods (Varbanov et al., 2012) provide a useful set of technologies for the analysis and design of similar systems. An increasing number of publications employ Pinch-based tools such as grand composite curve analysis (DiGenova et al., 2013) to investigate and improve the performance of pre-specified ORC configurations, or combine process integration principles with optimization methods to design efficient ORC flowsheets (Hipólito-Valencia et al., 2013). Despite obtaining promising results, improvements are mainly based on the design of heat-exchange networks around conventional ORC expansion operations using performance characteristics associated with energy analysis features (e.g. thermal efficiency etc.). The design of ORC flowsheets combining advances in both heat-exchange and expansion operations is clearly expected to result in considerable performance improvement. However, this requires the additional consideration of exergy ORC characteristics to identify configurations that better exploit the maximum useful work produced from heat sources of variable temperature and pressure. To date, few existing works have explored ORC design considering exergy analysis at different parts of the ORC flowsheet (Tchanche et al., 2010) or minimization of the exergy losses (Marechal and Kalitventzeff, 2004).

2. Proposed method

The consideration of exergy analysis in the investigation for promising ORC process configurations clearly deserves further attention in the context of systemic process integration methods. The presented work adopts the Exergy Composite Curves (ECCs) approach (Linhoff and Dhole, 1992) to explore the potential for ORC process improvements. The method is supported by a mathematical model representing a generic multi-pressure ORC cascade. The model facilitates interconnectivity at different temperature and pressure levels, also considering different types of turbines (e.g. expansion, induction turbines) to investigate the performance of different ORC configurations (e.g. independent pressure loops or pressure loops contacted through induction turbines). Such configurations are updated with new features within an iterative procedure supporting the systematic identification of the optimum number of pressure loops, together with several operating optimization parameters.

2.1. Model development

A major concern in the optimization of a standard ORC (Figure 1a) is the increase of the work extracted from a specific heat source or the reduction of exergy losses. This goal may be approached by modifications imposed on the ORC operating conditions which reflect on the shape of the ECCs, since the shaded area within the ECCs (Figure 1b) is directly associated with the observed exergy losses. Such modifications may be interpreted by different process configurations, as their practical implementation requires appropriate allocation of heat exchange and expansion equipment within the ORC flowsheet. In this context, different process configurations may be captured by a generic multi-pressure ORC cascade (Figure 2a) consisting of an arbitrary number of branches (*NLP*) to represent different pressure levels. The cascade considers two potential types of turbines, an expansion (*ET*) and an induction turbine (*IT*). The *ET* is used to generate work by expansion between any heat extraction and condenser pressure level, while the *IT* is used between successive pressure levels.

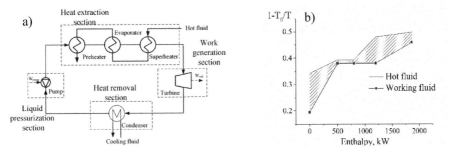

Figure 1. a) Scheme of a standard ORC, b) Exergy Composite Curves of heat extraction

The operating features of the cascade may be represented in a composite curve diagram (Figure 2b). The enthalpy intervals (*NWI*) for the working fluid (*wf*) curve follow a sequential, recursive pattern until the last interval where superheating of the *wf* takes place only at the highest pressure level. The system pressure levels are represented in the *wf* curve using three isothermal profiles (i.e. T_2-T_3, T_5-T_6, T_{3NLP-1}-T_{3NLP}). The hot fluid (*hf*) curve may also be composed of *NHI* temperature intervals (Θ_1-Θ_{NHI}). As the shaded area of Figure 1b corresponds to the observed exergy losses, the difference between the exergy contents of the hot fluid (Ex^{hf}) and the working fluid (Ex^{wf}) needs to be minimized whilst considering the minimum temperature driving force to ensure realistic heat transfer rate and exchange area. This is represented by Eq.(1), as follows:

$$\Delta E_{loss} = \sum_{l=1}^{NHI} \frac{\left(1-T_0/\theta_{l+1}\right)+\left(1-T_0/\theta_l\right)}{2}\Delta H_l^{hf} - \sum_{j=1}^{NWI} \frac{\left(1-T_0/T_{j+1}\right)+\left(1-T_0/T_j\right)}{2}\Delta H_j^{wf} \quad (1)$$

Based on the *wf* and *hf* curves the enthalpy (*ΔH*-kW) in each interval is calculated as:

$$\Delta H_{3i-2}^{wf} = \left(\sum_{i}^{NLP} F_i^{wf} \cdot C_{p_{liq},i}^{wf}\right)(T_{3i-1} - T_{3i-2}), i \in [1, NLP]$$

$$\Delta H_{3i-1}^{wf} = F_i^{wf} \cdot \Delta H_{vap}\left(T_{3i-1}\right), i \in [1, NLP]$$

$$\Delta H_{3i}^{wf} = F_i^{wf} C_{p_{vap},i}^{wf}\left(T_{3i+1} - T_{3i}\right) + \left(\sum_{i+1}^{NLP} F_i^{wf} \cdot C_{p_{liq},i}^{wf}\right)(T_{3i+1} - T_{3i}), i \in [1, NLP-1] \quad (2)$$

$$\Delta H_{3i}^{wf} = F_i^{wf} C_{p_{vap},i}^{wf}\left(T_{3i+1} - T_{3i}\right), i = NPL$$

$$\Delta H_l^{hf} = F_l^{hf} C_{p_{liq},l}^{hf}\left(\theta_{l+1} - \theta_l\right), l \in [1, NHI]$$

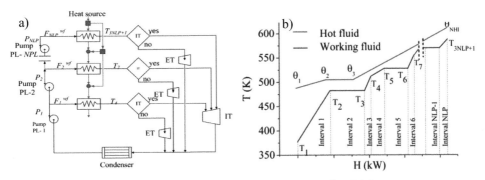

Figure 2. Generic a) multi-pressure ORC cascade, and b) corresponding ECCs

For the work generation (*turb*), heat removal (*cond*) and liquid pressurization (*pump*) sections of the cycle the following equations hold:

$$W_{turb,i} = -\int_{T_{turbout,i}}^{T_{3i+1}} C_{p,vap}(T) \cdot dT$$

$$W_{cond} = \lambda \left(Q^{hf} - \sum_{i=1}^{NLP} W_{turb,i} \right) \qquad (3)$$

$$W_{pump,i} = F_i^{wf} \cdot \upsilon^{sat} \left[P^{sat}(T_{3i-1}) - P^{sat}(T_i) \right] / \eta_{pump}, i \in [1, NLP]$$

where λ is a coefficient of the power input necessary to remove 100 kW of condenser heat, $C_{p,vap}$ and $C_{p,liq}$ are the vapor and liquid heat capacities (kJ/kmol.K), P^{sat} is the saturation pressure (Pa), υ^{sat} is the saturated liquid molar volume (m^3/kmol), F is the flowrate (kmol/s), W is the work (kW), Q is the heat transferred (kW) and η is the efficiency.

2.2. Optimization problem formulation and design approach

The minimization of exergy loss improves (i.e. maximizes) the quality of the extracted heat. The quantity of the work produced from the available exergy depends on the behaviour of the *wf* during the expansion process because it is a strong function of the fluid thermo-physical properties (Stijepovic et al., 2012).Therefore, the work generation in the expansion should be part of the objective function employed in optimization. Power requirements for liquid pressurization and condensation affect the overall power output. Higher operating pressures which are beneficial for exergy loss minimization require more power during the liquid pressurization process. Due to this trade – off the power requirement for pressurization should also be part of the objective function. The power requirement for the condensation process decreases as the quantity of the generated work increases. This affects the overall power output balance, therefore the power requirement for condensation should also be considered in the objective function. Hence the optimization problem can be defined as follows:

$$\min \Phi = \Delta Ex_{loss} - \left(\left| W_{turb} \right| - W_{pump} - W_{cond} \right) \qquad (4)$$

Subject to:

$$T_{j+1} - T_j \geq 0, \, j \in [1, 3NWI] \qquad (5)$$

$$\theta \left(\sum_{j=1}^{m} \Delta H_j^c \right) - T \left(\sum_{j=1}^{m} \Delta H_j^c \right) - \Delta T_{\min} \geq 0, \, j \in [1, m], m = NWI \vee NHI, c = wf \vee hf \qquad (6)$$

$$C_{p_{liq},i}(T_{3i-1} - T_0) + \Delta H_{vap}(T_{3i-1}) - C_{p_{vap},i}(T_{turbout,i} - T_0) \leq 0, \, i \in [1, NPL] \qquad (7)$$

$$T_{turbout,i+1} - T_{3i+1} = 0, i \in [1, NLP - 1] \qquad (8)$$

where Eq.(8) represents a case of an induction turbine where the outlet of a particular turbine stage has to be equal to the temperature of the stream with which it is mixed before entering the next turbine stage.

A systemic design approach is proposed consisting of the following stages: i) the quantity of the available heat is first determined based on the available hot stream (e.g. inlet temperature etc.), ii) an initial process configuration is then setup serving as a reference point to measure potential subsequent improvements, iii) the optimization problem is solved for this process, iv) a new process configuration is generated by adding a new pressure level, v) the new configuration becomes the reference process, hence steps (ii), (iii) and (iv) are repeated until no significant improvement is observed when adding new pressure levels (i.e. changing the process configuration).

3. Case study

3.1. Implementation details

The waste heat consists of water condensate with saturation temperature of 250 °C with mass flowrate of 267 t/h. The outlet temperature of the condensate should be decreased to 120 °C to recover part of the desired energy with an ORC. Dibromomethane is the *wf*, which is assumed to be appropriate for the specified hot fluid inlet temperature (Tchanche et al., 2011). A standard ORC process (Figure 1a) is optimized first using as decision variables the F^{wf}, the saturation temperature (T_2) and the outlet temperature at the heat extraction section (T_4). After determining the optimal values structural improvements are explored by introduction of a new pressure level (PL). Two alternative configurations are considered including (a) independent pressure loops with expansion turbines (PLET)and (b) pressure loops contacted trough an induction turbine (PLIT). For the 2^{nd}PL the type of optimization variables are the same but their number is doubled (one set for each level). Following the proposed optimization approach, the resulting 2-PLconfiguration will become the reference point for a 3-PL process if a significant performance improvement is achieved compared to the standard ORC process. The procedure is repeated fo 3PLs and so forth.

3.2. Results and discussion

Figure 3 shows the dependence of the net work output on the type of configuration and number of PLs. Configurations with 2-PLs have higher power output compared with a standard ORC with 1 PL (Figure 3a). This is because multi-PL processes are able to closely match the ECCs of the wf and hf, hence decreasing the exergy losses.

The recovered exergy loss is partially converted to power; this is why power production is increased with a multi-PL cascade compared to a standard process. The 3-PL configurations present slightly higher power output compared to the 2-PL ones. The 3-

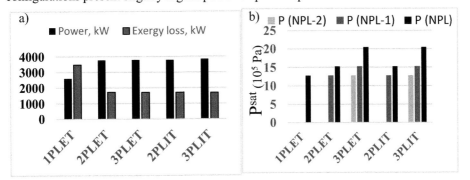

Figure 3. Type of ORC configuration vs. a) power output and exergy loss, b)saturation pressure distribution per pressure level

PL configuration matches the ECCs even more closely than the 2-PL case, but the improvement is not as significant. The induction turbine (e.g. 2-PLIT etc.) systems have higher power output than systems with expansion turbines (e.g. 1-PLET). In fact, a 3-PL with 3 expansion turbines (3-PLET) has the same power output as a 2-PL with 1 induction turbine (2-PLIT), while the 3-PLIT power output (3-PL, 1 induction turbine) is even higher (this is not clearly visible due to space restrictions). Figure 3a shows that the power output in multi-PLs is 44.5% higher than in a standard ORC.

Optimal values of pressure levels for each ORC configuration are given in Figure 3b. Figure 3b shows that the optimal value of pressure for each additional level is higher. This is because the working fluid operating parameters are limited by the pinch temperature. By adding new pressure levels the limitations introduced by the pinch point are reduced, and the system produces more power, reducing exergy losses if the new pressure level is higher. As a result exergy loss reduction is key for design of ORCs with improved performance. Future work should focus on the employment of mixtures in multi-pressure systems.

4. Conclusions

This work proposes an efficient approach for exploring potential ORC process improvements by introducing multi-pressure configurations. The consideration of exergy analysis in this investigation shows high potential to identify and reduce losses that occur due to process irreversibility. The method is used to explore different ORC configurations, which are updated with new features within an iterative procedure supporting the systematic identification of the optimum number of pressure loops together with several operating parameters. The optimization is performed using an inclusive objective function. The case study indicates significant improvements in power output from the introduction of multiple pressure loops.

References

K.J. DiGenova, B.B. Botros, J.G. Brisson, 2013, Method for customizing an organic Rankine cycle to a complex heat source for efficient energy conversion, demonstrated on a Fischer Tropsch plant, Applied Energy, 102, 746–754.

B.J. Hipólito-Valencia, E. Rubio-Castro, J. M. Ponce-Ortega, M. Serna-González, F. Nápoles-Rivera, M.M. El-Halwagi, 2013, Optimal integration of organic Rankine cycles with industrial processes, Energy Conversion and Management, 73, 285-302.

A. Kapil, I. Bulatov, R. Smith, J.K. Kim, 2011, Site-wide process integration for low grade heat recovery, Computer Aided Chemical Engineering, 29, 1859-1863.

B. Linnhoff, V.R. Dhole, 1992, Shaftwork targets for low-temperature process design, Chemical Engineering Science, 47, 2081–2091.

F. Marechal, B. Kalitventzeff, 2004, A Methodology for the Optimal Insertion of Organic Rankine Cycles in Industrial Processes, 2nd International Symposium of Process Integration, Dalhousie University, Halifax, Canada, <infoscience.epfl.ch/record/53483/files/[LENI-CONF-2004-006].pdf>, accessed on 4/8/2013.

M. Stijepovic, P. Linke, A.I. Papadopoulos, A. Grujic, 2012, On the role of working fluid properties in organic Rankine cycle performance, Applied Thermal Engineering, 36, 406–423.

B.F. Tchanche, G. Lambrinos, A. Frangoudakis, G. Papadakis, 2010, Exergy analysis of micro-organic Rankine power cycles for a small scale solar driven reverse osmosis desalination system, Applied Energy, 87, 1295–1306.

B.F. Tchanche, G. Lambrinos, A. Frangoudakis, G. Papadakis, 2011, Low-grade heat conversion into power using organic, Rankine cycles – A review of various applications, Renewable and Sustaianable Energy Reviews, 15, 3963–3979.

P.S.Varbanov, Z.Fodor, J.J.Klemeš, 2012, Total Site targeting with process specific minimum temperature difference (ΔTmin), Energy, 44, 1, 20-28.

Jiří Jaromír Klemeš, Petar Sabev Varbanov and Peng Yen Liew (Editors)
Proceedings of the 24th European Symposium on Computer Aided Process Engineering – ESCAPE 24
June 15-18, 2014, Budapest, Hungary.

MINLP Optimization Algorithm for the Synthesis of Heat and Work Exchange Networks

Viviani C. Onishi[a]*, Mauro A. S. S. Ravagnani[a], José A. Caballero[b]

[a]*Department of Chemical Engineering, State University of Maringá, Av. Colombo 5790, Maringá-PR 87020-900, Brazil*
[b]*Department of Chemical Engineering, University of Alicante, Ap Correos 99, Alicante03080, Spain.*
viviani.onishi@hotmail.com

Abstract

This paper introduces a new optimization model for the simultaneous synthesis of heat and work exchange networks. The work integration is performed in the work exchange network (WEN), while the heat integration is carried out in the heat exchanger network (HEN). In the WEN synthesis, streams at high-pressure (HP) and low-pressure (LP) are subjected to pressure manipulation stages, via turbines and compressors running on common shafts and stand-alone equipment. The model allows the use of several units of single-shaft-turbine-compressor (SSTC), as well as helper motors and generators to respond to any shortage and/or excess of energy, respectively, in the SSTC axes. The heat integration of the streams occurs in the HEN between each WEN stage. Thus, as the inlet and outlet streams temperatures in the HEN are dependent of the WEN design, they must be considered as optimization variables. The proposed multi-stage superstructure is formulated in mixed-integer nonlinear programming (MINLP), in order to minimize the total annualized cost composed by capital and operational expenses. A case study is conducted to verify the accuracy of the proposed approach. The results indicate that the heat integration between the WEN stages is essential to enhance the work integration, and to reduce the total cost of process due the need of a smaller amount of hot and cold utilities.

Keywords: optimization; mixed-integer nonlinear programming (MINLP); work exchange network (WEN); heat exchanger network (HEN); heat integration.

1. Introduction

Heat and work are two forms of energy frequently available in processing plants. The optimization of energy integration through the application of innovative strategies, and development of more efficient processing techniques is the most effective way to reduce process costs, and minimize environmental impacts related to high energy consumption (Lara et al., 2013). The pressure manipulation of streams is extremely important in many industrial processes, such as production of ammonia and natural gas, wherein is responsible for the consumption of large energy amounts and, consequently, high operating expenses. Although the synthesis of heat exchanger networks (HENs) has been intensively studied since the energy crisis in the 1970s (Ravagnani and Silva, 2012), with significant impact on the industry (Huang and Karimi, 2013), the literature about the problem of work integration is rather limited (Onishi et al., 2013). Huang and Fan (1996) introduced the work exchange network (WEN) problem, defining operational principles for work exchange among two process streams. Aspelund et al. (2007) presented a method based on Extended Pinch Analysis and Design (ExPAnD) to minimize energy requirements of the system. In their work, compressors and turbines are used separately, with any mention to the use of pressure manipulation equipment operating in a common axis. Moreover, only the aspects related to the exergy analysis were evaluated. Razib et al. (2012) presented a preliminary model for WENs synthesis, with the goal of minimizing the total cost of the network. The authors proposed a superstructure to optimize the pressure recovery of streams, via equipment running in a single-shaft-turbine-compressor (SSTC). Nevertheless, the model allows the use of only one SSTC axis unit restricted to a fixed rotational speed. In addition, the heat integration is not considered and the cooling and heating of streams is performed by heaters and coolers located in the end of each WEN stage.

A new optimization model is proposed for the simultaneous synthesis of WEN with heat integration of streams. In the WEN design, streams at high-pressure (HP) and low-pressure (LP) exchange work in pressure manipulation stages, via turbines and compressors running on common shafts and stand-alone equipment. The model allows the use of several SSTC axes units operating at any rotational speed. Generators and helper motors are used, respectively, to convert work excess into electricity and to fill for power shortage on the SSTC axes. Between the compression and expansion stages of the WEN, the streams are sent to the HEN to promote heat integration. The pressure and heat recovery of streams are performed in a multi-stage superstructure, formulated as a mixed-integer nonlinear programming (MINLP) problem, in order to minimize the total annualized cost. A case study is conducted to verify the accuracy of the proposed model. The results indicate that the heat integration between WEN stages is essential to enhance the work integration, and to reduce the total cost of the network.

2. Problem statement

Given a set of HP and LP gaseous streams with known mass flows, heat capacities, supply state (inlet pressure and temperature) and target state (outlet pressure and temperature); besides electricity, thermal utilities for heating and cooling, equipment for pressure manipulation and heat transfer, and their respective costs. The main objective is to synthesize an optimal WEN by minimizing the total annualized cost composed by the operational expenses—including the revenue from electricity generation—and capital cost of investment in the various units of the network. The leading idea of the WEN synthesis is to promote the work exchange between HP and LP streams, via turbines and compressors running on a common SSTC axis. The SSTC axis allows the pressure recovery among different streams in several expansion and compression stages through single-stage and parallel equipment, as well as the use of helper motors and generators to respond to any shortage and/or excess of energy, respectively. Moreover, stand-alone compressors, turbines and valves are also used to compose the WEN in addition to several SSTC axes units. The HEN synthesis is performed simultaneously to the WEN design, by recovering heat from process streams aiming to improve the pressure recovery. Thus, while the HEN only involves the heat integration of streams, the WEN involves the work integration or work and heat integration, using SSTC equipment, stand-alone turbines and compressors, valves, helper motors and generators and, when necessary, heat exchangers, heaters and coolers.

3. MINLP optimization model

In this paper, the proposed model for the WEN synthesis with heat integration is developed in a MINLP formulation. The proposed WEN superstructure is composed by

n stages of compression or expansion for each stream. Consequently, each HP stream goes through n expansion stages and, analogously, each LP stream undergoes n compression stages. The pressure recovery is performed by single-stage and/or parallel equipment—namely compressors and turbines—associated to a common shaft (SSTC). Several units of SSTC axes can be used. However, the global energy balance should be respected in each SSTC axis unit, i.e., the expansion work must be equal to the compression work:

$$Wg_e + \sum_{i=1}^{LP}\sum_{n=1}^{N}\sum_{k=1}^{K} We_{i,n,e,k} = Wm_e + \sum_{j=1}^{HP}\sum_{n=1}^{N}\sum_{k=1}^{K} We_{j,n,e,k} \quad i \in LP, j \in HP, n \in N, k \in K, e \in E \qquad (1)$$

For this reason, helper motors and generators (turbines) allocated on the SSTC axes, and stand-alone compressors, turbines and valves are also used in the network. At each compression and expansion stage, the overall mass flow is splitted between various flows, through the pressure manipulation equipment that compose each of these stages. In the end of each stage, the sub-streams pass through a mixer, reforming the parent streams. Although the outlet pressure is the same in all equipment of each expansion stage, the temperature in the outlet of each device is different. Thus, energy and mass balances should be performed at the mixing points. Besides the work integration, the HP and LP streams are submitted to simultaneous heat integration in the HEN. As a result, the inlet temperatures in the HEN should be connected to the outlet streams temperatures from the WEN stages. The formulation is based on the model for HEN design proposed by Yee and Grossmann (1990), wherein streams splits is considered, and isothermal mixing and constant heat transfer coefficients are assumed. However, the model is extended to include the unknown intermediate temperatures from the WEN, which are treated as optimization variables. The HEN superstructure is divided in stages according to temperature at mixing point, in which all hot streams can exchange heat with all cold streams. Thus, the HP streams are considered as cold streams and the LP streams as hot streams, since high temperatures favor the expansion process, as well low temperatures improve the compression process. Heaters and coolers are placed on the end of the streams, in order to guarantee that their target temperature can be achieved. The objective function is composed by capital cost associated to the various units of the network and operational expenses.

The resulting model is highly complex, due the need to simultaneously optimize all parameters relating to WEN and HEN design. For simplification, the same number of stages is considered in both WEN and HEN, and the ideal gas model is used to describe the thermodynamic behavior of real gases. However, an isentropic efficiency factor is considered to adjust inevitable losses of efficiency of real processes. The proposed MINLP model is optimized with the DICOPT solver under GAMS software (version 24.02). The high non-convexity and nonlinearity of the mathematical formulation does not guarantee the global optimum. However, some numerical experiments with this model showed that increasing the number of major iterations, and solving feasibility problems that may arise from NLP, allow obtaining good solutions. For the solution of the model is crucial to adequately establish all limits of the variables.

4. Case study

An example is studied to verify the applicability of the proposed approach for the simultaneous synthesis of heat and work exchange networks. In this case study, the WEN is designed allowing work integration between two streams at high-pressure (HP1 and HP2), and two streams at low-pressure (LP1 and LP2).The goal is to obtain a network that presents minimum total annualized cost through the optimal energy integration. The maximum number of four compression stages and four expansion stages of the streams are considered for the WEN synthesis. The process streams are sent to the HEN to promote heat recovery between the stages of compression and expansion. Thus, the high-pressure streams HP1 and HP2 are considered as cold streams, and the low-pressure streams LP1 and LP2 are regarded as hot streams for the HEN design. The stream HP1 originates the cold streams C1 to C5 and the stream HP2 gives rise to cold streams C6 to C10. Similarly, the stream LP1 originates the hot streams H1 to H5 and the stream LP2 gives rise to hot streams H6 to H10. For the HEN synthesis, a superstructure with four stages of heat exchange and the possibility of streams splits are considered, and isothermal mixing is assumed. The flow rates (F) and heat capacities (Cp) of all the streams are known constants. The problem data are presented in Table 1. The hot and cold utilities are available on 500 K and 288 K, respectively. In addition, all unknown intermediate temperatures of streams are restricted between 288 K and 600 K, and $f = 0.18$, $\Delta T_{min} = 5$ K, $\eta = 0.7$, $\mu = 1.961\text{e-}3$ K/kPa, $RC_{max} = 3$ are also regarded.

In this case study, the use of two SSTC axes units is analyzed. The optimal WEN obtained is composed by two valves, two stand-alone turbines, four stand-alone compressors, four SSTC turbines, and three SSTC compressors. The stream HP1 is subjected to three expansion stages through two parallel SSTC turbines (1,480.1 kW and 100 kW) associated to the shaft 2, one valve, and one stand-alone turbine (848.4 kW). The stream HP2 undergoes four expansion stages through one valve, two single-stage SSTC turbines (950 kW and 100 kW) located on shaft 1 and shaft 2, respectively, and one stand-alone turbine (698.3 kW). Both streams LP1 and LP2 undergo three compression stages. The stream LP1 passes through two stand-alone compressors (282 kW and 950 kW), and one single-stage SSTC compressor (950 kW) located on the shaft 1. The stream LP2 passes through one stand-alone compressor (950 kW), two parallel SSTC compressors (950 kW and 730.1 kW) associated to the shaft 2, and one stand-alone compressor (950 kW). The total work of expansion (compression) performed (consumed) by the SSTC turbines (SSTC compressors) is equal to 950 kW for the shaft 1, and 1,680.1 kW for the shaft 2. In the HEN design, four heat exchangers with heat exchanger areas (A) of 390.5 m² ($Q = 603.6$ kW), 432.7 m² ($Q = 742.1$ kW), 581.3 m² ($Q = 1,083.7$ kW) and 918.2 m² ($Q = 1,748.6$ kW) are needed. Moreover, two coolers ($A = 424.1$ m² with $Q = 836.2$ kW, and $A = 462.7$ m² with $Q = 747.9$ kW) are used for the heat recovery. Figure 1 shows the optimal WEN configuration with heat integration obtained for this example. In this case, as there are no remains or lacks of energy in the shafts, no helper motor or generator is needed to satisfy the energy balance. However, two stand-alone turbines are used in the network configuration. Consequently, 1,546.7 kW of energy are produced in the WEN, and can be used in other stages of the process and/or for sale of electricity. The total annualized cost estimated is 6,279k US$y⁻¹, in Table 1.

Table 1. Streams data for the example.

Streams	F (kg/s)	Cp (kJ/kg K)	h (kW/m²K)	T_{IN} (K)	T_{OUT} (K)	P_{IN} (kPa)	P_{OUT} (kPa)
HP1	15	1.432	0.1	380	380	850	100
HP2	18	0.982	0.1	400	400	980	180
LP1	15	1.432	0.1	400	400	100	520
LP2	18	1.432	0.1	400	400	100	850

Cost data: $CE = 455.04$ US$y⁻¹ kW; $CV = 400$ US$y⁻¹ kW; $CS = 337$ US$y⁻¹ kW; $CW = 100$ US$y⁻¹ kW

which 5,314k US$y^{-1} is the capital cost, 158k US$y^{-1}are the total expenses with heating and cooling streams, and 807k US$y^{-1} is the annual cost of electricity already discounted the revenue generated by stand-alone turbines (619k US$y^{-1}). In this example, if the network is synthetized with only one SSTC axis, the same equipment obtained with two axes is needed for the WEN design with heat integration. Clearly, as the networks obtained in both cases (i.e., with one and two SSTC axes) differ only in the number of SSTC axes used; both have the same total cost. Moreover, if the use of three SSTC axes units is forced, the total annualized cost increases that represent a sub-optimal solution. The mathematical model contains 3,900 continuous variables, 232 binary variables and 5,105 constraints with 17,710 Jacobian elements (non-zeros), in which 2,482 are nonlinear. The CPU time is 6.46 min and the optimal solution is found in the sixth major iteration. The example was solved using a personal computer with an Intel Core 2 Duo 2.40 GHz processor and 3.00 GB RAM under Windows 7 Ultimate.

5. Conclusions

A new optimization model is proposed for the simultaneous synthesis of WEN with heat integration concomitant in the HEN. The multi-stage superstructure is developed in a MINLP formulation, aiming the optimal integration between heat and work of LP and HP streams, by minimizing the total annualized cost of the network. The results obtained indicate that the heat integration between the WEN stages of expansion and compression is essential to enhance the work integration. Furthermore, the heat recovery from streams reduces the total annualized cost in 29 % as a consequence of the decrease of the operational expenses related to the use of thermal utilities. The total cost is also reduced in 10 % due the revenue generated from the expansion work produced by the stand-alone turbines. In the case study, the same WEN with heat integration can be designed with the use of one or two SSTC axes units. Thus, besides the economic

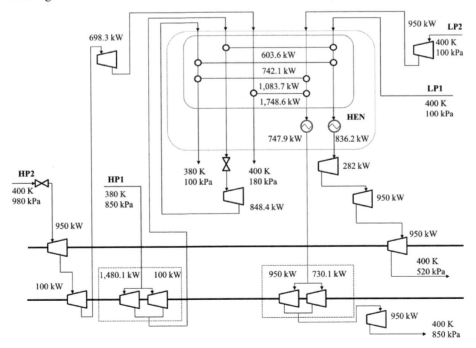

Figure 1. Optimal configuration of the WEN with heat integration obtained for the case study.

factor, the space available in the processing plant should be considered to choose the best WEN design. The larger number of equipment running on the same SSTC unit, the larger the difficulty to keep them under the same operating conditions will be, since all must be kept under the same rotational speed. In contrast, the use of a larger number of shafts may request a bigger space in the process plant.

Nomenclature

CE	cost parameter for electricity	We	SSTC compressor/turbine work
CR_{max}	maximum compression ratio	Wg	generator work
CS	cost parameter for the heating	Wm	helper motor work
CV	cost parameter for the electric power revenue	η	isentropic efficiency
		μ	Joule-Thompson coefficient
CW	cost parameter for the cooling	Subscripts	
f	annualization factor for the cost	e	SSTC axes units
P	pressure	i	LP streams (hot)
T	temperature	j	HP streams (cold)
ΔT_{min}	minimal approximation of temperature	k	streams splits
		n	stages in the WEN

Acknowledgements

The financial supports by the Brazilian agency "Coordenação de Aperfeiçoamento de Pessoal de Nível Superior – CAPES" (process n° 10758/12-7), and the Spanish Ministry of Science and Innovation and Ministry of Economy and Competitiveness (under project CTQ2012-37039-C02-02) are gratefully acknowledged.
Viviani C. Onishi also has the following affiliation: CAPES Foundation, Ministry of Education of Brazil, Brasília-DF 7004020, Brazil

References

A. Aspelund, D.O. Berstad, T. Gundersen, 2007, An extended pinch analysis and design procedure utilizing pressure based exergy for subambient cooling, Applied Thermal Engineering, 27, 2633–2649.

K.F. Huang, I.A. Karimi, 2013, Simultaneous synthesis approaches for cost-effective heat exchanger networks, Chemical Engineering Science, 98, 231–245.

M.A.A.S. Ravagnani, A.P. Silva, 2012, Retrofit of heat exchanger networks including the detailed equipment design, Computer Aided Chemical Engineering, 31, 235–239.

M.S. Razib, M.M.F. Hasan, I.A. Karimi, 2012, Preliminary synthesis of work exchange networks, Computers and Chemical Engineering, 37, 262–277.

T.F. Yee, I.E. Grossmann, 1990, Simultaneous optimization models for heat integration - II. Heat exchanger network synthesis, Computers and Chemical Engineering, 14, 10, 1165–1184.

V.C. Onishi, M.A.S.S. Ravagnani, J.A. Caballero, 2013, Simultaneous synthesis of heat exchanger networks with pressure recovery: Optimal integration between heat and work. AIChE Journal, doi:10.1002/aic.14314.

Y. Lara, P. Lisbona, A. Martínez, L.M. Romeo, 2013, Design and analysis of heat exchanger networks for integrated Ca-looping systems, Applied Energy, 111, 690–700.

Y.L. Huang, L.T. Fan, 1996, Analysis of a work exchanger network, Industrial and Engineering Chemistry Research, 35, 3528–3538.

Jiří Jaromír Klemeš, Petar Sabev Varbanov and Peng Yen Liew (Editors)
Proceedings of the 24th European Symposium on Computer Aided Process Engineering – ESCAPE 24
June 15-18, 2014, Budapest, Hungary. Copyright © 2014 Elsevier B.V. All rights reserved.

Sustainable Development of the Shale Gas Supply Chain and the Optimal Drilling Strategy for Nonconventional Wells

Diego C. Cafaro,[a] Ignacio E. Grossmann[b,*]

[a]INTEC (UNL – CONICET), Güemes 3450, Santa Fe, 3000, Argentina
[b]Dept. of Chem. Eng., Carnegie Mellon University, Pittsburgh, PA 15213, U.S.A.
grossmann@cmu.edu

Abstract

We present a long-term MINLP planning model for the development of shale gas fields. A key decision is the drilling/fracturing strategy yielding the freshwater consumption profile, which is critical in waterscarce regions with high cumulative demand for water. Results show that the model can help companies to reduce freshwater consumption by optimally planning drilling operations, at the expense of small reductions in the net present value of the projects.

Keywords: Shale gas, supply chain, sustainable plan, MINLP approach.

1. Introduction

Over the past decade, the combination of horizontal drilling and hydraulic fracturing has allowed access to large volumes of shale gas that were previously uneconomical to produce. The production of natural gas from shale formations has reinvigorated the natural gas and chemical industries, particularly in the U.S. Recent studies project U.S. shale gas production to double in the next 25 y (Energy Information Administration, 2012). In this context, the long-term planning and development of the shale gas supply chain network is a very challenging problem, from both economic and environmental points of view. However, to the best of our knowledge, it has not been addressed before in the literature. Regarding the design of natural gas Supply Chains (SC), Durán and Grossmann (1986) propose an MINLP model and a solution strategy deciding on the pipeline network design, compressors power and pipeline pressures. Van den Heever and Grossmann (2000) present a generalized nonlinear disjunctive programming model for oilfield infrastructure planning, while Gupta and Grossmann (2012) address new features of the same problem, accounting for oil, water, and gas flows explicitly in the formulation. More recently, Čuček et al. (2013) develop a multi-period model for the biorefinery's supply chain network design. On the other hand, some work has also been reported on the optimization of the hydraulic fracturing process (Rahman et al., 2001).

This work presents a mixed-integer nonlinear programming (MINLP) model for the sustainable planning and development of shale gas supply chains, which should optimally determine: (a) the number of wells to drill and fracture; (b) the size and location of new gas processing plants (and future expansions); (c) the section, length and location of new pipelines for gathering raw gas, delivering dry gas, and transporting natural gas liquids (NGL); (d) the location and power of new gas compressors; and (e) the amount of freshwater supplied from each reservoir for well drilling and fracturing; so as to optimize the results of the project, over a planning horizon comprising 10 y.

2. Problem Description

The raw gas extracted from shale formations is transported from wellbores to processing plants through gathering pipeline systems. The processing of shale gas consists of the separation of all the hydrocarbons and fluids from the pure gas (methane) to produce what is known as pipeline quality natural gas. This means that before the natural gas can be transported by midstream distributors, it must be purified to meet the requirement for pipeline, industrial and commercial uses. The associated hydrocarbons (ethane, propane, butane, pentanes and natural gasoline) known as NGLs can be valuable byproducts after the natural gas has been purified and fractionated. One of the most critical issues in the design and planning of the shale gas supply chain network is the sizing and location of natural gas processing plants due to their very high cost. Moreover, pipelines and compressors' sizes should be optimally determined. Typically, a superstructure of alternatives as the one partially depicted in Figure 1 is given.

From the operations perspective, the number of wells drilled in each location can dramatically influence costs and the ecological footprint of natural gas operations (Ladlee and Jacquet, 2011). The ability to drill multiple wells from a single pad is seen as a major technological breakthrough driving today's development. The utilization of multi-well pads also has large environmental and socio-economic implications, as the landscape disruption of as many as 20 or more natural gas wells and associated pipeline infrastructure can be concentrated in a single location. Furthermore, wells can be drilled in rapid-succession and the technology now exists to perform hydraulic fractures on multiple wells simultaneously. Hence, another key decision of the model is the drilling strategy, i.e. how many wells to set up or add on existing well pads at every period. Finally, a critical aspect in the shale gas production is water management. It is a highly water-intensive process, with a typical well requiring around 20 ML of water over a 3-month period to drill and fracture, depending on the basin and geological formation (Stark et al., 2012). The vast majority of this water is used during the fracturing process, with large volumes of water pumped into the well with sand and chemicals to facilitate the extraction of the gas. Although increasing amounts of water are being recycled and reused, freshwater is still required in high quantities as flowback water usually represents as low as 25-30 % of the water injected into the well.

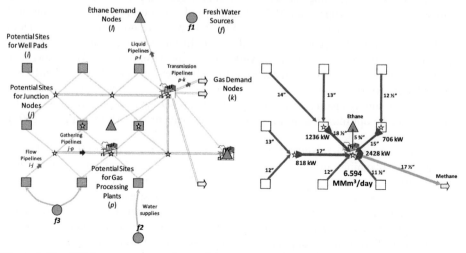

Figure 1. Simplified superstructure of a gas SC.   Figure 2. Optimal SC network design.

3. Mathematical Formulation

3.1. Gas Production and Flow Balances

The planning horizon is discretized in time periods (t), commonly quarters. Multiple wells can be drilled in a single pad over one time period, although not necessarily at the same time. It is assumed that all of them are fractured and completed within the same time period they are drilled. Hence, wells start to produce in the period following the drilling period. After that, its productivity rate is a decreasing function given by $pw_{i,a}$, where a is the well age. The number of wells drilled and fractured in the multi-well pad i during the period t is represented by the integer variable $N_{i,t}$. An upper bound on this variable is usually given due to technology limitations. Besides, the total number of wells that can be drilled in the same pad over the time horizon is also bounded. The total daily production coming from all the wells in pad i can be determined through Eq.(1). At time t, the age of a well drilled in time period $\tau < t$ is $a = t - \tau$.

$$\sum_{\tau=1}^{t-1} N_{i,\tau}\, pw_{i,t-\tau} = SP_{i,t} = \sum_{j\in J} GF_{i,j,t} \qquad \forall i \in I, t > 1 \tag{1}$$

Eq.(1) also states that the production of pad i during time period t is sent to one or more junction nodes j depending on the network design, which is also a model decision. In turn, Eq.(2) balances the input and output flows of shale gas at each junction node, collecting production from pads and sending them to processing plants.

$$\sum_{i\in I} GF_{i,j,t} = \sum_{p\in P} GF_{j,p,t} \qquad \forall j \in J, t > 1 \tag{2}$$

In each plant p, all the methane from the incoming flows of shale gas is separated and sent to one or more dry gas demand nodes k, as imposed through Eq.(3), where gc is the volume gas composition. The same also applies for NGL flows, which are received with the shale gas, separated and pumped to one or more petrochemical plants l in liquid state through pipelines p-l. In Eq.(4), lc is the NGL composition and s_g^L is the specific gravity of NGLs in standard conditions, given in $t/10^3 m^3$.

$$gc \sum_{j\in J} GF_{j,p,t} = \sum_{k\in K} MF_{p,k,t} \qquad \forall p \in P, t > 1 \tag{3}$$

$$lc\, s_g^L \sum_{j\in J} GF_{j,p,t} = \sum_{l\in L} LF_{p,l,t} \qquad \forall p \in P, t > 1 \tag{4}$$

3.2. Gas Processing Plants, Pipelines and Compressors

The total processing capacity of a plant p at time t ($SCap_{p,t}$) can increase due to new expansions started at the beginning of period ($t - \tau s$). In Eq.(5), $S_{p,t-\tau s}$ is the expansion size, and τs is the installation lead-time. Moreover, the sum of the shale gas flows coming from one or several junction nodes to a single separation plant during every period t should not exceed its processing capacity.

$$SCap_{p,t} = SCap_{p,t-1} + S_{p,t-\tau s} \quad ; \quad \sum_{j\in J} GF_{j,p,t} \le SCap_{p,t} \qquad \forall p \in P, t > 1 \tag{5}$$

Regarding gas flows, the diameter of the pipelines installed between a pair of nodes during a certain time period (a model decision) is substituted by such diameter raised to the power of 2.667, to preserve linearity in Eq. (6) (Weymouth, 1942). We assume that inlet/outlet pressures are given data, and diameters are treated as continuous variables.

$$GFlow_{i,j,t} = k_{i,j}\, l_{i,j}^{-0.5} \hat{D}_{i,j,t} \qquad \forall i \in I, j \in J, t > 1 \tag{6}$$

The gas transportation capacity between a pair of nodes i-j ($GCap_{i,j,t}$) is also followed period by period (Eq.(7)), accounting for the construction of new pipelines, which takes τp periods. The expected flow for period t should not exceed the transportation capacity. Other equations similar to Eqs.(6)-(7) control the liquid flow in pipelines connecting the gas processing plants p to the petrochemical industries demanding NGLs.

$$GCap_{i,j,t} = GCap_{i,j,t-1} + GFlow_{i,j,t-\tau p} ; \quad GF_{i,j,t} \le GCap_{i,j,t} \qquad \forall i \in I, j \in J, t > 1 \tag{7}$$

For transporting the shale gas, the model assumes that every junction node j collecting flows from the well-pads should have a gas compressor station, whose total power ($WCap_{j,t}$) may be expanded by incorporating new compressors ($W_{j,t-\tau c}$). In Eq.(8), τc is the compressor installation lead-time in quarters. If the suction and discharge pressures are given, and assuming that compressors are adiabatic, the required compression power is directly proportional to the total flow of gas being compressed (Weymouth, 1942).

$$WCap_{j,t} = WCap_{j,t-1} + W_{j,t-\tau c} ; \quad kc_j \sum_{p \in P} GP_{j,p,t} \le WCap_{j,t} \qquad \forall j \in J, t > 1 \tag{8}$$

Analogous equations deal with the size of compressors installed at the inlet section of dry gas pipelines, connecting plants to midstream distribution lines.

3.3. Freshwater Consumption

The total amount of water required by a single well during the drilling, fracturing and completion processes (wr_i) is known and may depend on the well location. Eq.(9) determines the total freshwater consumption in the pad i during period t, according to the number of wells drilled and fractured. This amount should be supplied from one or more freshwater sources f, as also stated by Eq.(9). The amount of freshwater supplied by source f for drilling and fracturing new wells is a key model decision represented by the continuous variable $WS_{f,i,t}$. In addition, if the well-pad i is able to process and reuse the flowback water, a factor rf_i (usually below 20 %) can reduce the need for freshwater.

$$N_{i,t}\, wr_i / (1+rf_i) = \sum_{f \in F} WS_{f,i,t} \quad \forall i \in I, t \in T \tag{9}$$

Freshwater resources (rivers, lakes, underground water, etc.) usually have an upper limit on the amount of water that can provide to the shale gas industry, often given by a seasonal profile ($fwa_{f,t}$). Hence, the total amount supplied from f to every pad i should be bounded by above as in constraint (10).

$$\sum_{i \in I} WS_{f,i,t} \le fwa_{f,t} \qquad \forall f \in F, t \in T \tag{10}$$

3.4. Gas and NGL Demands

Every potential market (or demand node) is assumed to buy a maximum amount of product (dry gas for gas distributors, NGLs for petrochemical plants) based on their own transportation or processing capacities. Such demand profile can be seasonal, especially in dry gas markets. Constraints (11) restrict the total flow of dry gas and NGLs that can be sold during every period of the planning horizon.

$$\sum_{p \in P} MF_{p,k,t} \le Dem_{k,t}^M \quad \forall k \in K, t > 1; \quad \sum_{p \in P} LF_{p,l,t} \le Dem_{l,t}^{NGL} \quad \forall l \in L, t > 1 \tag{11}$$

3.5. Objective Function

The objective function (12) comprises positive and negative terms for every period of the planning horizon, discounted back to its present value by the annual discount rate *dr*. Positive terms are dry gas and NGL sales incomes. Negative terms are shale gas production cost, the cost of drilling /completing wells, the cost of installing/expanding shale gas processing capacity at plants, the cost of new pipelines either for gathering raw gas or distributing dry gas and NGLs, the cost of installing new compressor stations at junction nodes and processing plants, and freshwater acquisition and transportation costs for drilling and fracturing purposes. Nonlinear expressions are used to represent economies of scale functions in some of the negative terms of Eq.(12), featuring exponents between 0 and 1. Hence, the objective function can be classified as non-convex, with strictly concave separable terms. However, all the constraints are linear.

$$
\begin{aligned}
NPV = \sum_{t \in T} (1 + dr/4)^{-t} \, [\sum_{p \in P} \sum_{k \in K} p_{k,t} \, nd_t \, GF_{p,k,t} + \sum_{p \in P} \sum_{l \in L} q_{l,t} \, nd_t \, LF_{p,l,t} \\
- \sum_{i \in I} \sum_{j \in J} c_{i,t} \, nd_t \, GF_{i,j,t} - \sum_{p \in P} ks \, S_{p,t}{}^{SExp} - \sum_{i \in I} kd \, N_{i,t} \\
- \sum_{i \in I} \sum_{j \in J} kp \, l_{i,j} \, \hat{D}_{i,j,t}{}^{GPExp} - \sum_{j \in J} \sum_{p \in P} kp \, l_{j,p} \, \hat{D}_{j,p,t}{}^{GPExp} - \sum_{p \in P} \sum_{k \in K} kp \, l_{p,k} \, \hat{D}_{p,k,t}{}^{GPExp} \\
- \sum_{p \in P} \sum_{l \in L} kp \, l_{p,l} \, \hat{D}_{p,l,t}{}^{LPExp} - \sum_{j \in J} kc \, W_{j,t}{}^{CExp} - \sum_{p \in P} kc \, W_{p,t}{}^{CExp} - \sum_{f \in F} \sum_{i \in I} \left(fx_f + v_f \, l_{f,i} \right) WS_{f,i,t}]
\end{aligned}
\tag{12}
$$

4. Results and Discussion

Since the proposed MINLP model is non-convex, a decomposition approach is used for the global optimization of the problem, based on successively refining a piecewise linear approximation of the objective function (Cafaro and Grossmann, 2014). For a simple example with 9 pads, 8 junction nodes, 3 processing plants, 6 demand nodes and 3 freshwater sources (rivers) as the one shown in Fig. 1, the model comprises 31,633 continuous variables, 360 integer variables and 28,900 equations, requiring almost 5 h of CPU time to obtain a solution with a GAP below 3 %, using GAMS/DICOPT, GUROBI and CONOPT as MINLP, MILP and NLP solvers (McCarl, 2011), on an Intel Core i7 CPU, 12 GB RAM. The optimal design for the network is depicted in Figure 2. As we are interested in reducing the environmental impacts of the project, we solve two different instances. In the first case, the freshwater consumption is bounded by above to 1 % of the river flow at every quarter. In the second case, it is reduced to 0.5 %.

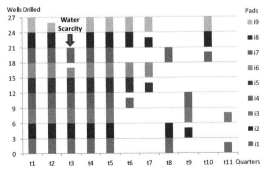

Figure 3. Optimal drilling strategy using up to 0.5 % of the river flow.

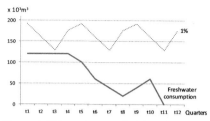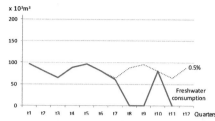

Figure 4. Water consumption from source *f2*, in both instances of the case study.

By comparing the results, the NPV of the project reduces merely by 0.78 % (from 1,674.27 to 1,661.18 M USD). To reduce freshwater consumption, a less intensive drilling strategy is planned (see Figure 3), while the network design remains the same. Freshwater resources are rationally used, in a more sustainable way. Pads are simultaneously supplied by two or three sources instead of just the closest one, and the drilling strategy strictly follows the seasonal pattern of water availability, reducing the number of wells drilled in those periods with water scarcity and high competition with other users. Fig. 4 shows the water consumption profile from source *f2*, in both instances of the case study.

5. Conclusions

We present the first comprehensive optimization tool for the sustainable design and planning of shale gas supply chains. It determines the structure of the network (plants of natural gas, pipelines and compressors) and the operations strategy (drilling, fracturing and water supply) in a single monolithic model. Results on realistic case studies show that the model can help companies to reduce freshwater consumption by optimally planning drilling operations, at the expense of small reductions in the net present value of the projects. This is critical to mitigate the ecologic footprint of shale gas production, particularly in waterscarce regions with high cumulative demand for water.

References

D.C. Cafaro, I.E. Grossmann, 2014, Strategic planning, design and development of the shale gas supply chain network, AIChE J., DOI: 10.1002/aic.14405.
L. Čuček, M. Martin, I.E. Grossmann, Z. Kravanja, 2013, Multi-period synthesis of a biorefinery's supply networks, Comput. Aided Chem. Eng., 32, 73-78.
M.A. Durán, I.E. Grossmann, 1986, A mixed-integer nonlinear programming algorithm for process systems synthesis, AIChE J., 32, 592-606.
Energy Information Administration (EIA), 2012, Annual Energy Outlook with Projects to 2035, US Department of Energy, Washington, USA.
V. Gupta, I.E. Grossmann, 2012, An efficient multiperiod MINLP model for optimal planning of offshore oil and gas field infrastructure, Ind. Eng. Chem. Res., 51, 6823-6840.
J. Ladlee, J. Jacquet, 2011, The implications of multi-well pads in the Marcellus shale, Research & Policy Brief Series, Cornell Univ. Comm. & Regional Develop. Inst. (CaRDI), Ithaca, USA.
B.A. McCarl, 2011, Expanded GAMS user guide v 23.6, GAMS Dev. Corp., Washington, USA.
M.M. Rahman, M.K. Rahman, S.S. Rahman, 2001, An integrated model for multiobjective design optimization of hydraulic fracturing, Journal of Petroleum Science and Engineering, 31, 41-62.
M. Stark, R. Allingham, J. Calder, T. Lennartz-Walker, K. Wai, P. Thompson, S. Zhao, 2012, Water and shale gas development, Accenture, Dublin, Ireland.
S.A. Van Den Heever, I.E. Grossmann, 2000, An iterative aggregation/disaggregation approach for the solution of a mixed-integer nonlinear oilfield infrastructure planning model, Ind. Eng. Chem. Res., 39, 1955-1971.
T.R. Weymouth, 1942, Problems in natural gas engineering, ASME Transactions, 34, 185-234.

Jiří Jaromír Klemeš, Petar Sabev Varbanov and Peng Yen Liew (Editors)
Proceedings of the 24th European Symposium on Computer Aided Process Engineering – ESCAPE 24
June 15-18, 2014, Budapest, Hungary. Copyright © 2014 Elsevier B.V. All rights reserved.

Design of Ionic Liquids by Principal Component Decision Trees

Zelimir F. Kurtanjek

University of Zagreb, Faculty of Food Technology and Biotechnology
Pierottijeva 6, 10 000 Zagreb, Croatia
zkurt@pbf.hr

Abstract

The aim of this work is to apply computer modelling approach based on principal component decision trees for possible design of ionic liquids (ILs) structure with desired physical properties and with emphasis on prediction of their potential toxicity. Based on the available MERCK data derived are predictions for toxicity effects at molecular, cellular, and environmental levels (at molecular level as inhibition of transmission of neuro signals, apoptosis and necrosis of test cell cultures, and environmental impact on living organisms). In view of possible application of ILs for integration of new biotransformations and extraction processes in microreactors derived are the models for prediction of viscosity in given temperature ranges (NIST, 2013). Modelling is based on principal component decomposition of planar (D2) molecular descriptors (elemental and group contributions). Projections of individual (distinctively for cations and anions) IL descriptors gave orthogonal targets on which are based random forest prediction models. For viscosity modelling the targets are applied for principal component regression PCR of ILs energy of activation. Based on the selected ILs the results indicate applicability of the approach and improved predictivity due to significant reduction and orthogonalization due to projections of the molecular descriptors and robustness of random forest algorithm.

Keywords: decision tree, random forest, ionic liquids, toxicity

1. Introduction

Research on ionic liquids (ILs) has become one of the most interesting application research areas in novel technology developments in view of focuses on lower energy consumption, lower carbon and water environmental footprints, biofuel production, process miniaturization (Kokorin, 2011). Their potential applications are widespread, with examples in new catalytic synthesis in microreactors (Cvjetko, 2012), recovery of high-tech metals using ionic liquids (SDEWES Fraunhofer Annual Report 2011-2012), for integration of chemical and bio-microrectors with separation processes, polymerization, nano-technology, enzyme-catalysis, composite preparation, and many others. There are several available databases with about 20 different physical and chemical properties collected from various sources (NIST, 2013; MERCK, 2013; Suojiang et al., 2009). Besides technological applications, ILs are also in a focus of theoretical and computational chemists (Plechkova et al., 2012). From mathematical view point, design of ILs structure is a combinatorial problem, with theoretically possible 10^6 combinations (Kokorin, 2011). Availability of numerous data on already explored combinations inspires a modelling approach based on transposition of chemical structural data into numerical data and application of various multivariate (chemometric) algorithms. Owing to their low pressures and specific properties, ILs are referred to as the basis of new "green chemistry/technology". However, due to recent concerns, one of the primary modelling tasks is prediction of their toxicity.

2. Model

Here is considering prediction functions, Eq.(1), of ILs physical properties θ and classes C of toxicity based on molecular descriptors of pairs of cations X_{Cation} and anions X_{Anion}. Considered are only low level 2D descriptors based on elemental chemical compositions, chemical bonds, cation "head" structure, position and length of cation side chains, and chemical groups attached to the chains (Fatemi et al., 2011).

$$\theta = f_P(X_{Anion}, X_{Cation}, T) \qquad C = f_c(X_{Anion}, X_{Cation}) \tag{1}$$

Due to high correlations between the descriptors, which greatly degrades quality and predictivity of the models, here are selected as model inputs targets T of the descriptors projected to the lower dimensional principal component spaces P, corresponding separately to principal component analysis (PCA) for cations and anions Eq.(2). As the criteria for selection of dimension of PCA space is the level of loss of information on descriptors of about 2 %.

$$X_{Anion} = T_{Anion} \cdot P_{Anion}^T + E_{Anion} \qquad X_{Cation} = T_{Cation} \cdot P_{Cation}^T + E_{Cation} \tag{2}$$

The principal components are selected on criteria of maximum similarity between projections of molecular descriptors, i.e. by minimisation of variance (Eq. (3-4)):

$$P_{Anion} \rightarrow \max(\mathrm{var}(T_{Anion})) \qquad P_{Anion} \cdot P_{Anion}^T = I \tag{3}$$

$$P_{Cation} \rightarrow \max(\mathrm{var}(T_{Cation})) \qquad P_{Cation} \cdot P_{Cation}^T = I \tag{4}$$

Numerical evaluation of the PCA vectors can be evaluated by SVD (singular value decomposition) or iteratively, starting with the first component p_1 corresponding to maximum eigenvalue λ_1, i.e. preserving maximum of information (Varmuza et al., 2009).

$$(X_{Anion}^T \cdot X) \cdot p_{Anion,i} = \lambda_{Cation,i} \cdot p_{Anion,i} \tag{5}$$

$$(X_{Cation}^T \cdot X_{Cation}) \cdot p_{Cation,i} = \lambda_{Cation,i} \cdot p_{Cation,i} \tag{6}$$

In Fig.1 are presented "scree" plots of eigenvalues for cations and anions. It can be observed that first 15 for cations and first 10 components for anions are sufficient for representation of the original sets of descriptors. Besides the reduction in dimension of the input space, important gain is orthogonalization of the inputs leading to robust regression and simplified decision tree classification. Obtained targets can be applied for principal component regression (PCR) of ILs physical properties. Here is only considered a model for viscosity, in view of ILs application for biotransformations in microreactors (Cvjetko, 2012). Here is adopted 3 parameter Polanyi's linearized model, Eq. 7

$$v(T) = v_0 \cdot T^\alpha \cdot e^{-E/R \cdot T} \tag{7}$$

The model parameters, for selected ILs, are predicted by the principal component regression (PCR) on cation and anion targets (T_{Cation}, T_{Anion}), and available viscosity data v_{exp} in temperature ranges T_{exp} from NIST database, Eq.(8-9).

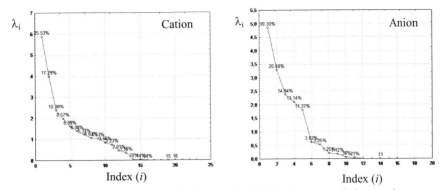

Figure 1. Scree plots of ILs cations and anions molecular descriptor correlation matrixes

$$\hat{E} = PCR\left(T_{Anion}, T_{Cation}, T_{exp}, T_{exp}^{-1}, \ln \upsilon_{exp}\right) \tag{8}$$

$$\ln \hat{\upsilon}_0 = PCR\left(T_{Anion}, T_{Cation}, T_{exp}, T_{exp}^{-1}, \ln \upsilon_{exp}\right) \tag{9}$$

3. Decision tree analysis

Modeling of ILs toxicity is based on data provided in MERCK database. Levels of EC_{50} are divided into 4 categories C: low (L > 1000 $\mu mol \cdot L^{-1}$), moderate (M 100 - 1000 $\mu mol \cdot L^{-1}$), high (H 10 - 100 $\mu mol \cdot L^{-1}$), and very high (VH < 10 $\mu mol \cdot L^{-1}$). Applied are decision tree (DT_{class}) models for prediction of categories of toxicity on molecular scale (inhibition of acetylcholinesterase), on cell level (IPC-81 leukemia cells), and population (ecological) level (test on *Vibrio fischeri*). Branching of the decision trees is based on mutually orthogonal (in statistical sense independent) targets of the cation and anion molecular descriptors, Eq. 10.

$$C_{toxicity} = DT_{class}\left(T_{Anion}, T_{Cation}\right) \tag{10}$$

The decision trees enabled "crisp" logical (nonlinear) separation of the target space leading to significant reduction of tree sizes and importantly, to high "purity" branching points (Gene index). Applied are numerical packages available in R (Development Core Team, 2011) for: chemometric evaluation (Wehrens and Varmuza, 2011); tree analysis "rpart" (Breiman and Cutler, 2009); and plotting "rpart.plot" (Themeau et al., 2013). Results are compared with DTREG software (Sherrod, 2013). In order to develop robust predictive models (avoid potential overfitting of an individual tree, Svetnik et al., 2013), decision trees were subject to sample randomization to create a weighted population of individual models named "random forest".

$$\hat{C}_{toxicity} = RF_{class}\left(T_{Anion}, T_{Cation}\right) \tag{11}$$

4. Results and Discussion

Results for individual DT models are shown in Fig.2. It is observed that almost all branching points are separations by the descriptor targets T_i. The top branching points for the cell line and population models are broken by the first target T_1 accounting 25

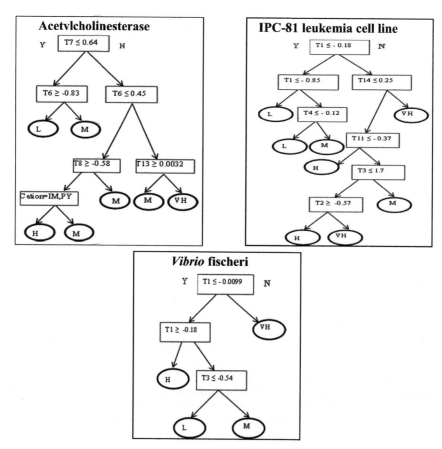

Figure 2. Decision trees for classification of ILs toxicity in low (L) medium (M), high (H), and very high (VH) categories on molecular, cell and population levels.

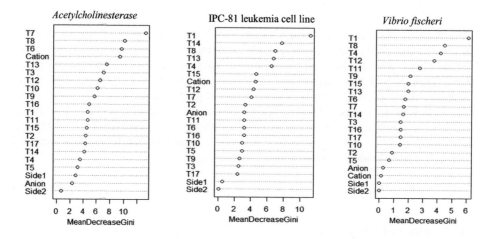

Figure 3. Variable importance distributions for ILs principal component descriptors (targets T) of toxicities for the corresponding random forest models

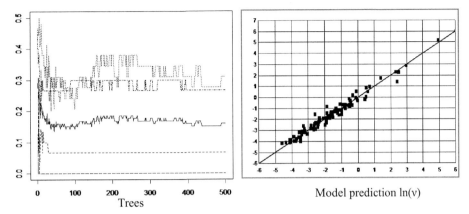

Figure 4. Random forest error rate distributions du-ring search of 500 decision trees for modelling acetylcholinesterase inhibition

Figure 5. Viscosity model predictions and experimental data in range 12 0C to 81 0C for selected 150 ILs.

and 30 % variance ("information") on cations and anions. However, for the enzyme level inhibition the first branching point is given by T_7 which accounts only for 2-3 % of the total variability of the descriptors. Besides the molecular descriptors, targets as decision variables also include names of "heads" of cation and anions (Cation, Anion), and numerical data for lengths of the alkane side chains (Side1, Side2).

The same results are confirmed by random forest models built on 500 trees. On Fig. 3 are given the lists of variable importance for each of the RF models. Tracks of the validation errors decrease during simulation of RF are depicted in Fig. 4

Analysis the residual errors in prediction (Statistica, 2013) gave the following average accuracy in predictions molecular level 90 %, cellular level 87 %, and population (ecological level) 91 %. Accuracy for prediction of temperature dependence of ILs viscosities is depicted on Fig. 5. Shown are logarithmic plots of dynamic viscosities given as experimental data versus the model predictions. Obtained are the following correlations: for training set r = 0.986, test set r = 0.968, and the validation set r = 0.915. It should be noted that for the given choice of ILs the covered range of viscosities is exceptionally high, of the order of magnitude 10^6.

5. Conclusions

The results obtained on relatively limited number of ILs combinations (150) showed that decision tree models and random forest predictors have high predictivity power. Robustness due to elimination of redundant model parameters by ensembling (randomisation of predictors) leads to significant elimination of the model overfitting.

Projection of the planar 2D molecular descriptors with basic chemical information on elemental compositions, bonds and structures can be effectively reduced to corresponding targets leading to significant size reduction and "purification" of the decision trees. Application of linear principal component regression for ILs properties (viscosity) also has the advantage of the model size reduction and elimination of overfitting and increase of prediction robustness.

As toxicity of ILs is the main concern for their application in "green chemistry/technology) obtained results indicate possible important effects. The toxicity data on three essentially different levels are "poorly" correlated. The problem of poor correlation is probably due to "dynamics of toxic effects", i.e. difference between immediate (acute) responses on molecular level and chronic effects on cell and population levels. Also data on cell and especially environmental level are relatively scarce and computer models are needed for preliminary assessment of their biological effects.

Overall average errors in prediction of ILs toxicity are 85-90 % which confirms the applicability of the proposed methodology. Reliable prediction algorithm enables computer design of ILs tailored for specific properties. The RF predictor can be used in a "design loop" serving as a pseudo inverse model enabling optimization of ILs structure for a given fitness function (specific to ILs application in a technology) by an "in loop" genetic algorithm.

Acknowledgement

This work was supported by Ministry of Science, Education and Sports of Republic of Croatia, project 058-1252086-0589.

References

L. Breiman, A. Cutler,< www.stat.berkeley.edu/~breiman/ RandomForests>, accessed on 14/12/2013

M. Cvjetko, 2012, Synthesis, application in biotransformations and cytotoxycity of selected imidazolium-based ionic liquids, Doctoral Thesis, (in Croatian) University of Zagreb, Faculty of Food Technology and Biotechnology, Zagreb, Croatia.

M.H. Fatemi, P. Izadiyan, 2011, Cytotoxicity estimation of ionic liquids based on their effective structural feature, Chemosphere, 84, 553-563.

A. Kokorin, 2011, Ionic Liquids: Theory, Properties, New Approaches, InTech, Rijeka, Croatia

NIST, Ionic Liquids Database Standard Reference Database #147, <ilthermo.bouder.-nist.gov /ILThermo/mainmenu.uix>, accessed on 18/07/2013

N.V. Plechkova, K.R. Seddon, E.I. Izgorodina, Theoretical Approaches to Ionic Liquids: From Past History to Future Directions, Ionic Liquids Uncoiled: Critical Expert Overviews, DOI: 10.1002/9781118434987.

R Development Core Team, 2011, R: A language and environment for statistical computing. R, Vienna, Austria,<www.R-project.org>, accessed on 14/12/2013

SDEWES, 2012, Fraunhofer-Allianz Annual Report. <www.allianz.com/en/investor_relations/ results_reports/annual-reports.html>, accessed on 14/12/2013

P.H. Sherrod, DTREG, Predicting modelling software, <www.dtreg.com>, accessed on 14/12/2013.

StatSoft, Inc. STATISTICA, v.10.< www.statsoft.com>, accessed on 14/12/2011.

Z. Suojiang, X. Lu, Q. Zhou, X. Li, X. Zhang, S. Li, 2009, Ionic Liquids, Physichochemical Properties, Elsevier, Amsterdam, The Netherlands.

V. Svetnik, A. Liaw, C. Tong, J.C. Culberson, R.P. Sheridan, B.P. Feuston, 2003, Random forest: a classification and regression tool for compound classification and QSAR modeling, J. Chem. Inf. Comput. Sci., 43, 6, 1947–1958.

The UFT/ Merck Ionic Liquids Biological Effects Database, <www.il-eco.uft.uni-bremen.de>, accessed on14/12/2013.

T. Therneau, B. Atkinson, B. Ripley, 2013, CRAN – Packagge rpart, <cran.rproject.org/web/ packages/rpart/index.html>, accessed on 14/12/2013.

K. Varmuza, P. Filzmoser, 2009, Multivariate Statistical Analysis in Chemometrics, CRC Press, Baton Rouge, Louisiana, USA.

R. Wehrens, 2011, Chemometrics with R, 2011, Springer, New York, USA.

Jiří Jaromír Klemeš, Petar Sabev Varbanov and Peng Yen Liew (Editors)
Proceedings of the 24th European Symposium on Computer Aided Process Engineering – ESCAPE 24
June 15-18, 2014, Budapest, Hungary. Copyright © 2014 Elsevier B.V. All rights reserved.

Model-Based Analysis for Acetone-Butanol-Ethanol Production Process through a Dynamic Simulation

Ricardo Morales-Rodriguez,[a*] Divanery Rodriguez-Gomez,[b] Mauricio Sales-Cruz,[c] Jose A. de los Reyes-Heredia,[a] Eduardo S. Pérez Cisneros[a]

[a]*Departamento de Ingeniería de Procesos e Hidráulica, Universidad Autónoma Metropolitana-Iztapalapa, Av. San Rafael Atlixco 186, C.P. 09340, México, D.F., México.*
[b]*Departamento de Biotecnología, Universidad Autónoma Metropolitana-Iztapalapa, Av. San Rafael Atlixco 186, C.P. 09340, México, D.F., México.*
[c]*Departamento de Procesos y Tecnología, Universidad Autónoma Metropolitana-Cuajimalpa, Artificios 40, CP. 01120, México D.F., México.*
rmro@xanum.uam.mx

Abstract

This study presents an analysis for acetone, butanol and ethanol production process. Firstly, a systematic methodology for model-based simulation is proposed in order to perform an appropriate modelling task in the analysis of production processes. The implementation of the systematic methodology allowed the evaluation of four ABE production processes with different operating scenarios such as, continuous and continuous with recycle in the enzymatic hydrolysis and ABE fermentation, relying on a benchmarking criterion (kg-butanol/kg-dry-biomass). The results show that recycle in both sections improve butanol production, but especially when this was present in the enzymatic hydrolysis section. The highest yield was found in the configuration with continuous and recycle mode for enzymatic hydrolysis and ABE fermentation.

Keywords: Acetone-butanol-ethanol production, model-based analysis, dynamic modelling.

1. Introduction

The European commission has established a gradual transfer from petroleum-based economy to a more carbohydrate-based economy for 2030, where 20 % of transportation fuel and 25 % of chemical should be produced from biomass (Biofuels in the European Union, 2006). Thus, research efforts have been conducted searching for new substitutes to overcome those issues for producing alternative carbohydrates-based fuels and high value-added products such as, bioethanol, biodiesel, biobutanol, xylitol, lactic acid, etc. Among the different research options on bioproducts, biobutanol is a biofuel to focus on, due to its advantages compared to bioethanol, for instance, better blending properties and higher energy content (Mayank et al., 2013).

The research on acetone, butanol and ethanol (ABE) production from a biological pathway where butanol is the principal product, have been focused from the feedstock and fermentation analysis point of view (e.g. use of different raw material, microorganisms, operating conditions, etc.) (Sukumaran et al., 2011), development of some mathematical models for the ABE fermentation phenomena including different levels of abstraction in the metabolic route (Mayank et al., 2013); and most recently looking for new technologies for purification of products and recovery of raw materials (Heitmann et al., 2013).

The current state of art shows that ABE process production has been analysed from separate perspectives, where the integrated economic and dynamic model-based analysis has not been considered yet. Previously, Morales-Rodriguez et al. (2011) presented some dynamic model-based evaluations for bioethanol production from lignocelluloses, therefore, based on the current computational platform and previous results. This study presents an extension of the previous modelling platform, in order to perform a model-based evaluation for the ABE process production using diverse process configurations, employing as benchmarking criterion among the different flowsheets the ratio of produced butanol from the fed dry-biomass in the process.

2. Acetone-Butanol-Ethanol production process

The ABE production process consists of 4 principal sections: 1) pre-treatment (PT): the main objective is breaking down the lignocellulosic matrix to leave the cellulose available for hydrolysis by the enzymes; 2) enzymatic hydrolysis (EH): this section employs some cellulases that produce the remaining glucose from the polysaccharide chain; 3) ABE fermentation: the glucose previously produced is processed by the microorganisms to produce acetone, butanol and ethanol; 4) downstream process: the main purpose of this section is the purification of butanol and high valued-added products, as well as the recovery of some reactants.

3. Methodology for the model-based simulation of the acetone-butanol-ethanol production process

The definition of the methodology is a key task for this type of model-based analysis, thus, this work proposes and pursues the following systematic methodology that consists of 5 steps: 1) data and mathematical model collection; 2) implementation of the selected model in a computer-aided modelling tool for mathematical model calibration and/or validation; 3) selection of the most promising mathematical model; 4) proposal of process configurations including different operating modes (such as, continuous, continuous with recirculation, etc.) in the core sections of the process; and 5) definition of benchmarking criteria for comparing the diverse process configurations. The implementation of the dynamic mathematical models was carried out in MatLab (The MathWorks, Inc., 2008).

4. Results

4.1. Data and mathematical model collection
The first step was the collection of some kinetic models for ABE production. Mayank et al. (2013) recently published a review of various mathematical models for the ABE fermentation. This was a significant source of information for performing the data and mathematical model collection.

4.2. Calibration and validation of the mathematical models
The implementation of some mathematical models available in the previous survey (Mayank et al., 2013) was performed with the aim of validating the presented results in the selected papers.

4.3. Selection of the most promising mathematical model

The model published by Shinto et al. (2007) was selected among the different evaluated mathematical models, due to this includes most of the steps of the metabolic route for ABE production from glucose by *Clostridium saccharoperbutylacetonicum* N1-4. In addition, this mathematical model includes some equations representing the conversion of xylose to ABE, which could be an alternative biological route. The original model proposed by Shinto et al. (2007) was initially for batch operation, therefore, an extension of the mathematical model was performed in order to analyse the behaviour in continuous operations for ABE production section.

4.4. Process configurations for ABE production process

The reactors for the PT, the EH and the ABE sections were modelled as continuous stirred tank reactors, relying on a previous process model structure presented by Morales-Rodriguez et al. (2011); moreover, the mathematical model for solid-liquid separators is also present in the supplementary material. The enzymatic hydrolysis and ABE fermentation are two of main steps of the process, due to the production of glucose and its subsequently metabolization to produce acetone butanol and ethanol are carried out in those sections, respectively. The extended mathematical model was employed to propose 4 process configurations with different operating modes in each section (see Figure 1). The models were selected based on previous results of the most promising process configurations. The first configuration was for a continuous operation in the enzymatic hydrolysis and ABE fermentations (ABE: C-C). The second process topology was also for a continuous operation in the enzymatic hydrolysis section and an operation in continuous and recycle for the ABE fermentation section (ABE: C-C-RECY). A configuration with continuous operation and recycle for enzymatic hydrolysis and the section of ABE fermentation with an operating mode in continuous (ABE: C_RECY-C) was also proposed. Finally, the continuous operation with recycle for both sections was performed (ABE: C_RECY-C_RECY). The Figure 1 illustrates different number of units for the enzymatic hydrolysis and ABE fermentation sections; this difference is mainly due to the fact that processes have different residence times in both sections. The average residence time for the material in the enzymatic hydrolysis reactor was 36 h in continuous operation and 46 h in the ABE fermentation section. The main characteristics and conditions for the simulations of the process configurations were obtained from Morales-Rodriguez et al. (2011) and Shinto et al. (2007).

4.5. Benchmarking criteria for selection of the most promising process configuration

The comparison of the performance of the different process flowsheets was performed by using as evaluation criterion as illustrated in Eq.(1).

$$R_{Butanol/dry-biomass} = \frac{Total\ mass\ of\ butanol}{Total\ dry-biomass} \tag{1}$$

The model-based simulation was performed to the 4 process configurations. The results are illustrated in Table 1

Table 1. Results of butanol yields from the model-based simulation for the analysed process configurations

ABE Process configuration	Butanol/dry-biomass ratio	Improvement in butanol
C-C	0.077	-
C-C_RECY	0.079	2 %
C_RECY-C	0.091	18 %
C_RECY-C_RECY	0.093	20 %

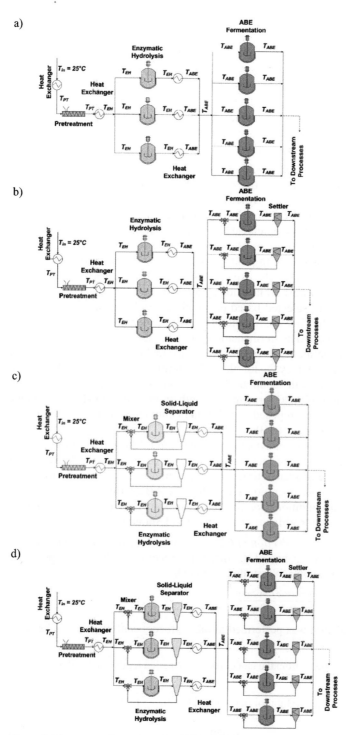

Figure 1. Process configurations for ABE production: a) ABE:C-C, b) ABE: C-C_RECY, c) ABE: C_RECY-C, d) ABE: C_RECY-C_RECY.

According to the results from Table 1, the best process configuration was the enzymatic hydrolysis and ABE fermentation operating in continuous with recycle of a fraction of the output flowrate in both sections (C_RECY-C_RECY), where the main purpose was to return part of the unconverted material to the reactor in order to increase the conversion of reactants. The second best process configuration was found to be the configuration operating in continuous with recycle in the enzymatic hydrolysis section and continuous mode in the ABE fermentation (C_RECY-C). The results illustrates that butanol/dry-biomass ratio was similar in C_RECY-C compared to C_RECY-C_RECY process configuration, with a difference of 2% in the produced butanol. The lowest value for the butanol/dry-biomass ratio was obtained in C-C configuration, followed the C-C _RECY configuration.

The configurations with recycle of not converted material showed higher butanol production as much as the recirculation was present, because butanol/dry-biomass ratio decreased when recycle mode disappeared in the process configuration.

On the other hand, comparing C-C_RECY and C_RECY-C process configurations, it was possible to identify that the bottleneck between these two sections of the process was found in the enzymatic hydrolysis section, since the C-C_RECY process decreases its butanol production when recycle was not present in the enzymatic hydrolysis section. Thus, the degradation of cellulose to glucose is the section of the process that should be improved in order to increase butanol production in the process.

Moreover, the comparisons of C-C with C-C_RECY and C_RECY-C with C_RECY-C_RECY allowed arguing that recycle is highly necessary only in the enzymatic hydrolysis section, since butanol/dry-biomass ratios were different for only 2% when the same operating mode was found in this section, but a difference of up to 20% in butanol yield was found with different operating conditions. The main reason is that the time necessary to metabolize glucose into ABE is enough in the fermentation section, thereby, the recycle of not converted materials is not necessary in this section of the process. From the process design point of view, these results would permit to plan in a better manner the necessary unit operations and configurations before constructing the plant; besides at the production stage, costs would be lower due to no pumping equipment would be included in the plant, therefore reducing the energy cost. Table 1 also illustrates the improvement on the butanol production taking as baseline case the operation in continuous for enzymatic hydrolysis and ABE fermentation.

5. General discussion

The continuation of the use of dynamic mathematical model was performed with the aim of extending the modelling platform, which will allow future analysis, such as, uncertainty and sensitivity analysis on the process configurations, implementations of control scenarios for the study of certain disturbances in the production process performance and optimization examination as previously performed to the second generation bioethanol production process (Morales-Rodriguez et al., 2012); even though it is well known that algebraic steady-state models have been employed for the last task, the advantage of creating a dynamic mathematical model would allow to extend this work from different perspectives of the computer-aided process engineering area.

The superstructure-based optimization approach could be an option for analysing and selecting the potential process configuration, unfortunately, most of those studies just consider a conversion in the reaction section or ideal separation unit, thereby, presenting results not considering rigorous mathematical models as it is considered in this work.

On the other hand, it seems trivial that recycle of reactants to the reactor could improve the production for almost all the desired products, but it is important to highlight that this assumption is not straightforward for all biological systems, due to there are several factors that could not allow it, for example, the inhibition effect by the product, microorganisms inhibition for high concentration environment, binding sites in the enzymes, etc. Therefore, this study must be of special interest for researchers interested on conceptual process design for ABE production.

6. Conclusion

This study has proposed a systematic methodology to perform a model-based simulation analysis where different scenarios for ABE production process were compared, in order to identify the process configuration (based on the operating mode) with higher butanol production. The best process was found when the section of enzymatic hydrolysis and ABE fermentation operate in continuous with recycle (0.093 kg-butanol/kg-dry-biomass). The result also allowed finding that recycle was more significant for the enzymatic hydrolysis than ABE fermentation, since the larger difference in the butanol/dry-biomass ratio was present when the enzymatic hydrolysis reactor was operating in continuous and continuous with recycle.

Acknowledgments

Ricardo Morales-Rodriguez acknowledges PROMEP-Mexico (identification number: UAM-PTC-454) for the financial support on the development of this work.

References

Biofuels in the European Union, 2006, A vision for 2030 and beyond, <ec.europa.eu/research/energy/pdf/biofuels_vision_2030_en.pdf.> Accessed on16/09/2013.

S. Heitmann, M. Stoffers, P. Lutze, 2013, Integrated Processing for Separation of Biobutanol. Part B: Model-based Process Analysis, Green Processing and Synthesis, 2, 121-141.

R. Mayank, A. Ranjan, V.S. Moholkar, 2013, Mathematical models of ABE fermentation: review and analysis, Critical reviews in Biotechnology, 33, 419-447.

R. Morales-Rodriguez, A.S. Meyer, K.V. Gernaey, G. Sin, 2011, Dynamic model-based evaluation of process configurations for integrated operation of hydrolysis and co-fermentation for bioethanol production from lignocelluloses, Bioresource technology, 102, 1174–1184.

R. Morales-Rodriguez, A.S. Meyer, K.V. Gernaey, G. Sin, 2012, A Framework for model-based optimization of bioprocesses under uncertainty: lignocellulosic ethanol production case, Computers and Chemical Engineering, 42, 115-129.

H. Shinto, Y. Tashiro, M. Yamashita, G. Kobayashi, T. Sekiguchi, T. Hanai, Y. Kuriya, M. Okamoto, K. Sonomoto, 2007, Kinetic modeling and sensitivity analysis of acetone–butanol–ethanol production, Journal of Biotechnology, 131, 45-56.

R.K. Sukumaran, L.D. Gottumukkala, K. Rajasree, D. Alex, A. Pandey, 2011, Butanol fuel from biomass: revising ABE fermentation, Biofuels: alternative feedstocks and conversion processes, Chapter 25, Amsterdam, The Netherlands, 571-586.

Jiří Jaromír Klemeš, Petar Sabev Varbanov and Peng Yen Liew (Editors)
Proceedings of the 24th European Symposium on Computer Aided Process Engineering – ESCAPE 24
June 15-18, 2014, Budapest, Hungary.

Heat Exchanger Network Synthesis using MINLP Stage-wise Model with Pinch Analysis and Relaxation

Natchanon Angsutorn[a], Kitipat Siemanond[a,*], Rungroj Chuvaree[b]

[a]The Petroleum and Petrochemical College, Chulalongkorn University, Bangkok 10330, Thailand
[b]PTT Public Company Limited, Bangkok 10900, Thailand
kitipat.s@chula.ac.th

Abstract

Heat exchanger network (HEN) is important for energy saving in industry. HEN synthesis is the heat integration between hot and cold process streams to reduce heating and cooling utility consumption in the industrial processes. Since the HEN synthesis problem contains nonlinear equations and constraints, the mathematical programming difficulties for large-sized HEN are long computational time and divergence problem. This research work applies Pinch Analysis and MINLP stage-wise model with relaxation technique to synthesize HEN. Pinch Analysis helps identify the optimal Pinch Point or the heat recovery approach temperature (HRAT) which decomposes all process streams into two parts; above-pinch and below-pinch parts. Next MINLP stage-wise model helps design HEN in above-pinch and below-pinch parts. After that, relaxation technique by mathematical programming will reduce number of exchangers and generate the final HEN design. The stage-wise model combined with Pinch Analysis and relaxation has several advantages over the stage-wise model alone. The computational time per solving cycle is reduced due to HEN synthesis of two smaller sized parts separated by optimal Pinch Point. Optimal Pinch Point helps avoid large-area exchangers located at this point. The relaxation technique allowing heat transfer across Pinch Point helps improve HEN design with less number of process exchangers. Hot-and-cold-process-stream data from gas separation plant in Thailand will be used as a case study for this research work.

Keywords: Pinch Analysis, heat integration, MINLP, mathematical programming.

1. Introduction

Heat exchanger network (HEN) is important for energy saving in industry. HEN synthesis is the heat integration between hot and cold process streams to reduce heating and cooling utility consumption in processes. Research works on HEN synthesis have been done for more than 40 years by many researchers; for examples; Linnhoff and Hindmarsh (1983) using Pinch Analysis and pinch design method, Yee and Grossmann (1990) using MINLP model with stage-wise superstructure, Barbaro and Bagajewicz (2005) using MILP model with linearization technique, Escobar and Trierweiler (2013) using MINLP model with initialization strategy, Anantharaman and coworkers (2013) using heuristics to develop optimal energy efficient design of the fossil fuel power plants, and Huang and Karimi (2014) developing the efficient algorithm without feasible starting point for HEN design. Since the HEN synthesis problem contains nonlinear equations and constraints, the mathematical difficulties for large-sized HEN are long computational time and divergence problem. This research work applies Pinch Analysis and MINLP stage-wise model (Yee and Grossmann, 1990) with relaxation technique to synthesize HEN. The heuristics from Pinch Analysis and optimization from MINLP and relaxation technique can help the stage-wise model generate the large-sized HEN with lower annualized cost compared to other research study.

2. Methodology

For this work, there are three steps to synthesize HEN, as shown in Figure 1.

2.1. Targeting step by Pinch Analysis

Pinch Analysis is performed by Grassroots Potential Program (Siemanond and Kosol, 2012) based on Excel Visual Basic for Applications (VBA). The program predicts the optimal heat recovery approach temperature (HRAT) or optimal utility consumption and vertical heat transfer area of heat exchangers with minimum number of process heat exchangers.

2.2. HEN synthesis step by stage-wise model with pinch temperature

The stage-wise model with Pinch Point is the MINLP stage-wise model (Yee and Grossmann, 1990) where pinch temperatures of hot and cold process streams are located in the model as shown in Figure 1. In this model, the problem is partitioned into smaller subproblems, above-pinch and below-pinch parts, and utility load is fixed at the optimal HRAT. The model is simplified by minimizing number of heat exchangers and their area.

2.3. HEN improvement step by relaxation

The number of process exchangers is larger compared to one from heuristic rule; the Euler's general network theorem observed by Hohmann (1971), stating that the minimum number of heat exchangers equals to number of all process streams and all utility types subtracted by one. In this step, the stage-wise model with relaxation can be done by applying stage-wise model with variable bounding strategy, as shown in Table 1 and 2 for nomenclature, to reduce the number of heat exchangers of the previous step. The HRAT changes in this step because cross-pinch heat transfer occurs. Therefore, the number of heat exchangers must be equal or less than one from previous step and the utility consumption increases a little more because HRAT changes.

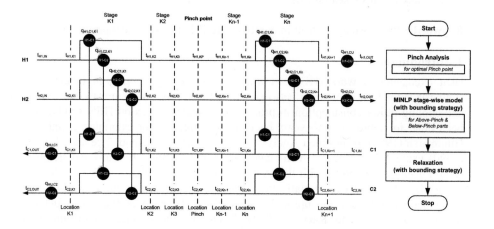

Figure 1. Stage-wise model with Pinch Point and flow chart of this work.

Table 1. Lower and upper bounds of some variables.

Variables	Controlling index	Upper Bound	Lower Bound
$th_{i,k}$	$th_{i,1}, i \in HS$	$TINH_i$	$TINH_i$
	$th_{i,k+1}, i \in HS, k \in ST$	$TINH_i$	$TOUTH_i$
$tc_{j,k}$	$tc_{j,NOK+1}, j \in CS$	$TINC_j$	$TINC_j$
	$tc_{j,k}, j \in CS, k \in ST$	$TOUTC_j$	$TINC_j$

Variables	Lower Bound	Variables	Upper Bound
$th_{i,k}$(cont)		$tc_{j,k}$(cont)	

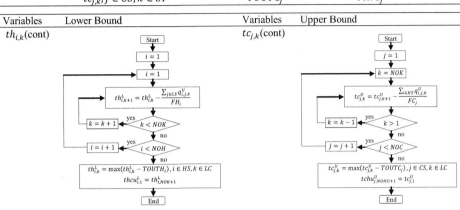

Table 2. Nomenclature of indices, parameters, and variables.

Indices		Sets	
i	hot stream	HS	$\{\, i \mid i$ is a hot stream $\}$
j	cold stream	CS	$\{\, j \mid j$ is a cold stream $\}$
k	temperature location or stage	ST	$\{\, k \mid k$ is a stage, $k = 1, \dots, NOK\, \}$
n	cold utlity temperature location or cold utility	CU	$\{\, n \mid n$ is a cold utility $\}$
m	hot utlity temperature location or hot utility	HU	$\{\, m \mid m$ is a hot utility $\}$

Parameters		Variables	
$TINH_i$	inlet temperature of hot stream i, °C	$th_{i,k}$	temperature of hot stream i at temperature location k, °C
$TINC_j$	inlet temperature of cold stream j, °C	$tc_{j,k}$	temperature of cold stream j at temperature location k, °C
$TOUTH_i$	outlet temperature of hot stream i, °C	$thcu_{i,n}$	temperature of hot stream i at cold utility temperature location n, °C
$TOUTC_j$	outlet temperature of cold stream j, °C	$tchu_{j,m}$	temperature of cold stream j at hot utility temperature location m, °C
FH_i	heat capacity flow rate of hot stream i, kW/°C	$LMTD_{i,j,k}$	log mean temperature difference for match of hot stream i and cold stream j at stage k, °C
FC_j	heat capacity flow rate of cold stream j, kW/°C		
$TINCU_n$	inlet temperature of cold utility n, °C	$LMTDcu_{i,n}$	log mean temperature difference for match of hot stream i and cold utility n, °C
$TOUTCU_n$	outlet temperature of cold utility n, °C		
$TINHU_m$	inlet temperature of hot utility m, °C	$LMTDhu_{j,m}$	log mean temperature difference for match of cold stream j and hot utility m, °C
$TOUTHU_m$	outlet temperature of hot utility m, °C		
$EMAT_{i,j,k}$	exchanger minimum approach temperature for match of hot stream i and cold stream j at stage k, °C	*Positive variables*	
		$q_{i,j,k}$	heat load for match of hot stream i and cold stream j at stage k, kW
		$qcu_{i,n}$	heat load for match of hot stream i and cold utility n, kW
		$qhu_{j,m}$	heat load for match of cold stream j and hot utility m, kW
$EMATCU_{i,n}$	exchanger minimum approach temperature for match of hot stream i and cold utility n, °C	$dt_{i,j,k}$	temperature approach for match of hot stream i and cold stream j at temperature location k, °C
$EMATHU_{j,m}$	exchanger minimum approach temperature for match of cold stream j and hot utility m, °C	$dtcul_{i,n}$	temperature approach for match of hot stream i and cold utility n at cold utility temperature location n, °C
NOK	total number of stages	$dtcur_{i,n}$	temperature approach for match of hot stream i and cold utility n at cold utility temperature location $n + 1$, °C
$NOCU$	total number of cold utlities		
$NOHU$	total number of hot utlities	$dthul_{j,m}$	temperature approach for match of cold stream j and hot utility m at hot utility temperature location m, °C
$U_{i,j}$	overall heat transfer coefficient for match of hot stream i and cold stream j, kW/m² °C	$dthur_{j,m}$	temperature approach for match of cold stream j and hot utility m at hot utility temperature location $m + 1$, °C
$UCU_{i,n}$	overall heat transfer coefficient for match of hot stream i and cold utility n, kW/m² °C	$AREA_{i,j,k}$	area for match of hot stream i and cold stream j at stage k, m²
		$AREAcu_{i,n}$	area for match of hot stream i and cold utility n, m²
$UHU_{j,m}$	overall heat transfer coefficient for match of cold stream j and hot utility m, kW/m² °C	$AREAhu_{j,m}$	area for match of cold stream j and hot utility m, m²
		$splith_{i,k}$	number of splitting of hot stream i at stage k, times
		$splitc_{j,k}$	number of splitting of cold stream j at stage k, times
		Binary Variables	
		$z_{i,j,k}$	existence for match of hot stream i and cold stream j at stage k
		$zcu_{i,n}$	existence for match of hot stream i and cold utility n
		$zhu_{j,m}$	existence for match of cold stream j and hot utility m

3. Results and discussion

The case study consists of 11 hot and 4 cold streams, 1 cold and 1 hot utility. The stream data and utility and cost data are shown in Table 3 and 4, respectively. The objective functions are to minimize net present cost (NPC). The mathematical models were programmed in GAMS 21.2 and solved with DICOPT2x-C (CONOPT3 and CPLEX 8.1) using default option. MIP time was limited at 30,000 s per one cycle. The CPU times are reported corresponding to runs performed in VPCCB15FH with Intel(R) Core(TM) i5-2410M CPU @ 2.30 GHz processor, 4.00 GB of ram memory.

Pinch Analysis predicts that the optimal HRAT at 21 °C, as shown in Table 5, gives the optimal NPC of $ 12,100,007 and number of exchangers of 20. Next, stage-wise model with optimal Pinch Point is applied to generate HEN with number of exchangers of 28, as shown in Table 6. And relaxation step is applied to improve HEN by reducing number of exchangers from 28 to 23, as shown in Table 7, resulting in HRAT increase from 21 °C to 24.3 °C. The final HEN, as shown in Figure 3, is compared to one generated by stage-wise model (Yee and Grossmann, 1990), as shown in Figure 4.

Table 3. Stream data.

Stream	F*Cp (kW/°C)	T_{in} (°C)	T_{out} (°C)	h (kW/m²·°C)
H1	1,197.80	134.0	108.2	0.31
H2	396.19	224.7	190.8	0.31
H3	447.31	268.1	198.8	0.31
H4	136.03	232.7	40.0	0.31
H5	48.43	238.2	45.0	0.31
H6	76.57	279.3	68.0	0.31
H7	159.55	335.9	262.7	0.31
H8	78.65	335.9	186.1	0.31
H9	263.30	235.4	176.2	0.31
H10	85.23	176.2	90.0	0.31
H11	160.04	115.2	56.0	0.31
C1	583.35	39.0	153.0	0.31
C2	689.80	153.0	165.2	0.31
C3	635.68	155.3	348.0	0.31
C4	194.80	150.0	270.0	0.31

Table 4. Utility stream and cost data.

Utility	T_{in} (°C)	T_{out} (°C)	h (kW/m²·°C)
CU1	20	40	0.31
HU1	600	590	0.31

Cost Data		
CU1	$/kW-y	11.98
HU1	$/kW-y	29.96
Heat exchanger cost	$	8,572 + 124.63A
Splitting cost	$/Time	3,000
Project life time	y	5
Interest rate	%	10
EMAT (exchanger minimum approach temperature)	°C	10

Table 5. Pinch Analysis.

Supertargeting results		
Optimum HRAT	°C	21
Hot pinch temperature	°C	134
Cold pinch temperature	°C	113
Optimum CU load	kW	23,111
Optimum HU load	kW	60,949
Optimum no. of heat exchangers	Units	20
Optimum total vertical area	m²	31,750
NPC (Objective function)	$	12,100,007

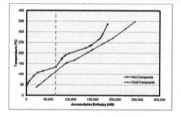

Figure 2. Composite Curves at optimal Pinch.

Table 6. Stage-wise model with Pinch.

Stage-wise model with pinch temperature results		
No. of cycle	Cycles	8
No. cycle that MIP limit reached	Cycles	1
Total time	s	70,253
Average time per cycle	s/cycle	8,782
HRAT	°C	21
CU load	kW	23,111
HU load	kW	60,949
No. of heat exchangers	Units	28
Total area	m²	36,837
Total splitting	Times	11
No. of splits	Splits	17
Payback period	y	2.3
NPC (Objective function)	$	12,835,560

Table 7. Relaxation step.

Stage-wise model with topology control results		
No. of cycle	Cycles	2
No. cycle that MIP limit reached	Cycles	-
Total time	s	2.5
Average time per cycle	s/cycle	1.25
HRAT	°C	24.3
CU load	kW	25,064
HU load	kW	62,902
No. of heat exchangers	Units	23
Total area	m²	34,324
Total splitting	Times	9
No. of splits	Splits	13
Payback period	y	2.1
NPC (Objective function)	$	12,784,080

The NPC of the synthesized HEN is very close to that predicted by Pinch Analysis. This ensures the reliability of the predicted HRAT. However, some differences may come from non-vertical heat transfer in actual network. Its time requirement is also reasonable for large problem. The HEN improved by relaxation has less complexity and better NPC with some penalty of utility consumption and very short computational time.

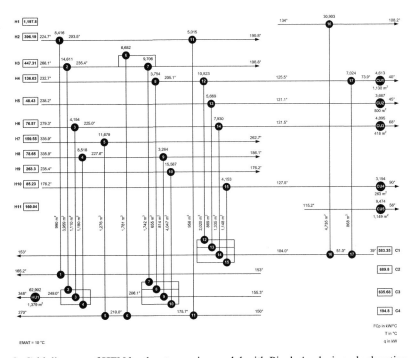

Figure 3. Grid diagram of HEN by the stage-wise model with Pinch Analysis and relaxation.

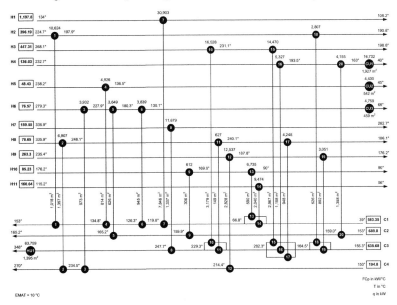

Figure 4. Grid diagram of HEN by the stage-wise model (Yee and Grossmann, 1990).

Table 8. Summary of HEN results.

		Stage-wise model with Pinch Analysis and relaxation	Stage-wise model
Total time	s	70,256	60,008
HRAT	°C	24.3	25.8
Cooling utility usage	kW	25,064	25,921
Heating utility usage	kW	62,902	63,759
No. of heat exchangers	Units	23	24
Total area	m^2	34,324	36,180
Total splitting	Times	9	5
No. of splits	Splits	13	9
Operating cost	$/y	2,184,797	2,220,741
Capital cost	$	4,501,983	4,729,787
Payback period	y	2.1	2.1
Net present cost	$	12,784,080	13,148,140

4. Conclusions

MINLP stage-wise model with Pinch Analysis and relaxation for HEN synthesis was presented in this paper. This method consists of three steps; targeting, HEN synthesis, and HEN improvement. The first step predicts optimal HRAT. Next HEN is generated by stage-wise model with Pinch Point. Finally, HEN is improved by reducing number of exchangers. From case study in previous section, as shown in Table 8, this work provides less computational time per cycle than method using only stage-wise model. It also gives HEN with less NPC. In another word, the method with stage-wise model alone will take larger computational time than the method using stage-wise model with Pinch Point and relaxation to generate the HEN with the same NPC. For application case, the gas separation plant in Thailand is applied using this work to synthesize HEN.

Acknowledgements

Authors would like to express our gratitude to the Petroleum and Petrochemical College, Chulalongkorn University, National Center of Excellence for Petroleum, Petrochemicals and Advanced Materials, Government Budget Fund, PTT Public Company Limited, and Research and Researcher for Industry for funding support.

References

A. Barbaro, M.J. Bagajewicz, 2005, New rigorous one-step MILP formulation for heat exchanger network synthesis, Computers and Chemical Engineering, 29, 1945-1976.

B. Linnhoff, E. Hindmarsh, 1983, The pinch design method for heat exchanger networks, Chemical Engineering Science, 38, 5, 745-763.

K. Siemanond, S. Kosol, 2012, Heat exchanger network retrofit by pinch design method using stage-model mathematical programming, Chemical Engineering Transactions, 29, 367-372.

K.F. Huang, I.A. Karimi, 2014, Efficient algorithm for simultaneous synthesis of heat exchanger networks, Chemical Engineering Science, 105, 53-68.

M. Escobar, J.O. Trierweiler, 2013, Optimal heat exchanger network synthesis: A case study comparison, Applied Thermal Engineering, 51, 801-826.

R. Anantharaman, K. Jordal, D. Berstad, T. Gundersen, 2013, The role of process synthesis in the systematic design of energy efficient fossil fuel power plants with CO_2 capture, Chemical Engineering Transactions, 35, 55-60.

T.F. Yee, I.E. Grossmann, 1990, Simultaneous optimization models for heat integration—II. Heat exchanger network synthesis, Computers and Chemical Engineering, 14, 10, 1165-1184.

Jiří Jaromír Klemeš, Petar Sabev Varbanov and Peng Yen Liew (Editors)
Proceedings of the 24th European Symposium on Computer Aided Process Engineering – ESCAPE 24
June 15-18, 2014, Budapest, Hungary. Copyright © 2014 Elsevier B.V. All rights reserved.

Study of Energy Efficient Distillation Columns Usage for Multicomponent Separations through Process Simulation and Statistical Methods

Sandra S. Florindo, Isabel M. João, João M. Silva*

Chemical Engineering Department, Instituto Superior de Engenharia de Lisboa-ISEL, Instituto Politécnico de Lisboa, R. Cons. Emídio Navarro 1, 1959-007 Lisboa Portugal.
jmsilva@deq.isel.ipl.pt

Abstract

This paper studies the optimal design conditions for the fully thermally coupled distillation columns, FTCDC, through process simulation with Aspen HYSYS and statistical methods. A fractional factorial design was used in order to screen the main operational and structural factors that minimize the total cost. Following the process characterization a steepest descent method was iteratively performed in the direction of total cost optimization. The best combination of levels of structural and operational variables obtained by the designed experiments allowed to a reduction of 9.6 % in the total costs. The factors' levels obtained in steady state simulation were then tested in dynamic simulation. It is important to carry out the dynamic simulation to test the conditions obtained by steady state simulation in a more realistic way because it is well known that FTCDC systems are difficult to control and operate.

Keywords: FTCDC, factorial design, Aspen HYSYS, Dynamic Simulation

1. Introduction

Most chemical processes require the separation of mixtures of chemical components. Distillation is mainly used for liquid separations, driving nearly all other separation techniques out of the process industry. The distillation processes have a huge impact on both operation and investment costs in chemical plants and this has motivated the development of several types of fully thermally coupled distillation columns (FTCDC) that can lead to savings in energy and capital costs (Agrawal and Fidkowski, 1998). Despite the high potential of the FTCDC economic benefits, a lack of reliable design methods has contributed for the low number of commercial solutions (Caballero and Grossmann, 2006). Therefore, it is still a challenging task for engineers to define near optimal design conditions for the FTCDC in a simple and efficient manner in the initial stage of the design procedure. Several distinct configurations of the FTCDC can be implemented in commercial process simulators, but the challenge is to find optimal or near optimal solutions for the problem due to the large number of design variables of the FTCDC system which lead to tedious iterative simulations in order to find a proper structure. Additionally the trial and error simulation can lead to an inadequate structure unable to converge in the process simulation for design (Kim, 2002).

Statistical methods like factorial and fractional factorial designs can be used to investigate the effects of many different factors by varying them simultaneously instead of changing one factor at time (OFAT). This is a great advantage of experimental statistical design over the OFAT traditional experimentation, because it provides a full comprehension of the interactions between the design factors allowing to reach better design solutions with lower number of experiments when compared with OFAT (Montgomery, 2009).There are few studies concerning the use of statistical designed experiments in the optimization of energy efficient columns usage for multicomponent separations through process simulation in steady state (Long and Lee, 2012). A more recent study from Sangal et al. (2013) shows the use of Box–Behnken statistical design coupled with simulation for the optimization of the main process parameters in divided wall distillation columns.

Simulation was coupled with statistical designed experiments in the first place to factor screening, that is to identify the main variables that affect the total cost followed by process optimization in order to find the variables' conditions that result in a lower total cost.

Knowing that FTCDC systems are difficult to control and operate (Wolff and Skogestad, 1995) it was also an aim of this work to verify if the conditions obtained by steady state simulation could be run using Aspen HYSYS in a dynamic simulation mode which translates in a more realistic way the process performance.

2. The problem– Separation of a ternary mixture

In this work, we start the design using the methodology proposed by Triantafyllou and Smith (1992) by means of the preliminary design equations based on short-cut Fenske-Underwood-Gilliland-Kirkbride method (FUGK) to find the initial configuration for the Petlyuk column. It was chosen a mixture of 2-methylpropan-1-ol, butan-1-ol and butan-2-ol. The design was implemented in Aspen HYSYS v7.3 and for the computation of the thermodynamic properties it was used the UNIQUAC model with the binary parameters from the Aspen HYSYS database. The Petlyuk configuration for the separation of a ternary mixture is a special case of the FTCDC. A prefractionator followed by a product column characterizes this system.

For the first step of the design procedure, it was applied the short-cut distillation method (FUGK) to obtain a first approximation for the Petlyuk structure (Figure 1). In this step it was possible identify the values for the main variables of this system and it was implemented a new structure consisting on an absorber and a distillation column. The absorber corresponds to the prefractionator.The main design factors identified can be aggregated into two types: six structural related with the number of stages in the prefractionator and main column and position of the feed and draw of the midle product; and two operational related with the flow rates of liquid and vapor transferred between

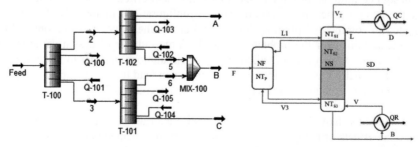

Figure 1. Implementation of the FUGK method in Aspen HYSYS and identification of the main variables of the Petlyuk system.

the prefractionator and the product column. The main variables are identified and the starting values for the optimization process by design of experiments are displayedin Table 1.

3. Process optimization with designed experiments

Some special types of factorial designs are very useful in process development and improvement. One of such kinds are factorials of the type 2^k with k factors, each at two levels usually referred as low level (-1) and high level (+1) of the factor. As the number of factors in a factorial experiment grows the number of effects to estimate also grows. In the present case we have a total of 8 factors and so we would need a total of 256 simulations (experiments) with no replication in order to perform all the combinations. In order to reduce the number of simulations and assuming the sparsity of effects principle a fractional factorial design can be used to obtain information on the main effects and low order interactions. The fractional factorial chosen was 2_{IV}^{8-4}. In this design no main effect is aliased with any other main effect or two factor interaction being a good design to use in a screening experiment due to its high resolution. This design only requires 16 experiments reducing considerably the number of runs required for a full factorial experiment. For the fractional factorial design four generators were used, E=BCD, F=ADC, G=ABC and H=ABD. In order to interpret the results of fractional factorial designs it is necessary to take into account the alias relationships (Montgomery, 2009).

For the design of experiments simulations, a variation of ±1 stage was used for the structural factors and a variation of ± 5 kgmol/h for the operational factors in relation to the starting values. The response variable selected was the total cost obtained with the Aspen Economic Evaluator using the default definition. With this tool, it is possible to obtain a rapid estimation of the capital and operational cost of each run. After performing the 16 experiments, the effects were estimated and a normal probability plot of the effects was built in order to graphically judge the relevance of the factors and interactions. The estimates that behave like a random sample drawn from a normal distribution have zero mean and the plotted effects will lie approximately along a straight line. Those effects that do not plot on the line are probably the significant effects as we can observe in Figure 2a).The analysis of variance (ANOVA) was performed in order to test which factors and interactions are significant. The mean

Table 1. Description of the main variables and starting values

Structural factors	
A – Position of the feed stream in the prefractionator, $N_F=8$	D – Number of stages in the middle section of the main column, $NT_{S2}=51$
B – Number of stages of the prefractionator, $NT_P=19$	E – Position of the extraction of B product (middle), $N_{SD}=42$
C – Number of stages in the top section of the main column, $NT_{S1}=15$	F – Number of stages in the bottom section of the main column, $NT_{S3}=8$
Operational factors	
G – Vapor Molar flow of the interconnection stream in the bottom, V3=280 kgmol/h	H – Liquid molar flow of the interconnection stream in the top, L1=240 kgmol/h

square of each of the factors and interactions that did not plot on the line (i.e. a total of seven) were calculated and divided by the mean square error. Each of these ratios follows an F distribution, with the numerator degrees of freedom equal to the number of levels minus one (i.e 1 degree of freedom) an the denominator degrees of freedom equal to 8 (i.e 15-7). The computed F should be compared with the tabular value (i.e. $F_{5\%,1,8} = 5.32$) and the null hypothesis is rejected if the computed F exceed the tabular value for the significance level of 5 %. After ANOVA computation we were able to conclude that all the seven, factors and interactions, affect significantly the total cost (response variable), a result already observed graphically (Figure 2a) and tested with ANOVA. We concluded that factors A, B, G and H are significant as well as the interactions AB, BG and GH. Figure 2(b) represents the plots of the AB, BG and GH interactions and A, B, G and H main effects. The plot of the interaction GH shows that the interaction is very strong, and the effect of changing H from the lower level to the higher level is dependent of the level in which factor G is settled (the interaction hide the main effects). Looking at Figure 2(b) it was easy to conclude that it is better to work with factors A and B in their higher levels in order to minimize the cost. In relation to factors G and H it is better to work with factor H in the lower level an also factor G in the lower level due to the effect of the interaction GH that is stronger than the effect of the individual factors.

After performing the fractional factorial design for process characterization and once the appropriate set of structural and operational factors as well as their levels is identified, the next step was the process optimization in order to find the set of conditions that result in the lowest total cost. In order to optimize we used the method of steepest descent, which is a procedure for moving sequentially along the path of steepest descent that is in the direction of the minimization of the response. A second cycle of simulations were performed varying the factors considered significant. The experiments were conducted along the path of steepest descent with a full factorial design2^4 with the factors A, B, G, and H varying in the direction of the better level in which the total cost reduces. The results of ANOVA for a level of significance of 5 % allowed to the conclusion that the factors A, B, G and H still affect the response. After that, a third designed experiment was performed in order to further move along the path of steepest descent. After the whole process of optimization, the better conditions of the eight factors (structural and operational variables) in order to minimize the total cost are:

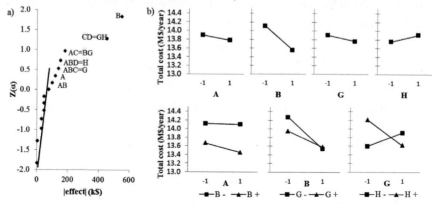

Figure 2. Factorial fractional experiments results: a) Probability plot to identify the significant factors and interactions; b) Influence of the factors and interactions level in the total cost.

A $-N_F$=13; B $-NT_P$=32; C $-NT_{S1}$=15; D $-NT_{S2}$=51; E $-N_{SD}$=42; F $-NT_{S3}$=8; G – V3=265kgmol/h; H – L1 = 225 kgmol/h. The use of these conditions in the Petlyuk column allows a reduction of the total cost of 9.6 % relative to the starting values.

4. Dynamic simulation

After the statistical design experiments performed, the optimal solution obtained was tested by dynamic simulation using the Aspen HYSYS in dynamic mode. This type of system is more complex than a traditional distillation column with more degrees of freedom. Taking in consideration the control objective and previous works done by Wolf and Skogestad (1995) and Hwang et al. (2011) was chosen a LV configuration with SISO feedback control loops, adapted from the LV configuration used in traditional distillation columns.

The control structure implemented present eight control loops. The control loop for pressure with the pressure in the top stage of the main column is the variable to control and the manipulated variable is the flow of utility used in the condenser. The two levels control loops in the condenser and reboiler use the flow rates of the distillate and bottom products as manipulated variables respectively. The composition of the distillate is controlled by manipulating the reflux flow rate. The composition of the bottom product is adjusted by manipulating the flow rate of the utility used in the reboiler. For the control of the composition of the middle product a cascade control loop was adopted were the set point for the side draw flow rate was obtained by the control of the composition of this stream. The two remaining control loops concern the control of the flow rates of interconnection streams between the prefractionator and the main column. One is for the liquid stream leaving the main column and the other is for the vapor stream exit from the main column. Figure 3 presents the simulation of the control loops. All the controllers are configured as PI and the parameters were obtained by the internal auto-tuning function. In the auto-tuning, it is possible to adjust the relay hysteresis to take into account the non-linearity observed in the distillation columns. As an example of the performance obtained with this control configuration, it is showed in Figure 4 the response of the composition control loops in the bottom and middle products to a change in the set-point. The control of the FTCDC system is more complex than in a traditional distillation column and the results obtained showed that the response time of the system is higher when compared with a system of two columns for the same separation, but even so possible to control. The FTCDC control can be improved using model predictive control strategies.

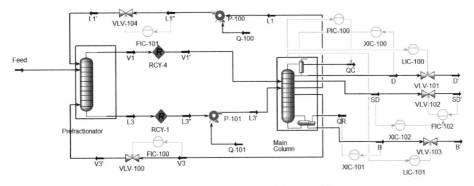

Figure 3. Implementation of FTCDC in Aspen HYSYS with control loops.

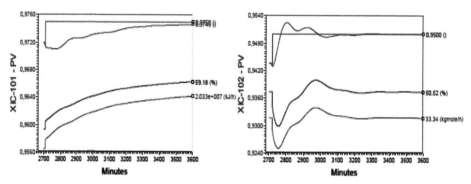

Figure 4. Response of the composition control loops for the middle and bottom products.

5. Conclusions

The combination of statistical tools like design of experiments proved to be useful in the simulation of multicomponent separation reducing the number of simulation runs to achieve an optimized solution for a particular problem. In the case of this Petlyuk column a reduction of the total cost estimation of almost 10 % was obtained with a reduced number of runs. The dynamic simulation of the optimized Petlyuk column shows the possibility of operation of this system, but it is necessary to implement new control strategies to overcome the high response time observed. The use of model predictive control can be a strategy to improve the performance of these systems.

Acknowledgements

I.M. João is also with CEG-IST and J.M. Silva is also with CRERG-IBB, research units of Instituto Superior Técnico, Universidade de Lisboa, Lisboa, Portugal.

References

R. Agrawal, Z.T. Fidkowski, 1998, Are thermally coupled distillation columns always thermodynamically more efficient for ternary distillations?, Ind. Eng. Chem. Res., 37, 8, 3444–3454.

J.A. Caballero, I.E. Grossmann, 2006, Structural considerations and modeling in the synthesis of heat-integrated–thermally coupled distillation sequences, Ind. Eng. Chem. Res., 45, 25, 8454–8474.

K.S. Hwang, B.C. Kim, Y.H. Kim, 2011, Design and Control of a Fully Thermally Coupled Distillation Column Modified from a Conventional System, Chem. Eng. Technol., 34, 2, 273–281.

Y.H. Kim, 2002, Structural design and operation of a fully thermally coupled distillation column, Chem. Eng. J., 85, 2–3, 289–301.

N.V.D. Long, M. Lee, 2012, Design and optimization of a dividing wall column by factorial design, Korean J. Chem. Eng., 29, 5, 567-573.

D.C. Montgomery, 2009, Introduction to Statistical Quality Control, 6th ed. John Wiley & Sons, Inc., Hoboken, NJ, USA.

V.K. Sangal, V. Kumar, I.M. Mishra, 2013, Optimization of a divided wall columnfor the separation of c4-c6 normalparaffin mixture using box-behnkendesign, Chem. Ind. Chem. Eng. Q., 19, 1, 107–119.

C. Triantafyllou, R. Smith, 1992, The design and optimization of fully thermally coupled distillation, Trans IChemE, 70, Part A, 118–132.

E.A. Wolff, S. Skogestad S., 1995, Operation of Integrated Three-Product (Petlyuk) DistillationColumns, Ind. Eng. Chem. Res., 34,2094-2103.

Jiří Jaromír Klemeš, Petar Sabev Varbanov and Peng Yen Liew (Editors)
Proceedings of the 24th European Symposium on Computer Aided Process Engineering – ESCAPE 24
June 15-18, 2014, Budapest, Hungary.

Structure Generation of Candidate Reactants Using Signature Descriptors

Vikrant A. Dev[a], Nishanth G. Chemmangattuvalappil[b], Mario R. Eden[a],*

[a]*Department of Chemical Engineering, Auburn University, USA*
[b]*Department of Chemical and Environmental Eng., University of Nottingham, Malaysia*
edenmar@auburn.edu

Abstract

Integrated process and product design techniques in a reverse problem formulation are successful in selecting optimal chemicals and maximizing process efficiency. However most of these techniques are limited to non-reactive systems. Previous efforts to optimize products and generate candidate reactants have generally been restricted to a single reactant being an unknown, utilization of property prediction models that are linear functions of topological indices (TIs) and implementation of independent-site approximation among others. In this work, a molecular design algorithm has been developed that incorporates property models that are non-linear functions of TIs for the design of optimal products without restriction on number of unknown reactants and products. Property operators that are tailored functions obeying linear mixing rules and molecular signature descriptors that are novel molecular descriptors have been utilized to generate structures of reactants. Signature descriptors are capable in capturing the interactions between neighboring atoms. The algorithm can generate reactant structures of any reaction as it focuses on the design of the products and then considers the change in the various chemical bonds due to the reaction chemistry.

Keywords: Signature Descriptors, Reactive Systems, Molecular Design

1. Background

1.1. Molecular Design Challenges

Molecular design has previously been investigated by independent utilization of Group Contribution Models (GCMs) and Quantitative Structure Activity/Property Relationships (QSARs/QSPRs). Both these types of models have non-linear structures that can make it computationally difficult to handle molecular design problems that involve combinations of physico-chemical and biological properties (Eden et al., 2004). In reactive systems, molecular design is increasingly playing a role in selecting optimal solvents for enhancing reaction kinetics and for generating candidate reactants. Chemmangattuvalappil et al. (2012) developed an algorithm for the design of an unknown reactant using linear property models. De Vleeschouwer et al. (2012, 2013) optimized photoacidity and intrinsic stability of single unknown candidates by constructing on a molecular template using a stochastic version of best first search (BFS) heuristic algorithm. The sites were optimized individually by carrying out chemical changes after presuming their independence. This increases the possibility of getting stuck in local optima. In the acidity/photoacidity optimization problem, additional approximations involved utilizing the energy difference between conjugate base and acid as a measure of acidity instead of the change in Gibbs free energy due to the reaction, restricting analysis to single point calculations in gas phase, etc. which can introduce sizeable errors. There is also a disagreement in the optimized structures obtained in ground and excited states. In this work, a deterministic algorithm has been developed that is valid for any number of unknown reactants and products, incorporates non-linear property models, provides a global optima for the case of convex property functions and captures the interactions between neighboring atoms.

1.2. Simplification of Integrated Process and Product Design

Reverse Problem Formulation (RPF) simplifies integrated process and product design problems by decoupling them into two reverse problems (Eden et al., 2004). The first reverse problem identifies property targets to achieve optimum process performance and the second reverse problem generates molecular structures that meet the identified property targets. The first reverse problem is linearized using property operators which are tailored functions obeying linear mixing rules.

1.3. Molecular Design using Signature Descriptors

The signature descriptor is a systematic codification system over an alphabet of atoms describing the extended valence of the atoms of a molecule (Faulon et al., 2003). If G is a molecular graph and x is an atom of G, the atomic signature of height h of x is a canonical representation of the subgraph of G containing all atoms that are at a distance h from x. Increasing the height of the signature descriptors, increases the amount of information captured of the interactions with the neighbouring atoms. The signature of a molecule can be obtained as a linear combination of its atomic signatures. Signature descriptors enable utilization of QSARs/QSPRs and GCMs on a single platform and thus can track a wide variety of property targets (Chemmangattuvalappil et al., 2010). Thus, in the second reverse problem, property targets can be related to the molecular structures of interest. Faulon et al. (2003) identified the relationship between topological indices (TIs), which constitute QSARs/QSPRs, and signatures. If k is a constant, $^h\alpha_G$ is the vector of occurrences of atomic signature of height h and $TI(root\,(^h\Sigma))$ is the vector of TI values calculated for each root of atomic signature:

$$TI(G) = k.^h\alpha_G.TI\left(root\left(^h\Sigma\right)\right) \tag{1}$$

2. Signature Descriptors in Reactive Systems

To track the target properties in reactive systems, the concept of signature of a reaction, $^h\sigma(R)$, was defined by Faulon et al. (2003):

$$^h\sigma(R) = f\big(\sigma(A)\sigma(B)\big) \tag{2}$$

When a reaction occurs, one or more of the molecular groups in the reactants are replaced by new groups from the other reactants to form corresponding products. Thus the signature of a reaction is a function of the signatures of the reactants, $\sigma(A)$, and the signatures of the products, $\sigma(B)$. Since the groups are replaced, the signatures of the atoms close to the groups also change. Thus $^h\sigma(R)$ is also related to the property operator associated with the change in signatures.

$$\Delta\Omega = f(^h\sigma(R)) \tag{3}$$

The height of the signature considered for tracking the target property decides which atoms' signatures will change and which atoms will have the same signature as before. For example, consider the transesterification reaction on the next page.

If signatures of height two are generated, the signatures for the C atoms at parent and child level of the root O atom marked as "*" and that of the double bonded O atom at the parent level will change after the reaction occurs because the OR'' group leaves and is replaced by the OR group. The signatures of the other C atoms in the R' group are unaffected. Similarly one can describe the change in the signatures of the reactant alcohol.

Instead of relating the change in property operator to the signature of the reaction, alternatively, optimal reactants can be generated by obtaining corresponding shared groups and/or other common structural features from the products that have been generated to meet design targets. For example, in the transesterification reaction, the optimal product ester and product alcohol are designed first using the property targets. Since the product ester and the reactant alcohol share the R group, identifying the R group from the generated structure(s) of optimal product ester identifies the required reactant alcohol. Similarly identifying the R' and R'' groups from the generated optimal structure(s) of product ester and product alcohol respectively identifies the structure of the required reactant ester. Separate molecular design problems are set up for each of the products. For property operators that are linear functions of the TIs, the property operator relationship for the unknown products in terms of the unknown reactants taking into account the change in signatures can be expressed as:

$$\sum_{i=1}^{Np} {}^hP_i = \sum_{j=1}^{Nu} {}^hU_j + \sum_{k=1}^{h}\sum_{l=1}^{Nc} {}^hC_{k,l} \tag{4}$$

Where, $\sum^hP_i$ = sum of the property operators of the products such that the constituent atoms have signature of height h, $\sum^hU_j$ = sum of the property operators associated with the signatures of height h for the atoms that belong to the unchanged part of the reactants and $\sum\sum^hC_{k,l}$ = sum of the property operators associated with the signatures of height h for the atoms of the products that were at a height k ($k \leq h$) from the groups in the reactants that were replaced due to the reaction. Np and Nu represent the number of products and reactants while Nc represents the number of atoms that were at a height k from the groups in the reactants that were replaced due to the reaction. For property operators that are non-linear functions of TIs, the relationship will depend on the defined function.

2.1. General Problem Statement

Design molecules that have the best dominant property and fulfil property constraints obtained from process design taking into account the chemical reaction involved.

2.2 Problem Formulation

The property operator $\Omega(P)$ of the property P obeys linear mixing rules and is expressed in terms of the occurrence numbers of the atomic signatures ($x_i = {}^h a_i$) for molecular design (Chemmangattuvalappil and Eden, 2013). An optimization problem for each product is set up such that the dominant property operator Ω_j is maximized/minimized as per the requirements and the constraints (Ω_j^{min} and Ω_j^{max}) placed on other properties

(Ω_{ij}) are satisfied. The optimization problem which also accounts for Eq. (4) is formulated as:

$$Max / Min \ \Omega_j \tag{5}$$

$$\Omega_j^{min} \leq \Omega_{ij} \leq \Omega_j^{max} \tag{6}$$

$$\Omega(P) = f(TI) \tag{7}$$

$$TI = \sum_{i=1}^{N} {}^h\alpha_i \cdot TI(root({}^h\Sigma)) = \sum_{i=1}^{N} x_i L_i \tag{8}$$

$$\Omega_{ij} = \sum_{i=1}^{N} x_i S_i \tag{9}$$

$$\Omega_{ij} = \sum_{i=1}^{N} x_i C_i \tag{10}$$

Where, S_i is the coefficient of x_i obtained by substituting Eq. (8) in Eq. (7) and C_i is the property contribution ascribed to the corresponding signature(s) after utilizing GCMs.

By employing graph theory principles structural constraints are generated in terms of occurrence number of signatures to ensure generation of feasible molecules (Chemmangattuvalappil and Eden, 2013).

2.3 Problem solution steps
1. Calculate property targets for optimum process performance.
2. Identify QSARs/QSPRs/GCMs that predict the target properties.
3. The maximum height corresponding to the utilized TIs is identified and all the possible signatures are generated for that height.
4. Identify the contributing signatures taking into consideration the various structural and property constraints after setting up design problems for each of the product molecules. The structure of the product molecules is generated using the algorithm developed by Chemmangattuvalappil and Eden (2013).
5. Trace back the unknown groups to the reactants from the products by addition and/or removal of groups and/or rearrangements by utilizing the general chemical equation and the general structural formula of the reactants and products.

3. Case Study

The aim of this case study is to identify the unknown structures of the reactant alcohol (ROH) and the reactant ester (R′COOR″) that produce the ester (R′COOR) and alcohol (R″OH) such that the soil sorption coefficient $\log(K_{oc})$ of products is minimized. The product ester is constrained by boiling point and toxic limit concentration, $\log(TLC)$, and the product alcohol is constrained by boiling point and lethal concentration, $\log(LC_{50})$, with the values listed in Table 1 and Table 2. Table 3 lists the models used to predict these target properties. The $\log(LC_{50})$ QSAR is applicable only for alcohols. The boiling point GCM by Joback and Reid (1987) has been utilized for alcohols since it provides a better estimate in the given temperature range.

Table 1. Property Constraints on Product Ester

Property	Upper Bound	Lower Bound
Boiling Point, BP (°C)	170	110
log(TLC) (ppm)	-	1
log(K_{oc})	Minimum	

Table 2. Property Constraints on Product Alcohol

Property	Upper Bound	Lower Bound
Boiling Point, BP (°C)	85	10
log(LC_{50}) (ppm)	-	1.2
log(K_{oc})	Minimum	

Table 3. Property Models

Property	Property Model
log(K_{oc}) (Bahnick and Doucette, 1988)	$\log(K_{oc}) = 0.53(^{1}\chi) - 1.25(\Delta^{1}\chi^{v}) - 0.72(\Delta^{0}\chi^{v}) + 0.66$
Boiling Point, BP (Marrero and Gani, 2001)	$T_b = t_{b0} \cdot \ln\left[\sum_{g=1}^{n_g} n_i t_{b1} + \sum_{s=1}^{N_s} n_s t_{b2} + \sum_{t=1}^{N_t} n_t t_{b3} \right]$
log(TLC) (Koch, 1982)	$\log(TLC) = 4.066 - 0.9915(^{1}\chi^{v})$
Boiling Point, BP (Joback and Reid, 1987)	$T_b = 198.2 + \sum_{i=1}^{n_g} n_i t_{bi}$
log(LC_{50}) (Juric *et al.*, 1992)	$\log(LC_{50}) = 2.975 + 1.169(\log{}^{0}\chi^{v}) - 7.309(\log{}^{0}\chi^{v})^2$

Property models are ultimately expressed in terms of molecular signatures via molecular descriptors. The maximum height of the signature in this case is 2. The following is a set of few of the signatures that have the potential to constitute an optimal ester:
[O2(C2(CO)C4(=OOC)), C1(O2(CC)), C2(C3(OCC)C1(C)), O2(=C4(=OOC)), C3(C3(CCC)C2(CC)C1(C)), C2(C4(=OOC)C1(C)), C4(=O2(=C)O2(CC)C1(C))]

Signatures for the product alcohol can be similarly generated. Two optimization problems for each of the product molecules were set up in the GAMS software using Eqs. (4)-(10) along with structural constraints and solved using DICOPT solver for minimum values of soil sorption coefficient. DICOPT tends to ber very fast and provides a globally optimal solution for convex functions while for non-convex functions often serves as a successful heuristic approach (Bonami et al., 2012). The best candidates for the product ester and alcohol were found to be:
- Product ester: 2-methylpropyl ethanoate ($CH_3(CH_3)CHCH_2OC(=O)CH_3$)
- Product alcohol: methanol (CH_3OH)

Since, the reaction is a transesterification reaction, one knows what fragments of the reactant ester and alcohol carbon chain become part of the product alcohol and ester.

From the optimal products, the R, R′ and R″ groups have been identified as 'CH$_3$(CH$_3$)CHCH$_2$', 'CH$_3$' and 'CH$_3$' respectively. Thus the structures of the reactant ester and alcohol are:

- Reactant ester: methyl ethanoate (CH$_3$OC(=O)CH$_3$)
- Reactant alcohol: 2-methyl propan-1-ol (CH$_3$(CH$_3$)CHCH$_2$OH)

4. Conclusions

An algorithm has been developed to solve molecular design problems in reactive systems with unknown reactants and products. The algorithm can track the changes in the properties for different types of reactions. The algorithm is based on the fact that changes in the reaction sites of the unknown molecules are deciding the nature of the product. Since the introduced algorithm focuses on the design of products first and then uses the chemical equation to generate the reactant structures, it can be used irrespective of the type of reaction and the number of reactions in the system. Future efforts in this direction would be to develop a solution scheme that treats property/activity functions that are discontinuous, non-differentiable and/or highly nonlinear.

References

D.A. Bahnick, D.J. Doucette, 1988, Use of molecular connectivity indices to estimate soil sorption of organic chemicals, Chemosphere, 17, 9, 1703-1715.

P. Bonami, M. Kilinc, J. Linderoth, 2012, Algorithms and software for convex mixed integer nonlinear programs, In: J. Lee, S. Leyffer (Eds.), Mixed Integer Nonlinear Programming, The IMA Volumes in Mathematics and its Applications, 154, Springer, New York, US, 1-39.

N.G. Chemmangattuvalappil, M.R. Eden, 2013, A Novel Methodology for Property-Based Molecular Design Using Multiple Topological Indices, Industrial and Engineering Chemistry Research, 52, 7090-7103.

N.G. Chemmangattuvalappil, C.B. Roberts, M.R. Eden, 2012, Signature Descriptors for Process and Molecular Design in Reactive Systems, Computer Aided Chemical Engineering, 31, 1356-1360.

N.G. Chemmangattuvalappil, C.C. Solvason, S. Bommareddy, M.R. Eden, 2010, Reverse problem formulation approach to molecular design using property operators based on signature descriptors, Computers and Chemical Engineering, 34, 12, 2062-2071.

F. De Vleeschouwer, A. Chankisjijev, W. Yang, P. Geerlings, F.D. Proft, 2013, Pushing the Boundaries of Intrinsically Stable Radicals: Inverse Design Using the Thiadiazinyl Radical as a Template, Journal of Organic Chemistry, 78, 7, 3151-3158.

F. De Vleeschouwer, W. Yang, D.N. Beratan, P. Geerlings, F.D. Proft, 2012, Inverse Design of molecules with optimal reactivity properties: acidity of 2-naphthol derivatives, Physical Chemistry Chemical Physics, 14, 16002-16013.

M.R. Eden, S.B. Jorgensen, R. Gani, M.M. El-Halwagi, 2004, A novel framework for simultaneous separation process and product design, Chemical Engineering and Processing, 43, 5, 595-608.

J.L. Faulon, D.P. Visco Jr., R.S. Pophale, 2003, The Signature Molecular Descriptor 1. Using Extended Valence Sequences in QSAR and QSPR Studies, Journal of Chemical Information and Computer Sciences, 43, 707-720.

K.G. Joback, R.C. Reid, 1987, Estimation of Pure-Component Properties from Group-Contributions, Chemical Engineering Communications, 57, 233-243.

A. Juric, M. Gagro, S. Nikolic, N. Trinajstic, 1992, Molecular topological index: An application in the QSAR study of toxicity of alcohols, Journal of Mathematical Chemistry, 11, 1, 179-186.

R. Koch, 1982, Molecular connectivity and acute toxicity of environmental pollutants, Chemosphere, 11, 9, 925-931.

J. Marrero, R. Gani, 2001, Group-contribution based estimation of pure component properties, Fluid Phase Equilibria, 183-184, 183-208.

Jiří Jaromír Klemeš, Petar Sabev Varbanov and Peng Yen Liew (Editors)
Proceedings of the 24th European Symposium on Computer Aided Process Engineering – ESCAPE 24
June 15-18, 2014, Budapest, Hungary. Copyright © 2014 Elsevier B.V. All rights reserved.

Validation of a New Double-Column System for Heteroazeotropic Batch Distillation by Experiments and Dynamic Simulation

Ferenc Denes[a], Xavier Joulia[b,c], Peter Lang[a*]

[a] *BME Department of Building Service and Process Engineering, H-1111 Budapest, Muegyetem rkp. 3-5, Hungary*
[b] *University of Toulouse, INPT, UPS, Laboratoire de Génie Chimique, 4, allée Emile Monso, F-31432 Toulouse Cedex 4, France*
[c] *CNRS, Laboratoire de Génie Chimique, F-31062 Toulouse, France*
lang@mail.bme.hu

Abstract

The separation of a binary heteroazeotropic mixture (1-butanol – water) by batch distillation is studied in a new Double-Column System (DCS) by pilot plant experiments and dynamic simulation performed with a professional flowsheet simulator. The DCS is operated in closed mode. At the end of the process products of high purity were obtained with high recoveries in the reboilers. However the limited facility of setting accurately the ratio of the reboiler heat duties caused difficulties concerning the optimal operation of the new system.

Keywords: batch heteroazeotropic distillation, closed system, experiment, dynamic simulation

1. Introduction

If the components of a mixture form a heteroazeotrope, or by the addition of an entrainer a heteroazeotrope can be formed, the separation can be performed by heteroazeotropic distillation (HAD). So far the batch heteroazeotropic distillation was applied in the industry only in batch rectifiers (equipped with a decanter, BR) in open operation mode. Different operation modes of the batch HAD and their strategies are presented in the book of Luyben and Chien (2010). The batch HAD is studied experimentally among others by Ooms et al. (2013, ethyl acetate – isooctane by using methanol and acetonitrile as entrainer).

We developed a new batch double-column HAD configuration (double-column system, DCS, Figure 1) operated in closed mode (without continuous product withdrawal), (Denes et al., 2009). The results of feasibility studies and dynamic simulation calculations showed that comparing with the BR significant reduction of the energy demand can be achieved. Then the DCS was experimentally validated for the separation of a binary heteroazeotropic mixture in a simple laboratory glass equipment (Denes et al., 2010). After that the DCS was extended to a generalised double-column system (GDCS, Denes et al., 2012) for the batch HAD separation of binary homoazeotropic mixtures by using entrainer. The GDCS has three further degrees of freedom compared with the DCS (locations of two continuous feedings, reflux ratio in Column β) and is more advantageous for the separation of binary homoazeotropic mixtures with a heterogeneous entrainer.

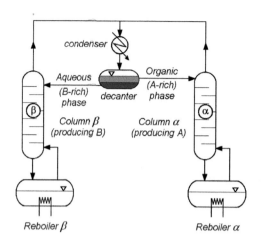

Figure 1. Theoretical scheme of the DCS for the separation of a binary heteroazeotropic mixture

In the next a pilot plant was installed, by which comparing with the laboratory column much more information can be acquired about the process (temperature profiles, pressure drop etc.), and whose operation is more flexible (variable reflux ratio) and appropriate (higher decanter holdup). The goal of this paper is
- to validate the DCS by pilot plant experiments,
- to evaluate the results with dynamic simulation.

2. Pilot plant experiment

2.1. The pilot plant equipment and its operation
The columns (D = 80 mm, H = 4x1 m) of the pilot plant equipment (Figure 2) are filled with structured packing: Sulzer CY (Column α), Kühni Rombopak (Column β). Both columns have an own condenser, reflux divider and aftercooler. Hence both condensates can be refluxed bypassing the decanter, too. The heating medium (oil) is circulated and heated by electricity (maximal performances: $Q_\alpha = 6$ kW, $Q_\beta = 4$ kW). The temperature of the oil entering into the reboiler heating spiral is set.

The charge (of 18.6 °C) contains 1-butanol (A, 7.5 dm^3) and water (B, 9.5 dm^3). Into the reboilers 8.0 dm^3 saturated organic and 9.0 dm^3 aqueous phases are filled. The decanter is filled with heterogeneous liquid (Figure 2). The two columns are operated simultaneously. There are three operational steps:
1. Boiling-up: until the liquid in the reboiler begins to boil.
2. Heating-up: until the vapour arrives at the top of the column.
3. Purification: until the end of the process.

In the boiling-up and heating-up steps both columns are operated under total reflux Since Heater α generates too high vapour flow rate, therefore 60 % of the condensate was directly refluxed in order to avoid the too short residence time in the decanter.
The purification steps of both columns were started at the same time. However, the durations of the boiling-up and heating-up steps were different because of the limited controllability of the reboiler heat duties.

The charge in Reboiler α would have boiled up much earlier than in the other reboiler therefore its heating was strongly reduced until the heating-up of the other column approached to the end (for 76 min). Table 1 shows the lengths of the different operation steps. (The optimal lengths if they are different are in parentheses.) The experiment was finished when either reboiler temperature did not significantly increase more.

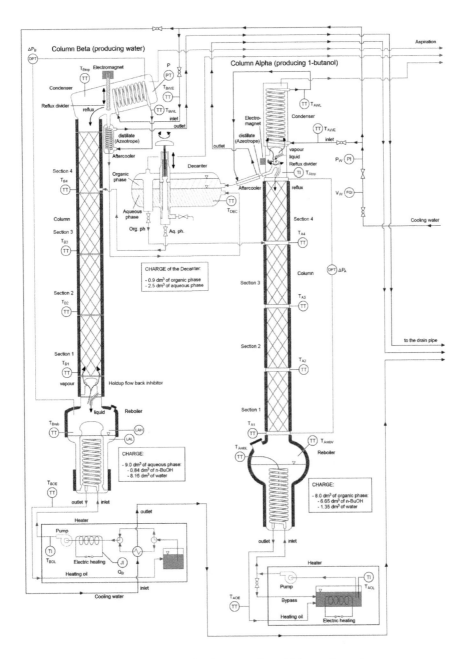

Figure 2. DCS pilot plant equipment for the separation of 1-butanol – water

Table 1. Duration of the different operation steps [min]

Step	Column α		Column β	
	Time at the end	Duration	Time at the end	Duration
Boiling up	148	148 (53)	93	93
Heating-up	175	27	175	82 (63)
Purification	357	182	357	182

2.2. Experimental results

The reboiler temperatures (Figure 3) verify that products of very high purity were obtained at the end of the purification step with very high recoveries: 1-butanol: 99.9 mass%, 7.4 dm^3; water: 99.9 mass%, 9.5 dm^3. At the end of heating-up both reboiler temperatures are near to the azeotropic one.

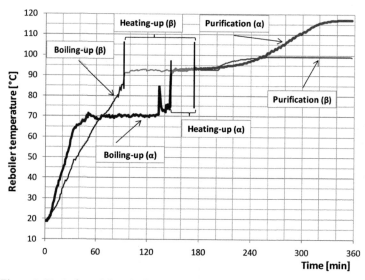

Figure 3. Evolution of the reboiler temperatures (experiment)

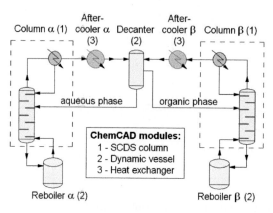

Figure 4. ChemCAD model of the DCS

3. Posterior simulation

3.1. Simulation method

We performed rigorous simulation applying the following simplifying assumptions: theoretical trays, constant volumetric liquid holdup on the trays and in the decanter, negligible vapour holdup. The model equations to be solved are non-linear ODEs (material and heat balances) and non-linear algebraic equations (VLLE, hold-up and physical property models etc.). The phase equilibrium is described by the NRTL model (BIPs, K^{-1}: 215.427 and 1468.34; $\alpha = 0.3634$). For the solution of the above equations the dynamic simulator of ChemCAD 6.4 (CCDCOLUMN) is applied. The model of the pilot plant is shown in Figure 4.

3.2. Input data

The number of theoretical stages of the columns (of holdup 25 cm³/stage) without condenser, decanter and reboiler is estimated to 20. The levels of the liquid phases (of 60 °C) are kept constant in the decanter. The net heat duties of the reboilers (Q_{reb}^{net}) are so chosen to give the same durations of the operation steps as in the experiment (Figure 5).The calculations are started with dry plates. The boiling-up step of Column α was started by 76 minutes later in order to avoid the "waiting period" of the experiment (Figure 5, Table 2).

Table 2. Operation steps in the simulation

No.	1	2	3	4	5
Column α	No heating	Boiling-up		Heating-up of the column	Purification
Column β	Boiling-up			Heating-up of the column	

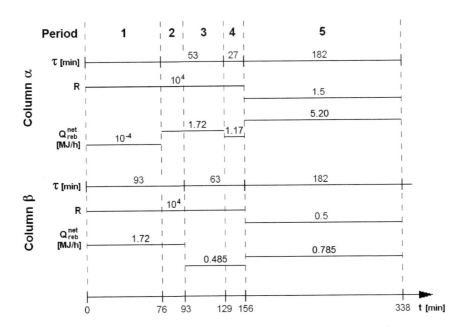

Figure 5. Operational parameters in the different operation steps

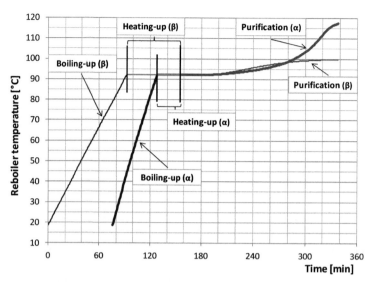

Figure 6. Evolution of the reboiler temperatures (simulation)

3.3. Results

The posterior simulation verified the production of high purity products: 1-butanol: 99.9 mass%, 7.72 dm^3; water: 99.9 mass%, 9.48 dm^3. The product quantities and qualities are in good agreement with those of the experiment. Figure 6 shows the evolution of the reboiler temperatures.

4. Conclusions

The separation of the mixture 1-butanol – water by batch heteroazeotropic distillation is studied in a new closed Double-Column System (DCS) by pilot plant experiments and posterior dynamic simulation with ChemCAD 6.4. At the end of the process products of high purity were obtained in the reboilers with high recoveries. However the experiment highlighted the importance of the accurate control of the reboiler heat duties in order to operate the DCS at optimal conditions and to avoid the loss of time and energy. This is even more important for the GDCS used for the separation of a binary homoazeotropic mixture with a heterogeneous entrainer where the composition of the condensate may get outside the heterogeneous region if the ratio of the heat duties is not appropriate.

References

F. Denes, P. Lang, G. Modla, X. Joulia, 2009, New double column system for heteroazeotropic batch distillation, Computers and Chemical Engineering, 33, 1631-1643.

F. Denes, P. Lang, X. Joulia, 2010, Experimental validation of a new double-column system for heteroazeotropic batch distillation, Distillation and Absorption 2010, IChemE Symposium Series, 289-294.

F. Denes, P. Lang, X. Joulia, 2012, Generalised closed double-column system for batch heteroazeotropic distillation, Separation and Purification Technology, 89, 297-308.

W. L. Luyben, I-L. Chien, 2010, Design and Control of Distillation Systems for Separating Azeotropes, Wiley-VCH, New York, USA.

T. Ooms, S. Vreysena, G. V. Baelena, V. Gerbaud, I. Rodriguez-Donis, 2013, Separation of ethyl acetate–isooctane mixture by heteroazeotropic batch distillation, Chemical Engineering Research and Design, DOI:10.1016/j.cherd.2013.10.010.

Jiří Jaromír Klemeš, Petar Sabev Varbanov and Peng Yen Liew (Editors)
Proceedings of the 24th European Symposium on Computer Aided Process Engineering – ESCAPE 24
June 15-18, 2014, Budapest, Hungary.

MINLP Model for the Synthesis of Heat Exchanger Networks with Handling Pressure of Process Streams

Viviani C. Onishi[a]*, Mauro A. S. S. Ravagnani[a], José A. Caballero[b]

[a]*Department of Chemical Engineering, State University of Maringá, Av. Colombo 5790, Maringá-PR 87020-900, Brazil*
[b]*Department of Chemical Engineering, University of Alicante, Ap Correos 99, Alicante03080, Spain*
viviani.onishi@hotmail.com

Abstract

This paper introduces a new mathematical model for the simultaneous synthesis of heat exchanger networks (HENs), wherein the handling pressure of process streams is used to enhance the heat integration. The proposed approach combines generalized disjunctive programming (GDP) and mixed-integer nonlinear programming (MINLP) formulation, in order to minimize the total annualized cost composed by operational and capital expenses. A multi-stage superstructure is developed for the HEN synthesis, assuming constant heat capacity flow rates and isothermal mixing, and allowing for streams splits. In this model, the pressure and temperature of streams must be treated as optimization variables, increasing further the complexity and difficulty to solve the problem. In addition, the model allows for coupling of compressors and turbines to save energy. A case study is performed to verify the accuracy of the proposed model. In this example, the optimal integration between the heat and work decreases the need for thermal utilities in the HEN design. As a result, the total annualized cost is also reduced due to the decrease in the operational expenses related to the heating and cooling of the streams.

Keywords: optimization, mixed-integer nonlinear programming (MINLP), heat exchanger network (HEN), heat integration, handling pressure.

1. Introduction

Optimizing energy use through the application of more efficient processing technologies is essential to improve the energy conservation in industrial processes (Onishi et al., 2013). The increasing global energy demand allied with the current high cost of energy, and the tightening environmental regulations on gaseous emissions are among the many driving forces behind the need for energy conservation (Razib et al., 2012) and efficiency in processing plants. The synthesis of heat exchanger networks (HENs) has been extensively studied over the past few decades (Huang and Karimi, 2012), due to the importance of thermal integration in the reduction of energy consumption and efficient energy usage (Ravagnani and Silva, 2012). Amongst the major research areas, mathematical programming stands out for treating the HEN design as an optimization problem, in order to obtain an optimal network in economic and thermodynamic terms. Although the simultaneous methods are, generally, more difficult to implement and solve, it can lead to larger economic advantages (Kamath et al., 2012).

Handling pressure is extremely important in many industrial plants, such as oil refineries and cryogenic processes, due to being responsible for large energy consumption. Despite the numerous efforts to solve the problem of HEN synthesis, few studies related to processes optimization involving pressure manipulation and heat integration of streams are available in the literature. Aspelund et al. (2007) proposed an approach based on Extended Pinch Analysis and Design (ExPAnD) to study the expansion of streams at sub-ambient conditions. In their work, only a graphical interpretation of pressure exergy are considered to minimize energy requirements of the system. Wechsung et al.(2011) presented a model for the HEN synthesis with streams that are subject to compression and expansion. The authors combine pinch analysis, exergy analysis and mathematical programming in a formulation to minimize the total irreversibility of the process. However, the costs involved in the network design as well as the possibility of coupling equipment are not evaluated, only the aspects related to heuristics and exergy analisys are taken into account during the HEN synthesis.

This paper introduces a new mathematical model for the simultaneous HENs synthesis, wherein the handling pressure of process streams is used to enhance the heat integration. The proposed model combines generalized disjunctive programming (GDP) and mixed-integer nonlinear programming (MINLP) formulation, in order to minimize the total annualized cost composed by operational and capital expenses. The superstructure is based on the model of Yee and Grossmann (1990), allowing for stream splits and assuming constant heat capacity flow rates and isothermal mixing. However, the streams pressure and temperature should be treated as optimization variables. In addition, the model allows for coupling of compressors and turbines, increasing further its complexity. A case study is performed to verify the accuracy of the proposed model. The results indicate that optimal integration between the heat and work decreases the total annualized cost, due to reduced need for thermal utilities in the HEN design.

2. Problem statement

Given a set of hot and cold process streams with a known supply state—temperature and pressure—and a target state in which some streams have pressures that differ from the inlet conditions, energy supplies for heating and cooling, and pressure manipulation equipment, with their respective costs. The main objective of the model is to synthetize an optimal HEN with handling pressure of streams that minimizes the total annualized cost, considering the operational expenses and the capital investment in the various units of the network. In the proposed approach, some flows should follow a specific route of expansion and compression via turbines and compressors. This route is selected based on the work of Wechsung et al. (2011), wherein the "plus–minus" principle is used to identify the best way of pressure manipulation of streams so that the energy requirements may be reduced. Thus, considering a maximum of three pressure manipulations, the hot streams can potentially be cooled, compressed, cooled, expanded, heated, compressed and cooled. Similarly, the cold streams can be heated, expanded, heated, compressed, cooled, expanded and heated. The processes of streams expansion and compression are formulated as an isentropic process, through the introduction of a constant efficiency factor to model real processes. In addition, the proposed model allows for coupling of turbines and compressors as long as the cost-benefit ratio is respected in order to save energy. This fact, added to the high nonlinearity and non-convexity of the cost correlations, confer an even higher degree of complexity on the model. For simplification, all streams should behave as ideal gases.

3. MINLP-based model

The proposed model is developed in generalized disjunctive programming (GDP) and mixed integer non-linear programming (MINLP) formulation. The mathematical model is based on the MINLP model for HEN design presented by Yee and Grossmann (1990), assuming isothermal mixing and constant heat capacity flow rates, and allowing for streams splits. The superstructure is represented by stages according to temperatures. In each of these stages, a hot stream can exchange heat with all cold streams, and vice versa. The number of stages is equal to the maximum number of possible heat exchanges between hot and cold streams. Moreover, heaters and coolers are allocated in the ends of the streams.

The main difference between the proposed model and the Yee and Grossmann (1990) superstructure is that, in this model, the streams are subjected to handling pressure, and they must be connected to the HEN through turbines and compressors. Consequently, the outlet temperatures of the HEN should correspond to the temperatures of the inlet streams in the respective pressure equipment. Thus, the process conditions (i.e., stream temperature and pressure) are considered as unknown variables that must be optimized in order to obtain an optimal design with a minimal cost. In consequence, this proposed approach is significantly more complex than the standard problem of heat integration as formulated by Yee and Grossmann (1990). In fact, the streams can temporarily change their identity; as a result, a hot stream can behave as a cold stream and, analogously, a cold stream can behave like a hot stream. Furthermore, some process streams can operate as thermal utilities, mitigating problems related to excess or deficit of energy in the system. Therefore, there is no clear distinction among hot and cold streams, nor between thermal utilities and streams. Moreover, the heat exchange among parts of the same stream that assume other identity, like as the placement of thermal utilities between stages of expansion and compression should be forbidden, through the implementation of constraints in the model that increases further the difficult to solve it. As the conventional problem of HENs synthesis is extended to include streams subjected to handling pressure, a operator for pressure manipulation and a GDP-based operator for the coupling of compressors and turbines are added in the formulation:

$$
\begin{bmatrix}
y_{c,e} \\
WC_c = WE_e \\
C_{electricity} = CE \cdot WC_c = 0
\end{bmatrix}
$$

Using the big-M reformulation, the disjunction may be expressed as follows:

$$WC_c - WE_e \leq M_1\left(1 - y_{c,e}\right)$$

$$WC_c - WE_e \geq -M_1\left(1 - y_{c,e}\right)$$

$$C_{electricity} \leq M_2\left(1 - y_{c,e}\right) \tag{1}$$

$$C_{electricity} \geq CE \cdot WC_c - M_2 \cdot y_{c,e}$$

In which M is a positive parameter that is large enough to validate the formulation (1). The parameter M_1 is calculated as the difference between the upper bound of the expansion work and the lower bound of the compression work, and the parameter M_2 is calculated as the difference between the upper and lower bounds of the electricity cost.

The superstructure is written in GAMS and solved with the SBB solver. As the model is highly nonlinear and non-convex, it is very difficult to solve it to global optimality with the available global solvers due the large CPU time required. Nevertheless, the use of a simple branch and bound based solver, such as the SBB solver, allows obtaining a solution near the global optimum. To solve the model, one must impose limits (i.e., upper and lower bounds) on all variables, and provide initial values with physical meaning.

4. Case study

A case study is performed to verify the applicability of the developed MINLP model, for obtaining an optimal HEN synthesis with handling pressure of streams at sub-ambient conditions. The example was extracted from Wechsung et al. (2011), considering a two-fold flow in all streams. One hot stream H1 and one cold stream C1 are at constant pressure, whereas a second cold stream C2 is expanded from 0.4 to 0.1 MPa. The pressure manipulation route for C2 includes the stages of expansion, compression and expansion, and requires heat integration in the HEN between each of these stages. Thus, C2 behaves as C3 after the first expansion, as H2 after compression, and finally, as C4 after the last expansion. The heat capacity and flow rates of all streams are known constants. The problem data are presented in Table 1. A superstructure with four stages, and the possibility of stream splits is considered for the HEN synthesis.The unknown inlet temperatures can vary between 103–373 K, the pressure of the C3 stream is restricted to 0.1–0.4 MPa, and the pressure of the H2 stream is restricted to 0.1–0.6 MPa. The individual heat transfer coefficients for all streams are maintained at 0.1 kW/m^2K, and a hot and cold utility coefficient of 1.0 kW/m^2K is considered. An annualized capital cost factor of $f = 0.18$ (10 % interest rate over 8 years) is assumed. In addition, $T^h_U = 383$ K, $T^c_U = 93$ K, and $\Delta T_{min} = 4$ K. The HEN synthesis considers the possibility of coupling equipment with an efficiency of $\eta = 0.7$ and $\kappa = 1.51$ for both the turbine and the compressor.

Firstly, the HEN is designed without handling pressure of stream C2, i.e., all streams are at constant pressure. The optimal HEN is obtained with two heat exchangers ($A = 42.47$ m^2, $Q = 77.87$ kW; and $A = 95.88$ m^2, $Q = 371,64$ kW), two heaters with areas of $A = 20.33$ m^2($Q = 222.14$ kW), and $A = 19.73$ m^2 ($Q = 223.36$ kW) located at the ends of streams C1 and C2, and one cooler placed at the end of H1 ($A = 102.48$ m^2, $Q = 540.50$ kW). In this case, no compression and/or expansion work is produced in the network. The total annualized cost of the HEN with this configuration is 866,171 US$y^{-1}, in which 690,634 US$y^{-1}derives from the hot and cold services, and 175,537 US$y^{-1} is related to the capital investment in equipment. Secondly, the proposed MINLP model is used to solve the problem.The results indicate that the optimal HEN is obtained with four heat exchangers ($A = 90.39$ m^2, $Q = 171.61$ kW; $A = 287.51$ m^2, $Q = 506.47$ kW; A

Table 1. Problem data for the case study.

Stream	F_sCp_s(kW/K)	$T_{s,in}$(K)	$T_{s,out}$(K)	p_s(MPa)
H1	6.0	288	123	0.1
C1	4.0	213	288	0.1
C2	3.4	113	-	0.4
C3	3.4	-	-	-
H2	3.4	-	-	-
C4	3.4	-	288	0.1

Cost data: $CC = 1,000$ US$y^{-1} kW; $CE = 455.04$ US$y^{-1} kW; $CH = 337$ US$y^{-1} kW

= 134.79 m², Q = 179.86 kW; and A = 176.94 m², Q = 300 kW), one cooler located in the end of H1 (A = 25.57m², Q = 132.07 kW), and one heater with area of 7.74 m² (Q = 141.99 kW) placed at the end of stream C4. In this second case, two turbines and one compressor are also required, in which the expander EX1 is coupled to CO1 ($WC = WE$ = 108.13 kW); therefore, the cost of electricity is zero. The expansion work produced by EX2 is equal to 104.92 kW. The results obtained for the decision variables and optimal HEN configuration are presented in Figure 1. The total annualized cost of the HEN with this configuration is 603,844 US$y^{-1} (composed by $C_{operational}$ = 179,924 US$y^{-1} and $C_{capital}$ = 423,920 US$y^{-1}), which represents 30 % of savings in the total annualized cost of the HEN over that obtained in the first case, i.e., without pressure manipulation of the stream C2. The mathematical model has 322 continuous variables, 25 discrete variables, and 460 constraints with 1,411 Jacobian elements (non-zeros), of which 200 are nonlinear. The CPU time is 57 s with the SBB solver under the software GAMS (version 24.0.2). The problem was solved using a personal computer with an Intel Core 2 Duo 2.40 GHz processor and 3.00 GB RAM running Windows 7 Ultimate.

5. Conclusions

A new MINLP model for HEN synthesis with handling pressure of streams is proposed to optimize the integration between heat and work. The developed approach, involves generalized disjunctive programming (GDP) and mixed-integer nonlinear programming (MINLP) formulation. The conventional HEN synthesis problem is expanded to harness energy from streams that undergo pressure manipulation. As a result, intermediate pressures and temperatures are treated as unknown variables that must be optimized. The streams subjected to handling pressure should be connected to the HEN via compressors and turbines. The hot and/or cold streams should follow a specific pressure manipulation route to reduce the energy requirements. The possibility of coupled equipment is studied to optimize the HEN design by minimizing the total annualized cost, composed by operational and capital expenses of the network.

The results indicate that the handling pressure of streams enhances the heat integration, decreasing significantly the amount of necessary thermal utilities in the HEN design.

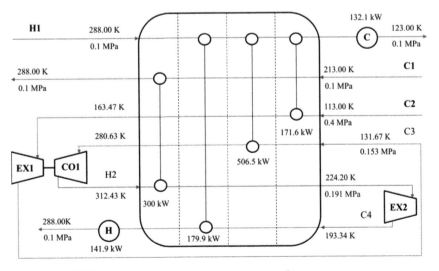

Figure 1. Optimal HEN configuration obtained for the case study.

Consequently, the total annualized cost is reduced in 30 % due the diminution of operational expenses related to heating and cooling of process flows. The total annualized cost also decreases in 8 % when compressors and turbines are coupled, to allow the expansion work to satisfy the energy requirement of the compressors. In this case, the operational expenses associated to electricity are zero. In the example, up to three pressure manipulations of streams are allowed. However, a larger number of pressure changes can easily be implemented in the model through the use of a larger quantity of compressors and turbines in each stream subjected to pressure manipulation.

Nomenclature

A	heat exchanger area	WE	expansion work
C	cost	WC	compression work
CC	cost parameter for cooling	y	binary variable that define the coupling equipment
CE	cost parameter for electricity		
CH	cost parameter for heating	η	isentropic efficiency
Cp	heat capacity	κ	polytrophic exponent
F	streams flow rate		
p	pressure	Subscripts	
Q	heat duty	e	expander (turbine)
T	temperature	c	compressor
ΔT_{min}	minimal approximation of temperature	s	streams
		U	utility

Acknowledgments

This study was financed by the Brazilian agency "Coordenação de Aperfeiçoamento de Pessoal de Nível Superior – CAPES" (process nº10758/12-7), and the Spanish Ministry of Science and Innovation and Ministry of Economy and Competitiveness (project CTQ2012-37039-C02-02).

Viviani C. Onishi also has the following affiliation: CAPES Foundation, Ministry of Education of Brazil, Brasília-DF 7004020, Brazil.

References

A. Aspelund, D.O. Berstad, T. Gundersen, 2007, An extended pinch analysis and design procedure utilizing pressure based exergy for subambient cooling, Applied Thermal Engineering, 27, 2633–2649.

A. Wechsung, A. Aspelund, T. Gundersen, P.I. Barton, 2011, Synthesis of heat exchanger networks at subambient conditions with compression and expansion of process streams, Process Systems Engineering, 57, 8, 2090–2108.

K.F. Huang, I.A. Karimi, 2012, Heat exchanger network synthesis using a hyperstructure of stagewise stream superstructures, Computer Aided Chemical Engineering, 31, 1552–1556.

M.A.A.S. Ravagnani, A.P. Silva, 2012, Retrofit of heat exchanger networks including the detailed equipment design, Computer Aided Chemical Engineering, 31, 235–239.

M.S. Razib, M.M.F. Hasan, I.A. Karimi, 2012, Preliminary synthesis of work exchange networks, Computers and Chemical Engineering, 37, 262–277.

R.S. Kamath, L.T. Biegler, I.E. Grossmann, 2012, Modeling multistream heat exchangers with and without phase changes for simultaneous optimization and heat integration, AIChE Journal, 58, 190–204.

T.F. Yee, I.E.Grossmann, 1990, Simultaneous optimization models for heat integration. II. Heat exchanger network synthesis, Computers and Chemical Engineering, 14, 10, 1165–1184.

V.C. Onishi, M.A.S.S. Ravagnani, J.A. Caballero, 2013, Mathematical programming model for heat exchanger design through optimization of partial objectives, Energy Conversion and Management, 74, 60–69.

Jiří Jaromír Klemeš, Petar Sabev Varbanov and Peng Yen Liew (Editors)
Proceedings of the 24th European Symposium on Computer Aided Process Engineering – ESCAPE 24
June 15-18, 2014, Budapest, Hungary. Copyright © 2014 Elsevier B.V. All rights reserved.

Modelling of an Amine Based CO_2 Absorption Plant: an Alternative Approach through the Identification of the Number of Stages

Roberto Baratti[a], Massimiliano Errico[a*], Daniele Pinna[a], Paolo Deiana[b], Marcella Porru[a]

[a]Dipartimento Ingegneria Meccanica, Chimica e dei Materiali, Università degli Sudi di Cagliari , Via Marengo 2, 09123 Cagliari, Italy
[b]ENEA Centro Ricerche Casaccia - S.P. 081, Via Anguillarese 301, 00123 S. Maria di Galeria, Roma, Italy
massimiliano.errico@dimcm.unica.it

Abstract

In the last decades, a huge number of studies on carbon dioxide removal have been presented in the literature. The non-equilibrium nature of the process involves an accurate definition of the parameters' correlations and of the model's assumptions. One of the most important assumptions when developing a process model is the definition of the number of discretization points. In this paper an alternative methodology has been presented for the definition of the number of stages of the absorption column in order to fit all the transport phenomena taking part in the carbon dioxide removal process. Then, it was developed a rigorous model of the absorption unit and finally implemented in Aspen Custom Modeler® environment to manage with a high level of complexity. The results obtained demonstrate that the number of stages is fundamental for the correct representation of the process and its incorrect evaluation could lead to huge errors in the prediction of the performance of the plant.

Keywords: carbon dioxide capture, process modelling, number of stages definition

1. Introduction

Considering the possible relation between climate changes and the anthropogenic carbon dioxide (CO_2) emission, carbon's capture represents one of the most challenging topics for the international scientific community. Indeed, according to ICPP (2007), CO_2 consists in the 57 % of the total greenhouse gas emitted in the atmosphere. As results of the data published by IEA (2012), the 41 % of the world CO_2 emissions come from the electricity and heat sector and the 21 % from the industry sector. In order to respect the environmental constrains and to minimize the costs of plants integrations needed, the sectors aforementioned are focusing in developing a strategy for the reduction of CO_2 emissions.

In the current state of art, post-combustion carbon capture and storage(CCS) technology based on chemical absorption with alkanolamine solutions is considered one of the most reliable options for a mid-term full scale application due to the possibility to be implemented in retrofitting of pre-existing power plants and for the experience gained in gas sweetening (Posch and Haider, 2013).

In this work a post-combustion CCS plant has been designed to purify the flue gases coming from an ultrasupercritic (USC) Power Plant of 250 MWe capacity. The carbon dioxide removal plant consists in an absorption and stripping unit. In the absorption unit the transfer flow of CO_2 from the gas to the liquid phase is enhanced by the chemical reactions with a 30 %wt of monoethanolamine (MEA) aqueous solution. This solvent is then regenerated in the stripping unit.

2. Number of Stage Analysis

It is a very common practice to use the concept of equilibrium stage when absorption or stripping units are modelled. This is reliable when a very close contact between the phases is realized, together with a residence time long enough to consider the outlet streams in thermodynamic equilibrium. Anyway, this approach seems to be inadequate in particular situations characterized by component's diffusion, reaction and phase changing as considered in this specific case.

In the present work a dynamic model of the absorber has been developed using the mass transfer calculation approach. The two-film theory was used to describe the segments defined to discretize both units, the ENRTL thermodynamic model has been selected to describe the CO_2-H_2O-MEA chemical system and the kinetics of the carbammate and carbonate formation have been added (Kvamsdal et al., 2009). MEA, CO_2 and water are the only components considered in both liquid and vapour phases. Commonly, the number of stages is defined in steady state simulations by a sensitivity analysis focused on the stage minimization for a fixed carbon dioxide removal or for the target concentration in the clean gas coming out from the absorber. Although the variation of the number of stage has a limited effect whether it is considered only the total amount of carbon dioxide removed from the flue gas, it was proved that this type of approach can lead to misleading results in dynamic modelling. Thus, the column height was discretized considering a different number of segments and the relative differences in the temperature and composition profiles were registered in Figures 1 and 2. At this point, it has been found that above 300 stages the profiles differences cannot be appreciate. On the bases of this, a reference case of 300 stages was fixed as a basis for comparison to define the differences between the several options considered. A solution is considered valid if the temperature profile has a 1 °C maximum deviation from the reference case.

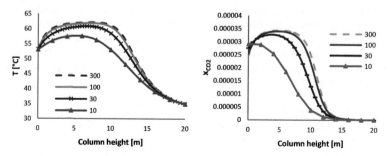

Figure 1. Effect of the number of stages on absorber's temperature profile (left) and CO_2 concentration (right).

The initial and final temperature of the liquid phase, for both absorber and stripper unit, is not influenced by the number of stages. Otherwise the absorber's composition profile, depends on the number of segments because it is evident a different value for the outlet composition of CO_2. Thus, it means that the number of stages influences both the steady-state and the dynamic simulation. On the other hand, the difference of the calculated values in the several profiles, especially in the mid region of the column, demonstrates that the dynamic model is closely dependent to this parameter. For this reason, it is required an accurate estimation in order to avoid mistakes in its further applications.

In addition Table 1, shown below, reported the maximum temperature difference along the column calculated varying the number of stages. According to the results, it was decided to set hundred segments to develop the dynamic model.

3. Mathematical model

Once the number of segments was defined the mathematical model has been developed applying the conservation laws to a small element of volume of the column and then allowing the dimension of the volume tending to zero. In the used notation the "zero point" corresponds to the bottom of the column.

The Peclet Number, in both liquid and vapour phase, has been calculated as defined in Eq. (1).

$$N_{Pe_i,j} = u_i d / h_i \varepsilon \, D^i_{j,mix}$$ (1)

Where u_i is the velocity for the i-th phase [m/s], d the diameter [m], h_i the hold-up, ε is the void fraction [m³/m³] and $D^i_{j,mix}$ is the molecular diffusivity for the j-th component in the i-th phase. The diffusional contribution in the all balances was been neglected since a N_{Pe} of 10^7 and 10^5 for the liquid and vapour phase was respectively obtained. The model has been built considering (i) Plug Flow regime for each phase, (ii) non-ideal behaviour in liquid and gas mixture, (iii)

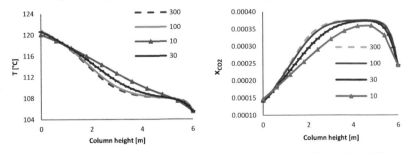

Figure 2. Effect of the number of stages on stripper's temperature profile (left) and CO_2 concentration (right).

Table 1. Maximum of temperature difference

Unit \ Stage	10	30	50	75	100	120	150	200
Absorber	8.27	3.28	2.05	1.36	0.93	0.77	0.56	0.35
Stripper	3.00	1.59	0.98	0.65	0.42	0.32	0.22	-

thermodynamic equilibrium in gas/liquid interface, (iv) linear pressure profile and (v) no energy transfer to the environment.

The mass balances are reported in Eq. (2) and Eq. (3) for liquid and vapour phase respectively.

$$\varepsilon h_L S \frac{\partial \rho_L}{\partial t} = \frac{\partial (L\,PM_{MIX})}{\partial z} - S \frac{\partial}{\partial z}\left[\rho_L D^L_{i,mix}\frac{\partial \omega_{L,i}}{\partial z}\right] + \sum_{i=1}^{NC}\frac{(N_i M_i)}{dz} \tag{2}$$

$$\varepsilon h_V S \frac{\partial \rho_V}{\partial t} = -\frac{\partial (V\,PM_{MIX})}{\partial z} + S \frac{\partial}{\partial z}\left[\rho_V D^V_{i,mix}\frac{\partial \omega_{V,i}}{\partial z}\right] - \sum_{i=1}^{NC}\frac{(N_i M_i)}{dz} \tag{3}$$

Where L and V are the liquid and the vapour molar flow [kmol/s] respectively, ω represents the mass fraction in the respective phase, ρ is the mass density [kg/m^3], M the molecular weight [kg/m^3], N is the mole transfer rate [kmol/s] between phases and S is the cross sectional area of the column [m^2].

Eq. (4) reports the component balance for the liquid phase and Eq. (5) for the vapour phase.

$$\varepsilon h_L S \rho_L^m \frac{\partial x_i}{\partial t} = \frac{\partial (L\,x_i)}{\partial z} - S \frac{\partial}{\partial z}\left[\rho_L^m D^L_{i,mix}\frac{\partial x_i}{\partial z}\right] + \frac{N_i}{dz} + \frac{\varepsilon h_L}{dz}R_i \tag{4}$$

$$\varepsilon h_V S \rho_V^m \frac{\partial y_i}{\partial t} = -\frac{\partial (V\,y_i)}{\partial z} + S \frac{\partial}{\partial z}\left[\rho_V^m D^V_{i,mix}\frac{\partial y_i}{\partial z}\right] - \frac{N_i}{dz} \tag{5}$$

Where x and y are the liquid and the mole fraction respectively, ρ^m is the molar density [kmol/m^3] and R the mole production/consumption by reaction [kmol/s]. Finally the energy balances are reported in Eq.(6) and Eq.(7) for both phases.

$$\varepsilon h_L S \rho_L^m C_{p,L}\frac{\partial T_L}{\partial t} = \frac{\partial (L\,H_L)}{\partial z} - S \frac{\partial}{\partial z}\left[k\frac{\partial T_L}{\partial z}\right] +$$
$$+\left[h_{L/V}a_w(T_L - T_V) - \sum_{j=1}^{NR}\left(\frac{(-\Delta H_{R,j})N_j}{dz}\right) + \sum_{i=1}^{NC}\left(\frac{(\Delta H_{v,i})N_i}{dz}\right)\right] \tag{6}$$

$$\varepsilon h_V S \rho_V^m C_{p,V}\frac{\partial T_V}{\partial t} = -\frac{\partial (V\,H_V)}{\partial z} + S \frac{\partial}{\partial z}\left[k\frac{\partial T_V}{\partial z}\right] - \left[h_{L/V}a_w(T_L - T_V) + \sum_{i=1}^{NC}\left(\frac{(\Delta H_{v,i})N_i}{dz}\right)\right] \tag{7}$$

Where T is the temperature [K], H is the molar enthalpy [kJ/kmol], k is the thermal conductivity [kW/m K], a_w is the wetted packing area [m^2/m^3], C_p is the specific heat [kJ/kmol K], $h_{l/v}$ is the transfer coefficient between the liquid and vapour phase [kW/m^{2}K], ΔH_R is the enthalpy of reaction [kJ/kmol] and ΔH_v is the heat of vaporization [kJ/kmol]. Mass transfer coefficients and interfacial packing area have been calculated using the Onda's method according to Lawal et al. (2009).

The equilibrium relation rate has been modelled as reported in Eq.(8).

$$r = \frac{K}{K_{eq}}\left(K_{eq} - \prod_{i}^{NC}C_i\right) \tag{8}$$

The larger K, the less is the deviation from equilibrium. In order to consider that the kinetic reactions are mainly developed in the liquid film, the liquid transfer coefficient was multiplied by the enhancement factor, derived according to Harun et al. (2012). The heat transfer coefficients were calculated using Chilton and Colburn analogy and the liquid hold-up was taken as the ratio of the liquid volume to the column volume, calculated with the correlation proposed by Billet and Schultes according to Kvamsdal and Hillestad (2012). The phase equilibrium of the volatile components at the interface was modelled using Henry's law coefficient for CO_2 and the saturation vapour pressure for water and MEA. Consequently, it is possible to calculate the mole transfer fluxes for each phase and finally the combination among (i) the fluxes equality and (ii) interfacial phase equilibriums have been solved to get the interfacial compositions and fluxes value. The system was finally scaled to simplify the convergence and implemented in Aspen Custom Modeler®. The Central Finite Difference (CFD2) method used to discretize the spatial derivate. In the steady state run the solution was found just by solving a Non-Linear Algebraic Equation system using the Hybrid's method with residual as convergence criterion. The results obtained are shown in Figure 3 and Figure 4 for liquid, vapour composition and temperature profiles.

The amount of CO_2 in the flue gas is absorbed along the column, at the same time some of the MEA vaporize from the liquid to the vapour phase. In the liquid phase the CO_2 absorbed, reacts with MEA generating the carbammate. The temperature in the down-coming solvent increases as the CO_2 is absorbed in the solvent, with the consequent water vaporization. The colder solvent feed in the top of the column causes water condensation. The resulting temperature profiles along the column present a bulge which location and magnitude might affect the absorber performance when it is located in the middle, whereas seems not to have any effect when it is located in the top or in the bottom of the column (Kvamsdal and Rochelle, 2008)

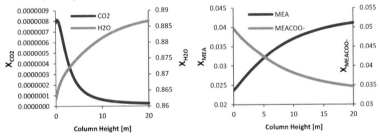

Figure 3. Liquid composition profile in the absorber.

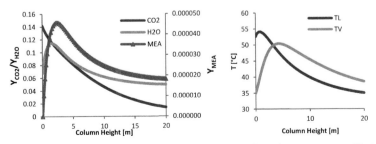

Figure 4. Vapour composition profile in the absorber (left) and temperature profile in the absorber (right).

4. Conclusions

CO_2 removing process via absorption with MEA represents a concrete solution for both new plant design and power plant retrofitting, necessary to accomplish the stringent environmental targets. Disposing of reliable tools, essentials for the economic performance evaluation of the entire production, it is possible to analyse and optimise the process.

In the present work the influence of the number of stage on the dynamic model of the absorption and stripping unit has been analysed. The 300 stage profile was used as reference to evaluate the composition and temperature profile one hundred stages is the suggested value for an accurate representation of the process. Although difficulty have been met in the development of the mass transfer model, cause of several relation are present in the literature, a dynamic model with suitable level of complexity for the absorber unit has been developed using Aspen Custom Modeler®. The results obtained reproduce the correct behaviour of all variables, but it put the basis for further optimization with the introduction of a control system as well.

References

N. Harun, T. Nittaya, P. Douglas, E. Croiset, L. A. Ricardez-Sandoval, 2012, Dynamic simulation of MEA absorption process for CO2 capture from power plants, International Journal of Greenhouse Gas Control, 10, 295-309.

IEA-International Energy Agency, 2012, CO_2 emissions from fuel combustion, Paris, France.

IPCC, 2007, Climate Change 2007: Mitigation of Climate Change, Cambridge University Press, Cambridge, United Kingdom and New York, NY, USA.

H. M. Kvamsdal, M. Hillestad, 2012, Selection of model parameter correlations in a rate-based CO_2 absorber model aimed for process simulation, International Journal of Greenhouse Gas Control, 11, 11-20.

H. M. Kvamsdal, J. P. Jakobsen, K. A. Hoff, 2009, Dynamic modeling and simulation of a CO2 absorber column for post-combustion CO_2 capture, Chemical Engineering and Processing, 48, 135-144.

H. M. Kvamsdal, G. Rochelle, 2008, Effects of the temperature bulge in CO_2 absorption from flue gas by aqueous monoethanolamine, Industrial and Engineering Chemistry Research, 47,867-875.

A. Lawal, M. Wang, P. Stephenson, H. Yeung, 2009, Dynamic modelling of CO2 absorption for post combustion capture in coal-fired power plants, Fuel, 88, 2455-2462.

S. Posch, M. Haider, 2013, Dynamic modeling of CO_2 absorption from coal-fired power plants into an aqueous monoethanolamine solution, Chemical Engineering Research and Design, 91, 977-987.

Jiří Jaromír Klemeš, Petar Sabev Varbanov and Peng Yen Liew (Editors)
Proceedings of the 24th European Symposium on Computer Aided Process Engineering – ESCAPE 24
June 15-18, 2014, Budapest, Hungary. Copyright © 2014 Elsevier B.V. All rights reserved.

Optimal Superstructure-Based Design and Synthesis of Hydrocarbon Biorefinery via Fast Pyrolysis, Hydrogen Production and Hydroprocessing Pathway

Qiao Zhang, Jian Gong, Fengqi You*

Northwestern University, 2145 Sheridan Rd., Evanston, IL, 60208, USA
you@northwestern.edu

Abstract

This paper is concerned with the process design and synthesis of hydrocarbon biorefinery under economic and environmental considerations. A superstructure is developed that consists of fast pyrolysis, bio-crude collection, hydroprocessing, and hydrogen production sections. Multiple process alternatives are included in the superstructure for process optimization. Three hydrotreating feed options with different bio-crude ratios and hydrotreating catalysts are placed; natural gas steam reforming, bio-crude steam reforming and biomass gasification are employed for hydrogen generation. A bi-criteria mixed integer nonlinear programming (MINLP) model is proposed to maximize the economic performance measured by the net present value (NPV) and minimize the environmental impact quantified by global warming potential (GWP). The bi-criteria MINLP model is solved with the ε-constraint method, and the resulting Pareto curve reveals the trade-off between the economic and environmental behaviour of the process. The two "good choice" optimal designs indicate a unit cost of $3.43 and $5.26 per gallon of gasoline equivalent (GGE), corresponding a net greenhouse emission of 1.95 and 2.04 kg CO2-eq/GGE, respectively.

Keywords: superstructure, hydrocarbon biorefinery, fast pyrolysis, hydroprocessing, MINLP.

1. Introduction

Petroleum and its chemical derivatives is environmentally unfriendly and becoming a diminishing energy resource. Among all currently available renewable energy alternatives, biofuels, especially hydrocarbon biofuels, emerge as the most promising near-term solution to the increasing environmental concerns. Various pathways for the production of hydrocarbon biofuels were proposed and improved by researchers in the past decades, among which the pyrolysis pathway is recognized as a promising option. Fast pyrolysis (Jones et al., 2009) is a thermal process that rapidly heats biomass to around 500 °C in the absence of oxygen and cools the gaseous products quickly to simultaneously obtain biogas, bio-crude oil and char. Martin and Grossmann (2011) investigated the design of the bioethanol production from switchgrass via gasification pathways. Gabriel and EI-Halwagi (2013) recently studied the optimal bioethanol plant capacity, configuration and operating conditions based on the existing technologies. To the best of our knowledge, few works ever focused on the optimal economic performance as well as environmental footprint of a hydrocarbon biorefinery via fast pyrolysis, hydrogen production and hydroprocessing pathways simultaneously.

In this paper, we develop a superstructure for the design and synthesis of the hydrocarbon biorefinery through fast pyrolysis and hydroprocessing pathway. The process consists of four major sections: fast pyrolysis, bio-crude collection, hydroprocessing, and hydrogen production. Potential technology alternatives are considered in the superstructure. For hydroprocessing, three types of technologies with different catalysts are considered to produce gasoline and diesel; for hydrogen production, we consider three alternatives: natural gas steam reforming, bio-crude steam reforming and biomass gasification. A mixed integer nonlinear programming model for the optimization of the superstructure-based biorefinery is established and solved. The objective of the MINLP model is to simultaneously maximize the net present value (NPV) and minimize the global warming potential (GWP) subject to mass balance, energy balance, economic analysis and environmental evaluation constraints. The ε-constraint method is introduced to make trade-off between NPV and GWP, and then generate Pareto-optimal solutions that constitute the Pareto curve. The novelties of this work are summarized below:

> A novel superstructure developed for the sustainable design and operation of hydrocarbon biorefinery based on fast pyrolysis and hydroprocessing
> A bi-criteria MINLP model simultaneously maximizing the economic performance and minimizing environmental impact of the hydrocarbon biorefinery according to life cycle optimization framework
> Insights and suggestions for future developments based on the resulting Pareto optimal curve, optimal process configuration, cost and emission profile, etc.

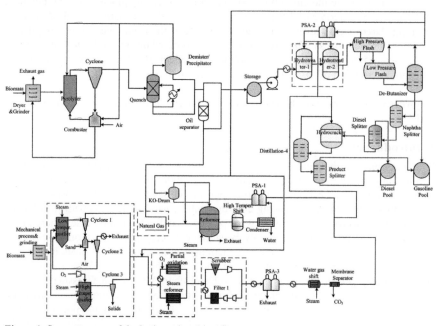

Figure 1. Superstructure of the hydrocarbon biorefinery.

2. Process Description

The process superstructure for the optimal design of hydrocarbon biorefinery through fast pyrolysis and hydroprocessing is shown in Figure 1. Four major sections, including fast pyrolysis, bio-crude collection, hydroprocessing and hydrogen production emphasized by dashed rectangles, are employed. Firstly, the harvested biomass is dehydrated and grounded to small particles. The pre-treated biomass then enters the pyrolyzer where it is converted into a tri-phase mixture. After separation by a cyclone, a quench and a demister, the biogas and solids are recycled. Meanwhile, the remaining bio-crude product is sent to the following section. Given that water soluble oil in the bio-crude oil is able to produce hydrogen through steam reforming, we consider three options for the hydrotreating feed:(1) the bio-crude is fully utilized for hydroprocessing and cobalt-molybdenum (Co-Mo) is chosen as the hydrotreating catalyst; (2) part of water soluble oil is used for hydrogen production and the rest goes to hydroprocessing, in which palladium on carbon (Pd-C) is chosen as the catalyst; (3) apply similar conditions to (2), except that nickel molybdenum (Ni-Mo) is chosen as the catalyst. After hydrotreating, the stabilized bio-crude is separated by consecutive splitters and distillation columns and gasoline range products are directly harvested. The long chain hydrocarbons are sent to the hydrocracker to be broken down into gasoline and diesel range products. Hydrogen is produced by one of the following three technologies: send a natural gas feed into a steam reformer, a high temperature shift reactor, a condenser and a pressure swing adsorption (PSA) successively; apply the same process to a bio-crude feed; prepare an extra biomass feed for gasification, cyclone separation, tar reforming, gas clean-up, PSA, water gas shift and membrane separation successively. For gasification conditions, we provide two options: "low-temperature gasifier + hot clean-up" and "high-temperature gasifier + cool clean-up". Also, the tar reforming step includes steam reforming and partial oxidation as alternatives. Note that the selections of hydroprocessing feedstock options and hydrogen production options are not independent. When (1) is selected as the feed of hydrotreating, the hydrogen can be produced from natural gas steam reforming or biomass gasification. Otherwise, hydrogen must be derived from bio-crude steam reforming.

3. Model formulation

A bi-criteria MINLP mathematical model is formulated for the superstructure optimization (Gebreslassie et al., 2013b). For mass balance constraints, the separation operations are modeled by linear mass conservation relationship of each species while chemical reaction units are modeled by atomic balance and product distribution. The energy constraints consist of steam and electricity consumption and generation. The economic constraints quantify annualized investment cost and annual operating cost based on flow rate of each stream. Specifically, the investment cost of each unit is estimated by empirical power functions and the operating cost accounts for steam, electricity, natural gas, biomass feedstock, catalysts etc (Gong and You, 2014). As for environmental impact, it is evaluated according to the principles of LCA (You and Wang, 2011). Conventional LCA cannot automatically generate design alternatives and identify the optimal one. In order to overcome the drawback, we integrate LCA with multiobjective optimization and apply life cycle optimization (LCO) framework (You et al., 2012) to our biorefinery superstructure model. GWP with a time horizon of 100 years is chosen as the indicator of LCO (Wang et al., 2013). The model simultaneously optimizes two objective functions. The economic objective is to maximize NPV while environmental objective is to minimize GWP. (Yue et al., 2013)

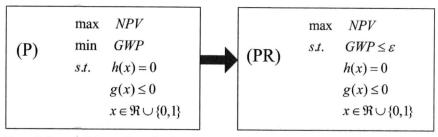

Figure 2. Formulation transformation for ε-constraint method

4. Solution approaches

The mathematical model can be written in a compact form as problem (P), which focuses on the major features of this bi-criteria MINLP model. Two objectives are maximizing the NPV and minimizing the GWP, respectively. The constraints involve both equalities and inequalities. The equalities represent the mass and energy balance constraints, as well as equalities related to cost evaluation and LCA. The inequalities are employed to describe the design specifications (e.g., capacity limits, process variable bounds). The continuous variables include the flow rates, capacities, etc. and binary 0-1 variables, however, indicate the selection of superstructure alternatives.

Since multiple objectives are involved in the proposed mathematical model, conventional single-objective optimization methods cannot be applied directly. Among the various multiobjective optimization methods, ε-constraint method (Gebreslassie et al., 2013) is proved to be efficient and straightforward to formulate. Therefore, we employ the ε-constraint method to solve the proposed bi-criteria MINLP problem. According to the ε-constraint method, the Pareto-optimal solutions of problem (P) can be obtained by solving a series of sub-problems (PR) with different ε-parameter.

5. Result and discussion

The MINLP model is coded in GAMS 24.0.2 and solved using BARON 10.2.0 to achieve the global optimality with 0 % relative gap. The 13 Pareto-optimal points are obtained in 10,800 CPU seconds, and then compose the "Pareto curve" as in Figure 3.

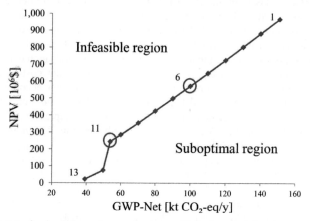

Figure 3. Pareto-optimal solutions of superstructure optimization model.

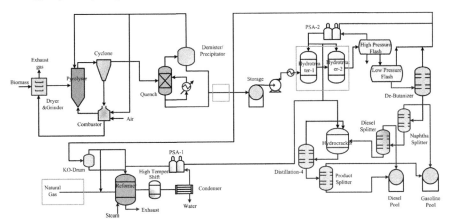

Figure 4. Optimal configuration of point 1 where all bio-crude is upgraded in hydroprocessing
and hydrogen is generated from natural gas.

In this figure, vertical coordinate is the NPV in unit of 10^6\$ while horizontal coordinate
is the GWP in unit of kt CO2-eq/y. Solutions above the curve are infeasible, while
solutions below the curve are feasible but sub-optimal. Each point on the Pareto curve
represents an optimal design and operation of the biorefinery. Point 1 on the top right
has the maximum NPV of \$9.68×10^8 as well as the largest GWP of 150.8 kt CO2-eq/y
among all the feasible solutions. The optimal design of this point selects all the bio-
crude for upgrading and natural gas steam reforming for hydrogen production as shown
in Figure 4. In contrast, point 13 on the bottom left has the minimum GWP, 39.2 kt
CO2-eq/y and the smallest NPV of \$2.21×10^7. The optimal configuration of point 13
demonstrates that part of the bio-crude is utilized for hydroprocessing with Ni-Mo
catalyst and the remaining part is sent to steam reforming for hydrogen production.
From the cost perspective, Figure 5 presents the breakdown of the equipment purchase
cost for point 1 and point 13. In both cases, the equipment purchase cost is dominated
by establishing the steam reformer in the hydrogen production section.

Point 10 is a turning point on the Pareto curve, indicating change in the process design.
The Pareto-optimal solutions from point 1 to 10 have the same process design where
hydrotreating feedstock option (1) is chosen and hydrogen is produced from natural gas
steam reforming. In other words, the binary decisions, such as the selection of
technologies and equipment units, are the same among these solutions. On the other
hand, the solutions from point 11 to 13 select hydrotreating feedstock option (3). Note
that, none of the Pareto-optimal solutions select the hydrogen production from biomass
gasification, because producing hydrogen from biomass requires a higher capital cost
compared to that from natural gas. Even worse, producing hydrogen from biomass leads
to higher GHG emissions due to higher utility consumption.

6. Conclusions

In this paper, we proposed a new superstructure for the design of a hydrocarbon
biorefinery to produce biofuels via fast pyrolysis and hydroprocessing pathway and its
bi-criteria MINLP mathematical model to maximize the NPV and minimize the GWP
simultaneously. The optimal solutions result in a Pareto curve indicating the trade-off
between NPV and GWP objectives. Two optimal production designs are identified from

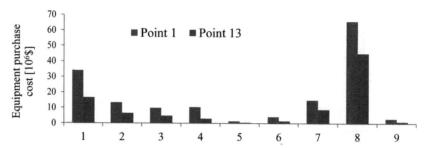

Figure 5. Equipment purchase cost distribution for both point 1 and point 13. 1, dryer; 2, pyrolyzer; 3, liquid collection; 4, hydrotreating; 5, separation; 6,pressure swing adsorption; 7, hydrocracking; 8, steam methane reforming; 9, storage.

the results: one upgrades all bio-crude in hydroprocessing section catalysed by Co-Mo while hydrogen is supplied by natural gas steam reforming; the other splits part of the bio-crude to hydroprocessing catalysed by Ni-Mo while hydrogen production is fulfilled by reforming the remaining bio-crude.

References

K. J. Gabriel, M. M. El-Halwagi, 2013, Modeling and optimization of a bioethanol production facility, Clean Technologies and Environmental Policy, 15, 6, 931-944.

B. H. Gebreslassie, M. Slivinsky, B. L. Wang, F. Q. You, 2013a, Life cycle optimization for sustainable design and operations of hydrocarbon biorefinery via fast pyrolysis, hydrotreating and hydrocracking, Computers and Chemical Engineering, 50, 71-91.

B. H. Gebreslassie, R. Waymire, F. You, 2013b, Sustainable design and synthesis of algae-based biorefinery for simultaneous hydrocarbon biofuel production and carbon sequestration, AIChE Journal, 59, 5, 1599-1621.

J. Gong, F. You, 2014, Optimal Design and Synthesis of Algal Biorefinery Processes for Biological Carbon Sequestration and Utilization with Zero Direct Greenhouse Gas Emissions: MINLP Model and Global Optimization Algorithm, Industrial and Engineering Chemistry Research, 53, 4, 1563-1579.

S. B. Jones, C. Valkenburg, C. W. Walton, D. C. Elliott, J. E. Holladay, D. J. Stevens, C. Kinchin, S. Czernik, 2009, Production of gasoline and diesel from biomass via fast pyrolysis, hydrotreating and hydrocracking: A design case, Pacific Northwest National Laboratory Richland, WA.

M. Martín, I. E. Grossmann, 2011, Energy optimization of bioethanol production via gasification of switchgrass, AIChE Journal, 57, 12, 3408-3428.

B. Wang, B. H. Gebreslassie, F. Q. You, 2013, Sustainable design and synthesis of hydrocarbon biorefinery via gasification pathway: Integrated life cycle assessment and technoeconomic analysis with multiobjective superstructure optimization, Computers and Chemical Engineering, 52, 55-76.

F. Q. You, L. Tao, D. J. Graziano, S. W. Snyder, 2012, Optimal design of sustainable cellulosic biofuel supply chains: Multiobjective optimization coupled with life cycle assessment and input-output analysis, AIChE Journal, 58, 4, 1157-1180.

F. Q. You, B. Wang, 2011, Life Cycle Optimization of Biomass-to-Liquid Supply Chains with Distributed-Centralized Processing Networks, Industrial and Engineering Chemistry Research, 50, 17, 10102-10127.

D. J. Yue, M. A. Kim, F. Q. You, 2013, Design of Sustainable Product Systems and Supply Chains with Life Cycle Optimization Based on Functional Unit: General Modeling Framework, Mixed-Integer Nonlinear Programming Algorithms and Case Study on Hydrocarbon Biofuels, ACS Sustainable Chemistry and Engineering, 1, 8, 1003-1014.

Jiří Jaromír Klemeš, Petar Sabev Varbanov and Peng Yen Liew (Editors)
Proceedings of the 24th European Symposium on Computer Aided Process Engineering – ESCAPE 24
June 15-18, 2014, Budapest, Hungary. Copyright © 2014 Elsevier B.V. All rights reserved.

Rate-based Modelling of Chilled Ammonia Process (CAP) for CO_2 Capture

Dawid P. Hanak*, Chechet Biliyok, Hoi Yeung, Vasilije Manovic

Energy and Power Engineering Division, School Of Engineering, Cranfield University, Bedford, Bedfordshire, MK43 0AL, UK
d.p.hanak@cranfield.ac.uk

Abstract

Chilled ammonia process (CAP) has been identified as a promising alternative to the monoethanolamine based capture process for post-combustion CO_2 capture. Therefore, a full-scale rate-based CAP capture plant model has been developed. First, the aqueous NH_3 process was modelled in Aspen Plus and validated with pilot-plant data. The model was modified to meet the CAP operating conditions, and then scaled-up to process the flue gas from 660 MW_{el} coal-fired power plant. The full-scale rate-based CAP model showed a substantial performance improvement through reducing the energy requirement for solvent regeneration by 27 % compared to the reference MEA process.

Keywords: rate-based modelling chilled ammonia process, carbon capture, coal-fired power plant.

1. Introduction

As imposed by the European Union, up to 99 % of the CO_2 emission from the power sector needs to be eliminated by 2050. Meeting this target is, however, expected to be challenging as a substantial part of power generation is based upon coal combustion. Therefore, post-combustion CO_2 capture (PCC) with chemical solvents will need to be implemented on coal-fired power plants to meet emission reduction targets.

Being relatively cheap, commercially available and characterised by a high CO_2 absorption capacity, NH_3 has been identified as a viable alternative to monoethanolamine (MEA) for PCC (Zhao et al., 2012). Compared to the MEA solvent, CO_2 absorption by NH_3 is characterised by a lower heat of reaction, which means less energy required for solvent regeneration. Also, NH_3 is not as corrosive as MEA and can be used as a multicomponent capture solvent such as SO_x and NO_x (Zhao et al., 2012). Moreover, the stripping process can be conducted at much higher pressure, up to 138 bar, having a positive impact on the overall electricity consumption of the capture plant (Gal, 2006). However, the main drawbacks of using NH_3 are its relatively slow CO_2 absorption kinetics and NH_3 slip in the absorber (Strube and Manfrida, 2011).

The concept for using NH_3 as an alternative to MEA scrubbing was first proposed by Bai and Yeh (1997), who experimentally analysed the chemical absorption of CO_2 into NH_3 solution, and found that a capture level of 95 % can be achieved. Two options for NH_3 based PCC are commonly identified (Linnenberg et al., 2012): aqueous ammonia process (AAP) with CO_2 absorption taking place at ambient temperature (>20 °C) and chilled ammonia process (CAP) in which the CO_2 is absorbed at a low temperature (<20 °C). As NH_3 is characterised by high volatility, which increases with temperature, lower temperatures in the CAP absorber results in a significant reduction in NH$_3$ evaporation and, hence NH$_3$ slip (Darde et al., 2010). This not only ensures that fugitive NH$_3$ emissions to the environment are avoided, but also reduces the heat requirement of washing sections. This makes the CAP process a more feasible option for integration into the coal-fired power plants.

2. Modelling Approach

There are two approaches for modelling the chemical absorption in packed columns: equilibrium-based and rate-based modelling. In the equilibrium-based approach, it is assumed that vapour and liquid phases exist in equilibrium on a number of theoretical stages, with the performance of each stage characterised by height equivalent to a theoretical stage and Murphee efficiencies. While the rate-based approach involves multi-component mass and heat transfer, as well as chemical reactions, which can be represented either by a chemical equilibrium or reaction kinetics (Kothandaraman, 2010).

Although the CAP process has been investigated in literature through thermodynamic modelling (Darde et al., 2010) and process simulation (Linnenberg et al., 2012), most of the studies performed were equilibrium based. A comparison of the equilibrium and rate-based modelling of the CAP conducted by Strube and Manfrida (2011) revealed that the equilibrium modelling results in large deviations from rate-based models. However, in their work the lean solvent temperature is 20 °C, and there is no intercooling of solvent in the absorbers, therefore absorption takes place under AAP conditions (>20 °C). Niu et al. (2012) validated a rate-based model of the AAP absorber and found a good agreement between the model performance and experimental data. Moreover, accuracy of the rate-based approach was confirmed Qi et al. (2013) and Zhang and Guo (2013b) who validated their AAP models against the experimental data from the Munmorah pilot plant. However, the large-scale model developed by Zhang and Guo (2013a) to match the scale of 500 MW$_{el}$ coal-fired power plant achieved the capture efficiency of 50 % only. All of these studies have focused on models for the AAP, with few considering the solvent regenerator, and only one attempting to model a large scale capture process. Therefore this work is undertaken to build a large scale rate-based model of CAP, which is expected to provide good prediction of the performance of the CAP at a scale that has not been previously reported.

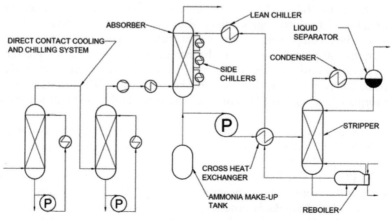

Figure 1. Simplified process flow diagram of full-scale CAP capture plant

3. Model development and validation

Due to no CAP pilot plant performance data available, a rate-based AAP model is first developed in Aspen Plus V8.0 and validated with the Munmorah plant data (Table 1), so as to provide a basis for a large-scale CAP model development. The packed columns are modelled using RadFrac units with a closed recycle to achieve a more reliable prediction of the process performance (Biliyok et al., 2012). The model utilises the electrolyte NRTL method for the liquid phase and Redlich-Kwong equation of state for the vapour phase properties. Furthermore, CO_2, NH_3 and N_2 are modelled as the Henry components with the Henry's constants with water retrieved from the Aspen Plus databanks. Also, the CAP chemistry, which involves equilibrium and kinetic reactions, as well as salt precipitation, is implemented in the model (AspenTech, 2008). The rate-based model performance is compared with the pilot plant data in Table 2. It is concluded that the rate-based model prediction is in a good agreement with the pilot-plant performance. Therefore, this model will provide a reliable initial point for the full-scale CAP capture plant development.

4. CAP process modelling and scale up

The operating conditions in the model are modified to match CAP process, using process information provided by Gal (2006). As illustrated in Figure 1, the flue gas and lean solvent are chilled to 7 °C in the direct contact cooler and 10 °C in the chiller, respectively, before being fed to the absorber. Temperature in the absorber is kept below 10 °C using side chillers, to maximise the CO_2 absorption rate and limit the NH_3 slip in the absorber. The rich solvent leaving the absorber bottom is pressurised to 10.1 bar, then fed to the stripper via a cross heat exchanger, where it is heated up by the lean solvent leaving the stripper reboiler. The stripper condenser operates at 25 °C and stripper reboiler at 150 °C, preventing NH_3 and water from evaporating, and ensuring that pure and high pressure CO_2 stream is collected at the top of the stripper. Moreover, the lean solvent is characterised by the initial NH_3 content of 15 wt% and loading of 0.295. This is due to reported increase in CO_2 absorption capacity and limited NH_3 slip of solvents having moderate NH_3 contents (Zhao et al., 2012) compared to NH_3 content of 28 wt% suggested by Gal (2006).

Table 1. Design and operating parameters of the rate-based AAP model (Yu et al., 2011)

Design		Operations	
Absorber column number	2	Absorber temperature (°C)	26
Absorber packing height (m)	3.9	Absorber pressure (bar)	1.01
Stripper column number	1	Stripper temperature (°C)	120
Stripper packing height (m)	3.4	Stripper pressure (bar)	6.00
Column packing type	25mm Pall Ring	Lean solvent NH_3 content (wt%)	5

Table 2. Validation of the rate-based AAP model against the Munmorah pilot-plant data

Parameter	Experiment ID 31	Simulation
CO_2 lean loading (molCO₂/molNH₃)	0.24 ± 0.01	0.24
CO_2 rich loading (molCO₂/molNH₃)	0.32 ± 0.03	0.34
CO_2 absorption rate (kg/h)	80 ± 2	82.3
CO_2 capture level (wt%)	87.7	87.0

Finally, using generalised pressure drop correlation, the model is scaled up to meet the requirement of 90 % CO_2 capture level from a 660 MW_{el} supercritical coal-fired power plant, which was modelled and validated with data provided by Suresh et al. (2009). The required cross sectional areas of the absorber and stripper columns are determined. Process stream information and initial design parameters are given in Table 3. A parametric study is carried out using the cross sectional areas to determine the number of columns required depending on design diameters selected (Figure 2). With the column structural limitations in mind, three absorber and one stripper columns, all with 12 m in diameter, were selected. Such configuration is expected to perform well from the plant controllability point of view during part-load operation.

Table 3. CAP preliminary design

Parameter	Value
Flue gas flow rate (kg/s)	619.4
Flue gas CO_2 content (wt%)	22.73
Captured CO_2 flow rate (kg/s)	126.7
Required lean solvent flow rate (kg/s)	2,920.6
Absorber cross sectional area requirement (m^2)	294.7
Stripper cross sectional area requirement (m^2)	116.7
Absorber and stripper packing height (m)	30
Absorber and stripper packing type	Mellapak 350X

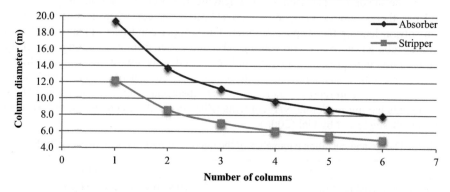

Figure 2. Determination of a column number for the large-scale chilled ammonia process

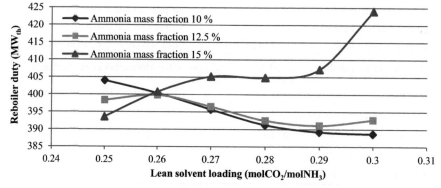

Figure 3. Impact of lean solvent loading and initial NH_3 content on the reboiler duty

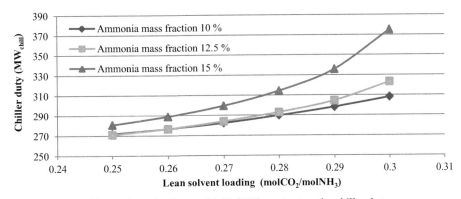

Figure 4. Impact of lean solvent loading and initial NH_3 content on the chiller duty

5. Sensitivity analysis

Sensitivity studies are conducted to determine optimal operating conditions of the CAP capture plant. Lean solvent NH_3 content is varied between $10 - 15$ wt% and lean loading between $0.25 - 0.30$, while other parameters are tuned to maintain a 90 % capture level. The results are presented in Figure 3 and Figure 4, respectively.

From Figure 3, it is seen that at a 90 % CO_2 capture level, the reboiler duty decreases with lean solvent NH_3 content for the lean loadings above 0.26. Below this value, the reboiler duty is lower when NH_3 content is higher. This reveals that there is a threshold of solvent loading below which a higher NH_3 contents appears to be beneficial. The reason behind this is the solvent heat capacity, which increases with NH_3 content. Therefore, it is expected that the reboiler duty will follow the trend observed at 15 wt% NH_3 content for the scenarios with greater NH_3 content. Yet, a combination of low solvent loading and high solvent NH_3 content would result in the additional problem of increased NH_3 slip in the absorber. Furthermore, it is observed from Figure 4 that the chilling duty requirement decreases with the lean solvent loading and NH_3 content. From the sensitivity study results, the optimum operating conditions for the full-scale CAP plant, where energy utilized is lowest, is at lean solvent content of 10 wt% and loading of 0.28. Such operating conditions results in heat requirement reduced from 3.24 MJ_{th}/kgCO_2 to 3.08 MJ_{th}/kgCO_2, compared to the first run performed with initial lean solvent NH_3 content of 15 wt%. For the considered operating range, CAP reboiler duty is always smaller than 4.2 MJ_{th}/kgCO_2, which has been reported for the MEA process (Yang and Zhai, 2010). Moreover, the chilling power requirement falls from 0.38 MJ_{el}/kgCO_2 to 0.29 MJ_{el}/kgCO_2, yet the implication on parasitic energy demands on a power plant performance is significant. Thus, a global optimization study of the CAP plant integrated into the power plant is required to determine operating conditions of the capture plant to minimise the energy penalty imposed on the power plant.

6. Conclusions

This study is undertaken to develop a large-scale rate-based model of CAP to explore its expected advantages over MEA and AAP processes. First, a pilot-plant scale AAP rate-based model was developed and validated with the Munmorah pilot-plant data to prove the efficacy of the proposed modelling approach. As the model was found to represent the plant performance accurately, it was then tuned to operate under CAP conditions, before it was scaled-up to handle the flue gas from a 660 MW_{el} coal-fired power plant. A parametric study identified the dimensions and number of columns required at this scale. It was identified that three absorbers and single stripper are required to accommodate this volume of flue gas. Such configuration is expected to be beneficial under part-load operation. The impact of the lean solvent NH_3 content and loading are analysed, and it was found the optimum operational point for the conditions under consideration is achieved at the NH_3 content of 10 wt% and loading of 0.28. At this point, CAP performance resulted in a 27 % reduction in the energy required for solvent regeneration compared to the MEA process, although a significant chilling duty is also imposed. Nevertheless, a global optimization study of the CAP plant integrated to the power plant is needed to minimise the energy penalty.

References

AspenTech, 2008, Rate-based model of the CO_2 capture process by NH_3 using Aspen Plus, Aspen Technology Inc., Cambridge, MA, USA.

H. Bai, A. C. Yeh, 1997, Removal of CO_2 greenhouse gas by ammonia scrubbing, Ind. Eng. Chem. Res., 36, 2490-2493.

C. Biliyok, A. Lawal, M. Wang, F. Seibert, 2012, Dynamic modelling, validation and analysis of post-combustion chemical absorption CO_2 capture plant, Int. Jour. of GHG Control, 9, 428-445.

V. Darde, K. Thomsen, W. van Well, E. Stenby, 2010, Chilled ammonia process for CO_2 capture, Int. Jour. of GHG Control, 4, 131-136.

E. Gal, 2006, Ultra cleaning of combustion gas including the removal of CO_2, Patent no. WO/2006/022885, <www.patentscope.wipo.int/search/en/WO2006022885>, accessed on 19/01/2014.

A. Kothandaraman, 2010, Carbon dioxide capture by chemical absorption: a solvent comparison study, PhD thesis, Massachusetts Institute of Technology, Cambridge, MA, USA.

S. Linnenberg, V. Darde, J. Oexmann, A. Kather, W. van Well, K. Thomsen, 2012, Evaluating the impact of an ammonia-based post-combustion CO_2 capture process on a steam power plant with different cooling water temperatures, Int. Jour. of GHG Control, 10,1-14.

Z. Niu, Y. Guo, Q. Zeng, W. Lin, 2012, Experimental studies and rate-based process simulations of CO_2 absorption with aqueous ammonia solutions, Ind. Eng. Chem. Res., 51, 14, 5309-5319.

R. Strube and G. Manfrida, 2011, CO_2 capture in coal-fired power plants - Impact on plant performance, Int. Jour. of GHG Control, 5, 4, 710-726.

M. Suresh, K. Reddy, A. K. Kolar, 2009, 3-E analysis of advanced power plants based on high ash coal, Int. Journal of Energy Research, 34, 8, 716-735.

Y. Yang, R. Zhai, 2010, MEA-based CO_2 capture technology and its application in power plants, Paths to Sustainable Energy, A. Ng (Ed.), InTech, <www.intechopen.com/books/paths-to-sustainable-energy>, accessed on 19/01/2014

H. Yu., S. Morgan., A. Allport, T. Cottrell, J. Do, L. McGregor, P. Wardhaugh, P. Freon, 2011, Results from trialling aqueous NH_3 based post-combustion capture in a pilot plant at Munmorah power station: Absorption, Chem. Eng. Res. Des., 89, 1204-1215.

M. Zhang, Y. Guo, 2013a, Process simulations of large-scale CO_2 capture in coal-fired power plants using aqueous ammonia solution, Int. Jour. of GHG Control, 16, 61-71.

M. Zhang, Y. Guo, 2013b, Rate based modeling of absorption and regeneration for CO_2 capture by aqueous ammonia solution, Applied Energy, 111, 142-152

B. Zhao, Y. Su, W. Tao, L. Li, Y. Peng, 2012, Post-combustion CO_2 capture by aqueous ammonia: A state-of-the-art review, Int. Jour. of GHG Control, 9, 355-371.

Jiří Jaromír Klemeš, Petar Sabev Varbanov and Peng Yen Liew (Editors)
Proceedings of the 24th European Symposium on Computer Aided Process Engineering – ESCAPE 24
June 15-18, 2014, Budapest, Hungary. Copyright © 2014 Elsevier B.V. All rights reserved.

Coupled Population Balance-CFD Modelling of a Continuous Precipitation Reactor

Botond Szilágyi[a,*], Paul Şerban Agachi[a], Réka Barabás[b], Béla G. Lakatos[c]

[a]*Babeş-Bolyai University, Department of Chemical Engineering, Cluj Napoca 40002, Romania*
[b]*Babeş-Bolyai University, Department of Chemistry and Chemical Engineering of Hungarian Line of Study, Cluj Napoca 400028, Romania*
[c]*University of Pannonia, Department of Process Engineering, Veszprém 8200, Hungary*
botiszilagyi@yahoo.com

Abstract

Precipitation of amorphous calcium phosphate in a Y-mixer-tubular reactor device is investigated using a population balance equation including nucleation, growth and agglomeration of particles and a three-dimensional CFD flow model. The population balance equation is reduced into a moment equations system the quadrature form of which is coupled with the detailed CFD model. Simulation results obtained by the detailed CFD flow model provided results comparable to those produced by assuming ideal mixing conditions. This comparison reveals that under the given process conditions of precipitation of amorphous calcium phosphate application of a simple ideal mixing model, for instance in controlling such processes can be justified.

Keywords: Calcium phosphate, Continuous precipitation, CFD modelling, Population balance model, Simulation.

1. Introduction

Due to its excellent biocompatibity, hydroxyapatite (HAp) has various practical applications but is mainly used in modern implant production: Zhou et al. (2012) synthetized, Salimi and Anuar (2013) characterized the HAp coatings for biomedical applications. A cheap, clean and environmentally friendly way to produce HAp is precipitation: Wu (2007) prepared HAp using an impinging stream, and later Dejeu et al. (2009) a Y mixer–tubular reactor, in a multistep crystallization, which results in a high quality product with reduced environmental impact and costs. The first step in the process is the formation of amorphous precursor calcium phosphate (ACP) precipitate from a chemical reaction and this step is followed by transformation of ACP to HAp.

Veljović et al. (2011) proved that the mechanical properties of the HAp are strongly affected by the particle sizes and N. L. D'Elía et al. (2013) studied the effects of HAp coating morphology on bioactivity, thus it seems to be important to control the particle formation starting already on the precipitation step. Characterization and preparation of ACP have been studied extensively (Dorozhkin et al., 2010) while only a few works were published considering the kinetics. Montrastuc et al. (2003) presented an agglomeration model for ACP in a pellet reactor, Lai et al. (2005) studied the nucleation kinetics in a reverse micelle solution, and Castro et al. (2012) investigated the mechanism of the HAp preparation.

Szilágyi (2013) investigated the precipitation kinetics of ACP in a Y-mixer-tubular reactor device. A detailed population balance model was established including nucleation, growth and agglomeration of particles but an approximating piston flow model were used for describing the flow conditions of the device. However, an important question arises if a detailed flow model would improve the predictions of the model compared with those provided by the ideal mixing since this seems to be a significant point when developing and solving process optimization problems of such systems.

The aim of the paper is to examine this problem by simulating precipitation of ACP using more detailed flow conditions coupling the corresponding population balance equation with a CFD flow model. The population balance equation is reduced into a moment equations system and the quadrature form of that is coupled with a three-dimensional CFD model. The kinetic parameters used in simulation were determined formerly by Szilágyi (2013).

2. Mathematical model

The reactor used in experiments had 5 mm diameter, 300 mm length and the angle of Y-mixer was 80°. The process was started at moment $t=0$ feeding solutions of reagents in given composition, prepared from analytical purity reagents diluted with distilled water, to the Y-mixer-tubular reactor device. The reaction, approximately instant, occurs in the Y-mixer producing the precipitating material. In tubular reactor, followed by further mixing of streams, nucleation, growth and agglomeration of particles take place what results in a well specified particle size distribution (PSD) that was measured experimentally with a Coulter Counter nano-particle analyser at the outlet of the reactor. The details of the system and experiments are described by Szilágyi (2013).

2.1. The population balance model

The particle formation process, i.e. nucleation, growth and agglomeration along the tubular reactor is modelled by means of transported population balance equation governing the size distribution of the solid particulate phase:

$$\frac{\partial n(L,r,t)}{\partial t} + \nabla[v(r)n(L,r,t)] + \frac{\partial}{\partial L}[G(r)n(L,r,t)] = B_p(r,t) -$$

$$- n(L,r,t)\int_0^\infty \beta(L,\lambda)n(\lambda,r,t)d\lambda + \frac{L^2}{2}\int_0^L \frac{\beta\left[\left(L^3-\lambda^3\right)^{1/3},\lambda\right]}{\left(L^3-\lambda^3\right)^{2/3}} n\left[\left(L^3-\lambda^3\right)^{1/3},r,t\right] n(\lambda,r,t)d\lambda \tag{1}$$

In Eq.(1), $n(L,r,t)$ denotes the population density function of particles at the position $r=(x,y,z)$ of the reactor at time t that provides the size distribution of particles with respect to the linear particle size L, B_p denotes the nucleation rate, G is the growth function of particles and β is the agglomeration kernel. The first two terms on right hand side describes the temporal and spatial evolutions of PSD, the third term denotes the growth of particles, and the terms on the right side describe nucleation and agglomeration. The kinetic equations for nucleation, growth and agglomeration are as follows:

$$B_p(S) = k_{p0}\exp\left(-\frac{k_B}{RT}\right)\exp\left(-\frac{k_e}{\ln^2 S}\right) \tag{2}$$

$$G(S) = k_{g0} \exp\left(-\frac{k_G}{RT}\right)(S-1)^g \tag{3}$$

$$\beta(L,\lambda) = b_0(L+\lambda)^3 \tag{4}$$

where $S = c/c_s$ denotes the supersaturation ratio of ACP (c – concentration, c_s – saturation concentration).

The population balance equation was solved within the Population Balance Module of Ansys Fluent program, using the Quadrature Method of Moments (QMOM) approximation which stands on the next transformation:

$$\mu_k(r,t) = \int_0^\infty L^k n(L,r,t)dL \cong \sum_{i=1}^I w_i(r,t)L_i^k(r,t), \quad k = 0,1,2... \tag{5}$$

The integral of Eq.(5) is the moment transformation rule which enables computation of the moments of the linear size of particles which can be numerically approximated using the quadrature rule as it was showed by McGraw (1997). In Eq.(5), w_i are the weights while L_i are the abscissas of the quadrature form. In the current study the first 6 moments ($k=0,1, ...5$) were used from the infinite set of moment equations.

2.2. The CFD model and the mass balance
The model of the experimental device was built within Ansys and solved with the Fluent program, but there exists different software's also for solving similar problems, as Akroyd et al. (2011) showed.

The Mixture multiphase model was used to describe the multiphase conditions. For modelling the flow, the realizable k-ε turbulence model was applied which seemed to be the best choice to the current problem. This model defines a transport equation for the turbulent kinetic energy (k) and for turbulent dissipation rate (ε) which are used to compute the turbulent viscosity (for more details see Ansys INC (2011)).

The Species Transport module was used to simulate the chemical reaction after defining the materials missing from the Fluent database as user-defined materials. The finite rate volumetric chemical reaction concept was considered having very low activation energy (100 J/kg) to simulate the instant, temperature independent chemical reaction. The QMOM approximation was used from population balance module to simulate the precipitation process, Eqs (1)-(5), and the kinetics of nucleation, growth and agglomeration were embedded as compiled user-defined subroutines. The mass balance for the liquid phase precipitating material, neglecting the dispersion of concentration, was given as follows

$$\frac{\partial c(r,t)}{\partial t} + \nabla[v(r)c(r,t)] = -k_V \rho L_n^3 B_p(r,t) - v\rho k_V \nabla[v(r)\mu_3(r,t)] \tag{6}$$

The first term on the left side of Eq.(6) denotes the time evolution of concentration, the second term denotes the convective transport of concentration while the right side computes the concentration due to nucleation and growth of solid particles.

3. Numerical details and simulation settings
Numerical simulation was carried using the Ansys Fluent CFD software, with a 3D double precision parallel steady state solver. To save computational time, a symmetry

plane was defined which cuts the reactor in longitudinal direction and the lengths of conduits feeding the Y-mixer was minimized to 0. For this, the input velocity was not given as constant value but the fully developed flow profile of velocity, k and ε, corresponding to the given flow-rate was computed initially and loaded into the simulation. The convergence criterion was set to 0.001 and in order to achieve the convergence, the under relaxation factors of Volume Fraction, Moments and Species were set to 0.05. The discretization scheme was Phase-Coupled SIMPLE for Pressure-Velocity Coupling, SIMPLE for Pressure, Least Square Cell Based for the Gradient, QUICK for the Volume Fraction, First Order Implicit for Transient Formulation and Second Order Upwind for all other quantities. A high quality mesh was built in Icem CFD software, applying more dense spacing in zone of micro-mixer and near to the walls. The mesh was validated based on the Grid Convergence Index. In order to fully ensure the grid independency, the mesh was validated for the highest concentration, temperature and for double of highest flow-rate used in simulations.

4. Simulation results and discussions

The flow and mixing conditions in reactor, computed by the realizable k-ε turbulence model are presented in Figure 1. As it seen the flow in the reactor is not piston flow and the mixing in Y-mixer is not perfect. The steady state value of the product concentration is achieved approximately after 50 mm from the mixer, (16.67 % of the reactor length).

Table 1 presents the computed moments of particle size. Due to the increased computational costs of CFD, three simulations were run. Based on the data presented, the idealized flow model slightly overestimates the lower moments of distribution. The 0.010 sample standard deviation between the computed moments could be interpreted as the accuracy loss of the kinetic model estimation which, taking into consideration the highly nonlinear kinetics of the process seems to be a reasonable trade-off between the accuracy and faster simulation of IFM.

Knowing the leading moments, the PSD can be reconstructed using different methods. In this work, the gamma density function corrected with Laguerre polynomials, both having only moment dependent terms, was used (Randolph and Larson, 1988). The reconstructed particle size distributions are presented in Figure 2.

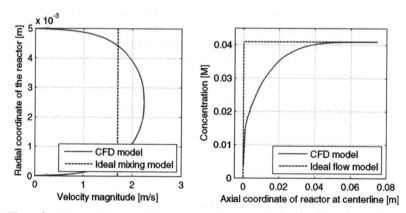

Figure 1. The real mixing and flow conditions computed

Table 1. Simulated moments of distribution (IFM – Idealized Flow Model)

Quant.	T=295 K, Ca_0=0.27 M		T=318 K, Ca_0=0.01 M		T=333 K, Ca_0=0.09 M	
μ_i [m^i/kg]	IFM	CFD	IFM	CFD	IFM	CFD
$\mu_0 * 10^{-11}$	1.408	1.325	0.383	0.365	2.510	2.448
$\mu_1 * 10^{-5}$	3.297	3.225	1.041	1.018	5.958	5.726
μ_2	2.010	1.937	0.327	0.323	2.136	2.046
$\mu_3 * 10^5$	3.054	3.054	0.113	0.113	1.018	1.018
$\mu_4 * 10^{10}$	7.768	7.890	0.042	0.044	0.596	0.623
$\mu_5 * 10^{15}$	25.86	27.67	0.016	0.018	0.407	0.428

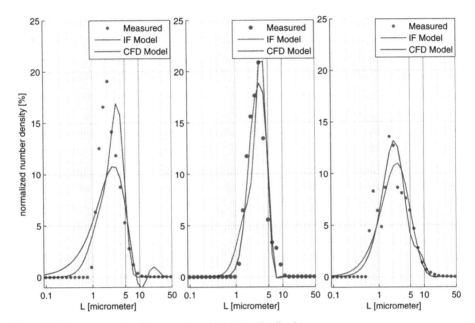

Figure 2. The computed and measured particle size distributions

As it is seen in Figure 2, the CFD model coupled simulation generally result in wider PSD's but the mean particle size is not significantly affected because of the very high growth rate of the newly formed nuclei. The wider PSD can be explained with the non-perfect mixing: the nuclei have formed not only in the mixer but in the first part of length 50-70 mm of the tubular reactor.

5. Conclusions

In the current study the effects of mixing and flow conditions on a precipitation process were investigated by modelling and simulation. The case study analysed was precipita-tion of the ACP coupling the corresponding population balance equation with an idealized flow and a detailed CFD model. The moments of the PSD computed with the two models had standard deviation of $\sigma = 0.010$. Simulation using idealized flow con-ditions usually overestimated the lower order moments (k<3) and underestimated the higher order ones. The real mixing model resulted in wider particle size distributions while the mean particle size was not significantly affected. As a final conclusion we can state that the CFD modelling approach can improve the accuracy of simulations but, as long as in experiments a good mixing is ensured, the idealized flow model approach can be used with acceptable accuracy when computing the moments of the particle size in a precipitation process of amorphous material. Based on these results, our kinetics estimation was also validated with $\sigma = 0.010$ reliability.

Acknowledgements

This research was realized in project by the Hungarian Scientific Research Fund under Grant OTKA K77955. The support of Collegium Talentum, Forerunner Federation and World Federation of Scientists is also acknowledged.

References

X. Zhou, R. Siman, L.P. Mohanty, 2012, Argon atmospheric plasma sprayed hydroxyl-apatite/Ti composite coating for biomedical applications, Surface Coating Techology, 207, 343-349.

M. N. Salimi, A. Anuar, 2013, Characterizations of Biocompatible and Bioactive Hydroxyapatite Particles, Procedia Engineering, 53, 192-196.

Y. Wu, 2007, Preparation of Ultrafine Powders by Reaction-Precipitation in Impinging Streams: Nano Hydroxyapatite, Impinging Streams, 317 – 327.

V.R. Dejeu, R. Barabás, A. Pop, E.S. Bogya, P.S. Agachi, 2009, Kinetic studies for the trans-formation process of beta-whitlockite in hydroxyapatite, Revista de chimie, 12, 1251-1253.

D. Veljović, R. Jančić-Hajneman, I. Balać, B. Jokić, S. Putić, R. Petrović, D. Janaćković, 2011, The effect of the shape and size of the pores on the mechanical properties of porous HAP-based bioceramics, Ceramics International, 37, 471-479.

N. L. D'Elía, A. N. Gravina, J. M. Ruso, J. A. Laiuppa, G. E. Santillán, P. V. Messina, 2013, Manipulating the bioactivity of hydroxyapatite nano-rods structured networks: Effects on mineral coating morphology and growth kinetic, Biochimica et Biophysica Acta - General Subjects, 1830-11, 5014-5026.

S.V. Dorozhkin, 2010, Amorphous calcium (ortho)phosphates, Acta Biomaterialia, 6, 4457–4475.

L. Montastruc, C. Azzaro-Pantel, B. Biscans, M. Cabassud, S. Domenech, L. Dibouleau, 2003, A general framework for pellet reactor modelling: application to p-recovery, Translations of the IChemE A, 81, 1271-1278.

C. Lai, J,Y. Wang, K. Wei, 2008, Nucleation kinetics of calcium phosphate nanoparticles in reverse micelle solution, Colloid Surface A., 315, 268–274.

F. Castro, A. Ferreira, F. Rocha, A. Vicente, J. A. Teixeira , 2012, Characterization of intermediate stages in the preparation of hydroxyapatite at 37°C, Chemical Engineering Science, 77, 150-156.

B. Szilágyi, 2013, Modelling and simulation the reactive crystallization of hydroxyapatite, MSc Dissertation, Babes Bolyai University, Cluj Napoca, Romania.

R. McGraw, 1997, Description of Aerosol Dynamics by the Quadrature Method of Moments, Aerosol Science and Technology, 27-2, 255-265.

Ansys INC, 2011, Ansys Fluent Theory Guide, <cdlab2.fluid.tuwien.ac.at/LEHRE/TURB/Fluent.Inc/v140/flu_th.pdf>, accessed on 04/07/2013.

J. Akroyd, A. J. Smith, R. Shirley, L. R. McGlashan, M. Kraft, 2011, A coupld CFD – population balance approach for nanoparticle synthesis in turbulent reacting flows, Chemical Engineering Science, 66, 17, 3792-3805.

A. Randolph, M. Larson, 1988, Theory of Particulate Processes, Academic Press, San Diego, California.

Jiří Jaromír Klemeš, Petar Sabev Varbanov and Peng Yen Liew (Editors)
Proceedings of the 24th European Symposium on Computer Aided Process Engineering – ESCAPE 24
June 15-18, 2014, Budapest, Hungary. Copyright © 2014 Elsevier B.V. All rights reserved.

Process Design for Extraction of Soybean Oil Bodies by Applying the Product Driven Process Synthesis Methodology

Aleksandra Zderic[a,*], Tugba Tarakci[a], Nasim Hooshyar[b], Edwin Zondervan[a], Jan Meuldijk[a]

aEindhoven University of Technology, Den Dolech 2, Eindhoven 5600 MB, The Netherlands
bUnilever R&D, Olivier van Noortlaan 120, Vlaardingen, The Netherlands
a.zderic@tue.nl

Abstract

The present work describes the product driven process synthesis (PDPS) methodology for the conceptual design of extraction of intact oil bodies from soybeans. First, in this approach consumer needs are taken into account and based on these needs application of the final product (oil bodies) is defined to use extracted oil bodies for food industry as natural antioxidant agents. Furthermore, we defined fundamental tasks followed by an appropriate mechanism to convert an input (soybeans) into a desired output (intact oil body structure). Based on these fundamental tasks logical alternative process flow sheet was generated. The most promising of these alternatives were experimentally tested. It has been found that ultrasound reduced the remaining insoluble fraction and increased the amount of solids (around 60 %) extracted into the aqueous phase which also resulted into higher protein extraction up to 26 %. This has a positive effect on the stability of extracted oil bodies.

Keywords: PDPS methodology, extraction, oil bodies.

1. Introduction

Soybeans are the most important bean source in the world, providing vegetable protein and oil for millions of people and supplying functional ingredients for the food, health care, pharmaceutical and chemical industry (Rosenthal et al., 1996). However, during classical processing of soybeans, the natural ordering, protection and preservation of components (protein and oil) are destroyed. This results in a number of undesired effects, such as loss in quality and/or a more difficult separation of these components afterwards.

In soybean seeds, the oil fraction is stored in discrete subcellular structures known as oil bodies (OBs) or oleosomes. OBs obtained from oilseeds have been exploited for a variety of applications in biotechnology and these applications are based on their non-coalescing nature, easy of extraction and presence of unique membrane proteins (oleosins). In a suspension, OBs exist as separate entities and hence they can be used as emulsifying agent for a wide variety of products, ranging from vaccines, food, cosmetics and personal care products (Serrato, 1981).

The present work describes the product driven process synthesis (PDPS) methodology proposed by Bongers and Almeida-Rivera (2012) for the conceptual design of an economic and sustainableprocess for the extraction of oil bodies from soybeans. This methodology delivers flow sheets that allow economical and environmentally responsible conversion of specific feed stream(s) into desired and specific product(s). Moreover, the PDPS methodology has several hierarchical levels and focuses on finding fundamental tasks that could be performed by different mechanisms. These mechanisms are then linked with unit operations that are running under defined optimum operating conditions. A case of extraction of oil bodies from soybeans is taken here as an example to demonstrate some of the key steps of the PDPS methodology.

2. Product driven process synthesis methodology (PDPS)

2.1. Current process

Existing oil bodies extraction techniques were primarily developed for biochemical isolation and structural analysis of OBs without concern for their practical application within the food industry. The need for effective extraction of biologically active components from plants, without any loss of functionality and high purity, has resulted in development of a novel extraction process (Chen et al., 2007). Nevertheless, for any alternative to the current hydrocarbon solvent extraction to be economically valuable, high oil extraction yields have to be achieved. A simplified process flow diagram of the existing process is shown in the Figure 1.

2.2. Conceptual design of extraction process of oil bodies

We followed a fundamental approach focusing on the physical transformations during processing from raw material to desired product and linked them with equipment selection. In this PDPS approach, we started from a white paper sheet, specified the input, the output streams, and their key properties and treated the "process" as a black box. Subsequently the definition of fundamental tasks required to convert input (soybeans) into output streams (intact oil bodies, proteins and carbohydrates) was done. The idea is to have these streams as separate fractions, because further purification and isolation (downstream processing) of these compounds should not be needed. Furthermore, we generated a conceptual process diagram by combining these fundamental tasks together with logical combination of the process flows. In a later stage, a brainstorming is required with engineering judgment and the analysis and evaluation of experimental data. All these steps are called "levels" which start with consumer needs and end with a complete conceptual process design. Moreover, Bongers and Almeida-Rivera (2012) define all these levels. In the following sections, the PDPS levels as well as some of the relevant experiments and results are discussed.

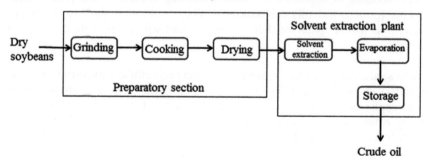

Figure 1. Simplified process flow diagram of existing soy oil production process

2.2.1. Level 0: consumer needs

Nowadays, people want to eat healthy food that includes avoidance of synthetic antioxidants on the product label (no E3XX additives on the back product labels). Food containing fats and oil is most likely to have problems with oxidation. Fats react with oxygen and even if food has a very low fat content it may still need the addition of an antioxidant. Synthetic antioxidants are added to food to decrease the rate of oxidation and if used properly they can extend the shelf life of the food in which they have been used. Looking from a consumer point of view having synthetic antioxidant agents in the food product is not favorable. A very promising alternative to the synthetic antioxidants are oil bodies (OBs). Intact OBs are considered as a natural form of antioxidant (as well as self-emulsifying agent), where 95 % of oil is protected with only 5 % of proteins which provides stable structure.

2.2.2. Level 1: input and output

Most of the soybean protein and oil are stored in the cotyledon tissue in organelles called protein bodies and oil bodies (oleosomes), respectively. The typical soybean composition is 20 % oil, 40 % protein, 35 % carbohydrate (soluble and insoluble) and 5 % ash on dry basis (Hsieh and Huang, 2004).

The output of the process has to be a fraction of intact oil bodies. Visual inspection of the microstructure is used as indicator for intact OBs. A desired microstructure could be identified by microscopy and Confocal Scanning Laser Microscopy (CSLM) was used to analyze the obtained fraction. Figure 2 shows CSLM pictures of the intact OBs and protein bodies as well as shape and size of the compounds and their placement in the microstructure.

2.2.3. Level 2: task network and mechanisms

The next step is to identify the fundamental tasks to convert input into output. The aim is to extract intact OBs from soybean, originally present inside cotyledon cells. To reach the OBs the first step is the reduction of the particle size after this cell wall disruption and at the end, extraction of OBs has to be performed. Taking these steps as a starting point, the logical "process flow" is presented in the Table 1. This is theoretically the critical and minimum required number of tasks based on the definition of the final structure of the product (intact oil bodies). These three steps (size reduction, cell wall disruption and separation) would lead to six (3!=3x2x1=6) process flow sheets, which would not be practical to validate experimentally. Domain knowledge and experience are used to limit these options.

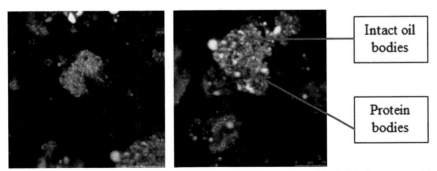

Figure 2. Confocal Scanning micrographs of intact oil bodies (small individual green particles, smaller than 1μm) and protein bodies (bigger particles stained in red).

Table 1. List of selected tasks for extraction process of oil bodies from soybeans.

Level 1 Class of task
Level 2 Fundamental task
C Change the distribution properties
C2 size reduction of particulates (solids / fibres / proteins)
C3 cell wall disruption
G Separation of two phases
G1 separation of a system into two systems with different composition

Among all listed tasks in the Table 1, task G is the most critical one. In conventional industrial processes, edible oil is extracted from oil seeds using organic solvents, mainly hexane. Hexane is derived from a non-renewable source (petroleum distillates) and it is highly flammable and explosive, posing hazards to plant, person and property. Moreover, the harsh conditions used during hexane extraction can lead to severe degradation of protein functionality and production of off-flavour (Serrato, 1981) due to the presence of a significant amount of polyunsaturated fatty acids. Use of hexane for removal of oil increases process costs. Potential cost saving based on preliminary economic calculation is 20 % if hexane is not used in the process.

Therefore, there is a need for alternative process routes under mild conditions. The aqueous extraction process (AEP) was suggested as an alternative to the solvent extraction (Rosenthal et al., 1996). In AEP water is used as an extracting medium to remove oil as an emulsion or free oil, unlike organic solvents which dissolve the oil.
To carry out defined fundamental tasks, mechanisms are identified. A list of tasks and mechanisms is presented in the Table 2 (which is extension of Table 1).

Based on the end user requirements, some mechanisms have been rejected immediately. For example, use of chemicals for cell wall disruption is out of scope, because organic solvents are not food grade. Moreover, removal of organic solvents would bring an additional complexity into the process line. However, some of the remaining feasible ideas were experimentally tested in the lab. In addition, for the presented fundamental tasks an operating window was defined.

The definition of the operating window requires previous knowledge and/or further experiments to be performed. In this case, some information is collected from a

Table 2. Selected fundamental tasks and mechanisms taken from process synthesis tasks proposed by Bongers and Almeida-Rivera (2012)

C Change the distribution properties
C2 size reduction of particulates (solids / fibres / proteins)
C21 attrition
C3 cell wall disruption
C32 electro-magnetic fields (ultrasound)
C34 enzymes
G Separation of two phases
G1 separation of a system into two systems with different composition
G11 molecular size
G12 particle size
G13 electrical charge
G14 solubility

previous research project, for example, soaking time, soaking temperature, incubation time, etc. Information such as ultrasound frequency in the ultrasonic bath and type and concentration of enzymes are gathered experimentally. In Table 3 the operating windows of the selected tasks are shown.

In the last part of PDPS methodology, the fundamental tasks are translated to suitable processing equipment. In Figure 3, the proposed process flow sheet is presented.

Table 3. Operating windows of the selected tasks

C Change the distribution properties	Operating window
C2 size reduction of particulates (solids / fibers / proteins)	
C21 attrition	Milling / size ring: 0.2 µm
C3 cell wall disruption	
C32 ultrasound	Frequency: 25 kHz
C34 enzymes	Concentration: 5 % (v/w); incubation: 3 h at 40 °C
G Separation of two phases	
G1 separation of a system into two systems with different composition	
G11 molecular size	Membrane size: ≥0.6 µm
G12 particle size	Centrifuge: 4700 rpm at 4 °C
G13 electrical charge	Buffer: 250 mM NaCl
G14 solubility	Hydration for 30 min at 4 °C in sodium phosphate buffer 0.1 M pH7.2

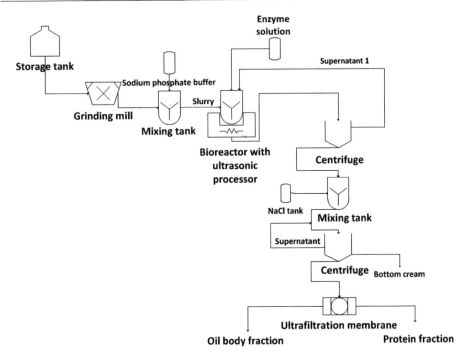

Figure 3. Proposed flow sheet for the process of extraction of OBs from soybeans

Table 4. Comparison between conventional and proposed process routes

	Conventional	Proposed process route
Starting material	Hexane defatted soyflour/flakes	Full fat soy flour
Hexane residue	Possible	No
Extracted intact OBs	Destroyed	Detected/identified by microscopy (CSLM)
Economic potential	0.6 M€/y	2.1 M€/y
Protein solubility	30 % (commercial SUPRO 661)	90 % (extracted protein)

The highest yields were obtained for the ultrasound experiment with 60.5 % of the solids in the protein fraction, resulting in higher protein extraction (26.1 %). This has a positive effect on the stability of extracted oil bodies. The economic potential presented in Table 4 was calculated for both process routes: conventional and proposed.

Comparison of the solubility of the extracted protein from the present study with the commercial protein (SUPRO 661) showed that the extracted protein had about 90 % solubility, while commercial one only had about 30 % solubility. The nutritional value of the extracted protein is not impacted and solubility is very high which leads to the conclusion that the proposed process route did (Rosenthal et al., 1996) not affect the state of the proteins. Moreover, it could be concluded that due to the complete avoidance of hexane (as organic solvent for removal of oil) not only potential cost savings could be made, but also the process itself is labeled as natural and denaturation of proteins is prevented.

3. Conclusion

The findings presented in the current work have clearly pointed out that the aqueous extraction of oil bodies is possible following alternative route while applying mild conditions. This mild alternative route provided one more advantage: denaturation of proteins is prohibited, which means that proteins are still in the native state representing added value products.

References

P. Bongers, C. Almeida-Rivera, 2012, Product Driven Process Design Method, Computer Aided Chemical Engineering, 31, 195-199.

B. Chen, D. McClements, D. Gray, E. Decker, 2007, Physical and oxidative stability of pre-emulsified oil bodies extracted from soybeans, Food Chemistry, 55, 21, 8711-8716.

K. Hsieh, A. Huang, 2004, Endoplasmic reticulum, oleosins, and oils in seeds and Tapetum cells, Plant Physiology, 136, 3, 3427-3434.

A. Rosenthal, D. Pyle, K. Niranjan, S. Gilmour, L. Trinca, 1996, Aqueous and enzymatic processes for edible oil extraction, Enzyme and microbial technology, 19, 6, 402-420.

A. Serrato, 1981, Extraction of oil from soybeans, Journal of American Oil Chemical Society, 58, 3, 157-159.

Jiří Jaromír Klemeš, Petar Sabev Varbanov and Peng Yen Liew (Editors)
Proceedings of the 24th European Symposium on Computer Aided Process Engineering – ESCAPE 24
June 15-18, 2014, Budapest, Hungary. Copyright © 2014 Elsevier B.V. All rights reserved.

Global Optimization for Flexible Heat Exchanger Network Synthesis of Chemical Plant

Lautaro Braccia[a], Lucas Nieto Degliuomini[b], Patricio Luppi[b], Marta S. Basualdo[a,b*]

[a] Computer Aided Process Engineering Group (CAPEG) Technological National,University Tecnológica Faculty of Rosario (UTN-FRRo) Zeballos 1341, S2000BQA, Rosario, Argentina
[b] French Argentine International Center for Information and Systems Sciences (CIFASIS - CONICET - UNR – AMU) 27 de Febrero 210 bis, S2000EZP, Rosario, Argentina
basualdo@cifasis-conicet.gov.ar

Abstract

In this work a new systematic methodology of global optimization to perform synthesis of a flexible heat exchanger network (HEN) is presented. It is based on a previous model, named SynFlex, which uses a promising superstructure to obtain flexible HEN. The synthesis is projected to operate over a specified range of expected variations in the inlet temperatures and flow rates of the process streams. The main objective of SynFlex is that the total annual cost (TAC) involving the utility consumption and the investment be optimized simultaneously. The framework is based on the operability analysis where the design variables are chosen and favors to follow with the control structure design as a next step. Hence, SynFlex is enhanced by introducing a new special-purpose global optimization procedure, which relies on turning as convex specific non convex terms. Two examples are given in this work to illustrate the achievements since the SynFlex model can exclude optimal configurations due to the isothermal mixing assumption. Specially, the obtained application results from a hydrogen production plant from bioethanol with fuel cell, illustrates about the global optimization and computational efficiency for this complex case study.

Keywords: Energy Integration, Flexible Heat Exchanger Network, Global Optimization Synthesis.

1. Introduction

The energy integration is motivated by economic benefits, the HEN configuration impacts the process behavior introducing interactions, and in many cases, making the process more difficult to control and operate. In addition, the HEN configuration may impose control limitations which may make the control extremely difficult, if the network is improperly designed. The conventional heat exchanger network synthesis is performed under the assumption of fixed operating parameters at nominal conditions. However, it is possible that significant changes could occur in the environment of a plant. In this context, taking into account the flexibility in the synthesis stage using the SYNFLEX model, developed by Escobar et al. (2011), as a basis gives more confidence on achieving a successful control design. However, SYNFLEX can be enhanced by performing the HEN design through a global optimization strategy (GOS). Then, the work developed by Björk and Westerlund (2002) is considered for this purpose. Their GOS relies on a convex transformation of the non-convex terms instead of a using a branching procedure. This transformation technique will give rise to a sequence of convex problems that needs to be solved to ensure a global optimal solution. Finding the global optimum for a model assuming isothermal mixing, however, is less time consuming than for a model that does not. Without a global optimization procedure, one cannot easily know if it is possible to obtain better solutions or not, since there is no information as to whether the solution is a local optimum or the global one. The complete strategy presented here is tested with two examples. The first one is the same studied by Björk and Westerlund (2002) to have elements for doing a proper comparison. The other one consists on designing a flexible HEN able to perform the energy integration for a hydrogen production plant from bio-ethanol. It is expected that the obtained HEN would be the best candidate to implement multivariable control structure in the context of that overall complex plant. Finally, according to the application results obtained here the conclusions and future works are given in the last session.

2. New Strategy Proposed

2.1. Multiperiod Flexible Heat Exchanger Networks Synthesis.

The incorporation of uncertainty into the HEN design may be possible through a deterministic approach based on the postulation of a finite number of periods (scenarios) to characterize the uncertainty and can be formulated as multiperiod optimization problem. The solution of the multiperiod design problem can be embedded in two stage strategy in order to generate flexible HEN. Therefore, the synthesis of the network is accomplished based on uncertainty on the inlet temperatures. The first step consists on choosing the existence and dimension of the equipments. The second one is an operation stage, for which is checked whether the design selected in the previous step is able to operate over the space of uncertain parameters. If the design is feasible it is assumed to be flexible; otherwise, the critical point obtained from the flexibility evaluation is included in the current set of periods, and a new multiperiod formulation is solved in order to obtain a new design.

2.2. Strategy of Global Optimization

The developed strategy by Björk and Westerlund (2002) is used in this work to find the global optimization solution for a real case. In this strategy, an alternative to global optimization is applied in the Multiperiod SYNFLEX model to obtain flexible HEN synthesis. The strategy firstly proposes transforming non-convex terms in convex to ensure a global optimization solution which will be an underestimation of the solution to the original non convex problem. The necessary time to find the solution for this transformed problem will be increased respect to the solution time for the original problem, but it can be found with standard MINLP-solvers. Adding the solution of a previously solved transformed into convex problem as new gridpoints will, therefore, make the new problem more accurate. If a solution of a subproblem is at some gridpoints, on the other hand, it will also be a feasible solution to the original problem, since the approximation is exact at the gridpoints. This fact can be used as a convergence criterion instead of a difference between upper and lower bounding problems. The proposed new strategy is schematically shown at Figure 1.

3. Results

3.1. Example #1

The data for the first illustrative example is given at Table 1 where the proposed methodology is applied to do global optimization strategy and simultaneous synthesis of

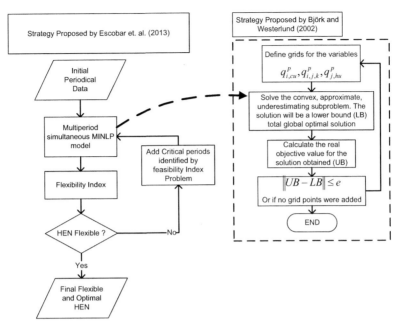

Figure 1. New methodology scheme

multiperiod heat exchanger network. The results can be seen at Table 2 and the Upper Bound (UB) and Lower Bound (LB) calculated during the global optimization procedure are shown at Table 3 and Table 4.

In Table 2, can be seen that the value of the objective function (TAC) when the problem is solved by SYNFLEX model is equal to that obtained by the global optimization procedure. It guarantees that the solutions given by SYNFLEX at both periods correspond to global optimum points for the required operating conditions for each case. Hence, including this global optimization procedure prevents that SYNFLEX model get stuck in a local optimum when the number of period is increased or for a higher dimension problems. In this example the achievable flexibility index is increased up to 20 °C with a global optimal solution of 5 heat exchangers producing a reasonable higher investment and operating cost corresponding to higher TAC.

3.2. Example # 2

The proposed methodology is applied to design the flexible HEN to a plant which consists of a bio-ethanol processor system. It has an Ethanol Steam Reforming (ESR) plug flow reactor, where most of the conversion of ethanol to H_2 is made. Carbon monoxide (CO) which poisons the fuel cell catalyst is produced in the ESR, so additional processing is needed to remove this substance. There are three reactors that configure the cleaning system. These are two Water Gas Shift (WGS), one of high temperature (HTS) and the other of low temperature (LTS), that favors the equilibrium of the reaction to higher conversion rates of CO. The third is a Preferential Oxidation of Carbon monoxide (CO-Prox) reactor, where oxidation of CO into CO_2 is made. Ethanol and vaporized water are mixed and then supplied to the jacket of the ESR reactor, to produce ethanol decomposition such that $CH_3CH_2OH + 3.H_2O \leftrightarrow 6.H_2 + 2.CO_2$.

Table 1. Problem data for Example #1

Stream	Tin (°C)	Tout (°C)	Flow Capacity (kW°C^{-1})	Heat transfer coefficient (kW°C^{-1}m^{-2})
CU	5	15		1
HU	210	210		1
H1	150	45	20	2
C1	60	120	13	2
C2	20	120	12	2

Cost of heat exchanger ($y^{-1})= 4000+ 700 x Area$^{0.8}$/ Cost of utility ($y^{-1})= 4000+ 560 x Area $^{0.8}$/ Cost of Cooling utility ($ kW^{-1} y^{-1}) =20/Cost of Heating utility ($ kW^{-1} y^{-1}) =20

Table 2. Results for example #1

Period	Number of required heat exchangers	Operating Cost ($ y^{-1})	Investment Cost ($ y^{-1})	TAC-Global Optimization ($ y^{-1})	TAC-SynFlex ($ y^{-1})	Flexibility Index (°C)
1	4	2,400	50,029	52,429	52,429	2.667
2	5	1,200	55,802	57,002	57,002	20

Table 3. Lower and Upper bound for first period of example #1.

Iteration	Lower Bound ($ y^{-1})	Upper Bound ($ y^{-1})	Gap (%)
1	45,080.03	52,429	16.3
2	52,309.13	52,429	0.23
3	52,414.77	52,429	0.02
4	52,427.28	52,429	0.003

Table 4. Lower and Upper bound for second period of example #1.

Iteration	Lower Bound ($ y^{-1})	Upper Bound ($ y^{-1})	Gap (%)
1	51,919.74	57,002	9.78
2	56,819.26	57,002	0.32

The overall reaction is endothermic. The amount of oxygen (in air) injected into the CO-PrOX is about twice of the stoichiometric relation to have a good selectivity and satisfy the requirements of the fuel cell (FC). It converts chemical energy directly into electrical energy. This new strategy is applied to Hydrogen production to determine which set of cold streams must be heated with specific hot streams. The following cost data is considered for doing the calculations given at Table 5. Therefore, a good HEN design is important in order to obtain great efficiency of the process and to decrease the operating cost, specially for systems involving valuable bio fuels as raw material.

In this example the application of the new methodology allows increasing the flexibility index up to 15 °C. However, for this case the flexibility index of 8.7 °C is acceptable for the operating conditions required at period 1. Again, the new methodology is able to guarantee a global optimum point for both periods.

Table 5. Problem data for Example # 2

Stream	Tin (°C)	Tout (°C)	Flow Capacity (kW°C-1)	Heat transfer coefficient (kW°C-1m-2)
CU	25	28		87.77
HU	807	807		10.22
H1	709.00	500.00	0.6268	87.15
H2	538.92	150.00	0.5966	31.54
H3	405.67	94.98	0.6223	34.41
H4	94.98	80.00	2.3012	97.43
H5	810.84	286.64	1.6787	10.22
C1	41.76	98.25	0.9482	190.01
C2	98.25	99.25	111.9641	190.01
C3	98.25	126.50	10.8001	31.77
C4	126.50	709.00	0.5482	9.78
C5	25.00	300	0.0178	194.02
C6	80.00	500.00	1.5921	13.23

Cost of heat exchanger ($y^{-1})= 1+ 379.5 x area $^{0.65}$/ Cost of utility ($y^{-1})= 1+ 379.5 x area $^{0.65}$/ Cost of Cooling utility ($ kW^{-1} y^{-1}$) =1000/ Cost of Heating utility ($ kW^{-1} y^{-1}$) =1000

Tabla 6. Results for example #2

Period	Number of required heat exchangers	Operating Cost ($ y-1)	Investment Cost ($ y-1)	TAC-Global Optimization ($ y-1)	Flexibility Index (°C)
1	15	45,338.8	817.2	46,156	8.7
2	15	111,742	988	112,730	15

Table 7. Lower and Upper bound for first period of example #2

Iteration	Lower Bound ($ y^{-1}$)	Upper Bound ($ y^{-1}$)	Gap (%)
1	45,879.49	46,224	0.75
2	46,131.93	46,182	0.109
3	46,135.37	46,156	0.044

Table 8. Lower and Upper bound for second period of example #2.

Iteration	Lower Bound ($ y^{-1}$)	Upper Bound ($ y^{-1}$)	Gap (%)
1	112,391.17	112,668	0.24
2	112,568.11	112,730	0.14

4. Conclusions and Future Works

A novel strategy to obtain an optimal and flexible heat exchanger network has been presented in this work where it is obtained from the integration of different models available in the literature. Hence, the first part of the strategy ensures proper operation under a certain working temperature range according to the obtained flexibility index. The second part ensures that the obtained HEN is the optimal solution found between lower bound (LB) and upper bound (UB). To achieve this result a set of convex subproblems (MINLPs) is solved. It was found through the examples analyzed here that a higher flexibility index was obtained at expense of higher TAC values. However, the operational conditions can be significantly improved when higher flexibility index is achievable.

This new strategy was applied to two examples, the first one more simple to show the steps of the procedure. The second one, consisted of the process to obtain hydrogen from bio-ethanol coupled to PEM fuel cells, where the optimal and flexible heat energy integration is important in order to obtain great efficiency. The next step is the integration with the developed strategy by Luppi et. al. (2014) to design reconfigurable control structure. It is based on the sum of square deviations of non controlled variables and other useful indexes. The objective is to find a proper plant wide control for a nominal working point and redundant control loops for critical situations that can occur in the chemical plant with energy integration.

Acknowledgements

The authors want to acknowledge the financial support from CONICET (Consejo Nacional de Investigaciones Cientificas y Técnicas), ANPCyT and Universidad Tecnologica Nacional-Facultad Regional Rosario from Argentina.

Referentes

Z. A. R. Ciric, C. A. Floudas, 1991, Heat Exchanger Network Synthesis without decomposition, Computers and Chemical Engineering, 15, 6, 385-396.

Y. K. Björk, T. Westerlund, 2002, Global Optimization of heat exchanger network synthesis problems with and without the isothermal mixing assumption, Computers and Chemical Engineering, 26, 1581– 1593.

W. P. Luppi, L. Nieto Degliuomini, M. P. Garcia, M. S. Basualdo, 2014, Fault-tolerant control design for safe production of hydrogen from bioethanol, International Journal of Hydrogen Energy, 39, 1, 231–248

V. M. Escobar, J. O. Trierweiler, I. E. Grossman, 2013, Simultaneous synthesis of heat exchanger networks whit operability considerations: Flexibiliy and controllability, Computers and Chemical Engineering, 55, 158– 180.

U. M. Escobar, J. O. Trierweiler, I.E. Grossman, 2011, SynFlex: a computational framework for synthesis of flexible heat exchanger networks, Computer Aided Chemical Engineering, 32, 2, 2276–2290.

T. T. F. Yee, I. E. Grossman, 1990, Simultaneous Optimization Models for Heat Integration- II. Heat Exchanger Network Synthesis, Computers and Chemical Enginerring, 14, 1165-1184.

S. L. Nieto Degliuomini, S. Biset, P. Luppi, M. Basualdo, 2012, A rigorous computational model for hydrogen production from bio-ethanol to feed a fuel cell stack, International Journal of Hydrogen Energy, 37, 4, 2012, 3108 – 3129.

Jiří Jaromír Klemeš, Petar Sabev Varbanov and Peng Yen Liew (Editors)
Proceedings of the 24th European Symposium on Computer Aided Process Engineering – ESCAPE 24
June 15-18, 2014, Budapest, Hungary.

A Systems Approach for the Holistic Screening of Second Generation Biorefinery Paths for Energy and Bio-based Products

Marinella Tsakalova[a],*, Aidong Yang[b], Antonis C. Kokossis[a]

[a]School of Chemical Engineering, National Technical University of Athens, Greece
[b]Faculty of Engineering and Physical Science, University of Surrey, United Kindom
marintsa@mail.ntua.gr

Abstract

One of the key challenges in the area of biorefining is to screen over the multiple possibilities and combinations among the numerous bio-based sources, processes and products that form a biorefinery. The methodology proposed in the current paper makes use of the systems technology to deal with the overflow of degrees of freedom originated from different sources of information and different granularities and aspects of the problem (engineering, supply chain, agricultural). The proposed holistic approach is based on the formulation of a generic and modular superstructure comprising common elements of the synthesis involved and tested against the development of an evolving real-life lignocellulosic biorefinery. Building elements include feedstock, processes, blocks of intermediates and final products. Different studies scope the impact on deviating from single-product to multi-product processes, the selection of co-products when a fixed production of a primal product (methane) is considered, implications of variations in market conditions and supplies as well as the significance of the cost for transport in the optimal solution. This study reveals a clear advantage of multi-product plants, essentially pointing to the fact that single-product plants are not feasible.

Keywords: Synthesis, Optimization, Biorefinery

1. Introduction

Biomass technologies have been inundated with new ideas and innovations posing new challenges to chemical engineering. Individual bio-based paths and production schemes featuring a single chemical product or fuel have gradually taken a significant position in markets. The production of individual biofuels, and biochemicals (Demirbas, 2007) has steadily led to the development of the concept of biorefining (Clark, 2007). Exploring possible chemical products from biomass processing, NREL and PNNL (Werpy et al., 2004) produced an impressive list of potential building blocks, secondary chemicals, intermediates and final products.

The area of biorefinery is attractive and can be approached from different perspectives. Thus literature is increasingly enriched with new ideas related to catalysts, enzymes, types of feedstock, technology efficiencies, portfolio of products and associated co-products, techno-economic assessment, supply chain, LCA analysis, environmental impacts, social factors, optimization etc. A possible way to get out of the maze is by a systematic approach to biorefineries.

An essential challenge of process engineering is to employ the existing knowledge and experience of systems technology to guide the innovative design of biorefineries towards competitiveness through integration of bio-based processes with the existing conventional infrastructure. Different types of biomass feedstock, possible intermediate and final products and processing technologies and options can be used as yeast for systems technology and integration to offer solutions to the challenging area and assist vital decisions that have to be taken (Kokossis and Yang, 2010).

A great discussion is made over the integration of biorefineries either with other type of biomass or even with other type of bio refineries such as marine bio refineries. Additionally waste water systems can be integrated within the refinery (Ryan et al., 2009). However, systematic screening of a large amount of options in general and exploring integration opportunities between flows, chemicals, processing routes etc, although all important for optimal biomass utilization, are still largely unnoticeable in the literature.

The contribution of this paper is the presentation of a holistic and structured way of formulating problems involved in a biorefinery in terms of feedstock, intermediate and final products and processing technologies enabling a screening process to deal with a variety of solutions engaging links among economic and environmental aspects. For illustration purposes, a case study of biogas (methane) productions is presented. This example will be imposed to several scenarios such as the limited availability of biomass. In this case, the optimal solution should cover the market demand of the desired products with the goal to sustain the biorefinery economically and environmentally.

2. Methodology Overview

2.1. Problem Description
The problem can be described as follows: Given a set of feedstocks j that through the processes l can be converted to either intermediate product i or final products k. For the feedstock, intermediate and final products prices are known. For the processes conversions and investment cost to final or intermediate products are known. Additionally for the processes energy needs are know in terms of steam, fuel and electricity (consumption or production) and LCA performance indicators such as CO_2 equivalent. The degrees of freedom of the problem are the selection of the paths, the capacity of the plant, the product portfolios, the selection of feedstock and the level of integration required to optimise technical, economic, and/or environmental performance.

2.2. Proposed Approach
The problem described above is to be handled by a holistic approach. The screening for the appropriate paths should be carried out simultaneously, not assessing each path separately. To account for multiple entries of chemicals and intermediates, the overlapping between processes and the complementary production of more than one product, an integrated approach and a synthesis representation have to be adapted. The representation is composed by building blocks that include feedstock points, intermediate bulk chemicals, products, as well as conventional and non-conventional processes. Network connectivities enable possible links between synthesis blocks, essentially describing a superstructure representation for the biorefinery. The superstructure is a superset of all individual biorefinery schemes.

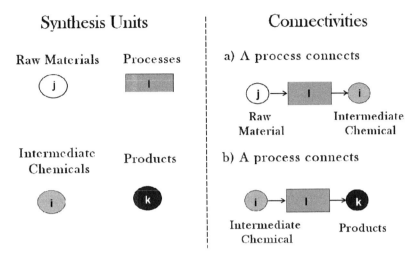

Figure 1. (a) Synthesis Units and (b) Connectivities

2.2.1. Synthesis

2.2.1.1 Synthesis Units

The synthesis units of the superstructure consist of nodes and blocks. Nodes include raw materials, products, and intermediates chemicals. Blocks include processes whereas process streams account for the connections between blocks and nodes. Figure 1(a) illustrates the units of the superstructure with nodes for feedstocks (yellow), products (brown), and intermediates (orange). Processes are represented by blocks (green).

2.2.1.2 Synthesis Connectivities

The connectivity between units is then determined by their input-output structure. If a node makes a possible feed for a process then a connection is established. Whether it is activated or not will be decided by the optimization of the superstructure. The possible set of connections is illustrated in Figure 1(b). Figure 2 illustrates the superstructure of ethylene production based on 5 different biomass types, 9 processes and 6 intermediate chemicals.

2.2.2. Optimization

The superstructure model is subsequently formulated as an optimization problem. Its solution produces the optimal paths to deploy. The formulation of the model uses sets of variables and parameters that describe the function of each unit. Parameters include prices, market demands, conversions and energy efficiencies. Constraints include mass and energy balances, market constrains, cost equation and logical constraints. The model deploys continuous and binary variables. The continuous variables include process inlet and outlet flows, as well as variables to account for economic performance. Binary variables select and deselect units. The model takes the form of a mixed-integer programming problem and is optimized using commercial software.

3. Case Study: Biogas (Methane) production

For the particular problem, the following synthesis units (nodes and blocks) are available: 4 different types of biomass (corn stover, woodchips, municipal waste, plant oil); 19 conventional and non conventional processes (Syngas fermentation to ethanol, Glycerol to Propylene Glycol, Propylene to Butanol, Biomass Fermentation to Ethanol,

Methanol synthesis from Syngas, Biogas reforming to Syngas, Plant oil to biodiesel & Glycerol, Propylene to Propylene Glycol, Ethanol dehydration to Ethylene, Alcohol synthesis from Syngas, Propylene to acetone, Indirect Biomass Gasification, Methanol to olefins- MTO, Direct Biomass Gasification, Anaerobic Digestion of MSW for Biogas, ABE fermentation, Syngas to NH3, Glycerol Anaerobic Digestion to Biogas); and 12 intermediate and final products (ethanol, ethylene, methane, syngas, methanol, acetone, butanol, propylene, biodiesel, glycerol, propylene glycol, ammonia).

Using routes to compose a superstructure, an optimisation problem was solved, where the optimiser was to choose the optimal route for market demand of methane (biogas) 1,000 kt/y. Note that biogas can be an intermediate or a final product. For the particular problem the solution seems to be obvious (via the anaerobic digestion of municipal waste). However, taking into considerations sustainability and feasibility of the production route and using proper constraints to the mathematical problem, the selection of the optimal solution seems to be more complex. Using profitability as the objective function to the problem, the selection provides a strong preference towards the multi-product plants. Acetone, butanol, ethylene and syngas are selected as co-products in order to enhance the profitability of methane production (Table 1, Selection A). The mathematical model that has been developed also enables uncertainty analysis that might involve changes in market, transport cost, environmental issues etc. Taking into consideration the effect of limiting biomass availability, the optimization model gave as a result termed Selection B (in Table 1) where the woodchip use is restricted and the biorefinery is based on corn stover and municipal waste to sustain the profitability of the plant.

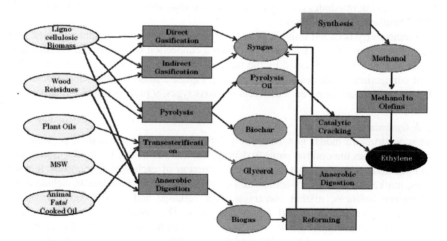

Figure 2. Ethylene superstructure example

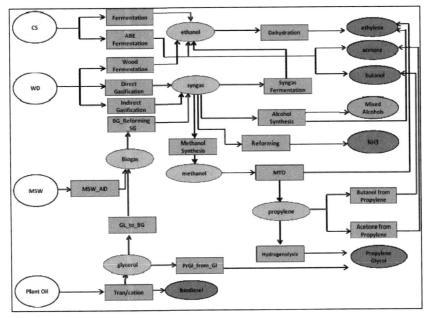

Figure 3. Superstructure of biogas production problem

Taking into consideration environmental constraints compared to the Selection A and B the optimization model provided a solution that tends to keep the CO_2-equivalent GHG emission of the biorefinery paths as low as possible, Thus Selection C was taken as the optimal environmentally path where the corn stover manufacture processes (as feedstock to the fermentation to ethanol and ABE fermentation) possesses negative carbon footprints. The selection of biorefinery C having one more process that of corn stover fermentation constitutes a more environmentally friendly solution compared to that of biorefinery B. From the above results it is essential to address a solution based on multi-objective criteria in order to get a comprehensive solution that will deploy simultaneously economic and environmental aspects.

Table 1. Input and data results for the optimization problem of biogas production

Summary Result Table			
Selections	Feedstock	Processes	Products
A	Corn Stover Wood Chips MSW	Biomass Fermentation to Ethanol Ethanol dehydration to Ethylene Anaerobic Digestion of MSW for Biogas ABE fermentation Direct Biomass Gasification Biogas reforming to Syngas	Syngas Ethylene Acetone Butanol Biogas
B	Corn Stover MSW	Anaerobic Digestion of MSW for Biogas ABE fermentation	Acetone Butanol Ethanol Biogas
C	Corn Stover MSW	Anaerobic Digestion of MSW for Biogas ABE fermentation Biomass Fermentation to Ethanol	Acetone Butanol Ethanol Biogas

4. Conclusion

Introducing renewable biomass into the manufacturing of energy and chemical products poses great challenges as well as opportunities to process systems engineering. This requires extensions of established methods and tools to address new problems in this area. This paper presents a systematic and holistic methodology to screen and select products and processing paths by combining a superstructure scheme and an optimisation model. The selection produced combination of products, energy products and chemicals affirming the advantage of multi-product plants. The selected paths conclude that environmental feasibility can be sustained via integrated paths that can simultaneously retain profitability. The set of paths and processes still contains a large number of degrees of freedom to optimize. A number of additional criteria can be accordingly considered (risk analysis, flexibility, supply chain etc). The methodology is now being further developed and applied to more sophisticated case studies, multi-objective criteria, different types of biorefineries touching areas of energy sufficiency and integration towards the design of a sustainable and feasible biorefinery in means of economics, environment and energy use.

References

J. H. Clark, 2007, Green chemistry for the second generation biorefinery – sustainable chemical manufacturing based on biomass, J Chem Technol Biotechnol, 82, 603–609.

A. Demirbas, 2007, Progress and recent trends in biofuels, Progress in Energy and Combustion Science, 33, 1–18.

M. FitzPatrick, P. Champagne, M. Cunningham, R. Whitney, 2010, A biorefinery processing perspective: Treatment of lignocellulosic materials for the production of value-added products, Bioresource Technology, 101, 8915-8922.

Ch. Floudas, J. Elia, R. Baliban, 2012, Hybrid and single feedstock energy processes for liquid transportation fuels: A critical review, Computers and Chemical Engineering, 41, 24– 51.

L. F. Gutierrez, O. J. Sanchez, C. A. Cardona, 2009, Process integration possibilities for biodiesel production from palm oil using ethanol obtained from lignocellulosic residues of oil palm industry, Bioresource Technology, 100, 1227-1237.

H. Huang, S. Ramaswamy, W. Al –Dajani, U. Tschirner, 2010, Process modeling and analysis of pulp mill-based integrated biorefinery with hemicellulose pre-extraction for ethanol production: A comparative study, Bioresource Technology, 101, 2, 624-613.

A. Kokossis, A. Yang, 2010, On the use of systems technologies and a systematic approach for the synthesis and the design of future biorefineries, Computers and Chemical Engineering, 34, 1397–1405.

A. Kokossis, A. Yang, M. Tsakalova, T.-C. Lin, 2010, A systems platform for the optimal synthesis of biomass based manufacturing systems, Computer Aided Chemical Engineering, 28,1105-1110.

A.C. Kokossis, A. Yang, M. Tsakalova, T.-C. Lin, 2012, Systematic Screening of Multiple Processing Paths in Biorefineries: the ABC (Accessing Biomass to Chemicals) Project and Its Potential to BuildProcess Synthesis Capabilities, Integrated Biorefineries: Design, Analysis, and Optimization, CRC Press, Florida, USA.

R. Raymond, J.-A. Ballacillo, K. Aviso, A. Culaba, 2009, A fuzzy multiple-objective approach to the optimization of bioenergy system footprints, Chemical Engineering Research and Design, 87, 1162–1170.

M. Tsakalova, A. Yang, A. Kokossis, 2011, Implementation and initial evaluation of a decision support platform for selecting production routes of biomass-derived chemicals, Computer Aided Chemical Engineering, 29,1470-1474.

T. Werpy, G. Petersen, A. Aden, J. Bozell, J. Holladay, J. White, A. Manheim, 2004, Top Value Added Chemicals From Biomass, Volume I: Results of Screening for Potential Candidates from Sugars and Synthesis Gas, National Renewable Energy Lab, Colorado, USA.

Jiří Jaromír Klemeš, Petar Sabev Varbanov and Peng Yen Liew (Editors)
Proceedings of the 24th European Symposium on Computer Aided Process Engineering – ESCAPE 24
June 15-18, 2014, Budapest, Hungary. Copyright © 2014 Elsevier B.V. All rights reserved.

Full Bivariate MWD in RAFT Copolymerization using Probability Generating Functions

Cecilia Fortunatti[*], Adriana Brandolin, Claudia Sarmoria, Mariano Asteasuain

PLAPIQUI, Camino La Carrindanga km 7, Bahía Blanca (8000), Argentina
cfortunatti@plapiqui.edu.ar

Abstract

In this work, we develop a model for RAFT copolymerization able to predict the full bivariate molecular weight distribution (MWD). To the best of our knowledge, this is the first model to do so. For this purpose, the 2D probability generating functions (pgf) technique was used. Our results show that the pgf technique allows obtaining the bivariate MWD without simplifying assumptions or any a priori knowledge of the MWD shape. In this way, the model provides useful information about the copolymer molecular structure and can aid scientific and industrial practitioners to establish design parameters and operating policies to produce desired copolymer structures. Moreover, the results underline the importance of simulation as a powerful tool in process design.

Keywords: probability generating function, MWD, RAFT, copolymerization, model.

1. Introduction

Reversible addition-fragmentation chain transfer (RAFT) polymerization is one of the most promising controlled radical polymerization (CRP) techniques. This approach has attracted considerable interest in both the scientific and industrial communities thanks to its effectiveness in achieving the living/controlled behavior and a wide range of polymerizable monomers (Braunecker and Matyjaszewski, 2007).

Although RAFT polymerization has been extensively studied, there are still unresolved fundamental issues regarding the kinetics of this process (Tobita, 2013). In some systems, an induction period and a retardation of the propagation rate is produced by the augmentation of the RAFT agent concentration. This may indicate that the RAFT moiety is not acting just as a chain transfer agent, and therefore different theoretical kinetic models were developed to explain these phenomena. Barner-Kowollik et al. (2001) proposed that the intermediate radical of two arms is relatively stable and, therefore, fragments slowly (slow fragmentation model, SF). Since this theory failed to predict the actual radical concentrations, Monteiro and de Brouwer (2001) proposed the intermediate radical termination model (IRT). This model assumes that the two-arm adduct cross-terminates with the active radicals. However, experimental measures showed that the three-arm star material is negligible, well below the amount predicted by the IRT model. In an effort to unify the experimental data with the model predictions, Konkolewicz et al. (2008) proposed that the cross-termination of the two-arm adduct can only occur with oligomers up to two monomers length (intermediate radical termination with oligomers, IRTO). In another line of thought Buback et al. (2007) claimed that the cross-termination products may undergo the so-called "missing steps" reactions, in which the third weakly bonded branch in the three-arm species reacts with propagating radicals. Ultimately, as Klumperman et al. (2010) stated, the differences between the proposed models may not be as incompatible as it appears, even though more careful kinetic measurements are needed.

In any case, to make the most of this polymerization technique, it is clear that precise modeling studies are necessary in order to determine process and design conditions for producing tailor-made materials that meet pre-specified properties. However, since this mechanism involves the formation of an adduct with two arms, the obtainment of a rigorous description of the reacting system requires computing bivariate molecular weight distributions even for homopolymerization reactions (Fortunatti et al., 2013).

Published studies on simulation (Wang et al., 2012) and optimization (Wang et al., 2006; Ye and Schork, 2009) of RAFT copolymerization systems do not include the prediction of the full molecular weight distribution (MWD). Some works do include the obtainment of the MWD either using PREDICI commercial software (Wulkow et al., 2004), by assuming the MWD shape (Jung and Gomes, 2011), or by direct integration of mass balances (Zapata-González et al., 2011). However they have only dealt with homopolymerization systems.

In previous works we developed a mathematical model for RAFT homopolymerization that predicts average properties together with the full MWD in an accurate and efficient way using probability generating functions (pgf) (Fortunatti et al., 2013). In this paper we extend that work in order to deal with RAFT copolymerization. The new model is able to predict properties of the copolymer as well as the full MWD. As a case study, Styrene (St)-Methyl methacrylate (MMA) copolymerization is addressed. The model could help establish operating conditions and design parameters conducive to the production of tailor-made copolymers. The results also showcase the power of simulation as a tool in process design.

2. Methods

2.1. Mathematical Model

The mathematical model presented in this work considers the SF approach for the RAFT polymerization. Nevertheless, extension to the IRT or IRTO models is straightforward. The kinetic mechanism for the RAFT copolymerization is:

Initiation:
$$I \xrightarrow{f\,k_d} 2I° \quad, \quad I° + M_j \longrightarrow R^j_{2-j,j-1}, \quad j=1,2 \tag{1}$$

Thermal initiation of styrene:
$$3M_1 \xrightarrow{k_{th}} R^1_{1,0} + R^1_{2,0} \tag{2}$$

Propagation:
$$R^i_{n,s} + M_j \xrightarrow{k_{p,ij}} R^j_{n+2-j,s+j-1}, \quad i=1,2; j=1,2 \tag{3}$$

Pre-equilibrium

Addition:
$$R^i_{n,s} + TR_0 \xrightarrow{k^0_{ai}} R^i_{n,s}TR_0 \tag{4}$$

Fragmentation:
$$R^i_{n,s}TR_0 \xrightarrow{(\frac{1}{2})k^0_{fi}} TR^i_{n,s} + R_{0,0}$$
$$R^i_{n,s}TR_0 \xrightarrow{(\frac{1}{2})k^0_{fi}} TR_0 + R^i_{n,s} \tag{5}$$

Core-equilibrium

Addition:
$$R^i_{n,s} + TR^j_{g,h} \xrightarrow{k_{ai}} R^i_{n,s}TR^j_{g,h} \tag{6}$$

Fragmentation:

$$R_{n,s}^i TR_{g,h}^j \xrightarrow{(1/2)k_{fi}} R_{n,s}^i + TR_{g,h}^j$$

$$R_{n,s}^i TR_{g,h}^j \xrightarrow{(1/2)k_{fj}} TR_{n,s}^i + R_{g,h}^j$$

(7)

Chain termination:

by coupling:

$$R_{n,s}^i + R_{g,h}^j \xrightarrow{k_{tc,ij}} P_{n+g,s+h}$$

(8)

by disproportionation:

$$R_{n,s}^i + R_{g,h}^j \xrightarrow{k_{td,ij}} P_{n,s} + P_{g,h}$$

(9)

Chain transfer to monomer:

$$R_{n,s}^i + M_j \xrightarrow{k_{trm,ij}} P_{n,s} + R_{2-j,j-1}^j$$

(10)

The chemical species involved are: initiator (I), monomers St (M_1) and MMA (M_2), active radicals ending in monomer i with n units of M_1 and s units of M_2 ($R_{n,s}^i$), dormant radicals of one arm ending in M_i with n units of M_1 and s units of M_2 ($TR_{n,s}^i$), two-arm adduct with n units of M_1 and s units of M_2 in one branch ending in M_i and g units of M_1 and h units of M_2 in the other branch ending in M_j ($R_{n,s}^i TR_{g,h}^j$), RAFT chain transfer agent (TR_0), and terminated chains with n units of M_1 and s units of M_2 ($P_{n,s}$).

A bulk RAFT copolymerization of St and MMA mediated by cumyl phenyldithioacetate (CPD) with AIBN as initiator was modeled. The operation was considered isothermal at 60 °C. Values of the addition and fragmentation constants were taken from Barner-Kowollik et al. (2001), who conducted experiments for the RAFT homopolymerizations of St and of MMA. It was assumed that the pre-equilibrium and core-equilibrium stages proceed at the same rate ($k_{ai}^0 = k_{ai}$ and $k_{fi}^0 = k_{fi}$). The addition and fragmentation rate constants were taken equal to those for the homopolymerization of each individual monomer. When the active sites involved are of different sort, the kinetic constant used corresponds to the end-monomer of the branch that is either added or split from the RAFT agent moiety. It should be mentioned that no data of the addition and fragmentation constants were found for a copolymerization system. The remaining kinetic parameters were taken from Asteasuain et al. (2011).

Average properties were modeled using the method of double index moments. Accordingly, mass balances of the polymeric species are transformed to obtain balances for the first moments of the copolymer MWD. Then, average properties can be computed from these moments. For the two-arm adduct both partial moments (Zapata-González et al., 2011), and conventional double index moments were considered in order to take into account the units of each monomer in the reacting branch and the total amount of each monomer in the species, respectively.

The full bivariate MWD was modeled using 2D probability generating functions (pgf). This modeling technique is based on transforming the infinite mass balances of the polymer species with two internal coordinates -the number of each monomer in the chain- to the 2D pgf domain (Brandolin and Asteasuain, 2013). In this way a finite set of equations is obtained for the 2D pgf transform of the bivariate MWD of the copolymer. After solving the pgf equations, the MWD distribution is recovered by numerical inversion of the pgf (Asteasuain and Brandolin, 2010). This technique has great potential to simulate polymer properties since it does not need any a priori knowledge of the MWD shape and can deal with complex mechanisms. Besides, no simplification or modification of the kinetic mechanism is needed.

All the simulations were performed in gPROMS (Process Systems Enterprise, Ltd.) in a standard desktop computer. The resulted differential algebraic equation system was solved using the solver DASOLV.

3. Results and Discussion

As a previous step, the developed model was run for a RAFT St homopolymerization in order to reproduce the experimental data reported by Barner-Kowollik (2001). It can be seen in Figure 1 that the model shows good agreement with the experimental data.

Then, the CPD mediated copolymerization of St and MMA was modeled considering the following initial reagents concentration: $[St]_0 = [MMA]_0 = 4.39$ mol L^{-1}, $[I]_0 = 3.7$ x 10^{-3} mol L^{-1} and $[TR_0]_0 = 8.5$ x 10^{-3} mol L^{-1}.

The final properties of the resulting resin are shown and Table 1. It can be observed that although slow fragmentation rate constants were used, the predicted two-arm adduct concentration is low, even at the beginning of the reaction (see Figure 2). The model also predicts an induction period of approximately one hour during which dormant radicals reach a maximum concentration.

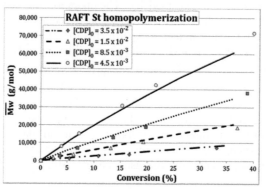

Figure 1. RAFT homopolymerization of St with $[I]0 = 3.7$ x 10^{-3}. (Lines: model output – Symbols: experimental data.)

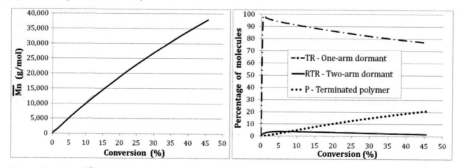

Figure 2. pSt-r-MMA properties development during reaction.

Table 1. pSt-r-MMA properties at final reaction time of 12 h.

Condition	Value after 12 h
$\overline{M_n}$	37,953 g/mol
PDI	1.214
Global composition (% St)	52.2 %
Global conversion	45.5 %
$\overline{M_n}$ One-arm Dormant (TR)	38,440 g/mol
$\overline{M_n}$ Two-arm Dormant (RTR)	76,995 g/mol
$\overline{M_n}$ Dead Polymer(P)	32,841 g/mol

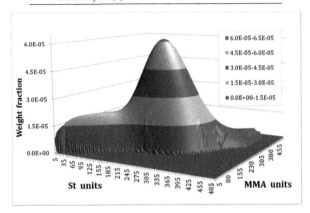

Figure 3. pSt-r-MMA MWD at final reaction time of 12 h.

At final time, the amount of dead polymer chains exceeds 20 %. Even though this value may be considered large for a controlled polymerization, the polydispersity index (PDI) is still low and the $\overline{M_n}$ vs. conversion profile is close to the linear behavior characteristic of living polymerizations.

Finally, the full bivariate MWD can be observed in Figure 3. It can be seen that, albeit the polymer growth is controlled, the distribution shows a "shoulder" in the region of low molecular weights. This may be ascribed to the 20 % of dead polymer since it has lower molecular weight than the dormant chains and the overall polymer. Similarly, the high molecular weight tail observed can be attributed to the two-arm adduct.

4. Conclusions

The RAFT copolymerization with the slow fragmentation kinetics has been successfully modeled, including the prediction of the full MWD of the copolymer. For this purpose, the 2D pgf technique was employed. The model allows obtaining the MWD without simplifying assumptions or any a priori knowledge of the MWD shape. This can be achieved in spite of the high complexity features of the polymerization system, such as the fourth-dimensional nature of the MWD of the intermediate adduct. Finally, it can be seen that the full bivariate MWD can provide detailed information about the copolymer that is useful to predict its characteristics and determine its end-use properties.

References

M. Asteasuain, A. Brandolin, 2010, Mathematical modeling of bivariate polymer property distributions using 2D probability generating functions, 1 - Numerical inversion methods, Macromolecular Theory and Simulations, 19, 6, 342-359.

M. Asteasuain, D. Covan, C. Sarmoria, A. Brandolin, C. Leite de Araujo, J. C. Pinto, 2011, Comprehensive Mathematical Modeling of Controlled Radical Copolymerization in Tubular Reactors, Computer Aided Process Engineering, 29, 51-55.

C. Barner-Kowollik, J. F. Quinn, T. L. U. Nguyen, J. P. A. Heuts, T. P. Davis, 2001, Kinetic investigations of reversible addition fragmentation chain transfer polymerizations: Cumyl phenyldithioacetate mediated homopolymerizations of styrene and methyl methacrylate, Macromolecules, 34, 22, 7849-7857.

A. Brandolin, M. Asteasuain, 2013, Mathematical modeling of bivariate distributions of polymer properties using 2D probability generating functions. part II: Transformation of population mass balances of polymer processes, Macromolecular Theory and Simulations, 22, 5, 273-308.

W. A. Braunecker, K. Matyjaszewski, 2007, Controlled/living radical polymerization: Features, developments, and perspectives, Progress in Polymer Science (Oxford), 32, 1, 93-146.

M. Buback, O. Janssen, R. Oswald, S. Schmatz, P. Vana, 2007, A missing reaction step in dithiobenzoate-mediated RAFT polymerization, Macromolecular Symposia, 248, 158-167.

C. Fortunatti, C. Sarmoria, A. Brandolin, M. Asteasuain, 2013, Prediction of the full molecular weight distribution in raft polymerization using probability generating functions, Computer Aided Process Engineering, 32, 859-864.

S. M. Jung, V. G. Gomes, 2011, Miniemulsion polymerisation via reversible addition fragmentation chain transfer in pseudo-bulk regime, Macromolecular Reaction Engineering, 5, 7-8, 303-315.

B. Klumperman, E. T. A. Van Den Dungen, J. P. A. Heuts, M. J. Monteiro, 2010, RAFT-mediated polymerization- A story of incompatible data?, Macromolecular Rapid Communications, 31, 21, 1846-1862.

D. Konkolewicz, B. S. Hawkett, A. Gray-Weale, S. Perrier, 2008, RAFT polymerization kinetics: Combination of apparently conflicting models, Macromolecules, 41, 17, 6400-6412.

M. J. Monteiro, H. De Brouwer, 2001, Intermediate radical termination as the mechanism for retardation in reversible addition-fragmentation chain transfer polymerization, Macromolecules; 34, 3, 349-352.

H. Tobita, 2013, On the discrimination of RAFT models using miniemulsion polymerization, Macromolecular Theory and Simulations, 22, 8, 399-409.

D. Wang, X. Li, W. J. Wang, X. Gong, B. G. Li, S. Zhu, 2012, Kinetics and modeling of semi-batch RAFT copolymerization with hyperbranching, Macromolecules, 45, 1, 28-38.

R. Wang, Y. Luo, B. Li, X. Sun, S. Zhu, 2006, Design and control of copolymer composition distribution in living radical polymerization using semi-batch feeding policies: A model simulation, Macromolecular Theory and Simulations, 15, 4, 356-368.

M. Wulkow, M. Busch, T. P. Davis, C. Barner-Kowollik, 2004, Implementing the Reversible Addition-Fragmentation Chain Transfer Process in PREDICI, Journal of Polymer Science, Part A: Polymer Chemistry, 42, 6, 1441-1448.

Y. Ye, F. J. Schork, 2009, Modeling and control of sequence length distribution for controlled radical (RAFT) copolymerization, Industrial and Engineering Chemistry Research, 48, 24, 10827-10839.

I. Zapata-González, E. Saldívar-Guerra, J. Ortiz-Cisneros, 2011, Full molecular weight distribution in RAFT polymerization. New mechanistic insight by direct integration of the equations, Macromolecular Theory and Simulations, 20, 6, 370-388.

Jiří Jaromír Klemeš, Petar Sabev Varbanov and Peng Yen Liew (Editors)
Proceedings of the 24th European Symposium on Computer Aided Process Engineering – ESCAPE 24
June 15-18, 2014, Budapest, Hungary. Copyright © 2014 Elsevier B.V. All rights reserved.

Numerical Investigations of Packed Bed Reactors with Irregular Particle Arrangements

Theodoros Atmakidis[a], Eugeny Y. Kenig[a,b]⋆

[a]*University of Paderborn, Faculty of Mechanical Engineering, Chair of Fluid Process Engineering, Pohlweg 55, D-33098 Paderborn, Germany*
[b]*Gubkin Russian State University of Oil and Gas, Moscow, Russian Federation*
eugeny.kenig@upb.de

Abstract

In this work, a computational fluid dynamics (CFD) approach is developed and applied to study the main design and operating parameters in packed bed reactors with moderate tube-to-particle diameter ratios. Packed bed reactors consist of irregular particle arrangements generated using a modified ballistic deposition method. The focus of these investigations is put on the pressure drop, mass transfer and dispersion phenomena in such reactors. Different numerical methods are applied and compared. The suggested numerical analysis represents a valuable tool towards deeper understanding of the fundamental transport phenomena in packed bed reactors and, consequently, for the improvement of the reactor performance.

Keywords: packed bed reactors, CFD, pressure drop, mass transfer, dispersion.

1. Introduction

Packed bed reactors represent one of the most important reactor type widely used in the chemical industry, among others for large-scale manufacturing of basic chemicals and intermediates as well as for the removal of harmful or toxic chemicals from gas or liquid streams. The main advantage of packed bed reactors that makes them very attractive compared to other more sophisticated and novel reactor types is their low cost.

Pressure drop, residence time distribution, mass and heat transfer characteristics are crucial for the optimal design and operation of packed bed reactors, and, hence, their accurate estimation is very important. These characteristics have been studied both experimentally and numerically by several groups.

Pressure drop is a crucial design parameter of packed bed reactors. An overview of the most important pressure drop correlations can be found in Eisfeld and Schnitzlein (2001). The influence of the confining walls is important for packed bed reactors with tube-to-particle diameter ratios smaller than 20. Taking account of this fact, Eisfeld and Schnitzlein (2001) suggested an improved experimental pressure drop correlation

Several groups have studied the mass transfer phenomena existing in packed bed reactors using different experimental methods for both liquid and gas systems. An extensive review on mass transfer in packed beds was published by Wakao and Funazkri (1978) who summarised and revised the developed correlations. Furthermore, they suggested a correlation to describe mass transfer phenomena which still remains popular nowadays. Most of the correlations revised by Wakao and Funazkri (1978) were obtained for large tube-to-particle diameter ratios and only few more recent studies are focused on small tube-to-particle diameter ratios (Tsotsas and Schluender, 1990).

A similar situation also exists in literature for the dispersion studies in packed bed reactors. Although several experimental studies on the dispersion in reactors with large tube-to-particle diameter ratios are reported (see, e.g., Froment and Bischoff, 1979), only few consider small tube-to-particle diameter ratios. However, just for the latter case dispersion can play a very important role, mainly due to the high impact of the confining wall resulting in flow inhomogeneity.

Two different numerical approaches can be found in literature to describe hydrodynamic and transport properties of packed beds. In the first one, packed beds are treated as pseudo-homogeneous media, while modified Navier-Stokes equations are applied in conjunction with the Ergun pressure drop correlation to account for the fluid-solid interaction. To govern local phenomena, overall averaged quantities are replaced by functions describing the radial change of these quantities. For instance, to account for the radial porosity variation, the overall averaged porosity of the whole packed bed reactor is replaced with a function accounting for the porosity distribution along the reactor radius. Different empirical correlations have been developed for the radial porosity profiles (Giese et al., 1998), and, thus, their application may result in large differences in these profiles. This is especially true for the case of packed beds with moderate tube-to-particle diameter ratios, due to significant influence of confining walls to the particle arrangement. As a consequence, substantially different radial velocity profiles are expected. These correlations do not account for the axial variations of the local void fraction which can vary substantially in a packed bed reactor (Atmakidis and Kenig, 2009).

Furthermore, additional, experimentally determined correlations are required to simulate mass transfer, heat transfer or dispersion phenomena. Winterberg et al. (2000) updated correlations for the effective radial thermal conductivity and the effective radial dispersion coefficient. Both correlations depend on the local flow velocity and the radial position, and a good agreement is found between the developed model and the experimental results, both with and with exothermic reactions.

In the second approach, the packed bed is simulated based on the consideration of the actual packed bed geometry. This yields a detailed description of the liquid flow between the particles. In this way, no additional empirical correlations are required for the porosity distribution. To resolve the fluid flow between particles, two different numerical methods are used. These methods are revised and presented in a review paper published by Dixon et al. (2006).

The first method is the lattice Boltzman method (LBM). Using the LBM, the calculation of the local velocity, pressure drop, axial and radial dispersion coefficients in irregular arrangements of spheres in cylindrical containers is possible with good accuracy (Freund et al., 2003). However, the simulation of non-isothermal conditions poses serious challenges, and thermal LBM models are still in the state of development (Tsotsas, 2010).

In the second method, the Navier-Stokes equations are applied to the void between the spheres, and they are solved using the traditional finite volume methods. Models for the heat and mass transfer are already developed and validated for this methodology. The main drawback of the method is in the mesh generation near the particle-particle and particle-wall contact points. At these contact points, highly skewed mesh elements may appear when a relative course mesh is selected. This may lead to an inappropriate spacial discretisation and causes convergence problems. The latter can be avoided using mesh element refinement. However, this refinement increases the number of mesh elements and, consecutively, the necessary computational power and time.

To avoid low quality mesh elements at the contact points between particles as well as between the particles and the confining wall, different alternatives have been suggested in literature, all modifying locally the particle geometry. The most popular methods are the local flattening of the particles in the particle proximity (Eppinger et al., 2011), the generation of small cylinders (bridges) at the particle contact points, and the particle shrinkage or expansion (Calis et al., 2001). Dixon et al. (2013) revised all the different alternatives using two simplified geometries. The first one comprises two particles in a contact; the second one consists of one particle in contact with the confining wall. For this simplified case, it was found that the method suggested by Eppinger et al. (2011) gives better results in terms of drag coefficient and heat flow than the other alternatives.

To summarise, reliable heat and mass transfer models based on the LBM are not available yet. Nowadays, packed beds can also be simulated using traditional, more rigorous finite volume methods supplemented by advanced solution algorithms. The focus of the current work is to develop and validate reliable CFD models in order to study the most important parameters affecting design and operation of packed beds. To avoid low quality mesh, the particle shrinkage approach is employed. This methodology is tested for all considered parameters.

2. Model description and implementation

For the generation of irregular particle arrangements, a ballistic deposition method is employed and modified using the Monte Carlo approach. This method allows the generation of random configurations that are close to reality. Moreover, it requires significantly less computational time and programming work complexity than the most rigorous ballistic deposition algorithms. A detailed description of the employed method for the geometry construction and its validation can be found in Atmakidis and Kenig (2009). To describe the complex 3-D velocity and concentration field between the particles of a packed bed reactor, classical equations of continuity, momentum and species transfer are used (Bird et al., 2002). The void between the particles remains constant, since all solid particles keep fixed positions. The flow is considered to be incompressible and steady-state. The simulations are performed for Reynolds numbers below 100 (laminar flow regime).

The numerical solution was obtained using the commercial CFD code ANSYS CFX 11.0® by ANSYS Inc. based on a second-order discretisation scheme. Special attention was paid to ensure an accurate resolving of the boundary conditions near the particle surface. This was achieved with the help of prismatic elements, while 5 layers were found to be sufficient for the good fulfilment of the boundary conditions. A grid independence study was performed for all simulated cases. The velocity and concentration fields obtained for varying process conditions were further processed to yield important flow and mass transport characteristics described in the following section.

3. Results

3.1. Hydrodynamics

As the first step, the hydrodynamic behaviour has been studied. In Figure 1a, stream line plots are shown for the air system, illustrating the velocity distribution within a packed bed. Channelling is observed near the wall due to the higher local void fraction compared to the centre of the tube. In Figure 1b, the calculated pressure drop is compared with the established correlations, namely, the Ergun, the Carman, the Zhavoronkovet al. and the Reichelt correlations (these correlations can be found, e.g., in Eisfeld and Schnitzlein, 2001). Numerical results agree better with the latter two correlations, in which the wall effect on pressure drop is included.

3.2. Dispersion

To study dispersion phenomena in packed beds, two different methods, namely the tracer and the post-processing method, are applied. The first method imitates the experimental procedure in which a non-diffusive tracer is injected into the packed bed. The use of a non-diffusive traced is based on the assumption that molecular diffusion is slow and the overall residence time is too low for diffusion to be an influencing factor. The residence time can be evaluated from the evolution of the tracer concentration. The second method is purely numerical and allows fast residence time estimation. Provided that the velocity field is determined and assuming no reactions in the packed bed, local residence time can be obtained numerically, by solving the following equation:

$$u \, \nabla \, \tau = 1 \qquad\qquad\qquad\qquad\qquad\qquad\qquad\qquad (1)$$

where u is local velocity and τ is local residence time. Using the tracer method, useful conclusions can be drawn based on the calculated residence time distribution (RTD) curves. At low flow rates, the residence time is large and the RTD curve has a long tail. At higher liquid flow rates, the RTD curve becomes narrow with reduced tailing. This implies that the flow inside the packed-bed tends to plug flow as the flow rate increases, because, at these flow conditions, the influence of stagnant zones on the overall flow is reduced.

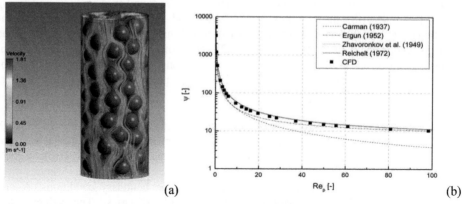

(a)   (b)

Figure 1. Velocity field of the air inside a packed bed for λ=3.77: Re= 14.1 (a); dimensionless pressure drop as a function of the particle Reynolds number (b).

In Figure 2a, the calculated Peclet numbers as functions of the Reynolds number are shown together with the reported values from literature (the grey area). As one can see, there is a big scattering of the reported values. It is worth noting that the Peclet numbers for the moderate tube-to-particle diameter ratio packed beds estimated from our simulations are in the same range as those from literature. A comparison of the two proposed methods is illustrated in Figure 2b. They yield almost identical local average residence time values, with deviations smaller than 5 %. The post-processingmethod can be used for a fast estimation of the flow field in homogeneities.

3.3. Mass transfer

Two different case studies are selected for numerical analysis of the mass transfer in packed beds, basically imitating the relevant experimental procedures. The first one is the dissolution of benzoic acid particles in water, the second one is the sublimation of naphthalene particles in air. In Figure 3a, the concentration field of naphthalene is presented for Re = 61.5. To validate the simulation results, experimental mass transfer correlations from literature are used (Figure 3b), and a good agreement between numerical and experimental results is found. A similar behaviour is observed for the dissolution of benzoic acid particles in water.

4. Conclusions

This work presents a comprehensive study of coupled flow and mass transport phenomena in packed bed reactors. Both the generation of irregular bed geometries and

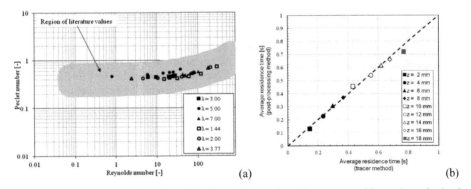

Figure 2.Peclet number as a function of the Reynolds number (a);average residence time obtained for λ=3 by the post-processing and by the tracer method at different packed-bed reactor heights (b).

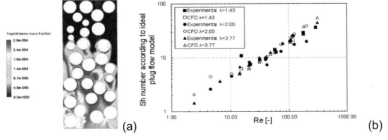

Figure 3. Naphthalene mass fraction of packed bed for λ=3.77 and Re=61.5 (a); Sherwood number as a function of the Reynolds number: experiments vs. simulation (b).

the solution of the governing fluid dynamics equations were performed numerically, using a modified ballistic deposition method and CFD. Based on the obtained velocity and concentration fields, critical process parameters, namely pressure drop, residence time distribution and Sherwood numbers, could be determined. All CFD models were validated against experimental data found in literature, and a satisfying agreement was found. The error introduced due to the geometry modification (particle shrinkage) has just limited effect on the results which ensures the model reliability.

In most cases, the proposed approach allows the derivation of fluid dynamics and mass transfer correlations with high accuracy and robustness; this helps to reduce the necessary number of real measurements. The numerical correlations obtained can further be extended to account for the influence of specific process parameters, e.g. density or viscosity, which cannot be easily done experimentally. In general, the developed numerical approach provides knowledge that is often difficult to obtain by experiments, and hence, it can help to significantly improve the design of packed bed units with low and moderate tube-to-particle diameter ratios.

References

T. Atmakidis, E.Y. Kenig, 2009, CFD-based analysis of the wall effect on the pressure drop in packed beds with moderate tube/particle diameter ratios in the laminar flow regime, Chemical Engineering Journal, 155, 404-410.

R.B. Bird, W.E. Stewart, E.N. Lightfoot, 2002, Transport Phenomena, 2nd ed., Wiley, New York, USA.

H.P.A. Calis, J. Nijenhuis, B.C. Paikert, F. M. Dautzenberg, C.M. Van den Bleek, 2001, CFD modelling and experimental validation of pressure drop and flow profile in a novel structured catalytic reactor packing, Chemical Engineering Science, 56, 1713-1720.

A.G. Dixon, M. Nijemeisland, E. H. Stitt, 2006, Packed tubular reactor modelling and catalyst design using computational fluid dynamics, Advances in Chemical Engineering, 31, 307-389.

A.G. Dixon, M. Nijemeisland, E.H. Stitt, 2013, Systematic mesh development for 3D CFD simulation of fixed beds: Contact points study, Computers and Chemical Engineering, 48, 135–153

B. Eisfeld, K. Schnitzlein, 2001, The influence of confning walls on the pressure drop in packed beds, Chemical Engineering Science, 56, 4321-4329.

T. Eppinger, K. Seidler, M. Kraume, 2011, DEM-CFD simulations of fixed bed reactors with small tube to particle diameter ratios, Chemical Engineering Journal, 166, 324-331.

H. Freund, J. Bauer, T. Zeiser, G. Emig, 2005, Detailed Simulation of Transport Processes in Fixed-Beds, Industrial and Engineering Chemistry Research, 44, 6423- 6434.

G.F. Froment, K.B Bischoff, 1979, Chemical Reactor Analysis and Design, Wiley, New York.

M. Giese, K. Rottschfer, D. Vortmeyer, 1998, Measured and modeled superficial flow profiles in packed beds with liquid flow, AIChE Journal, 44, 484-90.

E. Tsotsas, 2010, VDI Heat atlas, Springer-Verlag, Berlin Heidelberg, Germany.

E. Tsotsas, E.-U. Schluender, 1990, Measurements of mass transfer between particles and gas in packed tubes at very low tube to particle diameter ratios, Warme Stoffubertrang, 2, 245-256.

N. Wakao, T. Funazkri, 1978, Effect of fluid dispersion coefficients on particle-to-fluid mass transfer coefficients in packed beds, Chemical Engineering Science, 33, 1375-1384.

M. Winterberg, E. Tsotsas, A. Krischke, D. Vortmeyer, 2000, A simple and coherent set of coefficients for modelling of heat and mass transport with and without chemical reaction in tubes filled with spheres, Chemical Engineering Science, 55, 967-979.

Jiří Jaromír Klemeš, Petar Sabev Varbanov and Peng Yen Liew (Editors)
Proceedings of the 24th European Symposium on Computer Aided Process Engineering – ESCAPE 24
June 15-18, 2014, Budapest, Hungary. Copyright © 2014 Elsevier B.V. All rights reserved.

Stabilization of Empty Fruit Bunch (EFB) derived Bio-oil using Antioxidants

Chung Loong Yiin[a], Suzana Yusup[a,*], Parncheewa Udomsap[b], Boonyawan Yoosuk[b], Sittha Sukkasi[b]

[a]*Biomass Processing Lab, Centre for Biofuel and Biochemical, Green Technology, Mission Oriented Research, Chemical Engineering Department,Universiti Teknologi PETRONAS, Bandar Seri Iskandar, 31750 Tronoh, Perak, Malaysia.*
[b]*National Metal and Materials Technology Center, Pathumthani, Thailand*
drsuzana_yusuf@petronas.com.my

Abstract

Bio-oil is a promising alternative source of energy which can be produced from empty fruit bunch (EFB). Bio-oil comprises a mixture of highly oxygenated compounds, carboxylic acids and trace water. Bio-oil can be used as a substitute for conventional fuels after it is upgraded. However, the oil can react through many chemical reactions such as polymerization and lead to an increase in viscosity of bio-oil during storage. Thus, this paper explores the stabilization of empty fruit bunch derived bio-oil. The objective of this project is to select the optimum condition, to study the accelerated aging of bio-oil and the effect of addictive in stabilizing the bio-oil. The bio-oil is produced from the catalytic pyrolysis of EFB. The optimum reaction condition applied is 5 wt% of H-Y catalyst at reaction temperature of 500 °C and nitrogen flow rate of 100 ml/min. At this optimum condition, it is able to obtain the maximum bio-oil yield. The method used in this research to improve the stability of the bio-oil is through addition of antioxidants. Four different types of antioxidants which are propyl gallate (PG), tert-Butylhydroquinone (TBHQ), butylated hydroxyanisole (BHA) and calcium chloride salts ($CaCl_2$) are added to the bio-oil separately in the amount of 1,000 ppm. All the test samples are subjected to accelerated aging involving exposure to high temperature of 80 °C for 7 d. The properties of samples which are chosen as the indicator of aging are viscosity, water content and acidity. The effectiveness of antioxidants increase in the following order: $CaCl_2$, BHA, TBHQ and PG. The antioxidants used are able to improve the stability of bio-oil in terms of viscosity and water content during aging. All the antioxidants helped to reduce the acidity of bio-oil except for $CaCl_2$. The results from Gas Chromatography-Mass Spectrometry (GC-MS) analysis showed that the chain reaction of polymerization stopped by phenolics and decrease in carbonyls and ethers can lead to decreased in water content during aging. In addition, molecule decomposing reactions also reduced and resulted in lower acidity.

Keywords: Stabilization; Empty Fruit Bunch; Catalytic Pyrolysis; Antioxidants; Gas Chromatography-Mass Spectrometry (GC-MS)

1. Introduction

The use of renewable energy sources is becoming increasingly important to address the impacts of global warming (Heinzerling 2010). Renewable fuels from biological sources such as biodiesel, bioethanol and pyrolysis liquid are becoming more crucial. Biomass is the most common form of renewable energy and generates very low net greenhouse emissions. The energy from biomass can be obtained by various techniques, such as combustion or by upgrading it into a more valuable fuel, gas or oil. Biomass can also be transformed into a source of value-added products for the chemical industry by using a thermochemical method such as pyrolysis of bio-oil. Iliopoulou et al. (2012) pointed out that raw bio-oil that has not been upgraded yet has several undesired characteristics; high water and oxygen content, corrosive, instable under storage and heating conditions, high viscosity, low calorific value and immiscible with petroleum fuels.

Malaysia is the world's second largest producer of palm oil which covers about 59 % of the world's needs and 23 % of empty fruit bunch (EFB) can be obtained from the substantial fresh fruit bunch produced. Empty fruit bunch can be utilized as the feedstock for biomass pyrolysis. The reaction condition for the bio-oil used are 5 wt% of H-Y zeolite catalyst at temperature of 500 °C and nitrogen flow rate of 100 ml/min (Sukiran et al. 2009). Catalytic pyrolysis offers some advantages over slow pyrolysis. The reaction can be improved and enhanced by the introduction of catalyst. Since pyrolysis requires the breaking of carbon-carbon bonds, the introduction of catalyst is able to catalyze the reaction and to facilitate the cracking reactions and de-oxygenation reaction, improve the quality of bio-oil produced compared to that of slow pyrolysis and makes downstream upgrading processes less expensive (Gopakumar et al. 2011). This process is able to remove oxygenated groups in bio-oil and improves the stability of bio-oil. Introduction of catalyst in catalytic pyrolysis decreased the amount of organic yield (bio-oil) and increase the amount of gas yield, water content and polyaromatic hydrocarbons (PAHs). The oxygenated compounds in the bio-oil undergo dehydration, decarboxylation, cracking, aromatization, alkylation, condensation and polymerization with deoxygenation simultaneously (French 2010). Higher water content reduced the heating value of the bio-oil (Crocker 2010). The most important factor driving the aging rate is temperature. Heating bio-oil to 60 °C or higher will promote internal reactions and polymerization that can be significant over a prolonged period (Corporation 2006).

Antioxidants play an important role in maintaining the bio-oil's stability. Generally the antioxidants used are monohydroxy or polyhydroxy phenol compounds with various ring substitutions. This can help to delay the beginning of the aging of slow rate of chemical reaction (Mittelbach 2003). The objective of this project is to select the optimum condition to study the accelerated aging of bio-oil as well as to study the effects of antioxidants in stabilizing the bio-oil. The chosen optimum operating condition is aging the bio-oil at temperature of 80 °C for 7 d (Udomsap et al. 2011). The upgraded bio-oil should have higher stability than the original bio-oil such as lower value of viscosity, water content and acidity.

2. Materials and Methods

2.1. Materials

Fresh empty fruit bunches (EFB) are taken from nearby palm tree plantation area "Kilang Sawit FELCRA Berhad Nasaruddin, KM 37, Jalan Tronoh, 32600 Bota, Perak, Malaysia". These empty fruit bunches are washed and dried in oven at 100 °C for 3 d. The dried EFB are manually chopped and cut into smaller pieces. They are washed with water to remove the sand or dust particles and then dried in the oven at 100 °C for 24 h. The dried EFB is then grinded with FRITSCH Cutting Mill to particle size below 500 μm. The grinded EFB is sieved to obtain the desired particle size (< 500 μm). Ultimate analysis of the EFB is carried out using LECO 932 CHNS Analyzer and the higher heating value (HHV) is measured using IKA C5000 Bomb Calorimeter. The zeolite catalyst used in catalytic pyrolysis which is purchased from Sigma-Aldrich has surface area of 780 m^2/g and 30 wt% by SiO_2/Al_2O_3. The properties of EFB measured are summarized in Table 1.

All the antioxidants used in this research are purchased from Sigma-Aldrich except for commercial calcium chloride ($CaCl_2$) with purity of 100 %. The antioxidants are butylated hydroxyanisole (BHA) with purity of $\geq$ 98.5 %, tert-Butylhydroquinone (TBHQ) with purity of $\geq$ 96.5 % and propyl gallate (PG) powder with purity of $\geq$ 98 %.

2.2. Experimental

2.2.1. Catalytic pyrolysis of empty fruit bunch (EFB)

In each run, 15 gram of dried EFB was mixed well with zeolite catalyst and loaded into the borosilicate glass tube, which is inserted inside the furnace. A glass wool is used to prevent the elutriation of reactant particles and blocked the gas inlet to the condenser. Before the reaction started, nitrogen gas is allowed to flow through the tube for a few minutes to remove any oxygen presents. The desired temperature of the reaction which is 500 °C, the furnace heating rate of 20 °C/min and the nitrogen gas flow rate of 100 ml/min are set. During the pyrolysis, the pyrolysis vapor produced is carried out by the nitrogen gas and passed through an ice bath condenser, where the condensable vapor is condensed to form bio-oil. The reaction takes about 35 min. The weight of the bio-oil produced is determined by measuring the difference between the weight of the condenser before and after the experiment. The liquid yield is calculated using Eq. 1 below (Nilsen et al. 2007):

$$Liquid\ Yield\ (wt\%) = \frac{Weight\ of\ bio-oil\ produced}{Weight\ of\ biomass} \times 100\% \tag{1}$$

The bio-oil obtained from all the experimental runs are stored in a container and placed in a refrigerator in order to slow down the rate of aging.

2.2.2. Stabilization of EFB derived bio-oil

The aging of EFB derived bio-oil is studied at 80 °C. The value of viscosity, water content and acidity of the bio-oil with respective antioxidant is measured. The effect of commercial antioxidant such as calcium chloride salts ($CaCl_2$) on the EFB derived bio-oil is also studied. The salt is in pellets form. The salt is grinded into powder form of around 500 μm. In separate samples, 1,000 ppm of propyl gallate (PG), tert-Butylhydroquinone (TBHQ) and butylated hydroxyanisole (BHA) and calcium chloride salts ($CaCl_2$) are added to the EFB derived bio-oil.

Table 1. Properties of EFB (mf wt%)

Properties	Measured value
Ultimate Analysis	
Carbon	46.830
Hydrogen	6.277
Nitrogen	0.664
Sulfur	0.237
Oxygen (by difference)	45.992
HHV (MJ/kg)	19.643

2.2.3. Characterization of EFB derived bio-oil

The water content of bio-oil samples were determined by using Metrohm 870 Karl Fischer Titrino Plus. The viscosity of the bio-oil in this study is measured with Brookfield CAP 2000+ Viscometer and the setting temperature for measuring the viscosity is 40 °C. The acidity which is the pH value of bio-oil samples were measured by using EUTECH Instruments pH 510 pH/mV/°C Meter. The GC/MS analyses were conducted on samples diluted (0.1 g : 1.9 g) in acetone using GCMS-QP2010 Plus.

3. Results and Discussions

3.1. Effects of Antioxidants on Bio-oil's Stability

The percentage changed in viscosity, water content of bio-oil and change in acidity of bio-oil with and without antioxidants, that were subjected to accelerated aging are presented in Figure 1 - 3. Based on Figure 1, the percentage change of viscosity of bio-oil with PG, TBHQ, BHA and $CaCl_2$ are 78.98 %, 107.23 %, 116.55 % and 150.81 % respectively after 7 d of aging at 80 °C. According to Figure 2, after 7 d, the percentage change of water content of bio-oil with PG, TBHQ, BHA and $CaCl_2$ are 25.60 %, 17.80 %, 13.40 % and 9.4 %. In addition, all the antioxidants manage to reduce the acidity of bio-oil except for $CaCl_2$. Based on Figure 3, the pH value of pure bio-oil is 2.33 after 7 d of aging whereas the pH value of bio-oil with PG, TBHQ, BHA and $CaCl_2$ are 3.44, 3.11, 2.91 and 2.02. The accelerated aging of bio-oil can bring negative effects to the properties of bio-oil such as viscosity, water content and acidity. From the results obtained, the viscosity of bio-oil without any addictive increased with the viscosity

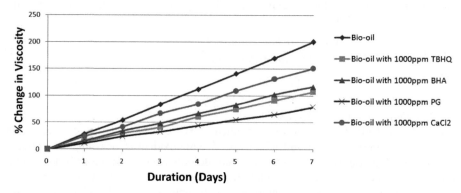

Figure 1. Percentage Change in Viscosity of Bio-oil with and without Antioxidants

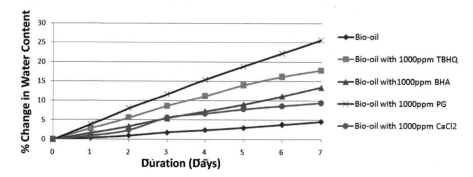

Figure 2. Percentage Change in Water Content of Bio-oil with and without Antioxidants

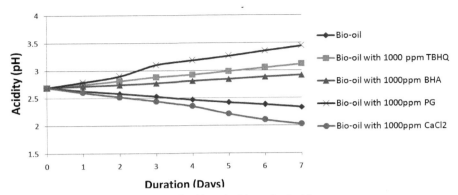

Figure 3. Change in Acidity of Bio-oil with and without Antioxidants

change addictive increased with the viscosity change of 200.04 % after 7 d. This phenomenon is due to the reactive organic compounds in the bio-oil that interact to form larger molecules or undergone polymerization during the aging. Storage of bio-oil at higher temperature will lead to faster polymerization (Moens et al. 2009). Meanwhile, the rate of increase of viscosity values of the bio-oil with antioxidants is lower than that of pure bio-oil. In addition, the water content of pure bio-oil decreased with a change of 4.6 % after 7 d. Addition of antioxidants helps to increase the rate of reduction of water content. The effectiveness of antioxidants increase in the following order: $CaCl_2$, BHA, TBHQ and PG. Bio-oil with PG and $CaCl_2$ are undergone Gas chromatography–mass spectrometry (GC-MS) analysis. The analysis is aim to study on how PG and $CaCl_2$ being the best antioxidant and increased the acidity of bio-oil after aging respectively.

3.2. Gas Chromatography-Mass Spectrometry (GC-MS) Analysis

Antioxidants restrict the entry of air to the bio-oil which can help to diminish the potential of forming peroxides that catalyze olefinic polymerization (Diebold 1999). Bio-oil apparently does not contain enough free-radical trap molecules for stabilization due to the disappearance of olefinic compounds in bio-oil as shown in Table 2. Hence, the phenolics formed will be used as free-radical traps and stopped the chain reaction of polymerization. Many phenolics are good free-radical traps and can be used to prevent olefins from the polymerizing effect of free-radicals. In addition, decrease in carbonyls and ethers may result in decreases of water content during aging. Furthermore, all the antioxidants reduced molecule decomposing reactions which led to lower acidity after aging except calcium chloride salts ($CaCl_2$) due to the presence of propanoyl chloride in the bio-oil.

Table 2. Chemical Composition of Pure Bio-oil, Bio-oil with PG and Bio-oil with $CaCl_2$

Functional Group	Pure bio-oil (wt%)	Bio-oil with PG (wt%)	Bio-oil with $CaCl_2$ (wt%)
Alcohol	3.97	4.11	4.03
Ester	7.10	7.95	7.88
Phenol	18.24	20.16	19.08
Furan	6.17	7.23	4.87
Carboxylic acid	32.91	30.16	34.59
Ketone	13.87	14.84	14.11
Olefin	4.62	3.42	3.67
Others (carbonyls, ethers, etc)	13.12	12.13	11.77

4. Conclusions

In conclusion, the optimum condition for accelerated aging of bio-oil at 80 °C for 7 d is studied. These conditions enable the effectiveness of additives used to stabilize the bio-oil. The antioxidants used are able to improve the stability of bio-oil in terms of viscosity, water content and acidity during aging. All the antioxidants helped to reduce the acidity of bio-oil except for $CaCl_2$. From this study, the effectiveness of antioxidants increased in the following order: $CaCl_2$, BHA, TBHQ and PG. Antioxidant had larger impact on viscosity compared to water content and acidity due to its low activation energy to donate hydrogen in order to affect the propagation of the free radical chain. This could help to delay the beginning of the aging or slow the rate of chemical reaction. In addition, all the antioxidants managed to reduce the acidity of bio-oil after aging except $CaCl_2$ due to the formation of propanoyl chloride after mixing with bio-oil.

Acknowledgement

The authors would like to acknowledge Universiti Teknologi PETRONAS for the support given to undertake the research work.

References

D. E. S. Corporation, 2006, Dynamotive; the Bio-oil Information Book, <www.wikinvest.com/stock/Dynamotive_Energy_Systems_(DYMTF)/Biooil_Production_Facilities_Markets>, accessed on 15/09/2013.

J. P. Diebold, 1999, A review of the chemical and physical mechanisms of the storage stability of fast pyrolysis bio-oils, <home.rmi.net/diebolic>, accessed on 26/02/2013.

R. French, S. Czernik, 2010, Catalytic pyrolysis of biomass for biofuels production, Fuel Processing Technology, 91, 25-32.

S. T. Gopakumar, S. Adhikari, R. B. Gupta, M. Tu, S.Taylor, 2011, Production of hydrocarbon fuels from biomass using catalytic pyrolysis under helium and hydrogen environments, Bioresource Technology, 102, 6742-6749.

A. Heinzerling, 2010, Carbon Emissions, <www.earth-policy.org/indicators/C52>, accessed on 12/03/2012.

E. F. Iliopoulou, S. D. Stefanidis, K.G. Kalogiannis, A. Delimitis, A. A. Lappas, K. S. Triantafyllidis, 2012, Catalytic upgrading of biomass pyrolysis vapors using transition metal-modified ZSM-5 zeolite, Applied Catalysis B: Environmental, 127, 281-290.

L. Moens, S. K. Black., M. D. Myers, S. Czernik, 2009, Study of the neutralization and stabilization of a mixed hardwood bio-oil, Energy and Fuels, 23, 2695-2699.

M. E. Crocker, 2010, Thermochemical Conversion of Biomass to Liquid Fuels and Chemicals, The Royal Society of Chemistry, United Kingdom.

M. Mittelbach, S. Schober, 2003, Influence of antioxidants on the oxidation stability of biodiesel, Journal of American Oil Chemist's Society, 80, 817-823.

M. H. Nilsen, E. Antonakou, A. Bouzga, A. Lappas, K. Mathisen, M. Stöcker, 2007, Investigation of the effect of metal sites in the Me-Al-MCM-41 (Me = Fe, Cu or Zn) on the catalytic behavior during the pyrolysis of wooden based biomass, Microporous and Mesoporous Materials, 105, 189-203.

M. A. Sukiran, C. M. Chin, N. K. A. Bakar, 2009, Bio-oils from Pyrolysis of Oil Palm Empty Fruit Bunches, Am. J. Applied Sci., 6, 869-875.

P. Udomsap, H. Y. Yapp, H. H. Tiong, B. Yoosuk, S. Yusup, S. Sukkasi, 2011, Towards Stabilization of Bio-oil by Addition of Antioxidants and Solvents, and Emulsification with Conventional Hydrocarbon Fuels, The International Conference and Utility Exhibition, Thailand.

Jiří Jaromír Klemeš, Petar Sabev Varbanov and Peng Yen Liew (Editors)
Proceedings of the 24th European Symposium on Computer Aided Process Engineering – ESCAPE 24
June 15-18, 2014, Budapest, Hungary.

Three-scale Modeling and Simulation of a Batch Suspension Polymerization Vinyl Chloride Reactor

Ágnes Bárkányi*, Sándor Németh, Béla G. Lakatos

University of Pannonia, Department of Process Engineering, 10 Egyetem Street, Veszprém, H-8200, Hungary
barkanyia@fmt.uni-pannon.hu

Abstract

A three-scale mathematical model of batch suspension polymerization reactors of vinyl chloride is presented and analyzed by simulation. The multidimensional population balance equation which is a meso-scale model of the monomer-polymer droplets population is completed with the macro-scale heat balance equations for the continuous phase and the cooling medium. This hybrid model includes polymerization reactions inside the droplets, random breakage and aggregation of droplets as well as heat and mass exchange between droplets induced by binary collisions. The model equations are solved by a coupled continuous time-Monte Carlo method. The effects of constitutive and process parameters, and, because of polymerization is a strongly exothermic process, the influence of the cooling strategy are investigated by simulation. The simulation results demonstrated that the temperature rise in droplets causes differences in the polymer properties.

Keywords: Suspension polymerization, Vinyl chloride, Population balance equation, Coupled continuous time–Monte Carlo solution, Simulation

1. Introduction

In suspension polymerization of vinyl chloride (VC) the water-insoluble monomer containing oil-soluble initiator is dispersed in the continuous aqueous phase by a combination of intensive stirring and the use of small amounts of suspending agents (stabilizers). The droplets behave as individual micro-reactors with continuous deterministic chemical reactions which are disturbed by collision induced coalescence and break up of droplets. The collision induced meso-scale interactions results in component and heat exchange between the colliding droplets. As this breakage-coalescence process of droplets proceeds parallel with polymerization inside the droplets their interactions may have significant effects on the final particle size distribution of polymer powder what is one of the most important issues in suspension polymerization (Hashim and Brooks, 2004).

The population balance approach can be applied to describe the temporal evolution of droplet size distribution adequately (Kotoulas and Kiparissides, 2006). However, in suspension polymerization, because of changes of droplet volume, concentrations of species and even of the temperature of droplets are important thus the population balance equation becomes, in principle, multivariable. Solution of multivariable population balance equations is a crucial problem. Although a number of solution methods have been published for single variable population balance equations for multivariable ones can be found only a few. The methods available for solution of multivariable population balance equations can be divided into deterministic and stochastic ones. In contrast to deterministic integration, stochastic methods utilize Monte Carlo (MC) procedures to simulate the evolution of a finite sample of droplets or particles population (Zhao and Zheng, 2013). However, in the case of suspension poly-merization besides the multivariable problem we see other problems as well. Namely, here time continuous processes inside the droplets and in the continuous phases and discrete event interactions between the droplets occur in parallel thus solution of the system of equations requires a special technique: combination of a continuous time and discrete event treatment. This phenomenon was studied by Salikas et al. (2008) and Irrizary (2008) but they have not described the problem in details.

The temperature of the PVC polymerizing process is nonlinear and difficult to control (Gao et al., 2013). It is commonly assumed that in suspension polymerization heat transfer between the polymerizing droplets and the continuous phase is rapid and both phases have the same homogeneous temperature (Meyer and Keurentjes, 2005). The aim of our work is to present a detailed population balance equation which includes the time continuous and discrete event processes of suspension polymerization completed with the macro-scale heat balance equations for the continuous phase and the cooling medium allowing investigating this assumption by simulation. The model equations are solved by a coupled continuous time-MC method taking the heat transfer between the polymerizing droplets and the continuous phase into consideration analyzing in this way the effects of heat transfer interactions between the droplets and continuous phase on the monomer conversion and polymer properties.

2. Model development

The model developed contains micro-, meso- and macro-scale processes inside the polymerization reactor, forming a complex three-scale system.

Micro-scale: Polymer reactions, related with the kinetic mechanism and micromixing occur at the micro-scale.

Meso-scale: At meso-scale occur the collision induced coalescence and break up of droplets.

Macro-scale: At this scale, the overall mass and energy balances, the heat and mass transfer from the reactor as well as the reactor dynamics and control can be described.

In order to take the interdependence of micro- and meso-scale processes into consideration, suspension polymerization of vinyl chloride is modeled by using the population balance approach. If the reactor is well mixed at macro-scale, the population of droplets can be described by the population density function $n(.,.,.,t)$ by means of which $n(\upsilon, c, T, t)d\upsilon dc dT$ provides the number of droplets from the droplets volume and temperature intervals $(\upsilon, \upsilon + d\upsilon)$ and $(T, T + dT)$, and from the region $(c, c + dc)$ of concentrations in a unit volume of suspension at time t. Under such conditions the behavior of droplets population in a batch reactor is governed by the population balance equation (Lakatos, 2011)

$$\frac{\partial n(\upsilon, c, T, t)}{\partial t} + \frac{\partial}{\partial c}\left[\frac{dc}{dt} n(\upsilon, c, T, t)\right] + \frac{\partial}{\partial T}\left[\frac{dT}{dt} n(\upsilon, c, T, t)\right] =$$

$$\boldsymbol{M}_b\left[n(\upsilon, c, T, t)\right] + \boldsymbol{M}_a\left[n(\upsilon, c, T, t)\right] + \boldsymbol{M}_{c/r}\left[n(\upsilon, c, T, t)\right] \qquad (1)$$

where the second and third terms on the left hand side provide the rates of continuous changes of the population density function due to the mass and heat effects of chemical reactions while the terms on the right hand side of Eq.(1) provide, in turn, the rates of jump-like changes of population density function because of coalescence, break up and collision induced heat exchange between the colliding droplets (Lakatos, 2011).

In suspension polymerization, mass transfer between the dispersed and continuous phases is negligible, therefore the detailed model of the reactor consists of Eq.(1) completed with the macro-scale heat balance equations for the dispersed and continuous phases and the cooling medium making possible to analyze the effects of temperature changes of the continuous phase on polymer properties.

The heat balance for a droplet is

$$\rho_d c_{p,d} \upsilon_d \frac{dT_d}{dt} = \upsilon_d \left(-\Delta H_r\right) \cdot \boldsymbol{R}_r \left(\boldsymbol{c}_d, T_d\right) - a_d h_{dc} \left(T_d - T_c\right) \tag{2}$$

where T_d, ρ_d, υ_d and $c_{p,d}$ are the temperature, density, volume and heat capacity of a droplet, T_c is the temperature of the continuous phase, a_d is the surface of a droplet, h_{dc} is the heat transfer coefficient between a droplet and the continuous phase, $\boldsymbol{R}_r$ and $-\Delta H_r$ are the vectors of the reaction rates and reaction heats, and $\boldsymbol{c}_d$ is the vector of concentrations of species in a droplet. The convective heat transfer coefficient (h_{dc}) is calculated by empirical expressions.

The heat balance for the continuous phase takes the form

$$\rho_c c_{p,c} \varepsilon V \frac{dT_c}{dt} = V \int_{T_{min}}^{T_{max}} \int_0^{c_m} \int_0^{\upsilon_m} a_d h_{dc} \left(T - T_c\right) n\left(\upsilon, \boldsymbol{c}, T, t\right) d\upsilon d\boldsymbol{c} dT - A_{cj} h_{cj} V\left(T_c - T_j\right) \tag{3}$$

where T_c, ρ_c, ε and $c_{p,c}$ are the temperature, density, volumetric ratio and heat capacity of the continuous phase, V is the volume of the suspension, h_{cj} and A_{cj} denote the coefficient and the effective surface of heat transfer between the continuous phase and the cooling medium. In Eq.(3), T_j denotes the temperature of the cooling medium in the jacket assumed to be a step-wise process at the initial moment of time.

The heat balance for the cooling medium is

$$V_j c_{p,j} \rho_j \frac{dT_j}{dt} = c_{p,j} F_j \left(T_{j,in} - T_j\right) - A_{cj} h_{cj} V\left(T_c - T_j\right) \tag{4}$$

where F_j, $c_{p,c}$ and $T_{j,in}$ denote the mass flow rate, the heat capacity and the inlet temperature of the cooling medium.

The mixed set of the integral-differential Eq.(1) with the ordinary differential Eqs.(2)-(3) of macro-scale heat balances was solved by developing a Monte Carlo procedure (Bárkányi et al., 2013a) combining the deterministic processes of chemical reactions inside the droplets and the heat transfer in the continuous phase with the effects of random collisions of droplets. This procedure provides, in principle, a Monte Carlo method of solution of the multivariable population balance equation.

3. Coupled continuous time–Monte Carlo method

MC methods can be divided into two classes according to the treatment of the time step. These are referred to as "time-driven" and "event-driven" MC. Here we used an event-driven MC method. The developed solution method is suitable to calculate the deterministic polymerization reactions and the stochastic meso-scale interactions of monomer droplets, simultaneously. Figure 1 presents the algorithm of solution which was described in details in a previous work (Bárkányi et al., 2013b).

In present work the effects of the temperature change in the reactor was analyzed on the monomer conversion and polymer properties. The number of droplets in a 1 m^3 reactor was calculated and the transferred heat from droplets was proportionally increased. After that the temperature of the continuous phase and cooling jacket were calculated by Eqs.(3)-(4). It was assumed that the temperature of the continuous phase is homogeneous.

4. Simulation results and discussion

The computer program was written and all simulation runs were carried out in MATLAB environment. In our previous papers, we presented the effects of the initial initiator distribution (Bárkányi et al., 2013a), the initial droplet size distribution (Bárkányi et al., 2013b) and the temperature rise in droplets (Bárkányi et al., 2012) on the monomer conversion and polymer properties. The kinetic data of VC polymerization were taken from the literature (Sidiropoulou and Kiparissides, 1990). In the present work we studied the influence of cooling of the reactor.

During the course of simulation a simple proportional controller was applied for controlling the reactor temperature. The total reaction heat released due to the polymerization reactions was computed that provided the needed inlet flow rate of the cooling water.

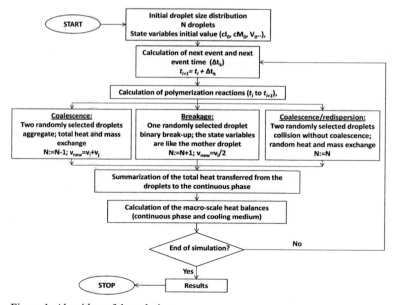

Figure 1. Algorithm of the solution

We calculated this flow rate in every simulation step. Naturally this is not a perfect temperature controller but in this study it was enough that the temperature staid in the stable range. The inlet temperature of the cooling water was 293 K. In Figure 2a we see the average temperature of droplets that is about 0.5 K higher at the maximum point than the temperature of the continuous phase. Figure 2b presents the temperature of the cooling jacket during the polymerization. We can see it follows really well the changing of temperature in the dispersed and continuous phase in spite of the very simple control system.

In Figure 3a the effects of these small temperature differences on monomer conversion are shown. Under isothermal conditions the temperature of continuous phase was constant 323 K but we calculated the temperature rise in droplets. Under non-isothermal conditions we calculated the temperature rise in the droplets and the heat transfer between the droplets and the continuous phase, too. We can see at the middle of the process the differences are remarkable. Figure 3b presents the effect of the non-isothermal conditions on number average molecular weight. We can see similar difference between the cases as in Figure 2a. Note, that in these cases the maximum temperature difference of the continuous phase was only about 1 K, so we can see that it is important to control the temperature in order to ensure the proper quality of the product.

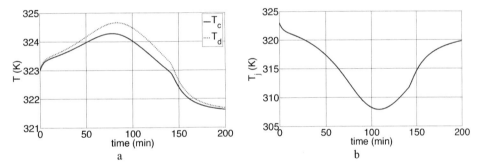

Figure 2. Temporal evolution of temperature of the continuous phase and the average temperature of the disperse phase (a) and of the cooling jacket (b). The amount of initiator was 0.0029 mole % based on monomer, initially the initiator distribution was uniform and the temperature of polymerization was 323 K. The inlet temperature of the cooling medium was 293 K.

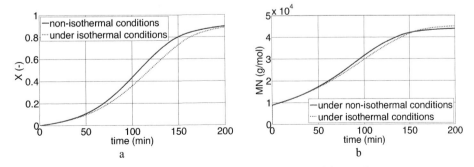

Figure 3. Temporal evolution of the monomer conversion (a) and of the number average molecular weight (b) compared under isothermal and non-isothermal conditions. The amount of initiator was 0.0029 mole % based on monomer, initially the initiator distribution was uniform and the temperature of polymerization was 323 K.

5. Conclusions

A population balance equation was presented for modeling the time continuous and discrete event processes of droplets population in suspension polymerization of vinyl chloride, completed with the macro-scale heat balance equations for the continuous phase and the cooling medium. The developed coupled continuous time-Monte Carlo method allowed computing the heat transfer processes between the polymerizing droplets and the continuous phase. The results obtained by simulation showed that the non-perfect cooling strategy causes remarkable differences in monomer conversion and polymer properties. Furthermore, the simulation results revealed that the heat transfer between the droplets and the continuous phase is not negligible. Our further plan is to model the particle formation inside the polymerizing droplets.

Acknowledgements

This research was supported by the TÁMOP-4.2.2.A-11/1/KONV-2012-0071 and the Hungarian Scientific Research Fund under Grant K77955.

References

Á. Bárkányi, B.G. Lakatos, S. Németh, 2012, Modelling of heat exchange between drops in suspension polymerization of vinyl chloride, Periodica Polytechnica Chemical Engineering, 56, 2, 55-64.

Á. Bárkányi, S. Németh, B.G. Lakatos, 2013a, Modelling and simulation of suspension polymerization of vinyl chloride via population balance model, Computers and Chemical Engineering, 59, 211-218.

Á. Bárkányi, S. Németh, B.G. Lakatos, 2013b, Modelling and Simulation of a Batch Poly(vinyl chloride) Reactor, Chemical Engineering Transactions, 32, 769-774.

S.Z. Gao, J.S. Wang, X.W. Gao, 2013, Modeling and advanced control method of PVC polymerization, Journal of Process Control, 23, 664-681.

S. Hashim, B.W. Brooks, 2004, Mixing of stabilised drops in suspension polymerisation, Chemical Engineering Science, 59, 2321-2331.

R. Irizarry, 2008, Fast Monte Carlo methodology for multivariate particulate systems – I: Point ensemble Monte Carlo, Chemical Engineering Science, 63, 95-110.

C. Kotoulas, C. Kiparissides, 2006, A generalized population balance model for the prediction of particle size distribution in suspension polymerization reactors, Chemical Engineering Science, 61, 332-346.

B.G. Lakatos, 2011, Multi-scale approach to population balance modelling of disperse systems. Proceedings of Simultech 2011, 186-191.

T. Meyer, J. Keurentjes, 2005, Handbook of Polymer Reaction Engineering, Free-radical Polymeriztaion: Suspension, 213-248, WILEY-VCH, Weinheim, Germany.

V. Salikas, C. Kotoulas, D. Meimaroglou, C. Kiparissides, 2008, Dynamic evolution of the particle size distribution in suspension polymerization reactors: A comparative study on Monte Carlo and sectional grid methods, The Canadian Journal of Chemical Engineering, 86, 924-936.

E. Sidiropoulou, C. Kiparissides, 1990, Mathematical modeling of PVC suspension polymerization: A unifying approach and some new results, Journal of Macromolecular Science – Chemistry, A27, 3, 257-288.

H. Zhao, C. Zheng, 2013, A population balance-Monte Carlo method for particle coagulation in spatially inhomogeneous systems, Computers and Fluids, 71, 196-207.

Jiří Jaromír Klemeš, Petar Sabev Varbanov and Peng Yen Liew (Editors)
Proceedings of the 24th European Symposium on Computer Aided Process Engineering – ESCAPE 24
June 15-18, 2014, Budapest, Hungary. Copyright © 2014 Elsevier B.V. All rights reserved.

Biodiesel Production from Waste Vegetable Oils: Combining Process Modelling, Multiobjective Optimization and Life Cycle Assessment (LCA)

Luis-Fernando Morales Mendoza, Marianne Boix,* Catherine Azzaro-Pantel, Ludovic Montastruc, Serge Domenech.

Laboratoire de Génie Chimique,UMR5563, INP- ENSIACET, 4 Allée Emile Monso BP 84234, 31432 Toulouse Cedex 4, FRANCE
Marianne.boix@ensiacet.fr

Abstract

The objective of this work is to propose an integrated and generic framework for eco-design that generalizes, automates and optimizes the evaluation of the environmental criteria at earlier design stage. The approach consists of three main stages. The first two steps correspond to process inventory analysis based on mass and energy balances and impact assessment phases of LCA methodology. The third stage of the methodology is based on the interaction of the previous steps with process simulation for environmental impact assessment and cost estimation through a computational framework. Then, the use of multi-objective optimization with a multicriteria choice decision making allows to select optimal solutions. The methodology is illustrated through the acid-catalyzed biodiesel production process.

Keywords: multiobjective optimization, biodiesel, process simulation, multiple choice decision making, acid-catalyzed.

1. Introduction

The exhaustion of stocks of fossil fuel supplies in combination with significant environmental and human impacts of petroleum fuel usage make urgent the development of alternative fuels that come from renewable resources. In this context, biofuels are a very promising solution. They include fuels derived from biomass conversion, as well as solid biomass, liquid fuels and various biogases. The scientific community was first interested in the production of biofuel with vegetable oils because it is derived from renewable resources which make biodiesel greener than petroleum diesel (Huynh et al., 2011). However, the main drawback of producing a great quantity of biodiesel from vegetable oil is the lack of feedstock and then, some ethical problems arise because of the utilization of a food product to make biofuel. Recently, lignocellulosic biomass and waste vegetable oils seem to be good candidates to be feedstock for the production of biodiesel (Atapour et al., 2014).

Biodiesel is a renewable fuel for diesel engines and can be produced by vegetable oils or animal fats. Made from agricultural co-products and by-products such as soybean oil, other vegetable oils or animal fats, it is an advanced biofuel. To be called biodiesel, it must meet strict quality specifications and biodiesel can be used in any blend with petroleum diesel fuel. Biodiesel reduces net carbon dioxide emissions by 78 % on a life-cycle basis when compared to conventional diesel fuel. It has also been shown to have dramatic improvements on engine exhaust emissions. Moreover, it is biodegradable and non-toxic and has a more favorable combustion emission profile than diesel, such as lower emissions of carbon monoxide, particulate matter and unburned hydrocarbons. The utilization of waste oils can produce cheap biodiesel and it can also solve the problem of waste oil disposal, so they are very good candidates to the production of biodiesel (Huynh et al., 2011).

In this study, a biodiesel production process design alternative is studied using an approach based on a previous work from Ouattara et al. (2012). This work takes into account economic and environmental considerations to obtain an eco-friendly and economically viable process design. The methodology carried out environmental impact analysis taking into account not only process but also impact of energy requirements. The current work intends to carry on a generic approach cradle-to-gate and a compliant software framework to implement an efficient LCA method and automate environmental impact analysis.

2. Methodology and tools

The originality of this study is to present an approach for eco-efficient process design, coupling process flow-sheeting and an energy plant simulator with a life cycle assessment module that generalizes and automates the evaluation of the environmental criteria. The approach consists of three main stages; the first two correspond to process inventory analysis and impact assessment phases of LCA methodology. The third stage performs environmental impact assessment and cost estimation through a computational framework. Process simulation has been performed with AspenHysys simulation software, and environmental performances are analyzed through Life Cycle Assessment (LCA, Impact 2002+) with Simapro. The energy requirements are evaluated by the use of Ariane software. The criteria are adapted to perform multi-criteria optimization taking into account the economic and environmental aspect by the IMPACT 2002+ method. An attributional LCA is considered: impacts from the production of biodiesel from vegetable oil would be attributed based on the inputs and outputs from the considered system, not taking into account what happened with the other related activities in the economy. In other words, no consequential LCA approach is targeted here. Optimizations have been solved with the genetic algorithm NSGAIIb. This procedure belongs to the genetic algorithm library (MULTIGEN) recently developed in Gomez et al. (2010). The MULTIGEN tools (written in Visual Basic for Applications VBA), use Excel sheets as interface. The general methodology is illustrated on a biodiesel production process from vegetable oils which is one of the foremost alternative fuels to those refined from petroleum products.

3. Biodiesel production simulation with Hysys

3.1. Overview of the biodiesel production process

Among the several routes to transform oil in biodiesel such as pyrolysis or micro-emulsion, the transesterification reaction process is the most common method to obtain biodiesel (Morais et al., 2010). Biodiesel is produced by the transesterification of the oil composing the feedstock (1) in presence of an excess of alcohol and a catalyst:

$$\text{Triglyceride + Alcohol (excess)} \xrightarrow{\textit{Catalyst}} \text{Fatty Acid Ester (BD) + Glycerol} \tag{1}$$

The catalyst can be either a base (alkali-catalyzed process) or an acid (acid-catalyzed process). A particular focus on the latter is made in this study. In this process, methanol (molar ratio methanol: oil of 50:1) and sulphuric acid (used as a catalyzer) feed the transesterification reactor with a stream of pre-heated oil. The excess of methanol is removed from the biodiesel in a distillation column and recycled back to the transesterification reactor. Introduction of calcium oxide is needed to remove sulfuric acid from the transesterification products in the neutralization reactor.

3.2. Simulation of the process with Aspen Hysys

This section defines the conditions and parameters used to model the bio-diesel process using waste cooking oil with HYSYS software. In this work, tri-olein ($C_{57}H_{104}O_6$). (i.e., triglyceride of oleic acid) is considered as the triglyceride in the waste cooking oil. The reaction set is established before starting flowsheet modelling. Two reactions are involved, one for transesterification and one for neutralization of sulphuric-acid:

$$\text{Transesterification} \quad 3MeOH + Triolein \rightarrow 3MethylOleate + Glycerol \tag{2}$$

$$\text{Neutralization} \quad CaO + H_2SO_4 \rightarrow H_2O + CaSO_4 \tag{3}$$

Raw material inputs are represented as process input streams, Table 1 illustrates the operating conditions.

Table 1. Process inputs for the simulation model in Hysys

	Input 1	**Input 2**	**Input 3**	**Input 4**	**Input 5**
Components	Methanol	Triolein	Sulphuric acid	Water	Calcium oxide
Flow rate	210 kg/h	1,000 kg/h	150kg/h	110 kg/h	80 kg/h
Temperature	25°C	25°C	25°C	25°C	25°C
Pressure	1 bar	1 bar	1 bar	1 bar	1 bar

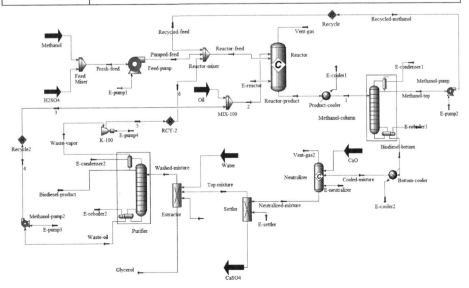

Figure 1. Flowsheet of the acid-catalyzed process obtained with Hysys

The following analysis is based on the environmental impact assessment using the IMPACT 2002+ LCIA (Life cycle impact assessment) method in order to perform a cradle to gate analysis. Methanol in vent gas output of the purifier column and triolein in reboiler liquid output are recycled with a purity of 99.97 % and 99.99 %. Through recycling about 34 kg/h of methanol and 111 kg/h of triolein are recovered and injected into the process

4. Inventory data and identification of potential factors

Inventory data elements are then identified in the EcoInvent database provided in SIMAPRO tool. Table 2 summarizes the inventory data of the biodiesel production process and their related database names.

5. Optimization of biodiesel production

5.1. Formulation of the problem

The formulation optimization problem proposed in this work is to maximize profit and minimize the environmental impact of biodiesel production process. The economic model used is based on the calculation of profit. The calculation is carried out using the basic operation:

$$PROFIT = (Flow_{bd} * \text{Pr}ice_{bd}) - \sum_{x=1}^{i} QE_x * CostE_x - \sum_{y=1}^{j} QRM_y * CostRM_y - \sum_{z=1}^{k} Qw_z * Costw_z \qquad (4)$$

Where:
$CostE_x$	Energy cost of type x
$CostRM_y$	Raw material cost of type y
$Costw_z$	Waste cost of type z
$Flow_{bd}$	Biodiesel flowrate in output stream
$Price_{bd}$	Price of biodiesel ($/kg)
QE_x	Energy amount of type x
QRM_y	Raw material amount of type y
Qw_z	Waste amount of type z

With regard to the environmental aspect, the end-point categories of IMPACT 2002+ LCIA method are used as criteria to minimize.

Table 2. Inventory data of the biodiesel production process

Category	Sub-category	Inventory data	Database elements names	Unit
Process	Raw materials	Methanol	Methanol	kg
		Sulphuric acid	Sulphuric acid	kg
		Water	Water	kg
		Calcium oxide	Calcium oxide	kg
Energy	Fuels	Natural gas	Heat, natural gas, at industrial furnace >100kW/RER S	MJ
				MJ
	Emissions	Carbon dioxide	Carbon dioxide	kg
		Sulphur dioxide	Sulphur dioxide	kg
		Nitrogen oxides	Nitrogen oxides	kg
		Carbon monoxide	Carbon monoxide	kg

The optimization problem can thus be formulated as follows:

Determine the decision variables (i.e., process operating conditions) in order to satisfy simultaneously the following objectives:

Maximization (Profit)
Minimization (Human Health)
Minimization (Ecosystem Quality)
Minimization (Climate Change)
Minimization (Resources)

Subject to:

Amount of calcium oxide must be exact to remove sulphuric acid
Decision variables ranges

5.2. Optimization results

The eco-design framework was then applied combining the process simulator (HYSYS), the energy plant simulator (Ariane), the environmental sub-module based on life cycle assessment and the genetic algorithm (NSGA IIb in Multigen) and an MCDM tool based on M-TOPSIS (the other decision tools are not applied here). The optimization approach uses the NSGA-IIb genetic algorithm embedded in Multigen environment, with the following parameters: number of individuals in the population: 200; generation number: 50; crossover rate: 0.9; mutation rate: 0.5.

The first step is to carry on a mono-objective optimization by maximizing the profit (Eq.1). The multi-criteria optimization then follows considering simultaneously five criteria i.e.: one economic (Profit) and four environmental ones corresponding to the endpoint of IMPACT 2002+ (Human Health, Ecosystem Quality, Climate Change and Resources). Pareto fronts are represented on figure 2. The results are then analyzed with an M-TOPSIS (Ren et al., 2007) application (Profit and end-point categories) with a same weight allocated for all criteria. The best solution found by M-TOPSIS maintains a balance between all the criteria and, with regard to the mono-criterion solution, (Min Profit) it is not so environmentally unfriendly. The mono-criterion solution is in red in Figure 2 whereas the best solution with TOPSIS is in green in Figure 2.

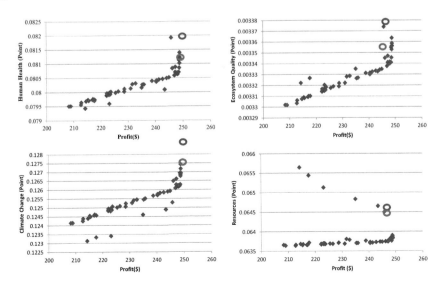

Figure 2. Two dimensionally comparisons of Pareto front (Profit – Environment)

6. Conclusion

The environmental gain obtained by the multi-objective framework is slight which can be attributed to the recycling steps that are introduced in the flowsheet. Figure 3 shows the individual analysis of the environmental impact of M-TOPSIS (Rank 1) solution. The figure confirm the "hot spot" of the system described above, but also indicate other, such as emissions of carbon dioxide and nitrogen oxide in addition to the methanol raw material.

Biodiesel is an alternative to fossil fuel use, which requires further studies to optimize the process in economic and environmental aspects. This work implements an eco-design framework to the production of biodiesel through waste vegetable oils. A cradle-to-gate assessment was then performed and the study was conducted with IMPACT 2002 + LCIA method. The results show that the step of multiple choice decision making with M-TOPSIS leads to an optimal solution not far away from the mono-criterion optimization solution. This kind of analysis can be further developed in order to revisit LCA objectives and carry out consequential analysis that is particularly sound in the case of alternative fuels. Future works will also take into account uncertainties as it was underlined in a recent study of Luna and Martinez (2013).

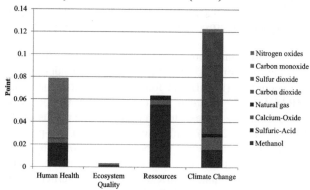

Figure 3. End-point analysis of the M-TOPSIS solution

References

M. Atapour, H.-R. Kariminia, P. M. Moslehabadi, 2014, Optimization of biodiesel production by alkali-catalyzed transesterification of used frying oil, Process Saf. Environ. Prot., 92, 2, 179-185.

A. Gomez, L. Pibouleau, C. Azzaro-Pantel, S. Domenech, C. Latgé, D. Haubensack, 2010, Multiobjective genetic algorithm strategies for electricity production from generation IV nuclear technology, Energy Convers. Manag., 51, 4, 859–871.

L. H. Huynh, N. S. Kasim, Y. H. Ju, 2011, Biodiesel production from waste oils in Biofuels: alternative feedstocks and conversion processes, USA, Academic press, Elsevier, 375 – 396.

M.F. Luna, E.C. Martinez, 2013, Model-based run-to-run optimization under uncertainty of biodiesel production, Comput. Aided Chem. Eng., 32,103-108.

S. Morais, T. M. Mata, A.A. Martins, G.A. Pinto, C.A.V. Costa, 2010, Simulation and life cycle assessment of process design alternatives for biodiesel production from waste vegetable oils, J. Clean. Prod., 18, 13, 1251–1259.

A. Ouattara, L. Pibouleau, C. Azzaro-Pantel, S. Domenech, P. Baudet, B. Yao, 2012, Economic and environmental strategies for process design, Comput. Chem. Eng., 36, 174–188.

L. Ren, Y. Zhang, Y. Wang, Z. Sun, 2010, Comparative Analysis of a Novel M-TOPSIS Method and TOPSIS, Appl. Math. Res. eXpress, 2007, 1–10.

Jiří Jaromír Klemeš, Petar Sabev Varbanov and Peng Yen Liew (Editors)
Proceedings of the 24th European Symposium on Computer Aided Process Engineering – ESCAPE 24
June 15-18, 2014, Budapest, Hungary. Copyright © 2014 Elsevier B.V. All rights reserved.

A Novel Cross-decomposition Multi-cut Scheme for Two-Stage Stochastic Programming

Sumit Mitra, Pablo Garcia-Herreros, Ignacio E. Grossmann*,

Department of Chemical Engineering, Carnegie Mellon University, Pittsburgh, PA 15213, United States
grossmann@cmu.edu

Abstract

We describe a decomposition algorithm that combines Benders and scenario-based Lagrangean decomposition for two-stage stochastic programming investment planning problems with complete recourse. The first-stage variables are mixed-integer and the second-stage variables are continuous. The algorithm is based on the cross-decomposition scheme and fully integrates primal and dual information in terms of primal-dual multi-cuts added to the Benders and the Lagrangean master problems for each scenario. The benefits of the cross-decomposition scheme are demonstrated with an illustrative case study for a facility location problem with risk of disruptions.

Keywords: Cross-decomposition, stochastic programming, investment planning.

1. Motivation

Two-stage stochastic programming investment planning problems (Birge and Louveaux, 2011) can be hard to solve since the resulting deterministic equivalent programs can lead to very large-scale problems. There are two major approaches, to address the resulting computational challenge. First, sampling methods (Linderoth et al., 2006) and scenario reduction techniques (Heitsch and Romisch, 2003) can be used to limit the number of required scenarios. Second, decomposition schemes, such as Benders decomposition (Benders, 1962; Geoffrion, 1972), also known as L-shaped method (Van Slyke and Wets, 1969) can be applied to exploit decomposable problem structures induced by the presence of complicating variables (e.g. stage-one variables). Lagrangean decomposition (Guignard and Kim, 1987; Caroe and Schultz, 1999), on the other hand, can be applied to exploit decomposable structures induced by the presence of complicating constraints (e.g. non-anticipativity constraints).

While there is extensive literature focused on improvements for one or the other decomposition method, only few research efforts have tried to combine the complementary strengths of both decomposition schemes. First proposed by Van Roy (1983), the cross-decomposition algorithm is a framework that unifies Benders and Lagrangean relaxation, which can be seen as duals of each other. The cross-decomposition algorithm iterates between the primal and dual subproblems, where each of the subproblems yields the input for the other one. Convergence tests are used to determine when the iteration between the problems needs to be augmented with the solution of a primal or dual master problem in order to prevent cycling of the algorithm and restore convergence. Holmberg (1990) generalizes the idea of cross-decomposition and introduces a set of enhanced convergence tests. One of the main ideas in cross-decomposition is to avoid solving the master problems since the solution of these problems, potentially MIPs, is regarded as a hard task. Some variations of the method, e.g. mean value cross-decomposition (Holmberg, 1997a,b), in which a new solution is obtained by averaging over a set of solutions from previous iterations, even completely eliminate the use of master problems at the cost of potentially slow convergence. Sohn et al. (2011) derive a mean value cross-decomposition approach for two-stage stochastic programming problems (LP) based on the scheme proposed by Holmberg (1997a).

2. Problem statement

We consider a two-stage stochastic programming problem (SP) of the following form:

$$(SP) \quad \min TC = c^T x + \sum_{s \in S} \tau_s d_s^T y_s \tag{1}$$

$$\text{s.t.} \quad A_0 x \qquad\qquad \leq b_0 \tag{2}$$
$$A_1 x + B_1 y_s \leq b_1 \quad \forall s \in S \tag{3}$$
$$B_s y_s \leq b_s \quad \forall s \in S \tag{4}$$
$$x \in X \tag{5}$$
$$y_s \geq 0 \tag{6}$$

The objective function (1) minimizes the total expected cost TC, which consists of investment cost ($c^T x$) and expected operational cost ($\sum_{s \in S} \tau_s d_s^T y_s$), where τ_s is the probability for scenario $s \in S$ with $\sum_{s \in S} \tau_s = 1$. The first-stage decisions, x are mixed-integer and correspond to discrete choices for investments and associated capacities:

$$X = \{x = (x_1, x_2)^T : x_1 \in \{0,1\}^n, x_2 \in \mathbb{R}^+\} \tag{7}$$

All second-stage decisions, y_s, which correspond to operational decisions in scenario s, are continuous. In Eq. (2), constraints on the investment decisions are specified, e.g. logic constraints on the combination of investments. Eq. (3) links the investment decisions with operational decisions, e.g. if capacity is expanded, additional operational decisions are available. In Eq. (4) operational constraints are specified.

Note that the problem naturally decomposes into scenarios once the investment decisions x are fixed. Furthermore, we can explicitly formulate the so-called non-anticipativity constraints, which are derived by duplicating the investment decisions for each scenario (x_s) and enforcing equality constraints across all scenarios. We use the formulation by Caroe and Schultz (1999) and re-write problem (SP) in the following way $(SPNAC)$, where Eq. (12) represents the non-anticipativity constraints, ($x_1 = x_2 = \cdots = x_n$), with a suitable matrix $H = (H_1, H_2, \ldots, H_{|S|})$:

$$(SPNAC) \quad \min TC = \sum_{s \in S} \tau_s (c^T x_s + d_s^T y_s) \tag{8}$$

$$\text{s.t.} \quad A_0 x_s \qquad\qquad \leq b_0 \quad \forall s \in S \tag{9}$$
$$A_1 x_s + B_1 y_s \leq b_1 \quad \forall s \in S \tag{10}$$
$$B_s y_s \leq b_s \quad \forall s \in S \tag{11}$$
$$\sum_{s \in S} H_s x_s = 0 \tag{12}$$
$$x_s \in X_s \tag{13}$$
$$y_s \geq 0 \tag{14}$$

In Eq. (13), X_s is defined analogously to X:

$$X_s = \left\{ x_s = (x_{1,s}, x_{2,s})^T : x_{1,s} \in \{0,1\}^n, x_{2,s} \in \mathbb{R}^+ \right\} \qquad \forall s \in S \tag{15}$$

It should be noted that problems (*SP*) and (*SPNAC*) are equivalent, which follows simply by substituting the non-anticipativity constraints (12).

3. Ingredients of the decomposition algorithm

Our cross-decomposition scheme is based on Benders and Lagrangean decomposition, which both exploit the decomposable problem structure. We assume complete recourse, which means that all scenarios are feasible regardless of the first-stage decisions. This assumption can be relaxed, but requires including primal feasibility cuts and addressing dual unboundedness.

The proposed algorithm implies solving four problems per iteration: the primal (Benders) subproblems that yield upper bounds, the dual (Lagrangean) subproblems, the dual (Lagrangean) master problem, and the primal (Benders) master problem that yields lower bounds. The sequence of the algorithm is presented in Fig. 1. The basic idea is to use Benders decomposition in order to predict the upper and lower bounds. The intermediate Lagrangean steps are used to generate cuts that strengthen the primal (Benders) master problem, while the primal (Benders) subproblems are used to strengthen the dual (Lagrangean) master problem. In this way, we avoid the need to rely on a heuristic to generate feasible solutions from the dual (Lagrangean) subproblems.

The primal (Benders) subproblems based on (*SPNAC*), can be obtained by fixing the first-stage variables at iteration k to a candidate solution $\hat{x}^k$. The resulting problem (BSP^k) is formulated for each scenario s as follows:

$$(BSPp_s^k) \quad \min \quad \tau_s(c^T\hat{x}^k + d_s^T y_s) \tag{16}$$
$$\text{s.t.} \quad B_1 y_s \leq b_1 - A_1\hat{x}^k \tag{17}$$
$$B_s y_s \leq b_s \tag{18}$$
$$y\_s \geq 0 \tag{19}$$

A valid relaxation of (*SPNAC*) can be obtained by formulating its Lagrangean dual, in which the non-anticipativity constraints (12) are dualized (Guignard and Kim, 1987; Caroe and Schultz, 1999). The dual (Lagrangean) subproblems (LD^k) are formulated for a fixed set of Lagrange multipliers μ^k. The mixed-integer linear formulation can be decomposed by scenario s as shown in (LD_s^k).

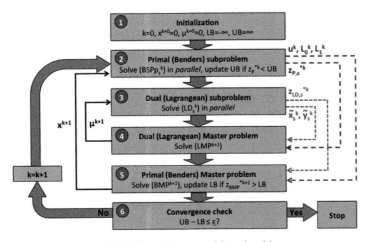

Figure 1. Sequence of the Cross-Decomposition algorithm.

(LD_s^k) min $\displaystyle\sum_{s \in S} \tau_s(c^T x_s + d_s^T y_s) + \mu^k H_s x_s$ (20)

$$
\begin{aligned}
\text{s.t.} \quad A_0 x_s &\leq b_0 & \forall s \in S && (21)\\
A_1 x_s + B_1 y_s &\leq b_1 & \forall s \in S && (22)\\
B_s y_s &\leq b_s & \forall s \in S && (23)\\
x_s &\in X_s & && (24)\\
y_s &\geq 0 & && (25)
\end{aligned}
$$

The previously described dual (Lagrangean) subproblems yield a solution in which some of the original non-anticipativity constraints (12) are most likely violated. Therefore, a primal solution needs to be obtained, which also provides a valid upper bound. In the framework of Lagrangean decomposition, a heuristic is applied to generate a first-stage feasible $\hat{x}^k$, which is used in $(SPNAC)$ to obtain the primal solution. However, the heuristic can be avoided since the Lagrangean primal subproblem for scenario s is equivalent to the Benders subproblem for scenario s in its primal form $(BSPp_s)$.

The multi-cut version of the cutting planes and the upper bounds form the primal (Benders) subproblems given in (29) can be used to formulate the strengthened dual (Lagrangean) master problem (LMP^{k+1}), in which we add a cut for every scenario at each iteration. The derivation is presented in Mitra (2014). The dual (Lagrangean) master problem yields the next set of Lagrangean multipliers (μ^{k+1}). The resulting quadratic program is formulated as follows.

(LMP^{k+1}) max $\eta_{LMP} + \dfrac{\delta}{2}\|\mu - \bar{\mu}\|_2^2$ (26)

$$
\begin{aligned}
\text{s.t.} \quad \eta_{LMP} &\leq \sum_{s \in S} \kappa_s & && (27)\\
\kappa_s &\leq \tau_s(c^T \tilde{x}_s^k + d_s^T \tilde{y}_s^k) + \mu H_s \tilde{x}_s^k & \forall s \in S, \forall k \in K && (28)\\
\kappa_s &\leq z_{P,s}^{*k} + \mu H_s \hat{x}_s^k & \forall s \in S, \forall k \in K && (29)\\
\eta_{LMP} &\in \mathbb{R}^1, \quad \mu \in \mathbb{R}^{(|S|-1) \times n}, \quad \kappa_s \in \mathbb{R}^1 & \forall s \in S && (30)
\end{aligned}
$$

The objective function (26) contains the additional quadratic stabilization term $\frac{\delta}{2}\|\mu - \bar{\mu}\|_2^2$ that defines a trust-region for the update of the Lagrangean multipliers (Lemarechal, 1974; Zowe, 1985; Kiwiel, 1990; Frangioni, 2005). The stabilization requires initial values and update strategies for the penalty δ, which defines the size of the trust region, and the stabilization center $\bar{\mu}$.

Let z_{LMP}^{*k+1} be the optimal objective function value of (LMP^{k+1}). Note that the valid inequalities (29) make the dual (Lagrangean) master problem bounded. Furthermore, they guarantee that the dual (Lagrangean) master problem will yield a bound at least as tight as the best known primal upper bound obtained from the primal (Benders) subproblems.

Using the multi-cut version for the optimality cuts and the Lagrangean dual bounds derived by Mitra (2013) and given in (34), we formulate the mixed-integer linear primal (Benders) master problem (BMP^{k+1}) that yields the next primal vector $\hat{x}^{k+1}$.

(BMP^{k+1}) min η_{BMP} (31)

$$\text{s.t.} \quad \eta_{BMP} \leq \sum_{s \in S} \theta_s \tag{32}$$

$$\theta_s \geq \tau_s c^T x + (A_1 x - b_1)^T u_s^k - b_s^T v_s^k \qquad \forall s \in S, \forall k \in K \tag{33}$$

$$\theta_s \geq z_{LD,s}^{*k} - \mu^k H_s x \qquad \forall s \in S, \forall k \in K \tag{34}$$

$$A_0 x \leq b_0 \tag{35}$$

$$x \in X, \quad \eta_{BMP} \in \mathbb{R}^1, \quad \theta_s \in \mathbb{R}^1 \qquad \forall s \in S \tag{36}$$

Let z_{BMP}^{*k+1} be the optimal objective function value of (BMP^{k+1}). Note that (BMP^{k+1}) is a relaxation of $(SPNAC)$ that provides the following lower bound:

$$z_{BMP}^{*k+1} \leq TC \qquad \forall k \in K \tag{37}$$

Note that by adding the dual Lagrangean cuts given in Eq. (34) to the primal (Benders) master problem, we strengthen its formulation, and we can guarantee that the lower bound obtained from the Benders master problem is at least as tight as the best known solution from the Lagrangean dual.

4. Illustrative case study

We apply the cross-decomposition scheme to a facility location problem with distribution centers (DCs) under the risk of disruptions. In the problem, demand points need to be satisfied from a set of candidate DCs in order to minimize the sum of investment cost and expected transportation cost. The capacitated reliable facility location problem is formulated as a two-stage stochastic program. First-stage decisions involve the selection of DCs and their capacities. Second-stage decisions are the demand assignments to DCs in the scenarios, which are defined by combinations of active and disrupted locations. Penalties are applied to unsatisfied demands, such that the second-stage subproblems have full recourse. The details of the model are presented by Garcia-Herreros et al. (2013).

The illustrative example includes 12 candidate locations for DCs and 49 demand sites. The disruption probability of all candidate locations is set to 0.05. The scenarios are generated assuming that disruptions at candidate locations are independent. Given the very small probabilities of scenarios with more than 5 simultaneous disruptions, they have been grouped into a single scenario in which all demands are penalized. As a consequence, the instance has 1,587 scenarios, 99,996 constraints, and 1,012,534 variables (12 binaries).

The resulting fullspace model is hard to solve. Table 1 shows the computational results for the different solution methods. It can be observed that it takes 722 min (over 12 h) to solve the fullspace problem. Interestingly, multi-cut Benders decomposition fails to solve the example faster than the fullspace method. Benders decomposition is terminated after a time limit of 4,000 min, with a remaining optimality gap of 18.8 %.

Table 1. Computational results for the illustrative example.

	Fullspace	Benders	Cross
Objective ($)	1,004,855.83	1,028,650.66	1,004,855.83
LP relaxation ($)	479,563.62	-	-
Optimality gap (%)	0	18.8	0
Iterations (#)	-	130	36
Runtime (min)	722	4,000[a]	474

[a]Terminated after 4,000 min time limit.

In contrast, the proposed cross-decomposition algorithm solves the example to optimality in 36 iterations and 474 min. Hence, it outperforms the fullspace model in terms of runtime by 34 %, which demonstrates the potential of the cross-decomposition method for stochastic programming.

5. Conclusion

We have described a cross-decomposition algorithm that combines Benders and scenario based Lagrangean decomposition for two-stage stochastic MILP problems with complete recourse, where the first-stage variables are mixed-integer and the second-stage variables are continuous. The algorithm fully integrates primal and dual information with multi-cuts that are added to the Benders and the Lagrangean master problems for each scenario. Computational results for an illustrative case study on a facility location problem with risk of disruptions demonstrate the conceptual strength of the cross-decomposition such as a reduction of iterations and stronger lower bounds compared to pure multi-cut Benders decomposition.

References

J. Benders, 1962, Partitioning Procedures for Solving Mixed-variables Programming Problems, Numer Math, 4, 238-252.

J. Birge, F. Louveaux, 2011, Introduction to Stochastic Programming. New York, NY: Springer.

C.C. Caroe, R. Schultz, 1999, Dual Decomposition in Stochastic Integer Programming, Oper Res Lett, 24, 37-45.

A. Frangioni, 2005, About Langrangian Methods in Integer Optimization, Ann Oper Res, 139, 163-193.

P. Garcia-Herreros, J.M. Wassick, I.E. Grossmann, 2013, Design of Supply Chains under the Risk of Facility Disruptions, Computer Aided Chemical Engineering, 32, 577-582.

A. Geoffrion, 1972, Generalized Benders Decomposition, J Optimiz Theory App, 10, 237-260.

M. Guignard, S. Kim, 1987, Lagrangean Decomposition - a Model Yielding Stronger Lagrangean Bounds, Math Program, 39, 215-228.

H. Heitsch, W. Romisch, 2003, Scenario Reduction Algorithms in Stochastic Programming, Comput Optim Appl, 24, 187-206.

K. Holmberg, 1990, On the Convergence of Cross Decomposition, Math Program, 47, 269-296.

K. Holmberg, 1997a, Linear Mean Value Cross Decomposition: A Generalization of the Kornai-Liptak Method, Eur J Oper Res, 62, 55-73.

K. Holmberg, 1997b, Mean Value Cross Decomposition Applied to Integer Programming Problems, Eur J Oper Res, 97, 124-138.

K. Kiwiel, 1990, Proximity Control in Bundle Methods for Convex Nondifferentiable Minimization, Math Program 46, 105-122.

C. Lemarechal, 1974, An Algorithm for Minimizing Convex Functions, Proceedings IFIP'74 Congress, 552-556.

J. Linderoth, A. Shapiro, S. Wright, 2006, The Empirical Behavior of Sampling Methods for Stochastic Programming, Ann Oper Res, 142, 215-241.

S. Mitra, P., 2013, Optimal Multi-scale Demand-side Management for Continuous Power-intensive Processes, Ph.D. thesis, Carnegie Mellon University, Pittsburgh, Pennsylvania, USA.

H.S. Sohn, D. Bricker, T.L. Tseng, 2011, Mean Value Cross Decomposition for Two-Stage Stochastic Linear Programming with Recourse, TOORJ, 5, 30-38.

T.J. Van Roy, 1983, Cross Decomposition for Mixed Integer Programming, Math Program, 25, 46-63.

R. Van Slyke, R. Wets, 1969, L-shaped Linear Programs with Applications to Optimal Control and Stochastic Programming, SIAM J Appl Math, 17, 638-663.

J. Zowe, 1985, Nondifferentiable Optimization, In K. Schittkowski, Computational Mathematical Program, NATO ASI Series F: Computer and Systems Science, 15, 323-356.

Jiří Jaromír Klemeš, Petar Sabev Varbanov and Peng Yen Liew (Editors)
Proceedings of the 24th European Symposium on Computer Aided Process Engineering – ESCAPE 24
June 15-18, 2014, Budapest, Hungary. Copyright © 2014 Elsevier B.V. All rights reserved.

Optimal Wavelet-Threshold Selection to Solve Dynamic Optimization Problems

Lizandro S. Santos, Argimiro R. Secchi*, Evaristo C. Biscaia Jr.

Chemical Engineering Program-PEQ/COPPE, Universidade Federal do Rio de Janeiro, CT -Bloco G, Sala G116,Cidade Universitária, Ilha do Fundão, Cx.P. 68502, CEP: 21941-914, Rio de Janeiro, RJ, Brazil
arge@peq.coppe.ufrj.br

Abstract

In this work, the influence of different wavelet thresholding rules coupled to the single-shooting algorithm applied to solve dynamic optimization problems is analyzed. Three wavelet thresholding strategies: Sureshrink, Visushrink, and Cross Validation are used for comparison purposes. These rules have many applications to denoise and compress large datasets. However it has not been investigated its effects on adaptive strategies for grid treatment of dynamic optimization algorithms. The wavelet thresholding algorithms attempt to find optimal thresholds which objectives are twofold: reducing the computation time of the dynamic optimization algorithm and improving the quality of control vector parameterization (number and time-location of control decision variables). We show here that the optimal threshold not only depends on the wavelet level, but also on the control profile shape, and its influence on the optimization algorithm is very pronounced, allowing to drastically reduce the NLP dimension and CPU time.

Keywords: wavelets, thresholding, wavelets shrinkage, optimal control, single shooting, multigrid.

1. Introduction

In dynamic optimization with single-shooting methods, the use of high resolution grid to accurately capture any discontinuities in the state and/or control variables is necessary. It requires a large computational cost because of the high dimension of the NLP problem. Additional numerical problems can appear in intervals, where model states are constrained by path constraints or singular arcs, where the sensitivity of the objective function in relation to the control variables can be small (Schlegel et al, 2005).

This work deals with the evaluation of different adaptive strategies that applies different wavelet thresholding policies in order to solve dynamic optimization. The influence of different thresholding rules on adaptation procedure and its effects upon optimal solution are investigated. The challenge is to demonstrate that there is a relation between the computed threshold value and the algorithm performance.

Some researchers have shown that thresholding procedure is crucial for wavelets application to denoising and compression. Donoho and Johnstone (1994) developed some thresholding rules, as Visushrink and Sureshrink, and proved that different rules affect the quality of image and data. Wieland (2009) carried out a deep study of the Cross Validation thresholding algorithm for signal processing.

In a previous study, Santos et al. (2012), we demonstrated that heuristic wavelet-thresholds (fixed thresholds and norm of wavelet details) may affect the optimization performance and, in some occasions: the adaptive algorithm can be slower than a non-adaptive (with fixed discretization) one. Moreover, heuristics strategies have been used by some researchers, such as Schlegel et al. (2005) for single shooting methods and Assassa and Marquardt (2014) for multiple shooting methods. Recently, Logist et al. (2012) suggested the strategy used by Schlegel et al. (2005) to solve dynamic optimization with multiple objectives. Therefore, it is instructive to compare the performance of these thresholding procedures due to its different characteristics to deal with wavelet details coefficients and its direct impact on the refinement procedure. This introductory study is particularly new for dynamic optimization area, and our objectives are to show that wavelet thresholds are not simple parameters for tuning control vector parameterization. The novelty is also the application of these strategies upon problems with two or more control variables. As the control profiles may present different shapes, the expectation is that the relevance of the choice of threshold is clearer for these cases.

2. Wavelets

Wavelet analyses are relatively recent numerical concepts that allow representing a function in terms of a set of basis functions, called wavelets, which are localized both in location and scale. These functions are generated from one single function ψ called the mother wavelet by the simple operations of dilation and translation, Daubechies (1992):

$$\psi_{n,m}(t) = 2^{n/2} \psi\left(2^n t - m\right), \quad m \in 0, \ldots, 2^n - 1, \quad n \in 0, \ldots, K-1 \tag{1}$$

where the integer index n denotes the scale or wavelet decomposition level and m denotes the translation index on a specific level and K is the maximum decomposition level.

Compactly supported wavelets are localized in the space, which means that the solution can be refined in regions of high gradient without having to generate the mesh for the entire problem. This particular property reduces the need of function evaluations. Therefore it is possible to generate the coefficients at different scales by different sections of one signal. These coefficients are results of a regression of the original signal performed on the wavelets. Considering a function $u(t)$ on Hilbert space $L_2[0,1]$, it can be transformed into wavelet domain as:

$$d_{n,m} = \left\langle u(t), \psi_{n,m}(t) \right\rangle \tag{2}$$

$d_{n,m}$ is the scalar wavelet detail that captures the characteristics of the function at (n,m) indexes. Consequently, a function $u(t)$ can be approximated by the following wavelet expansion:

$$u(t) \approx c\varphi + \sum_{n=0}^{K-1} \sum_{m=0}^{2^n-1} d_{n,m} \psi_{n,m}(t) \tag{3}$$

where c is the approximation coefficient and φ is the wavelet scale function. Eq. 3 is the inverse wavelet transform ($\mathbf{DWT^{-1}}$) which calculates a function profile from wavelets coefficients. Both $\mathbf{DWT}$ and $\mathbf{DWT^{-1}}$ can be performed through the pyramidal algorithm (Mallat, 1989). Actually, $\mathbf{DTW}$ is realized at specific stages, $\upsilon = u\left(t_i\right)_{i=1,\ldots n_s}$.

3. Wavelets Thresholding

This section presents a description of three thresholding algorithms using wavelet transforms. These algorithms are Visushrink, Sureshrink, and Cross Validation. The term wavelet thresholding is explained as decomposition of the data or the image into wavelet coefficients, comparing the detail coefficients with a given threshold value, and shrinking these coefficients close to zero to take away the effect of noise in the data (Donoho and Johnstone, 1994).The wavelet threshold algorithm is summarized as:

$$\mathbf{d} = \mathbf{DWT}(\upsilon) \rightarrow \mathbf{d}_\delta = \mathbf{Thr}(\mathbf{d},\delta)\mathbf{d} \rightarrow \upsilon_\delta = \mathbf{DWT}^{-1}(\mathbf{d}_\delta) \qquad (4)$$

In the above equation, function **Thr** is the threshold rule that depends on the threshold value δ. In this work, the hard threshold rule was considered:

$\mathbf{Thr}(d_{n,m},\delta) = \begin{cases} 0, & |d_{n,m}| \leq \delta \\ 1, & |d_{n,m}| > \delta \end{cases}$. The demand for good threshold means to find the minimal

mean squared error between the thresholded polluted data and the original cleaned data.

3.1. Visushrink (VS)

The Visushrink threshold was derived by Donoho and Johnstone (1994), showing that for n_s independent, identically distributed, standard normal variables, the expected maximum is $\sqrt{2\ln(n_s)}$, leading to the formulation of $\delta = \sigma\sqrt{2\ln(n_s)}$, where σ is the noise standard deviation. An estimate of σ is defined based on the median absolute deviation given by: $\hat{\sigma} = median\left(\left\{\|d_{n-1,m}\| : m = 0,1,\ldots,2^{n-1}-1\right\}\right)/0.6745$.

3.2. Sureshrink (SS)

A threshold chooser based on Stein's Unbiased Risk Estimator (SURE) was proposed by Donoho and Johnstone (1994) and was called Sureshrink. It is a combination of the Visushrink and the SURE threshold defined as: $\delta = \min\left(\theta, \sigma\sqrt{2\ln(n_s)}\right)$, where θ denotes the value that minimizesSURE. The Sureshrink is adaptive and calculates a threshold at each wavelet decomposition level.

3.3. Cross Validation (CV)

Like SS, CV can be seen as a function of a threshold parameter and is an estimate of the Unbiased Risk Estimator function. The concept of CV is given by the construction of several estimates, never using the whole data set. Using these estimates one predicts what the expelled data could have been. Finally one compares the prediction with the actual values of the expelled data (Wieland, 2009). The estimate of each expelled data is based on the mean between two neighbours' data. The deduction of this procedure can be seen in Wieland (2009) and is defined as:

$$CV(\delta) = \min\left[\frac{1}{n_s}\sum_{i=1}^{n_s}(z_i - \tilde{z}_i)^2\right] \qquad (5)$$

where z_i is the true data and $\tilde{z}_i$ is the estimated cross validation version of z_i.

3.4. Numerical details

The algorithm was implemented in Matlab 7.6$^{\copyright}$, using the function fmincon (SQP), the DASSLC integrator (Secchi, 2012), and Matlab wavelet routines (wavedec, wden, waverec) were used. More details can be seen in Santos et al. (2012).

4. Case-studies

Twelve case studies taken from the literature are examined. Detailed description of the problems shown here are given in the cited references in Table 1. For each example, such steps were followed: (i) Reference solution determination: In this case, the adaptive algorithm starts with 8 elements for each control variable and the number of elements is doubled at each iteration; (ii) Wavelet adaptive algorithm: Again, the algorithm starts with 8 elements for each control variable. However, after the second iteration, with 16 elements, the wavelet thresholding procedure starts.

For each wavelet thresholding procedure, it is compared the CPU time, the number of elements, the objective function value, convergence and the values of computed thresholds.Figure1 summarizes these different wavelet thresholding procedures applied to 12 problems. According to the results, we note that in several cases (cases 1, 2, 5, 6, 7, 8, 9, 10, 11 and 12) more than 50 % of reduction in CPU was possible.

4.1. Visushrink Analysis

In problems that result in control profiles with three or more different arcs (i.e., cases 3 and 12) the VS strategy performs worse than SS and CV. In fact, it is expected because VS is not indicated for detecting strong variations in control profile. Contrary to this, when the control profile is smooth, this method presents better results. This behavior is clearly observed in problem 7 (Figure 2), where VS strategy is superior to SS. We also checked that in problems 1, 2, 5, 6, 9 and 10, VS performed relatively well, with similar SS CPU values. It can be explained by the fact that the convergence occurs very fast in these cases, with no more than five iterations of the adaptive.

4.2. Sureshrink Analysis

As mentioned, SS loses for VS only in problems 5, 6 and 7. In fact SS is level dependent and most of the important details are collected at coarse wavelet levels in smooth control, which may have few sufficient details for satisfactory threshold estimation. Thus, the algorithm can calculate too small thresholds and the convergence may be slow. On the other hand, for very irregular control profiles the SS works relatively well, as observed in problems 3 (Figure 3) and 12. Problem 12, in particular, has 3 control variables. In these cases, the level dependency analysis appears to be a good choice, because significant control profile variations are kept in high wavelet levels and SS performs well to calculate it.

Table 1. List of dynamic optimization problems.

Case	Problem (reference)
1	CSTR Reactor (Srinavasan et al., 2003)
2	The mixed catalyst problem (Bell and Sargent, 2000)
3	Park and Ramirez Bioreactor (Canto et al., 2001)
4	Time Free Bang Bang Control (Liang et al., 2003)
5	Batch Reactor Problem (Ciznia et al., 2006)
6	Pressure-constrained Batch Reactor (Huang, 2002)
7	Van der Pol Oscillator (Vassiliadis et al., 1999)
8	Singular Control (Luus, 2002)
9	Linear Bang Bang Control (Luus, 2002)
10	Lee & Ramirez Bioreactor $Q = 0$ (Canto et al., 2001)
11	Lee & Ramirez Bioreactor $Q = 2.5$ (Canto et al., 2001)
12	Non-linear CSTR with three control variables (Canto et al., 2001)

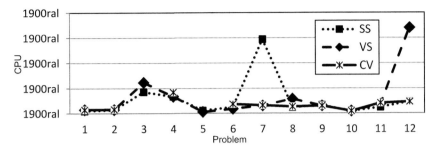

Figure 1. Performance of the thresholding algorithms.

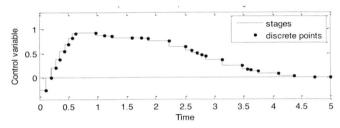

Figure 2. Typical control profile of problem 7.

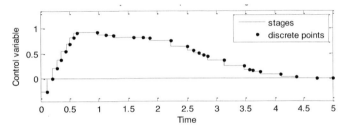

Figure 3. Typical control profile of problem 3.

4.3. Cross Validation Analysis

It is also observable in Figure1 that CV presents a profile very similar to SS profile, however quite often reporting equal or inferior performances. According to the theory (Wieland, 2009), it is really expected that CV and SS coincide in most cases. The exceptions can occur in two situations: (i) In control profiles with refinement errors strongly dependent on wavelet levels. In these cases it is expected better performance of SS; (ii) When level dependent fails due to low number of wavelet details at coarser levels. If coarser levels are most relevant ones, SS can fail in calculating the optimal threshold, which can be observed in problem 7.

5. Conclusions

Three wavelet-threshold procedures have been analyzed here: Visushrink, Sureshrink, and Cross Validation. According to obtained results, we can summarize:

(i) VS presents better results for smooth control profiles, or control profiles with low number of switch points and irregularities. In fact, VS calculates a universal threshold which does not take into account the different wavelet decomposition levels.

(ii) SS presents better results for control profiles with switch points, singular arcs, and irregularities. It is level dependent and calculates an optimal threshold for each level. Therefore it causes a large impact in cases with very irregular control profiles.

(iii) CV and SS have similar performances. However, for cases where SS fails, CV uses to have a better performance, with results very similar to VS. It is observable that this rule is capable to calculate a threshold based on the most important wavelet decomposition level. In other words, when SS fails in calculate a threshold for a particular level, CV appears to be more appropriate.

References

F. Assassa, W. Marquardt, 2014, Dynamic optimization using adaptive direct multiple shooting, Computer and Chemical Engineering, 60, 242-259.

M.L. Bell, R.W.H. Sargent, 2000, Optimal control of inequality constrained DAE systems, Computer and Chemical Engineering, 24, 11, 2385-2404.

E.B. Canto, J.R. Banga, A.A. Alonso, V.S. Vassiliadis, 2001, Dynamic optimization of chemical and biochemical processes using restricted second-order information,Computer and Chemical Engineering, 254, 539-546.

M. Cizniar, M. Fikar, M.A. Lati, 2006, MATLAB dynamic optimisation code DYNOPT, User's Guide, Bratislava, Slovak Republic.

I. Daubechies, 1992, Ten Lectures on Wavelets, Society for Industrial and Applied Mathematics, Philadelphia,USA.

D.L. Donoho, I.M. Johnstone, 1994, Ideal Spatial Adaptation by Wavelet Shinkage, Biometrika, 81, 425-455.

J.I. Huang, G.V. Reklaitis, V. Venkatasubramanian, 2002, Model decomposition based method for solving general dynamic optimization problems,26, 863-873.

J. Liang, M. Meng, Y. Chen, R Fullmer, 2003, Solving tough optimal control problems by network enabled optimization server (NEOS), Technical report, School of Engineering, Utah State University USA.

F. Logist, F. Assassa, J.V.Impe, W. Marquardt, 2012, Computer Aided Chemical Engineering, 30, 782-786.

R. Luus, 2002, Iterative dynamic programming, Chapman and Hall/CRC, USA.

S. Mallat, 1989, A theory for multiresolution signal decomposition: the wavelet representation, IEEE Transactions on Pattern Analysis and Machine Intelligence, 2, 674-693.

L.S. Santos, A.R. Secchi, E.C.Biscaia Jr., 2012, Wavelet-threshold influence in optimal control problems, Computer Aided Chemical Engineering, 30, 1222-1226.

M. Schlegel, K. Stockmann, T. Binder, W. Marquardt, 2005, Dynamic optimization using adaptive control vector parameterization,Computer and Chemical Engineering, 29, 1731-1751.

A.R. Secchi, 2012, DASSLC version 3.8: Differential-Algebraic Systen Solver in C, <www.enq.ufrgs.br/enqlib/numeric> accessed on 20/03/2013.

B. Srinavasan, S. Palanki, D. Bonvin, 2003, Dynamic optimization of batch processes: I. characterization of the nominal solution,Computer and Chemical Engineering, 27, 1, 1-26.

V.S. Vassiliadis, J.R. Banga, E. Balsa-Canto, 1999, Second-order sensitivities of general dynamic systems with application to optimal control problems, Chemical Engineering and Sciency, 54, 3851-3860.

B. Wieland, 2009, Speech signal noise reduction with wavelets, PhD Thesis, Universität Ulm, Deutschland.

Jiří Jaromír Klemeš, Petar Sabev Varbanov and Peng Yen Liew (Editors)
Proceedings of the 24th European Symposium on Computer Aided Process Engineering – ESCAPE 24
June 15-18, 2014, Budapest, Hungary.

Incorporating Green into Production and Consumption Behaviours toward Sustainable Logistics Optimization in Process Systems

Yoshiaki Shimizu

Department of Mechanical Engineering, Toyohashi University of Technology, 1-1 Hibarigaoka, Tenpaku-cho, Toyohashi 441-8580, Japan
shimizu@me.tut.ac.jp

Abstract

Recently, realizing low carbon society has attracted a great interest under a provision for essential infrastructure aligned with sustainable development. Deployment of green logistics incorporating co-existence of manufacturers and consumers will be a new key issue for such technologies. Noticing such circumstance, in this paper, we have extended our approaches for logistics optimization to cope with green logistics associated with production and consumption behaviours in process systems. Taking a multi-layer logistics network, we have developed a novel approach that tries to evaluate the minimum total cost and CO2 emission under appropriate constraints through adjusting prone and aversion consciousness on sustainability among the logistics members. Numerical experiment has been carried out to validate effectiveness of the proposed approach. Moreover, to enhance usability toward real-world applications, we provide a system development aimed at using Google map API.

Keywords: Sustainability, Green Logistics Optimization, Hybrid Meta-Heuristic Method, Co-Exist of Production and Consumption.

1. Introduction

Recently, realizing low carbon society has attracted a great interest under a provision for essential infrastructure aligned with sustainable development. Deployment of green logistics incorporating co-existence of manufacturers and consumers will be a new key issue for such technologies. Noticing such circumstance, in this paper, we have extended our hybrid approach (Wada and Shimizu, 2006) for green logistics optimization in process systems (Nikolopoulou and Ierapetritou, 2012) by adjusting decision making on production methods. Taking a multi-layer logistics network, we have developed a novel approach that tries to evaluate the minimum total cost and CO_2 emission under appropriate constraints through controlling prone and aversion consciousness on sustainability among the logistics members).

After providing a general formulation and proposed solution procedure, numerical experiments are carried out to validate effectiveness of the proposed approach and to explore the prospects for sustainable logistics. Moreover, to enhance

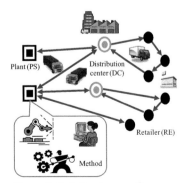

Figure 1. Solution image of concerned problem

usability toward real-world applications, we aim at a system development for collection of real distance data and visualization of result using Google map API. The final scope of this study is to make a rational decision that can consider trade-off between economical interests and CO_2 emissions for incorporating sensitivity on sustainable consciousness into production and consumption behaviors.

2. Problem Formulation

Taking a global logistics network composed of plant or production site (PS), distribution center (DC), and customer or retailer (RE) as shown in Figure 1, we try to decide the available PSs and their production methods, paths from PSs to DCs and circular routes from every DC to its client REs. The goal of this problem is to minimize either total cost or CO_2 emission so that we can consider a trade-off for green logistics. This problem for cost minimization is formulated as the following mixed-integer programming problem under mild assumptions, e.g., round-trip transport between PS and DC, circular transport over REs, certainly defined system parameters, etc. Just replacing the cost coefficients in the objective function with those of CO_2 emission, we can give the formulation for another problem.

(p.1) Minimize

$$\sum_{i\in I}\sum_{j\in J}TcL_{ij}(f2_{ij}+2w_0t_i)+\sum_{i\in I}\sum_{i'\in I'}Hp_{ii'}f1_{ii'}+\sum_{i\in I}Sh1_i(\sum_{j\in J}f2_{ij})+\sum_{j\in J}Sh2_j(\sum_{i\in I}f2_{ij})$$
$$+\sum_{v\in V}\sum_{p\in P}\sum_{p'\in P}c_v d_{pp'}(g_{pp'v}+w_v)z_{pp'v}+\sum_{v\in V}F_v y_v+\sum_{i\in I}\sum_{i'\in I}Fc_{ii'}x_{ii'}$$

subject to

$$\sum_{p\in P}z_{kpv}\le 1, \quad \forall k\in K;\forall v\in V \tag{1}$$

$$\sum_{p'\in P}z_{pp'v}-\sum_{p'\in P}z_{p'pv}=0, \quad \forall p\in P;\forall v\in V \tag{2}$$

$$\sum_{j'\in J}z_{jj'v}=0, \quad \forall j\in J,\forall v\in V \tag{3}$$

$$g_{pp'v}\le W_v z_{pp'v}, \quad \forall p\in P;\forall p'\in P;\forall v\in V \tag{4}$$

$$\sum_{p\in P}\sum_{p'\in P}z_{pp'v}\le My_v, \quad \forall v\in V \tag{5}$$

$$\sum_{j\in J}\sum_{k\in K}z_{jkv}=y_v, \quad \forall v\in V \tag{6}$$

$$\sum_{j\in J}\sum_{k\in K}z_{kjv}=y_v, \quad \forall v\in V \tag{7}$$

$$\sum_{k\in K}g_{kjv}=0, \quad \forall j\in J;\forall v\in V \tag{8}$$

$$\sum_{v\in V}\sum_{p\in P}g_{pkv}-\sum_{v\in V}\sum_{p\in P}g_{kpv}=D_k, \quad \forall k\in K \tag{9}$$

$$\sum_{p\in P}(g_{pkv}-D_k z_{pkv})=\sum_{p\in P}g_{kpv},\forall k\in K,\forall v\in V \tag{10}$$

$$\sum_{p\in\Omega}\sum_{p'\in\Omega}z_{pp'v}\le|\Omega|-1,\forall\Omega\subseteq P\setminus\{1\},|\Omega|\ge 2,\forall v\in V \tag{11}$$

$$\sum_{j \in J} f2_{ij} = \sum_{i' \in I'} f1_{ii'}, \quad \forall i \in I \tag{12}$$

$$\sum_{i \in I} f2_{ij} = \sum_{v \in V} \sum_{k \in K} g_{jkv}, \quad \forall j \in J \tag{13}$$

$$\sum_{i \in I} f2_{ij} \leq U_j, \quad \forall j \in J \tag{14}$$

$$f1_{ii'} \leq S_{ii'}^{\max} x_{ii'}, \quad \forall i \in I, \forall i' \in I' \tag{15}$$

$$P_i^{\min} t_i \leq \sum_{j \in J} f2_{ij} \leq P_i^{\max} t_i, \quad \forall i \in I \tag{16}$$

$$x_{ii'} \in \{0,1\}, \forall i \in I, \forall i' \in I'; \ y_v \in \{0,1\}, \forall v \in V; \ t_i \in \{0,1\}, \forall i \in I;$$

$$z_{pp'v} \in \{0,1\}, \forall p \in P; \forall p' \in P; \forall v \in V$$

$$f1_{ii'} \geq 0, \forall i \in I; \forall i' \in I'; \ f2_{ij} \geq 0, \forall i \in I; \ \forall j \in J;$$

$$g_{pp'v} \geq 0, \forall p, \forall p' \in P; \forall v \in V$$

Variables

$f1_{ii'}$: amount of production at PS i by method i'

$f2_{ij}$: shipping amount from PS i to DC j

$g_{pp'v}(t)$: load of vehicle v on the path from $p \in P$ to $p' \in P$

t_i= 1 if PS i is selected; otherwise 0

$x_{ii'}$= production method i' is selected at PS i; otherwise 0

$y_v(t)$= 1 if vehicle v is used; otherwise 0

$z_{pp'v}(t)$= 1 if vehicle v travels on the path from $p \in P$ to $p' \in P$; otherwise 0

Parameters

c_v: transportation cost per unit load per unit distance of vehicle v

D_k: demand of retailer k

$d_{pp'}$: path distance between $p, p' \in P$

$Fc_{ii'}$: fixed charge to take production method i' at PS i

F_v: fixed charge to operate vehicle v

$Hp_{ii'}$: production cost per unit load at PS i for method i'

L_{ij}: distance between PS i and DC j

M: auxiliary constant (Large real number)

$P_i^{\max}$: maximum production amount at PS i

$P_i^{\min}$: minimum production amount at PS i

$S_{ii'}^{\max}$: maximum production at PS i for method i'

$Sh1_i$: shipping cost per unit load at PS i

$Sh2_j$: shipping cost per unit load at DS j

T_c: transportation cost per unit load from PS to DC

U_j: maximum capacity at DC j

w_0, w_v: own weight of vehicle used at PS and DC, respectively

W_v: maximum capacity of vehicle v

Index set

I: PS; I': Method; J: DC; K: RE

In (p.1), the objective function is composed of round-trip transportation costs between PS and DC, circular transportation costs for covering every customer, production cost at PS, shipping costs at PS and DC, and fixed charges for production and vehicle operation. On the other hand, constraints mean that Eq.(1): vehicles cannot visit a customer twice; Eq.(2): vehicles entering a certain RE must leave it; Eq.(3): no travel between DCs; Eq.(4): upper bound on loading capacity for vehicle; Eq.(5): each vehicle must travel once on a certain path; Eqs.(6) and (7):each vehicle leaves only one DC and returns there; Eq.(8): vehicles return to the DC with empty; Eq.(9): customer demand is satisfied; Eq.(10): sum of inlet must be greater than that of outlets by the demand; Eq.(11): Sub-tour elimination; Eqs.(12) and (13): material balances at PS and DC, respectively; Eq.(14): holding capacity at DC is upper bounded; Eq.(15): production is upper bounded at PS per method; Eq.(16): total production at PS is within the prescribed range.

From this problem, we can decide the available PSs and their production methods with different structures regarding cost accounting and CO_2 emission, paths from PSs to DCs and circular routes touring the client REs from every DC under the relevant constraints. However, it is almost impossible to solve this problem with practical size using any currently available commercial software. Against this, we have successfully solved various logistics optimization problems, including complicated situations resulting from a variety of real-life conditions, by using the hybrid method (Wada & Shimizu, 2006). This method is not only a practical and powerful method but also flexible and suitable for a variety of applications. So, we can extend such idea to the problem under consideration.

3. Hybrid Tabu Search Incorporating Multi-depot Vehicle Routing Problem

To cope with the above problem, we have majorly invented two new ideas and similarly integrated them into the framework of our hybrid method. In its first level, we choose the available PSs and their production methods using the modified tabu search. In the second level, we tentatively decide the paths from PSs to REs via DCs by solving the minimum cost flow (MCF) problem through graph algorithm. Letting the retailers thus allocated as the clients for each DC, we deploy a new idea to solve multi-depot vehicle routing problem (M-VRP).

Since transportation cost and CO_2 emission depend not only on distance traveled but also on loading weight, it is practical to consider these two factors in parallel or to adopt the bilinear model of distance and load (Weber) or nonlinear model (generalized Weber). Moreover, it had better to consider the fixed operational cost F_v of vehicle for practical accounting. However, these ideas have been never considered in previous studies. This aspect is also essential for consistent evaluation of the transportation cost from PS to DC and that of circular route. To derive such circular route from each DC, we developed the modified saving method to derive an initial solution and the modified tabu search to improve it (Shimizu and Sakaguchi, 2013).

Then, the result obtained so far will be fed back to the first level and this procedure will be repeated until a certain convergence condition has been satisfied. The procedure of this algorithm is illustrated in Fig.2. In this algorithm, the modified swing method is outlined as follows.
Step 1: Create direct outward-and-return routes from every DC to each RE. Compute the saving value by $s_{i,j}=(d_{0,j} - d_{0,i} - d_{i,j})D_j+(d_{0,j}+d_{i,0} - d_{i,j})w$. Sort the savings in descending order.
Step 2: Starting from the top of the saving list, determine whether there exist two routes, one containing $(i, 0)$ and the other containing $(0, j)$. If so, merge the route as long as the combined demand is less than the vehicle capacity and the saving is greater than $-F_v/c_v$.

Since the modified saving method derives only an approximated solution, we try to update such initial route through the modified tabu search. Moreover, we derive the

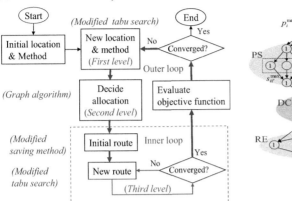

Figure 2. Flow chart of the proposed procedure

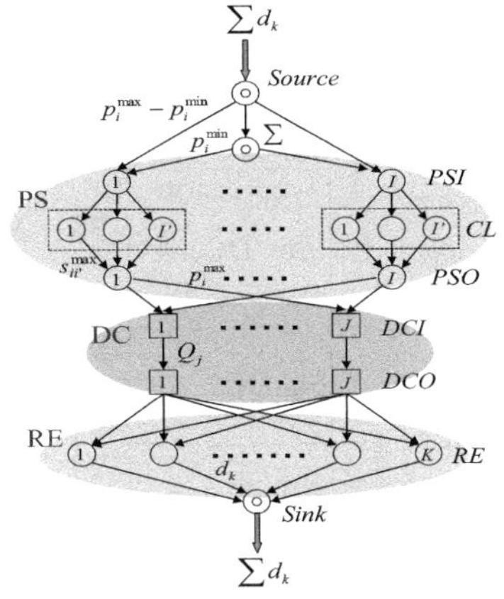

Figure 3. MCF graph for the concerned problem

can consider the respective production method at each PS and client REs for each DC. In terms of the MCF graph thus derived, we can solve the original allocation problem extremely fast through a graph algorithm like RELAX4. Moreover, its sensitivity analysis can accelerate the speed to solve the similar problem repeatedly.

4. Numerical Experiments and Discussion

We prepared a few benchmark problems with different problem sizes, i.e., $\{|I|, |I'|, |J|, |K|\}$. Basically, system parameters are set randomly within the respective prescribed intervals. First, we solved the smaller size problem like $|I|=3$, $|I'|=2$, $|J|=3$ and $|K|=17$ incorporated with the Google map API. Actually, real distance data are retrieved from the map for the assumed locations, and also the resulting routes are drawn in the map after the optimization. We show the result in Table 2 where we obtained the different decisions depending on the adopted objective function and can observe the trade-off relation between the cost and CO_2 emission.

Then, concentrating on the cost minimization problem, we solved the larger problems to examine the solution ability of the proposed approach, and obtained the results as shown in Table 3. Threat, improved rate is defined by $(Cost^{(1)}-Cost^*)/Cost^*$, where $Cost^{(1)}$ and $Cost^*$ respectively denote the values at the first and the converged stages in the outer loop iteration whose number is shown in "Iteration" column. We can ascertain

Table 1. Labeling on the edge for MCF graph

Edge (from to)	Cost	Capacity
Source - $\sum$ (Dummy)	$-M$	$\sum_{i \in I} P_i^{min}$
Source - PSI i	0	$P_i^{max} - P_i^{min}$
$\sum$ - PSI i	0	P_i^{min}
PSI i – CL ii'	$Hp_{ii'}$	$S_{ii'}^{max}$
CL ii' – PSO i	0	$S_{ii'}^{max}$
PSO i – DCI j	$TcLij + Sh1_i$	P_i^{max}
DCI j - DCO j	$Sh2_j$	U_j

DCO j- RE k	$c_v d_{jk}$	D_k
RE k - Sink	0	D_k

Table 2. Results of optimization

Kind of problem		Total cost [cost unit]	CO_2 emission [kg-co2]
Objective value	Total cost	**1,193,215**	1,636,735
	CO_2 emission	7,764.45	**5,293.51**
Path from PS to DC & (Method)		PS1: *NA* PS2 (M1)→{DC1, DC2} PS3 (M1)→{DC1}	PS1 (M1)→{DC3} PS2 (M1)→{DC1} PS3 (M2)→{DC1, DC3}
Circular route around RE	From DC1	V1: RE8→17→16→13→ 12→7 V2: RE14→5→2→1→11	V1: RE6→15→3→9→ 10→4 V2: RE11
	From DC2	V1: RE15→6→3→10→9 →4→11	*NA*
	From DC3	*NA*	V1: RE8→17→14→13 →12→7 V2: RE16→5→2→1

Table 3. Results of larger benchmark problems

Problem size*	Cost	Improved rate	Iteration	CPU [s]
(5, 2, 3, 20)	683663.0	0.316	496.0	1.03
(10, 2, 5, 50)	1436566.3	0.237	1600.0	14.29
(10, 2, 10, 100)	2092999.0	0.357	1612.0	51.62

* ($|I|$, $|I'|$, $|J|$, $|K|$), Results are averaged over 10 samples.

the high performance of the proposed approach. On the other hand, the required CPU time increase exponentially with the size as expected a priori. Even for these larger size problems, however, we can obtain the results within a reasonable time.

5. Conclusion

Provision for essential infrastructure aligned with sustainable development requires us to realize green logistics incorporating co-existence of manufacturers and consumers. This paper has concerned the green logistics optimization in process systems associated with decision making on production method that has not concerned elsewhere. Taking a multi-layer logistics network, we have developed a novel approach to optimize either the minimum total cost or CO_2 emission through adjusting prone or aversion consciousness on sustainability. Numerical experiment has been carried out to validate the solution ability and the visualization of result from the proposed approach.

Future studies should be devoted to establish a total decision support system associated with multi-objective optimization. Real-world applications are also interesting issues.

References

A. Nikolopoulou, M.G. Ierapetritou, 2012, Optimal design of sustainable chemical processes and supply chains: A review, Computers and Chemical Engineering, 44 , 9, 94-103.

Y. Shimizu, T. Sakaguchi, 2013, Generalized vehicle routing problem forreverse logistics aiming at low carbon transportation, Industrial Engineering and Management Systems, 12, 2, 161-70.

T. Wada, Y. Shimizu, 2006, A Hybrid metaheuristic approach for optimal design of total supply chain network, Transactions of the Institute of Systems, Control and Information Engineers, 19, 2, 69-77 (in Japanese).

Jiří Jaromír Klemeš, Petar Sabev Varbanov and Peng Yen Liew (Editors)
Proceedings of the 24th European Symposium on Computer Aided Process Engineering – ESCAPE 24
June 15-18, 2014, Budapest, Hungary.

Parametric Solution Algorithms for Large-Scale Mixed-Integer Fractional Programming Problems and Applications in Process Systems Engineering

Zhixia Zhong, Fengqi You*

Department of Chemical and Biological Engineeirng, Northwestern University, Evanston, IL, 60208, USA
you@northwestern.edu

Abstract

In this work, we proposed novel parametric algorithms for solving large-scale mixed-integer linear and nonlinear fractional programming problems. By developing an equivalent parametric formulation of the general mixed-integer fractional program (MIFP), we propose exact parametric algorithms based on the root-finding methods for the global optimization of MIFPs. We also propose an inexact parametric algorithm that can potentially outperform the exact parametric algorithms for some types of MIFPs. Extensive computational studies are performed to demonstrate the efficiency of these parametric algorithms and to compare them with the general-purpose mixed-integer nonlinear programming methods. The applications of the proposed algorithms are illustrated through a case study on process scheduling and demonstrate the economic benefits of applying the proposed algorithms to practical application problems.

Keywords: global optimization, root-finding, MILFP, MIQFP, production scheduling.

1. Introduction

A mixed-integer fractional programming (MIFP) problem has a general form given in problem **(P)**: $\max\{Q(x) = N(x)/D(x) \mid x \in S\}$, where the variables x contain both continuous and discrete variables, the denominator $D(x)$ is always positive in S, i.e. $D(x) > 0$. The numerator $N(x)$ and denominator $D(x)$ can be any linear or nonlinear function. MIFP applications in process systems engineering can be categorized into three types. The first one is to optimize the productivity of a process system, such as the overall cost or profit over the makespan. Cyclic scheduling problems can be formulated as a mixed-integer linear fractional programming (MILFP) problem by optimizing the productivity, or as a mixed-integer quadratic fractional programming (MIQFP) problem if the objective function involves the trade-off between inventory and setup cost (Chu and You, 2012). Another MIFP application is optimization for sustainability (Yue and You, 2013), such as sustainable or environmental-conscious scheduling of batch processes (Capón-García et al., 2010) and the functional-unit based life cycle optimization (Yue et al., 2013). The third application field is on the optimization for return rate, such as return on investment (Bradley and Arntzen, 1999).

Most tailored MIFP solution algorithms in the literature focus on the special case of MILFP problems. Li (1994) proposed a global optimization approach based on the branch-and-bound method to solve 0-1 fractional programs. Yue et al. (2013) proposed an exact mixed-integer linear programming (MILP) reformulation for MILFP, although it cannot be applied to mixed-integer nonlinear fractional programs. The goal of this paper is to propose novel and efficient parametric approaches for solving MIFP problems with improvements of computational efficiency by orders of magnitude, and to illustrate their effectiveness for process scheduling application. The proposed algorithm would be efficient enough to solve previously intractable MIFP problems.

2. Parametric approach for MIFP problems

2.1. Equivalent parametric formulation and exact parametric algorithms
Considering the following parametric problem (P$_q$):

$$(P_q)\ F(q) = \max\{N(x) - q \cdot D(x) | x \in S\}\ \text{ for } q \in \mathbb{R}^1 \tag{1}$$

where x contains continuous variables and integer variables, S is compact and bounded, $D(x) > 0$, and q is a parameter. It is easy to show that the function $F(q)$ is convex, strictly monotonic decreasing, continuous and has bounded subgradients, and that $F(q) = 0$ has a unique solution q^* which is exactly the global optimal objective value of the problem (P). Thus, we have the following proposition:

Proposition: $q^* = N(x^*)/D(x^*) = \max\{N(x)/D(x) | x \in S\}$ if   and   only   if $F(q^*) = F(q^*, x^*) = \max\{(N(x) - q^* D(x) | x \in S\} = 0$, i.e. the variable x* is a global optimal solution to the fractional programming problem (P) if and only if x* is a global optimal solution to the parametric problem (P$_q$) with $F(q^*) = 0$.

We note that the equivalence proposition only requires that the denominator is always positive, i.e. D(x)>0, no matter whether the functions N(x) and D(x) are linear or nonlinear. The proposition holds true when the problem contains both continuous and integer variables. Though there are no assumptions on the convexity of the two functions N(x) and D(x), the equivalence is only valid based on the global optimal solutions of both problems. Because the ratio function in the objective is transformed into the difference, the parametric problem (P$_q$) has fewer nonlinearities than the MIFP problem (P), and might be easier to solve. For example, if (P) is an MILFP problem, (P$_q$) is a (parametric) mixed-integer linear program (MILP); if (P) is an MIQFP problem with a convex N(x) and a concave D(x), (P$_q$) is a convex mixed-integer quadratic program (MIQP). MILP and convex MIQP problems can be solved very efficiently using state-of-the-art branch-and-cut methods implemented in solvers like CPLEX. Thus, solving MIFP problem (P) ends up with the root finding of nonlinear equation $F(q) = \max\{N(x) - q \cdot D(x) | x \in S\} = 0$. Because F(q) does not have a close-form analytical expression, it can be solved through numerical root-finding algorithms, such as the bisection method, Newton's method, secant method, false position method and others. In principle, all root-finding methods for nonlinear equations are applicable for the parametric problem (P$_q$). In this paper, we only apply these four well-known root-finding algorithms to solve the equivalent parametric form of MIFP. Due to the space limit, we only introduce the Newton's method in details in this paper.

In Newton's method, q_{n+1} is defined by, $q_{n+1} = q_n - F(q_n)/F'(q_n)$. As shown by You et al. (2009), we can use the approximated subgradient at point q_n to estimate the derivate, $F'(q_n) \approx -D(x_n^*)$, which is the negative value of the denominator evaluated at x_n^*, a global optimal solution of $\max\{N(x) - q_n \cdot D(x) | x \in S\}$.

Thus, $q_{n+1} = q_n - \dfrac{F(q_n)}{-D(x_n^*)} = q_n + \dfrac{N(x_n^*) - q_n \cdot D(x_n^*)}{D(x_n^*)} = \dfrac{N(x_n^*)}{D(x_n^*)}$ (2)

The full procedure of the Newton's method for solving $(\mathbf{P_q})$ is as follows:

STEP 1: Set $q_1 = 0$, initialize n by $n = 1$.

STEP 2: Solve $F(q_n) = \max\{N(x) - q_n \cdot D(x) \mid x \in S\}$ and let optimal solution be x_n^*.

STEP 3: If $|F(q_n)| < \delta$ (optimality tolerance), stop and output x_n^* as the optimal solution
and q_n as optimal objective. If $|F(q_n)| \geq \delta$, let $q_{n+1} = N(x_n^*)/D(x_n^*)$, update n with $n + 1$
and update q_n with q_{n+1}. Go to *Step 2*.

In this method, the function is approximated by its tangent line and one computes the q-
intercept of this tangent line. The method can iterate and converge to $q*$ due to the
properties of the function $F(q)$. We note that this is an exact Newton's method that
requires each parametric subproblem to be solved to the global optimum, i.e. 0 % gap.
This algorithm converges superlinearly at a rate of $\left[1 - D(x^*)/D(x')\right]$.

2.2. Inexact parametric algorithm

The parametric algorithms presented in the previous section are all global convergent
exact methods. In each step of those algorithms, the parametric subproblem needs to be
solved to the global optimality, i.e. 0 % gap. Mixed-integer programming problems are
usually NP-hard and the solution to 0 % optimality gap might require significant
computational effort when the problem size is large. In this section, we present an
inexact solution approach based on the Newton's method for solving MIFPs, of which
both the numerator and denominator functions are non-negative, i.e. $N(x) \geq 0$ and $D(x) >$
0. The main idea is that we start the iterations with the initial value of $q = 0$, and apply
the same procedure as the Newton's method, except that the parametric subproblem in
each iteration does not need to be solved to the global optimality, i.e. 0 % gap. Instead,
we show that the algorithm will still converge to $q*$, as long as that we set the initial
value of $q = 0$ and that each subproblem is solved to a pre-defined relative optimality
criterion less than 100 %. Here we consider the same definition of relative optimality
criterion as used by GAMS, i.e. (|BP - BF|)/|BP| $< \varepsilon$, where BP is the best possible
solution, BF is the best solution found, and ε is the relative optimality criterion. The
procedure of the inexact parametric algorithm based on Newton's method is similar to
the one presented in Section 2.1, except that Step 2 is now revised to the following one:

Step 2: Solve $F(q_n) = \max\{N(x) - q_n \cdot D(x) \mid x \in S\}$ to a relative optimality gap ε, where
$\varepsilon < 100\%$. Denote the near-optimal solution as x_n^*.

In this way, each subproblem does not need to be solved to global optimum. This can
potentially reduce the computational time required for each iteration, although the
number of iterations might increase. It is easy to prove that this inexact algorithm
converges linearly with a rate of $\left[1 - D(x^*)/(\eta \cdot D(\overline{x_k}))\right]$, where $\overline{x_k}$ is the near-optimal
solution with a relative optimality gap ε obtained in iteration k and $\eta = 1/(1 - \varepsilon)$.
Although the convergence rate of this inexact algorithm is slower than that of the exact
Newton's method, it may need shorter solution time in each iteration due to the large

optimality gap. Thus, this inexact method can potentially outperform the exact parametric algorithms as will be shown in the next section.

3. Comparison with general-purpose MINLP algorithms

In order to test the computational efficiency of the proposed solution algorithms for solving large-scale mixed-integer linear and nonlinear fractional programming problems, we conduct computational experiments based on two testing problems below.

MILFP testing problem **(TP1)**:

$$\max \quad \frac{A_0 + \sum_{i \in I} A1_i x_i + \sum_{j \in J} A2_j y_j}{B_0 + \sum_{i \in I} B1_i x_i + \sum_{j \in J} B2_j y_j}$$

s.t. $\quad B_0 + \sum_{i \in I} B1_i x_i + \sum_{j \in J} B2_j y_j \geq 0.001$

$\quad \sum_{i \in I} C1_{ik} x_i + \sum_{j \in J} C2_{jk} y_j \leq D_k, \ \forall k \in K$

$\quad x^L \leq x_i \leq x^U, \ \forall i \in I, \ y_j \in \{0,1\}, \ \forall j \in J$

MIQFP testing problem **(TP2)**:

$$\max \quad \frac{A_0 + \sum_{i \in I} A1_i x_i + \sum_{j \in J} A2_j y_j - \sum_{i \in I} A3_i x_i^2}{B_0 + \sum_{i \in I} B1_i x_i + \sum_{j \in J} B2_j y_j + \sum_{i \in I} B3_i x_i^2}$$

s.t. $\quad B_0 + \sum_{i \in I} B1_i x_i + \sum_{j \in J} B2_j y_j \geq 0.001$

$\quad \sum_{i \in I} C1_{ik} x_i + \sum_{j \in J} C2_{jk} y_j \leq D_k, \ \forall k \in K$

$\quad x^L \leq x_i \leq x^U, \ \forall i \in I, \ y_j \in \{0,1\}, \ \forall j \in J$

The MILFP testing problem **(TP1)** has an objective function as the ratio of two linear functions, and the MIQFP testing problem **(TP2)** has an objective function as the ratio of a concave quadratic function and a convex quadratic function. The first constraint in both testing problems is to ensure that the denominator is positive. Both problems consists of $|I|$ continuous variables, $|J|$ binary variables, and $|K|+1$ constraints. The values of $|I|$, $|J|$ and $|K|$ range from 100 to 2,000. For each testing problem, we solve 45 large-scale, randomly generated instances to demonstrate the efficiency of the solution algorithms, including the exact Newton's method, bisection method, secant method, false position method and the general MINLP algorithms via SBB solver, DICOPT and the global optimizer BARON 11.3. A tailored MILFP algorithm, the reformulation linearization method (Yue et al., 2013), is also used to solve the MILFP problem **(TP1)**. The MILP and MIQP problems in the parametric algorithms are solved using CPLEX 12 with 10^{-9} gap. The optimality tolerance for the parametric algorithms are set as $\delta = 10^{-3}$. The maximum solution time for each instance is limited to 7,200 CPU seconds.

Figure 1(a) shows the performance profiles of solving the MILFP testing problems **(TP1)** using the aforementioned algorithms. The x-axis is the maximum computational time needed for solving the problem and the y-axis is the number of instances. If a solution method has a performance profile towards the upper left corner, it implies that this method can solve more problems within shorter time, i.e. better computational performance. We can see from Figure 1(a) that the performances of the parametric algorithms and reformulation-linearization method are in general better than those tested MINLP solvers in solving the MILFP problems. Among the parametric algorithms, Newton's method and secant method, which both converge quadratically, have better performance than the bisection method and the false position method with linear convergence rates. Generally speaking, among the four tested parametric algorithms, both exact Newton's method and the secant method are good choices in solving large-scale MILFP problems. Reformulation-linearization method has comparable performance with the exact Newton's method and the secant method for solving MILFP problems. The performance profiles of solving the MIQFP testing problems **(TP2)** are given in Figure 1(b). We can clearly see that the exact Newton's method is the "champion" among all the solution methods considered in this test, similar to the

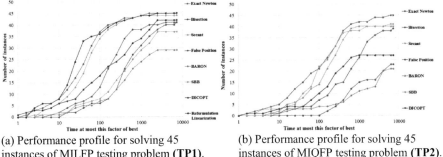

(a) Performance profile for solving 45 instances of MILFP testing problem **(TP1)**.

(b) Performance profile for solving 45 instances of MIQFP testing problem **(TP2)**.

Figure 1. Performance profiles for comparing the proposed algorithm with MINLP methods

MILFP cases. It is then followed by the secant method. However, the secant method needs two staring points with opposite signs in $F(q)$ that might be less convenient to implement than the exact Newton's method. For this MIQFP cases, the performance of the general-purpose MINLP solvers SBB exceeds those of another MINLP solver DICOPT and the global optimizer BARON, as well as the bisection method and the false position method. In general, exact Newton's method has obvious advantages in solving linear and nonlinear MIFP due to its high computational efficiency and guarantee of finding global optimal solutions.

4. Case Study

In this section, we consider a case study on a multipurpose batch plant scheduling problem originally from The Dow Chemical Company (Wassick et al., 2012), in order to illustrate the application of the proposed inexact parametric algorithms. The process structure of this scheduling problem is given in Figure 2(a) (Chu et al., 2013). The scheduling model ends up with a mixed-integer linear fractional program which maximizes the productivity defined by total profit over the makespan. The main tradeoff in this problem is that more time points |t| would potentially lead to better objective value, i.e. higher productivity, but it could also lead to larger problem size. The detailed formulation is omitted due to the space limit. We specifically compare the exact Newton's method with the proposed inexact approach. The results are shown in Figure 2(b). By using the inexact parametric algorithm, each MILP subproblem only needs to be solved to a pre-defined relative optimality gapless than 100 %. We implemented this inexact algorithm to solve the scheduling problem with different relative optimality gaps, where the case of 0 % gap corresponds to the exact Newton's method, while the rest cases with 1%, 10 % and 90 % gaps are for the inexact parametric algorithm.

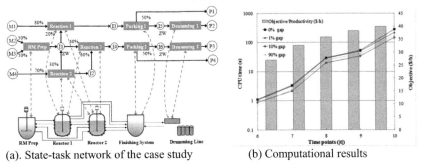

(a). State-task network of the case study

(b) Computational results

Figure 2. The comparison of the computational results and efficiency of using inexact Newton's method in the scheduling problem at different relative optimality gaps (optcr).

For all the instances, the inexact algorithm returns the same global optimal solution as the exact one, but only requires around 50 % ~ 70 % of the CPU times of the exact Newton's algorithm. The time-saving is more significant for large instance with 10 time points. Over all, the inexact Newton's method with a proper gap can use less time than the exact one. The case study shows the economic benefits and significances of the proposed, more efficient inexact parametric algorithms for large-scale MIFP problems.

5. Conclusions

In this paper, we presented exact parametric algorithms for solving the general MIFP problems based on a parametric reformulation and root-finding algorithms. We further propose an inexact parametric algorithm, which is a variation of exact algorithm based on the Newton's method, for the global optimization of MIFPs problem. We solved randomly generated instances to test the efficiency of the four parametric algorithms for on large-scale MILFP and MIQFP problems, and also to compare their performance with the general-purpose global optimization methods. Through a case study on process scheduling, the applicability and performance of the proposed algorithms were further illustrated. The results show that inexact parametric algorithms based on Newton's method can outperform other solution algorithms for large-scale MILFP problems by improving the computation speed at least 20 times and led to economic benefits when the proposed algorithms are applied to practical production scheduling problems.

References

J. R. Bradley, B. C. Arntzen, 1999, The simultaneous planning of production, capacity, and inventory in seasonal demand environments, Operations Research, 47, 795-806.

E. Capón-García, A. D. Bojarski, A. Espuña, L. Puigjaner, 2010, Multiobjective optimization of multiproduct batch plants scheduling under environmental and economic concerns, AIChE Journal, 57, 2766-2782.

Y. Chu, F. You, 2012, Integration of scheduling and control with online closed-loop implementation: Fast computational strategy and large-scale global optimization algorithm, Computers and Chemical Engineering, 47, 248-268.

Y. Chu, J. Wassick, F. You, 2013, Efficient scheduling method of complex batch processes with general network structure via agent-based modeling, AIChE Journal, 59, 2884-2906.

H. L. Li, 1994, A Global Approach for General 0-1 Fractional-Programming, European Journal of Operational Research, 73, 590-596.

J. M. Wassick, A.Agarwal, N. Akiya, J. Ferrio, S. Bury, F. Q. You, 2012, Addressing the operational challenges in the development, manufacture, and supply of advanced materials and performance products, Computers and Chemical Engineering, 47, 157-169.

F. You, P. M. Castro, I. E. Grossmann, 2009, Dinkelbach's algorithm as an efficient method to solve a class of MINLP models for large-scale cyclic scheduling problems, Computers & Chemical Engineering, 33, 1879-1889.

D. Yue, M. Kim, F. You, 2013, Design of Sustainable Product Systems and Supply Chains with Life Cycle Optimization Based on Functional Unit, ACS Sustainable Chemistry and Engineering, 1, 1003-1014.

D. Yue, G. Guillén-Gosálbez, F. You, 2013, Global optimization of large-scale mixed-integer linear fractional programming problems: A reformulation-linearization method and process scheduling applications, AIChE Journal, 59, 4255-4272.

D. Yue, F. You, 2013, Sustainable scheduling of batch processes under economic and environmental criteria with MINLP models and algorithms, Computers and Chemical Engineering, 54, 44-59.

Jiří Jaromír Klemeš, Petar Sabev Varbanov and Peng Yen Liew (Editors)
Proceedings of the 24th European Symposium on Computer Aided Process Engineering – ESCAPE 24
June 15-18, 2014, Budapest, Hungary. Copyright © 2014 Elsevier B.V. All rights reserved.

Optimal Valve Spacing for Next Generation CO_2 Pipelines

Solomon Brown, Vikram Sundara, Sergey Martynov, Haroun Mahgerefteh[*]

Department of Chemical Engineering, UCL, London, UK
h.mahgerefteh@ucl.ac.uk

Abstract

Pipeline transportation is considered as the primary mode of transporting CO_2 for future carbon capture and storage (CCS) projects. The failure of such pipelines could lead to the release of a significant amount of inventory, which in high enough concentrations is toxic and presents a significant risk to life. To mitigate this hazard, emergency shutdown valves (ESDVs) are installed at regular intervals along the pipeline, to minimise the amount of inventory released in the event of failure. This paper presents a methodology and the required metrics for optimising valve spacing as a trade-off between the reduction in hazard against the cost of installation and maintenance.

Keywords: CO_2 pipeline, valve spacing, hazard optimisation

1. Introduction

As part of the portfolio of technologies aimed at reducing global CO_2 emissions, the application of Carbon Capture and Sequestration (CCS) is projected to make a significant contribution, with some 1.4 and 83 Gt of CO_2 expected to be captured and stored by 2030 and 2050 respectively (IEA, 2010). As the majority of the captured CO_2 will be transported by pipelines, the pipeline infrastructure required is estimated to between 95,000 and 500,000 km in length by 2050 depending on the uptake of CCS (Element Energy, 2010; IEA, 2010). Given that CO_2 is increasingly toxic at concentrations above 7 % (vol./vol.) (Kruse and Tekiela, 1996), the safety of these pipelines is of great importance and indeed pivotal to the public acceptability of CCS as a viable means of tackling the impact of global warming.

As part of the design of a pipeline network it is common practice to split the pipeline into segments, separated by valve and venting stations. While the primary motivation for this is routine maintenance, valves may also play an important role in the event of a pipeline failure. Given that a typical 100 km long, 0.8 m i.d. highly pressurised pipeline transporting dense-phase CO_2 contains ca. 9,000 t of inventory, the unhindered escape of the CO_2 following Full Bore Rupture (FBR) of the pipeline near a populated area, i.e. the worst case failure scenario, represents a major hazard. The use of Emergency Shutdown Valves (ESDVs) to limit the amount of inventory released could go some way to mitigating this safety issue.

The effectiveness of ESDVs is dependent on both the valve response time and importantly the spacing between the valves themselves (Mahgerefteh et al., 2000). Since it is intuitively obvious that the total inventory released decreases with the spacing of the valves, it would be beneficial from a safety point of view to have ESDVs sited at short distances along pipelines. However, the installation and operation of such valves represents a significant financial cost. Thus, defining the valve spacing requires a trade-off between the cost to install and maintain the valves on one hand, and the level of mitigation offered by ESDVs in the event of a pipeline failure on the other. This can be formulated as a multi-objective optimisation problem. Methods for solving such problems differ mainly in the time at which the decision maker is involved in guiding the solution selection. Techniques are classified as a priori (for example Arnaud et al. 2011), interactive (e.g. Eduardo et al. 2011; de Boer et al. 1998) or a posteriori. The latter, i.e. where the decision maker applies their preferences at the end of the multi-objective optimisation search (Zio and Bazzo 2011), is most useful in the present context as the decision maker will have further constraints which cannot be accounted for, e.g. the availability of sites for valve construction.

Furthermore, in contrast to the cost of valves along a pipeline, it is difficult to quantify the hazard presented by a pipeline failure, as it is a function of the CO_2 concentration and its variation with time and distance from the release point, as well as other factors such as the population density in the locality of the failure. The definition of a reasonable metric must therefore account for the amount of CO_2 released, its dispersion and its effect on the local population. In this work we use an appropriate measure of the cost incurred through the spacing of ESDVs and define a metric for the hazard associated with a pipeline failure.

2. Mathematical Model

2.1. Description of the optimal valve spacing problem

The optimization problem is summarised in mathematical form below:

$$\min_{d \in D} J_1(d), J_2(d) \tag{1}$$

Here $J_1(d)$ is the metric defined for the hazard associated with a pipeline failure and $J_2(d)$ is the valve installation and maintenance costs and d is the spacing between valves (km). In this study, we define the objective function, J_1, to be the area bounded by the 7 % (vol./vol.) concentration contour of the dispersing CO_2 cloud. The evolution of the CO_2 cloud is described using a dense-gas dispersion model coupled with a model for predicting the outflow of CO_2 from the failed pipeline. These models will be described in the following sections.

The total valve cost for installation, J_2, is calculated using the following expression (Medina et al., 2012):

$$J_2(d) = \frac{V_{PN} r (1 + r)^n L}{\left((1 + r)^{n+1} - 1\right) d}, \tag{2}$$

where VPN is the single valve cost (€), r is the discount rate, n is the average life time of the equipment (y) and L is the overall length of the pipeline (km).

It is further observed that the two objective functions are expected to move in opposite directions, i.e. one increases for a change in the valve spacing while the other decreases.

2.2. Optimisation methodology

Due to the conflicting nature of the objective functions the solution of a multi-objective optimisation problem is usually not unique. In general, only a set of optimal solutions, known as the Pareto set can be obtained. The Pareto set can however be used to determine a particular optimum solution given the subjective preferences of a decision maker. To obtain the Pareto set, or a discrete approximation of it, the objective functions are sampled using differing values of the independent variables.

2.3. Outflow model

The background theory of the multi-phase fluid dynamics model employed for predicting the fluid flow parameters including the transient fluid temperature and pressure following pipeline failure has been described elsewhere (Mahgerefteh et al., 2008) and hence only a brief account is given here. Assuming that the constituent fluid phases are in thermal and mechanical equilibrium, the mass, momentum and energy conservation are given by (see for example Zucrow and Hoffman, 1975):

$$\frac{\partial \rho}{\partial t} + \frac{\partial \rho u}{\partial x} = 0 \qquad (3)$$

$$\frac{\partial \rho u}{\partial t} + \frac{\partial \rho u^2 + P}{\partial x} = -\frac{2 f_w \rho u^2}{D_p} - \rho g \sin(\theta) \qquad (4)$$

$$\frac{\partial \rho \left(e + \frac{1}{2} u^2\right)}{\partial t} + \frac{\partial u \left[\rho \left(e + \frac{1}{2} u^2\right) + P\right]}{\partial x} = -u \frac{2 f_w \rho u^2}{D_p}. \qquad (5)$$

where u, P, D_p and f_w are the mixture velocity, pressure, pipeline diameter and Fanning friction factor, calculated using the correlation of Chen (1979), as functions of time, t, and space, x. g and θ are the gravitational acceleration and the angle of inclination of the pipeline to the horizontal. e and ρ are the mixture specific internal energy and density:

$$e = x_{eq} e_v + (1 - x_{eq}) e_l, \qquad \frac{1}{\rho} = \frac{x_{eq}}{\rho_v} + \frac{(1 - x_{eq})}{\rho_l} \qquad (6)$$

and, x_{eq} is the equilibrium vapour quality. The subscripts v and l refer to the vapour and liquid phases.

The above conservation equations are solved numerically using the method of characteristics (Zucrow and Hoffman, 1975). A modified Peng-Robinson Equation of State (Wu and Chen, 1997) is employed to obtain the relevant thermodynamic and phase equilibrium data for the CO_2. To describe the pressure drop and flowrate during valve closure boundary conditions are applied between pipeline segments connected by such valves. In this study, the ESDV is modelled as a ball valve with the discharge coefficient $C_d(t)$ being a function of the area of the valve opening, $A_f(t)$ (Wylie and Streeter, 1993) defined as:

$$A_f(t) = 2 \left[\frac{\pi R^2}{180} \cos^{-1} \left(\frac{B}{R}\right) - B \left(\sqrt{R^2 - B^2}\right) \right], \quad B = \left(\frac{R - \frac{2R - z(t)}{2}}{R} \right) \qquad (7)$$

where R and z are the radius of the pipe and the linear closure rate of the valve . The pressure drop across the valve is given by:

$$Q(t) = C_d(t) A_f(t) \sqrt{\frac{2 \Delta P(t)}{\rho}} \qquad (8)$$

where $Q(t)$ and $\Delta P(t)$ are the volumetric flowrate and pressure drop across valve.

2.4. Dense gas dispersion model

In order to predict the concentration contours of the released CO_2 the dense-gas integral model SLAB is used. The SLAB model uses steady-state one-dimensional convection-diffusion equations to describe the variation of average concentration along the centre-line of the cloud, and applies the Gaussian distribution functions to reconstruct the concentration profiles in the crossflow direction (Koopman et al., 1989).

As input conditions for the SLAB model the results of the outflow calculations using the model presented in section 2.3 are applied. To enable simulation of dispersion cloud for transient pipeline decompression scenarios, the outflow data fed into SLAB code is sampled at discrete times. The steady state concentration profiles predicted for these discrete time intervals are then used to produce the average area spanned by 7 % (vol./vol.) concentration.

3. Results and discussion

The methodology described in section 2 for optimising the valve spacing is applied to a hypothetical pipeline transporting dense phase CO_2, for which a FBR occurs in the middle of the pipeline. Table 1 presents the pipeline characteristics and fluid conditions assumed for the pipeline failure scenario.

In order to generate the Pareto set 30 different valve spacings were sampled, while 6,000 nodes were used to discretise the pipeline. The values used here are $\in V_{PN} = 15,556$, $r = 0.035$ and $n = 10$. The valve spacing, d, lies in the interval $D = [5,40]$ km. The valves are assumed to close 900 s following pipeline failure at a rate of 1.904 cm/s.

Figure 1 shows the 7 % (vol./vol.) concentration contours, representing the shape of the cloud in a horizontal half-plane at a height 1 m above the ground, as calculated at various times after the beginning of the release.

As can be seen from figure 1, the dimensions of the cloud vary significantly during the initial period of the release. In particular, during the times from 180 to 2,340 s the half-width of the cloud increases from ca 10 to 30 m, while its downwind length decreases from ca. 170 to 90 m. After ca. 2,340 s the area of the cloud bounded by 7 % (vol./vol.) concentration contour is gradually shrinking with time. Figures 2 (a) shows the variation of J_1 and J_2. As can be observed, the cost of the valves shows the expected hyperbolic decrease as the valve spacing is increased from the smallest value of 4 km used in this study. In contrast, the J_1 shows a near linear increase from 0 to 1 as the valve spacing increases from ca. 5 to 24 km. As the valve spacing increases beyond 24 km the normalised area falls to a near constant value of ca. 0.7, this is believed not to be due a real effect but a result of the model integration which also leads to the numerical noise observed throughout.

Figure 2 (b) shows the Pareto set of the optimisation problem. The variation of the area spanned is observed to increase from ca. 0.65 to ca. 0.95 at normalised costs of 0 and ca. 0.1 respectively. Following this, the normalised area decreases hyperbolically to ca. 0.2 at a normalised cost of ca. 0.5, and approaches 0 at a normalised area of 1. The implication of these results is that the hazard reduction obtained by increasing the number of valves becomes marginal above a certain range.

Table 1. Pipeline characteristics and fluid conditions for failure scenario.

Parameter	Value	Parameter	Value
Pipeline		Boundary Conditions	
Pipeline external diameter	610 mm	Upstream end	Constant pressure
Pipeline wall thickness	19.4 mm	Downstream	No back flow
Pipeline wall roughness	0.005 mm	Initial Conditions	
Pipeline length	96 km	Pressure in pipe	151 bara
Pipeline angle	Horizontal	Temperature in pipe	30 °C
		Ambient temperature	10 °C

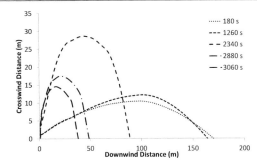

Figure 1. Variation of 7 % concentration half-contours with time

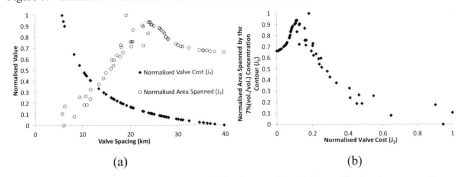

(a)   (b)

Figure 2. Valve spacing multi-objective optimisation results: (a) Normalised valve cost and area spanned by 7 % concentration (b) Pareto set.

4. Conclusions

This work presented a methodology for optimising the spacing of Emergency Shutdown Valves for CO_2 transportation pipelines. This was based on the definition of a metric for the hazard associated with pipeline failure and formulating the trade-off of this with the cost of valve installation and maintenance as a multi-objective optimisation problem.

The application of the methodology to a hypothetical pipeline showed that the spacing of ESDVs has a complex, non-linear impact on the hazard presented by a pipeline failure. The results also indicated the existence of a threshold beyond which decreasing valve spacing provided little protection with substantial cost. The design of pipelines is often performed using the ALARP (As Low As Reasonably Practicable) (Melchers,

2001) principle; the work presented here provides a framework on which this criterion may be assessed rigorously. The validity of the results is, however, dependent, on the accuracy of the metric used to assess the hazard. As such, given the relatively simple metric postulated here, further studies are required to investigate the impact of the choice of metric on the results obtained as well as other important variables such as the pipeline length, operating pressure and temperature.

Acknowledgements

The research leading to this work has received funding from the European Union 7th Framework Programme FP7-ENERGY-2012-1-2STAGE under grant agreement number 309102.

References

N. H. Chen, 1979. An Explicit Equation for Friction Factor in Pipe, Ind. Eng. Chem. Fund. 18, 3, 296-297.

E. Fernandez, E. Lopez, C. Fernando Lopez, 2011, Increasing selective pressure towards the best compromise in evolutionary multiobjective optimization: The extended NOSGA method. Inform. Sciences., 181, 1, 44-56.

Element Energy, 2010, CO_2 pipeline infrastructure: An analysis of global challenges and opportunities, Technical report, Final report for IEA Greenhouse Gas programme, UK.

IEA, 2010, Energy technology perspectives 2010: Scenarios and strategies to 2050, Technical report, OECD/IEA, France.

R. Koopman, D.Ermak, S. Chan, 1989, A review of recent field tests and mathematical modelling of atmospheric dispersion of large spills of Denser-than-air gases, Atmos. Environ., 1967, 23, 4, 731-745.

H. Kruse, M. Tekiela, 1996, Calculating the consequences of a CO_2-pipeline rupture. Energ. Convers. Manage., 37, 95, 1013-1018.

A. Liefooghe, L. Jourda, T. El-Ghazali, 2011, A software framework based on a conceptual unified model for evolutionary multiobjective optimization: ParadisEO-MOEO, Eur. J. Oper. Res., 209, 2, 104-112.

H. Mahgerefteh, G. Denton, Y. Rykov, 2008, A hybrid multiphase flow model, AIChE J., 54, 9, 2261-2268.

H. Mahgerefteh, P. Saha, I. G. Economou, 2000, Modeling fluid phase transition effects on dynamic behavior of ESDV, AIChE J., 46, 5, 997--1006.

H. Medina, J. Arnaldos, Casal, J., Bonvicini, S., Cozzani, V., 2012, Risk-based optimization of the design of on-shore pipeline shutdown systems, J. Loss Prevent. Proc., 25, 3, 489-493.

R. Melchers, 2001, On the ALARP approach to risk management, Reliab. Eng. Syst. Safe. 71, 2, 201-208.

D. Wu, S. Chen, 1997, A Modified Peng-Robinson Equation of State, Chem. Eng. Comm., 156, 1, 215-225.

E. B. Wylie, V. L. Streeter, 1993, Fluid Transients in systems, Prentice-Hall, Englewood, NJ, USA.

E. Zio, R. Bazzo, 2011, Level Diagrams analysis of Pareto Front for multiobjective system redundancy allocation, Reliab. Eng. Syst. Safe, 96, 5, 569-580.

M. J. Zucrow, J. D. Hoffman, 1975, Gas Dynamics, Wiley, NY, USA.

Jiří Jaromír Klemeš, Petar Sabev Varbanov and Peng Yen Liew (Editors)
Proceedings of the 24th European Symposium on Computer Aided Process Engineering – ESCAPE 24
June 15-18, 2014, Budapest, Hungary. Copyright © 2014 Elsevier B.V. All rights reserved.

SMART: An Integrated Planning and Decision Support Tool for Solid Waste Management

Sie Ting Tan[a], Haslenda Hashim[a]*, Chew Tin Lee[a], Jeng Shiun Lim[a], Wai Shin Ho[a], Jinyue Yan[b]

[a]*Process System Engineering Centre (PROSPECT), Faculty of Chemical Engineering, Universiti Teknologi Malaysia, 81310 UTM Skudai, Johor, Malaysia*
[b]*School of Sustainable Development of Society and Technology, Mälardalen University, SE-72123 Västerås, Sweden*
haslenda@cheme.utm.my

Abstract

Solid waste management (SWM) system combined waste streams, waste collection, treatment and disposal methods are critically important to a regional, to achieve environmental economic and societal benefits. Decision-makers often have to rely on optimization models to examine a cost effective, environmentally sound waste management alternative. This paper presents a new systematic framework for long term effective planning and scheduling of SWM. This framework has been converted into software called Solid Waste Management Resource Recovery Tool (SMART). SMART is a first-of-a-kind SWM tool to facilitate the tradeoffs analysis between technical, economical, and environmental at national, regional, state, province, or community level. This simple tool is useful for decision makers for the selection of MSW technology including incineration, landfill, composting and recycling are while minimising the costs and meet CO_2 reductions target. The developed tool was applied in Iskandar Malaysia as a case study.

Keywords: Solid Waste Management (SWM); Optimisation; Solid Waste Management Resource Recovery Tool (SMART); Economical Assessment

1. Introduction

As the global population increases dramatically, with the change of consumption patterns, economic development, rapid urbanization and industrialization, the generation of solid waste is at a rate that outstrips the ability of the natural assimilation of the municipal wastes. The substantial growth of waste generation and the complexity of the waste composition make the waste management system more challenging. In addition, inadequate storage, collection and disposal practices with lack of legislation and policies for long term solid waste management (SWM) planning are of major concern for many countries in Asia and Pacific region. For instance, Malaysia received approximately 19,100 t of municipal solid waste (MSW) in 2005, 21,000 t in 2009, and this is expected to rise to 31,000 t/d by 2020. The present SWM methods in Malaysia are highly dependent on landfill as in 2009, only 5.5 % of the MSW was recycled and 1% was composted, while the remaining 94.5 % of MSW was disposed on the landfill site Malaysian government spent about € 151 M on SWM in year 2005 and this is estimated to rise to € 240 M by year 2020 (Ministry of Housing and Local Government (MHLG), 2005). Ineffective waste management causes high cost to the government so as contributing towards detrimental environmental impacts. Waste management contributes approximately 3-5 % of the total anthropogenic emission in year 2005 (The Intergovernmental Panel on Climate Change (IPCC), 2006).

The complexity of municipal solid waste management (MSWM) includes the prediction of solid waste generation, selection of waste treatment technologies, selection of facility sites, estimation of facility capacity, operation of the facility, scheduling of the system and transportation of the wastes, can be modelled through a system perspective. SWM can be modelled and optimised using a software tool where an optimum feasible solution can be developed. Decision-makers often have to rely on optimisation models to examine the impacts of mass balance, capacity limitation, operation and site availability as well as the selection different of a cost effective and environmentally sound waste management alternative. Most of the models for ISWM and the corresponding tools need to handle large quantity of data and complex equations. The complexity associated with the formulation of optimization models may hinder its use, and hence user friendliness is a major concern. Several decision making tool on SWM have been developed by researchers with various objectives. For example, a SWM tool termed as CO2ZW was developed by Sevigné et al. (2013) to estimate the GHG emissions for the management of MSW in Green, Italy, Slovenia, and Spain. Apart from CO2ZW, there are others similar tools on GHG emission assessment of SWM, such as the Environmental Assessment of Solid Waste Systems and Technologies (EASTEWASTE) (Kirkeby et al., 2009), Waste Management Planning System (WAMPS) (Swedish Environmental Research Institute, 2010), LCA-IWM (den Boer, 2007), and Organic waste research (ORWARE) tool (Eriksson, 2002). EASEWASTE not only estimates the emission from GHG but also for all emissions to air, soil, surface water and groundwater. WAMPS is designed to estimate the environmental consequences of final disposal materials. LCA-IWM included temporary storage of waste, collection and transport, and treatment disposal and recycling in the waste management assessment. ORWARE focus mainly on life cycle assessment of organic waste which calculated the substance flows, environmental impacts, and costs of waste management. These system assessment tools however do not provide any optimal solution for a waste management system. There is a need of study to develop user friendly tool to find a cost effective solution for SWM as well as to comply with the environmental obligations. This paper presents a new SWM tool named Solid Waste Management Resource Recovery Tool (SMART). SMART is useful for decision makers for long term effective planning and scheduling of MSWM system which can be used to analyse the tradeoffs between technical, economic, and environmental concerns at the national, regional, state or province, or community level. It requires a minimum number of input data the results has been graphically visualize for easy understanding, thus it is user friendly for decision makers. This paper highlighted the framework for the development of SMART includes mathematical modeling, input data, and optimization results. A case of Iskandar Malaysia (IM) was evaluated to demonstrate the potential abilities of SMART. The SMART software has been designed to work at regional and municipality level. It can also be used at national level as long as the related data are provided.

2. Development of SMART

SMART is developed as a management tool for the identification and quantification of the optimal process network for MSWM. The tool examines the impacts of introducing alternative waste treatment technologies including incineration, landfill, composting and recycling to the economic benefits and environmental protection as compared to the existing MSWM system. SMART also incorporates the environmental indicator of carbon footprint of waste management. The tool has been designed to function most effectively at municipality scales; however, it can also be applied at any scale (i.e. state, country, and region) if sufficient data is provided. The tool used the Visual Basic interface to integrate the General Algebraic Modelling System (GAMS) with CPLEX optimization solver (GAMS Development Corporation, 2013), a computer software commonly used for complex optimisation problems. It allows the easy use and simple presentation of input data and output result of the optimal processing network. Figure 1 presents the framework of SMART integrated with GAMS. The SMART is presented in Figure 2.

2.1 Input data

Various input data are encoded into the optimisation system to specify the system boundary. In the normal optimisation system, the user needs to code all the data into system, with specific programming language, which hindered the non-programming user to perform optimal analysis. SMART used Visual Basic as an interface, and linked the data input to the optimisation software. It enables user to perform optimal analysis by simple input. The input data required for the tool are presented in Table 1. User needs to key in the key data such as waste generation, composition, waste moisture content, and policy target. Other data such as efficiency of specific waste treatment plant, costing, and selling prices are keyed-in in the tool as default data based on the Malaysian scenario.

2.2 Optimisation model

The input data from SMART will be transformed into an optimizer language, it is then further linked with the model to analyse and obtain the optimal result. The optimisation model for a MSW is conducted by applying the mixed integer linear programming (MILP) mathematical model due to its simplicity and common use for solving the complex SWM issues (Tan et al., 2013). The objective and model constraints incorporated several aspects of economics, energy, recycling, waste segregation and waste to value-added product to represent the MSWM case.

Table 1. Input data for SMART tool from user and by default in the system

Data	User provide data	Default value set in the system
Annual Waste generation	✓	
MSW composition and moisture content	✓	
MSW chemical element composition and residue fraction from treatment composition		✓
Efficiency of recovery by type of material		✓
Production rate of by-products		✓
Landfill biogas capture		✓
Capital cost, operating cost and variable cost of waste treatment technology and selling price of by-products		✓
Renewable energy (heat and electricity) and recycling target	✓	
Waste treatment plants specification		✓

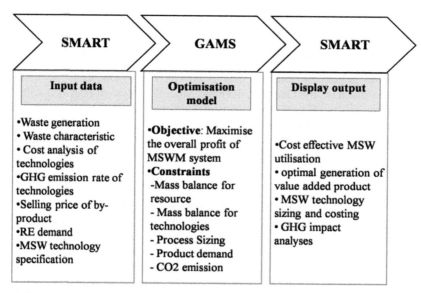

Figure 1. Framework of SMART with integrated GAMS Objective function

The optimisation model is formulated with an objective function and several constraints. The objective function aims to maximise the overall profit (PROFIT) of the MSWM system, the mathematical model is obtained from previous study of Tan et al. (2013), as described by Eq. (1). This function consists of the revenue from product selling (REV), processing cost (PCOST), total capital cost (CCOST) and the variable cost (VCOST).

$$PROFIT = REV\text{-}PCOST\text{-}CCOST\text{-}VCOST \tag{1}$$

REV represents the product revenues from the MSWM system as described in Eq. (2). PRO_{it} is the production rate of product i during period t. $PRICE_{it}$ denotes the unit price of product i in period t.

$$REV = \sum_{it} PRICE_{it} \times PRO_{it} \tag{2}$$

PCOST is the total processing cost of producing the value-added product, as shown in Eq. (3). MAT_{ipt} denotes the input rate of waste i into process p during period t. $UPCOST_{pt}$ is the unit processing cost of process p at period t.

$$POST = \sum_{ipt} UPCOST_{pt} \times MAT_{ipt} \tag{3}$$

VCOST represents the total variable operating and maintenance costs of the system as described in Eq. (4). $UVCost_{pt}$ is the unit variable cost of process p at time t.

$$VCOST = \sum_{ipt} UVCost_{pt} \times MAT_{ipt} \tag{4}$$

The capital cost $CCOST$ is described by Eq. (5), where YP_{pz} is the binary decision variable for purchasing technology p with capacity z, while $ACPCOST_{pzt}$ is the annualised capital cost of technology p with capacity z at period t.

$$CCOST = \sum_{pzt} YP_{pz} \times ACPCOST_{pzt} \tag{5}$$

In order to define the relationship among the variables and parameters in this model, several linear inequality and matrix manipulation constraints are developed such as the mass balance for resources, mass balances for processing unit, the process sizing, product demands, and CO_2 emissions. The mathematical models are encoded in GAMS software and processed by SMART

3. Case study – Iskandar Malaysia (IM)

Several regional default data are encoded in the SMART tool. One of the default data is from the region of Iskandar Malaysia (IM). IM is the third largest metropolis and the most developed region in the Southern Peninsula of Malaysia, with the aim to be transformed into a metropolitan by 2020. Solid waste generation in IM increased by approximately 30 % from 2005 to 2010 and it is expected to increase 50 % by 2025. More than 95 % of the waste is directly disposed in three final disposal landfill sites located around the region (Iskandar Regional Development Authority (IRDA), 2010).

4. Results of scenario analysis

To evaluate the impacts of different waste management options on the utilization system for MSW, four scenarios were constructed in this study. The base scenario presents the current situation of the SWM system in the case study using the data from the base year (year 2005). The base scenario is the baseline for which all scenarios have been compared. In Scenario A, it has been assumed that MSW utilization through MRF and organic waste recycling via composting technology is introduced. Under this scenario, no WTE-related technologies will be considered. Scenario B is a variation of Scenario A in which the MSW is sent to the incineration plant instead of MRF. WTE production will be maximized according to the energy demand targeted by the policy makers. Finally, Scenario C represents a combination of Scenario A and B in which the potential MSWM practices available are included in the scenario, i.e. LFGRS, incineration, MRF, and composting. This scenario is designed to achieve the maximum net profit for the proposed MSW processing network without exceeding the product demand. An optimal solution for MSWM in the case study will be proposed as it is anticipated to fulfill every demand without over- or under-production. Table 2 presents the optimal results of the SMART system for four scenarios.

5. Conclusion

MSWM is a complex system which involves various variables and uncertainties. With the assistance of a user-friendly optimization tool it provides reliable results for decision makers at speedy pace. SMART tool was developed with the objective to provide the interface for user-friendly key-in of input data, system assessment and optimal solutions for SWM. The robustness of SMART can be presented on the capability of scenario analysis under on-going and dynamic changes of policy framework. The result shows that with the SMART system, a maximum net profit of USD 474.04 M/y can be achieve for the case study in IM, which is under scenario A with focus on maxima energy production through WTE alternatives. It also has the lowest net carbon emission as compared to other scenario and base scenario. This scenario however is less optimal as it does not integrate all MSW treatment alternatives and there is overproduction of energy. The optimal scenario found in scenario C where all types of MSW treatment alternatives is integrated with result optimal profit and GHG emission without exceed the production demand.

Table 2. Optimal results of SMART system for MSWM of IM in four scenarios.

Scenario	Unit	Base	A	B	C
Financial planning					
Net Profit	M USD/y	-43.09	34.67	474.04	101.85
Total System Cost	M USD/y	58.53	233.37	7692.86	1787.14
Total Revenue	M USD/y	15.44	268.04	8164.29	1889.29
Unit Treatment Cost	M USD/t	0.0015	0.0034	0.1100	0.0400
GHG Emission	Mt $CO_{2\,eq}$ / y	3.285	1.459	0.195	0.992
Energy Production	G Wh/y	n/a	250.30	9594.13	2285.71
Fraction of waste allocation to technologies					
Incineration	%	n/a	0	15	3
Landfill	%	93	n/a	n/a	n/a
LFGRS	%	n/a	2	59	14
MRF	%	7	56	27	56
Composting	%	n/a	42	n/a	27

Acknowledgement

The authors gratefully acknowledge the University Teknologi Malaysia (UTM) for providing the research grant (Vote No. Q.JI3.2525.01H52) and the Japan International Cooperation Agency (JICA) under the scheme of Science and Technology Research Partnership for Sustainable Development (SATREPS). Besides, the acknowledgement also goes to the Ministry of Higher Education (MOHE) and Erasmus Mundus IDEAS Program for providing Ph.D. scholarship for the first author.

References

J.den Boer,E. den Boer,J. Jager, 2007, LCA-IWM: A Decision Support Tool for Sustainability Assessment of Waste Management Systems, Waste Management, 27, 8, 1032-1045.

O.Eriksson, B.Frostell, A.Björklund, G.Assefa, J.O.Sundqvist, J.Granath, M. Carlsson, A. Baky, L. Thyselius, 2002, ORWARE-A Simulation Tool for Waste Management, Resources, Conservation and Recycling, 36, 4, 287-307.

GAMS Development Corporation, 2013, GAMS: General Algebraic Modeling System (version 22. 9), Washington, United States.

IPCC, 2007, IPCC Fourth Assessment Report: Climate Change 2007 (AR4), Cambridge University Press, Cambridge, United Kingdom and New York, U.S.A.

J.T.Kirkeby, H.Birgisdottir, G.S.Bhander, M.Hauschild, T.H.Christensen, 2007, Modelling of Environmental Impacts of Solid Waste Landfilling within the Life-cycle Analysis Program EASEWASTE, Waste Management, 27, 7, 961-970.

Ministry of Housing and Local Government, 2005, National strategic plan for solid waste management,Putrajaya, Malaysia.

E. Sevigné Itoiz, C.M. Gasol, R.Farreny, J.Rieradevall, X.Gabarrell, 2013, CO2ZW: Carbon Footprint Tool for Municipal Solid Waste Management for Policy Options in Europe. Inventory of Mediterranean countries, Energy Policy, 56, 623-632.

Swedish Environmental Research Institute, 2011, Waste Management Planning System (WAMPS), European Union.

S.T.Tan., C.T.Lee, H.Hashim, W.S.Ho, J.S.Lim, 2013, Optimal Process Network for Municipal Solid Waste Management in Iskandar Malaysia, Journal of Cleaner Production, DOI: 10.1016/j.jclepro.2013.12.005

Jiří Jaromír Klemeš, Petar Sabev Varbanov and Peng Yen Liew (Editors)
Proceedings of the 24th European Symposium on Computer Aided Process Engineering – ESCAPE 24
June 15-18, 2014, Budapest, Hungary. Copyright © 2014 Elsevier B.V. All rights reserved.

Mass Transfer in a Porous Particle – MCMC Assisted Parameter Estimation of Dynamic Model under Uncertainties

Petteri Suominen*, Teuvo Kilpiö, Tapio Salmi

Laboratory of Industrial Chemistry and Reaction Engineering, Åbo Akademi University, Biskopsgatan 8, 20500 Åbo Finland
tisuomin@abo.fi

Abstract

In this paper a method based on Markov Chain Monte Carlo simulations to estimate kinetic parameters for a chemical reaction within a porous particle is presented. It uses distributions for parameter values rather than a single value, like average particle values which are thought to be representative values for a large population of particles. The results show how the variance in parameters affect the time needed to reach steady-state operation and in extreme cases even the proportion of the catalytic material which does not participate in catalysis due to mass transfer limitations. This helps in recognizing possible process conditions for heterogeneously catalyzed reactions. The work illustrates how hard it is to identify single, representative parameter values for phenomena which include non-homogenous material properties.

Keywords: Markov Chain Monte Carlo, parameter estimation, mass transfer.

1. Introduction

Mass transfer within a porous particle is a crucial factor for the performance in heterogeneous catalysis. On a theoretical level, the transport phenomena are well known but in modelling, there exist challenges to be solved. Conventionally, particle size, form and porosity are given as single parameter values, even though; they are in most real-life applications different kind of distributions. This makes the determination of kinetic parameter values in laboratory scale, a challenging, non-trivial task.

For instance, the porosity value of a typical catalyst carrier, activated carbon (AC), can vary ±10 %, even within AC material produced in identical conditions as presented by Drazer et al. (2000). Particle form in heterogeneous catalysis is given conventionally as an integer, 0 for an infinite long slab, 1 for a cylinder and 2 for a sphere. It is totally possibly, though, to use real numbers to represent the irregular shape of milled or crossed particles. The numerical values of particle form can vary a lot in practical applications. Particle size for milled or crossed particles varies based on the fineness of the sieves used. Parameters have, depending on the situation, positive or negative covariance and therefore a simple mathematical operation, such as finding mean or mode value for all parameters does not result in representative parameter values for a large population.

Therefore, some statistical procedure needs to be applied. Markov Chain Monte Carlo (MCMC) methods are established computer intensive methods to simulate the posterior distributions when parameter distributions are known or they can be approximated.

During past decades many papers utilizing MCMC techniques are published. A book with good examples was edited by Doucet et al. (2001).

A dynamic reaction-diffusion equation, needed for modelling the mass transfer with chemical reaction in a porous particle, is in form of partial differential equation (PDE). In this article PDE is solved by finite element method (FEM). Recent example for using FEM in mass and heat transfer in porous particle is given by Kilpiö (2013).

The aim of this article is to illustrate the magnitude of the error in parameter values for a reaction-diffusion problem in a porous particle when parameter values for average particle are used in comparison to estimating parameters with a MCMC method. This is measured in two ways: time needed to reach the steady state operation and quantity of catalytic material which participates in catalysis.

The paper is organized as follows. In the section II, the used computational methods and software are presented. Following section, number III, gives the details of the example model. The results are presented in section IV together with discussion about them. Last section presents the conclusions.

2. Computational methods and used software

2.1. Finite element method
In our previous article, Kilpiö et al. (2013), a backward difference scheme in time dimension was used but the computational burden of it, especially in non-isothermal cases was deemed too high to be practical in MCMC assisted parameter estimation. Therefore, a forward difference scheme was selected. The numerical instability of such an algorithm is well documented and it is not presented here. When this computational scheme is used, it is necessary to scale the problem to the stability region of the algorithm.

2.2. Markov Chain Monte Carlo
Markov Chain Monte Carlo (MCMC) methods are established computer intensive methods to simulate the posterior distributions when parameter distributions are known or they can be approximated.

Important results from MCMC include the mean value of the simulations and highest posterior distribution (HPD) estimates. Often, graphical illustrations include 95 % HPD which gives the area which includes 95 % of the simulation results. Even in this work, figures are presented with 95 % HPD area.

2.3. Python programming language and packages NumPy and PyMC
Object-oriented, interpreted programming language Python 2.7 was used in work. This language is often criticized for poor performance in computationally heavy tasks but this situation is drastically improved by NumPy package and especially its array data structure. PyMC is a package for Monte Carlo routines in Python.

3. Model

The model consists of mass transfer in a porous particle and a simple, heterogeneously catalyzed, chemical reaction as given in Eq.(1) following Langmuir-Hinshelwood kinetics presented in Eq.(2). The surface concentration is assumed to be constant. Concentration and particle diameter were made dimensionless and time was scaled so that the problem stays within numerically stable region. The reaction-diffusion equation for arbitrary particle geometry is presented in Eq.(3).

$$A + B \xrightarrow{\;cat\;} C \tag{1}$$

$$r_i = k \cdot C_s \cdot \frac{K_A \cdot K_B \cdot C_A \cdot C_B}{(1 + K_A \cdot C_A + K_B \cdot C_B)^2} \tag{2}$$

$$\frac{1}{r^s} \cdot \frac{d(D_{ei}(dc_i / dr)r^s)}{dr} + r_i \cdot \rho_p \tag{3}$$

Parameters were chosen to be particle size, form factor and Thiele modulus. This choice was made even though particle size is an intrinsic factor in Thiele modulus. The reason is that of these parameters, particle size distribution is the easiest one to be controlled in practical applications. Thiele modulus on the other hand, is a parameter often referred to in literature concerning heterogeneous catalysis and therefore comparisons to published data are easier.

Generalized Thiele modulus for arbitrary kinetics is presented in Eq.(4) All the equations taken from Salmi et al. (2009).

$$\phi^2 = \frac{\upsilon_i \cdot \rho_p \cdot R^2 \cdot r_i(c^s)}{D_{ei} \cdot c_i^s} \tag{4}$$

The resulting partial differential equation (PDE) was then discretized to yield a finite difference scheme. The procedure is similar to one presented in Kilpio et al. (2013) with the exception that the backward difference was replaced by forward difference.

4. Results and discussion

4.1. Results

The graphical illustration on how the uncertainty in concentration profiles develops in time is given in Figures 1-4. The time points which are chosen to graphical illustrations are related to time needed to reach a steady state operation according to simulation with average particle parameters.

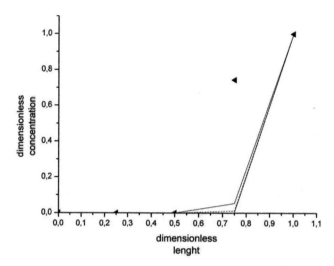

Figure 1. Concentration profile in a particle at time point 0.333·τ. Solid lines give the 95 % HPD area, dashed line profile simulated by mean value of the MCMC simulations and markers show simulated values for average physical parameter values

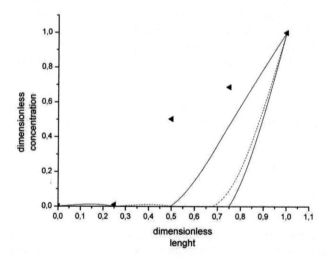

Figure 2. Concentration profile in a particle at time point 0.5·τ. Solid lines give the 95 % HPD area, dashed line profile simulated by mean value of the MCMC simulations and markers show simulated values for average physical parameter values

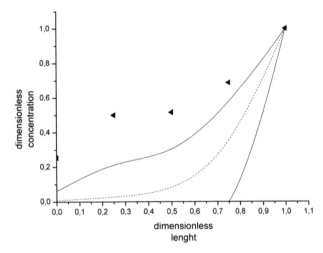

Figure 3. Concentration profile in a particle at time point τ. Solid lines give the 95 % HPD area, dashed line profile simulated by mean value of the MCMC simulations and markers show simulated values for average physical parameter values

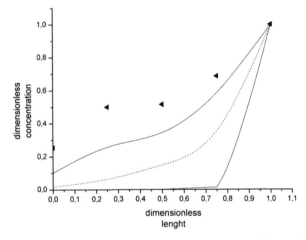

Figure 4. Concentration profile in a particle at time point 1.25·τ. Solid lines give the 95 % HPD area, dashed line profile simulated by mean value of the MCMC simulations and markers show simulated values for average physical parameter values

4.2. Discussion

The method can be applied to non-isothermal case. This increases naturally the computational cost. For chemical reaction model, the method is not limited to Langmuir-Hinshelwood kinetics. Langmuir-Hinshelwood kinetics was chosen to this illustrative example of the method as it is commonly used kinetic model in heterogeneous catalysis.

The results show that the uncertainty of the concentration profiles increases as time elapses. The most important observations are that the time needed to reach the steady state operation is 25 % higher according to parameters estimated by MCMC method than for average particle parameter values and that the simulation based on the average particle parameter values, constantly overestimates the concentrations within the particle.

5. Conclusions

The presented method applies finite element schemes and MCMC methods to estimate kinetic parameters for a heterogeneously catalyzed chemical reaction in a porous particle. The parameters for mean value of MCMC simulations significantly differ from those obtained by average values of the physical parameters. The MCMC estimated parameters yield more accurate predictions for time needed to reach steady-state operation in system and reveal the efficiency of the catalytic particle.

It is shown that there are cases where the simple statistical measures of statistical analysis are not enough to give representative parameter values for a large population of catalytic particles. The MCMC method intrinsically heeds the covariance of the parameters and produces more accurate parameter estimates for a large population of particles.

In our model case, the simulated steady state operation for a large population of catalyst particles was obtained 25 % later than for simulation with average particle parameters. The simulation results for average particle values severely overestimate the concentrations within the particle due to covariance of the parameters.

References

A. Doucet, N. de Freitas, N. Gordon, 2001, Sequential Monte Carlo Methods in Practice, Springer, New York, USA.

G. Drazer, M. Rosen, D.H. Zanette, 2000, Anomalous transport in activated carbon porous samples: power-law trapping-time distributions, Physica Am 283, 181-186.

T. Kilpiö, 2013, Mathematical Modeling of Laboratory Scale Three-Phase Fixed Bed Reactors, PhD Thesis, Åbo Akademi University, Painosalama, Turku, Finland

T. Kilpiö, P. Suominen, T. Salmi, 2013, Hydrogenation of sugars – combined heat and mass transfer, Computer Aided Chemical Engineering, 32, 67-72,

T. Salmi, J.-P. Mikkola, J. Wärnå, 2009, Chemical Reaction Engineering and Reactor Technology, CRC Press, Taylor & Francis Group, Boca Raton, FL, USA.

Jiří Jaromír Klemeš, Petar Sabev Varbanov and Peng Yen Liew (Editors)
Proceedings of the 24th European Symposium on Computer Aided Process Engineering – ESCAPE 24
June 15-18, 2014, Budapest, Hungary. Copyright © 2014 Elsevier B.V. All rights reserved.

Inventory Pinch Based Multi-Scale Model for Refinery Production Planning

Pedro A. Castillo Castillo, Vladimir Mahalec*

Dept. of Chemical Engineering, McMaster University, 1280 Main Street West, Hamilton, ON, L8S 4L8, Canada
mahalec@mcmaster.ca

Abstract

In this work, we introduce a new two-level decomposition algorithm for production planning. The top level optimizes operating conditions via a nonlinear (NLP) model, while the lower level computes an optimal production plan by solving a mixed-integer linear (MILP) model which uses operating states computed at the top level. Time periods at the top level are delineated by inventory pinch points. The algorithm solves mixed-integer nonlinear (MINLP) models much faster than current MINLP solvers for our case studies associated with gasoline blend planning and refinery production planning.

Keywords: inventory pinch, production planning, two-level decomposition

1. Introduction

In order to increase profit margins, supply chain optimization is becoming a common tool in modern industry. Mathematical programming is one of the main techniques to carry out such optimization. The supply chain of an oil refinery is a complex network that has to face a dynamic market and strict regulations. In the last decades, several researchers have worked developing and/or improving models and algorithms to optimize such network. Menezes et al. (2013) developed a single-period MINLP planning model for crude-oil distillation units which computes solutions closer to those observed in practice since they consider swing-cuts to have different properties than the final-cuts. Alhajri et al. (2013) proposed a single-period MINLP model to optimize the production planning in a refinery while reducing the CO_2 emissions. Oddsdottir et al. (2013) presented an MINLP model for procurement planning for oil refineries that considers the blending operations occurring in the refinery unloading section. Assuming fixed blend recipes, Guajardo et al. (2013) developed an MILP model to integrate production and sales tactical planning in oil refineries. Simplified empirical nonlinear equations have been used in refinery planning models as well as hybrid models, i.e. models that use first-principle rigorous relations and empirical linear correlations together (e.g. Mahalec and Sanchez, 2012).

Multi-level decomposition techniques have been implemented to solve the integrated planning and scheduling problem. Li and Ierapetritou (2009) developed a bilevel decomposition algorithm to solve separately the production planning and scheduling levels and proposed an iterative procedure to solve it. Terrazas-Moreno and Grossmann (2011) presented a bilevel decomposition for integrated production planning and scheduling where the upper level is decomposed using a spatial Lagrangean relaxation in order to solve a planning subproblem for each plant site. Leiras et al. (2013) developed an iterative algorithm to integrate the mid-term and short-term planning of multirefinery networks using a bilevel decomposition and the two-stage stochastic programming framework to handle uncertainty.

2. Inventory Pinch Based Planning Algorithm

This work introduces inventory pinch concept as a basis for refinery production planning using a two-level decomposition. An inventory pinch point on the cumulative total demand (CTD) curve is a point where cumulative average total production (CATP) curve intersects the CTD curve, so the CATP curve is above the CTD curve and if we extrapolate the CATP curve from this point onwards it will not cross the CTD curve (Castillo et al., 2013). The inventory pinch points delineate the periods where optimal operating states are likely to remain constant. This observation leads to the following approach to solving the planning problems:

(i)   Average production rates in intervals delimited by the pinch points are different from each other. In refinery planning the pinch points may be separated by 5 or 6 months or more.
(ii) Since plant efficiency and raw material utilization depends on the throughput and the properties of the feeds, let's compute optimal operating conditions corresponding to each of these periods (for a given average throughput in each of the intervals).
(iii) Compute more detailed production plan by using optimal operating conditions computed in (ii).

Above reasoning leads to our two-level decomposition algorithm, denoted as multi-period inventory pinch algorithm (MPIP), shown in Figure 1. The full-space model (i.e. the original single model) is decomposed into two levels. The top level is modelled as a discrete-time, multi-period NLP model. It optimizes the operating conditions of the different type of processing units in the refinery and sets the production targets for the lower level. The periods of the top level are initially defined by the inventory pinch points. At the top level, storage tanks are aggregated into inventory pools of each product, and parallel units are aggregated into a single processing unit. The lower level is formulated as a discrete-time, multi-period MILP model. This level computes the detailed production plan (i.e. how much to produce in each unit and in each time period of the lower level). The lower level periods are defined by the planner. IPOPT solver is used at the top level, and CPLEX is used at the lower level.

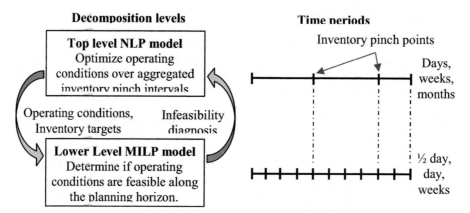

Figure 1. Multi-period Inventory Pinch (MPIP) decomposition.

3. Gasoline Blend Planning

Sample gasoline blending system is shown in Figure 2. The storage tanks are defined as dedicated tanks (DT) if they can only hold one type of product during the entire planning horizon, or as swing tanks (ST) if they are allowed to hold different type of products along the horizon (but not at the same time). We have studied systems with 1 to 3 blenders operating in parallel. There are 9 quality properties; one of them, the Reid vapour pressure (RVP) blends nonlinearly according to Eq. (1) (used by Singh et al., 2000) where I is the set of blend components, J the set of products, and $x_{i,j}$ is the volume fraction of component i in product j. In addition, there is a minimum threshold constraint on each gasoline blend (this introduces integer variables). Length of time periods at the lower level is set to 1 d each and the planning horizon is 14 d. It is assumed that the length of the time periods at the lower level is equal to the minimum length of time that a swing tank would stay in any given service (if the minimum service time is shorter, then the periods at the lower level need also to be shorter, correspondingly). This enables us to compute (if required) allocation of swing tanks as a part of the production plan.

$$RVP_j = \left(\sum_{i \in I} x_{i,j} RVP_i^{1.25} \right)^{0.8} \qquad \forall \, j \in J \tag{1}$$

Performance of inventory pinch based algorithm is compared to DICOPT, a current commercial MINLP solver. DICOPT is selected because, for our case studies, it requires shorter execution times than global MINLP solvers. Inventory pinch algorithm at the lower level has the same number of periods as the full-space MINLP model that is solved by DICOPT.

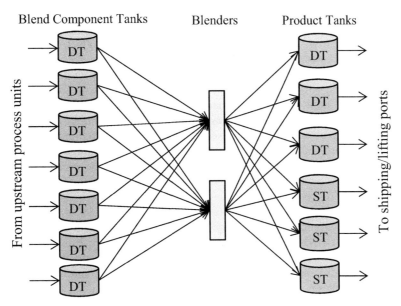

Figure 2. Sample gasoline blending system.

Table 1. Comparison of MPIP algorithm (IPOPT + CPLEX) and full-space MINLP (DICOPT).

Case study ID	# pinch points	# blenders	Blend Cost (×10³ $)	Full-space MINLP		MPIP Algorithm		
				# Recipes	CPU Time (s)	# Recipes	CPU Time (s)	# Its.
1	0	1	37,542.5	6	152.2	1	0.625	1
2	1	1	38,309.8	6	240.5	2	0.778	1
3	1	1	37,991.1	7	227.9	2	0.969	1
4	1	2	37,991.1	8	192.9	2	0.938	1
5	2	2	37,681.1	8	312.6	3	0.960	1
6	2	2	37,324.3	9	258.5	6	10.634	4
7	3	3	37,377.5	10	366.4	4	1.277	1

Results in Table 1 show that, for gasoline blend planning, MPIP algorithm is two orders of magnitude faster than DICOPT. Moreover, the number of different blend recipes is reduced significantly (a blend recipe is considered different if the absolute change of composition percentage of any component is greater than 1%). In addition, in most of our case studies the number of iterations (shown as "# Its." in Table 1) required by the MPIP algorithm is one. Due to the form of the RVP nonlinear constraints used, it was possible to also create a linear version of these constraints, construct an MILP model and check if DICOPT and the MPIP algorithm reach the global optimum. Both DICOPT and MPIP algorithm compute the global optimum in these cases studies.

4. Refinery production planning

In many countries across the world, consumption of refining products varies as the seasons change. In the summer, there is a high demand for gasoline. In the winter, the demand for diesel fuel increases significantly, while the demand for gasoline decreases. A refinery meets such varying demands by shifting the operation of various process units from e.g. maximum gasoline to maximum diesel mode. Current practice in refinery production planning is to define several modes of operation for a process unit and define each mode of operation by a fixed set of yields and fixed product qualities. Since refinery units are nonlinear and since several units produce similar products, it is possible that the optimal operating states are different than those predetermined in advance and entered as parameters in the linear planning model. Hence, it is desirable to use nonlinear models for refinery planning.

Figure 3 shows configuration of the refinery used in our case studies. It is comprised of crude distillation unit (CDU), fluid catalytic cracking (FCC) unit, catalytic reformer (CR), and hydrotreaters (HT). The nomenclature of the streams is the following: sr = straight run, hc = hydrocracker, fcc = fluid catalytic cracker, ln = light naphtha, hn = heavy naphtha, ds = diesel, kero = kerosene, lgo = light oil, hgo = heavy oil, lco = light catalytic oil, hco = heavy catalytic oil, f = feed, lf = light feed, and hf = heavy feed. Only the blending operations in the gasoline and diesel pools are considered. Figure 4 shows cumulative curves for a sample refinery case study. There is a pinch point at period 8 for gasoline pool and a pinch point at period 4 for diesel pool. In one case study, MPIP algorithm solves the planning problem in 3.03 s, while corresponding MINLP problem is solved by DICOPT in 12.59 s. Complete mathematical models and results will be presented in a full length paper.

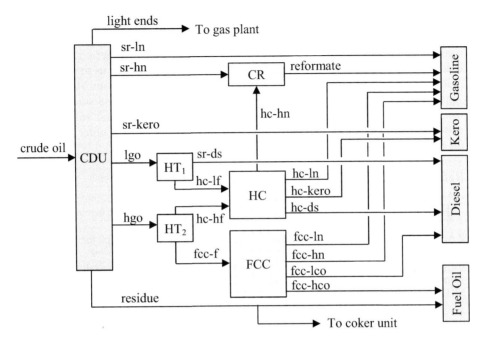

Figure 3. Sample refinery system.

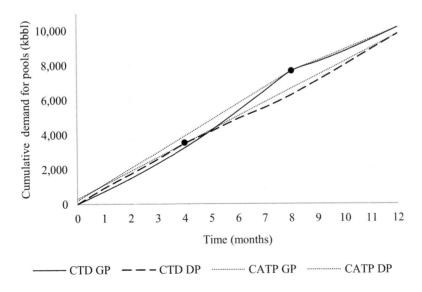

Figure 4. Cumulative curves and pinch points for gasoline pool (GP) and diesel pool (DP).

5. Conclusions

Inventory pinch provides a basis for two-level decomposition of the planning problems; this decomposition enables us to use nonlinear refinery models to solve nonlinear or mixed-integer nonlinear problems in a very efficient manner. Compared to the traditional, fixed-period planning models (e.g. 12 monthly periods for refinery planning, or 14 daily periods for gasoline blending), inventory pinch algorithm optimizes nonlinear models using significantly smaller number of periods. Moreover, decomposition introduced in the inventory pinch algorithm enables us to solve MINLP problems by first solving aggregate NLP problem and then solve an MILP problem. Application of the algorithm to the refinery operations planning case studies (gasoline blending, process units operations) shows that it leads to the same solutions as the multi-period MINLP models. Moreover, the solution times are one order of magnitude (or even more) faster than DICOPT MINLP solver.

References

I. Alhajri, Y. Saif, A. Elkamel, A. Almansoori, 2013, Overall integration of the management oh H_2 and CO_2 within refinery planning using rigorous process models, Chemical Engineering Communications, 200, 139-161.

P.A.C. Castillo, J.D. Kelly, V. Mahalec, 2013, Inventory pinch algorithm for gasoline blend planning, AIChE Journal, 59, 3748-3766.

K. Glismann, G. Gruhn, 2001, Short-term scheduling and recipe optimization of blending processes, Computers and Chemical Engineering, 25, 627-634.

M. Guajardo, M. Kylinger, M. Ronnqvist, 2013, Specialty oils supply chain optimization: From a decoupled to an integrated planning approach, 229, 540-551.

A. Leiras, G. Ribas, S. Hamacher, A. Elkamel, 2013, Tactical and operational planning of multirefinery networks under uncertainty: An iterative approach, Industrial & Engineering Chemistry Research, 52, 8507-8517.

Z. Li, M.G. Ierapetritou, 2009, Integrated production planning and scheduling using a decomposition framework, Chemical Engineering Science, 64, 3585-3597.

V. Mahalec, Y. Sanchez, 2012, Inferential monitoring and optimization of crude separation units via hybrid models, Computers and Chemical Engineering, 45, 15-26.

B.C. Menezes, J.D. Kelly, I.E. Grossmann, 2013, Improved swing-cut modelling for planning and scheduling of oil-refinery distillation units, Industrial & Engineering Chemistry Research, 52, 18324-18333.

T.A. Oddsdottir, M. Grunow, R. Akkerman, 2013, Procurement planning in oil refining industries considering blending operations, Computers and Chemical Engineering, 58, 1-13.

A. Singh, J.F. Forbes, P.J. Vermeer, S.S. Woo, 2000, Model-based real-time optimization of automotive gasoline blending operations, Jourbal of Process Control, 10, 43-58.

S. Terrazas-Moreno, I.E. Grossmann, 2011, A multiscale decomposition method for the optimal planning and scheduling of multi-site continuous multiproduct plants, Chemical Engineering Science, 66, 4307-4318.

Jiří Jaromír Klemeš, Petar Sabev Varbanov and Peng Yen Liew (Editors)
Proceedings of the 24th European Symposium on Computer Aided Process Engineering – ESCAPE 24
June 15-18, 2014, Budapest, Hungary. Copyright © 2014 Elsevier B.V. All rights reserved.

Estimation of Specific Fluxes in Metabolic Networks using Non-linear Dynamic Optimization

Dominique Vercammen, Filip Logist, Jan Van Impe*

KU Leuven, BioTeC & OPTEC, Department of Chemical Engineering, Willem de Croylaan 46, 3001 Leuven, Belgium
jan.vanimpe@cit.kuleuven.be

Abstract

Metabolic network models describing the biochemical reaction network and material fluxes inside micro-organisms open interesting routes for the model based optimization of bioprocesses. Dynamic metabolic flux analysis (dMFA) has lately been studied as an extension of regular metabolic flux analysis (MFA), rendering a dynamic view of the fluxes, also in non-stationary conditions. Recent dMFA implementations suffer from some drawbacks, though. More specifically, the fluxes are not estimated as specific fluxes, which are more biologically relevant. The flux profiles are not smooth, and additional constraints cannot be taken into account. In this work, a new methodology based on a B-spline parameterization of the fluxes is presented. These are estimated using state-of-the-art dynamic optimization tools, i.e., orthogonal collocation, an interior-point optimizer and automatic differentiation. The approach is validated on a small-scale network, and proven to yield an accurate representation of the metabolic fluxes.

Keywords: Dynamic metabolic flux analysis, B-splines, non-linear optimization, parameter estimation

1. Introduction

The modeling and estimation of fluxes in metabolic reaction networks (Metabolic Flux Analysis (MFA)) enables a more detailed view of what is happening inside the cell. The dynamic variant (dynamic Metabolic Flux Analysis (dMFA)) allows furthermore to build dynamic models for cellular growth. Including this micro-scale knowledge in macro-scale bioprocess models will yield more accurate predictions. dMFA has been treated in different ways. In the most recent approach (Leighty and Antoniewicz, 2011), the fluxes are not estimated as specific fluxes, but are multiplied with the biomass concentration to non-specific fluxes. These are parameterized as piecewise linear functions, resulting in a non-dynamic parameter estimation problem. This approach, however, introduces some drawbacks, i.e., (i) the fact that specific fluxes, which are most descriptive from a biological kinetics point of view, cannot be estimated directly, (ii) the non-smoothness of the flux profiles due to the piecewise linear description, and (iii) the fact that irreversibility constraints on the fluxes are not taken into account. The approach which is presented in this work addresses these disadvantages by establishing the true non-linear, dynamic nature of this problem and using state-of-the-art optimization approaches for solving it. The smoothness of the free flux profiles is ensured by using B-spline functions. By using all data at once in the estimation process, the goodness-of-fit of the resulting model can be assessed in a consistent way. Section 2 presents the background on dMFA. Section 3 introduces the novel method and results are presented in Section 4. Finally, Section 5 summarizes the conclusions.

2. Background

2.1. Metabolic reaction networks

A metabolic reaction network represents (a subset of) all metabolic reactions that occur inside a cell (Van Impe et al., 2013). In these networks, m_{int} intracellular and m_{ext} extracellular metabolites are connected to each other through n reactions, which can be intracellular reactions or exchange reactions between the cell and the environment. The reaction rates of these reactions, the so called fluxes, are summarized in the $(n \times 1)$ flux vector $\mathbf{v}$ [mol/(gDW·h)]. Growth of the cell is represented as a pseudo-reaction to biomass, which is defined as an extracellular compound, yielding $m_{ext} + 1$ extracellular metabolites in total. All reactions are classified as reversible or irreversible, based on thermodynamic information. All this information is represented by the stoichiometric matrix $\mathbf{S}$, which contains the stoichiometric reaction coefficients. This matrix can be subdivided into $\mathbf{S}_{int}$, $\mathbf{S}_{ext}$ and $\mathbf{S}_{bio}$, which are the row(s) corresponding to intracellular and extracellular metabolites, and biomass, respectively.

2.2. Dynamic metabolic flux analysis

The dynamic metabolic flux analysis problem consists of identifying the free flux profiles over time, based on measurements of the states, i.e., the extracellular metabolite concentrations, or the fluxes themselves (Antoniewicz, 2013). This problem can be written as a dynamic input estimation problem using a least-squares objective function:

$$\min_{\mathbf{u}(t), \mathbf{x}_0} \sum_{i=1}^{n_{time}} \sum_{j=1}^{n_{out}} \left(\frac{y_j(t_i) - m_{ij}}{\sigma_{ij}} \right)^2 \tag{1}$$

subject to:

$$\dot{\mathbf{x}}(t) = \mathbf{S}_e \cdot \mathbf{K} \cdot \mathbf{u}(t) \cdot c_{bio}(t), \quad \mathbf{x}(0) = \mathbf{x}_0, \quad \mathbf{x}(t) \geq 0 \tag{2}$$

$$\mathbf{z}(t) = \mathbf{IR} \cdot \mathbf{u}(t), \quad \mathbf{z}(t) \geq 0 \tag{3}$$

with:

$$\mathbf{x}(t) = \begin{bmatrix} \mathbf{c}_{ext}(t) \\ c_{bio}(t) \end{bmatrix}, \mathbf{S}_e = \begin{bmatrix} \mathbf{S}_{ext} \\ \mathbf{S}_{bio} \end{bmatrix}, \mathbf{y}(t) = \mathbf{f}(\mathbf{x}(t), \mathbf{u}(t)), \mathbf{v}(t) = \mathbf{K} \cdot \mathbf{u}(t) \tag{4}$$

Here, $\mathbf{c}_{ext}$ is the $(m_{ext} \times 1)$ vector of extracellular concentrations [mol/L], and c_{bio} is the scalar biomass concentration [gDW/L]. These two variables are concatenated into the dynamic state vector $\mathbf{x}$. $\mathbf{u}(t)$ is the $(d \times 1)$ vector of free fluxes, which represent the degrees of freedom left in the metabolic reaction network after the pseudo steady state assumption (Van Impe et al., 2013). The $(n \times d)$ matrix $\mathbf{K}$ is a suitable basis for the null space of $\mathbf{S}_{int}$, which is used to calculate the values of all fluxes based on the free fluxes. The system also includes algebraic states $\mathbf{z}(t)$, which represent the irreversible fluxes. These are calculated through the $\mathbf{IR}$ matrix, which contains the rows of $\mathbf{K}$ that correspond to irreversible fluxes. By constraining the algebraic states to be positive, the irreversible fluxes are also kept positive. Furthermore, $\mathbf{y}(t)$ is the $(n_{out} \times 1)$ vector of outputs of the system, which can be any non-linear function $\mathbf{f}$ of the states and free fluxes, and $y_j(t_i)$ is the model output j at time t_i. The objective function is a weighted sum of least squares, with n_{time} the total number of time points at which measurements were taken, m_{ij} and σ_{ij} respectively the average and the standard deviation for the measurement of output j at time point t_i, and, at last, $\mathbf{x}_0$ the vector of initial values for the states.

3. Methods

3.1. Parameterizing the free fluxes using B-splines

In the current approach, every free flux is parameterized as a polynomial spline function, based on B-spline basis functions (Dierckx, 1993). These B-spline functions are defined by (i) the degree k, (ii) the locations of the $g + 2$ knots $t_0, t_1, ..., t_g, t_{g+1}$, of which the middle ones are the g internal knots, and (iii) the control points, or spline parameters $\mathbf{p}_u$. To get a smooth flux profile, i.e., a function with continuous first derivative, the degree of the spline function should be at least two, and hence the degree is fixed to two in this work, i.e., $k = 2$. Also, the start and end knots (t_0 and t_{g+1}) are fixed at the start and end times of the experimental time horizon. This leaves three entities to calibrate: the number of internal knots, their locations, and the spline parameters. Based on these values, the spline functions can be efficiently evaluated using the Cox-de Boor algorithm (de Boor, 2001). Each free flux is represented by its own spline function, and thus has its own set of internal knot locations and spline parameters. The total number of parameters for each free flux is given by:

$$n_p = 2 \cdot g + k + 1 \tag{5}$$

Three main operations on the splines are used. The first operation is constraining a knot to the specific measurement interval it is in. This is done to prevent knots from straying too far from their initial optimal location. The second operation is inserting a knot at the end of a specified time frame. In this operation, knot insertion, a feature inherent to B-splines, is used to insert a knot without changing the spline profile. This way, the next optimization can be started from a good initial guess, with an extra knot inserted. This operation also takes into account the bounds which were placed on previously added knots, i.e., the knot is inserted in the time frame at the end, where no knot has yet been inserted. The last operation prolongates the splines, which only changes the ending knot t_{g+1} to the new value. This means that the spline profile is slightly changed, because the spline parameters stay the same, but is still close to the previous profile.

3.2. Discretizing the dynamic parameter estimation problem using collocation

The dynamic optimization problem (1)-(4) must be discretized to solve it. In this work, direct collocation on finite elements is chosen (Biegler, 2010). Cubic Lagrange polynomials are adopted, with a Radau collocation scheme. The finite element borders are put at the measurement time points. The resulting NLP is solved with the interior-point solver IPOPT (Wächter and Biegler, 2006). Gradient, Jacobians and Hessian are generated using automatic differentiation with CasADi (Andersson et al, 2012).

3.3. Incremental free flux estimation

The number of internal knots directly controls the number of other parameters. As the least squares objective keeps on decreasing with increasing number of parameters, the optimal number of knots is infinity, rendering a perfect fit of the measurement noise instead of the trend. For this reason, a mechanism to prevent overfitting has to be used. Furthermore, although the polynomial spline functions are linear functions of the spline parameters, the system of ODE's is non-linear, and the splines are also non-linear in the knot locations. These non-linearities in the constraints lead to local minima in the optimization problem. To address these issues, a systematic, incremental strategy for estimating the free flux parameters and knot locations has been devised, based on the Akaike model discrimination criterion. This criterion (AIC, Burnham and Anderson, 2004) is used to discriminate between different model structures which can describe the same phenomenon. It takes into account both the model error and the number of

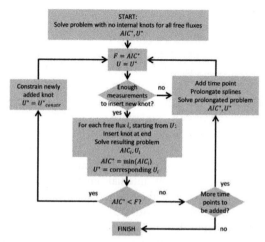

Figure 1. Iterative algorithm for dynamic metabolic flux analysis.

parameters needed. The corrected AIC criterion (AIC_c) is used, as it is more suited in cases where the number of measurements is close to the number of parameters:

$$AIC_c = f + \frac{2 \cdot n_p \cdot (n_p + 1)}{n_{meas} - n_p - 1} \qquad (6)$$

with f the weighted least squares error, as defined in Eq.(1), and n_{meas} the total number of measurements, i.e., $n_{time} \cdot n_{out}$. From this definition it is clear that $n_{meas} \geq n_p + 2$, as otherwise the denominator can become zero or negative.

An algorithmic description of the methodology is given in Figure 1. The method is started by estimating splines without knots, i.e., just second degree polynomials, on a reduced dataset, i.e., the first l timepoints, where l is the number of timepoints needed to make sure that the denominator of Eq.(6) is strictly positive:

$$l \cdot n_{out} \geq 3 \cdot d + 2 \qquad (7)$$

After selecting the correct number of timepoints, the polynomials are fitted and the optimal AIC value is saved as F, together with the optimal splines U. After this, d optimization problems are generated, in which every time one knot is inserted into one free flux spline at a time. The three problems are solved, and the minimum AIC value over these problems is saved as AIC^*, along with the corresponding optimal splines U^*, in which there is now one knot in one of the splines. Now, two possibilities arise. If AIC^* is smaller than F, a new, better solution is found, and another knot can be added. If AIC^* is bigger than F however, the old optimum was better than the new one, and so the old one is kept. An optimal solution for this number of time points has been found, and a new time point can be added if there is still one left to be added. After adding the time point, the splines are prolongated, and the prolongated problem is solved to get the new starting values for F and U for the next iteration. Once all time points have been added, U contains the final, optimal set of free flux profiles for the specified dataset.

4. Results

4.1. Description of case study

The proposed methodology was tested on a small-scale network with simulated measurements. The small-scale network is shown in Figure 2. The network consists of 4 extracellular metabolites, 6 intracellular metabolites and 9 fluxes. Thus, the number of free fluxes is 3. These were chosen as flux 1, 5 and 9. Measurements were simulated by choosing reference profiles (Figure 3, left) for these three fluxes, and simulating the states using the dynamic system. Measurements were generated at 21 equidistant points in time between time 0 and 20 for all 4 states, with added noise, rendering 84 measurements in total.

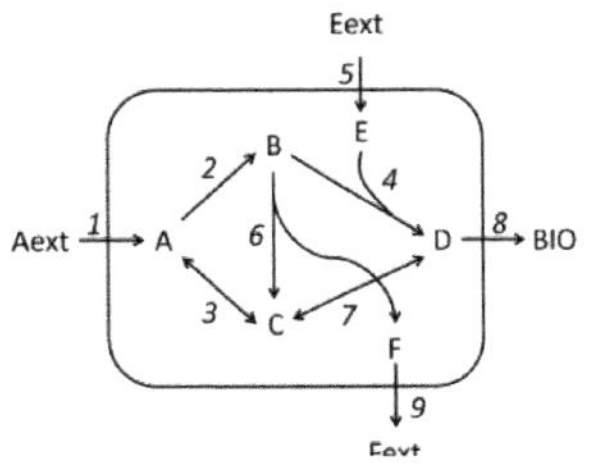

Figure 2. Small-scale network used in the case study.

4.2. Flux estimation for the small-scale network

The methodology is executed on the small-scale case study to validate it and to clarify its operation. An overview of the different iterations is given in Table 1. For this network, $n_{out} = 4$ and $d = 3$, so the number of time points needed to start is 3, based on Eq.(7). In the first iteration, three second degree polynomials are fitted for each of the fluxes. At this point it is not possible to insert a knot since after insertion the number of parameters would be 11, and Eq.(7) would not be satisfied. So a new time point is added at the end, and the problem is solved again for this extended dataset. Now, it is possible to insert a knot. Three subproblems are generated, one for each flux spline in which a knot is inserted. The minimum AIC for these subproblems (88.0) is however bigger than the previous one (48.0), so no new minimum is found, and the dataset is extended again. This pattern goes on until iteration 9, where a better minimum is found when inserting a knot into the spline for flux 1. The optimal location of the knot is 7.94, so it is constrained to lie inside data interval 8. Also, in the next subproblems knots can only be inserted after time 8. In the next subproblem, no better minimum is found, and the horizon is elongated again. The algorithm ends in iteration 19, because the full dataset is used at that point, rendering the optimal flux profiles for the full horizon, shown in Figure 3, together with the optimal state trajectories and the knot locations. These estimated profiles resemble the reference profiles accurately, empirically proving the usefulness of this method. In total, 88 NLP problems are solved, taking 90 seconds on a 3.2 Ghz Intel Core2 Duo CPU with 4 GB of RAM. It is clear that, by using this algorithm, a good starting point can be given to each of these subproblems, reducing the computational time and making sure that the global minimum is approached as close as possible, if not estimated exactly.

Table 1. Overview of the iterations done by the proposed dMFA algorithm.

Iter. #	n_{time}	AIC before insertion	Min. AIC	Comment
1	3	108.0	-----	No insertion possible
2	4	48.0	88.0	No better minimum
...	...	...	...	...
9	11	43.8	31.1	Knot inserted in flux 1 in interval 8
		31.1	38.5	No better minimum
10	12	72.5	40.7	Knot inserted in flux 1 in interval 10
		40.7	45.4	No better minimum
11	13	1,546.2	1,382.3	Knot inserted in flux 1 in interval 11
		1,382.3	79.7	Knot inserted in flux 1 in interval 12
		79.7	62.2	Knot inserted in flux 3 in interval 9
		62.2	73.2	No better minimum
...	...	...	...	...
15	17	74.8	63.6	Knot inserted in flux 3 in interval 13
		63.6	71.6	No better minimum
...	...	...	...	...
19	21	64.4	67.5	No better minimum

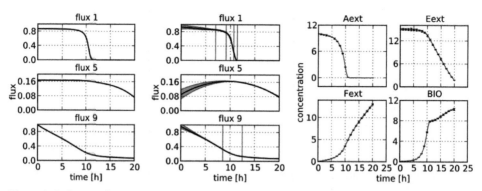

Figure 3. Reference fluxes (left), estimated fluxes (middle) and states (right) for the case study.

5. Conclusions

In this work, a novel methodology for dynamic metabolic flux analysis is described, which uses B-spline parameterizations for the fluxes, non-linear dynamic optimization techniques to estimate the knot locations and an iterative procedure based on model discrimination tools to estimate the number of knots per free flux. The methodology is proven to remove the drawbacks in previous implementations, and is validated on a small-scale in silico case study, in which a good resemblance between the estimated and reference fluxes is found.

Acknowledgements

D. Vercammen holds a PhD grant of the Agency for Innovation through Science and Technology in Flanders (IWT). J. Van Impe holds the chair Safety Engineering sponsored by the Belgian Chemistry and Life Sciences Federation essenscia. The research was supported by the KU Leuven Research Fund: PFV/10/002 (OPTEC), OT/10/035; the Research Foundation Flanders (FWO): FWO KAN2013 1.5.189.13, FWO-G.0930.13 and the Belgian Federal Science Policy Office: IAP VII/19 (DYSCO).

References

J. Andersson, J. Akesson, M. Diehl, 2012, CasADi – A symbolic package for automatic differentiation and optimal control, Recent Advances in Algorithmic Differentiation, Lecture Notes in Computational Science and Engineering, 87, 297–307.

M.R. Antoniewicz, 2013, Dynamic metabolic flux analysis--tools for probing transient states of metabolic networks, Curr. Opin. Biotechnol., 24, 6, 973-8.

L.T. Biegler, 2010, Nonlinear Programming: Concepts, Algorithms, and Applications to Chemical Processes, MPS-SIAM, Philadelphia, USA.

C. de Boor, 2001, A Practical Guide to Splines, Springer-Verlag, New York, USA.

K.P. Burnham, D.R. Anderson, 2004, Multimodel inference: understanding AIC and BIC in Model Selection, Sociol. Meth. and Res., 33, 261–304.

P. Dierckx, 1993, Curve and surface fitting with splines, Oxford Univ. Press, New York, USA

R.W. Leighty, M.R. Antoniewicz, 2011, Dynamic metabolic flux analysis (DMFA): a framework for determining fluxes at metabolic non-steady state, Metab. Eng., 13, 6, 745–55.

J.F. Van Impe, D. Vercammen, E. Van Derlinden, 2013, Toward a next generation of predictive models: A systems biology primer, Food Control, 29, 2, 336–42.

A. Wächter, L.T. Biegler, 2006, On the Implementation of a Primal-Dual Interior Point Filter Line Search Algorithm for Large-Scale Nonlinear Programming, Math. Progr., 106, 1, 25–57.

Jiří Jaromír Klemeš, Petar Sabev Varbanov and Peng Yen Liew (Editors)
Proceedings of the 24th European Symposium on Computer Aided Process Engineering – ESCAPE 24
June 15-18, 2014, Budapest, Hungary.

Optimal Design of Heat Exchanger Networks by Using SQP Algorithm Based on GPU Acceleration

Lixia Kang,[a] Yongzhong Liu,[a,*] Yuxing Ren,[b] Yazhe Tang[b]

[a]*Department of Chemical Engineering, Xi'an Jiaotong University, Xi'an, 710049, China*
[b]*Department of Computer Science and Technology, Xi'an Jiaotong University, Xi'an, 710049, China*
yzLiu@mail.xjtu.edu.cn

Abstract

To increase computational efficiency and quality of solutions on large-scale mixed-integer nonlinear programming (MINLP) models of heat exchanger network synthesis (HENs), a paralleled sequential quadratic programming (SQP) algorithm based on graphic process unit (GPU) acceleration is proposed. It features that the HENs model is decomposed into independent nonlinear programming (NLP) sub-problems that are simultaneously solved by paralleled SQP algorithm on CPU-GPU heterogeneous architectures. The estimation formulae of speed-up ratios for single-GPU and multi-GPU are derived, and the acceleration performances of the proposed algorithm are demonstrated by two MINLP problems of HENs. Results present the effectiveness and the advantage to solve large-scale MINLP models of HENs problems.

Keywords: Heat Exchanger Network; Sequential Quadratic Programming; Graphic Process Unit; Acceleration

1. Introduction

Synthesis of heat exchanger network (HEN) is usually formulated as complex MINLP models. With the increasing complexity and scale of HENs in practical situation, solutions to the problems are commonly time-consuming tasks, and even occurrences of the solution become infeasible.

Parallel computing provides opportunities in solving large-scale HEN optimization problems, which solves the problems by dividing them into a set of sub-problems and computing in parallel units simultaneously. Gao and Kemao (2012) reported that a heterogeneous computing system that was constructed by central processing unit (CPU) and graphic processing units (GPUs) can solve large-scale problems efficiently. The system is also an effective platform to solve large-scale optimization problems (Owens et al., 2008). So far, GPU-based particle swarm optimization algorithm(PSO) (Li et al., 2007), ant colony optimization algorithm (ACO)(Li et al., 2009), adaptive genetic algorithm (GA)(Munawar et al., 2011), and tabu search algorithm (TS) (Zhou, et al., 2013a) have been developed. However, little attention has been paid on the parallelization of deterministic algorithms performed on GPU (Zhou, et al., 2013b).

In this paper, a paralleled sequential quadratic programming (SQP) algorithm based on GPU is proposed to solve HEN synthesis problems. In the proposed approach, the MINLP models are decomposed into NLP sub-problems that are solved simultaneously by paralleled SQP algorithm. The integrality of HEN structures is ensured by enumeration of binary variables in the models. The optimal HENs are finally obtained by parallel selection from the solutions of NLP sub-problems. The feasibility and acceleration characteristics of the proposed method are illustrated by two examples.

2. Paralleled SQP algorithm to solve problems of HEN synthesis based on GPU acceleration

2.1. Modified SQP algorithm in parallel mode

In SQP algorithm, QP sub-problems are constructed and solved in each iterative step, which includes tremendous high dimensional matrix operations. This is one of the major drawbacks that hinder further applications of SQP algorithm. However, GPU provide an opportunity to improve the algorithm via acceleration of large-scale matrix operation in parallel (Owens et al., 2008). Thus, for large-scale optimization problems, it is possible to modify the SQP algorithm in serial mode to a paralleled one by GPU acceleration.

2.2. Accelerating strategy for solutions to HEN synthesis problems.

Figure 1 shows the modified SQP algorithm in parallel mode for solving HENs model based on GPU acceleration. The accelerating strategy basically consists of four steps.

Step 1: Decomposition of HENs model

Suppose that the number of binary variables in the HEN model is n. The number of all possible HEN structures is 2^n. According to Euler theorem, when there are no independent sub-systems, all matches in HEN is restricted by

$$\sum_{i\in HP}\sum_{j\in CP}\sum_{k\in ST} z_{i,j,k} + \sum_{i\in HP} z_i^{cu} + \sum_{j\in CP} z_j^{hu} \geq u-1 \tag{1}$$

where u is the total number of streams. Hence, the number of candidate HEN structures reduces to

$$M = C_n^{u-1} + C_n^u + \ldots\ldots + C_n^n = 2^n - \sum_{i=0}^{u-2} C_n^i < 2^n \tag{2}$$

Then, the MINLP model of HEN synthesis can be decomposed into M sub-problems.

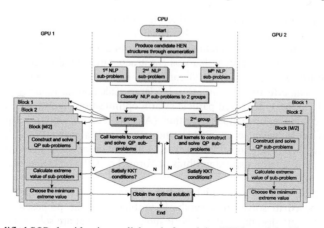

Figure 1 Modified SQP algorithm in parallel mode for solving HENs model with two GPUs

Step 2: *Assignment of NLP sub-problems*

In this work, blocks on GPU are considered the minimum coarse-grained parallel computing unit, which are used to solve NLP sub-problems. In single GPU case, all of NLP sub-problems are assigned to the GPU and be simultaneously solved. In multiple GPU case, NLP sub-problems are first classified according to the number of heat exchangers in HEN structures, and then assigned γ groups to γ GPUs in turn. In this way, the uniformity of assignment of NLP sub-problems in each GPU is ensured.

Step 3: *Parallel solutions to NLP sub-problems*

The CPU-GPU heterogeneous computing mode is adopted. As shown in Figure 1, start of kernel functions, complicated cycle and judgment statements are executed on CPU. Each NLP sub-problem is solved by parallel SQP algorithm in a block on GPUs. And large-scale matrix operations are also carried out by kernel functions on GPU. The optimum solutions to these NLP sub-problems are $f(i)$, $i = 1, 2, ..., M$.

Step 4: *Final selection of optimal solution*

The optimal solution of the HENs is finally obtained by comparing $f(i)$, which is realized by a reduction method in a block. In each step of comparison, the number of threads equals to half of the number of $f(i)$ requiring comparison. Each thread is used to compare the solutions corresponding to the position before and after a half.

3. Estimation of speed-up ratio for modified SQP algorithm in parallel

Each NLP sub-problem of the MINLP model for HEN synthesis is solved by SQP algorithm. Assume that the execution time of each NLP sub-problem is identical and equal to T_{s0}. When the computing is in serial mode, the total execution time should be

$$T_s = MT_{so} \tag{3}$$

Then the parallel execution time of each MLP sub-problem is

$$T_{p0} = T_{s0}\left(f_s + \frac{f_p}{a}\right) \tag{4}$$

where f_s and f_p are serial and parallel task ratios of total computing tasks according to Amdahl's law, constrained by $f_s + f_p = 1$. a is the number of GPU cores when the thread structure of CPU and GPU are the same. Therefore, the total parallel execution time can be expressed as

$$T_{pt} = MT_{s0}\left(f_s + \frac{f_p}{a}\right) + MT_{t0} \tag{5}$$

where T_{t0} is the delay time of communication between CPU and GPU in the course of solving a NLP sub-problem. In multiple GPU case, the total parallel execution time is

$$T_{pt} = \left\lceil \frac{M}{\gamma} \right\rceil T_{s0}\left(f_s + \frac{f_p}{a}\right) + MT_{t0} \tag{6}$$

Now, the speed-up ratio of the paralleled SQP algorithm for a single-GPU case is

$$S_1 = \frac{T_{st}}{T_{pt}} = \frac{MT_{s0}}{\left(f_s + \frac{f_p}{a}\right)MT_{s0} + MT_{t0}} \tag{7}$$

whereas for the multiple GPUs case is

$$S_m = \frac{T_{st}}{T_{pt}} = \frac{MT_{s0}}{\left(f_s + \frac{f_p}{a}\right)\left\lceil \frac{M}{\gamma} \right\rceil T_{s0} + MT_{t0}} \tag{8}$$

where the parameters, such as T_{s0}, T_{to}, f_s and f_p can be obtained by solving Eqs.(3) ~(8) when T_S, T_P, S_1 and S_2 of examples are known. And S_m can be estimated by fixing these parameters.

4. Application of paralleled SQP algorithm to solve HENs problems

4.1. Case studies

In this section, two case studies are employed to demonstrate the effectiveness of the proposed algorithm. All computations were performed over a PC system with NVIDIA TESLA C2050 GPU mounted on two motherboards with Intel(R) Xeon(R) E5640 2.67GHz as the host CPU. The total number of CUDA cores is 448. The selected computing environment of device is 4.0.

The first example is taken from Björk and Westerlund (2002). One hot and two cold streams are involved. Seven binary variables, 58 continuous variables and 130 constraints are included in HENs model. The HEN structure and the total annual cost of 42,163.5 $/a are obtained in this work, which are the same as those in literature.

Another example comes from Lee et al. (1970). There are two hot and two cold streams involved. The match between H1 and C1 is forbidden, which is not included in Lee's model. There are 12 binary variables, 88 continuous variables and 194 constraints in the HEN model. As shown in Table 1, the results show that the optimal solution obtained by the proposed approach is better than that in literature. From a practical perspective, the global astringency of SQP algorithm provides much more chances to ensure global optimal solutions to large-scale problems of HENs synthesis.

Table 1. Comparison of results for the second example

Method	H1-C1 Forbidden	C1-C2 Allowed	ΔT_{min} (K)	Total annual cost($/a)
Lee et al. (1970)			265.4	13,481
Papoulias and Grossmann (1983)	√	√	265.4	21,200
Yerramsetty and Murty (2008)	√		256.5	18,705
This work	√		256.5	17,843

4.2. Further discussion

Table 2 presents the execution time of a NLP sub-problem in a single thread. It indicates that the computing performance of GPU is poorer than that of CPU. However, the total execution time suggests that the paralleled SQP algorithm based on GPU has a better acceleration performance than that of on CPU, whatever a single GPU or double GPUs is used in computation, as shown in

Table 3. The speed-up ratio increases as the scale of the HENs problem increases. Thus, the proposed SQP algorithm based on GPU acceleration has advantages to solve large-scale problems of HENs synthesis.

5. Analysis of accelerating characteristics by using multiple GPUs

Figure 2 shows estimation of speed-up ratio with multiple GPUs. It indicates that if the scale of the HENs problem is fixed, the speed-up ratio increases with an increase in the number of GPUs, and finally tends to be constant. Thus the maximum speed-up ratio achieved by increasing the number of GPUs, and the required minimum number of GPUs corresponding to the maximum speed-up ratio can be obtained. It also reveals that the shares of the communication time in the total execution time increases as the number of GPUs increases. Subsequently, reasonably choosing the number of GPUs can improve acceleration performance; On the other hand, if the scale of the HENs model increases, the speed-up ratio still increases even if the number of GPUs is fixed, and the growth rate of speed-up ratio

Table 2. Comparison of execution time obtained by single thread

Item	Example 1	Example 2
Executive time T_S (in Serial) /s	63.37	63.43
Executive time T_P (in Parallel) /s	90.29	95.02
Ratio of execution time (=T_S/T_P)	1.42	1.50

Table 3. Comparison of results between serial and parallel computation

Item	Example 1	Example 2
Execution time (Serial) /s	3,013	250,384
Execution time in single-GPU case (Parallel) /s	239	9,120
Execution time in double-GPU case (Parallel) /s	206	4,953
Practical Accelerating Ratio S_1	12.62	27.46
Practical Accelerating Ratio S_2	14.62	50.55

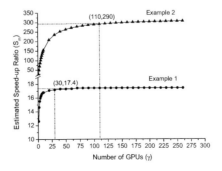

Figure 2. Estimation of speed-up ratio with multiple GPUs

increases with the increase of the number of GPUs. It is likely that the shares of communication time in total execution time decreases as the scale of HENs problem increases. This point is favorable of solving large-scale HENs problems. We infer that it is the shares of the communication time in the total execution time that mainly influences the speed-up ratio of parallel SQP algorithm in solving HENs problems by increasing the number of GPUs.

6. Conclusions

A paralleled SQP algorithm on GPU is proposed to solve large-scale HENs problems. The MINLP model is decomposed into independent NLP sub-problems, which are simultaneously solved by paralleled SQP algorithm on a CPU-GPU heterogeneous computation system. The solution quality and the acceleration performance of the proposed method are demonstrated by two MINLP problems of HENs. Results show that the proposed algorithm has a great advantage over the traditional SQP algorithm in serial mode for solving large-scale HENs problems. Reasonably choosing the number of GPUs can improve the acceleration performance. Exploring an effective method to reduce the number of sub-problems deserves further efforts.

Acknowledgements

The authors gratefully acknowledge funding by the projects (No. 21376188 and No. 21176198) sponsored by the Natural Science Foundation of China (NSFC).

References

K. M. Björk, T. Westerlund, 2002, Global optimization of heat exchanger network synthesis problems with and without the isothermal mixing assumption, Computers and Chemical Engineering, 26, 1581-1593.

W. Gao, Q. Kemao, 2012, Parallel computing in experimental mechanics and optical measurement: A review, Optics and Lasers in Engineering, 50, 608-617.

K. F. Lee, A. Masso, D. Rudd, 1970, Branch and bound synthesis of integrated process designs, Industrial and Engineering Chemistry Fundamentals, 9, 48-58.

J. Li, X. Hu, Z. Pang, K. Qian, 2009, A parallel ant colony optimization algorithm based on fine-grained model with GPU-acceleration, International Journal of Innovative Computing, Information and Control, 5, 3707-3716.

J. Li, D. Wan, Z. Chi, X. Hu, 2007, An efficient fine-grained parallel particle swarm optimization method based on GPU-acceleration, International Journal of Innovative Computing, Information and Control, 3, 1707-1714.

A. Munawar, M. Wahib, M. Munetomo, K. Akama, 2011, Advanced genetic algorithm to solve MINLP problems over GPU. In Evolutionary Computation (CEC), 2011 IEEE Congress, 318-325.

J. D. Owens, M. Houston, D. Luebke, S. Green, J. E. Stone, J. C. Phillips, 2008, GPU computing, In Proceedings of the IEEE, 96, 879-899.

S. A. Papoulias, I. E. Grossmann, 1983, A structural optimization approach in process synthesis - II: Heat recovery networks, Computers and Chemical Engineering, 7, 707-721.

K. M. Yerramsetty, C. V. S. Murty, 2008, Synthesis of cost-optimal heat exchanger networks using differential evolution, Computers and Chemical Engineering, 32, 1861-1876.

K. Zhou, X. Chen, Z. Shao, W. Wan, L. T. Biegler, 2013, Heterogeneous parallel method for mixed integer nonlinear programming, Computers and Chemical Engineering, DOI: 10.1016/j.compchemeng.2013.11.009.

K. Zhou, W. Wan, X. Chen, Z. Shao, L. T. Biegler, 2013, A Parallel Method with Hybrid Algorithms for Mixed Integer Nonlinear Programming, Computer Aided Chemical Engineering, 32, 271-276.

Jiří Jaromír Klemeš, Petar Sabev Varbanov and Peng Yen Liew (Editors)
Proceedings of the 24th European Symposium on Computer Aided Process Engineering – ESCAPE 24
June 15-18, 2014, Budapest, Hungary. Copyright © 2014 Elsevier B.V. All rights reserved.

Optimal Scheduling of Multi-stage Multi-product Biopharmaceutical Processes Using a Continuous-time Formulation

Miguel Vieira, Tânia Pinto-Varela[*], Ana Paula Barbosa-Póvoa

Center for Management Studies (CEG-IST), Instituto Superior Técnico, Universidade de Lisboa, Portugal
tania.pinto.varela@tecnico.ulisboa.pt

Abstract

In this paper, a scheduling model is presented for biopharmaceutical processes. The proposed Mixed Integer Linear Programing (MILP) formulation extends the unified continuous-time Resource-Task Network (RTN) representation presented by Castro et al. (2004). Two of the main characteristics required in the bioprocesses scheduling, which are the lots traceability of different productions and the shelf-life storage limitations, are considered. An illustrative example from the literature is used to demonstrate the applicability of the proposed formulation.

Keywords: Scheduling, RTN, lots traceability, shelf-life storage, biopharmaceutical process

1. Introduction

The process planning has become increasingly important in multi-product industries as a consequence of global competition and fast changing economic conditions. For that purpose, the optimal scheduling of operations is crucial for improving performance and adjust production flexibility to market demand. The general problems of planning and scheduling operations have been extensively researched, with relevance to the modeling optimization of short-term scheduling (Méndez et al., 2006). The application of such models to real industrial problems often stumbles either to address complex requirements of the manufacturing process, to tackle large temporal horizon or even to consider uncertainty. The development of efficient modeling techniques capable of solve large scale optimization problems remains a challenge, aiming the full integration with existing decision-making processes.

1.1. Planning and scheduling optimization

Research methodologies for solving planning and scheduling problems have been evolving from large sets of scatter optimization formulations, to more general approaches based on unified frameworks for process representation. Méndez et al. (2006) classified the scheduling problems according to its process topology: sequential, with single or multiple stages where one or several units may be working in parallel; and network, where arbitrary topology is handled, able to address more complex product recipes involving batch mixing/splitting or cyclic material flows. In the latter category are included the State-Task Network (STN) and the Resource-Task Network (RTN) formulations, two generic methodologies able to address the optimal allocation of resources to tasks. Both STN and RTN representations have been extensively used for modeling scheduling problems. Castro et al. (2004) developed a continuous RTN formulation based on a uniform time grid for the scheduling of multipurpose plants;

Pinto et al. (2008) addressed a comparative set of examples to evaluate the adequacy and effectiveness of STN/m-STN/RTN formulations to the design of multipurpose batch plants; and Shaik and Vooradi (2013) proposed a unified framework and developed two unit-specific event-based approaches for STN and RTN representations. Other authors have explored the complexity of industrial scheduling problems, developing MILP models integrating design, production planning and scheduling decisions for multistage multiproduct batch plants (Fumero et al., 2013).

Concerning the time representation, models are further classified as discrete or continuous. Discrete-time models divide the time horizon into equal length intervals, while continuous-time models can employ either common (global) or multiple unit-specific time grids, as well as slot-based or precedence-based approaches applied to sequential processes. Discrete formulations have shown to be a good approach for scheduling problems dealing with a reasonable small number of time intervals. Albeit, the major advantage of continuous-time formulation rely on the fact that scheduled tasks may occur at any instance of the scheduling horizon. Several authors have acknowledged that so far there is no single best representation, even for the same class of problems. The increasing model complexity have endured the discussion over alternative mathematical formulations exploring decomposition techniques and heuristic algorithms. A review over different model approaches for batch and continuous processes are presented by Floudas et al. (2004) and Sundaramoorthy et al. (2011) compared the performance capabilities of discrete and continuous-time formulations.

1.2. Biopharmaceutical processes

The pharmaceutical sector has been dominated by chemically synthesized drugs, representing more than 60 % the number of approvals of therapeutics in Europe. However, biopharmaceuticals have been gathering particular attention recently due to its efficiency in the treatment of complex diseases, such as cancer, diabetes or growth disturbances. These bioengineered molecules with pharmacological activity, used for therapeutic or in vivo diagnostic purposes, already account for eight out of top 10 selling drugs worldwide (Kontoravdi et al., 2013).

Biopharmaceuticals manufacturing processes are mainly composed by two complex steps referred as upstream and downstream processing, as depicted in Fig. 1. Upstream processing includes all tasks associated with culture and maintenance of cells, and downstream processing to those related to the chemical and physical separations necessary for the isolation and purifications of the drug product. The biopharmaceutical sector and the nature of the biochemical processes have risen specific optimization problems. In particular, the uncertainty associated with upstream processes and the high operating costs of downstream operations have endured an exponential research interest in this area (Liu et al., 2013). Long campaigns to minimize changeovers and cross-product contamination, intermediate products shelf-life limitations, biological variability of fermentation titers or track of production lots due to regulatory policies are considered relevant factors in the scheduling of these facilities.

Despite the extensive research over scheduling problems considering traditional chemical-based processes, applications to the biopharmaceutical sector are fairly unnoticed. Lakhdar et al. (2005) stated that there exists a gap yet to be explored, considering the bioprocesses a relevant case study for the application of these general model formulations. The same authors have later extended previous work proposing an

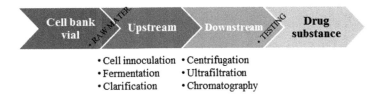

Figure 1. Outline of a biopharmaceutical manufacturing process

iterative algorithm to solve medium term biopharmaceutical manufacturing planning problems with uncertainty in fermentation titers (Lakhdar et al., 2008). More recently, Kabra et al. (2013) developed a continuous-time multi-period scheduling of a multi-stage multi-product process based on the STN framework.

Some of the identified scheduling problems are discussed in the present work. The remainder of the paper is structured as follows: the second section presents the problem characterization, followed by the modeling framework; the results of an illustrative case study are analyzed, followed by conclusions and future works remarks.

2. Problem Statement

This study explores the identified gap within the scheduling of a multi-stage multi-product process of the biopharmaceutical industry, proposing the development of a MILP model based on a continuous-time representation of the RTN formulation. The presented model will address some of the main scheduling constraints of bioprocesses, mainly, the traceability of different production lots and the storage constraints of intermediate products regarding inherent shelf-life limitations. The objective is profit maximization by determining the optimal schedule (tasks and quantities sequence), given: (i) the product recipes in terms of their respective RTN framework; (ii) the product demands and due dates; (iii) the characteristics of the processing units, processing times, operational costs and the task-unit suitability; (iv) the shelf-life limits of intermediates/products; (v) the value of the products and (vi) the storage costs for all materials (intermediaries and products).

3. Mathematical formulation

Due to the extent limitations of this paper, the mathematical formulation will focus only on the model extensions addressing two significant operational aspects of biopharmaceutical processes here presented: the lot traceability and shelf-life constraints. The RTN-base continuous formulation follows the work of Castro et al. (2004), considering a global-time points timing constraints. Without loss of generality of the formulations here presented, the approach concerning the interaction of discrete and continuous tasks proposed by the author was followed (I_r, I_c). Eq. (1) and (2) impose that the difference between the absolute times of two time events t and t' must be either greater than or equal (for zero-wait tasks I_{zw}) than the processing time of all tasks starting and finishing at those same time points. Parameters α_i and β_i account for the processing time of tasks given by, respectively, a fixed and/or a term proportional to amount being processed. The amount of each resource produced or consumed at the start and end of a task - $\mu_{ir}^{p,c}$ and $v_{ir}^{p,c}$ - are assumed to be proportional to the binary ($N_{iltt'}$) and/or continuous ($\xi_{iltt'}$) extents of the task. $N_{iltt'}$ is equal to one if task i starts lot l at event point t and ending at or before event point $t'>t$ and $\xi_{iltt'}$ gives the total amount of material being processed for the same instance.

$$T_{t'} - T_t \geq \sum_{i \in I_r}(\alpha_i N_{iltt'} + \beta_i \xi_{iltt'}) \quad \forall r \in E, l \in L_r, t < t', t \in H, t \neq |T| \tag{1}$$

$$T_{t'} - T_t \leq H\left(1 - \sum_{i \in I_{zw}} N_{iltt'}\right) + \sum_{i \in I_r}(\alpha_i N_{iltt'} + \beta_i \xi_{iltt'}) \quad \forall r \in E, l \in L_r, t < t', t \in H, t \neq |T| \tag{2}$$

3.1. Lots traceability constraints

As highlighted in the work developed by Moniz et al. (2013), the chemical-pharmaceutical industry relies on critical production features concerning regulatory policies to assure production quality. The same is verified within the biopharmaceutical sector. One of those aspects, which must be considered in our case, is the ability to trace the proportion/quantities of different lots of products that are mixed or split through the process. The resource balance is defined in Eq.(3), where R_{rlt} characterize the resource availability r at lot l and time point t. Considering a set of predefined global-time points T, where the first time point takes place at $T_1=0$ and the last at the end of the time horizon $T_i=H$. Eq.(4) performs the initial assignment of processing units E to lots and the amount of resource available is bounded by Eq.(5). Assuming that each task can be performed in a single processing unit, Eq.(6) account for capacity limitations.

$$R_{rlt} = \left(R_{rl}^0|_{(t=1)}, R_{rl,t-1}|_{t>1}\right) + \sum_{i \in I_r}\left(\sum_{t'<t}(\mu_{ir}^p N_{ilt't} + v_{ir}^p \xi_{ilt't}) + \sum_{t'>t}(\mu_{ir}^c N_{iltt'} + v_{ir}^c \xi_{iltt'})\right) + \sum_{i \in I_{st}}(\mu_{ir}^p N_{il(t-1)t} + \mu_{ir}^c N_{ilt(t+1)}) + \sum_{i \in I_c}(\mu_{ir}^p N_{il(t-1)t} + \mu_{ir}^c N_{ilt(t+1)} + \lambda_{ir} \xi_{il(t+1)t}) \quad \forall r, l \in L_r, t \in H \tag{3}$$

$$\sum_{l \in L_r} R_{rl}^0 \leq 1 \quad \forall r \in E \tag{4}$$

$$R_r^{min} \leq R_{rlt} \leq R_r^{max} \quad \forall r, t \in H \tag{5}$$

$$V_i^{min} N_{iltt'} \leq \xi_{iltt'} \leq V_i^{max} N_{iltt'} \quad \forall i \in I_r, l \in L_i, t < t', t \in H, t \neq |T| \tag{6}$$

3.2. Shelf-life constraints

Considering the limited shelf-life of intermediates and final products, the process should eliminate the lifetime-expired stored products by waste disposal, which represent an additional operational cost. Assuming a single storage task i per material resource r, Eq.(7) and Eq.(8) guarantee that if there is an excess amount of the resource r at time point t, the corresponding storage task will be activated for both intervals $t - 1$ and t. If the storage tasks I_{st} has extended the product lifetime λ_r (Eq.(9)), a binary variable $Sl_{itt'}$ is activated. The amount sent to waste disposal W_{rt} is defined by Eq.(10) and Eq.(11) and accounted in related resource balance.

$$V_i^{min} N_{ilt,t+1} \leq \sum_{r \in I^{st}} R_{rlt} \leq V_i^{max} N_{ilt,t+1} \quad \forall i \in I_{st}, l \in L_i, t \in H, t \neq |T| \tag{7}$$

$$V_i^{min} N_{ilt-1,1} \leq \sum_{r \in I^{st}} R_{rlt} \leq V_i^{max} N_{ilt-1,t} \quad \forall i \in I_{st}, l \in L_i, t \in H, t \neq 1 \tag{8}$$

$$Sl_{rt} \geq \left[|T_{t'} - T_t| - \lambda_r\right]\big/ H \quad \forall r \in P_{sl}, i \in I_{st}, t > t', t \in H, t \neq |T| \tag{9}$$

$$W_{rt} \geq \sum_{r \in I^{st}} R_{rlt} - V_i^{max}(2 - N_{iltt'} - Sl_{rt}) \quad \forall r \in P_{sl}, i \in I_{st}, t > t', t \neq |T| \tag{10}$$

$$W_{rt} \geq \sum_{r \in I^{st}} R_{rlt} - V_i^{max}(2 - N_{iltt'} - Sl_{rt}) \quad \forall r \in P_{sl}, i \in I_{st}, t > t', t \neq |T| \tag{11}$$

Based on the previous constraints and the profit maximization as the objective function, which considers total sales and manufacturing, storage, changeover or disposal costs, the model define the optimal tasks sequencing and the resources allocation for the time horizon *H*.

4. Illustrative case study

The presented model is applied to a literature example adapted from Lakhdar et al. (2005). The example considers a general problem in the biopharmaceutical industry: a two-stage facility, with two fermentation suites (J1 and J2) and two purification suites (J3 and J4) per stage, to produce three products (P1, P2 and P3) during a year-long production horizon. Figure 2 displays the outline of the process connections. To confine the integrality of the model and assess only the constraints formulation here presented, the original example was adapted assuming a single due date. This implied that storage constraints were only defined for intermediates. To detail the traceability of lots, for each intermediate/product demand was determined the lots size regarding its shelf-life limitations. The first step in the search for the global optimal solution started with the determination of the minimum number of event points. Was assumed a compromise for the shortest time-horizon that fulfills the demand, which determined 14 event points for *H* of 313 d. The model was implemented in GAMS (24.0.2 WIN VS8 x86) and solved with CPLEX in a Intel Xeon X5680 at 3.33GHz with 24GB RAM.

4.1. Results discussion

For the assumed time horizon, the schedule results are shown in a Gantt chart in Figure 3, as well as the optimal solution statistics. The chart depicts the sequencing of products in each unit, along with the identification of the lot and the amount produced. The black interspaces represent the units changeover time for each intermediate/product. Since a single due date is assumed for the end of the horizon, all lots of each intermediate/product are performed sequentially to minimize changeovers. The upstream tasks (units J1 and J2) have a higher processing time than the corresponding

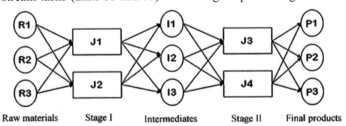

Figure 2. Example of a two-stage biopharmaceutical production process (Kabra et al., 2013)

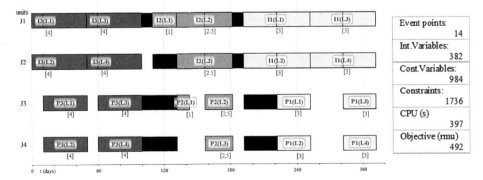

Figure 3. Production schedule and model statistics *H*=313 days (gap 0)

downstream tasks (units J3 and J4), leading to the activation of the storage tasks. The profit considers the fulfilled demand but was mostly penalized by the storage costs of intermediates and no shelf-life wastage was verified owing to extended shelf-life storage.

5. Conclusions

In this work, a MILP model based on a continuous global-time points RTN formulation has been proposed for solving a scheduling problem in the biopharmaceutical industry. The complexity of the production process enhances the challenge in the translations of the different operational constraints to a mathematical model. In this first study, two relevant operational constraints are presented: the tracing of the different lots and the shelf-life limitations in the products storage. An example involving two stages with parallel units for producing three products over a one year time horizon was used for demonstration. Future work will explore comparisons with other timing formulations and new formulations considering additional features, e.g. multiple due-dates deliveries.

Acknowledgements

The authors would like to acknowledge the financial support of Fundação para a Ciência e Tecnologia under the grant SFRH/BD/51594/2011

References

P. Castro, A. Barbosa-Póvoa, H. Matos, A. Q. Novais, 2004, Simple continuous-time formulation for short-term scheduling of batch and continuous processes, Ind Eng Chem Res 43, 1, 105-18.
C.A. Floudas, X. Lin, 2004, Continuous-time versus discrete-time approaches for scheduling of chemical processes: a review, Comput Chem Eng, 28, 11, 2109-2129.
Y. Fumero, M.S. Moreno, G. Corsano, J.M. Montagna, 2013, A multiproduct batch plant design model incorporating production planning and scheduling decisions under a multiperiod scenario, Comput Aided Chem Eng, 32, 505-510.
S. Kabra, 2013, Multi-period scheduling of a multi-stage multi-product bio-pharmaceutical process, Comput Chem Eng, 57, 95-103.
C. Kontoravdi, N.J. Samsatli, N. Shah, 2013, Development and design of bio-pharmaceutical processes, Curr Opin Chem Eng, 2, 4, 435-441.
K. Lakhdar, Y. Zhou, J. Savery, N.J. Titchener-Hooker, L.G. Papageorgiou, 2005, Medium term planning of biopharmaceutical manufacture using mathematical programming. Biotechnol Prog, 21, 1478-89.
K. Lakhdar, L.G. Papageorgiou, 2008, An iterative mixed integer optimisation approach for medium term planning of biopharmaceutical under uncertainty, Chem Eng Res Des, 86, 259-267.
S. Liu, A.S. Simaria, S.S. Farid, L.G. Papageorgiou, 2013, Mixed integer optimisation of antibody purification processes, Comput Aided Chem Eng, 32, 157-162.
C.A. Mendez, J.Cerda, I.E. Grossmann, I. Harjunkiski, M. Fahl, 2006, State-of-the-art review of optimization methods for short-term scheduling of batch processes, Comput Chem Eng, 30, 913-946.
S. Moniz, A.P. Barbosa-Póvoa, J. Pinho de Sousa, 2013, New General Discrete-Time Scheduling Model for Multipurpose Batch Plants, Ind Eng Chem Res 52, 48, 17206-17220.
T. Pinto, A.P.F.D Barbosa-Póvoa, A.Q. Novais, 2008, Design of multipurpose batch plants: A comparative analysis between the STN, m-STN, and RTN representations and formulations, Ind Eng Chem Res, 47, 16, 6025-6044.
M.A. Shaik, R. Vooradi, 2013, Unification of STN and RTN based models for short-term scheduling of batch plants with shared resources, Chem Eng Sci, 98, 104-124.
A. Sundaramoorthy, C.T. Maravelias, 2011, Computational Study of Network-Based MIP Approaches for Chemical Production Scheduling, Ind Eng Chem Res, 50, 9, 5023-5040.

Jiří Jaromír Klemeš, Petar Sabev Varbanov and Peng Yen Liew (Editors)
Proceedings of the 24th European Symposium on Computer Aided Process Engineering – ESCAPE 24
June 15-18, 2014, Budapest, Hungary. Copyright © 2014 Elsevier B.V. All rights reserved.

Spatial-based Approach of the Hydrogen Supply Chain in the Midi-Pyrénées Region, France

Sofía De-León Almaraz, Marianne Boix[*], Catherine Azzaro-Pantel, Ludovic Montastruc, Serge Domenech

Laboratoire de Génie Chimique, UMR 5563, INP- ENSIACET, 4 Allée Emile Monso BP 84234, 31432 Toulouse Cedex 4, France
Marianne.Boix@ensiacet.fr

Abstract

A mathematical programming approach is developed to optimize the hydrogen supply chain in Midi-Pyrénées, the largest region of France. The aim of this study is to use a Geographical Information System (GIS) as a new tool for multi-criteria decision making after multiobjective optimization step. To have a more precise snapshot of the results obtained, the map is confronted with the one constructed with ArcGis® that contains all the geographic and demographic data of the region. This study focuses on the need to take into account such geographic data so that the various facilities can really be positioned: the results show that the production centers (small, medium and large) and the refueling stations are near as possible to the main road. This post-optimization step allows analyzing the feasible and the best solutions considering geographic criteria.

Keywords: hydrogen supply chain, MILP, spatial-based approach, geographic information system, multiobjective optimization

1. Introduction

With the rising energy consumption, the scarcity of resources and the acceleration of global warming, it becomes urgent to reduce greenhouse gas emissions, to improve energy efficiency and to propose new solutions for developing cleaner energy pathways. In 2010, transportation was the largest consumer (32 %) of the total energy in Europe (Eurostat. European Commission, 2012). Transportation uses fossil fuels releasing CO_2 in the atmosphere, whereas fuel cell electric vehicles powered by hydrogen are considered to emit zero harmful emission in the tank-to-well point of view. The development of the hydrogen supply chain (HSC) can be a promising solution but currently, the lack of hydrogen infrastructure has been reported as one of the most important barrier to develop the hydrogen economy (Hugo et al., 2005; Murthy Konda et al., 2011). Hydrogen can be obtained from many energy sources and can embed various production and storage technologies. The HSC considers the different transportation modes to link hydrogen demand to its supply in the refueling stations (Figure 1).

2. Literature review

A literature review shows that the most common approaches to design and model the HSC are the optimization methods through mathematical programming. In that context, Mixed Integer Linear Programming (MILP) formulations have been widely used (Almansoori and Shah, 2012). Several mono-objective optimization approaches have been developed or extended (Ball et al., 2006; Liu et al., 2012; Yang and Ogden, 2013).

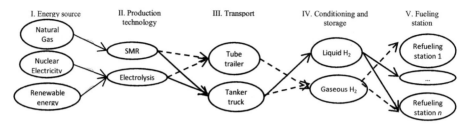

Figure 1. General framework of the hydrogen supply chain (HSC)

In these studies, the cost is the objective to be minimized. Multi-objective optimization studies are relatively scarce and criteria to be analyzed are based on economic and environmental performances (Guillén Gosálbez et al., 2010; Sabio et al., 2010; Han et al., 2013). Furthermore, Kim and Moon (2008) proposed a model that minimizes the total cost of the network and the total relative risk.

The Geographical Information System (GIS) is a package that can be usefully integrated with a modelling system for supply chain management. The ArcGis® software (developed by ESRI, Environmental Systems Research Institute) is a geographic information system used to organize, analyze and map spatial data. A typical GIS project contains an extensive database of geographical information, graphical capabilities of displaying maps with overlays pertaining to the company's supply chain activities. Literature review reveals that few researchers have used the spatial dimensions to build the infrastructure of hydrogen supply chain. Some examples include the study of Ball et al. (2006) who developed MOReHyS (Model for Optimization of Regional Hydrogen Supply), an approach that proposes an integration of geographical aspects by the GIS-based method in Germany. The authors identified the cost-optimal way for constructing and implementing an initial hydrogen supply infrastructure as well as possible trade-offs between hydrogen production and electricity generation. Johnson et al. (2008) also used ArcGis® for modelling regional hydrogen infrastructure deployment using detailed spatial data. They applied the methodology to a case study of a potential coal-based hydrogen transportation system in Ohio with CO_2 capture and storage (CCS). The objective was to optimize hydrogen infrastructure design for the entire state. More recently, Dagdougui (2011) highlighted that coupling a GIS component to a mathematical model could enhance and favour the exploitation of two different decision support systems.

In fact, the results of such an approach depend on national or regional specific conditions, with specific emphasis on local territorial constraints, such as transportation network, population, available resources or local policies. This work addresses this issue and is based on the development of a generic framework that can take into account the design of a HSC through multi-objective optimization with the use of a GIS as a tool for multi-criteria decision making after the optimization step.

3. Methodology and tools

The problem is formulated as a mixed-integer linear programming (MILP). The mathematical model previously published in De-León Almaraz et al. (2013) is solved within the GAMS 23.9 environment by using the CPLEX solver. In this study, three criteria are minimized: the daily cost of hydrogen, global warming potential (GWP) and a risk indicator. To take into account the multi-objective nature of the problem, the lexicographic strategy is adopted following the same method that has been implemented by Liu and Papageorgiou (2013). The territory is divided into districts in which the number, size and type of production and storage units have to be determined with the considered objective functions and constraints. The aim is to define the flow rate of hydrogen transported in the network. An average distance between the main cities is considered in the optimization model as an estimation of the delivery distances over the road network. The engineering-technical, financial and environmental data as well as demand are embedded in the model as input parameters. Once the optimization results are obtained, the districts where new facilities are to be established are known but the feasibility still depends on the geographic constraints.

ArcGis® is used to validate the best place for new hydrogen production plants and storage units. The energy sources map is produced using the GPS coordinates in Arc Map 10.2. Roads and geographical data maps are taken from the National Geographic Institute (IGN). The base layers to build the snapshot are: energy source location; initial conditioning centers and production plants; distances between main cities (national roads; intra-city delivery of hydrogen is not considered in this work) and refueling stations. The decision variables are the new production and storage sites as well as the flow rate links, following geographic constraints.

4. Case study

According to its geographic and administrative segmentation, Midi-Pyrénées region is divided into prefectures and sub-prefectures, representing 22 zones. This division has been used to obtain a realistic path between districts with the existence of major roads and to estimate the potential demand from regional statistics. Two time periods are analyzed (2020 and 2050). A deterministic demand of hydrogen for FCEV is considered, including fleets such as buses, private and light-good-vehicles and forklifts. Market demand scenarios selected for this project were based on previous studies (Mc Kinsey and Company, 2010).

It must be highlighted that for heavy transportation (e.g. tanker truck), only highways must be taken into account. In the proposed formulation, the hydrogen can be produced from an energy source e, delivered in a specific physical form i, such as liquid or gaseous, produced in a factory type involving different production technologies p, stored in a reservoir unit s and distributed by a transportation mode l from one district or grid g to another g' (with $g' \neq g$) in the time period t.

5. Multi-objective optimization results

In the lexicographic optimization, each time period (2020 and 2050) was treated for the three objective functions. The pay-off table was built and ε-constraint method was applied with 3 risk levels and 10 GWP points. The resulted configuration and results regarding the cost, the GWP and the risk are displayed in Figure 2. These networks use electrolysis as production process with wind and hydroelectricity as main energy sources.

In this first snapshot, new production and storage facilities are presented. The transportation flow among the districts is also indicated. It must be yet highlighted that the precise location within a district is not taken into account. In the next section, the snapshot of the same results is presented with the ArcGis® tool.

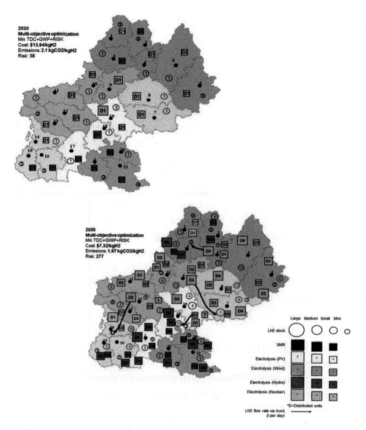

Figure 2. Cartographic representation of the optimal configuration for the HSC after multiobjective optimization at 2020 and 2050.

6. Midi-Pyrénées snapshot HSC with ArcGIS®

The results obtained from multi-objective optimization and previously displayed in Figure 2 are now treated with GIS use. The new snapshot is presented in Figure 3. The spatial analysis leads to localize very precisely the different components of the HSC. These new layers are built considering the geographic constraints for the studied region:

- the new production facilities are placed near the energy source and in the case of exporters, the production unit should be placed next to the main roads.
- for electrolysis plants using renewable energy, the facility must be close to the energy source and to the main road.
- for electrolysis plant using electricity with the French energy mix (based in nuclear energy with 78 % rate according the SimaPro 7.3 database), the main constraint is related to proximity to the refueling station to assure the on-site production.
- the storage centers (small, medium and large) are near to production plants, to the main road and refueling stations.

The distances considered before optimization do not necessarily correspond to the exact transportation links retained in ArcGIS® because in the pre-optimization step, data related to roads were obtained by Mappy®, with all kind of roads, and in the GIS

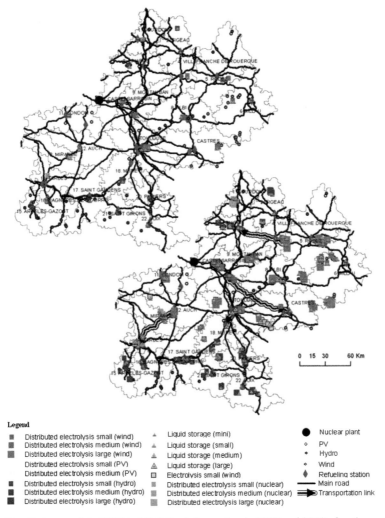

Figure 3. Detailed map of the HSC in Midi-Pyrénées region in 2020 and 2050 after the spatial analysis.

analysis, only motorways are taken into account. This change could vary the transportation cost, then, it is highly recommended to use ArcGis® before and after optimization.

7. Conclusions

This study focuses on coupling multi-objective optimization through a MILP with a GIS tool to take into account geographic data so that the various facilities can be really positioned after the HSC optimization. The GIS analysis represents a more precise snapshot compared to the locations resulting from the mathematical optimization results. From the optimization stage, the best option for the 2020 period is given with a cost of US\$ 13.94 per kg H_2 and a GWP of 2.1 kg CO_2-equiv per kg H_2 with a low risk level, for GWP and risk, very good results were found but, the cost may still be viewed as prohibitive. The spatial based approach by ArcGIS® allows analyzing the feasibility of the optimized HSC considering geographic criteria. The optimal solution has been proven to be realistic with the geographical analysis thus confirming the segmentation into districts following the first step of the methodology. The road network connects all the districts of the region, but the distances between the districts could vary from this approach where only motorways are considered and the distances obtained by Mappy where mainly roads for particular vehicles are displayed. Graphically, the spatial approach produces a more realistic snapshot that gives more information to the decision maker. The ArcGIS® tool highlights the need to consider real field constraints before and after optimization. Another perspective is to evaluate different region/district sizes to know if a more competitive cost could be reached.

References

A. Almansoori, N. Shah, 2012, Design and operation of a stochastic hydrogen supply chain network under demand uncertainty, Int. J. Hydrog. Energy 35, 3965-3977.

M. Ball, M. Wietschel, O. Rentz, 2006, Integration of a hydrogen economy into the German energy system: an optimising modelling approach, Int. J. Hydrog. Energy, 32, 1355–1368.

H. Dagdougui, 2011, Decision support systems for sustainable renewable energy systems and hydrogen logistics: modelling, control and risk analysis, UNIGE - Italy – CRC – MINES ParisTech- France.

S. De-León Almaraz, C. Azzaro-Pantel, L. Montastruc, L. Pibouleau, O.B. Senties, 2013, Assessment of mono and multi-objective optimization to design a hydrogen supply chain, Int. J. Hydrog. Energy, 38, 14121–14145.

Eurostat, European Commission, 2012, Energy Markets in the European Union in 2011, Belgium.

G. Guillén Gosálbez, F.D. Mele, I.E. Grossmann, 2010, A bi criterion optimization approach for the design and planning of hydrogen supply chains for vehicle use, AIChE J., 56, 650–667.

J.-H. Han, J.-H. Ryu, I.-B. Lee, 2013, Multi-objective optimization design of hydrogen infrastructures simultaneously considering economic cost, safety and CO2 emission, Chem. Eng. Res. Des., 91, 1427-1439.

A. Hugo, P. Rutter, S. Pistikopoulos, A. Amorelli, G. Zoia, 2005, Hydrogen infrastructure strategic planning using multi-objective optimization, Int. J. Hydrog. Energy, 30, 1523–1534.

N. Johnson, C. Yang, J. Ogden, 2008, A GIS-based assessment of coal-based hydrogen infrastructure deployment in the state of Ohio, Int. J. Hydrog. Energy, 33, 5287–5303.

J. Kim, I. Moon, 2008, Strategic design of hydrogen infrastructure considering cost and safety using multiobjective optimization, Int. J. Hydrog. Energy, 33, 5887–5896.

H. Liu, L.G. Papageorgiou, 2013, Multiobjective optimisation of production, distribution and capacity planning of global supply chains in the process industry. Omega, 41, 2, 369-382.

H. Liu, A. Almansoori, M. Fowler, A. Elkamel, 2012, Analysis of Ontario's hydrogen economy demands from hydrogen fuel cell vehicles, Int. J. Hydrog. Energy, 37, 8905–8916.

McKinsey & Company, 2010, A portfolio of power-trains for Europe: a fact-based analysis. The role of Battery Electric Vehicles, Plug-in Hybrids and Fuel Cell Electric Vehicles <ec.europa.eu/research/fch/pdf/a_portfolio_of_power_trains_for_europe_a_fact_based__analysis.pdf> Accessed on 20/02/2014.

N.V.S.N. Murthy Konda, N. Shah, N.P. Brandon, 2011, Optimal transition towards a large-scale hydrogen infrastructure for the transport sector: The case for the Netherlands, Int. J. Hydrog. Energy, 36, 4619–4635.

N. Sabio, A. Kostin, G. Guillén-Gosálbez, L. Jiménez, 2011, Holistic minimization of the life cycle environmental impact of hydrogen infrastructures using multi-objective optimization and principal component analysis, Int. J. Hydrog. Energy, 37, 5385–5405.

C. Yang, J.M. Ogden, 2013, Renewable and low carbon hydrogen for California – Modeling the long term evolution of fuel infrastructure using a quasi-spatial TIMES model, Int. J. Hydrog. Energy, 38, 4250–4265.

Jiří Jaromír Klemeš, Petar Sabev Varbanov and Peng Yen Liew (Editors)
Proceedings of the 24th European Symposium on Computer Aided Process Engineering – ESCAPE 24
June 15-18, 2014, Budapest, Hungary. Copyright © 2014 Elsevier B.V. All rights reserved.

Multi-Objective Meta-Heuristic Approach supported by an Improved Local Search Strategy for the Design and Planning of Supply Chain Networks

Nelson Chibeles-Martins[a,c], Tânia Pinto-Varela[a,b], Ana Paula Barbosa-Póvoa[b], A. Q. Novais[a,b]

[a]UAER/LNEG, Estrada do Paço do Lumiar, 22, 1649-038 Lisboa, Portugal
[b]CEG-IST, Instituto Superior Técnico, Universidade de Lisboa, A. Rovisco Pais, 1049-001 Lisboa, Portugal
[c]Centro de Matemática e Aplicações, Faculdade de Ciências e Tecnologia, Universidade Nova de Lisboa, Qta da Torre, 2829-516 Caparica, Portugal
npm@fct.unl.pt

Abstract

This paper explores alternative strategies for the Local Search mechanism of a Bi-Objective Simulated Annealing Algorithm. The algorithm is adapted to the planning and design of supply chain networks, where the Pareto Frontier approximations generated are compared with those based on an exact approach. Several strategies are proposed to improve the algorithm performance, which are exemplified through the solution of an example. The robustness and versatility of the proposed method is illustrated where a sensitivity analysis on two parameters of the model is performed: Final Product Demand and Facility Capacity.

Keywords: Multi-Objective; Meta-Heuristic; Simulated Annealing; Supply Chain Network.

1. Introduction

Traditionally the design and planning of supply chain networks (SCN) has been undertaken based an individual approach and applying only an economic objective, such as cost minimization or profit maximization. More recently, society is developing a higher level of awareness for environmental sustainability and the cost or profit are no longer the single concern, due to the high environmental impact that may result not only from implementing supply chain structures, but also from their operation. Additionally with the globalization phenomenon it is necessary to consider a worldwide spread of goods and hence the design and planning of SCN must be integrated, not only focusing the economic but also the environmental aspects. The most common approaches to this problem have been based on mathematical programming models (MILP and MINLP) (Papageorgiou, 2009), but the inclusion of several objective functions requires a multi-objective approach, which results in a high computational burden and, in many instances, when employing exact approaches the optimal solution cannot even be reached in a realistic time. In order to overcome this difficulty, Martins and Costa (2010) presented a modified Simulated Annealing algorithm for Bi-Objective problems with Economic and Environmental Objective Functions. Later on, Moncayo-Martinez et al. (2011) proposed a Meta-Heuristic for the design of SCN, excluding the planning perspective. Chibeles-Martins et al. (2012) presented a meta-heuristic approach, based on the Simulated Annealing (SA) methodology with a local search strategy, and attained promising results using a bi-objective approach (profit *vs* Eco-Indicator 99) applied to an instance previously solved with an exact method by Pinto-Varela et al (2011). These consisted of a high number of efficient solutions, organized into a Pareto Frontier (PF), where a comparison with the exact Pareto's frontier was made. The two sets of data were tight in both tails of the PF, but degradation of the SA solution in its central zone was observed (Figure 1).

Since this is the region of the PF most likely to contain the solutions offering the best trade-off between the economic and environment objectives, along with a higher SCN topology flexibility, further improvement is required in order to produce an expedient, exploratory tool for decision making. To meet this challenge, in this work several different methods are analyzed at handling a bi-objective approach, aiming at the improvement and control of the local search procedure of SA. A supply chain network case study is used as a test bed and its bi-objective optimum design and planning undertaken. The results obtained are compared with those from an exact approach, through the Pareto Frontier. A sensitivity analysis is performed over two selected parameters in order to reinforce the robustness and flexibility of the methodology.

2. Problem Statement and Modelling framework

Assuming an uniform discretization of time, the problem in study can be summarized as follows. Given: a fixed time horizon; a set of product recipes; a set of markets in which products are available to customers and their nominal demands and prices; a set of geographical sites for locating facilities, warehouses and distribution centres; a set of technologies for product manufacturing; lower and upper bounds for the capacity of facilities, warehouses/distribution centres and suppliers; fixed and variable costs associated to the setting up of facilities, warehouses and distribution centres; materials transportation; operational costs; raw-material costs; diesel, electricity consumptions and all the necessary environmental specifications. Determine: the facilities to be opened; the technology to be selected; the facilities, warehouses and distributions centres design (i.e. capacities); the amount of final products to be sold in different markets and the materials to be transported. So as to balance the maximization of the supply chain profit, while simultaneously considering the environmental impact minimization. The meta-heuristic approach explored in this paper is based on the

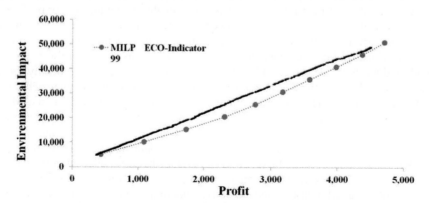

Figure 1. Pareto Frontier obtained with exact methods vs. SA before improvement.

Simulated Annealing algorithm proposed by Kirkpatrick (1983) and Cěrny. (1985). However, several adaptations were necessary in order to accommodate the bi-objective approach, due to the fact that the original algorithm was mono-objective. The proposed algorithm is initialized with a solution generated with a greedy constructive heuristic and is subsequently improved iteratively. Differently from the classical SA, the proposed SA algorithm has a multi-start procedure that allows the exploration of different regions of the efficient frontier. Whenever the stop criterion is verified the algorithm restarts, reinitializing all parameters and generating a new initial solution. The restart procedure is repeated several times and the number of restarts is determined empirically after a sensitivity analysis.

In what follows, s_i represents the current solution, s'_i the randomly generated neighbor solution, $f_1(s)$ and $f_2(s)$, respectively, the Profit and the Eco-Indicator 99 assessed for solution s, Pac the probability of accepting a neighbor solution, and $T1_i$ and $T2_i$ the temperatures associated respectively to objective functions $f_1(s)$ and $f_2(s)$ at iteration i. The algorithm considers the symmetric values of the Eco-Indicator function, so both functions have the same optimization direction. The algorithm generates a neighbor solution s' using one of four possible neighborhood moves: a) a small increase or decrease in one final product demand; b) a technological process being processed in a factory is delayed or anticipated 1 time unit; c) two equivalent technological processes being processed in different factories are agglomerated in just one facility or one process is divided in two different processes, which are simultaneously processed in different facilities; d) the location of a facility is changed.

During the algorithm run all non-dominated solutions are stored in the Pareto array. These solutions are sorted, from the highest to the lowest profit values. Due to the fact that the problem is bi-objective, all solutions in the Pareto array will be automatically sorted accordingly to f_2. In every iteration the algorithm verifies if the solution s'_i is non-dominated, comparing it with the solutions stored in the Pareto array. If necessary, this solution s'_i is added to the array, which is corrected and re-sorted using an Insertion Sort Algorithm. An independent procedure evaluates if solution s'_i is accepted as the current solution. The probability of acceptance, P_{ac}, depends on the adopted Local Search Strategy. Both temperatures are decreased every k[th] iteration, according to the following expression: $T_{k+1}=\alpha T_k$, where α is a constant close to *1*. The algorithm restarts when both $T1_i$ and $T2_i$ are smaller than a value assumed close to zero. Temperatures $T1_i$ and $T2_i$ are reset to their initial values and a new initial solution is randomly generated.

3. Case Study and Local Search Strategies

The proposed strategies are tested on a case study that was presented and explored using an exact approach by Pinto-Varela et al (2011). As it was mentioned above, in every iteration the algorithm generates a neighbour solution s'_i and the Local Search (LS) strategy defines the probability of acceptance of a worst solution, Pac. Different strategies will produce very different Pareto frontiers. Classic SA methodology, that uses only one objective function f, proposes the following:

$$Pac = \begin{cases} 1 & , f(s'i) > f(si) \\ e^{\frac{f(s'i) - f(si)}{Ti}} & , \quad \text{otherwise} \end{cases} \tag{1}$$

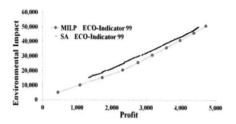

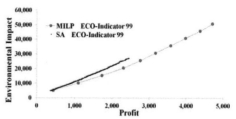

Figure 2. LS using OF Profit   Figure 3. LS using OF Enveronmental Impact

Figure 3 and Figure 2 illustrate the Pareto frontiers (PF) obtained when a LS strategy uses only one of the Objective Functions at a time. Both strategies produce inadequate approximations in the middle region of the exact PF, as the approximations are skewed towards the respective optimal values. Therefore, strategies that combine both objective functions had to be explored. The following strategy was to include always both OF, simultaneously, into the calculus of *Pac*, as shown on Equation (2). Unfortunately this Strategy kept the LS exploring only the middle region of PF, as can be seen in Figure 4. However, a LS Strategy that intends to reach the full range of the exact PF has to include the three approaches at once in an algorithm run.

$$Pac = \begin{cases} e^{\frac{f1(S'i)-f1(Si)}{Ti}} & ,f1(S'i) \leq f1(Si) \wedge f2(S'i) > f2(Si) \\ e^{\frac{f2(S'i)-f2(Si)}{Ti}} & ,f1(S'i) > f1(Si) \wedge f2(S'i) \leq f2(Si) \\ Min\left(e^{\frac{f1(S'i)-f1(Si)}{Ti}}, e^{\frac{f2(S'i)-f2(Si)}{Ti}}\right) & ,f1(S'i) \leq f1(Si) \wedge f2(S'i) \leq f2(Si) \\ 1 & otherwise \end{cases} \quad (2)$$

Due to the multi-start nature of the algorithm, it is a simple procedure to change the way *Pac* is computed every time the algorithm restarts on a different region of the Feasible Region, with a new Initial Solution. Three new Strategies are presented: A, B and C. Figure 5 presents a PF obtained with Strategy A, where 1/3 of restarts with LS are controlled by Profit, 1/3 controlled by Environmental Impact and the remaining restarts controlled by both OF, using Equation (2). The algorithm produced an approximated PF with a range similar to the exact one, and there was a slightly improvement of the tightness around the central zone. Strategy B is similar to Strategy A, but the two differ on *Pac* calculation, in that LS is controlled by both OF presented in Equation (3). For a given pair of Solutions *Si* and *S'i*, *Pac* calculated with Strategy B is higher or equal than *Pac* computed with Strategy A, meaning that worse *S'i* are accepted more often than in the case of *Si*. The tightness between the two data sets around the central zone seems similar to the one obtained with the previous Strategy and shown in Figure 5.

$$Pac = \begin{cases} Max\left(e^{\frac{f1(S'i)-f1(Si)}{Ti}}, e^{\frac{f2(S'i)-f2(Si)}{Ti}}\right) & ,f1(S'i) \leq f1(Si) \wedge f2(S'i) \leq f2(Si) \\ equal\ to\ (2) & ,otherwise \end{cases} \quad (3)$$

Finally, a different approach is used in Strategy C. It has the same multi-start mechanism, with 1/3 of restarts dedicated to each one of the OF, similarly to the previous two Strategies, but the third restarts, which includes both OF simultaneously, has the LS controlled alternately by only one of the OF for a fixed number of iterations. *Pac* is calculated with Equation (1). Strategy C results are shown in Figure 7, where the LS procedure shifts the controlling OF every other 5000 iterations. The improvement of

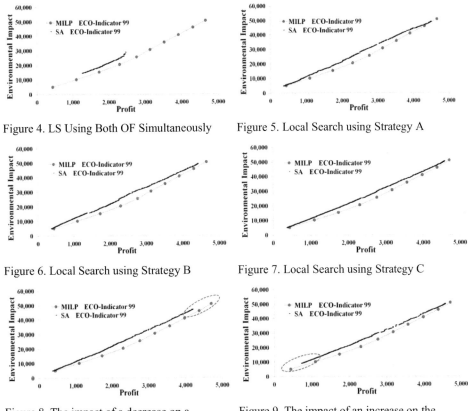

Figure 4. LS Using Both OF Simultaneously

Figure 5. Local Search using Strategy A

Figure 6. Local Search using Strategy B

Figure 7. Local Search using Strategy C

Figure 8. The impact of a decrease on a
Facility Capacity

Figure 9. The impact of an increase on the
demand of a Final Product

the tightness between the two data sets is visually noticeable and therefore Strategy C is
considered the most promising of the three strategies.

4. Algorithm Versatility

The algorithm versatility provides a tool for evaluating the impact of unexpected
fluctuations in the model parameters on the overall performance of the SCN. Figure 8
compares the result of an algorithm run considering a decrease in the capacity of a
Facility, against the original PF. Solutions with the highest profits are found to be
rejected by the algorithm in order to accommodate the loss of the production capacity.
The impact of the production demand increase on the final product is shown in Figure 9.
As expected, solutions with the lowest Environmental Impact were not able to satisfy
the new demand values and were ignored by the algorithm. These two analyses were
performed using Strategy C for the LS mechanism.

5. Conclusions

It this paper the authors propose several Local Search Strategies with the objective of
improving the performance of a Bi-Objective Simulated Annealing Algorithm adapted
to the planning and design of supply chain networks. The PF resulting from these
strategies were compared between each other and with a PF obtained through an exact

approach and the most promising strategy identified. The robustness and versatility of the proposed methodology is illustrated through a Sensitivity Analysis on two parameters, namely facility capacity and final product demand.

Acknowledgements

This work was partially supported by the FCT (Portuguese Foundation for Science and Technology) through PEst-OE/MAT/UI0297/2011 (CMA). The authors also gratefully acknowledge the support of the Portuguese National Science Foundation through the projects PTDC/SEN-ENR/102869/2008 and EXPL/EMS-GIN/1930/2013.

References

N. Chibeles-Martins, T. Pinto-Varela, A. P. Barbosa-Póvoa, A. Q. Novais, 2012, A Simulated Annealing Algorithm for the Design and Planning of Supply Chains with Economic and Environmental Objectives, Computer Aided Chemical Engineering, 30, 21-25.

F. Martins, C. A. V. Costa, 2010, Multi-Objective Optimization with Economic and Environmental Objective Functions using Modified Simulated Annealing, Computer Aided Process Engineering, 28, 919-924.

L. A. Moncayo-Martinez, D. Z. Zhang, 2011, Multi-objective ant colony optimisation: a meta-heuristic approach to supply chain design, International Journal of Production Economics, 131, 1, 407–420.

L. G. Papageorgiou, 2009, Supply chain optimisation for the process industries: Advances and opportunities, Computers and Chemical Engineering, 33, 12, 1931-1938.

T. Pinto-Varela, A. P. Barbosa-Povoa and A. Q. Novais, 2011, Bi-objective optimization approach to the design and planning of a supply chain: economic versus environmental performance, Computers and Chemical Engineering, 35, 1454-1468.

Jiří Jaromír Klemeš, Petar Sabev Varbanov and Peng Yen Liew (Editors)
Proceedings of the 24th European Symposium on Computer Aided Process Engineering – ESCAPE 24
June 15-18, 2014, Budapest, Hungary. Copyright © 2014 Elsevier B.V. All rights reserved.

Large-Scale Biorefinery Supply Network – Case Study of the European Union

Lidija Čuček,[a*] Mariano Martín,[b] Ignacio E. Grossmann,[c] Zdravko Kravanja[a]

[a]*Faculty of Chemistry and Chemical Engineering, University of Maribor, Smetanova ul. 17, Maribor, Slovenia*
[b]*Department of Chemical Engineering, University of Salamanca, Salamanca, Spain*
[c]*Department of Chemical Engineering, Carnegie Mellon University, Pittsburgh, USA*
lidija.cucek@um.si

Abstract

This contribution focuses on those renewable sources used within the transportation sector. As in the short-term only biofuels from biomass might provide an alternative that can be implemented (Martín and Grossmann, 2013), this contribution deals with biofuels production. A generic multi-period model is applied for the efficient synthesis of large-scale biorefinery supply networks. This model, which was previously developed by the authors (Čuček et al., 2013), is upgraded using different model reduction techniques (Lam et al., 2011) in order to be applied cross-regionally throughout the European Union (EU). Several first, second, and third generations of biofuel production technologies are considered (Čuček et al., 2013), and applied to a case study of the EU. The results show that miscanthus and algae are particularly promising raw materials for producing biofuels capable to economically substitute significantly more than 10 % of fossil fuels for transportation at the EU level.

Keywords: Biorefinery supply network, Biofuels, Model reduction, Multi-period synthesis, European Union.

1. Introduction

Renewable-based energies have attracted great attention due to shortages, non-sustainability, negative impacts on the environment and the increasing prices of fossil-based energy resources. Governments across the world have set mandatory renewable energy targets for increasing the share of renewables within the total consumption of energy. In particular, the EU has set binding targets by 2020: i) 20 % share of energy from renewable sources, ii) 20 % improvement in energy efficiency, iii) greenhouse gas emissions reduction to 20 % below the 1990 level (European Commission, 2009a), and iv) 10 % share of renewable sources regarding transportation (European Commission, 2009b).

In this study, a general multi-period mixed-integer linear programming (MILP) model for the synthesis of biorefinery supply networks at the continental level is synthesised. Several biofuels production technologies are considered including first, second, and third generations of biofuels – bioethanol, biodiesel, hydrogen, Fischer-Tropsch (FT)-diesel, and green gasoline (Martín and Grossmann, 2013). The main aim of this work is to compare these technologies for defining the most economically-efficient supply network at the continental level, by considering regional-specific conditions satisfying biofuels demands. These technologies, previously modelled and optimised by the authors, are embedded within the biorefinery supply network as surrogate models. In order to solve the corresponding MILP models with several millions of equations and constraints, different model reduction techniques (Lam et al., 2011) are used. The proposed model is applied cross-regionally during the case study of the EU, by exploring EU regionally-specific characteristics for the production and supply of biofuels and food. Economically-optimal solutions are obtained by accounting for the optimal planning of raw materials harvesting and supply, and biofuels and food production. The results show that the extent of renewable energy consumption within the transportation sector is more than satisfied within the EU whilst also satisfying food demand.

2. Methodology

2.1. Supply Network Synthesis

A four-layer (L1-L4) supply chain superstructure was formulated as a supply network superstructure for synthesising an optimally-integrated biorefinery system. The supply network contains sets of potential locations of: i) harvesting sites at supply zones at L1, ii) collection and pre-processing facilities at L2, iii) biorefineries at L3, and iv) end-users at L4, including logistics (Čuček et al., 2013). This model is an extension of the supply network synthesis (Čuček et al., 2010) to a multi-period optimisation model of a heat-integrated biorefinery supply network (Čuček et al., 2013) and accounts also for reduction of model size (Lam et al., 2011) in order to be applied cross-regionally. A set of biomass feedstocks was defined that can be converted into biofuels: food-based crops (corn grain, wheat), agricultural residues (corn stover, wheat straw), energy crops (miscanthus), wood residues (forest thinning), waste cooking oil and algae. Feedstocks from each zone are shipped to collection and pre-processing facilities to be dried and stored before shipping to the biorefineries. At the pre-processing facilities algal oil extraction is considered. At potential plant locations different technologies (Martín and Grossmann, 2013) can be applied for the conversion of biomass into biofuels and other by-products: i) dry-grind process (corn and wheat grain to bioethanol), ii) gasification and further catalytic synthesis, iii) gasification and further syngas fermentation (corn stover, wheat straw, miscanthus and forest thinning to bioethanol and hydrogen), iv) FT-diesel and green gasoline production (corn stover, wheat straw, miscanthus and forest thinning to FT-diesel and green gasoline), v) hydrogen production (corn stover, wheat straw, miscanthus and forest thinning to hydrogen), vi) biochemical process for lignocellulosic biomass (miscanthus to bioethanol), and vii) biodiesel production (algae and waste cooking oil to biodiesel). Using these technologies, biofuels such as bioethanol, biodiesel, hydrogen, FT-diesel, and green gasoline can be produced. Products such as ethanol, hydrogen or the excess of energy can be reused within the network. Food-based products can either be directly used at demand locations without transforming them to biofuels, or transformed in plants into biofuels and by-products in the plants.

2.2. Development of multi-period model and reduction of model size

In order to select the appropriate technologies for the production of biofuels, an initial pre-screening of technologies is performed and after that the detailed synthesis of individual technology's flowsheets (see contribution by Martin and Grossmann, 2013). Furthermore the surrogate models are developed based on conversion factors and cost correlations. The data from the detailed models are inserted as black-boxes into the renewable supply and demand network. The mathematical model (see Supplementary material by Čuček et al., 2013) includes mass and energy balances, production and conversion constraints and transportation, operating, storage and investment cost correlations, and the main objective of maximising the profit. In order to reduce the mixed-integer non-linear programming (MINLP) problem into a linear one (MILP), linearisation of nonlinear investment terms is performed by a piecewise linear approximation. Furthermore, in order to apply the model to the case study of the EU, the size of the model was reduced using various model reduction techniques, such as: i) reducing the connectivity within a biomass supply chain network (after Lam et al., 2011), ii) eliminating unnecessary variables and constraints (after Lam et al., 2011), iii) neglecting the heat loss, iv) neglecting heat distribution cost, and v) assuming that no utility is sold.

3. Demonstration Case Study

A multi-period MILP optimisation model of a heat-integrated biorefinery's supply network has been developed for the case study of a large region – the EU. The EU is divided into 138 zones, see Fig. 1. It is also assumed that at the centres of each zone there are possible locations for collection, storage, and intermediate pre-processing centres, biorefineries, and demand.

The model consists of approximately 1,150,000 single equations, 24,220,000 single variables, and 27,900 binary variables and can be solved in around 2,000 CPU-s with an optimality gap of maximum 5 % using a Server with 244 GB of RAM and processor Inter® Xeon® CPU E5-2670 0 @ 2.60 GHz (2 processors). The problem is formulated as an MILP in the modelling system GAMS 23.6 (GAMS Development Corporation, 2010) using a GUROBI 4.0 solver.

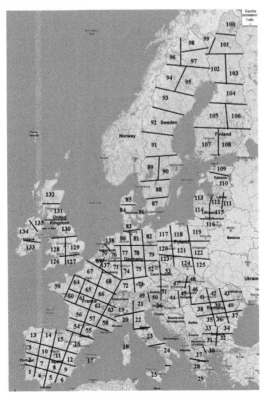

Figure 1. EU divided into 136 zones. The map is taken from Google Maps (2013)

Two different cases are considered where the production of biofuels and food can be greater than or equal to the demand for food – corn and wheat grain (≥ 100 %) and biofuels (≥ 10 %). The first case is when these restrictions are valid at the EU level (EU level in Table 1), whilst during the second case for each country level (Country level in Table 1). "EU level" means that the demand for transportation fuels is specified for the entire EU – 86,804 kt/y for gasoline and 196,896 kt/y for diesel. For the case "Country level", the demand for transportation fuels is specified for each country. 10 % of fuel consumption in regards to calorific value should be achieved by biofuels, at the EU level in general (first case) and in each country (second case). The demand for corn and wheat grain is taken from Cummans (2012), the demand for diesel from The World Bank (2013a), and the demand for gasoline fuel consumption from The World Bank (2013b). All the other data are taken from Čuček et al. (2013).

It is assumed that up to 10 % of the total area of each zone can be devoted to biofuels in order to be on the safe side regarding biodiversity loss. The restrictions for the model are the availability of cultivation areas for biofuels, maximum and minimum capacities for the plants, and also the required demand has to be at least satisfied. The main results from these two scenarios are presented in Table 1.

From the results it can be seen that the profit is significantly higher for those cases when the demand for biofuels and food is satisfied at the EU level, and not within each country. Thus, the demand for biofuels and food should be satisfied at the EU level. It can also be seen that the more profitable solutions are those using crop residues,

Table 1. Main results from optimisation

	EU level	Country level
Profit	231,831 M$/y	218,327 M$/y
Raw materials	Corn grain (83,687 kt/y)	Corn grain (83,687 kt/y)
	Corn stover (50,212 kt/y)	Corn stover (50,212 kt/y)
	Wheat (125,773 kt/y)	Wheat (125,773 kt/y)
	Wheat straw (128,289 kt/y)	Wheat straw (128,289 kt/y)
	Algae (66,310 kt/y)	Algae (66,310 kt/y)
	Miscanthus (263,714 kt/y)	Miscanthus (263,405 kt/y)
	Waste cooking oil (3,834 kt/y)	Waste cooking oil (750 kt/y)
Technologies	Biochemical conversion	Biochemical conversion
	Gasification and fermentation	Gasification and fermentation
	FT-diesel and green gasoline	FT-diesel and green gasoline
	Transesterification of oils with methanol	Transesterification of oils with methanol and ethanol
Investment cost	117,535 M$	127,117 M$
Production cost	124,264 M$/y	132,713 M$/y
Transportation cost	25,982 M$/y	34,581 M$/y
Water consumption	208,031 kt/y	209,136 kt/y
Biofuels	Bioethanol (91,194 kt/y)	Bioethanol (92,373 kt/y)
	Biodiesel (35,510 kt/y)	Biodiesel (32,549 kt/y)
	Hydrogen (7,285 kt/y)	Hydrogen (7,376 kt/y)
	Green gasoline (6,353 kt/y)	Green gasoline (6,157 kt/y)
	FT-diesel (23,901 kt/y)	FT-diesel (23,160 kt/y)
Gasoline and diesel substitution	Gasoline substitution (73.3 %)	Gasoline substitution (73.9 %)
	Diesel substitution (28.4 %)	Diesel substitution (26.7 %)
Solution time	1,249 CPU-s	1,978 CPU-s
Optimality gap	0.9 %	3.5 %

miscanthus, and algal biomass as raw materials. The selected technologies are biochemical conversion, gasification and further syngas fermentation, FT-diesel and green gasoline production, and the transesterification of oils with methanol. At the EU level more diesel is substituted and less gasoline when compared to the country level.

Figures 2a-d show the consumption of raw materials within the EU in the optimal scenario. As it can be seen, most of the corn grain for food and stover by gasification routes for bioethanol, hydrogen, FT-diesel and green gasoline is grown in southern countries, in Austria and in Hungary, wheat grain for food and straw by gasification routes for bioethanol, hydrogen, FT-diesel and green gasoline in northern countries, in Romania, Bulgaria and in Hungary, algae for biodiesel southern countries, and miscanthus by gasification and biochemical routes for bioethanol, hydrogen, FT-diesel

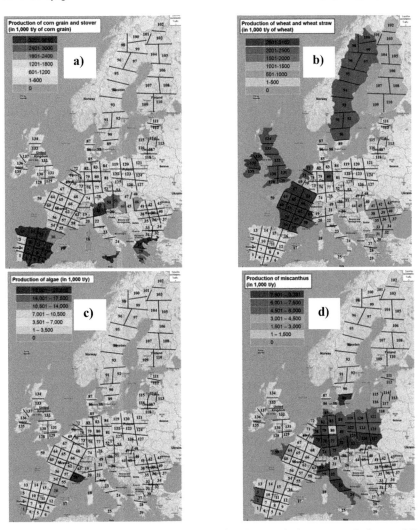

Figure 2. Consumption of a) corn grain and stover, b) wheat and wheat straw, c) algae and d) miscanthus

and green gasoline in Portugal, Germany, Slovenia, Italy, Denmark, Estonia, Latvia, Lithuania, Poland, Czech Republic, Slovakia and in south Sweden.

4. Conclusions and Future Work

The general MILP model for synthesis of biorefineries supply networks producing biofuels and food has been applied on a larger-scale level during a case study of the EU. It was shown that especially miscanthus and algae are promising raw materials for producing biofuels, as substitutes for gasoline and diesel. It was also shown that directives regarding biofuels production can be implemented economically by satisfying food demand within the EU by using a maximum 10 % of the area. Significantly more than 10 % of fuel demand for transportation can be achieved by biofuels. In the future, uncertainties related to prices and fluctuations in supply and demand will be dealt with. Also, direct, indirect, and total environmental impacts will be evaluated, and the proposed model extended to a multi-objective multi-period optimisation model under uncertainty. Finally, the synthesis should be extended to cover the time-span over the next decades.

Acknowledgments

The authors acknowledge the financial support from Slovenian Research Agency (Program No. P2-0032) and Centre for Advanced Process Decision-making.

References

J. Cummans, 2012, The Surging Demographic Trends Behind Grain Investing. <commodityhq.com/2012/the-surging-demographic-trends-behind-grain-investing/>. Accessed on 19/02/2013.

L. Čuček, H. L. Lam, J. J. Klemeš, P. S. Varbanov, Z. Kravanja, 2010, Synthesis of regional networks for the supply of energy and bioproducts, Clean Technologies and Environmental Policy, 12, 635-645.

L. Čuček, M. Martín, I.E. Grossmann, Z. Kravanja, 2013, Multi-period synthesis of optimally-integrated biomass and bioenergy supply network, Computers and Chemical Engineering, DOI: 10.1016/j.compchemeng.2014.02.020.

European Commission, 2009a, Directive 2009/28/EC of the European Parliament and of the Council of 23 April 2009 on the promotion of the use of energy from renewable sources and amending and subsequently repealing Directives 2001/77/EC and 2003/30/EC, L140/16-62, Official Journal of the European Union.

European Commission, 2009b, Directive 2009/29/EC of the European Parliament and of the Council of 23 April 2009 amending Directive 2003/87/EC so as to improve and extend the greenhouse gas emission allowance trading scheme of the Community, L140/63-87, Official Journal of the European Union.

GAMS Development Corporation, 2010. GAMS — A User's Guide. Washington, DC, US.

Google Maps, 2013, <maps.google.com/> Accessed on 16/10/2013.

H.L. Lam, J.J. Klemeš, Z. Kravanja, 2011, Model-size reduction techniques for large-scale biomass production and supply networks, Energy, 36, 8, 4599-4608.

M. Martín, I.E. Grossmann, 2013, On the systematic synthesis of sustainable biorefineries, Industrial & Engineering Chemistry Research, 52, 9, 3044-3064.

The World Bank, 2013a. Road sector diesel fuel consumption per capita (kg of oil equivalent). <data.worldbank.org/indicator/IS.ROD.DESL.PC/countries/1W-EU-US?display=graph>. Accessed on 19/02/2013.

The World Bank, 2013b. Road sector gasoline fuel consumption per capita (kg of oil equivalent). <data.worldbank.org/indicator/IS.ROD.SGAS.PC/countries/1W-EU-US?display=graph>. Accessed on 19/02/2013.

Jiří Jaromír Klemeš, Petar Sabev Varbanov and Peng Yen Liew (Editors)
Proceedings of the 24th European Symposium on Computer Aided Process Engineering – ESCAPE 24
June 15-18, 2014, Budapest, Hungary.

Optimal Chemical Product Design via Fuzzy Optimisation based Inverse Design Techniques

Lik Yin Ng, Nishanth G. Chemmangattuvalappil*, Denny K. S. Ng

*Department of Chemical and Environmental Engineering/
Centre of Excellence for Green Technologies, University of Nottingham Malaysia,
Broga Road, Semenyih 43500, Malaysia*
Nishanth.C@nottingham.edu.my

Abstract

While designing optimal products using molecular design technique for a specific application, product superiority is the only factor considered during design. It is noted that the effectiveness of this approach is highly dependent on the model accuracy which represents product robustness. Thus, to design an optimal product efficiently, the effect of property prediction uncertainty has to be addressed. This paper presents a systematic methodology for the design of optimum molecules used in chemical processes by considering both product superiority and robustness. Fuzzy optimisation approach is incorporated into inverse design techniques for this purpose. Inverse product design techniques utilize molecular design techniques to predict the molecular structure of the product from the target properties. Optimal solution is selected based on how much the solution satisfied the criteria of product superiority and robustness. The effectiveness of the developed methodology is shown by a case study on fungicide design, where the designed fungicide possess superior attributes than the conventionally used fungicide.

Keywords: Product design, inverse design techniques, fuzzy optimisation, property prediction uncertainties.

1. Introduction

1.1. Chemical product design via inverse design techniques

Chemical product design is the process of choosing the optimal product to be made for a specific application (Cussler and Moggridge, 2001). Most of the time, functionality of a product are defined in terms of physical properties rather than chemical structure of the product. Hence, chemical product design can be considered as an inverse property prediction problem where the preferred attributes of the product are represented in terms of physical properties (Gani and O'Connell, 2001). As product specifications are often extracted from customer needs, it is required to translate qualitative attributes into quantitative parameters in order to design a product (Achenie et al., 2003). The process of representing product attributes by using measurable parameters is often done by Computer Aided Molecular Design (CAMD) techniques. CAMD techniques are important for product design because they are able to predict and design molecules with a given set of properties. At present, most CAMD techniques use group contribution (GC) methods and topological indices (TI) to verify whether the generated molecules possess the specified set of desirable properties. Inverse design involves identification of molecules from the property targets of the product. Since different property prediction models utilize different calculation methods to predict chemical properties, there is no uniformity among these different types of models. Hence, it is difficult to use different TIs in inverse design problem.

Visco et al. (2002) developed a descriptor known as molecular signature descriptors. The signature is a systematic coding system of atom types and the signature of a molecule can be obtained as a linear combination of its atomic signatures. For a molecular graph G and an atom x of the graph, the atomic signature of height h of x can be represented as a sub graph containing all atoms that are at a distance h from x. The relationship between a TI and its signature can be represented as a dot product between the vector of the occurrence number of the atomic signature of height h and the vector of TI values computed for each root of those atomic signatures:

$$TI(G) = k \cdot {}^h\alpha_G \cdot TI(root({}^h\Sigma)) \tag{1}$$

here, ${}^h\alpha_G$ is the occurrence number of each signature of height h and $TI(root\,({}^h\Sigma))$ is the TI values for each signature root. Since all the molecular operators can be formed by molecular signatures, property models based on different topological indices and GC methods can be represented on the same property platform. Molecular signature descriptors are used in the optimisation model to solve the inverse problem by obtaining the molecular structures that targets the optimum properties.

1.2. Property prediction uncertainty and product optimisation

Typically, optimal product is the one which possesses most optimal property(s). This product superiority defines the quality of the product. Hence, in inverse property prediction, the product with optimal predicted property(s) will be regarded as optimal product. These property predictions are done by using property models. However, the effectiveness and usefulness of property model in identifying the optimum molecule rely heavily on the accuracy of the property prediction models. These models are usually developed from regression analysis which estimates the relationships between the property and the TI/groups from GC that correlate with each other. The accuracy of these property prediction models are expressed in terms of correlation coefficient (r^2) and standard deviation (σ). Traditionally, the accuracy of property models is used only as an indicator of the model ability in predicting the properties or the expected error that the model might produce. Abildskov et al. (2013) utilied GC methods in solvent screening for biocatalytic systems. Samudra and Sahinidis (2013) utilised GC^+ model for properties estimation in designing heat-transfer media components. It is noted that the identification of optimal solution is directly affected by the predefined product target ranges, which can be highly impinged by property model accuracy. Hence, the optimal solution for a design problem might differ accordingly to the accuracy of property model. In order to produce the optimal product by using inverse property prediction method, the effect caused by the imprecision/uncertainty of the property models have to be taken into consideration. This will be termed as product robustness in this work. In this work, by utilizing inverse design techniques, both product superiority and product robustness will be playing important roles in identifying the optimal molecular structure that possess optimal product properties.

2. Methodology

2.1. Signature based molecular design

To apply signature-based algorithm in designing a product that meets customers' requirements, signature-based algorithm developed by Chemmangattuvalappil et al. (2010) is adapted. Properties models which represent product properties can be expressed as a function of TI, θ as shown in Eq.(2):

$$\theta = f(TI) \tag{2}$$

By using Eqs.(1) and (2), property operator can be utilised to estimate the property of molecules. Property operators are functions of original properties which follow linear mixing rules. It can be obtained as the summation of products between number of occurrence and TI values for each signature, as represented as shown in Eq.(3):

$$\psi(P) = \sum_{i=1}^{N} x_i TI(root(^h\Sigma)) \tag{3}$$

where $\psi(P)$ is the property operator for property p and x_i is the occurrence for each signature. This algorithm identifies the product molecular structure that meets the target properties, V_{ip}. This can be written as two inequality expressions (Qin et al., 2004):

$$v_{ip}^L \leq V_{ip} \leq v_{ip}^U \qquad i = 1, 2, \ldots; \quad p = P \tag{4}$$

where the target property range is bounded by lower (v_{ip}^L) and upper (v_{ip}^U) constraints. Other than property constraints, structural constraints are imposed to ensure that a complete molecular structure can be formed from a collection of molecular signatures.

2.2. Fuzzy optimisation based inverse design techniques

This work incorporates both the effect of product superiority and robustness into the product design problem, where an optimal product is the product which fulfills these two criteria. Hence, it is required to identify a solution under the fuzzy environment of these both criteria. This can be formulated as fuzzy optimisation model. Fuzzy optimisation approach is a mathematical programming technique that is able to select the preferred alternative on a set of constraints under fuzzy environment (Bellman and Zadeh, 1970). Zimmermann (1978) extended the approach to address linear programming problems which involve multi-objectives. Tan et al., (2012) developed a fuzzy optimisation approach to optimise biomass production and trade under resourse availability and environmental footprint constraints. Recently, Zhang et al. (2014) utilised the approach for agricultural water quality management. This work presents an inverse design techniques incorporated with fuzzy optimisation approach. In the first step, property models that relate the properties of the chemicals to their molecular have been identified. These properties that are based on TI or GC methods are transformed to their signature equivalents. Upper and lower bounds for each of the properties to be optimized are then identified. To maximise the product superiority, trade-off between properties to be optimized is done by introducing a degree of satisfaction, λ which is bounded within the interval of 0 to 1. Each property to be optimised is assumed as linear function bounded by predefined fuzzy range (upper and lower limits), as shown below:

$$\lambda_{sp} - \frac{v_p^U - V_p}{v_p^U - v_p^L} \leq 0 \tag{5}$$

$$\lambda_{sp} - \frac{V_p - v_p^L}{v_p^U - v_p^L} \leq 0 \tag{6}$$

where λ_{sp} is the degree of satisfaction for product superiority, V_p is the value, v_p^U and v_p^L is the upper and lower bounds for property p. Eq.(5) is used for property to be minimised while Eq.(6) is used for property to be maximised. For property to be minimised, as lower values are desired, when the property approaches the lower bound, λ_{sp} approaches 1; when the property approaches the upper bound, λ_{sp} approaches 0. Vice versa applies to property to be maximised where higher values are preferred.

To maximise the product robustness, the effect of property model accuracy is taken into account. Product target range is divided into 3 different regions namely certain region (CR), lower uncertain region (LUR) and upper uncertain region (UUR). LUR is the region below the CR while UUR is the region above it. In certain region, it is assured that the property predicted by property model will fall within the region after taking the allowance of property prediction uncertainty. In uncertain regions, there is a possibility that the predicted property will within the region after the effect of property prediction uncertainty is considered. The lower and upper bounds for these regions can be obtained by adding and subtracting the standard deviation for that property model from v_p^L and v_p^U. Lower uncertain region is bounded by lower lower bound (v_p^{LL}) and lower upper bound (v_p^{LU}); certain region is constraint by v_p^{LU} and upper lower bound (v_p^{UL}) accordingly; upper uncertain region is bounded by v_p^{UL} and upper upper bound (v_p^{UU}). This is summarised in Table 1.

The nearer the property falls from the certain region, the better it is in terms of property robustness. This can be expressed and optimised by utilizing two-sided fuzzy optimisation, as described mathematically by the following equations:

$$\lambda_{rp} - \frac{v_p^{UU} - V_p}{v_p^{UU} - v_p^{UL}} \leq 0 \tag{7}$$

$$\lambda_{rp} - \frac{V_p - v_p^{LL}}{v_p^{LU} - v_p^{LL}} \leq 0 \tag{8}$$

where λ_{rp} is the degree of satisfaction for property robustness for property p. When V_p falls within lower uncertain region, λ_{rp} approaches 0 as V_p approaches B_p^{LL} and vise versa; when V_p falls within upper uncertain region, λ_{rp} approaches 0 as V_p approaches B_p^{UU} and contrariwise; when V_p falls within certain region, λ_{rp} remains as 1. To obtain the optimal solution, max-min aggregation is applied (Zimmermann, 1978), where the least satisfied fuzzy goal of these properties is maximised.

3. Case study: Optimal design of alkyl substituent for fungicide

Dialkyl dithiolanylidenemalonate (DD) is a common fungicide used to protect rice plants from insect pests and diseases. The design problem was solved by Raman and Maranas (1998) by quantifying the uncertainty of the property prediction models with stochastic formulation. Here, an optimal fungicide is produced by designing alkyl substituent to replace R_1 and R_2 of DD, as shown in Figure 1 by utilising the developed algorithm. The protective ability of fungicide is measured by its' ability to be transpor-

Table 1. Lower and upper bound for regions with different certainty.

Region	Lower bound	Upper bound
Lower uncertain	$v_p^{LL} = v_p^L - \sigma_p$	$v_p^{LU} = v_p^L + \sigma_p$
Certain	$v_p^{LU} = v_p^L + \sigma_p$	$v_p^{UL} = v_p^U - \sigma_p$
Upper uncertain	$v_p^{UL} = v_p^U - \sigma_p$	$v_p^{UU} = v_p^U + \sigma_p$

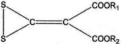

Figure 1. Chemical structure of dialkyl dithiolanylidenemalonate.

ted, distributed and retained in the plant. Hence, the effect of DD to be designed is quantified in terms of affinity ($\log V_E$), mobility ($\log \mu$) and retention ($\log[R/(1-R)]$). Uchida (1980) has published the correlation between these properties with hydrophobic factor $\log P$. Murray et al. (1975) developed a linear relation between $\log P$ and first order molecular connectivity index, $^1\chi$. The propery models for affinity, mobility and retention of the fungicide are shown by the following Eqs. (9)–(11). Toxicity of the DD is also a property of interest, which will be expressed in terms of lethal concentration (LC_{50}) as shown by property model of GC methods (Martin and Young, 2001) in Eq. (12).

$$\log(V_E) = 0.5751(^1\chi) - 0.2942 \tag{9}$$

$$\log(\mu) = -0.6983(^1\chi) + 2.0143 \tag{10}$$

$$\log\left(\frac{R}{1-R}\right) = 0.787(^1\chi) - 2 \tag{11}$$

$$\log(LC_{50}) = -\sum_{i=1}^{N} n_i \alpha_i \tag{12}$$

Affinity, mobility and retention of the fungicide are the properties to be optimised while toxicity is a constraint to be fulfilled. The product target range, standard deviation and shifted target range for each of the property are shown in Table 2. Together with the structural constraints, the model is formulated as mixed integer linear programming (MILP) problem and solved via fuzzy optimisation based inverse design techniques. Different solutions are generated by using integer cuts. Best five solutions are arranged according to their least satisfied fuzzy goal as summarized in Table 3. It can be seen that all of the substituents properties fall between the boundaries that represent customer requirements. Note that these values are the optimized properties subjected to the properties and structural constraints. These solutions are capable to replace R_1 and R_2 for optimal substituent selection for DD.

Table 2. Property targets and property operator targets.

Property	Standard deviation	Target range		Shifted target range			
		B_p^L	B_p^U	B_p^{LL}	B_p^{LU}	B_p^{UL}	B_p^{UU}
Affinity	0.10	1.00	1.60	0.90	1.10	1.50	1.70
Mobility	0.14	-0.30	0.10	-0.44	-0.16	-0.04	0.24
Retention	0.23	-0.20	0.60	-0.43	0.03	0.37	0.83
Toxicity	0.37	-3.51	-	-3.88	-	-	-

Table 3. Possible designs of alkyl substituents for DD.

No	Affinity			Mobility			Retention			Toxicity
	V_p	λ_{sp}	λ_{rp}	V_p	λ_{sp}	λ_{rp}	V_p	λ_{sp}	λ_{rp}	
1	1.40	0.62	1.00	-0.04	0.59	1.00	0.32	0.59	1.00	-3.05
2	1.38	0.60	1.00	-0.02	0.62	0.94	0.29	0.57	1.00	-3.02
3	1.32	0.53	1.00	0.05	0.73	0.67	0.21	0.51	1.00	-2.90
4	1.30	0.50	1.00	0.08	0.77	0.57	0.18	0.48	1.00	-2.90
5	1.47	0.71	1.00	-0.12	0.47	1.00	0.41	0.67	0.92	-3.18

4. Conclusions

This paper introduces a novel approach in chemical product design which consider product superiority and robustness while designing an optimal chemical product. Fuzzy optimisation approach is incorporated into the inverse design techniques in identifying the molecular structure which satisfied the product specification. By considering the prediction error of the property prediction models, the developed algorithm has been applied on a fungicide design problem. With the objective of maximisation of the least satisfied property, the predicted molecule by the algorithm has superior attributes than the conventionally used fungicide, which validates the predictive power of the novel method. Furthermore, all the properties of the optimal product predicted falls into the certain region of property robustness, hence confirming that the optimal product can be predicted after considering the property prediction error. Future efforts will be on extending the flexibility of this methodology in other related research areas where multiple objectives have to be optimised simultaneously.

References

J. Abildskov, M.B. van Leeuwen, C.G. Boeriu, L.A.M. van den Broek, 2013, Computer-aided solvent screening for biocatalysis, Journal of Molecular Catalysis B: Enzymatic, 85, 200–213.

L.E.K. Achenie, R. Gani, V. Venkatasubramanian, 2003, Computer aided molecular design: Theory and practice, Elsevier Science Inc, Amsterdam, Netherlands.

R. Bellman, L. Zadeh1, 1970, Decision-making in a fuzzy environment, Management Science, 17, 4, 141–164.

N.G. Chemmangattuvalappil, M.R. Eden, 2013, A novel methodology for property-based molecular design using multiple topological indices, Industrial and Engineering Chemistry Research, 52, 22, 7090–7103.

E.L. Cussler, G.D. Moggridge, 2001, Chemical product design, Cambridge University Press, Cambridge, Uniter Kingdom.

T.M. Martin, D.M. Young, 2001, Prediction of the acute tocixity (96-h LC50) of organic compounds to the fathead minnow (pimephales promelas) using a group contribution method, Chemical research in toxicology, 14, 10, 1378–1385.

W.J. Murray, L.H. Hall, L.B. Kier, 1975, Molecular connectivity III: relationship to partition coefficients, Journal of pharmaceutical sciences, 64, 12, 1978–1981.

X. Qin, F. Gabriel, D. Harell, M.M. El-Halwagi, 2004, Algebraic techniques for property integration via componentless design, Industrial and engineering chemistry research, 43, 14, 3792–3798.

V.S. Raman, C.D. Maranas, 1998, Optimization in product design with properties correlated with topological indices, Computers and Chemical Engineering, 22, 6, 747.

A. Samudra, N.V. Sahinidis, 2013, Design of Heat-Transfer Media Components for Retail Food Refrigeration, Industrial and Engineering Chemistry Research, 52, 25, 8518–8526.

R.R. Tan, K.B. Aviso, I. U. Barilea, A. B. Culaba, J. B. Cruz, 2012, A fuzzy multi-regional input-output optimization model for biomass production and trade under resource and footprint constraints, Applied Energy, 90, 1, 154–160.

M. Uchida, 1980, Affinity and mobility of fungicidal dialkyl dithiolanylidenemalonates in rice plants, Pesticide biochemistry and physiology, 14, 3, 249–255.

D.P.Jr. Visco, R.S. Pophale, M. D. Rintoul, J. L. Faulon, 2002, Developing a methodology for an inverse quantitative structure-activity relatioship using the signature molecular descriptor, Journal of Molecular Graphics and Modelling, 20, 429–438.

Y.M. Zhang, H.W. Lu, X.H. Nie, L. He, P. Du, 2014, An interactive inexact fuzzy bounded programming approach for agricultural water quality management, Agricultural Water Management, 133, 104–111.

H.J. Zimmermann, 1978, Fuzzy programming and linear programming with several objective functions, Fuzzy Sets and Systems, 1, 44–55.

Jiří Jaromír Klemeš, Petar Sabev Varbanov and Peng Yen Liew (Editors)
Proceedings of the 24th European Symposium on Computer Aided Process Engineering – ESCAPE 24
June 15-18, 2014, Budapest, Hungary. Copyright © 2014 Elsevier B.V. All rights reserved.

Numerical Analysis of Radiant Section of Fired Heater Focused on the Effect of Wall-Tube Distance

Jiří Hájek*, Zdeněk Jegla, Jiří Vondál

Institute of Process and Environmental Engineering,Faculty of Mechanical Engineering, Brno University of Technology, Technická 2, Brno 616 69, Czech Republic
hajek@fme.vutbr.cz

Abstract

Vertical cylindrical fired heater as used in crude oil atmospheric distillation unit is simulated numerically to analyse the distribution of thermal loading on the tubes. The model describes flow, gas combustion and radiative heat transfer inside the radiation section of the fired heater. Attention is focused on the tube-wall distance and the effect it has on circumferential distribution of heat flux on tube walls. It is shown that assumptions invoked in 1D design calculations of fired heaters are significantly underestimating heat flux variability.

Keywords: fired heater, heat transfer, wall-tube distance.

1. Introduction

The design of fired heaters for refinery processes is dominated by guidance of relevant standards, mostly by American Petroleum Institute Standard 560 (API, 2007), which can be considered as the main design reference worldwide (Jegla, 2008). Despite regular updates of this standard, the principle of calculation of important operating parameters of the fired heater radiant section remains the same, based on average heat flux to the radiant tubes. The significant variation of the real heat flux distribution around the length and circumference of fired heater tubes was studied in depth over the years by various authors resulting in estimation technique standardized in several updates of API Standard 530, with the latest version in (API, 2008). The calculation using the API Standard 530 (API, 2008) yields estimate of maximum tube temperature, which is a critical parameter for the safety and lifetime of the heater as shown in Moss et al. (2000). The maximum tube temperature is in design calculations estimated dominantly using the product of average radiant heat flux and several empirical correction factors, which can be insufficient for dependable decision support on the lifetime of tube systems under specific operating conditions. The purpose of the present work is thus to improve the accuracy of prediction of tube system lifetime. One of the parameters that influence uniformity of heat flux on the radiant tubes is the distance of tubes from furnace wall.

2. Motivation and method

2.1. Situation in fired heater numerical modelling methods and industrial experiments

Fired heater simulations reported in the literature have mostly concentrated on box or cabin types for various refinery processes. Thus e.g. Oprins and Heynderickx (2003) studied the flow and pressure fields in the radiation section of a thermal cracking furnace, Lan et al. (2007) performed a coupled simulation of transfer and reaction processes in ethylene furnace and Hu et al. (2012) performed a coupled simulation of a naphtha cracking furnace equipped with long-flame radiation burners. Of these, only (Lan et al., 2007) paid some attention to circumferential distribution of tube skin temperature and heat flux. In their case however, the tubes had flames on both sides.

Experimental works concerned with the measurement of heat flux in tubular furnaces and boilers have been mostly concerned with measurements and methods of measurement for the total heat flux along the whole circumference of a tube. Even such measurements are however scarce, and robust methods for such measurements are not widely used as discussed e.g. in Taler et al. (2009), where new method to measure the local heat flux to membrane water-walls in steam boilers is proposed. Experimental methods for the measurement of heat flux as reviewed by Arai et al. (1996) or more recently by Paist et al. (2002) are not suited to measure the heat transfer in much spatial detail. Novel approach proposed in Beckmann et al. (2006) is a promising method for membrane walls of steam generators, yet it is again not applicable to the case of free standing tubes immersed completely in the radiating medium.

Tube skin temperature measurements are obviously also very demanding. Durable thermocouples do not offer sufficient spatial detail as well as accuracy. Optical methods are limited by direct visibility of the tube surface, therefore making the measurement of circumferential profile of tube skin temperature very difficult. Even though interesting possibilities of 3D measurements in furnaces appeared recently (Cheng et al., 2014).

It therefore seems that numerical modelling is currently the best available technique to analyse in detail heat flux and tube skin temperature distribution on tubes in fired heaters.

2.2. Motivation from fired heater design point of view

Fired heaters designed for refinery applications are generally designed for allowable average radiant heat flux (q_r), which is one of the most closely watched design factors of fired heaters for given process application. For determination of average radiant heat flux it is necessary as a first step to determine the radiant heat duty (Q_r). All of existing well-established 1Dquasi-theoretical calculation techniques for radiant heat duty (Q_r) use global parameters of radiant tubular system, such as diameter of tubes and their spacing, distance of tube centre from lining surface etc. (e.g. Wimpress, 1978). For example influence of distance between furnace wall and tube centre is usually considered using so called view factor. For example, in case of typical vertical cylindrical fired heater with radiant tube coil designed as one single tube row against the lining wall, when the distance between wall surface and tubes centreline is less than spacing of tubes, the view factor can be read from Figure 1a) (drawn according to information from (VDI-Gesellschaft Verfahrenstechnik und Chemieingenieurwesen, 2010)), according to ratio of tube spacing (s) and tube outer diameter (D). In this figure we also can see how much of the total value of view radiation factor of tubes (red solid line) should come from direct radiation of flue gas (green dashed line) and reradiation from lining wall (blue dotted line). When the radiant heat duty (Q_r) is determined, the average radiant heat flux (q_r) is obtained by dividing Q_r by the total radiant heat transfer area (A_r).

The obtained average radiant heat flux (q_r) is then used for prediction of so-called local-maximum radiant heat flux q_m. According to API Standard 530(API, 2008), the local-maximum radiant heat flux q_m can be calculated from average radiant heat flux q_r as follows:

$$q_m = F_C . F_L . F_T . (q_r - q_{rc}) + q_{rc} \qquad (1)$$

where F_C is a tube-circumference heat flux variation factor, F_L is a tube-longitudinal heat flux variation factor, F_T is a tube-surface temperature heat flux variation factor and q_{rc} is the convective component of the average radiant section heat flux q_r.

Because the entire tube circumference is considered also in calculating q_r (as described in text above Figure 1) tube-circumference heat flux variation factor F_C tends to be in such 1D calculation somewhat higher. Factor F_C varies with tube spacing, as demonstrates Figure 1b).

Prediction of local-maximum radiant heat flux q_m from Eq. (1) may be sufficient for the purpose of calculation of maximum radiant section tube skin temperature and tube material selection. However, for dimensioning of tubular system of radiant section (sizing of tube coil) and prediction of its thermal properties this is rather insufficient, because real heat flux distribution in radiant section strongly influences character of two-phase flow regimes of heated fluid in radiant tubes. Insufficient prediction of real distribution of heat flux in radiation section is frequently the source of important fired heater operating troubles, as described for example in Jegla et al. (2011). These problems stem from the known fact that accurate determination of individual correction factors F_C, F_L and F_T for Eq. (1) is very difficult, since they depend on the fuel characteristics, combustion conditions, burner design, shape of flames and their interactions, arrangement and dimensions of radiant section and radiant coils, flue gas flow inside radiant section, etc.

3. Methodology

3.1. Fired heater design
The analysed radiant section of refinery fired heater and its tube system have been designed in accordance with the relevant abovementioned API Standards. Fired heater is of vertical cylindrical type with nominal firing capacity of 24 MW and working in process of atmospheric distillation of crude oil. There are a total of six staged-gas

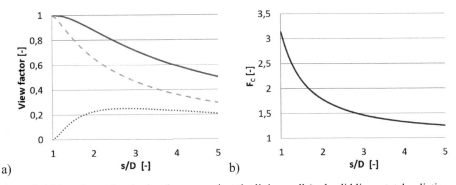

Figure 1 a) View factor for single tube row against the lining wall (red solid line – total radiation, green dashed line – direct radiation, blue dotted line – reradiation from wall), b) Tube-circumference heat flux variation factor F_C for single tube row against the lining wall (based on data from API, 2008)

burners vertically oriented and mounted on bottom of radiant section, equipped with guide-vane stabilizers (swirlers), each of nominal firing duty 4 MW. Radiant section's geometry and tube system have been deliberately designed with small imperfections to resemble a used system, where tubes are not in their precise design positions (nominal), but are slightly deformed in ways inspired by observations in real industrial units. This enables to study the influence of tube-wall distance.

3.2. Model setup

Numerical simulation includes the reactive flow in the flames of the radiant section. Turbulence is simulated by a two-equation model (Shih et al., 1995). Global single-step chemical mechanism is used to approximate the combustion reactions. Turbulence-chemistry interaction is included using eddy-dissipation model. Radiation is modelled by the discrete-ordinates method and absorption coefficient is determined by an updated weighted-sum-of-grey-gases model (Yin et al., 2010). Flow in the unit is unstable as caused mainly by processing vortices of the flames and internal recirculation; therefore simulation is performed in unsteady mode. To perform the computations, commercial system ANSYS FLUENT is employed.

3.3. Boundary conditions

Boundary condition on the tube walls assumes a constant inner skin temperature. This assumption is chosen in order to enhance direct comparability of data collected on individual tubes. Conduction in the tube walls is enabled in the radial direction as well as axially and tangentially (shell conduction). Shell conduction is enabled also in the wall of the furnace, the properties of which correspond to refractory bricks.

4. Results

Tubular system of analysed radiant section represents tube coil created by 60 tubes (placed in one row around circular lining wall) with the constant outer diameter (D) 194 mm and with tube spacing (s) 350 mm. Nominal distance of tube centre from lining surface is (e) 232 mm. The ratio s/D is then 1.8 and e < s. The height of radiant section is approx. 17 meters. In order to simulate poor fixation of individual tubes of the tube coil, some of the tubes are moved from the nominal position closer or farther from the wall and/or to neighbouring tubes.

When we take classic results from 1D global heat transfer analysis using the abovementioned method of view factors, we get for nominal position of the tube coil the following main data about tube-circumferential heat flux variation. The flame-side maximum local heat flux is predicted at 172 % of average heat flux, wall-side minimum local heat flux is predicted at 58 % of average heat flux.

The variability of local heat flux predicted by CFD simulation is however much higher than in the 1D design calculation. Flame-side maximum is 332 % of average heat flux, while wall-side minimum is 16 % of average heat flux.

Resulting heat loads around the circumference of individual tubes presented below are taken from a level 5 m above the floor of radiant section, which is the height with peak heat loads as documented by Figure 2b. Figure 2a displays a polar plot of typical heat flux profile around tube in nominal location (also neighbours in nominal positions).

The circumferential tube heat flux profiles predicted by the simulation display significant variability, as flow in the furnace is quite complex and non-symmetrical.

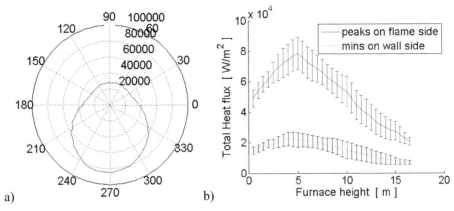

a)   b)

Figure 2a) Tube circumferential total absorbed heat flux variation on level 5 m from floor of
radiant section (tube in nominal position), b) vertical variation of total heat flux with error bars
displaying standard deviation in half-metre horizontal sections.

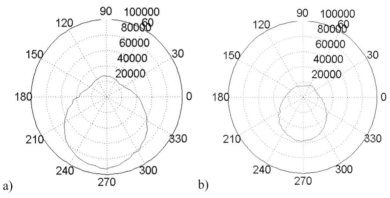

a)   b)

Figure 3 Tube circumferential total absorbed heat flux variation on level 5 m from floor of radiant
section, a) tube closer to flame than nominal, b) tube closer to wall.

When we predict local-maximum heat flux (q_m) for analysed radiant section using 1D
model by eq. (1) (with $F_C = 1.9$, $F_L = 1.1$ and $F_T = 1.0$, according to API (2008), we get
a value $q_m = 55.64$ kW/m^2.

However, from Fig. 2b it can be seen that CFD analysis shows value of maximum peak
of heat flux profile in radiant section higher by more than 40 %. Two examples of tubes
that are slightly shifted by D/2 towards the flame and to the wall, respectively, are
presented in Figure 3. The tube deformations however lead rather to qualitative
differences of the circumferential profiles, while peak levels of heat loads are influenced
mainly by flame inclination due to global flow pattern in the furnace, which is mainly
influenced by recirculation caused by large flue gas temperature differences.

5. Conclusions

Vertical cylindrical fired heater typical for crude oil atmospheric distillation units was
simulated numerically to analyse the distribution of thermal loading on the tubes.
Predictions were compared with classical design calculations and revealed significantly
greater variability. The effect of wall-tube distance has been shown to be relatively
small and qualitative as compared to other phenomena that influence distribution of heat

flux on the tube coil. Classical design calculation method has been shown to lead to overly optimistic predictions regarding heat flux uniformity on the tube coil.

Acknowledgements

The authors gratefully acknowledge financial support of the Ministry of Education, Youth and Sportswithin the framework of Operational Programme "National Sustainability Programme I" – NETME CENTRE PLUS (LO1202) and Operational Programme "Investment in education development", projects CZ.1.07/2.3.00/20.0020 and CZ.1.07/2.3.00/30.0039.

References

API, 2007, Standard 560, Fired Heaters for General Refinery Service, 4th edition, American Petroleum Institute, Washington DC, USA

API, 2008, Standard 530, Calculation of Heater-tube Thickness in Petroleum Refineries, 6th edition, American Petroleum Institute, Washington DC, USA

N. Arai, A. Matsunami, S.W. Churchill, 1996, A review of measurements of heat flux density applicable to the field of combustion, Experimental Thermal and Fluid Science, 12, 4, 452–60.

M. Beckmann, S. Krüger, W. Spiegel, 2006, A method for non-invasive heat flux detection in membrane walls of steam generators, IT3, Air and Waste Management Association, Savannah, USA, 531–550.

Q. Cheng, X. Zhang, Z. Wang, H. Zhou, S. Shao, 2014, Simultaneous measurement of three-dimensional temperature distributions and radiative properties based on radiation image processing technology in a gas-fired pilot tubular furnace, Heat Transfer Engineering, 35, 6-8, 770–779.

G. Hu, H. Wang, F. Qian, K.M. Van Geem, C.M. Schietekat, G.B. Marin, 2012, Coupled simulation of an industrial naphtha cracking furnace equipped with long-flame and radiation burners, Computers and Chemical Engineering, 38, 24–34.

Z. Jegla, 2008, Optimum arrangement of tube coil in radiation type of tubular furnace, Heat Transfer Engineering, 29, 6, 546–555.

Z. Jegla, J. Kohoutek, P. Stehlik, 2011, Design and operating aspects influencing fouling inside radiant coils of fired heaters operated in crude oil distillation plants, Proceedings of Heat Exchanger Fouling and Cleaning IX, Crete Island, Grece, 7-14

X. Lan, J. Gao, C. Xu, H. Zhang, 2007, Numerical Simulation of Transfer and Reaction Processes in Ethylene Furnaces, Chemical Engineering Research and Design, 85, 12, 1565–1579.

C.J. Moss, P. Barrien, A. Walczynski, 2000, Life management of refinery furnace tubing, International Journal of Pressure Vessels and Piping, 77, 2–3, 105–112.

A.J.M. Oprins, G.J. Heynderickx, 2003, Calculation of three-dimensional flow and pressure fields in cracking furnaces, Chemical Engineering Science, 58, 21, 4883–4893.

A. Paist, A. Poobus, T. Tiikma, 2002, Probes for measuring heat transfer parameters and fouling intensity in boilers, Fuel, 81, 14, 1811–1818.

T.-H. Shih, W.W. Liou, A. Shabbir, Z. Yang, J. Zhu, 1995, A new k-[epsilon] eddy viscosity model for high reynolds number turbulent flows, Computers and Fluids, 24, 3, 227–238.

J. Taler, P. Duda, B. Weglowski, W. Zima, S. Gradziel, T. Sobota, D. Taler, 2009, Identification of local heat flux to membrane water-walls in steam boilers, Fuel, 88, 2, 305–311.

VDI-Gesellschaft Verfahrenstechnik und Chemieingenieurwesen, 2010, VDI Heat Atlas, 2nd edition, Springer-Verlag Berlin Heidelberg, Germany.

N. Wimpress, 1978, Generalized method predicts fired-heater performance, Chemical Engineering (New York), 85,12, 95–102.

C. Yin, L.C.R. Johansen, L.A. Rosendahl, S.K. Kær, 2010, New Weighted Sum of Gray Gases Model Applicable to Computational Fluid Dynamics (CFD) Modeling of Oxy–Fuel Combustion: Derivation, Validation, and Implementation, Energy and Fuels, 24, 12, 6275–6282.

Jiří Jaromír Klemeš, Petar Sabev Varbanov and Peng Yen Liew (Editors)
Proceedings of the 24th European Symposium on Computer Aided Process Engineering – ESCAPE 24
June 15-18, 2014, Budapest, Hungary.

Logic-Based Outer Approximation for the Design of Discrete-Continuous Dynamic Systems with Implicit Discontinuities

Rubén Ruiz-Femenia[a]*, Jose A. Caballero[a], Ignacio E. Grossmann[b]

[a]*Department of Chemical Engineering, University of Alicante, Ap. 99, Alicante. Spain.*
[b]*Department of Chemical Engineering, Carnegie Mellon University. 5000 Forbes Avenue. 15213, Pittsburgh, PA. USA.*
Ruben.Ruiz@ua.es

Abstract

We address the optimization of discrete-continuous dynamic optimization problems using a disjunctive multistage modeling framework, with implicit discontinuities, which increases the problem complexity since the number of continuous phases and discrete events is not known a-priori. After setting a fixed alternative sequence of modes, we convert the infinite-dimensional continuous mixed-logic dynamic (MLDO) problem into a finite dimensional discretized GDP problem by orthogonal collocation on finite elements. We use the Logic-based Outer Approximation algorithm to fully exploit the structure of the GDP representation of the problem. This modelling framework is illustrated with an optimization problem with implicit discontinuities (diver problem).

Keywords: Logic-Based Outer Approximation, Discrete-Continuous Dynamic Systems, Mixed-Logic Dynamic Optimization, GDP, Orthogonal collocation method

1. Introduction

Many chemical process systems of practical interest are subject to discrete events that cause discontinuities in their dynamics. Dynamic models are required for batch and semi-batch processes which are inherently transient; for the operation of continuous processes in transient phases, including start-ups (Mynttinen and Li, 2012), shut-downs and changeovers from one to another steady state; and for safety analysis (Lotero-Herranz and Galán, 2013). Optimization of discrete-continuous dynamic problems (also referred as hybrid systems) requires the treatment of non-smooth conditions within the problem formulation. These problems can be formulated as mixed integer nonlinear programing (MINLP) models, that allow to handle logic conditions that lead to non-smoothness. However, the associated computational expense may be high for large systems with many discrete decisions. This is often the case in hybrid systems that can switch at any time. Raman and Grossmann (1994) developed the Generalized Disjunctive Programming (GDP), as an alternative modeling framework to the traditional mixed-integer formulations. The development of GDP has led to customized algorithms that exploit the disjunctive structure of the model. In particular, Turkay and Grossmann (1996) extended the outer approximation (OA) algorithm. We address the optimization of discrete-continuous dynamic optimization problems using a disjunctive multistage modeling framework that contains Boolean variables associated to alternative sets of differential equations for each stage (or continuous phase), and where switching from one continuous phase to the next occurs at some unknown time (implicit discontinuities). Before applying the logic-based OA algorithm, we transform the differential into algebraic equations by orthogonal collocation on finite elements.

2. Mathematical problem formulation

2.1. Disjunctive multistage model

The continuous phase of a process occurs in the time interval between two discrete events. When the process can reside in more than one mode for each stage, the dynamic system is described by an alternative sequence (Figure 1).

The first step is to extract a set of potential fixed direct sequences, which can be merged into one single fixed alternative sequence (i.e., the superstructure). A bypass stage maps the state variable values of one existing stage to the next. For further details on the general multistage modeling framework consult (Oldenburg and Marquardt, 2008).

2.2. Discretization using orthogonal collocation

We transform the disjunctive multistage problem into a discretized GDP problem by orthogonal discretization, a simultaneous method that fully discretizes the DAE system by approximating the control and state variables as piecewise polynomials functions over finite elements (Kameswaran and Biegler, 2006). Figure 2 shows how the time horizon is discretized. Accordingly, at each collocation point the state variable is represented by:

$$x_{sik} = x_{si}^0 + h_{si}\sum_{j=1}^{K}\Omega_j(\tau_k)\dot{x}_{sij}, \ s = 1,...,S, \ i = 1,...,I, \ k = 1,...,K \tag{1}$$

where x_{si}^0 is the value of the state variable at the beginning of element i in stage s, $\dot{x}_{sij}$ is the value of its first derivative in element i at the collocation point k in stage s, h_{is} is the length of element i in stage s, $\Omega_j(\tau_k)$ is the interpolation polynomial of order K for collocation point j, and τ_k is the non-dimensional time coordinate. We enforce continuity of the state variable across finite element boundaries in each stage by $x_{si}^0 = x_{s,i-1,K}$ for all $s = 1,...,S$, $i = 2,...,I$. Additional stage transition conditions map the differential state variable values across the stage boundaries:

$$x_{s1}^0 - x_{s-1,I,K} = 0, \ s = 2,...,S \tag{2}$$

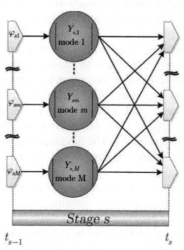

Figure 1. Alternative modes for each stage.

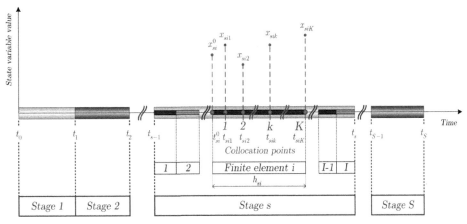

Figure 2. Discretization scheme used to apply the orthogonal collocation method.

For each stage, the collocation method requires the time to be discretized over each finite element at the selected collocation points t_{sik} :

$$t_{sik} = t_{si}^0 + h_{si}\tau_k, \quad s = 1,\dots,S, \quad i = 1,\dots,I, \quad k = 1,\dots,K \tag{3}$$

where t_{si}^0 is the value of the time at the beginning of element i in stage s. Time continuity between stages and between elements within a stage is also enforced by the following constraints:

$$t_{s,1}^0 = t_{s-1,I,K}, \quad s = 2,\dots,S$$
$$t_{si}^0 = t_{s,i-1,K}, \quad s = 1,\dots,S, \quad i = 2,\dots,I \tag{4}$$

3. Case study

The proposed modeling framework has been assessed with a benchmark case study, the diver problem (Barton, Allgor, 1998). The design task is to calculate the depth-time profile of a scuba diver who wishes to collect an item from the ocean floor with the minimum consumption of air. To prevent decompression sickness, the diver can make safety stops of 4 minutes during the ascent. The unknown switching structure arises from the number of decompression stops that the diver has to make during the ascent. The model comprises three state variables, which are the pressure in the tank $P^{tank}(t)$, the surrounding pressure $P(t)$ and the partial pressure of N_2 in the tissue $P^{tissue}(t)$. The control variable is the velocity of the descent/ascend of the scuba diver, $u(t)$:

$$\max_{u(t)} \quad P^{\text{tank}}(t^{final})$$

$$\text{s.t.} \quad \frac{dP^{\text{tank}}}{dt}(t) = \frac{-q}{V_{\text{tank}}} P(t)$$

$$\frac{dP^{\text{tissue}}}{dt}(t) = \frac{\ln 2}{5}(0.79P(t) - P^{\text{tissue}}(t)) \tag{5}$$

$$\frac{dP}{dt}(t) = -1 \times 10^5 \rho g u(t)$$

Ascent mode: $\underline{u} \le u(t) \le \bar{u}$

Switch to decompression mode if: $P^{\text{tissue}}(t) \ge 2 \times 0.79P(t)$

Decompression mode: $u(t) = 0$ and wait for 4 min and then switch to ascent mode.

3.1. Mixed-Logic Dynamic Optimization formulation

We formulate a disjunctive multistage representation of problem (5) by a fixing alternative sequence for a certain number of stages that may include a bypass term in the disjunction of any stage. Particularly, we use a fixed alternative sequence with three decompression stops. Hence, the MLDO problem is stated as:

$$\max_{u_s(t),t^{final},t^{bottom}} = P_S^{\text{tank}}(t_S) \tag{6}$$

s.t. $P(t_0) = 1, P(t^{bottom}) = P(t_1) = 6, P(t^{final}) = P(t_S) = 1$ \hfill (7)

$$
\begin{bmatrix}
Y_s^{\text{ascent}} \\
\varphi_s^1 : t - t_{s-1} = 0 \\
\dfrac{dP_s^{\text{tank}}(t)}{dt} = \dfrac{-q}{V_{\text{tank}}} P_s(t) \\
\dfrac{dP_s^{\text{tissue}}(t)}{dt} = \dfrac{\ln 2}{5}(0.79 P_s(t) - P^{\text{tissue}}(t)) \\
\dfrac{dP_s(t)}{dt} = -1. \times 10^5 \rho g u_s(t) \\
\underline{u} \le u_s(t) \le \overline{u} \\
P^{\text{tissue}}(t) \le 1.58 P(t)
\end{bmatrix}
\vee
\begin{bmatrix}
Y_s^{\text{bypass}} \\
\varphi_s^2 : t - t_{s-1} = 0 \\
P_s^{\text{tank}}(t_s) - P_s^{\text{tank}}(t_{s-1}) = 0 \\
P_s^{\text{tissue}}(t_s) - P_s^{\text{tissue}}(t_{s-1}) = 0 \\
P_s(t_s) - P_s(t_{s-1}) = 0 \\
u_s(t) = 0 \\
t_s - t_{s-1} = 0
\end{bmatrix}
\begin{array}{c} t \in [t_{s-1}, t_s] \\ s = 4,6,8 \end{array}
\tag{8}
$$

$$
\begin{bmatrix}
Y_s^{\text{deco}} \\
\varphi_s^1 : P^{\text{tissue}}(t) - \theta 0.79 P(t) = 0 \\
\dfrac{dP_s^{\text{tank}}(t)}{dt} = \dfrac{-q}{V_{\text{tank}}} P_s(t) \\
\dfrac{dP_s^{\text{tissue}}(t)}{dt} = \dfrac{\ln 2}{5}(0.79 P_s(t) - P^{\text{tissue}}(t)) \\
\dfrac{dP_s(t)}{dt} = -1 \times 10^5 \rho g u_s(t) \\
u_s(t) = 0 \\
t_s - t_{s-1} = 4
\end{bmatrix}
\vee
\begin{bmatrix}
Y_s^{\text{bypass}} \\
\varphi_s^2 : t - t_{s-1} = 0 \\
P_s^{\text{tank}}(t_s) - P_s^{\text{tank}}(t_{s-1}) = 0 \\
P_s^{\text{tissue}}(t_s) - P_s^{\text{tissue}}(t_{s-1}) = 0 \\
P_s(t_s) - P_s(t_{s-1}) = 0 \\
u_s(t) = 0 \\
t_s - t_{s-1} = 0
\end{bmatrix}
\begin{array}{c} t \in [t_{s-1}, t_s] \\ s = 3,5,7 \end{array}
\tag{9}
$$

$$Y_s^{\text{ascent}}, s = 1,2 \quad \therefore \quad Y_s^{\text{deco}} \Leftrightarrow Y_{s+1}^{\text{ascent}}, s = 3,5,7$$

3.2. MLDO Discretization

The time continuous MLDO problem is converted into a finite dimensional discretized GDP by a full orthogonal collocation of the three state variables using Eqs. (1)-(4):

$$\min_{P_{sik}^{\text{tank}},P_{si}^{\text{tank},0},\dot{P}_{sik}^{\text{tank}},P_{sik}^{\text{tissue}},P_{si}^{\text{tissue},0},\dot{P}_{sik}^{\text{tissue}},P_{sik},P_{si}^0,\dot{P}_{si},h_{si},u_s} Z = -P_{SIK}^{\text{tank}} \tag{10}$$

s.t., Time discretization: $t_{sik} = t_{si}^0 + h_{si}\tau_k, \; s = 1,...,S, \; i = 1,...,I, \; k = 1,...,K$

Time continuity finite element: $t_{si}^0 = t_{s,i-1,K}, \; s = 1,...,S, \quad i = 2,...,I$ \hfill (11)

Time mapping: $t_{si}^0 = t_{s-1,I,K}, \; s = 2,...,S$

$$
\text{State discretization: }
\begin{aligned}
P_{sik}^{\text{tank}} &= P_{si}^{\text{tank},0} + h_{si}\sum_{j=1}^{K}\Omega_{jk}\dot{P}_{sik}^{\text{tank}} \\
P_{sik}^{\text{tissue}} &= P_{si}^{\text{tissue},0} + h_{si}\sum_{j=1}^{K}\Omega_{jk}\dot{P}_{sik}^{\text{tissue}} \\
P_{sik} &= P_{si}^0 + h_{si}\sum_{j=1}^{K}\Omega_{jk}\dot{P}_{sik}
\end{aligned}
\left.\begin{array}{c} s = 1,...,S \\ i = 1,...,I \\ k = 1,...,K \end{array}\right\}
\tag{12}
$$

$$
\text{Time mapping: }
\begin{bmatrix}
P_{s,1}^0 - P_{s-1,I,K} = 0 \\
P_{s,1}^{\text{tank},0} - P_{s-1,I,K}^{\text{tank}} = 0 \\
P_{s,1}^{\text{tissue0}} - P_{s-1,I,K}^{\text{tissue}} = 0
\end{bmatrix}
, s = 2,...,S
\tag{13}
$$

State continuity finite element: $\left.\begin{array}{l} P_{si}^{\text{tank},0} = P_{s,i-1,K}^{\text{tank}} \\ P_i^{\text{tissue},0} = P_{i-1,K}^{\text{tissue}} \\ P_i^0 = P_{i-1,K} \end{array}\right\}, s = 1,\ldots,S, i = 2,\ldots,I$ $\qquad$ (14)

Common end point constraints: $P_{1,I,K} = 6, \; P_{S,I,K} = 1$ $\qquad\qquad$ (15)

$$
\begin{bmatrix}
Y_s^{\text{ascent}} \\
\text{Disjunctive switch function: } t_{s1}^0 - t_{s-1} = 0 \\
\text{Disjunctive differential equations:} \\
\left.\begin{array}{l} \dot{P}_{sik}^{\text{tank}} = \frac{-q}{V_{\text{tank}}} P_{sik} \\ \dot{P}_{sik}^{\text{tissue}} = \frac{\ln 2}{5}(0.79 P_{sik} - P_{sik}^{\text{tissue}}) \\ \dot{P}_{sik} = -1 \times 10^{-5} \rho g u_s \end{array}\right\}, i = 1,\ldots,I, k = 1,\ldots,K \\
\text{Disjunctive path constraints:} \\
\underline{u} \le u_s \le \bar{u} \\
P_{sik}^{\text{tissue}} \le \theta 0.79 P_{sik} \quad i = 1,\ldots,I, k = 1,\ldots,K
\end{bmatrix}
\underline{\vee}
\begin{bmatrix}
Y_s^{\text{bypass}} \\
\text{Disjunctive switch function:} \\
t_{s1}^0 - t_{s-1} = 0 \\
\text{Disjunctive path constraints:} \\
u_s = 0 \\
\text{Disjunctive end point constraints:} \\
P_{s,1}^{\text{tank},0} = P_{s,I,K}^{\text{tank}} \\
P_{s,1}^{\text{tissue},0} = P_{s,I,K}^{\text{tissue}} \\
P_{s,1}^0 = P_{s,I,K} \\
t_{s,1}^0 = t_{s,I,K}
\end{bmatrix}
\quad (16)
$$

$$
\begin{bmatrix}
Y_s^{\text{deco}} \\
\text{Disjunctive switch function: } P_{s1}^{\text{tissue},0} - 1.58 P_{s1}^0 = 0 \\
\text{Disjunctive differential equations:} \\
\left.\begin{array}{l} \dot{P}_{sik}^{\text{tank}} = \frac{-q}{V_{\text{tank}}} P_{sik} \\ \dot{P}_{sik}^{\text{tissue}} = \frac{\ln 2}{5}(0.79 P_{sik} - P_{sik}^{\text{tissue}}) \\ \dot{P}_{sik} = -1 \times 10^{-5} \rho g u_s \end{array}\right\}, i = 1,\ldots,I, k = 1,\ldots,K \\
\text{Disjunctive path constraints:} \\
u_s = 0 \\
\text{Disjunctive end point constraints: } t_{s,I,K} = t_{s,1}^0 + 4
\end{bmatrix}
\underline{\vee}
\begin{bmatrix}
Y_s^{\text{bypass}} \\
\text{Disjunctive switch function:} \\
t_{s1}^0 - t_{s-1} = 0 \\
\text{Disjunctive path constraints:} \\
u_s = 0 \\
\text{Disjunctive end point constraints:} \\
P_{s,1}^{\text{tank},0} = P_{s,I,K}^{\text{tank}} \\
P_{s,1}^{\text{tissue},0} = P_{s,I,K}^{\text{tissue}} \\
P_{s,1}^0 = P_{s,I,K} \\
t_{s,1}^0 = t_{s,I,K}
\end{bmatrix}
\quad (17)
$$

$Y_s^{\text{ascent}}, s = 1,2, \; \therefore \; Y_s^{\text{deco}} \Leftrightarrow Y_{s+1}^{\text{ascent}}, s = 3,5,7$ $\qquad\qquad$ (18)

3.3. Logic-based discretized NLP subproblem

The NLP subproblem is obtained by fixing the values of the Boolean variables Y_{sm}. Due to space limitations we omit stating the full discretized NLP subproblem.

3.4. Logic-based discretized Master problem

We formulate the discretized Master problem with the accumulated linearizations of the nonlinear constraints from previous solutions of each discretized NLP subproblem. For the shake of shortness, we exclude the representation of the discretized Master problem.

4. Results and discussion

The problem is solved by the logic based OA algorithm implemented in GAMS using the CONOPT solver for the NLP subproblems and the CPLEX 12.5.1.0 solver for MILP master problems. Our GAMS implementation allows writing disjunctions with more than two terms. The discretized linear master problem is reformulated as an MILP using the Hull Reformulation (HR). Figure 3 shows the optimal results of this case study, where we discretize the time domain using 3 collocation points per finite element.

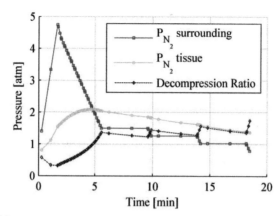

Figure 3. Optimal Pressure profiles.

5. Conclusions

The GDP modeling framework proposed coupled with logic-based OA algorithm can tackle with the optimization of continuous dynamic systems with implicit discontinuities. The methodology requires creating a superstructure with a certain number of stages and a fixed alternative sequence of modes. The application of the logic-based OA algorithm reduces the problem size in comparison when the model is directly reformulated into an MINLP, due to the differential equations corresponding to the non-active modes for a particular stage are discarded. Further work extends the proposed modeling framework to a multistage batch distillation process and the combination of scheduling with dynamic optimization.

Acknowledgements

The authors acknowledge financial support from «Estancias de movilidad en el extranjero "Jose Castillejo" (JC2011-0054)» of the Spanish "Ministerio de Educación", and from the Spanish "Ministerio de Ciencia e Innovacion" (CTQ2012-37039-C02-02).

References

I. Mynttinen, P. Li, 2012, A stop-and-restart approach to hybrid dynamic optimization problems, Computer Aided Chemical Engineering, 30, 822-826.

I. Lotero-Herranz, S. Galán, 2013, Automated HAZOP using hybrid discrete/continuous process models, Computer Aided Chemical Engineering, 32, 991-996.

R. Raman, I.E. Grossmann, 1994, Modelling and computational techniques for logic based integer programming, Computers and Chemical Engineering, 18, 7, 563-578.

M. Türkay, I.E. Grossmann, 1996, Logic-based MINLP algorithms for the optimal synthesis of process networks, Computers and Chemical Engineering, 20, 8, 959-978.

J. Oldenburg, W. Marquardt, 2008, Disjunctive modeling for optimal control of hybrid systems, Computers and Chemical Engineering, 32, 10, 2346-2364.

S. Kameswaran, L.T. Biegler, 2006, Simultaneous dynamic optimization strategies: Recent advances and challenges, Computers and Chemical Engineering, 30, 10-12, 1560-1575.

P.I. Barton, R.J. Allgor, W.F. Feehery, S. Galán, 1998, Dynamic optimization in a discontinuous world, Industrial and Engineering Chemistry Research, 37, 3, 966-981.

Jiří Jaromír Klemeš, Petar Sabev Varbanov and Peng Yen Liew (Editors)
Proceedings of the 24th European Symposium on Computer Aided Process Engineering – ESCAPE 24
June 15-18, 2014, Budapest, Hungary. Copyright © 2014 Elsevier B.V. All rights reserved.

Problem Diagnostics and Model Refinement in Dynamic Parameter Estimation

Neima Brauner,[a] Mordechai Shacham,[b*]

[a]*School of Engineering, Tel-Aviv University, Tel-Aviv, Israel*
[b]*Chem. Eng. Dept., Ben-Gurion University, Beer-Sheva, Israel*
shacham@exchange.bgu.ac.il

Abstract

In order to confront the problem of dynamic parameter estimation in face of the many uncertainties involved we propose to carry out an iterative process involving cycles of model specification, solution, analysis and diagnostics, and model modification if necessary. The objective is to suggest a systematic procedure that can ensure arriving at a maximal set of physically feasible parameter values, based on the available data and the suggested model. The proposed procedure is demonstrated using both the sequential and simultaneous approaches, gradient based and direct search minimization methods, and use of scaled compared to non-scaled data. The quality of the resulting model is assessed based on the comparison of the integrated values with the data, residual plots, confidence interval-to-parameter value ratios and the objective function value.

Keywords: model identification, parameter estimation, regression analysis

1. Introduction

Accurate mechanistic kinetic models of chemical/biological processes are essential for the understanding, design, optimization and control of such processes. Such models are often described by systems of ordinary differential equations (ODE's). The models usually contain unknown parameters that need to be determined using a set of measurements (experimental data). Typically, the estimation of the parameter values is performed using a maximum likelihood approach, where the objective is to minimize the weighted squared error between the set of the measured data and the corresponding model prediction. The role of parameter estimation for dynamic models has been recently discussed by Michalic et al. (2009) (for chemical processes) and Jia et al. (2012) (for biological processes).

The various stages of the mechanistic model development and the estimation of the model parameters in dynamic systems were described in detail by Maria (2004). Many methods have been developed in the attempt to find the global optimum of the parameter estimation problem for dynamic problems (for description of some recently developed methods and reviews of earlier methods, see for example Kravaris et al. (2013) and Dua (2011). However, researchers are still facing many challenges while solving practical problems belonging to this category. Kravaris et al. (2013) point out that fundamental models often contain more parameters than can be reliably estimated from data. McLean and McAuley (2012) emphasize that the models used by chemical engineers are generally nonlinear in the parameters, and mention the difficulties often arise from uncertainty regarding the suitability of the mathematical model to represent the data, availability of insufficient amount and/or low precision noisy experimental data and lack of sensible initial estimates for some (or all) of the parameter values.

In order to confront the problem of dynamic parameter estimation in face of the many uncertainties (related to the model, the data and the global minimum), we propose to carry out an iterative process involving cycles of model specification, solution, analysis and diagnostics, followed by model modification (if necessary). We assume that a "first estimate" of the model consisting of differential and algebraic equations, which are based on the mechanisms involved, already exists. The objectives of the regression, diagnostics and modification cycles is the adjustment of the model and the parameter values, so as to obtain the best possible fit between the model and the available experimental data with a stable set of parameter values. Typically, the model modification step may include increase or decrease of the number of equations, removal of superfluous parameters and terms from the equations, and the use of scaled or non-scaled data for regression.

For the solution stage, we have examined the use of several approaches. The parameter identification was carried out using both the sequential and simultaneous approaches. Using the sequential approach, the minimization of the objective function is carried out in an outer loop, while in the inner loop an integration routine is used to determine the state variable values at time intervals where experimental data are available. Using the simultaneous approach, the differential parameter estimation problem is converted to an algebraic estimation problem by fitting curves to the data of state variable vs. time and differentiating the resulting curves. Both gradient based (the Levenberg-Marquardt algorithm) and non-gradient based (the Nealder and Mead (1965) Simplex method) were applied for the objective function minimization. The possibility of partitioning a complex problem into a sequence of several simpler ones is also examined at this stage.

Due to space limitation only the sequential approach using gradient-based minimization methods are described. Results of one particular example are discussed in detail.

2. Basic Concepts

The ODE parameter estimation problem can be defined as:

$$\min_{\theta} \Phi(\theta) = \sum_{\mu=1}^{n} \sum_{i=1}^{m} \left(x_{\mu,i} - x_{\mu,i}^{c} \right)^2 * W_i \tag{1}$$

subject to:

$$\frac{d\mathbf{x}}{dt} = \mathbf{F}(\mathbf{x}, \theta, t); \quad \mathbf{x}(0) = \mathbf{x}_0 \tag{2}$$

where $\mathbf{F}$ is a system of m ordinary differential equations, $\mathbf{x}$ is a vector of m dynamic variables, θ is a vector of p parameters $\mathbf{x}_{\mu}$, $\mathbf{x}_{\mu}^{c}$ is a vector of m observed and calculated values at the μth data point, respectively and $\mathbf{W}$ is a vector of m weighting factors.

Using the initial problem formulation, the solution is carried out using the sequential (or the feasible path) approach. With this approach, the minimization defined in Eq. (1) is carried out in an outer loop, while in the inner loop an integration routine is used to determine the state variable values at time intervals where experimental data are available. In this study, the integration is usually carried out by the MATLAB *ode45* function, which is based on an explicit Runge-Kutta (4,5) formula, the Dormand-Prince (1980) pair. This algorithm monitors the estimate of the integration error and adjusts the integration step size in order to keep the error below a specified threshold. The accuracy requested is that both the relative and absolute (maximal) errors be less than the truncation error tolerance. The default value of this tolerance is 1.0E-6. The integration is carried out in a piecewise manner from the point t_μ to $t_{\mu+1}$. At this point the $(\mu+1)^{th}$ component of the objective function is calculated and added to the previous components. This process is continued until reaching the last set of data points at $t_{\mu+1} = t_n$. For integration of stiff systems, the MATLAB library function *ode15s* is used, which is based on the backward difference formulas (BDF) method of Gear (1971).

For the outer-loop minimization, the MATLAB *nlinfit* function that is based on the Levenberg-Marquardt (LM) algorithm (Seber and Wild, 2003) was used. It belongs to the gradient-based category, where the objective-function and constraints derivatives need to be evaluated. LM is a modification of the Newton method, where the second derivatives appearing in the Hessian matrix are neglected. The algorithm switches to the steepest descent method when the Hessian matrix becomes nearly singular.

In problems where the values of the state variables are associated with different units, or different magnitude, scaling is required. The scaling we introduce is: $W_i = 1/\max|x_{\mu,i}|$. This formulation actually scales all the variables in the objective function to the [-1,1] interval. With this scaling, the deviations of all of the state variable estimates from the measured values (e.g., due to miss prediction of the associated parameter values) have similar impact on the objective function.

The quality of the fit between the model and the available data can be assessed based on the visual inspection of the plot of the available data and the curve of the calculated values vs. time, for a particular variable. Deviations between the data and the calculated values may indicate inappropriate model and/or non-optimal parameter values. Residual plots are expected to show random error distribution in cases of adequate model and parameter values. Non-random residual distributions (which exhibit particular trends) may signal problems with the model and/or the parameter values.

Existence of superfluous parameters in the model may lead to "rank deficient" condition of the Jacobian matrix and/or inflated confidence intervals. The individual parameter confidence intervals $(\Delta\underline{\theta_i})$ in nonlinear regression are defined

$$\theta_i = \hat{\theta}_i \pm \Delta\theta_i ; \quad \Delta\theta_i \equiv t(v,\alpha)s\sqrt{a_{ii}} \tag{3}$$

where $\hat{\theta}_i$ is the estimated parameter value, a_{ii} is the ith diagonal element of the inverse of the Jacobian matrix, $t(v, \alpha)$ is the statistical t distribution corresponding to v degrees of freedom and a desired confidence level, α and s is the standard error of the estimate. Clearly, when $|\hat{\theta}_i| < \Delta\theta_i$, the zero value is included in the confidence interval, which implies that there is no statistical justification to include the associated term in the regression model.

3. Parameter estimation for catalytic hydrogenation of cinnamaldehyde (Zamostand Belohlav, 1999)

The reactions occurring in the catalytic hydrogenation of cinnamaldehyde are shown in Figure 1. Zamost and Belohlav (1999) report concentration data of an experiment that was carried out in an isothermal, isobaric, stirred semi-batch reactor. The mass balance and rate equations of the various reactions can be brought into the following form:

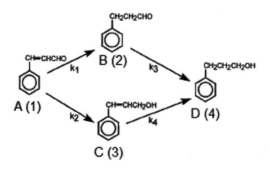

Figure 1. Reaction scheme of cinnamaldehyde hydrogenation (Zamostand and Belohlav, 1999)

$$\frac{dC_1}{dt} = -\frac{k_1 C_1}{\sigma} - \frac{k_2 C_1}{\sigma}; \qquad \frac{dC_2}{dt} = \frac{k_1 C_1}{\sigma} - \frac{k_3 \theta_2 C_2}{\sigma}$$

$$\frac{dC_3}{dt} = \frac{k_2 C_1}{\sigma} - \frac{k_4 \theta_3 C_3}{\sigma}; \qquad \frac{dC_4}{dt} = \frac{k_3 \theta_2 C_2}{\sigma} + \frac{k_4 \theta_3 C_3}{\sigma}; \qquad \sigma = C_1 + C_2 \theta_2 + C_3 \theta_3 + C_4 \theta_4 \qquad (7)$$

where t is the time, C_1, C_2, C_3 and C_4 are relative concentrations of compounds A, B, C and D, respectively, k_1, k_2, k_3 and k_4 are reaction rate coefficients and, θ_2, θ_3 and θ_4 are adsorption coefficient ratios with respect to the 1st compound (i.e., $\theta_1 = 1$). Thus, the parameters to be determined are k_1, k_2, k_3, k_4, θ_2, θ_3 and θ_4.

The experimental data reported by Zamostny and Belohlav (1999) are shown in Table 1. An arbitrary initial estimates: k_1, k_2, k_3, $k_4 = 0.1$ and θ_2, θ_3, $\theta_4 = 1$ were used to start the process of parameter identification. Using the sequential solution algorithm, approximately 500 iterations were required for the convergence of the LM algorithm. The calculated parameter values, the respective confidence intervals and the objective function value (Φ) are $k_1 = 0.073882 \pm 0.0105$, $k_2 = 0.0095684 \pm 0.00417$, $k_3 = 0.016988 \pm 0.0273$, $k_4 = 299.99 \pm 5.08E+07$, $\theta_2 = 1.3279 \pm 2.11$), $\theta_3 = 0.00011516 \pm 19.723$, $\theta_4 = 0.2493 \pm 0.24261$ and $\Phi = 0.00689$. Observe that for the parameters k_3, k_4, θ_2 and θ_3, the confidence interval is larger in absolute value than the corresponding parameter value. The parameters k_4 and θ_3 exhibit extreme ill-conditioning as the confidence intervals are by four orders of magnitude larger than the parameter values. To identify the cause for the ill-conditioning of k_4 and θ_3, the equations defining σ, dC_3/dt and dC_4/dt should be considered.

Considering the numerical values of C_3 (Table 1) and θ_3 shows that the term $C_3 \theta_3$ is by three orders of magnitude smaller than the other terms in the expression defining σ. Thus, the influence of θ_3 on the value of σ is infinitesimal and only the product $k_4 \theta_3$ can be identified from the values of dC_3/dt and dC_4/dt. Accordingly, the numerical ill-

Table 1. Relative concentration data for the example problem (Zamostny and Belohlav, 1999)

μ	t (min)	$C_{\mu 1}$	$C_{\mu 2}$	$C_{\mu 3}$	$C_{\mu 4}$
0	0	1	0	0	0
1	2	0.892	0.084	0.012	0.007
2	5	0.651	0.295	0.042	0.022
3	10	0.446	0.445	0.051	0.096
4	20	0.193	0.542	0.058	0.223
5	35	0.06	0.482	0.057	0.436
6	55	0.001	0.259	0.029	0.711
7	90	0	0.024	0	0.976

conditioning of the parameter identification problem can be alleviated by removing the term $C_3\theta_3$ from σ and defining a new parameter $k'_4 = k_4\theta_3$, which replaces the product of two parameters by a single (new) parameter.

The parameter identification process was repeated for the 6 parameter model, where $k_4\theta_3$ is replaced by k'_4. The convergence of the LM algorithm to the solution was much faster than in the 7 parameters case. The results in this case were: $k_1 = 0.081319 \pm 0.0058063$, $k_2 = 0.0091632 \pm 0.0034232$, $k_3 = 0.017872 \pm 0.0022194$, $k'_4 = 0.029887 \pm 0.020874$, $\theta_2 = 1.6118 \pm 0.265$, $\theta_4 = 0.4163 \pm 0.0985$ and $\Phi = 0.0185$. The parameter values are essentially identical to those obtained in the 7 parameter case (including the value of $k'_4 = k_4\theta_3$), however all the confidence intervals (absolute value) are now smaller than the respective parameter values. Plots of the calculated concentration curves obtained by the sequential solution technique with the six-parameter model (not shown), indicate good agreement of the calculated values with the data.

4. Conclusions

The proposed procedure for iterative diagnostics and model refinement in dynamic parameter estimation was utilized for improving the model proposed by Zamonstand and Belohlav (1999) for a cinnamaldehide hydrogenation process. For their model, the minimal sum of squares solution yielded two parameters (out of 7), that are not significantly different from zero. The reason for the ill-conditioning was diagnosed to be a high correlation between the two parameters. Replacing them by a single one yielded a stable and satisfactory solution. The proposed procedure was applied to additional problems, with the objective to find the maximal set of physically feasible parameter values, based on the available data and the suggested model. Because of space limitations the details for these problems are not included here, and only some conclusions follow.

The minimal sum of squares solution of the methanol to hydrocarbon process (Maria, 1989) yielded three parameter values (out of the five suggested) that were not significantly different from zero Using scaled variables in the objective function enabled inclusion of four stable parameter values in the optimal solution.

For the Dow chemical problem (Biegler et al., 1986), the 3 ODE model formulation (presented, for example, by Sulieman et al. 2009) was used. For this problem, accurate and stable 8-parameters solution was identified using scaled data (in the $0 - 1$ range), where all the parameters were identified simultaneously. On the other hand, solutions involving non-scaled data, or partitioning of the problem into sub-problems corresponding to the different temperature levels, yielded some unstable parameters with confidence intervals larger than the corresponding parameter values.

The modelling of the transient process of the Tobacco Mosaic Virus multiplication in a protoplast (based on the model of Ji and Luo, 2000) can be used for comparison of the efficiency, reliability and accuracy of the sequential and simultaneous solution techniques. This model comprises of six ODEs with 16 adjustable parameters. Only 8 of the parameters are identifiable with a stable solution and values for the rest of the parameters need to be assumed. The 8-parameters identification process, using arbitrary initial estimates and the simultaneous method, converges within <10 iterations and 0.019 CPU seconds to a solution with objective function value of $\Phi = 1.5762$.

Attempting to solve the same problem with the same initial estimates by the sequential method, required the application of stiff-integration algorithm and resulted in convergence to a local minimum. Using the simultaneous-method solution as initial estimate enabled convergence of the sequential method to the global optimum (Φ = 0.304) using the Runge-Kutta integration algorithm within <20 LM iterations, 4.2 CPU seconds.

Thus the simultaneous solution technique has proven to be by far computationally more efficient compared to the sequential method. However, it has been shown that in the case of noisy data, the parameter values calculated by the simultaneous method may yield solutions of the ODE for the state variables that deviate considerably from the data. Therefore, it is advisable to use the optimal parameter values obtained by the simultaneous method only as initial estimate for the final identification of the parameter values by a sequential method.

References

L. T. Biegler, J. J. Damiano, G. E. Blau, 1986, Nonlinear parameter estimation: a case study comparison, AIChE Journal, 32, 1, 29-45.

J. R. Dormand, P. J. Prince, 1980, A family of embedded Runge-Kutta formulae, J. Comp. Appl. Math., 6, 19-26.

V. Dua, 2011, An Artificial Neural Network approximation based decomposition approach for parameter estimation of system of ordinary differential equations, Computers and Chemical Engineering, 35, 545–553.

C. W. Gear, 1971, Numerical Initial Value Problems in Ordinary Differential Equations, Prentice Hall, Englewood Cliffs, USA.

F. Ji, L. Luo, 2000, A Hypercycle Theory of Proliferation of Viruses and Resistance to the Viruses of Transgenic Plant, J. Theor. Biol., 204, 453-465.

G. Jia, G. N. Stephanopoulos, R. Gunawan, 2011, Parameter estimation of kinetic models from metabolic profiles: two-phase dynamic decoupling method, Bioinformatics, 27, 1964-1970.

C. Kravaris, J. Hahn, Y. Chu, 2013, Advances and selected recent developments in state and parameter estimation, Computers and Chemical Engineering, 51, 111-123

G. Maria, 1989, An adaptive strategy for solving kinetic model coccomitant estimation-reduction problems., Can. J. Chem. Eng., 67, 825-832.

G. Maria, 2004, A Review of Algorithms and Trends in Kinetic Model Identification for Chemical and Biochemical Systems, Chem. Biochem. Eng. Q., 18, 3, 195–222.

K. A. P. McLean, K. B. McAuley, 2012, Mathematical modelling of chemical processes - obtaining the best model predictions and parameter estimates using identifiability and estimability procedures, Canadian Journal of Chemical Engineering, 90, 351-366.

C. Michalik, B. Chachuat, W. Marquardt, 2009, Incremental Global Parameter Estimation in Dynamical Systems, Industrial and Engineering Chemistry Research, 48, 5489–5497.

J.A. Nelder, R. Mead, 1965, A Simplex Method for Function Minimization, The Computer Journal, 7, 308.

G. A. F. Seber, C. J. Wild, 2003, Nonlinear Regression, Hoboken, NJ, Wiley-Interscience.

H. Sulieman, I. Kucuk, P. J. McLellan, 2009, Parametric sensitivity: A case study comparison, Computational Statistics and Data Analysis, 53, 2640-2652.

P. Zamostny, Z. Belohlav, 1999, A software for regression analysis of kinetic data, Computers and Chemistry, 23, 479-485.

Jiří Jaromír Klemeš, Petar Sabev Varbanov and Peng Yen Liew (Editors)
Proceedings of the 24th European Symposium on Computer Aided Process Engineering – ESCAPE 24
June 15-18, 2014, Budapest, Hungary. Copyright © 2014 Elsevier B.V. All rights reserved.

The Role of Mobile Devices in Computer Aided Process Engineering

Mordechai Shacham,[a*] Michael B. Cutlip,[b] Michael Elly[a]

[a]Chem. Eng. Dept., Ben-Gurion University, Beer-Sheva, Israel
[b]University of Connecticut, Storrs, CT 06269, US
shacham@exchange.bgu.ac.il

Abstract

The widespread and continuous availability of mobile devices (smart-phones and tablets) makes them attractive computational tools for CAPE applications. We have used a computational package developed by us for Android-based devices (PolyMathLite) to demonstrate a potential, important application of such packages. An example, involving the modelling and simulation of a semi batch, highly exothermic reaction is presented. The model of the reactor, operating at normal conditions is prepared, verified and saved. Whenever the need arises (as the result in changes in operating conditions) the model is updated and repeated simulations are used to determine what actions (if any) need to be taken in order to prevent temperature runaway in the reactor.

Keywords: process modelling and simulation, smart-phones, temperature runaway

1. Introduction

Large scale process modeling, simulation and optimization programs, such as Aspen Plus, Hysys, GAMS, gProms etc. (for details see for example, Seider et al., 2004) are routinely used for design and operation of chemical processes. However, they can be used only in locations where computers and the required programs are available. Often internet access is also essential. There can be instances where process design or operation related questions need to be dealt with when only mobile devices, such as smart-phones or tablets, are available. To enable engineers to use CAPE (computer aided process engineering) tools on mobile devices applications suitable to such devices need to be developed.

To fulfil this need, we have developed the PolyMathLite (PML) application for Android-based devices. This application is a slightly simplified version of the Polymath software package (Polymath is a product of Polymath Software). The Android operating system was selected because it is predicted that by 2017 it will be the dominant operating system for all computing devices (Wingfield, 2013).

PolyMathLite enables users to obtain numerical solutions to a wide range of problems including systems of linear and nonlinear algebraic equations (NLE), systems of ordinary differential equations (ODE, stiff and non-stiff) and carry out linear, multiple–linear, polynomial and non-linear regressions. The advanced numerical algorithms used in PML (and Polymath) were presented by Shacham et al. (2002) (for NLEs) and Alva et al. (2005) (for ODEs). The potential educational use of Polymath in in a process simalution course was described by Shacham (2011) and its application for modeling a complex unit operation was demonstrated by Shacham et al. (2012). Recently, it has been shown (Elly et al., 2013) that PML can can be applied for similar tasks in process modeling applications.

In order to use PML for CAPE related computations it is recommended to prepare, in advance, models of unit operation such as reactors, heat exchangers etc., verifying their operation using nominal process operating conditions and saving them in the mobile device. Whenever the need arises (like, when changing operating conditions) the parameters of the model can be changed to simulate the process behavior with the present operating conditions. Cooling failure in an exothermic reaction will be used to demonstrate the use of the proposed approach and highlight the importance of this new computational tool.

2. Cooling failure in a propylene oxide polymerization reactor

Propylene oxide polymerization is a highly exothermic process, which is carried out at high pressures. Nearly isothermal operation is required in order to prevent runaway conditions and the build-up of a pressure which is higher than the reactor's design pressure. Safety problems associated with the operation of such a reactor are described by Kneale and Forster (1968). Mathematical modelling and simulation of the reactor was carried out by Ingham et al. (1994). They considered the manufacture of a polyol lubricant through the following reaction:

$$C_4H_9OH + (n+1)\ C_3H_6O \rightarrow C_4H_9(OC_3H_6)nOCH_2CHOHCH_3 + heat \tag{1}$$

A schematic description of the reactor carrying out this reaction is shown in Figure 1. The catalyzed alcohol is initially charged into the reactor, up to the "initial level". The oxide is fed into the reactor at a constant rate until the batch is ready and the reactor is full. Excess heat of the reaction is removed via an external heat removal system. Economical considerations dictate that the reaction should be completed at the highest possible rate. The reaction rate is a function of the temperature, catalyst concentration and liquid phase oxide concentration (which is function of the pressure). The limits on the reactor temperature and catalyst concentration are set by considerations of thermal degradation and purification difficulties.

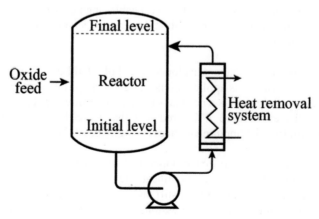

Figure 1. Propylene oxide polymerization reactor (Kneale and Forster, 1968).

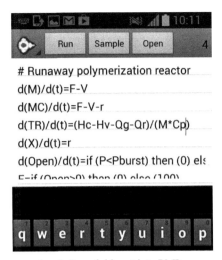

Figure 2. Polymerization reactor (partial) model input into PML

Table 1. Model equations for the polymerization reactor (normal operating conditions)

No.	Model equations	No.	Model equations
1	# Runaway polymerization reactor	20	C=MC/M
2	d(M)/d(t)=F-V	21	r=k*MC
3	d(MC)/d(t)=F-V-r	22	T0=80
4	d(TR)/d(t)=(Hc-Hv-Qg-Qr)/(M*Cp)	23	Lamda=670
5	d(X)/d(t)=r	24	Cp=3.5
6	d(Open)/d(t)=**if** (P<Pburst) **then** (0) **else** (0.001)	25	HR=-1660
7	F=**if** (Open>0) **then** (0) **else** (100)	26	Fc=3300
8	V=**if** ((P<=1) **or** (Open==0)) **then** (0) **else** (V1)	27	Pburst=8
9	V1=**if** (P<1.9) **then** (Vsubs) **else** (Vs)	28	R=1.987
10	Vs=0.85*Kv*P/*sqrt*(TR+273)	29	E=21000
11	Vsubs=Kv*P/*sqrt*((TR+273))**sqrt*(1+1/P^2)	30	M0=4400
12	MW=(M0+X)/(M0/74)	31	Kv=100
13	Hc=F*Cp*(T0-TR)	32	t(0)=0
14	Hv=V*Lamda	33	M(0)=4400
15	Qg=r*HR	34	MC(0)=0
16	Qr=Fc*Cp*(TR-T0)	35	TR(0)=80
17	P=**if** (P1<1) **then** (1) **else** (P1)	36	X(0)=0
18	P1=(*exp*(-3430/(TR+273)+11.7)+1.45e-3*MW)*C	37	Open(0)=0
19	k=9e9**exp*(-E/(R*(TR+273)))	38	t(f)=2000

To maximize the reaction rate, the pressure must be kept as high as possible for the entire duration of the batch. The higher limits on the pressure and reaction rate are dictated by the pressure suitability of the reactor system and the feasible heat removal rate. The model of the polymerization reactor can be entered into PML, as shown in Figure 2. Only the first few model equations are displayed in this Figure. The complete set of the equations corresponding to normal operating conditions is shown in Table 1.

Under normal operating conditions reacting mass is being re-circulated through the external heat removal system at flow rate of F_c, and cooled to temperature T_R, (see Eqs. 3 and 15 in Table 1). The bursting disk is intact (*Open* = 0, see Eq. 5) and the vapor discharge rate through the orifice, V, is zero (see Eq. 7). If for some reasons the pressure exceeds the limit of P_{burst}, the burst disk ruptures. In such a case, the variable '*Open*' becomes greater than zero (Eq. 5) and vapor discharge is initiated (Eq. 7) at either sonic (Eq. 9) or subsonic (Eq. 10) discharge rate. The latent heat of vaporization of the discharging oxide cools down the reactor (see Eqs. 3 and 13) and the reaction essentially stops. When the disk ruptures, the feed to the reactor is stopped (Eq. 6).

Parts of the results obtained when running this model with PML, for batch duration of 33 h and 20 min (2,000 min), under normal operating conditions, are shown in the first five rows of Table 2. The initial, maximal (absolute) and final values of the variables are shown. The PML report contains also tabular results that can be used for preparing plots of the changes of the variables with time. The variation of the reactor's temperature, T_R with time is shown in Figure 3. Observe that the temperature changes are quite moderate. After about 13 h, the temperature reaches a maximal value of 112 °C. The increased reaction rate associated with the high temperature (and pressure) reduces the oxide concentration. This, in turn, affects a reduction of the reaction rate (and the temperature) until the trend is reversed again, showing increasing temperature. The molecular weight of the final product in normal operation is $Mw = 2,895$.

The PML model of the polymerization reactor can be saved on the smart phone for future use and the report of the variable values obtained under normal operating condition can be kept for future reference. Simulation of the reactor's operation when some of the operating conditions change may be essential in many situations.

Consider, for example the situation where a cooling failure (stoppage of the re-circulation through the external heat removal system) of 10 min duration occurs after 700 min. from the start of the batch. The engineer, who is in charge of the operation of the reactor needs to determine what action (if any) should be taken in order to prevent temperature runaway and loss of the batch, while having only the smart-phone available for computation.

To simulate the cooling failure the equation defining the value of F_c (No. 25 in Table 1) need to be changed, in order to reflect the recirculation stoppage ($F_c = 0$) of 10 mins duration. The results obtained in this case are shown in the last 3 columns of Table 2 and in Fig. 3. Observe that the temperature reaches a maximal value of 265.7 °C about 23 min after the normal cooling re-circulation rate has been restored. The pressure reaches the threshold value of 8 bar 10 min earlier and the burst disk is ruptured. Because of the cooling caused by the latent heat of vaporization of the discharging oxide vapor and the reduction of reaction rate to zero due to diminishing oxide concentration, the temperature is reduced to 80 °C, about 2 h after the disk rupture. The pressure is reduced to 1 bar instantaneously. The molecular weight of the product in this case is an $Mw = 1,325$, which is far from the specifications. Thus, this particular batch is lost due to the cooling failure.

Investigating the options for preventing temperature runaway and loss of this particular batch shows that increase of the cooling re-circulation rate to its maximum, $F_c = 5,000$ kg min^{-1} after cooling is restored, enables reaching this objective.

Table 2. Initial, minimal, maximal and final variable values in the polymerization reactor

No.	Variable	Initial value	Normal operating cond.		Temperature runaway	
			Final value	Maximal (abs.) value	Final value	Maximal (abs.) value
1	C	0	0.1578	0.744704	-1.37E-24	0.744704
2	F	100	100	100	0	100
3	Fc	3,300	3,300	3,300	3,300	3,300
4	Hc	0	-3,955.89	-1.11E+04	0	-8,089.24
5	k	0.000895	0.002265	0.010554	0.000895	27.685
6	M	4400	2.04E+05	2.04E+05	7.55E+04	7.59E+04
7	MC	0	3.23E+04	3.99E+04	-1.03E-19	3.81E+04
8	MW	74	2895.18	**2,895.18**	1269.55	**1,269.55**
9	Open	0	0	0	0.013235	0.013235
10	P	1	2.21255	**6.35029**	1	**8.31067**
11	P1	0	2.21255	6.35029	-1.25E-23	8.31067
12	Qg	0	-1.21E+05	-3.98E+05	1.54E-19	-7.86E+05
13	Qr	0	1.31E+05	3.66E+05	1.64E-10	2.15E+06
14	r	0	73.0491	239.664	-9.26E-23	473.791
15	t	0	2,000	2,000	2,000	2,000
16	TR	80	91.3025	**111.897**	80	**265.669**
17	V1	7.5271	9.8533	28.4331	7.5271	35.8227
18	Vsubs	7.5271	12.7211	33.863	7.5271	42.4483
19	X	0	1.68E+05	1.68E+05	7.11E+04	7.11E+04

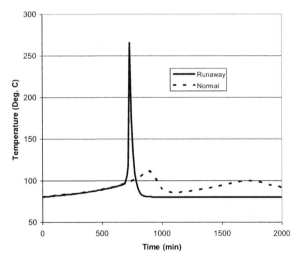

Figure 3. Temperature variation in the reactor under normal conditions and temperature runaway

3. Conclusions

With the introduction of the mobile phones the process engineer is expected to be available for answering process design and operation related questions at any time of the day, irrespective of his/her location. In this paper we have demonstrated that PML can serve as an "always available" computational tool that can help in reaching conclusions and decisions based on careful quantitative analysis of the problem in question. Because of the space limitation only one example of the use of PML was presented. This example involves an incident of cooling failure of limited duration in a semi batch, exothermic reaction and an attempt to determine what action (if any) should be taken in order to prevent temperature runaway and loss of the batch. Simulation of the reactor's operation using PML has shown that runaway conditions do develop if no action is taken, however this can be prevented by increasing the cooling recirculation rate after the cooling has been restored.

We expect that wider availability and accessibility of mobile device based computational tools will extend considerably the population of the users and the problems tackled by such tools. Use of this software can be introduced starting with problems that may be appropriate for users with only high school education background at the AP (advanced placement) levels in the sciences, math and introduction to engineering. More complex problems can be easily solved by students in the STEM (science, technology, engineering, and mathematics) subject areas in technical programs, community colleges, and four-year colleges and universities.

As PML uses very advanced and well proven numerical algorithms it can deal with very complex problems found in advanced coursework and in graduate scientific and engineering studies at the MS or PhD levels, in addition to the CAPE related applications that were demonstrated here. Thus, PolyMathLite represents an important and valuable contribution to the numerical computation toolbox of the practicing engineers, researchers and the chemical engineering students.

References

T. Alva, M. Shacham, N. Brauner, M. B. Cutlip, 2005, Construction of a Web–Based Library for Testing the Performance of Numerical Software for ODEs, Computer Aided Chemical Engineering, 20, 109-114

M. Elly, M.Shacham, M. B. Cutlip, 2013, The Role of Smartphones And Tablets In Numerical Problem Solving, Paper 668b, Presented at AIChE Annual Meeting, San-Francisco, Nov. 3-8.

J. Ingham, I. J. Dunn, E. Heinzle, J. E. Prenosil, 1994, Chemical Engineering Dynamics, VCH, Weinheim

M. Kneale, G. M. Forster, 1968, An Emergency Condensing System for a Large Propylene Oxide Polymerization Reactor, I. Chem. E. Symp. Series No. 25, 98

W. D. Seider, J. D. Seader, D. R. Lewin, 2004, Product and process design principles : synthesis, analysis, and evaluation, 2nd Ed., Wiley, New York.

M. Shacham, N. Brauner, M. B. Cutlip, 2000, Open Architecture Modelling and Simulation in Process Hazard Assessment, Comput. Chem. Eng, 24, 415-419.

M. Shacham, N. Brauner, M. B. Cutlip, 2002, A Web-based Library for Testing Performance of Numerical Software for Solving Nonlinear Algebraic Equations, Comput. Chem. Eng., 26, 4-5, 547-554

M. Shacham, 2011, Use of Advanced Educational Technologies in a Process Simulation Course, Computer Aided Chemical Engineering, 29, 1135-1139.

M. Shacham, M. B. Cutlip, M. Elly, 2012, Semi-Batch Steam Distillation of a Binary Organic Mixture – a Demonstration of Advanced Problem Solving Techniques and Tools, Chemical Engineering Education, 46, 173-181.

N. Wingfield, 2013, PC Sales Still in a Slump, Despite New Offerings, The New York Times, April 10.

Jiří Jaromír Klemeš, Petar Sabev Varbanov and Peng Yen Liew (Editors)
Proceedings of the 24th European Symposium on Computer Aided Process Engineering – ESCAPE 24
June 15-18, 2014, Budapest, Hungary. Copyright © 2014 Elsevier B.V. All rights reserved.

Modelling the Oxidation of Spent Uranium Carbide Fuel

James Shepherd,* Michael Fairweather, Peter Heggs, Bruce Hanson

School of Process, Environmental and Materials Engineering, University of Leeds, Leeds LS2 9JT, UK.
js08js@leeds.ac.uk

Abstract

Uranium/mixed carbide fuels are a candidate fuel for future nuclear reactors. However, in order to be implemented, a clear outline for their reprocessing must be formed so as to reduce the volume of nuclear waste produced as much as possible. One proposed method is to oxidise the uranium carbide into uranium oxide which can then be reprocessed using current infrastructure. A mathematical model has been constructed to simulate such an oxidation from a combination of finite-difference approximations of the relevant equations describing the heat and mass transfer processes involved. Available literature was consulted for reaction coefficients and information on reaction products, however the behaviour of the produced oxide is uncertain. The model was built accounting for this uncertainty and the resultant predictions will assist in characterising the proposed reprocessing method for carbide fuels.

Keywords: Nuclear, oxidation, finite-difference technique, heat/mass transfer.

1. Introduction

The oxidation of uranium carbide as a reprocessing step has the potential to significantly increase the efficiency of uranium (U) and plutonium (Pu) extraction from spent carbide fuel. However, it is not without its own difficulties. The oxidation in air is known to be highly exothermic (Mazaudier et al., 2010), especially if the carbide is in powder form (Le Guyadec et al., 2009), resulting in the risk of thermal run-away of the oxidation and perhaps even self-ignition. A model of this process, therefore, should define a safe operating envelope in which the exothermic nature of the reaction can be managed.

The only existing model of the oxidation of a carbide fuel pellet in the literature is that of Scott (1966), with no published literature on the simulated oxidation of carbide fuel since. Scott's model is a shrinking core model of a spherical graphite-uranium pellet in a fixed or moving bed. The model produced in this work elaborates on Scott's model by including a far more thorough description of the oxygen transfer through the uranium oxide (UO_2) product layer, including carbon dioxide transfer and affording the oxide layer the ability to spall off. This allows the oxidation behaviour of a uranium carbide pellet to be much more realistically modelled, given that under different conditions the oxide product layer may behave differently, and produces a valuable tool for research into carbide fuel reprocessing methods.

2. The Oxidation of Uranium Carbide

Taking the oxidation to occur in air, the reaction in its simplest form can be written as below:

$$UC(s) + 2O_2(g) \rightarrow UO_2(s) + CO_2(g) \tag{1}$$

The main products, therefore, are gaseous carbon dioxide and a solid, powdered oxide (in reality, a further oxidation to U_3O_8 can occur and a number of fission products are produced). It is unclear from the literature at this stage how the oxide product will behave, i.e. whether it adheres to the surface of the oxidising carbide, slowing the reaction, or if it continually spalls off the surface due to the density decrease from UC ($\sim$13.6 g cm^{-3}) to UO$_2$ ($\sim$11.0 g cm^{-3}). This has a significant effect as an adherent product layer will have a large limiting effect on the reaction rate. The model developed, therefore, will account for both possibilities as well as the possibility that the oxide layer adheres but cracks off sporadically. Regardless of the mechanism, when the reaction is complete the solid carbide pellet becomes a pulverised oxide powder (Maslennikov et al., 2009). The kinetics of the surface reaction described in Eq. (1) can be written as (Scott, 1966):

$$R_C = k_1 \exp\left(-E_A/RT|_{r_1}\right) AC_{O_2}\big|_{r_1} \tag{2}$$

where R_C = the rate at which oxygen is used up in the surface reaction, mol s^{-1}, k_1 = the surface reaction rate constant, m s^{-1}, E_A = the activation energy (given as 7 kJ mol^{-1} (Naito 1976)), kJ mol^{-1}, R = the gas constant, kJ (K·mol)$^{-1}$, $T|_{r_1}$ = the temperature at the carbide surface, K, A = the surface area of the carbide pellet, m^2, and $C_{O_2}\big|_{r_1}$ = the oxygen concentration at the carbide surface, mol m^{-3}.

3. Mathematical Model

The next stage is to characterise the physical processes involved that are to be included in the oxidation model, in particular, the heat and mass transfer processes. The pellet is assumed to be surrounded by an infinite gaseous region of stagnant oxidant. The oxidant, air in the case of the models, is held at a constant temperature. As shown in Figure 1, the pellet is assumed to be an equivalent volume sphere with a radius of 3.27

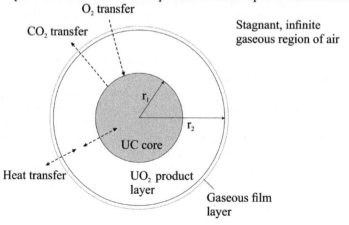

Figure 1. Diagrams of the transfer processes involved during the oxidation of a one dimensional, spherical carbide pellet with an adherent oxide layer forming.

mm allowing the system to be considered in one dimension. This assumption was made to simplify the calculations involved and because the pellets currently in use in fuel pins are roughly right cylinders 4 mm in length and 3 mm in diameter.

3.1. Heat and Mass Transfer
In order to calculate the rate from Eq. (2), the values of temperature and oxygen concentration must be known at the reaction surface, where $r = r_1$. Heat transfer was modelled using the Fourier equation for heat conduction as below:

For $t \geq 0$ and $0 \leq r \leq r_1(t) \leq r_2$:
$$\frac{\partial T_j}{\partial t} = \alpha_j \left(\frac{\partial^2 T_j}{\partial r^2} + \frac{2}{r} \cdot \frac{\partial T_j}{\partial r} \right) \tag{3}$$

where r = the radius, m, $r_1(t)$ = the radius to the surface of the carbide, m, r_2 = the radius to the surface of the solid (i.e. carbide and any oxide layer present), m, T = the temperature of the solid, K, t = the time passed, s, α_j = thermal diffusivity m² s⁻¹, and j = designates whether the carbide pellet or the oxide product layer is being considered. for $0 \leq r \leq r_1(t), j = UC$, and for $r_1(t) \leq r \leq r_2, j = UO_2$. As the reaction proceeds, r_1 decreases as the carbide pellet is oxidised. The overall volume of solid is assumed to remain constant (r_2 is constant) despite a volume expansion occuring in reality due to the density change. This representation is known as the shrinking core model (Smith, 1970).

The mass transfer of oxygen through the product layer can be considered similarly:

For $t \geq 0$ and $r_1(t) \leq r \leq r_2$:
$$\frac{\partial C_{O_2}}{\partial t} = D_e \left(\frac{\partial^2 C_{O_2}}{\partial r^2} + \frac{2}{r} \cdot \frac{\partial C_{O_2}}{\partial r} \right) \tag{4}$$

where D_e = the effective diffusivity of oxygen through the product layer, m² s⁻¹, and C_{O_2} = the oxygen concentration within the oxide layer, mol m⁻³.

The initial conditions for the two general Eqs. (3) and (4) are:

For t < 0: $\qquad\qquad r_1(0) = r_2 \tag{5}$

For t < 0 and $0 \leq r \leq r_2$: $\qquad T_j = fn(r) \tag{6}$

For t < 0 and $r_1(t) \leq r \leq r_2$: $\qquad C_{O_2} = fn(r) \tag{7}$

The boundary conditions that are then applied depend upon which behaviour of the oxide product layer the model is considering. The one shared condition, however, is for heat transfer at the centre of the sphere:

For $t \geq 0$ and $r = 0$:
$$\left. \frac{\partial T}{\partial r} \right|_{r=0} = 0 \tag{8}$$

3.1.1. No Oxide Layer
When there is no oxide layer present, $r_2 \to r_1(t)$ for the duration of the reaction. At $r = r_1$, the carbide surface, the pellet experiences a heat flux from the oxidising gas as well as heat generated from the reaction:

For $t \geq 0$ and $r = r_1(t)$:
$$-k_{UC} \left. \frac{\partial T}{\partial r} \right|_{r=r_1} = h_d \left(T|_{r_1} - T_g \right) + \Delta H_r R_C \tag{9}$$

where h_d = the convective heat transfer coefficient, m s^{-1}, k_{UC} = the thermal conductivity of the uranium carbide, m s^{-1}, T_g = the bulk gas temperature, K, and ΔH_r = the heat of reaction, kJ mol^{-1} (calculated theoretically as 1380kJ mol^{-1})

The mass transfer in this case is the diffusion of oxygen through the external gas film surrounding the pellet, assumed to comprise carbon dioxide. It can be expressed as:

$$R_c^* = k_g A \left(C_{O_2}^B - C_{O_2}\big|_{r_1} \right) \tag{10}$$

where R_c^* = the rate of oxygen diffusion, mol s^{-1}, k_g = the external diffusion coefficient, m s^{-1}, and $C_{O_2}^B$ = the bulk oxygen concentration, mol m^{-3}.

Equating the rate expressions in Eqs. (2) and (10) yields an equation for the reaction rate when no oxide layer is present:

$$R_C = \frac{k_g k A C_{O_2}^B}{k_g + k} \tag{11}$$

3.1.2. Oxide Layer With and Without Spallation

When there is an oxide layer present the boundary conditions must be adjusted. At the solid surface, the heat and mass transfer boundary conditions are:

For $t \geq 0$ and $r = r_2$:
$$-k_{UO_2} \frac{\partial T}{\partial r}\bigg|_{r=r_2} = h_d\left(T\big|_{r_2} - T_g\right) \tag{12}$$

$$-D_{UO_2} \frac{\partial C_{O_2}}{\partial r}\bigg|_{r=r_2} = k_g\left(C_{O_2}\big|_{r_2} - C_{O_2}^B\right) \tag{13}$$

where D_{UO_2} = the effective diffusivity of oxygen through the UO$_2$ product layer, m^2 s^{-1}.

At the reaction interface, where the carbide pellet and oxide product meet, the boundary conditions are:

For $t \geq 0$ and $r = r_1(t)$:
$$-k_{UC} \frac{\partial T_{UC}}{\partial r}\bigg|_{r=r_1} - \Delta H_r R_c = -k_{UO_2} \frac{\partial T_{UO_2}}{\partial r}\bigg|_{r=r_1} \tag{14}$$

$$T_{UC}\big|_{r=r_1} = T_{UO_2}\big|_{r=r_1} \tag{15}$$

$$-D_{UO_2} \frac{\partial C_{O_2}}{\partial r}\bigg|_{r=r_1} = k_1 \exp(-E_A/RT\big|_{r_1}) C_{O_2}\big|_{r_1} \tag{16}$$

The solution of these can then be substituted into Eq. (2) to calculate the rate of reaction with an oxide layer present. In the case where the oxide layer adheres but spalls off at regular time intervals of magnitude $t = t_{sp}$, the boundary conditions in section 2.1.2. apply when $nt_{sp} \leq t \leq (n+1)t_{sp}$ where $0 \leq n$ and n is a positive integer. The boundary conditions in Section 2.1.1 apply instantaneously when $t = t_{sp}$.

4. Results and Discussion

A finite-difference technique known as the fully implicit backward method (Smith, 1965) was then applied to the above equations with the resulting approximations then solved in a FORTRAN code using the Thomas algorithm (Chang and Over, 1981). The results calculated were then plotted into graphs showing the heat profiles of the solid as time passes, as well as the changing radius of the carbide, $r_1(t)$. Figure 2 is such a plot for the case where no oxide layer is present. The peak temperature reached is at the carbide surface and surpasses 1,250 K. This occurs at the beginning of the reaction as there is a large surface area of carbide exposed to the oxidant. The temperature then cools to the surrounding gas temperature, held at 773 K, as the reaction rate slows due to depletion of the carbide. The oxidation takes around 30s to complete overall.

Figure 3 is a plot of the case where an adherent oxide layer that spalls off is present. The reaction time is similar to the case with no oxide layer, suggesting that if the oxide layer is present but spalls off regularly, it has only a small effect on the reaction rate. Spallation of the oxide layer also causes the temperature at the carbide surface to drop to the gas temperature very quickly before increasing again as the layer re-builds. For the case where the oxide layer is present but does not spall off (not shown), the presence of the oxide layer greatly increases the time until the oxidation is complete to around 50s with similar maximum temperatures reached as in the spallation case.

The oxygen and carbon dioxide distributions through the oxide layer without spallation can be seen in Figures 4 and 5. The rate of carbon dioxide release is predicted in Figure 4, although the total amount released is dictated by the stoichiometry of Eq. (1).

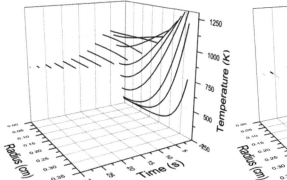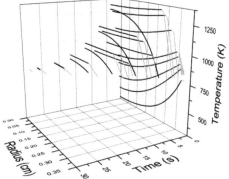

Figure 2. Radial temperature profiles through the carbide pellet during oxidation with no adherent oxide layer formed.

Figure 3. Radial temperature profiles for the case with an oxide layer undergoing regular spallation.

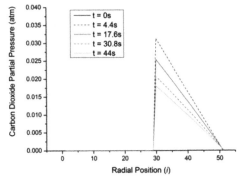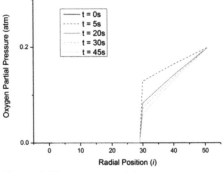

Figure 4. The carbon dioxide partial pressure throughout the oxide layer over time.

Figure 5. The oxygen partial pressure throughout the oxide layer over time.

From Figure 5, it can be seen that the oxygen concentration at the reaction interface (radial position $i = 30$) decreases over time. Therefore, it can be concluded that with the presence of an oxide layer the oxidation is diffusion limited.

5. Conclusions

A novel one-dimensional model of the oxidation of a spherical uranium carbide pellet has been derived for three different conditions to account for the uncertain nature of the oxide product. Notable features include non-linear boundary conditions that allow the calculation of co-dependent, transient heat and mass transfer. The model was completed using finite-difference approximations of the relevant heat and mass transfer equations as well as a first-order reaction rate of the reaction outlined in Eq. (1). The results confirmed the fact that a large temperature increase occurs, particularly at the surface of the carbide pellet where the reaction is taking place, which could be a potential problem if the process is employed in industrial reprocessing. It is also shown that the presence of an oxide layer has an influence on the peak temperature and reaction times. Therefore, it may be advisable to carry out the oxidation under a strong flow of air to prevent oxide layer formation. The temperature can also be controlled by lowering the oxygen concentration and temperature of the bulk gas. A 0.327 cm diameter pellet was found to completely oxidise within 30-50 s, depending on the oxide layer, with the first-order kinetics used (Scott, 1966). This is a very quick rate of reaction, which may be due to the idealised nature of the predictions (e.g. complete access of the infinite supply of oxidant to each surface of the pellet). However, it could also mean that the reaction coefficient used in Eq. (2) may need re-examining.

6. Acknowledgements

The research leading to the results contained in this paper received funding from the European Union 7th Framework Programme FP7-Fission-2011-2.3.1 under grant agreement number 295825 (Project ASGARD). The paper reflects only the authors' views and the European Union is not liable for any use that may be made of the information contained therein.

References

H.-Y. Chang, I. E. Over, 1981, Selected Numerical Methods and Computer Programs for Chemical Engineers, Sterling Swift, Manchaca, USA.

F. Le Guyadec, C. Rado, S. Joffre, S. Coullomb, C. Chatillon, E. Blanquet, 2009, Thermodynamic and Experimental Study of UC Powders Ignition, Journal of Nuclear Materials, 393, 2, 333-342.

A. Maslennikov, X. Genin, J. Vermeleun, P. Moisy, 2009, UC Oxidation with HNO_2 in Aqueous Solutions of HNO_3 and $HClO_4$, Radiochimica Acta, 97, 10, 571-580.

F. Mazaudier, C. Tamani, A. Galerie, Y. Marc, 2010, On the Oxidation of (U,Pu)C Fuel: Experimental and Kinetic Aspects, Practical Issues, Journal of Nuclear Materials, 406, 3, 277-284.

K. Naito, N. Kamegashira, T. Kondo, S. Takeda, 1976, Isothermal Oxidation, of Uranium Monocarbide Powder under Controlled Oxygen Partial Pressures. Journal of Nuclear Science and Technology, 13, 5, 260-267.

C. D. Scott, 1966, Analysis of Combustion of Graphite-Uranium Fuels in a Fixed Bed or Moving Bed, Industrial & Engineering Chemistry Process Design and Development, 5, 3, 223-233.

G. D. Smith, 1965, Numerical Solution of Partial Differential Equations, Oxford University Press, Oxford, UK.

J. M. Smith, 1970, Chemical Engineering Kinetics, McGraw-Hill, New York, USA.

Jiří Jaromír Klemeš, Petar Sabev Varbanov and Peng Yen Liew (Editors)
Proceedings of the 24th European Symposium on Computer Aided Process Engineering – ESCAPE 24
June 15-18, 2014, Budapest, Hungary.

Optimization of Performance Qualifiers during Oil Well Drilling

Márcia Peixoto Vega[a*], Marcela Galdino de Freitas[a], André Leibsohn Martins[b]

[a] DEQ - UFRRJ, BR 465, km7, CEP: 23890-000, Seropédica, RJ, Brazil
[b] PETROBRAS S.A./CENPES, Av. Hum Quadra 07, Ilha do Fundão, Rio de Janeiro, 21494-900, Rio de Janeiro, RJ, Brazil
vega@ufrrj.br

Abstract

An optimization analysis of the drilling process constitutes a powerful tool for operating under desired pressure levels (inside operational window) and, simultaneously, maximizing the rate of penetration, which must be harmonized with the conflicting objective of minimizing the specific energy. The drilling efficiency is improved as the rate of penetration is increased, however, there are conflicts with performance qualifiers, such as down hole tool life, footage, vibrations control, directional effectiveness and hydraulic scenarios. Concerning hydraulic effects, the minimization of the specific energy must be constrained by annulus bottom hole pressure safe region, using the operational window, placed above porous pressure and below fracture pressure. Under a conventional oil well drilling task, the pore pressure (minimum limit) and the fracture pressure (maximum limit) define mud density range and pressure operational window. During oil well drilling, several disturbances affect bottom hole pressure; for example, as the length of the well increases, the bottom hole pressure varies for growing hydrostatic pressure levels. In addition, the pipe connection procedure, performed at equal time intervals, stopping the drill rotation and mud injection, mounting a new pipe segment, restarting the drill fluid pump and rotation, causes severe fluctuations in well fluids flow, changing well pressure. Permeability and porous reservoir pressure governs native reservoir fluid well influx, affecting flow patterns inside the well and well pressure. The objective being tracked is operating under desired pressure levels, which assures process safety, also reducing costs. In this scenario, optimization techniques are important tools for narrow operational windows, commonly observed at deepwater and pre-salt layer environments. The major objective of this paper is developing an optimization methodology for minimizing the specific energy, also assuring safe operation (inside operational window), despite the inherent process disturbances, under a scenario that maximization of ROP (rate of penetration) is a target.

Keywords: efficiency, specific energy and rate of penetration.

1. Introduction

A drilling system consists of a rotating drill string, which is placed into the well. The drill fluid is pumped through the drill string and exits through the choke valve. An important scope of the drill fluid is to maintain a certain pressure gradient along the length of the well. During drilling, disturbances that produce fluctuations in the well pressure might occur. As the well is drilled, the hydrostatic pressure increases because of the well length grow. In addition, the reservoir fluid influx changes the well flow rate and density of the well fluid mixture. Finally, the pipe connection procedure, which requires stopping and starting of the drill fluid, produces severe fluctuations in the well flow rates. The pressure balance between the well section and the reservoir is important. If the pressure in the well is higher than the reservoir pressure, it is referred to as over-balanced drilling. This condition causes the circulation fluids to penetrate into the reservoir formation. On the other hand, if the pressure in the well is lower than the reservoir pressure, it is referred to as under-balanced drilling, and the reservoir fluids migrate into the well annulus (Nygaard and Nygaard, 2006).

2. Problem statement

An optimization analysis of a drilling process constitutes a powerful tool for operating under desired pressure levels and simultaneously maximizing the penetration rate, which reduces costs.

Since one of the first real-time drilling optimization studies, performed by Simmons (1986), developments in data acquisition and communication motivated drilling optimization studies on much more reliable basis. Dupriest and Koederitz (2005) effectively used Mechanical Specific Energy (MSE) concept in evaluating drilling efficiency of bits in real-time basis. They developed a system allowing the driller to continuously monitor MSE calculated through surface measurements alongside with other normal mechanical drilling logs. Remmert et al. (2007) performed an approach to manage rate of penetration using real time, continuously maximizing both bit cutter efficiency and transmission of energy from rig floor to the bit. They continuously monitored MSE and adjusted weight on bit (WOB) and rotary speed (RPM) to address downhole vibrations and reduce energy loss. The study provided the optimized independent drilling parameters following statistical synthesis.

Real time optimization of drilling parameters during drilling operations aims to optimize weight on bit, bit rotation speed for obtaining maximum drilling rate as well as minimizing the drilling cost. The process is formation specific.

Besides, performance qualifiers constitutes vibration control, operational life of drilling tools, rate of penetration (ROP), directional effectiveness and borehole quality. Improving drilling performance, as a means to reducing operational costs, requires optimization of performance qualifiers. Many factors influence the performance qualifies: hardness and/or abrasiveness of different formation types, weight on bit (WOB), rotary speed (RPM), flow rate (Q), and hydraulic horsepower per square inch (HSI), drilling fluid type and rheology.

Drilling efficiency has also been associated with mechanical specific energy (ES or MSE) through an inverse relationship. Mechanical specific energy ES, as a drilling efficiency quantification methodology, is defined as the energy input per unit rock volume drilled.

ES principles provide a means of predicting or analyzing bit performance. The ES parameter is a useful measure for predicting the power requirements (bit torque and rpm) for a particular bit type to drill at a given ROP in a given rock type, and the ROP that a particular bit might be expected to achieve in a given rock type. Eq.(1) shows Teale's specific energy equation derived for rotary drilling at atmospheric conditions.

$$ES = \frac{WOB}{A_B} + \frac{120 * \pi * RPM * T}{A_B * ROP} \qquad (1)$$

Teale (1965) also introduced the concept of minimum specific energy and maximum mechanical efficiency. The minimum specific energy is reached when the specific energy approaches or is roughly equal to the unconfined compressive strength (UCS) of the rock being drilled.

However, ES as an evaluation tool focuses only on the mechanical aspects of (drilling efficiency) DE. Most importantly, ES does not always have to be low to ensure DE improvement. Improvements in downhole tool life, borehole quality, directional drilling, hole cleaning, vibrations control and transitional drilling are events with similar effects on ES values and trends. As a result, mechanical and hydraulic aspects are important factors in order to implement real-time optimization during oil well drilling (Figure 1). As a result, the main objective of this paper is implementing real time optimization studies for assuring lowest cost and operational efficiency.

3. Results

A nonlinear mathematical model (gas-liquid-solid), representing the drilling system, was developed based on mass and momentum balances (Martins et al., 2013). The annulus bottomhole pressure was defined as the summation of annulus compression and hydrostatic pressures, frictional losses, pressure loss over the choke and atmospheric pressure. The state vector for the drilling problem includes liquid, gas and solid masses inside the drill string; liquid, gas and solid masses inside the annulus; well length; mass flow of the mixture at the bit and mass flow of the mixture at the choke, Eq. (2). The set of time varying control inputs (manipulated variables: choke opening index and WOB) to the process are shown in Eq. (3).

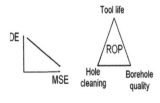

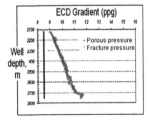

Figure 1. The mechanical and hydraulic aspects.

$$x(t) = \left[m_{gd}, m_{ld}, m_{sd}, m_{ga}, m_{la}, m_{sa}, L, W_{mix,bit}, W_{mix,choke} \right] \tag{2}$$

$$u(t) = \left[zchoke, WOB \right] \tag{3}$$

The mass balance comprised two systems: the drill string and the annulus between the wall of the well and the drill string. The momentum balance was evaluated at the drill bit and at the choke valve, taking into account frictional losses and compression and hydrostatic pressures. The flow from the reservoir into the well was modelled using a simple relation named productivity index, which is a constant scalar defining the mass flow rate based on the pressure difference between the reservoir and the well. The dynamic simulation of the drilling system phenomenological model for varying choke opening index and flow rates is shown in Figure 2.

The optimization problem solves a nonlinear system with constraints at each sampling interval. The optimization problem was solved using a Successive Quadratic Programming (SQP). Since its popularization in the late Sequential Quadratic Programming SQP has become the most successful method for solving nonlinearly constrained optimization problems. The basic idea of SQP is to model NLP at a given approximate solution say xk by a quadratic programming sub problem and then to use the solution to this sub problem to construct a better approximation xk+1. This process is iterated to create a sequence of approximations that it is hoped will converge to a solution x*. Perhaps the key to understanding the performance and theory of SQP is the fact that with an appropriate choice of quadratic sub problem the method can be viewed as the natural extension of Newton and quasi Newton methods to the constrained optimization setting. Thus one would expect SQP methods to share the characteristics of Newton like methods namely rapid convergence when iterates are close to the solution

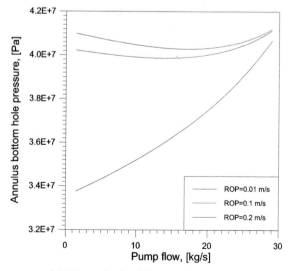

Figure 2. The drilling system model dynamic simulation.

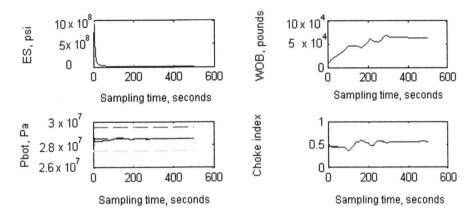

Figure 3. Optimization results (two input variables) —— fracture pressure ---- pore pressure.

but possible erratic behaviour that needs to be carefully controlled when iterates are far from a solution (Fletcher, 1981).

Figure 3 presents the minimization of the specific energy and annulus pressure set point tracking, using as constraint, the operational window placed above porous pressure and below fracture pressure. The SQP algorithm provided in line input variables for maintaining mechanical and hydraulic aspects. The input variables were weight on bit and choke opening index. It can be observed that the use of two input variables (WOB and choke opening index) in concert produced better results than can be obtained with only one input variable (WOB).

4. Conclusions

The present paper studied drilling operations inside desired pressure envelope, which assures process safety, also reducing costs for minimizing mechanical specific energy, assuring drilling efficiency. In this scenario, optimization techniques are important tools for narrow operational windows. Besides, in line optimization strategy is an useful tool due to the inherent dynamic behaviour of the process, as for example, the hydrostatic pressure increase because of the well length grown; the reservoir fluid influx, changing the well flow rate and density of the well fluid mixture and the pipe connection procedure, which requires stopping and starting of the drill fluid, producing severe fluctuations in the well flow rate.

5. References

R. Fletcher, 1981, Practical Methods of Optimization, Volume 2: Constrained optimization, John Wiley & Sons, New York, US.

E.L. Simmons, 1986, A Technique for Accurate Bit Programming and Drilling Performance Optimization, IADC/SPE 14784, Drilling Conference, Dallas, TX.

F.E. Dupriest, W. Koederitz, 2005, Maximizing Drill Rates with Real-Time Surveillance of Mechanical Specific Energy, IADC/SPE 92194, Drilling Conference, Amsterdam.

S.M. Remmert, J.W. Witt, F.E. Dupriest, 2007, Implementation of ROP Management Process in Qatar North Field, SPE 105521, SPE/IADC Drilling Conference, Amsterdam.

T. Eren, E. Ozbayoglu, 2010, Real Time Optimization of Drilling Parameters During Drilling Operations, SPE Paper 129126, SPE Oil and Gas India Conference and Exhibition, Mumbai, India.

A.L. Martins, R.A. Gandelman, M. Folsta, E.L. Resende, M.P. Vega, R.A. Dimitrios, Pirovolou, R. March, D. Gullo, 2013, On the Path for Offshore Drilling Automation, SPE/IADC Drilling Conference and Exhibition, Amsterdam, The Netherlands.

R. Teale, 1965, The Concept of Specific Energy in Rock Drilling, Int. J. Rock Mech. Mining Sci., 2, 57-53.

G.H. Nygaard, G. Naevdal, 2006, Nonlinear model predictive control scheme for stabilizing annulus pressure during oil well drilling, Journal of Process Control, 16, 719-732.

Jiří Jaromír Klemeš, Petar Sabev Varbanov and Peng Yen Liew (Editors)
Proceedings of the 24th European Symposium on Computer Aided Process Engineering – ESCAPE 24
June 15-18, 2014, Budapest, Hungary.

Modelling and Optimization of Natural Gas Networks

Tania Rodríguez[a*], Daniel Sarabia[b], Mar Valbuena[a], César de Prada[a]

[a] *Department of Systems Engineering and Automatic Control , Escuela superior de Ingenierías Industriales (University of Valladolid), Doctor Mergelina s/n,47011 Valladolid, Spain*
[b] *Department of Electromechanical Engineering, Escuela Politécnica Superior (University of Burgos), Avda. Cantabria s/n, 09006 Burgos , Spain*
tania.rodriguez@autom.uva.es

Abstract

Logistics planning and optimization are key activities for the competitiveness of companies. An important area which can benefit from the new optimization techniques is undoubtedly natural gas transmission networks.

The problem of gas network optimization deals with the question of how to operate the network, that is, taking decisions on quantity and quality of natural gas flow, minimizing at the same time the energy consumption of transport and such that, all demands of the gas network are satisfied (Martin et al., 2006). In this paper we use an sequential quadratic programming (SQP) algorithm implemented in SNOPT library for solving the optimization problem, whose objective is to minimize fuel gas consumption of the compressors whereas demands of consumers have to be satisfied.

Keywords: compressor station, gas networks, nonlinear programming, sequential quadratic programming.

1. Introduction

Transmission gas networks are formed basically by pipelines and compressor stations (controllable units) which transmit gas at high pressure from a gas source to demand points. The cost of fuel consumed by compressor stations is the most significant operation cost of transmission pipelines, they consume about 2 % of the natural gas running through them. For this reason, the aim is to minimize fuel gas consumption of the compressor whereas demands of consumers are satisfied and the compressors are operated in a cost-efficiently way.

The equations governing the dynamic behaviour of natural gas through pipelines and compressor stations are highly nonlinear. The compressors must be controlled in such a way that system constraints (such as minimum and maximum discharge pressure) are maintained at all times, while objective function (in this case compressor fuel consumed) is optimized. This results in a nonlinear constrained optimization problem. In addition to the highly nonlinear character, for a real network, this problem involves thousands of variables.

Optimization of gas networks has been treated widely for the stationary case (Pfetscha et al., 2013) but the transient case still is considered a challenge. The problem of time-dependent optimization in gas networks has been treated using different techniques as mixed integer approaches (Mahlke et al., 2010) or SQP methods (Haddad et al., 2013).

2. Modelling of natural gas networks

In order to analyse the natural gas network correctly, i.e. determine the actual state of the network, making predictions of its response to changes in operating variables, or making optimal management at low cost of the network, it is necessary to build a complete model of the gas network together with the use of optimization techniques.

A library of dynamic components has been developed in the simulation environment EcosimPro, which incorporates an object-oriented simulation language (Empresarios agrupados, 2013). This library contains rigorous pipelines models based on balance equations for mass, energy and momentum and additional equations for describing the dynamic of real gases where the longitudinal spatial coordinate in pipes has been discretized using finite differences (Rodríguez et al., 2013). Dynamic models represent typical elements, such as pipes, compressors, valves, regulation, measurement stations, etc.

Dynamic rigorous models of the behaviour of fluids in long and complex distribution networks carry a large computational load, especially when nonlinear optimization techniques are used. For this reason, it is necessary to use simpler models; in this case a new library has been created with a reduced model for the flow of natural gas in pipelines. This reduced model is based on steady state flow and energy balance equations for each pipe (Schroeder, 2001) Eqs.(1, 2), combined with several differential equations to capture the phenomenon of time delay in the union between pipelines, Eq.(4).

$$Q = C \cdot \frac{T_b}{P_b} \cdot D^{2.5} \cdot e \cdot \left(\frac{P_{in}^2 - P_{out}^2 - H_c}{L \cdot G \cdot T_a \cdot Z_a \cdot f} \right)^{0.5} \tag{1}$$

C: Constant; 0.0011493
D: Pipe diameter (mm)
e: Pipe efficiency (dimensionless)
f: Friction factor (dimensionless)
G: Gas specific gravity (dimensionless)
L: Pipe length (km)
P_b: Normal pressure (kPa)

P_1: Inlet pressure (kPa)
P_2: Outlet pressure (kPa)
Q: Flow rate (Nm^3/d)
T_a: Average temperature (K)
T_b: Normal temperature (K)
Z_a: Compressibility factor (dimensionless)
H_c: Correction factor static head (kPa^2)

$$F \cdot (T_{out} - T_{in} + \gamma_1) + \gamma_2 T_{out} F \cdot (P_{out} - P_{in}) + \gamma_3 (T_{out} - T_{soil}) = 0 \tag{2}$$

Where constants γ_1, γ_2, and γ_3 are calculated as follows, Eq. (3):

$$\gamma_1 = \frac{gsL}{C_P}, \qquad \gamma_2 = \frac{dZ_a/dT}{C_P rho_a Z_a}, \qquad \gamma_3 = \frac{\pi U_{ground} L}{C_P} \tag{3}$$

F: Natural gas mass flow (kg/s)
T_{soil}: Soil temperature (K)
U_{ground}: Heat transfer coef. (W/m^2 K)
g: Gravity (m/s^2)

C_P: Specific heat capacity (J/kg K)
rho_a: Average density (kg/m^3)
s: Pipeline slope (dimensionless)

$$\tau \cdot \frac{dP}{dt} = Q_{in}rho_{in} - Q_{out}rho_{out} \qquad (4)$$

Simulation's results should be practically the same using either library, for this reason, a proper parameterization of the reduced model is realized through nonlinear optimization algorithms. The algorithm used has been SNOPT that is typically used for large-scale constrained optimization (Gill et al., 2005). Due to the good results of parameterization obtained is concluded that the reduced model is a good simplification of the dynamic model more complete and can be used both for simulating gas networks and performing optimal management of the network. Furthermore the computation time of the simulations is reduced by 10 times using the reduced model.

In addition to gas pipelines, compressor stations are the main component of natural gas networks. They are formed by centrifugal compressors that have been modelled in order to get the required pressure ratio (discharge pressure control) and avoid the unstable operation that can be caused if at any given speed suction flow rate decreases (anti-surge control) (Acedo Sánchez, 2006). Most of authors use a simplified model of compressor stations, considering fuel gas consumed is directly proportional to the power required by the compressor, and operation limits as constraints in the optimization problem (Ehrhardt, 2005). In this paper compressor stations have been modelled adding two PID controllers in order to guarantee an efficient operation and the gas consumed is obtained depending on combustion gases produced.

The Figure 1 shows the schematic of compressor station developed in EcosimPro. The completed dynamic compressor model has been used for optimization due to the number of these units in gas networks is less than the number of pipelines and it does not imply more computational load and represents more exactly the operation of this type of installations. Fuel gas consumed by the combustor is directly related to the velocity of the turbo-compressor and thereby to discharge pressure. The lower discharge pressure necessary to satisfy a demand the lower fuel gas is consumed.

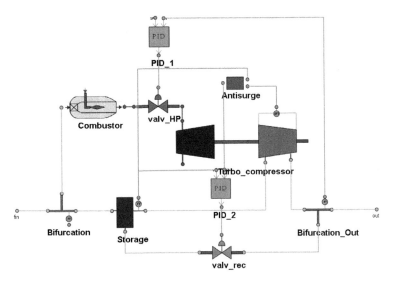

Figure 1. Schematic of compressor station in EcosimPro

Models will be validated from experimental data as normalized flow in pipelines, pressure drop or discharge temperature in centrifugal compressors. The parameterization of models will allow them represent correctly the dynamic of natural gas along the gas transmission network.

3. Optimization of natural gas transmission networks

In this paper the following problem is considered. A transmission gas network is given, there are consumers that need a certain amount of gas at a specified quality and pressure, and sources where some gas is delivered at a determined pressure, in addition, the number of compressors operating has been decided previously.

The Figure 2 shows the transmission gas network selected in order to optimize the distribution, it is based in a real gas network managed by Reganosa S.A, situated in the north of Spain, with a total length of 130 km and four measurement stations (Reganosa S.A., 2013). It has one source and six demand points; we have included two compressor stations, one of them in the supply point. They are the controllable units in order to get the normalized flow demanded by every consumer.

The optimization problem, constituting the minimization of fuel consumption of the gas transmission network is mathematically expressed by Eq. (5)

$$\min_{(SP(i))} J = \sum_{i=1}^{n} \int_{0}^{T} Q_{fuel}$$

s.t

Reduced pipeline model, Eq. (1-4), and compressor station model (5)
Minimum and maximum discharge pressure (kPa):
$5,500 \leq SP(i) \leq 9,000 \qquad \forall\, i = 1...n$
Flow demanded by every consumer:
$Q_j \geq Demand \qquad \forall\, j = 1...m$

Q_{fuel}: Natural gas flow consumed in compressor stations (m³/s)
Q_j: Natural gas flow received by every consumer (Nm³/s)
T: Total simulation time (s)
Demand: Minimum flow demanded by every consumer (Nm³/s)
Where i indicates the compressor station unit, j the consumer, n the total amount of compressor stations (in this case $n = 2$) and m the total number of consumers (in this case $m = 6$).

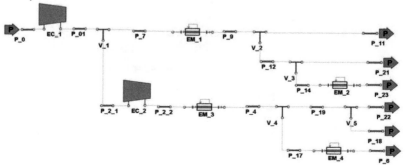

Figure 2. Gas transmission network

The optimization problem has 4 decision variables, discharge pressure for each compressor and each demand and 6 nonlinear constraints that represent the demand of every consumer. The gas network model has 2,593 variables and 2,430 equations using the reduced model whilst the complete model has 9,848 variables and 8,832 equations.
Total simulation time T has been 14,400 s (4 h) with a change in the consumer's demand at 7,200 s (2 h). With this experiment it has been checked that the optimizer is able to calculate the optimum pressure controller's set point despite variations in demand. In Figure 3 the more restrictive demands are presented, also, the experimented change at 7,200 s.

Figure 3 shows that the normalized flow which receives each consumer (dashed lines) is greater than or equal to the fixed demand (solid lines). In order to satisfy the amount of natural gas required for each consumer the optimum discharge pressure of compressor stations (solid line) must have the value presented in Figure 4 and Figure 5.

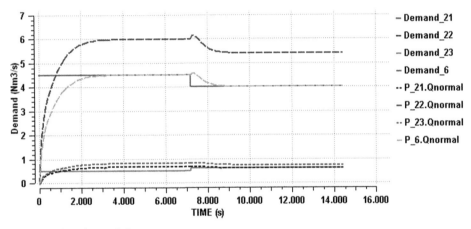

Figure 3. Flow demanded

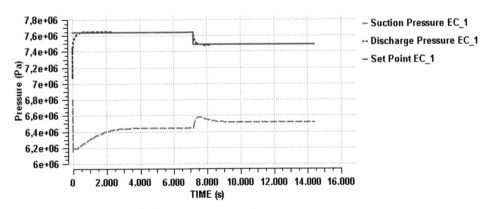

Figure 4. Optimum EC_1 discharge pressure set point

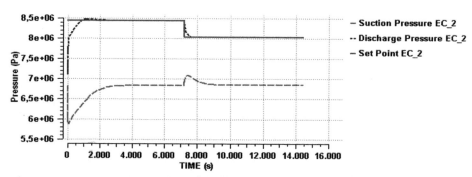

Figure 5. Optimum EC_2 discharge pressure set point

4. Conclusions

In this paper, optimization of gas transmission networks has been treated with the objective of minimizing fuel gas consumption of compressor stations satisfying demands of consumers. We have used SNOPT, an SQP algorithm that is typically used for large-scale constrained optimization.

We have developed a complete and rigorous model for compressor stations with antisurge and discharge pressure control which avoid unstable operation of the compressor. The rigorous model allows obtaining the fuel gas consumed accurately.
The results obtained have been tested simulating the complete rigorous library; we have checked that with the value of discharge pressure obtained we manage to satisfy the demands of all consumers with the minimum fuel gas consumption.

Compressor stations consume about 2 % of the natural gas running through them. With the optimization carried out and according to the dynamic rigorous library developed the percentage is reduced until 0.8 % approximately.

References

J. Acedo Sánchez, 2006, Advanced Process Control and Instrumentation, 431-449 (in Spanish).
K. Ehrhardt, Marc C. Steinbach, 2005, Nonlinear optimization in gas networks. Modeling, Simulation and Optimization of Complex Processes, 139-148
Empresarios Agrupados, 2013. EcosimPro.Versión 5.0.6, <www.ecosimpro.com> access on 17/01/2014
P. E. Gill, W. Murray, Michael A. Saunders, 2005, SNOPT: An SQP Algorithm for Large Scale Constrained Optimization, SIAM Review, 47, 1, 99-131
J. Haddad, R.M. Behbahani, 2013, Optimization of a Natural Gas Transmission System, International Journal of Computer Applications, 66, 11, 35-42.
D. Mahlke, A. Martin, S. Moritz, 2010, A mixed integer approach for time-dependent gas network optimization, Optimization methods and software, 25, 4, 625-644.
A. Martin , M. Moller, S. Moritz, 2006, Mixed integer models for the stationary case of gas network optimization, Mathematical programming, 105, 2-3, 563-582
M. E. Pfetscha, A. Fügenschuhb, B. Geißlerd, 2013, Validation of nominations in gas network optimization: Models, methods and solutions. Optimization online
S.A. Reganosa, 2013, <www.reganosa.com>, access on 17/01/2014
T. Rodríguez, D. Sarabia, C. de Prada, M. Valbuena, J.L Morales, 2013, Modelling and monitoring of natural gas networks, European Gas Technology Conference (EGATEC 2013).
D. W. Schroeder, 2001, A tutorial on pipe flow equations. <www. psig. org/Papers/2000/0112. pdf>, accessed on 17/01/2014

Jiří Jaromír Klemeš, Petar Sabev Varbanov and Peng Yen Liew (Editors)
Proceedings of the 24th European Symposium on Computer Aided Process Engineering – ESCAPE 24
June 15-18, 2014, Budapest, Hungary. Copyright © 2014 Elsevier B.V. All rights reserved.

Steel Production Scheduling Optimization under Time-sensitive Electricity Costs

Hubert Hadera[a,b], Iiro Harjunkoski[a]*, Ignacio E. Grossmann[c], Guido Sand[a], Sebastian Engell[b]

[a]*ABB Corporate Research, Wallstadter Str. 59, 68526 Ladenburg, Germany*
[b]*Technical University of Dortmund, Fraunhofer Str. 20, 4427 Dortmund, Germany*
[c]*Carnegie Mellon University, 5000 Forbes Ave., Pittsburgh, PA 15213, USA*
Iiro.Harjunkoski@de.abb.com

Abstract

Demand response of industrial production processes can support the transformation process of today's energy supply systems by enabling an active load management. For energy-intensive industries this can be seen as an opportunity to reduce costs taking advantage of process flexibility. In this study we extend a continuous-time scheduling model with generic energy-awareness to optimize the electricity purchase together with the load commitment problem. Considered electricity sources are volatile day-ahead markets, time-of-use (TOU) and base load contracts, as well as onsite generation together with a possibility to sell electricity. The model is applied to a batch process of a melt shop section in a stainless steel plant. Example case study scenarios show that the potential threat of high prices in day-ahead markets can be turned into an opportunity when optimally choosing the strategy for both scheduling the production and optimizing its net consumption cost.

Keywords: scheduling, steel plant, energy optimization, demand-side management.

1. Introduction

Today's electricity supply-demand systems face new challenges such as integration of renewables, increasing demand and liberalization of markets. One of the major technologies supporting the transformation is demand-side response. Apart from electricity producers, this technology is of special interest to heavy energy-intensive industries such as metals for which in many markets the order volumes have decreased substantially. Underutilization of production resources creates flexibility which can be exploited in order to reduce the cost for the plant and actively support the grid's reliability and safety via response to financial incentives. Energy-awareness in production scheduling is an enabler recognized as one of the emerging challenges of industrial application of scheduling as explained in the study by Harjunkoski et al. (2014), which includes also a literature survey on industrial scheduling problems. Recently Mitra et al. (2012) introduced volatile electricity markets in discrete-time scheduling of continuous processes. Less emphasis has been put on continuous-time scheduling of batch processes (Hadera and Harjunkoski, 2013), which is the focus of this work. In addition, most contributions consider a single volatile price curve (Castro et al., 2013), time-of-use (Ashok, 2006) or load tracking as a way to deal with the load commitment (Nolde and Morari, 2010). In contrast, we introduce a generic energy-awareness strategy for continuous-time based scheduling models of batch processes with optimization of multiple electricity sources.

Table 1. Model notation

Sets: $P-$ heats (products); $M-$ equipment; $S-$ energy-aware time slots; $ST-$ stages; $SM(ST,M)-$ production stages st corresponding to equipment m; $Node, I, J-$ nodes, $Node^{Pur}-$ purchase contracts node; $Node^{Dem}-$ process demand node; $Node^{Gen}-$onsite generation node; $Node^{Bal}-$ balancing node; $Node^{Sale}-$ sales node; $Arc^{Node,Node,s}-$ defined arc between nodes.
Variables: $t_{p,m}^{s}, t_{p,m}^{f}/t_{p,st}^{s}, t_{p,st}^{f}-$ starting and finishing time of heat p on equipment m/ at stage st; $q_{s}-$ electricity consumed in a time slot s; $Y_{p,st,s}^{s}, Y_{p,st,s}^{f}-$ event binaries, true when heat p starts/finishes on stage st in the slot s; $X_{m,p}-$ binary, true when heat p is processed on equipment m; $G_{s,i,j}-$ binary, true when generation is running in slot s; $g_{s,i,j}^{s}-$ continuous variables denoting startup of generation; $y_{p,m,st,s}^{saux}, y_{p,m,st,s}^{faux}-$ auxiliary continuous variables; $a_{p,m,st,s}, b_{p,m,st,s}, c_{p,m,st,s}, d_{p,m,st,s}-$ continuous variables accounting for task's time spent within a slot s; $f_{s,i,j}-$ flow from node i to j in time slot s; $c_{s}^{gen}-$ cost of generation in slot s
Parameters: $\tau_{p,m}-$ processing duration of heat p on equipment m; $\tau_{s}-$ electricity price boundary of time slot s; $h_{p,m}-$ specific power consumption of heat p on equipment m; $c_{s,i,j}-$ electricity cost in time slot s; $f_{s,i,j}^{min}, f_{s,i,j}^{max}-$ min and max flow between nodes i and j; minr, mind$-$ minimum run and down time intervals of onsite generation; $c^{start}-$ onsite generation startup cost; k$-$ percentage reduction of onsite generated power due to startup

2. Problem statement

An MILP formulation is applied to a power-intensive stainless steel melt shop process producing a set of products $p \in P$ on a set of machines $m \in M$ while satisfying various operational constraints. The batch scheduling model incorporates plant layout and features described in Hadera and Harjunkoski (2013). We generate a 24 h schedule minimizing the net electricity cost and the weighted makespan, while satisfying the production requirements for a fixed number of products. The electricity bill consists of the cost for electricity purchased from different contracts and penalties paid for the deviation from a pre-agreed load curve. The penalties occur when exceeding a certain penalty-free buffer and may differ for under- and over consumption. Possible sources of electricity include a negotiated base load contract having both constant price and volume of electricity delivered through the entire scheduling horizon. Another tariff considered is a time-of-use contract with two price levels. The plant is assumed to have an opportunity to buy from hourly changing day-ahead market and to produce electricity using own generation. The bill can be reduced by selling surplus of electricity.

3. Model formulation

3.1. Model structure and scheduling problem
The scheduling model uses continuous start time variables to link with the energy-aware part. The latter is defined in order to calculate a variable denoting the overall electricity consumption within any given time interval. Once the model is complemented by energy-awareness, both the electricity purchase and the committed load problem can be optimized. The scheduling part of the model uses assignment and precedence binaries following Equations (1-17) from Hadera and Harjunkoski (2013). The basic definitions of the mathematical formulation follow the notation as in Table 1.

3.2. Energy-awareness in continuous-time
In continuous-time models, it is challenging to account for resource consumption. The scheduling model is extended by energy-awareness by introducing a time grid with intervals corresponding to volatile electricity prices (Fig. 1) and committed load values.

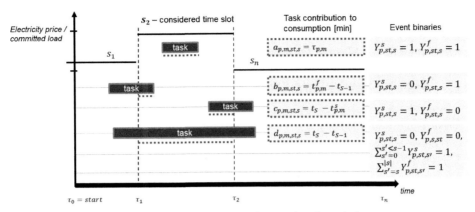

Figure 1. Electricity consumption tracking for a continuous-time formulation

For the case study we assume there are equidistant 1 h time slots. We define two event binary variables using a big-M formulation (Eqs. 1-2). The start variable is true if a task starts within a considered time slot. Similarly, the finish variable is true when a task finishes within the slot. Since the binary variables are stage specific, two corresponding auxiliary variables are defined to be equal to zero for cases when a task is not assigned to produce on a given machine (Eqs. 3-4). With the help of the auxiliary variables, a set of continuous variables is introduced in order to capture how much electricity a task consumes in a given time slot (Eqs. 5-10). A proper summation of a product of the continuous variables and machine-specific electricity consumption parameter accounts for the total consumption in a given time slot (Eq. 11). The above described approach yields less binaries than the one used by Nolde and Morari (2010).

$$\tau_s + M(1 - Y^s_{p,st,s}) \geq t^s_{p,m} \geq \tau_{s-1} - \tau_{s-1}(1 - Y^s_{p,st,s}) \quad \forall p \in P, m \in M, st \in ST, s \in S \tag{1}$$

$$\tau_s + M(1 - Y^f_{p,st,s}) \geq t^f_{p,m} \geq \tau_{s-1} - \tau_{s-1}(1 - Y^f_{p,st,s}) \quad \forall p \in P, m \in M, st \in ST, s \in S \tag{2}$$

$$Y^s_{p,st,s} \geq y^{saux}_{p,m,st,s} \geq X_{p,m} + Y^s_{p,st,s} - 1 \,; Y^f_{p,st,s} \geq y^{faux}_{p,m,st,s} \geq X_{p,m} + Y^f_{p,st,s} - 1 \tag{3}$$

$$y^{saux}_{p,m,st,s} \leq X_{p,m}; \; y^{faux}_{p,m,st,s} \leq X_{p,m} \tag{4}$$

$$a_{p,m,st,s} \geq y^{saux}_{p,m,st,s} + y^{faux}_{p,m,st,s} - 1; a_{p,m,st,s} \leq y^{saux}_{p,m,st,s}; \; a_{p,m,st,s} \leq y^{faux}_{p,m,st,s} \tag{5}$$

$$t^f_{p,m} - \tau_{s-1} + M(1 - y^{faux}_{p,m,st,s}) \geq b_{p,m,st,s} \geq t^f_{p,m} - \tau_{s-1} - M(1 - y^{faux}_{p,m,st,s} + y^{saux}_{p,m,st,s}) \tag{6}$$

$$b_{p,m,st,s} \leq (\tau_s - \tau_{s-1}) y^{faux}_{p,m,st,s}; \; b_{p,m,st,s} \leq (\tau_s - \tau_{s-1})(1 - y^{saux}_{p,m,st,s}) \tag{7}$$

$$\tau_s - t^s_{p,m} + M(1 - y^{saux}_{p,m,st,s}) \geq c_{p,m,st,s} \geq \tau_s - t^s_{p,m} - M(1 - y^{saux}_{p,m,st,s} + y^{faux}_{p,m,st,s});$$
$$c_{p,m,st,s} \leq (\tau_s - \tau_{s-1}) y^{saux}_{p,m,st,s}); c_{p,m,st,s} \leq (\tau_s - \tau_{s-1})(1 - y^{faux}_{p,m,st,s}) \tag{8}$$

$$(\tau_s - \tau_{s-1}) \sum_1^{s'<s} y^{saux}_{p,m,st,s'} \geq d_{p,m,st,s} \geq (\tau_s - \tau_{s-1})(\sum_1^{s'<s} y^{saux}_{p,m,st,s'} + \sum_{s'>s}^{|S|} y^{faux}_{p,m,st,s'} - 1);$$
$$d_{p,m,st,s} \leq (\tau_s - \tau_{s-1})(1 - y^{faux}_{p,m,st,s'}) \tag{9}$$

$$d_{p,m,st,s} \leq (\tau_s - \tau_{s-1}) \sum_{s'>s}^{|S|} y_{p,m,st,s'}^{faux} \; ; d_{p,m,st,s} \leq (\tau_s - \tau_{s-1})(1 - y_{p,m,st,s}^{saux}); \tag{10}$$

$$\forall p \in P, m \in M, st \in ST, s \in S, \{st, m\} \in SM$$

$$q_s = \frac{\sum_{p \in P, m \in M} h_{p,m}(a_{p,m,st,s}\pi_{p,m} + b_{p,m,st,s} + c_{p,m,st,s} + d_{p,m,st,s})}{60} \qquad \forall s \in S \tag{11}$$

$$\sum_{i \in Node} f_{s,i,j'} = \sum_{j \in Node} f_{s,j',j} \qquad \forall (i,j'),(j',j) \in Arc, j' \in Bal, s \in S \tag{12}$$

$$f_{s,i,j}^{max} \geq f_{s,i,j} \geq f_{s,i,j}^{min} \quad \forall (i,j) \in Arc, i, j \in Node, \ s \in S \tag{13}$$

$$q_s = \sum_{i \in Node, j \in Dem} f_{s,i,j} \qquad \forall (i,j) \in Arc, s \in S \tag{14}$$

$$M \cdot G_{s,i,j} \geq f_{s,i,j} \geq G_{s,i,j} \qquad \forall (i,j) \in Arc, i \in Gen, j \in Bal, s \in S \tag{15}$$

$$G_{s,i,j} \geq g_{s,i,j}^s \geq G_{s,i,j} - G_{s-1,i,j} \qquad \forall (i,j) \in Arc, i \in Gen, j \in Bal, s \in S \tag{16}$$

$$g_{s,i,j}^s \leq G_{s,i,j}; g_{s,i,j}^s \leq 1 - G_{s-1,i,j} \qquad \forall (i,j) \in Arc, i \in Gen, j \in Bal, s \in S \tag{17}$$

$$c_s^{gen} = \sum_{i \in Gen, j \in Bal} f_{s,i,j} \cdot c_{s,i,j} + c^{start} \cdot g_{s,i,j}^s \quad \forall (i,j) \in Arc, s \in S \tag{18}$$

$$f_{s,i,j} = f_{s,i,j}^{max} \cdot G_{s,i,j} - k \cdot f_{s,i,j}^{max} \cdot g_{s,i,j}^s \quad \forall (i,j) \in Arc, i \in Gen, j \in Bal, s \in S \tag{19}$$

$$\sum_{s'=s}^{s+minr-1} G_{s',i,j} \geq minr \left(G_{s,i,j} - G_{s-1,i,j} \right) \qquad \forall (i,j) \in Arc, i \in Gen, j \in Bal, s \in S \tag{20}$$

$$\sum_{s'=s}^{s+mind-1} G_{s',i,j} \leq mind(1 + G_{s,i,j} - G_{s-1,i,j}) \quad \forall (i,j) \in Arc, i \in Gen, j \in Bal, \ s \in S \tag{21}$$

$$\mu = \sum_{s \in S} \left(\sum_{i' \in Pur, j' \in Bal} f_{s,i',j'} + c_s^{gen} + \sum_{i \in Bal, j \in Sale} f_{s,i,j} \cdot c_{s,i,j} \right) \; \forall (i,j),(i',j') \in Arc \tag{22}$$

$$\min(\mu + \delta + c \cdot t^{ms}) \tag{23}$$

3.3. Time-sensitive electricity purchases optimization

The tracking of electricity consumption over the time intervals can be used for optimization of the purchase strategy. The idea here is based on a minimum cost flow network (Figure 2) with a balancing node for which all inflows must be equal to all outflows (Eq. 12). The inflow nodes represent possible sources of electricity. The outflow nodes are the process demand and the sale of electricity. The balancing node is connected with sink and source nodes by arcs defined by parameters and variables. An arc exists only if there is a cost defined for it. The parameters are minimum and maximum levels of flows between two given nodes (Eq. 13) and cost (Figure 2). The network is used to identify the most economical flow while always satisfying the load on the process demand node (Eq. 14). The onsite generation is modelled using a binary variable denoting if the plant is in production mode (Eq. 15) and an auxiliary continuous variable denoting generation start-up (Eqs. 16-17). The onsite generation constraints are kept simple by considering a constant generation cost with additional start-up cost (Eq. 18) and reduced production rate for time intervals where start-up occurs (Eq. 19).

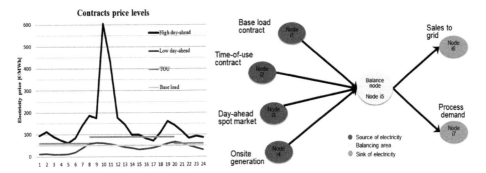

Figure 2. Price levels and flow network representation

Moreover, minimum runtime and downtime are enforced (Eqs. 20-21). Implementation of more detailed constraints available in literature is also possible here. The final net electricity purchase cost (Eq. 22) is composed of the cost associated with purchase from contracts, the cost of the generation and revenues from the electricity sold. The plant is assumed to commit to certain hourly varying levels of load. In case the actual consumption deviates from pre-agreed values (Figure 2) financial penalties are incurred. The part of the model accounting for the penalties is the set of Eq. (30-32) from Hadera and Harjunkoski (2013). The final objective function comprises of the net consumption cost, penalties paid due to load deviation and weighted makespan (Eq. 23).

4. Numerical case study

The model was implemented in GAMS/CPLEX and tested on a problem with 20 products. Since the scheduling problem itself (without energy-awareness) is intractable for large instances, its complexity is reduced in the case study by fixing both assignment and precedence variables. Different scenarios for input data concerning electricity contracts are investigated. Except for the "low day-ahead" (EPEX 2013, Germany/Austria 23/09/2013) scenario, the spot market is assumed to have high prices (EPEX 2013, France 10/02/2012). The base load is set to make up approximately 70 % of the peak consumption. The objective function weight coefficient for the makespan is a small number, the influence of it is assumed to have no impact on the economic objective, i.e. in-process heat losses are not considered. We assume penalty-free buffers of 5 % and 4 % buffers for over- and under-consumption respectively, with penalty cost equal to the day-ahead prices. The cost for onsite generation is assumed to be equal to the off-peak price of the TOU tariff, other price levels are shown in Fig. 2. The price of selling electricity is set to be between base load and onsite generation cost, i.e. 56 €/MWh, except for the case "sell as day-ahead" when it equals to the day-ahead prices.

Near optimal solutions of high value for industrial practice are always obtained within less than a minute, but proving the optimality of the last fraction of gap percentage (e.g. 0.1 %) takes relatively long for some instances. As shown in Table 2, for high prices of day ahead it does not pay off to buy from that market. Instead, base load, onsite generation and TOU contracts make up for the load and selling back to the grid pays off. For the same case, however with much lower volatile prices it is profitable to buy from that source and sell back even higher volume causing the net cost to drop. For the scenario without base load the electricity is made up mostly using TOU. When price of selling is set to be equal to the high day-ahead price levels it pays to exploit the negotiated contracts (base and TOU) and sell electricity, which creates large negative net cost.

Table 2. Numerical case study results

Purchase structure	Binaries/ Total var /Equations	CPUs (2% gap)	Net cost [k€]	Purchase [k €]	Penalties [€]	Day-ahead [MWh]	TOU [MWh]	Onsite [MWh]
High Day-ahead	5,257/29,588 /109,267	228 (12)	109	127.9	26	0	10	952
Low Day-ahead	5,257/29,588 /109,267	3081 (10)	76.8	166.6	13	1275	0	952
No base load	5,257/29,564 /109,267	570 (13)	143	96.4	24	190.4	1097.1	952
Sell as day-ahead	5,257/29,588 /109,267	771 (4)	-1,642	1,623	24	0	19734	952
Flow-min	5,253/29,588 /109,267	1 (1)	242	169.8	110,292	287.2	84	0

For flow minimal schedule the net cost increases substantially due to assumed committed load levels thus penalties incurred.

5. Discussion and conclusion

The proposed model benefits from the exact timing of the continuous-time scheduling representation. The model is able to capture complicated price structures and to optimally determine the exact amount of electricity to be purchased and sold. The flexible part of the purchase optimization can be further extended by more complicated dependencies between the contracts. The model might help assessing different price levels of negotiated contracts as well as reduce the risk associated with entering volatile markets. The main limitations of the model are concerned with computational performance for large instances and deterministic nature. The former can be dealt with by introducing decomposition approaches. Uncertainty in the process and the prices might heavily impact the robustness of the schedule, and therefore the final benefits. Further work could deal with the above mentioned issues.

Acknowledgements

The Marie Curie FP7-ITN research project "ENERGY-SMARTOPS", Contract No: PITN-GA-2010-264940 is acknowledged for financial support.

References

S. Ashok, 2006, Peak-load management in steel plants, App. Energy, 83, 5, 413-424

P. Castro, L. Sun, I. Harjunkoski, 2013, Resource–Task Network Formulations for Industrial Demand Side Management of a Steel Plant, Ind. Eng. Chem. Res., 52, 36, 13046–13058

EPEX Spot, 2013, European Power Exchange, <www.epexspot.com> accessed on 11/11/2013

H. Hadera, I. Harjunkoski, 2013, Continuous-time Batch Scheduling Approach for Optimizing Electricity Consumption Cost, Comput. Aided Chem. Eng., 32, 403-408

I. Harjunkoski, C. Maravelias, P. Bongers, P. Castro, S. Engell, I. E. Grossmann, J. Hooker, C. Méndez, G. Sand, J. Wassick, 2014, Scope for industrial applications of production scheduling models and solution methods, Comput. Chem. Eng., doi:10.1016/j.compchemeng.2013.12.001

S. Mitra, I. E. Grossmann, J. M. Pinto, N. Arora, 2012, Optimal production planning under time-sensitive electricity prices for continuous power-intensive processes, Comput. Chem. Eng., 38, 171–184

K. Nolde, M. Morari, 2010, Electrical load tracking scheduling of a steel plant, Comput. Chem. Eng, 34, 11, 1899–1903

Jiří Jaromír Klemeš, Petar Sabev Varbanov and Peng Yen Liew (Editors)
Proceedings of the 24th European Symposium on Computer Aided Process Engineering – ESCAPE 24
June 15-18, 2014, Budapest, Hungary. Copyright © 2014 Elsevier B.V. All rights reserved.

Integration Framework for Improving Quality and Cost-Effectiveness in Pharmaceutical Production Processes

Hirokazu Sugiyama*, Masahiko Hirao

Department of Chemical System Engineering, The University of Tokyo, 7-3-1 Hongo, Bunkyo-ku, 113-8656 Tokyo, Japan
sugiyama@chemsys.t.u-tokyo.ac.jp

Abstract

In the pharmaceutical industry, it is becoming increasingly important to realize superior production processes regarding quality and cost-effectiveness. Many companies are adopting so-called "continuous improvement" for retrofitting production and business processes even under strong constraints of quality regulations. Here, Computer Aided Process Engineering (CAPE) has a lot to offer in solving individual problems as well as in consolidating the process of problem solving. With an aim of enhancing the role of CAPE in this change of the pharmaceutical industry, we present a framework of process improvement that integrates data, methods and activities. The paper first describes the current situation of process improvement in pharmaceutical companies. With defining this as the As-Is model, To-Be models are presented, which emphasize the importance of defining the business processes as well as integrating data and methods. Activity modeling and integrated performance indicator are introduced as key enablers of the shift from As-Is to To-Be, together with industrial applications.

Keywords: Pharmaceutical production, continuous improvement, business process modeling, IDEF0, industrial application

1. Introduction

In pharmaceutical industry, it is becoming increasingly important to realize superior production processes regarding quality and cost-effectiveness. Many companies are adopting concepts of "Quality by Design" (QbD: ICH, 2009) for incorporating quality-thinking during process development, or "continuous improvement" for making running processes more reliable and efficient. Contributions can be found that illustrate introduction strategy of QbD (Kawai et al., 2012) as well as continuous improvement (Sugiyama and Schmidt, 2013). Applications of CAPE tools are also reported, such as optimization of scheduling with maintaining sufficient supply and minimizing operational costs for clinical supply (Chen et al., 2013) as well as for commercial batches (Siganporiaa et al., 2012). However, the overall picture is still missing regarding how these tools and concepts can be incorporated in the routine business, which focuses strongly on the quality standard namely Good Manufacturing Practice (GMP).

In this work, we present a framework for integrating data, methods and activities for realizing continuous improvement in the pharmaceutical industry. The paper first reviews the current situation of process improvement in pharmaceutical companies. With defining this as the As-Is model, two To-Be models and steps to achieve them are described. Here, it is recognized vital to define the business processes and to combine data and methods which would otherwise be scattered in the organization. In realizing the shift from the As-Is to the To-Be statuses, two CAPE-related methods and approaches play significant roles: (i) activity modeling method termed Integrated DEFinition type 0 (IDEF0: Ross, 1985) and (ii) integrated performance indicator. As an example, we revisit the results that the first author implemented in the industry and presented in the previous ESCAPE conference (Sugiyama and Schmidt, 2013).

2. Integration framework

2.1. Reviewing current industrial situation

Based on the experience in/with the pharmaceutical industry, we identify the following three points as the area for improvement in realizing continuous improvement:

- Data: Technologies such as Process Analytical Technology (PAT, e.g. Roggo et al, 2010) or Manufacturing Execution System (MES) are effectively increasing the data availability of the production processes. However, the primary focus of these technologies is to document manufacturing data for maintaining GMP compliance, and thus data are not stored in such a way that they can be directly used for improvement projects. Also, data are scattered in the organizations such as manufacturing, quality control (QC) or financial sections, and are managed in different ways. This limited readiness of data can lead to the difficulty in calculating even simple performance metrics such as overall product yield.

- Method: Generally, there are various methods that are commonly applied to continuous improvement such as statistical process control or Lean Six Sigma. These methods are originated from the machinery industry, which has different objectives compared to the pharmaceutical industry. For instance, minimizing inventory, one of the common interest of the machinery industry, is not necessarily regarded positive for medicinal products, and therefore, incorporation of pharma-specific aspects is needed.

- Activity: The GMP regulations can be a strong constraint in performing changes of manufacturing processes, and the activities of continuous improvement are still to be established. Generally in changing a process, different stakeholders need to participate, such as manufacturing, quality units or engineering, and especially the quality units play a significant role in examining the GMP compliance. For institutionalizing the activities of continuous improvement, interactions between these different stakeholders need to be clarified.

2.2. Integration Framework

For overcoming the above mentioned challenges, we propose a framework for integrating data, method and activities as shown in Figure 1. The As-Is status at the left side represents the current status: (i) the activities of process improvement are undefined (ii) interactions with related departments depend on the involved persons (iii) various data and methods are available but distributed in the organization. The model in the middle represents the To-Be status after the first integration step. In this To-Be 1 model, activities of process improvement are defined, and also, interactions with the related departments have become process-based with reducing dependency on individuals. Data and methods are restructured so that they are readily available for process improvement. For instance, performance indicators, e.g., yield or production lead time, can be tracked over time using data from different data management systems such as MES. This To-Be 1 model can be further integrated with other sites for exchanging challenges and achievements within the company, or with the supply chain network for tackling issues that cannot be solved by a maufacturing unit alone.

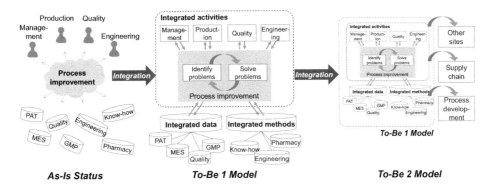

Figure 1. Two-step framework for integrating data, methods and activities

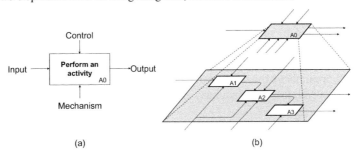

Figure 2. (a) Syntax of IDEF0 (b) Hierarchical expansion of an activity into sub-activities

The To-Be 2 model can also produce feed-forward information to the development of new processes in order to avoid issues that occurred in the running processes. This feed-forward system can help realize more effective deployment of PAT technologies for monitoring truly critical process parameters. In enabling the first shift from the As-Is to the To-Be 1 model, two CAPE-related methods can play central roles, i.e., IDEF0 and integrated performance indicator.

2.3. IDEF0 activity modeling

Figure 2 (a) shows the syntax of IDEF0. The box represents an activity, which has a verb as a name. The input arrows, entering the activity box from the left side, represent the objects that are transformed by the activity into the output arrows on the right side. The control arrows associated with the top side are conditions required to produce the correct output, e.g. business strategy or GMP regulations. The mechanism arrows on the bottom comprise the means to perform the function, e.g. enterprise resources or know-how. As shown in Figure 2 (b), every activity can be decomposed into sub-activities that have the same boundary condition as the parent activity. In supporting the integration steps in Figure 1, this IDEF0 can be a useful tool for defining activities of process improvement and information interactions.

2.4. Integrated performance indicator

Another useful tool for supporting data integration is an integrated performance indicator. As an example, a product loss indicator of Sugiyama and Schmidt (2013) is revisited here, which measures the overall loss of Parenterals or injectable products in a process shown in Figure 3. The first step is to compound the product solution by mixing Active Pharmaceutical Ingredients (APIs), excipients and water for injection, which are filled into glass vials and closed with rubber closures and caps in sterile environment. The last step, visual inspection, removes defectives from the good items.

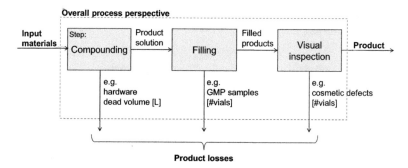

Figure 3. Typical process of Parenterals production with indicating product losses

The production is performed in a batch process, and no materials are recycled due to GMP regulations. In this process, there are various causes of product losses, e.g. dead volume of solution in the hardware, samples taken for GMP purposes, or products rejected due to cosmetic defects in visual inspection. These data are normally available in MES, however, managed in individual process steps, and stored in different units such as liter or number of vials. The indicator f for measuring contribution of individual causes to the overall loss over batches i is expressed as:

$$f^{a,b} = \sum_i m_i^{a,b} \Big/ \sum_i \sum_{a,b} m_i^{a,b} \tag{1}$$

where $m_i^{a,b}$ is the API mass [g] in the non-product output at step a in type b, i.e. loss due to hardware, GMP sample and poor operation. The values of m can be obtained by converting the data in MES to g-API equivalent. The indicator itself is simple, however, has a significant meaning in combining data scattered in the steps of compounding, filling and visual inspection from the overall process perspective. Such a performance indicator can be useful for supporting the shift of data integration from the As-Is to the To-Be 1 models shown in Figure 1.

3. Industrial Applications

In this chapter, the work of Sugiyama and Schmidt (2013) is interpreted as an industrial effort of making the the first step of the integration framework shown in Figure 1.

3.1. Applying IDEF0 for modeling business process of continuous improvement
Figure 4 is the business process model of continuous improvement using IDEF0 presented by Sugiyama and Schmidt (2013). The model was developed in an industrial production facility of Parenterals, and can be regarded as an example of defining the process improvement activities in the shift from As-Is to To-Be 1. The major aim of the IDEF0 model is to convert "process to improve" into "improved process" through three activities of A2: intake ideas, A3: execute projects, and A4: implement changes. The function of the activity A2 is to collect "initial ideas" for process improvement from the organization, and to select relevant ones considering "deployment strategy". The selected ideas are then summarized in a "project charter" together with goals, timeline and required resources, which is due to be approved by the management. According to the "approved project charter", projects are executed in activity A3 and action plans are produced, which are again to be approved by the management. According to the "approved action plan", changes are implemented in activity A4. The model in Figure 4 also contains activity A1: manage activities, which produces "deployment policy" for

managing the whole activities. Required resources are indicated at the bottom part of the model, and activity A5: provide resources allocates necessary personnel and budgets to activities A2 to A4.

This IDEF0 model can be interpreted as a first trial version of the defined activities of process improvement in the To-Be 1 model. This model also incorporates elements of GMP, expertise of process improvement, or process data into one business process model, which would otherwise be scattered in the organization.

3.2. Practicing integrated performance indicator
The integrated performance indicator in Eq. (1) was practiced by Sugiyama and Schmidt (2013) in identifying the significant product losses in an industrial Parenterals production facility. Figure 3 describes the investigated process. This facility was, at the time of practice, undergoing start-up activities and producing so-called validation batches in order to obtain the manufacturing licenses. By applying the indicator f to 17 validation batches, the result was obtained as shown in Figure 5. The largest contribution was minor defect or non-conforming items due to cosmetic appearance, e.g. scratch on the outer surface of the glass vials. Along with the IDEF0 model, improvement projects were deployed to reduce cosmetic defects, and the defect rate could be reduced to the half with regard to the mean and standard deviation.

In this case, the integrated performance indicator enabled comparison of loss causes from the different process units, i.e., compounding, filling and visual inspection, which had been managed individually before. The result in Figure 5 helped the management to focus on the important loss causes from the overall perspective, and preventive actions could be implemented on a prioritized manner. In this way, integrated data management as depicted in the To-Be model in Figure 1 can lead to effective process improvement.

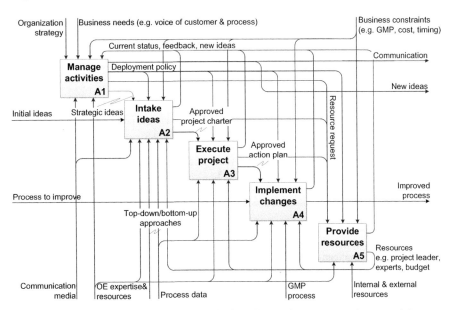

Figure 4. IDEF0-based business process model of continuous improvement (excerpted from Sugiyama and Schmidt, 2013)

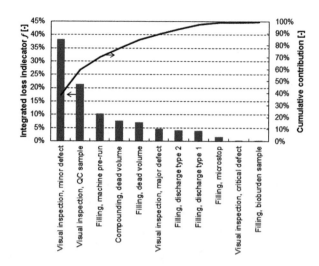

Figure 5. Result of applying integrated loss indicator in a Parenterals production process (excerpted from Sugiyama and Schmidt, 2013)

4. Conclusions and outlook

In this paper, we presented a framework of process improvement that integrates data, methods and activities towards better quality and cost-effectiveness. The paper first described the current status of process improvement in industry. With defining this as the As-Is model, two To-Be models were presented, which emphasized the importance of defining business processes as well as integrating data and methods that are distributed in manufacturing organizations today. IDEF0 and integrated performance indicator are introduced as helpful tools from the field of CAPE for realizing the first shift from the As-Is to the To-Be models. The effectiveness was illustrated with industrial applications. As future work, more case studies are desired in order to enhance applicability of CAPE methods in the pharmaceutical industry.

References

Y. Chen, J. M. Laínez, J. F. Pekny, G. V. Reklaitis, 2013, Risk pooling strategy in pharmaceutical for clinical trial supply chain, Ind Eng Chem Res, 52, 152-65.

International Conference on Harmonization (ICH), 2009, Pharmaceutical Development Q8 (R2), <www.ich.org/fileadmin/Public_Web_Site/ICH_Products/Guidelines/Quality/Q8_R1/Step4/Q 8_R2_Guideline.pdf> accessed on 20/08/2013.

H. Kawai, H. Seki, T. Fuchino,Y. Naka, 2012, Pharmaceutical engineering strategy for quality informatics on the IDEF0 business process model, Journal of Pharmaceutical Innovation, 7, 195-204.

Y. Roggo, K. Degardin, P. Margot, 2010, Identification of pharmaceutical tablets by Raman spectroscopy and chemometrics, Talanta, 81, 988-995.

D. T. Ross, 1985, Application and Extensions of SADT, Computer, 18, 25-34.

C. Siganporiaa, S. Ghosh, T. Daszkowski, L. Papageorgiou, S. S. Farida, 2012, Production planning of batch and semi-continuous bioprocesses across multiple biopharmaceutical facilities, Computer Aided Chemical Engineering, 30, 377-81.

H. Sugiyama, R. Schmidt, 2013, Business model of continuous improvement in pharmaceutical production processes, Computer Aided Chemical Engineering, 32, 697-702.

Jiří Jaromír Klemeš, Petar Sabev Varbanov and Peng Yen Liew (Editors)
Proceedings of the 24th European Symposium on Computer Aided Process Engineering – ESCAPE 24
June 15-18, 2014, Budapest, Hungary.

Optimal Design of Generalized Supply Chain Networks

Magdalini A. Kalaitzidou[a], Pantelis Longinidis[b], Panagiotis Tsiakis[c], Michael C. Georgiadis[a,*]

[a]*Department of Chemical Engineering, Aristotle University of Thessaloniki, University Campus, Thessaloniki, 54124, Greece*
[b]*Department of Engineering Informatics & Telecommunications, University of Western Macedonia, Karamanli & Lygeris Street, Kozani, 50100, Greece*
[c]*Wipro Consulting Services, 3 Sheldon Square, London W2 6PS, United Kingdom*
mgeorg@auth.gr

Abstract

This paper presents a mathematical programming model for the optimal design of Generalized Supply Chain Networks (GSCNs) that incorporates strategic flexibility in network's configuration. The model is formulated as a deterministic Mixed-Integer Linear Programming (MILP) problem and solved to global optimality using standard branch-and-bound techniques. Optimality is assessed in terms of SCN's overall cost while its applicability, benefits, and robustness are illustrated by using a real case study.

Keywords: Supply chain network design; Generalized nodes; MILP; Deterministic;

1. Introduction

In recent years, the problem of designing the SCN has gained much interest from business as its contribution to sustainable competitive advantages is universally acknowledged. Facility location is the core decision within strategic design of SCNs. According to Drezner and Hamacher (2004) facility location problems involve a set of spatially distributed customers whose location is known and a set of facilities to satisfy their demands, whose locations are to be determined. Melo et al. (2009) conduct a remarkable review on facility location models and demonstrate how their characteristics affect strategic SCN management. Likewise, Melo et al. (2006) revealed how the structure of the network is strongly affected by external supply of materials, inventory opportunities, storage limitations, relocation, expansion or reduction of capacities. In a very recently work, Cardoso et al.(2013) proposed a novel model for the design and planning of SCNs with reverse flows and demand uncertainty.

The vast majority of the relevant works on the research stream of SCN design assumes a structure of the network with distinct and consecutive echelons, constituted of nodes with predetermined function. Only the work of Laínez et al. (2009) considered a modeling framework with allowed flows within facilities in which equipment and tasks are determined by the optimization procedure. The aim of this paper is to introduce a flexible composition to network's structure, as the function of the proposed generalized nodes are optimally defined rather than selected from a set of available alternatives. Moreover, intra-layer material flow connection is permitted among these generalized nodes.

2. Mathematical formulation

2.1. Problem description

This work addresses the design of a multi-product, multi-echelon SCN. The model proposes an innovative configuration to network's structure by entering a level consisted of generalized production/warehousing nodes (P/W) whose function is not a priori assumed, as in mainstream fixed echelon SCNs. These nodes can receive material from any potential supplier (S) or any other P/W node and deliver material to any customer zone (C) or any other P/W node, as shown in Figure 1.

We denote the set of all nodes in the network as $n \in N$. This includes not only the generalized nodes $n \in P/W$ but also suppliers nodes $n \in S$ and customer zones nodes $n \in C$. Overall we have $N = S \cup P/W \cup C$. The objective is to minimize the overall capital and operational cost and determine the optimal structure of the network. The model defines: (i) suppliers; (ii) generalized node's location and role; (iii) material flow among SCN's levels; and (iv) functional elements (capacity, material flow, purchases etc.).

2.2. Mathematical model

A deterministic MILP model is formulated where each product can be produced at several generalized P/W nodes in different location with known and time-invariant product demand. All transportation flows determined are considered to be time-averaged quantities whereas customer zones are single sourced. The objective is to minimize the overall capital and operational cost of the network and is as follows:

$$
\min \sum_{n \in P/W} \left\{ C_n^P Y_n^P + \sum_e E_{en} Y_{en}^P + C_n^W Y_n^W + \gamma_n^W W_n + \sum_i C_{in}^{WH} \left(\sum_{n' \in S \cup P/W} Q_{in'n} + \sum_{n' \in C \cup P/W} Q_{inn'} \right) \right.
$$

$$
+ \sum_e \delta_{en}^P \sum_{k \in Kn} \lambda_{ek} \xi_{kn}
$$

$$
\left. + \sum_i \left(\sum_{n' \in S} C_{in'n}^T Q_{in'n} + \sum_{n' \in P/W} C_{inn'}^T Q_{inn'} + \sum_{n' \in C} C_{inn'}^T Q_{inn'} \right) \right\}
$$

$$
+ \sum_{n \in S} \left(C_n^S Y_n^S + \sum_i C_{in}^S S_{in} \right)
$$

Capital cost is consisted of infrastructure cost whereas handling, production, transportation and purchasing contribute to operational cost. Infrastructure cost is related to the establishment of a warehouse or a production plant at a particular node $n \in P/W$. If a production capability is established at a node $n \in P/W$ then its infrastructure cost has a stable element ($C_n^P Y_n^P$) and a variable element ($\sum_e E_{en} Y_{en}^P$). The former is the

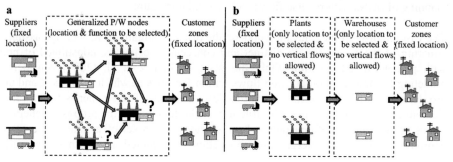

Figure 1. The proposed GSCN structure (a) against the typical fixed echelon SCN structure (b).

product of the annualized fixed cost required to establish a production capability (C_n^P) with the binary variable that expresses the establishment of this capability (Y_n^P). The latter element is the summary of the products of the continuous variable expressing the total rate of availability of manufacturing resource e (E_{en}) with a coefficient expressing the unit cost associated with the establishment of this manufacturing resource (γ_{en}^P).Similarly, if a warehousing capability is established at node n∈P/W then its infrastructure cost has a stable element ($C_n^W Y_n^W$), and a variable element ($\gamma_n^W W_n$), the product of a coefficient expressing the unit cost associated with the warehousing capacity (γ_n^W) with the continuous variable expressing the warehousing capacity (W_n).

Regarding operational cost, handling cost is expressed as a linear function of the total throughput at node n∈P/W. The total throughput is the sum of the summary of the continuous variables expressing the rate of flow of material i that arrives at node n∈P/W from node n∈S or/and from other node n∈P/W ($\sum_{n'∈S∪P/W} Q_{in'n}$) and the summary of the continuous variables expressing the rate of flow of material *i* that leaves node n∈P/W to node n∈C or/and to other node n∈P/W ($\sum_{n'∈C∪P/W} Q_{inn'}$). By multiplying the aforementioned total throughputs with the unit handling cost for material *i* (C_{in}^{WH}) and summarising the resulting products we gain the handling cost. Production cost is related to the utilization of various resources e at node n∈P/W and is determined as the summary of the products of the unit cost of consumption of resource e at node n∈P/W (δ_{en}^P) with the total utilization of each resource *e* ($\sum_{k∈Kn} \lambda_{ek} \xi_{kn}$). Utilization is the product of the amount of manufacturing resource e required to perform unit amount of task k (λ_{ek}) and the continuous variable expressing the rate of operation of task k at node n∈P/W(ξ_{kn}).Transportation cost is decomposed into three terms each of which summarizes the products of unit transportation cost of material i from a node n to another node n'($C_{in'n}^T$), and vise versa ($C_{inn'}^T$), and the corresponding continuous variables expressing the rate of flow of material i that arrives at a node n from another node n' ($Q_{in'n}$) and vise versa ($Q_{inn'}$). The first term expresess transportation cost of material i transferred from node n'∈S to node n∈P/W the second term expresses the transportation cost of material i transferred from node n∈P/W to other node n'∈P/W, and the third term expresses the transportation cost of material *i* transferred from node n∈P/W to node n'∈C. Finally, purchasing cost has a stable element ($C_n^S Y_n^S$), the product of the annualized fixed cost of establishing a relationship with node n∈S(C_n^S), and the binary variable that expresses the selection of node n∈S as a material provider in the network(Y_n^S), and a variable element ($C_{in}^S S_{in}$), the product of the unit purchase price of material i from node n∈S(C_{in}^S)and the continuous variable expressing the purchased amounts of material i from the selected node n∈S(S_{in}). By summarising this variable element for all materials and all suppliers we gain the purchasing cost.

The MILP optimization model has six sets of constraints that formulate the structure of the network. Constraints (1) and (2) demonstrate the conditions for the establishment of a node n∈P/W. In specific, constraint (1) states that if a production capability is established at a node n∈P/W($Y_n^P = 1$) then the corresponding node n∈P/W should be established as the binary variable that expresses its establishment is forced to take the value of one. In the same fashion, constraint (2) states that if a warehousing capability is established.

$$Y_n ≥ Y_n^P, \forall n ∈ P/W \tag{1}$$

$$Y_n \geq Y_n^W, \forall\, n \in P/W \tag{2}$$

If a node $n \in P/W$ is established ($Y_n = 1$) it should receive material from at least one other node $n' \in S \cup P/W$ and should provide material to at least one other node $n' \in P/W \cup C$. As shown in constraint (3), if a node $n \in P/W$ is established ($Y_n = 1$) the binary variable that expresses the establishment of a material transportation link($X_{n'n}$) is forced to take the value one for at least one pair of $n' \in S \cup P/W$ with $n \in P/W$ and provided that $n \neq n'$. In the same manner, constraint (4) shows that if a node $n \in P/W$ is established ($Y_n = 1$) the binary variable that expresses the establishment of a material transportation link ($X_{nn'}$) is forced to take the value one for at least one pair of $n \in P/W$ with $n' \in P/W \cup C$ and provided that $n \neq n'$.

$$Y_n \leq \sum\nolimits_{n' \in S \cup P/W \setminus \{n\}} X_{n'n}\,, \forall\, n \in P/W \tag{3}$$

$$Y_n \leq \sum_{n' \in C \cup P/W \setminus \{n\}} X_{nn'}\,, \forall\, n \in P/W \tag{4}$$

A connection between a node $n' \in S$ and a node $n \in P/W$ can exist only if both the supplier is contracted and the generalized node is established. Constraint (5) forces the binary variable expressing the contracting of node $n' \in S$ ($Y_{n'}^S$) to be unity when the material transportation link, between a node $n' \in S$ and a node $n \in P/W$, is established. On the other hand, constraint (6) forces the binary variable expressing the establishment of node $n \in P/W$ to be unity when the material transportation link, between anode $n' \in S$ and a node $n \in P/W$, is established ($X_{n'n} = 1$).

$$X_{n'n} \leq Y_{n'}^S, n' \in S, n \in P/W, n \neq n' \tag{5}$$

$$X_{n'n} \leq Y_n, n' \in S, n \in P/W, n \neq n' \tag{6}$$

Similarly, a connection between two nodes $n \in P/W$ and $n' \in P/W$ or $n' \in C$ can exist only if both nodes are established (constraints (7), (8) and (9)).

$$X_{nn'} \leq Y_n, \forall\, n \in P/W, \forall\, n' \in P/W, n \neq n' \tag{7}$$

$$X_{nn'} \leq Y_{n'}, \forall\, n \in P/W, \forall\, n' \in P/W, n \neq n' \tag{8}$$

$$X_{nn'} \leq Y_n\,, \forall\, n \in P/W, \forall\, n' \in C, n \neq n' \tag{9}$$

As the model does not allow reverse flows, intra-layer flows between suppliers and customer zones, and direct flows from suppliers to customer zones appropriate fixing to zero takes place for the binary variables ($X_{nn'}$)expressing the establishment of the above prohibited transportation links. Moreover, the flow of materials ($Q_{in'n}$) lies between upper and lower bounds. In nodes $n \in P/W$ where production capability is established the overall balance for the production of material i is the inflow ($\sum_{n' \in S \cup P/W \setminus \{n\}} Q_{in'n}$) minus the outflow ($\sum_{n' \in C \cup P/W \setminus \{n\}} Q_{inn'}$)of material i plus the rate of production of material i at that node, as shown in constraint (10).

$$\sum_{n' \in S \cup P/W \setminus \{n\}} Q_{in'n} + \sum_{k \in Kn} v_{ik}\, \xi_{kn} = \sum_{n' \in C \cup P/W \setminus \{n\}} Q_{inn'}\,, \forall\, i, n \in P/W \tag{10}$$

The term (v_{ik}) expresses the amount of material i produced by unit amount of task k and multiplied with the continuous variable expressing the rate of operation of task k at node $n \in P/W (\xi_{kn})$ we have the rate of production. The total utilization of each resource e $(\sum_{k \in Kn} \lambda_{ek} \xi_{kn})$ is limited to the total rate of availability of resource e at node $n \in P/W (E_{en})$ as shown in constraint (11).

$$\sum_{k \in Kn} \lambda_{ek} \xi_{kn} \leq E_{en} , \forall e, n \in P/W \tag{11}$$

Upper and lower bound are imposed for both the total rate of availability of resource e and purchased amounts of material i from the selected node. Additionally, appropriate constraints force the model to transfer all purchased material to generalized nodes and also to satisfy all demand. Finally, warehousing capacity (W_n) lies between higher and lower limits, while the is approached as linear function of handled material flow as shown in constraint (12) with $\left(a_{in}^{in}\right)/\left(a_{in}^{out}\right)$ expressing the relationship between capacity of warehouse at node $n \in P/W$, to material i handled that enters/leaves the node.

$$W_n \geq \sum_{i,n' \in SUP/W} Q_{in'n} a_{in}^{in} + \sum_{i,n' \in CUP/W} Q_{inn'} a_{in}^{out}, \forall n \in P/W, n \neq n' \tag{12}$$

3. Case study

The applicability of the GSCN design and operation model is illustrated by using a real case study in the European area. This study is being held for the interests of a European company. This network is comprised by total thirty-eight nodes, whose locations are sited among the European area. More specific there are, five potential suppliers, fifteen potential production plants/warehouses and eighteen customer zones. The number of materials/products provided by the suppliers is fourteen.

4. Results

The proposed model (GSCN) is compared with a counterpart model with fixed-echelons (FSCN), both of which were implemented in GAMS 24.1.3 software, using CPLEX 12solver. Identical data were used for both models and production process is approached in the same way. Figure 2, present the optimal network for GSCN and FSCN, respectively. The former establishes 3 P/W nodes with both capabilities in location countries: ES, IT, BE and 1 P/W node with only warehousing capability (CH), all of which are provisioned from 2 suppliers (BG, RO), while the latter establishes3 plants (PT, BE, CH) and 5 warehouses (IT, DK, PT, BE, CH) all of which are provisioned from the same suppliers.

The GSCN model shows its superiority firstly from the objective function, and secondly from the network's flexibility. Both models employ the same objective function that was counted 742,016 and 1,051,214 relative money units (rmu) for GSCN and FSCN, respectively. This cost gap, is due to the fact that FSCN model is forced by the a priori structure to build more facilities (sum of plants & warehouses) in order to satisfy customer demand. Furthermore, FSCN's model ends up in a structure where the more sizeable material flow connections are among the plants and warehouses that are located and build at the same country-area. This fact shows the necessity of a generalized node with both warehousing/manufacturing capabilities. Additionally, a sensitivity analysis

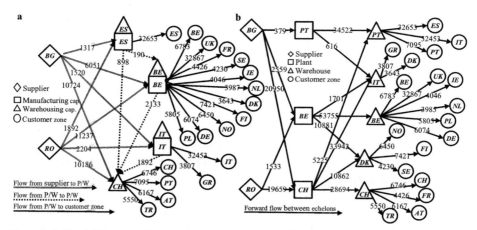

Figure 2.Optimal GSCN configuration (a) against the optimal FSCN configuration (b).

was performed and the outcome revealed that the GSCN model reacts fairly enough in demand changes and is insensitive to all other parameters.

5. Conclusions

This paper introduces a mathematical model that provides flexibility options on designing and operating SCNs. The model is capable of deciding the appropriate suppliers and material flow connections including intra-layer flows but mainly the location and role/capability of the generalized nodes. It is concluded that, giving the network the option to have nodes that act with both manufacturing and warehousing capability (or choose among them) and simultaneously to avoid having separated manufacturing and warehousing layers, minimizes the overall cost, but mostly benefits in material handling cost.

6. Acknowledgements

This research has been co-financed by the European Union (European Social Fund – ESF) and Greek national funds through the Operational Program "Education and Lifelong Learning" of the National Strategic Reference Framework (NSRF) - Research Funding Program: Thales. Investing in knowledge society through the European Social Fund.

References

S.R. Cardoso, A.P.F.D. Barbosa-Póvoa, S. Relvas, 2013, Design and planning of supply chains with integration of reverse logistics activities under demand uncertainty, European Journal of Operational Research, 226, 436-451.

Z. Drezner, H.W. Hamacher, 2004, Facility location: Applications and Theory, Springer, New York.

J. M. Laínez, G. Kopanos, A. Espuña, L. Puigjaner, 2009, Flexible design-planning of supply chain networks, AIChE Journal, 55, 1736-1753

M.T. Melo, S.Nickel, F. Saldanha-Da-Gama, 2006, Dynamic multi-commodity capacitated facility location: A mathematical modeling framework for strategic supply chain planning. Computers and Operations Research, 33, 181-208.

M.T. Melo, S. Nickel, F. Saldanha-Da-Gama, 2009, Facility location and supply chain management – A review, European Journal of Operational Research, 196, 401-412.

Jiří Jaromír Klemeš, Petar Sabev Varbanov and Peng Yen Liew (Editors)
Proceedings of the 24th European Symposium on Computer Aided Process Engineering – ESCAPE 24
June 15-18, 2014, Budapest, Hungary. Copyright © 2014 Elsevier B.V. All rights reserved.

Intelligent Process Management for Continuous Operations in Pharmaceutical Manufacturing

Arun Giridhar, Anshu Gupta, Matt Louvier, Girish Joglekar, Zoltan K. Nagy, Gintaras V. Reklaitis*,

School of Chemical Engineering; Purdue University; 480 Stadium Mall Drive, West Lafayette, Indiana 47907, USA
reklaiti@ecn.purdue.edu

Abstract

Over the last fifteen years, pharmaceutical manufacturing has moved cautiously from an exclusively batch-oriented system towards continuous production. Sensing and instrumentation for continuous production have improved much in that time, but the development and adoption of new process management technologies have lagged compared to instrumentation due to various barriers. In this work, we describe those barriers and present solutions in achieving continuous closed-loop operations in pharmaceutical manufacturing.

Keywords: pharmaceutical manufacturing, process operations, knowledge management

1. Introduction

Fifteen years ago, pharmaceutical manufacturing was exclusively batch-oriented, with every unit operation being filled, operated, emptied, and cleaned manually, with a large quantity of material in process at any given time, with laboratory-based quality assurance checks between unit operations, and with batch rejection being the primary quality assurance mechanism. More recently, online sensing and instrumentation, termed process analytical technology (PAT) within the pharmaceutical sector, have been adopted extensively and have reduced the turnaround times of laboratory tests. The industry has grown more comfortable with the notion of continuous operation with support from government agencies. However, the development and adoption of new process management technologies have lagged relative to instrumentation, with acceptance/rejection still being used as the primary product quality assurance mechanism. The pharmaceutical sector wishes to progress to a Quality by Design (QbD) worldview, wherein detailed knowledge of the process is used to predict product quality with good accuracy, and inversely product quality is maintained by adjusting process variables in real-time. The adoption of such process management techniques has faced two barriers. The first is the historical lack of online instrumentation, which has now been addressed for many but not all process variables and product quality attributes. The second is a broad range of challenges associated with powder processing in many fields, such as: high variance in particulate systems that hinder state estimation and fault detection; fat-tailed noise distributions in powder streams that make filtering non-trivial; the non-linear behavior of heterogeneous particles when compressed; and the complex, poorly predicted interaction of powder properties in blends.

In this work, we describe our progress towards addressing these challenges and achieving continuous closed-loop operations in pharmaceutical manufacturing.

Specifically, we focus on the integration of four key components of robust supervisory control: control system design, dynamic real-time optimization, fault detection and diagnosis, and process instrumentation. As the components by themselves are detailed in their own right, this work will describe their interaction and integration for a dry granulation case study.

2. Case Study: Dry Granulation Process

Dry granulation (Kleinebudde, 2004) is a process to convert powders into tablets. Powders including active pharmaceutical ingredients (APIs) and inert excipients are fed at a measured rate, blended, and compacted between rollers to make a ribbon, which is then milled to make granules, which are lubricated and compacted again to make tablets (Figure 1). The supervisory control challenges in this process are representative of many other solids-handling processes in pharmaceutical and other sectors.

3. System Design and Performance

3.1. Instrumentation and Process State Estimation

The dry granulation line (Figure 1) is mounted with near-infrared (NIR) spectrometers, microwave detectors (Austin et al, 2013), a vision-based particle analysis instrument and an X-ray mass flow meter. Spectroscopy is used to measure: compositions of blended powders, tablets and lubricated granules; densities of ribbon and tablets; and moisture content of material. Blend uniformity is quantified as the standard deviation of the composition divided by the mean composition, calculated over a fixed time window. The particle size distribution of the granules is measured online through a vision-based system. Mass flow is measured online with an X-ray instrument. In general, equipment-centric process data such as RPMs and pressures are easily incorporated into a plantwide distributed control system (DCS). Material-centric measurements are harder, usually reducing a spectrum or an image into scalar predictions like density or composition. Storing the predictions as well as the raw sensor data is a challenge, and requires novel techniques to manage data and knowledge scalably (Joglekar et al, 2013). We use principal components analysis (PCA) or partial least squares (PLS) to process spectra, autocorrelation and averaging for X-ray data, and numerical integration and feature extraction for particle analysis. We find that it is more

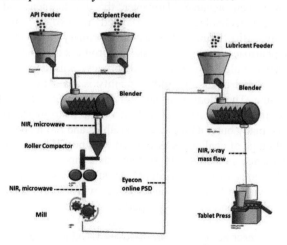

Figure 1. Schematic of a dry granulation line with instrumentation

reliable for long term use to dedicate separate computers for handling instrument data, but centralizing all data processing in the DCS is easier to start with. The DCS used in our work is Emerson DeltaV, which we use to store process history and communicate with individual process units. Production metadata (anything valuable that cannot be automatically recorded by instruments, such as the purpose of a production experiment, equipment configuration, who ran the experiment etc) are stored separately using a workflow management web application developed in-house (Howlett et al, 2013).

Data reconciliation and state estimation are straightforward when one can deduce a process variable through multiple instruments or a soft sensor such as a mass balance equation. The principle is to calculate the process state such that the weighted sum of squared residuals between instrument predictions and the process state is minimized; we found good success when the instruments are assigned weights as a reciprocal of their standard deviation over the last 15 samples, with numerical protection against singularities. Gross error detection is challenging due to fat-tailed distributions often exhibited by powder stream properties. A common physical cause of fat-tailed measurement noise is powder stickiness: when sticky powder accumulates in hoppers or nozzles, the flow out of the unit is artificially low. Eventually the accumulated material breaks and falls as a lump, causing a large (over two standard deviations from the mean) spike in the measured values. Such brief deviations are common and should not be construed as sensor failures by the gross error detection system. We find that a better indicator of sensor failure is a sudden and sustained increase in sensor noise: non-sustained increases in sensor noise are routine and the sensor returns to normal within 3 or 4 samples; a sustained but gradual increase in sensor noise is usually a genuine material property change and not a sensor fault per se.

3.2. Feedback and Feedforward Control System

Process robustness is vital in pharmaceutical manufacturing. Since raw materials exhibit significant variation in physical properties, feedback control is required to maintain product quality. Unlike cases in the oil and paper industries, model-predictive control (MPC) strategies based on sophisticated mechanistic models are neither used nor preferred in powder processes except in extenuating circumstances. The main limitation of mechanistic models is the lack of mixing rules for materials: for example the overall bulk density or cohesion of a blended powder stream are very difficult to calculate from the composition and individual property values. As such, data-driven MPC is preferred over mechanistic MPC, and PID is preferred over MPC for its simplicity. Another practical reason is that PID and simple data-driven MPC can usually be implemented natively in the DCS, whereas advanced mechanistic models require external software that would need to be additionally validated by government regulatory agencies.

Simple PID suffices to control powder feeding and blending, where blend uniformity is controlled, and the blender and feeder setpoints are manipulated. However denoising is a challenge because the measured composition tends to have fat-tailed distributions as described above. Accordingly a simple low-pass or adaptive filter is usually not adequate to distinguish signal from noise, and more advanced techniques like Bayesian wavelet transforms are required. A similar PID subsystem is used for the lubricant blender, which lubricates the granules.

In theory, by using high-speed spectroscopy on the tablet press measuring density and composition. off-spec tablets can potentially be rejected in real-time while press settings are adjusted to make future tablets on-spec. More realistically, the material composition in the tablet press hopper is used for a feed-forward accept/reject decision on the final tablets, with a suitable time delay corresponding to the residence time, using a Smith predictor. Thus acceptance/rejection is still important in so-called "real-time release" but it operates on a smaller scale than entire batches of material. Work is currently in progress to implement such feedforward accept/reject schemes in other unit operations and manufacturing processes: known off-spec intermediates are diverted to a reject stream instead of being sent downstream for further processing.

The roller compactor, which compacts powders into ribbons and breaks the ribbon into granules, has three manipulated variables (roller RPM, roll pressure, and a material feed screw RPM), and two controlled variables (ribbon thickness and ribbon density). The input-output transfer matrix is coupled, with each controlled variable depending on all three manipulated variables. Traditionally control systems have used two decoupled PID loops, one controlling ribbon thickness and the other controlling ribbon density. Hsu et al (2010) found such schemes to perform poorly for common tuning rules due to interacting loops, and they proposed an MPC strategy instead. Practical implementation of such MPC requires heavy computation; consequently we find a good tradeoff in practice is to use such high-fidelity models in offline simulations to train a data-driven online controller such as a neural network. Such simpler controllers can also be directly implemented inside a DCS, making it attractive from a software validation perspective.

3.3. Dynamic Real-time Optimization

Starting up or shutting down a powder processing line without automatic setpoint adjustment is very difficult and tedious, requiring coordinated manual input across multiple unit operations while chasing an elusive steady-state and wasting material in the form of off-spec intermediates or products. Accordingly a dynamic real-time optimization (DRTO) approach was used to develop optimized startup and shutdown procedures for dry granulation. A dynamic flowsheet model of the entire process is used to predict the instantaneous throughput and the quality attributes of intermediates and products. We defined the objective function to be the amount of material that is lost during process transients due to being off-spec. For example, if the roll pressure is increased suddenly, all the ribbon made until the new steady state is reached is off-spec, but if the roll pressure is increased gradually, the ribbon produced is within specifications even though the new steady state takes longer to reach. In effect, by changing process settings slowly and smoothly, we impose a quasi-steady-state on the quality attributes, making the product quality acceptable. The optimizer seeks a balance between transition time and product quality, weighting quality more than throughput.

Such a flowsheet model was implemented and optimized in gPROMS using dynamic models for individual unit operations. The end result indicates a rapid 150-second startup time from cold shutdown to steady production rate. The optimum strategy is to have a high throughput on upstream units and a low throughput (ramping up) on downstream units; this ensures that hoppers are filled as preliminary product is being made, and minimizes material loss. As seen in Figure 2, the roller compactor is started about 90 seconds after the feeders are started, and while the ribbon mass flow rate (quantity) ramps up over the next 120 seconds, the ribbon density (quality) is constant

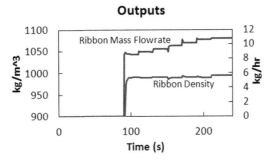

Figure 2. Performance of an optimized startup procedure. Observe that the ribbon density (quality) is nearly constant even though the production rate is still ramping up.

over nearly the entire range, meaning that very little material needs to be discarded for being the wrong density. Such dynamic RTO profile optimization can readily br developed for many other processes besides dry granulation.

3.4. Intelligent Alarm Management

As large variations in material properties are routine, a process management system needs to smoothly transition between normal operations and a process fault condition, failing which the usual result is an alarm cascade and unplanned shutdown. A wide variety of mathematical tools and techniques are used in our intelligent alarm management system: PCA and PLS are useful for fault detection and localization; wavelet transforms are very useful in distinguishing signal from noise with fat-tailed distributions, and also give early warning of process variables trending out of normal operation zone (Gupta et al, 2013); fast Fourier transforms (FFTs) are useful in isolating periodically repeating variations (Hamdan et al, 2012); and trend analysis and signed digraphs serve as confirmation of the fault diagnosis (Hamdan et al, 2010). Going beyond traditional alarm systems, the intelligent alarm management system helps mitigate a fault by identifying its root cause and guiding the operator in fixing it.

As seen in Figure 3, the intelligent alarm management system automatically defines zones like "normal operating condition" or "feasible but not ideal" and alerts the operator about any incipient faults in progress, which can be fixed before they become crises. The size of the zones is calculated automatically and dynamically depending on the process variable's inherent variability and its desired upper and lower limits. The intelligent alarm management system identifies the following kinds of faults well: unit operations running out of material; flow blockages in hoppers; material sticking to rotating equipment; off-spec compositions; excessive humidity; and off-spec size distribution for powders or granules. These findings are currently being extended to other solids-based and fluids-based processes, as the underlying mathematical techniques are identical for all process applications.

The handing of control back and forth between the alarm management and the rest of the control system is an interesting practical aspect. Our approach is to set "flag variables" in the DCS that indicate whether the alarm management system has identified any abnormal events. If no such flags are set, the process is assumed to be normal and routine subsystems such as feedback control and setpoint optimization are active. If any such flag is set, the feedback control and setpoint optimization routines simply skip their scheduled execution and wait for the next time interval, waiting until the flag is cleared. In the interregnum, only the state estimation and the alarm management

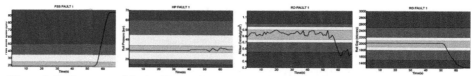

Figure 3. Performance of the intelligent alarm management system

systems have control authority. The net effect is that if the operator is fixing the process fault manually, he or she will not be interfered with by the feedback controllers or setpoint optimizers, and if the fault is being fixed automatically, the alarm management system carries that out and waits for steady state before handing control back to the feedback control systems by resetting the flag variables.

4. Conclusion

Pharmaceutical manufacturing poses many challenges for continuous manufacturing that are not commonly encountered in traditional chemical industries. This work describes some of those challenges and their solutions. A good real-time process management system for dry granulation requires multiple subsystems such as state estimation, robust feedback control, dynamic setpoint optimization for startup and shutdown, and intelligent alarm management to guide the operator in fixing process faults. Our process management system enables dry granulation to be run continuously, a necessary step for the pharmaceutical industry to transition to continuous operations. The methods described in this work are directly applicable to most continuous solids-handling processes at a wide variety of production scales.

Acknowledgements

This work was funded by the National Science Foundation under grant EEC-0540855 and the industrial members of the Engineering Research Center for Structured Organic Particulate Systems (ERC-SOPS).

References

J. Austin, A. Gupta, R. McDonnell, G. V. Reklaitis, M. T. Harris, 2013, The Use of Near-Infrared and Microwave Resonance Sensing to Monitor a Continuous Roller Compaction Process, Journal of Pharmaceutical Science, 102, 6, 1895-1904.

A. Gupta, A. Giridhar, V. Venkatasubramanian, G. V. Reklaitis, 2013, Intelligent Alarm Management Applied to Continuous Pharmaceutical Tablet Manufacturing: An Integrated Approach, Industrial and Engineering Chemistry Research, 52, 35, 12357-12368.

I. M. Hamdan, G. V. Reklaitis, V. Venkatasubramanian, 2010, Exceptional Events Management Applied to Roller Compaction of Pharmaceutical Powders, Journal of Pharmaceutical Innovation, 5, 4, 147-160.

I. M. Hamdan, G. V. Reklaitis, V. Venkatasubramanian, 2012, Real-Time Exceptional Events Management For a Partial Continuous Dry Granulation Line, Journal of Pharmaceutical Innovation, 7, 3-4, 95-118.

G. A. Howlett, G. S. Joglekar, A.Giridhar, 2013, Workflow editor, <pharmahub.org/resources/558> accessed on 01/31/2014.

S.-H. Hsu, Reklaitis, G. V., Venkatasubramanian, V., 2010, Modeling and Control of Roller Compaction for Pharmaceutical Manufacturing, Journal of Pharmaceutical Innovation, 5, 1-2, 14-36.

G. Joglekar, A. Giridhar, G. V. Reklaitis, 2013, Knowledge Management in Pharmaceutical Manufacturing, Paper 710e, AIChE Annual Meeting, San Francisco, CA.

P. Kleinebudde, 2004, Roll Compaction / Dry Granulation: Pharmaceutical Applications, European Journal of Pharmaceutics and Biopharmaceutics, 58, 2, 317-326.

Jiří Jaromír Klemeš, Petar Sabev Varbanov and Peng Yen Liew (Editors)
Proceedings of the 24th European Symposium on Computer Aided Process Engineering – ESCAPE 24
June 15-18, 2014, Budapest, Hungary.

Statistical Process Control based Energy Monitoring of Chemical Processes

Tibor Kulcsar[a,]*, Peter Koncz[a], Miklos Balaton[b], Laszlo Nagy[b], Janos Abonyi[a]

[a]University of Pannonia, Department of Process Engineering, POB. 158, Veszprem, HU
[b]MOL Hungarian Oil and Gas Company Szazhalombatta, HU
tibor.kukcsar@hotmail.com

Abstract

Advanced chemical process systems expected to maximize productivity and minimize cost and emission. Cost reduction needs Energy Monitoring and Targeting Systems that calculate actual energy usage, estimate energy needs at normal operation and highlight issues related to energy efficiency. Monitoring is based on continuous comparison of actual and estimated energy consumption. We developed Partial Least Squares (PLS) regression based targeting models that not only predict the expected value of energy consumption, but also visualize the operating regimes of the process. Soft-sensors working with PLS regression are widely used in chemical industry. The development of PLS models could be problematic because previous feature selection is needed. Since complex set of process variables determines Key Energy Indicators (KEIs) we applied Self-Organizing Map (SOM) models of that support visualization and feature selection of the process variables. Local linear target-models of different operating regions can be automatically determined based on the Voronoi diagram of the codebook of the SOM. We used Statistical Process Control (SPC) techniques to monitor the difference between the targeted and the measured energy consumption. We applied the concept of the resulted energy monitoring system at Heavy Naphtha Hydrotreater and CCR Reforming Units of MOL Hungarian Oil and Gas Company.

Keywords: Energy monitoring, Operating regime based modelling, PLS, SOM, SPC

1. Introduction

Energy Monitoring and Targeting systems should provide better understanding of how energy is used (Thiede, 2012). Energy efficiency has the following four components: performance efficiency, operation efficiency, equipment efficiency and technology efficiency (Xia, 2010). A systematic overview of the state of the art in energy and resource efficiency improving methods is given by Duflou (2012). Energy monitoring improves energy efficiency in process plants by helping plant operators, engineers and managers to track actual and target energy consumption by allowing the user to: (1) Detect avoidable energy waste that might otherwise remain hidden - this waste occurs at random, due to poor control, unexpected equipment faults or human error; (2) Quantify savings achieved by projects and campaigns; (3) Identify fruitful lines of investigation for energy surveys; (4) Provide feedback for staff awareness - improve budget setting and undertake benchmarking.

Methods for calculating expected consumption fall into two categories: Precedent based methods that compare consumption and efficiency measures with previous periods of operations; and activity-based methods that relate expected consumption to its driving factors (Behrendt, 2012). For complex applications precedent-based targeting models can be too simplistic. Activity-based targeting is particularly appropriate when there are clear drivers for changing energy consumption, for example, changes in production throughput. These targets can be useful to reduce energy consumption through real-time comparisons of the actual energy flow vs. the targeted rates. Activity based methods require accurate models to represent the effects of the driving factors. In case of complex processes the first principle modelling (also referred as white-box, mechanistic or *a priori* models) approach is insufficient because it is difficult to build precise first-principle models that can explain how malfunctions appear in productions. Since many companies have built integrated databases to store historical process data from all plants, and in many cases no detailed knowledge is available about the process we should build data driven (black-box or *a posteriori*) models. Data-based approaches and statistical regression methods have become popular techniques for process modeling because these methods determine the relationship between inputs and outputs based on historical process data only. Process modelling and monitoring needs accurate prediction models (also known as soft-sensors) these models are generally statistical regression models, especially PLS models that bears some relation to principal components regression because both the input and output data are projected to new spaces, the PLS family of methods are known as bilinear factor models (Vinzi, 2010).

Self-Organizing Maps - which we use for modeling and data visualization - performs a topology preserving mapping from high dimensional space onto a two dimensional grid of neurons so that the relative distances between data points are preserved. As SOM provides a compact representation of the data distribution, it has been widely applied in analysis and visualization of high-dimensional data (Kohonen, 1990). In this paper a method to use SOM for the identification of targeting model is presented where SOM is used to partition the input space (operating regime) of piecewise linear models. Our idea is to quantize the available input-output data to get a set of operating regimes to build global nonlinear prediction tool containing piecewise linear models. It should be noted that since historical process data is extensively used our methodology can be considered as a mixture of precedent and activity-based targeting approaches.

The monitoring of the process is based on the difference between the targeted and the measured energy consumption. To provide a sophisticated analysis of this deviation we propose the application of statistical process control (SPC) techniques (Montgomery, 2009). Control charts are industry-accepted techniques to ascertain the in-statistical-control status of the process (MacGregor, 1995). As we will show this technique connected to data-driven targeting models is also suitable to provide informative feedback about energy consumption.

2. SOM based models of energy monitoring

Data driven activity-based energy monitoring is based on the predicted value of energy consumption, $\hat{y}_k$. When the predicted consumption $\hat{y}_k$ is higher than the measured value y_k, the technology is considered to be efficient, while the $\hat{y}_k < y_k$ relation suggests that the technology could/should work at lower energy consumption. The structure of the model is the following:

$$\hat{y}_k = f(x_k, \theta) = [x_k^T \ 1]\theta \tag{1}$$

where the calculated output $\hat{y}_k$ that represents an energy consumption or efficiency related variable is modelled by the linear combination of process variables (drivers),

$\boldsymbol{x}_k = [x_{1,k}, \ldots, x_{n,k}]$, where k represents the k-th sampling time and n stands for the number of process variables having significant effect to energy consumption. At the development of this model it is important to ensure that data are synchronised as closely as possible with the required assessment intervals. Based on a synchronized set of data $\boldsymbol{z}_k = [y_k, \boldsymbol{x}_k]$, $k = 1, \ldots, N$ least squares method can be applied to find optimal parameters of the model $\boldsymbol{\theta}$ by minimizing the $\sum_{k=1}^{N}(y_k - \hat{y}_k)^2$ quadratic cost function. In this case the application of operating regime based models could be beneficial:

$$\hat{y}_k \sum_{i=1}^{s} \omega_i(\boldsymbol{x}_k) \left(\boldsymbol{a}_i^T \boldsymbol{x}_k + b_i\right) \tag{2}$$

where $\omega_i(\boldsymbol{x}_k)$ describes the operating regime of the i-th local linear model defined by the parameter vector $\boldsymbol{\theta}_i = [\boldsymbol{a}_i^T \ b_i]^T$. Piecewise linear models are special case of operating regime based models. If we denote the input space of the model by $T: z \in T \subset \mathbb{R}^n$, the piecewise linear model consists of a set of operating ranges $T_1, T_2, \ldots, T_s$ which satisfy $T_1 \cup T_2 \cup \cdots \cup T_s = T$ and $T_j \cap T_i = \emptyset$ when $i \neq j$. Hence, the model can be formulated as

If $\boldsymbol{x}_k \in T_i$ then $\hat{y}_k = [\boldsymbol{x}_k \ 1]\boldsymbol{\theta}_i$ (3)

where $\boldsymbol{\theta}_s$ denotes the parameter estimate vector used in the i-th local model. In this paper we apply SOM to partition the input space to define piecewise linear models. SOM performs a topology preserving mapping from high dimensional space onto map units so that relative distances between data points are preserved. The map units (also referred as neurons or codebooks) form usually a two dimensional regular lattice. Each neuron i of the SOM is represented by an l-dimensional weight, or model $m_i = [m_{i,1}, \ldots, m_{i,l}]^T$. These weigh vectors of the SOM form a codebook. The partitioning is obtained by the Voronoi diagram of the codebook of the SOM. The application of Voronoi diagrams of SOM has already been suggested in the context of time series prediction. Our idea is to quantize the available input-output data to get a set of operating regimes and use the obtained regimes to identify parameters of local targeting models. SOM can be used to predict the output $\hat{y}_k$ of the process from the input vector $\boldsymbol{x}_k$. Regression is accomplished by searching for the Best Matching Unit(BMU) using the known vector components $\boldsymbol{x}_k$ (please remember SOM was trained based on $\boldsymbol{z}_k = [y_k, \boldsymbol{x}_k]$. Since the output of the system is unknown, the BMU is determined as

$$i^0 = \arg\min_i \|\boldsymbol{p}_i - \boldsymbol{x}_k\| \tag{4}$$

where $\boldsymbol{p}_i = [m_{i,2}, \ldots, m_{i,n+1}]$. The output of the model can be estimated by the local model of BMU, which could be piecewise constant model $(\hat{y}_k = d_{i^0})$ or piecewise linear regression model $(\hat{y}_k = [\boldsymbol{x}_k^T \ 1]\boldsymbol{\theta}_{i^0})$. (1) The piecewise constant output model results a d_{i^0} constant value for each Voronoi cell; (2) The piecewise linear regression model estimates y_k using the parameter estimate vector θ_{i^0}, where i^0 is the index of BMU.

3. Results and discussion

The concept of the resulted historical data based energy monitoring system is demonstrated at Heavy Naphtha Hydrotreater and CCR Reforming Units of MOL Hungarian Oil and Gas Company. The plant's heating steam production is analysed as demonstrating example. The steam is produced in a furnace operated by fuel gas from the fuel gas network of the refinery. The energy content is calculated based on flow, density, heat capacity and temperature of steam, so the unit of production is $[GJ/h]$. The targeting model is identified based on one-year historical data. We assume that the range of this dataset is wide enough, so it covers operation rages with high and low energy consumptions.

We applied Self-Organizing Maps to identify the most relevant driving factors of heating steam production. These maps are useful for correlation hunting. Figure 1 compares process variables related to the Key Energy Indicator (KEI). We ranked the variables based on the similarity of maps measured by absolute value of 2D correlation coefficient. Using this method we can find also the variables with opposite behaviour to KEI, which are as important as the variables with same behaviour (red→blue is similar to blue→red). As Figure 1 and Table 1 show the Process Variable 1 is the most similar to the Key Energy Indicator, 2nd is Variable 7, the 3rd is Variable 8, etc

Following the industrial practice we applied PLS regression to obtain a targeting model. Figure 2 compares the PLS models (Vinzi, 2010) with different complexity related to numbers of model inputs and latent variables. We selected the PLS model that has 7 input and 5 latent variables. Models having 8-9 inputs and complex latent space have better performance, but the last two inputs have much worse map correlation (0.005, 0.003) than the others and the benefit of usage of these inputs is only 0.5 %. We identified a SOM model based on the same one-year historical data. This model estimates the steam production using the method described in Section 2. We can identify the operating regimes of the technology and identify a local model for each cell. Historical data related to the regimes are used to build local models. The prediction performance and the SPC charts based on this targeting model are shown in Figure 4. It should be noted that this nonlinear model gives almost the same prediction performance than the linear PLS model. Figure 3 shows the correlation diagrams of the examined models. SOM regression has almost the same result than PLS but it can show also the operating regimes (See Figure 1).

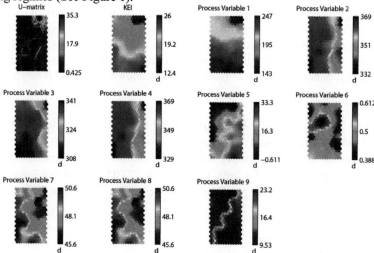

Figure 1. Self-Organizing Maps of process variables related to the Key Energy Indicator (KEI). The first Map shows the dissimilarity matrix (euclidean distance) of Voronoi Cells. The 2nd Map show the Key Energy Indicator (KEI) that is the heating steam production. Table 1 shows the correlations of process variables and ranking related to KEI's Map.

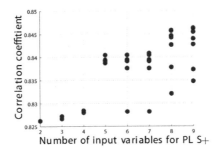

Figure 2. Correlation coefficients of PLS models width different number of input and latent variables. Horizontal axis represents the number of model inputs. We select the first n variables from the ranked series (See Table 1 We calculate the correlation with different latent space complexity from 2 to n ($n - 1$ point for each n).

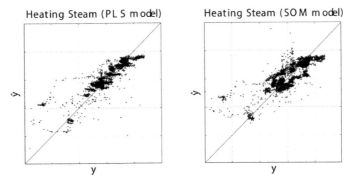

Figure 3. Time series of the latent variables and modelling error of PLS model.

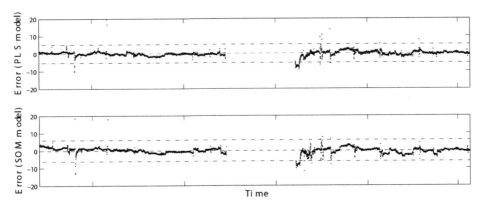

Figure 4. I-Chart of the modelling error for the three different models (PLS, SOM). The control limits are also shown determined using six-sigma rule. It should be noted that tracking only single value of energy consumption does not give detailed information about the operating situation.

Table 1. Ranking of variables using 2D correlation coefficient of maps of variables.

Variable	1	2	3	4	5	6	7	8	9
Correlation	0.987	0.005	0.473	0.003	0.456	0.262	0.511	0.504	0.492
Rank	1	8	5	9	6	7	2	3	4

The Statistical Process Control practice provides useful tools (Montgomery, 2009) for monitoring like I-Charts and MR-Charts, which are well supported in the most monitoring systems. To examine the prediction error we used standard I-Charts with control limits. Limit ware calculated using the six-sigma rule. Applying SPC monitoring we can detect the outlier samples (Montgomery, 2009) and indicate that the technology could operate more efficiently.

4. Conclusion

Energy monitoring improves energy efficiency in process plants by helping plant operators, engineers and managers to track actual and target energy. Energy monitoring is based on the comparison of Key Energy Indicators (KEIs) and their target vales. These targets depend on operating regimes determined by a complex set of process variables. We developed advanced data-driven modelling techniques to support on-line targeting. We also showed that deviations from the target should be investigated based on the analysis of the variance of the model error. Based on this analysis the aggressive or conservative behaviour of energy monitoring can be easily tuned. PLS and SOM models were identified. SOM gives an accurate and interpretable operating regime and feature selection methodology. We proposed statistical process control charts for monitoring. The resulted tools can be effectively used to support systematic improvement of energy efficiency. Summarizing the results: PLS models are ideal for Energy Monitoring and Targeting as well as Self-Organizing Map is powerful tool to support and supervise the model development process.

Acknowledgements

This research was supported by the European Union and the State of Hungary, co-financed by the European Social Fund in the framework of TÁMOP 4.2.4.A/2-11-1-2012-0001 'National Excellence Program' and TÁMOP 4.2.2.C-11/1/KONV-2012-0004 - National Research Center for Development and Market Introduction of Advanced Information and Communication Technologies.

References

J. R. Duflou, J. W. Sutherland, D. Dornfeld, C. Herrmann, J. Jeswiet, S. Kara, M. Hauschild, K. Kellens, 2012, Towards energy and resource efficient manufacturing: A processes and systems approach, CIRP Annals - Manufacturing Technology, 61, 587-609.

L.C. Braga, A.R. Braga, C.M.P. Braga, 2013, On the characterization and monitoring of building energy demand using statistical process control methodologies, Energy and Buildings, 65, 205-219.

J.F. MacGregor, T. Kourti, 1995, Statistical process control of multivariate processes, Control Engineering Practice, 3, 3, 403-414.

T. Kohonen, 1990, The self-organizing map, Proceedings of the IEEE 78, 1464-1480.

D. C. Montgomery, 2009, Jefferson City, Introduction to Statistical Quality Control, Sixth Edition, John Wiley Sons, New Jersey, US.

S. Thiede, G. Bogdanski, C. Herrmann, 2012, A systematic method for increasing the energy and resource efficiency in manufacturing companies, Procedia CIRP, 2, 28-33.

T. Behrendt, A. Zein, S. Min, 2012, Development of an energy consumption monitoring procedure for machine tools, CIRP Annals - Manufacturing Technology, 61, 43-46.

V. E. Vinzi, 2010, Berlin, Handbook of Partial Least Squares: Concepts, Methods and Applications, Springer Handbooks, Heidelberg, Germany.

X. Xia, J. Zhang, 2010. Energy Efficiency and Control Systems-from a POET Perspective, Control Methodologies and Technology for Energy Efficiency, 1, 255-260.

Jiří Jaromír Klemeš, Petar Sabev Varbanov and Peng Yen Liew (Editors)
Proceedings of the 24th European Symposium on Computer Aided Process Engineering – ESCAPE 24
June 15-18, 2014, Budapest, Hungary. Copyright © 2014 Elsevier B.V. All rights reserved.

A Bi-Criterion Optimization Planning Model for Process Networks with Multiple Scenarios and Environmental Impact

Ahmad M. Alothman[a], Ignacio E. Grossmann[b,*],

[a] Saudi Aramco, Process & Control Systems Dep., Dhahran 31311, Saudi Arabia
[b] Carnegie Mellon University, Department of Chemical Engineering, 5000 Forbes Avenue, Pittsburgh, PA-15213, USA
grossmann@cmu.edu

Abstract

This work proposes an optimization model for planning operations, capacity expansions, and other process retrofitting for a chemical process network considering uncertainties in products prices and demands, and also considering environmental impact. The formulated MILP is a bi-criterion problem such that the first objective function is to maximize the net present value (NPV) and the second objective function is to minimize the total environmental impact for the chemical process network. Multiple scenarios are incorporated to account for uncertainties in products prices and demands. The bi-criterion problem is solved using the epsilon constraint method. The model is tested with an industrial scale chemical network to illustrate the advantages of using an integrated approach for this planning problem.

Keywords: optimization, planning, process network, uncertainty, environmental impact

1. Introduction

Investment decisions on capacity expansions and other process retrofitting in chemical networks are affected by many factors like raw materials availabilities and cost, and products demands and prices. The planning problem can be even more complex when considering uncertainties in these factors. Also with today's interest of having sustainable supply chain, planning does not only aim to maximize profits, but also to minimize environmental impact generated by the network. One of the major decisions that are taken as part of the planning for a given supply chain network is the expansion of facilities in the network (Shah, 2005). There are many studies in the literature that address the problem of capacity expansion in a given network. Sahinidis et al. (1989) presented a multi-period MILP for planning capacity expansions in a chemical process network over a long-range time horizon. The MILP model considers a forecast of product demands and pricing data and its objective function was to maximize the NPV of the network operations and capacity expansions decisions. This MILP model was expanded later to account for flexible and dedicated processes operating in continuous or batch modes (Sahinidis and Grossmann, 1991). In the latter work, the type of flexible processes that were considered, were those that have different main products. Also, Norton and Grossmann (1994) extended the MILP to account for dedicated and flexible processes with the flexibility being characterized by feedstocks, products, or any combinations. Later, Iyer and Grossmann (1998) also extended the MILP model of Sahinidis et al. (1989) to account for uncertainties in demands and prices by assuming a set of independent scenarios for each time period. For process retrofitting, Jackson and

Grossmann (2002) proposed a strategy for analyzing both, an entire process network at a high level and also analyzing a specific process flow sheet in a low level. They presented a methodology for the high level for selecting process retrofits of a given network using a multi-period generalized disjunctive programming (GDP) model.

In this work, the problem formulations highlighted above are followed to solve the expansion and other process retrofitting planning problem under multiple scenarios and further extended to account for environmental impact minimization.

2. Problem Statement

The problem addressed in this work assumes a given network of processes and chemicals. The model involves multiple time periods that can be either short (e.g. 1 y) or long periods (e.g. 4 y).The network contains both existing and potential processes and chemical products. Given also are multiple scenarios for forecasted chemical prices and demands for each time period. The problem consists of determining the following items: process retrofit projects for existing processes; selection of new processes and their capacity expansion policy; production profiles; selection of feedstocks for flexible processes; and sales and purchases of chemicals at each time period.

3. Model Formulation

It is assumed that there is a given network consisting of a set of NP chemical processes. These processes are either existing $i \in I_e$ or potential $i \in I_p$ (where i = 1,NP). The processes can be interconnected in a finite number of ways. The network also has a set of NC chemicals that include raw materials, intermediates and products. A finite number of NT time periods is also considered. The time periods are either short periods $t \in T_s$ or long periods $t \in T_l$ (where t = 1, NT). Uncertainty is included in the problem such that, for each time period, it is assumed that there are NS independent scenarios. Those are obtained from discrete random uncertainty in demands and prices. Raw materials, intermediates and products are represented by NC nodes of chemicals where purchases and sales are considered on one of several markets, l= 1,NM.

Similar to Sahinidis et al. (1989) and Iyer and Grossmann (1998), the network is represented by two types of nodes: one for the processes and the other for the chemicals. Accordingly, we have used the same material balances equations for these nodes (the reader may refer to the mentioned articles for more details on these equations).

Flexibility addressed in this work is the ability for some processes in the network to use more than one type of raw material. For this type of processes, it is assumed that for every feedstock, there is a hypothetical process such that $i \in I_f$ (where i = 1,NP, and I_f is the subset of processes for flexible process f. Figure 1). For this case, processes $i \in I_f$, if desired, can have one overall capacity such that

$$\sum_{i \in I_f} Q_{it} \geq \sum_{i \in I_f} W_{ijst} \qquad j \in MP(i) \qquad t = 1, NT \qquad s = 1, NS \qquad (1)$$

The subset MP(i) corresponds to the main product produced by process i. The amount produced of that product, W_{ijst}, cannot exceed the flexible process f total capacity, Q_{it}, available at time period t.

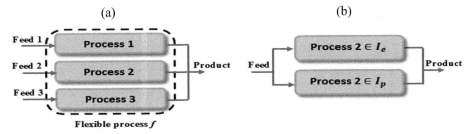

Figure 1. a) Superstructure for flexible processes. b) Superstructure existing and potential process of the same type

For potential processes, Q_{i0} has a value of zero. Unlike process retrofit projects, which normally have short project time (i.e. one year) and can be implemented within one short time period, capacity expansion projects have long project implementation times (i.e. 4 y). Accordingly, newly added capacities take more than one short time period to be available. The equation for calculating the total capacity Q_{it} of potential process i at short time periods $t \in T_s$ is given by the below relation:

$$y_{it}QE_{it}^L \leq QE_{it} \leq QE_{it}^U y_{it} \qquad y_{it} = 0,1 \quad i \in I_p \ t = 1, NT \qquad (2)$$

$$Q_{it} = Q_{i,t-1} + QE_{it-PT} \qquad i \in I_p \quad t \in T_s \qquad (3)$$

where QE_{it} represents the capacity expansion of process i installed at time period t. y_{it} are the 0-1 binary variables which indicate the occurrence of the expansions for each process i at each time period t. QE_{it}^L and QE_{it}^U are lower and upper bounds for the capacity expansions and PT is the implementation time for the expansion project. For the first long time period t = FL, where $t \in T_l$, capacity expansions projects started during the last few short time periods need to be included in the overall capacity. Defining a subset $t \in T_{ls}$ which represents the set of time periods such that $FL - PT < t < FL$, the equation for calculation the total capacity Q_{it} at this time period is:

$$Q_{it} = Q_{i,t-1} + QE_{it} + \sum_\tau QE_{i\tau} \quad i \in I_p \ t = \text{FL} \ where, \ \tau \in T_{ls} \qquad (4)$$

For other long time periods the equation is:

$$Q_{it} = Q_{i,t-1} + QE_{it-PT} \qquad i \in I_p \ t > FL \ t \in T_l \qquad (5)$$

For existing processes i $\in$ I$_e$, the equation for the plant capacity at any time period t is:

$$Q_{it} = Q_{i,t-1} + RE_{it} \qquad i \in I_e \quad t = 1, NT \qquad (6)$$

where the variable RE_{it} is the increase in process capacity, if there is any, as a result of implementing a process retrofit project in time period t. Note that when there is a decision to expand the production on an existing chemical product (capacity expansion), the expansions in capacity will assume to have different process number i such that $i \in I_p$ as shown in Figure 1.

Retrofit projects for existing processes can be mainly design modifications and/or debottlenecking. An implementation of a retrofit project r $\in$ R$_i$ on an existing process may result in increasing plant throughput and/or reducing operating cost. The below disjunctions are used for selecting retrofit projects for existing processes:

$$V_{r \in R_i} \begin{bmatrix} Z_{ir}^t \\ \overline{OC}_{ist} = \delta_{ir}^t W_{ijsr}^t \end{bmatrix} \quad j \in MP(i) \quad i \in I_e \quad t = 1..NT \quad s = 1, NS \tag{7}$$

$$V_{r \in R_i} \begin{bmatrix} X_{ir}^t \\ RC_{it} = \omega_{ir}^t \\ RE_{it} = \theta_{ir} \end{bmatrix} i \in I_e \qquad \qquad t = 1..NT \tag{8}$$

The Boolean variables Z_{ir}^t in (7) are for selecting the operating mode of retrofit project r of process i. X_{ir}^t variables in (8) represent the decision to implement retrofit project r. So X_{ir}^t can be considered as the Boolean variable for project selection, while Z_{ir}^t as the Boolean variable that defines the operating cost as a function of the decisions X_{ir}^t. The variable $\overline{OC}_{it}$ is the operating cost for a given process retrofit project r. Note that the existing operating cost is when r is $r_0 \in R_i$. Parameter θ_{ir} in (8) is the additional capacity that will be gained by existing process $i \in I_e$, as a result of implementing process retrofit r. The parameter ω_{ir}^t in (8) represents the fixed cost of the retrofit project, so the variable RC_{it} is the fixed cost spent at time period t for project retrofit r. Similar to what was done in Jackson and Grossmann (2002), an equation is used to ensure that not more than one retrofit project for an existing process is selected at time period t. The above disjunctions are converted into linear inequalities by convex hull reformulations.

The primary objective function is the maximization of NPV for the process network:

$$maxNPV =$$
$$-\left(\sum_{i \in I_e} \sum_{t=1}^{NT} RC_{it} + \sum_{i \in I_p} \sum_{t=1}^{NT} (y_{it}\beta_{it} + \alpha_{it}QE_{it}) \right) - \sum_{i=1}^{NP} \sum_{t=1}^{NT} \sum_{s=1}^{NS} \pi_{st} OC_{ist} +$$
$$\sum_{l=1}^{NM} \sum_{t=1}^{NT} \sum_{i=1}^{NP} \sum_{s=1}^{NS} \pi_{st} (\gamma_{jlst}S_{jlst} - \Gamma_{jlst}P_{jlst}) \tag{9}$$

where the parameter π_{st} is the probability of scenario s at time period t such that:

$$\sum_{s=1}^{NS} \pi_{st} = 1 \qquad t = 1, NT \tag{10}$$

The first two terms in (9) are for calculating the total investments in process retrofitting and capacity expansions, respectively. The third term is for total operating cost and the last two are the total chemical sales and raw materials purchases, respectively.

One of the life cycle assessment (LCA) methods used to calculate the environmental impact is EDIP97 method. To estimate the total environmental impact for a given process network during a given time horizon and with using this (LCA) method, the following equation can be used:

$$EIMP = \sum_{t=1}^{NT} \sum_{S=1}^{NS} \sum_{EP=1}^{NEP} \sum_{i=1}^{NP} \pi_{st} W_{ijst} (EPC_{i\,EP}/EPN_{EP}) EPW_{EP} \quad j \in MP(i) \tag{11}$$

where NEP is a set of environmental impact categories. Parameters EPN_{EP} and EPW_{EP} are the normalization references and weighting factors of these impacts, respectively. The parameter $EPC_{i\,EP}$ is the environmental potential impact caused by producing one unit mass of main product $j \in MP(i)$ of process i. The above equation is introduced to the problem as a second objective function that needs to be minimized. The resulted bi-criterion problem can be solved using the epsilon constraint (ε-constraint) method (Haimes et al., 1971).

4. Case Study

4.1. Industrial Scale Chemical Process Network Description

To demonstrate the use of the proposed MILP model, we apply using it on an industrial scale chemical process network. The network consists of 60 types of processes (with assigning different numbers to new capacities, the number of processes in the model is 120). A total of 108 different chemicals that are either raw materials, intermediates, byproducts or final products. There are four process types that are actually one flexible process which can process four different raw materials and produce three main products but with different yields for each raw material. Eleven time periods are considered in this example. The first 8 periods, t = 1, 2,..8, are short ones with a length of one year for each, and the last three periods, t = 9, 10, 11, are long ones with a length of 4 y for each giving a total length of the time horizon of 20 y. Two markets are considered in this problem. Minimum sales for most of the main products in the network are specified. The network has some existing processes at the beginning of the planning horizon (t = 0). These existing processes have two possible process retrofit projects: process debottleneck and energy reduction. Three different scenarios are considered: normal products prices and demands when s = 1, high products prices and demands when s = 2, and low products prices and demands when s = 3.

4.2. Results

The proposed model was implemented in GAMS using MILP solver XPRESS. To show the effect of considering uncertainties in the planning problem, the MILP problem of maximizing the NPV was first solved with only one scenario for prices and demand (normal). Results showed that when considering prices and demand scenarios, the total new added capacities to the network was reduced by about 13 % and the objective function value was reduced by about 6 %. This due to the fact that there is some probability that the chemical products prices and demands will be less than projected (low prices and demands scenario). Decisions for process retrofits for existing processes were almost the same for both cases. Table 1. Shows the MILP model computational statistics for the MILP problem with one and multiple scenarios.

When considering the minimization of the total environmental impact generated by the process network, equation 11 is introduced as a second objective function. The bi-criterion is solved using the ε-constraint method. The upper bound for ε is obtained by solving the maximization of NPV problem, and the lower bound is obtained by solving the minimization of EIMP problem. Figure 3displaysthe Pareto-optimal solution set for the bi-criterion problem. The total CPU time needed to generate the points on this curve with an optimality tolerance of 1.0 % is 3,859 s.

Table 1. Model computational statistics

	One scenario	Three scenarios
No. of continuous vars.	163,153	470,977
No. of binary vars.	5,940	5,940
No. of constraints	181,168	495,149
CPU, sec (optimality tolerance of 0.5 %)	2,104	3,828

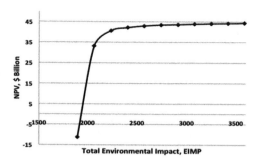

Figure 2. Pareto set: NPV vs. total environmental impact (in million targeted person-equivalent, mPET)

When analyzing the NPV vs the environmental impact curve, one can see that the slope at NPV values higher than $ 40 billion (in short scale) is quite small. This means that significant reduction in the environmental impact can be achieved with very little reduction in NPV. For example, reducing the NPV by 8.4 % (to $ 40.7 billion) from its highest possible value of $ 44.4 billion would result in reducing the total environmental impact by more than 37 %. Note that below some EIMP level (about 2,233 mPET), the NPV value will fall rapidly and accordingly, big drop in NPV will only cause little reduction in the total environmental impact.

5. Conclusions

In this work, a bi-criterion optimization planning model for process networks was developed. The model considers multiple scenarios for products prices and demands and also, includes the total environmental impact generated when producing the various chemical products in the network. The use of the model was tested in a large industrial scale process network. It was shown that the proposed model can define an optimal investment plan for a given process network that has potential capacity expansions and other process retrofits projects. The model can also define optimum production plan for the network like specifying production levels at each process and identifying feedstocks for flexible processes. It was also shown how the model can define an optimum investment plan that has minimum environmental impact.

References

Y. Y. Haimes, L. S. Lasdon, D. A. Wismer, 1971, On a bicriterion formulation of the problems of integrated system identification and system optimization. IEEE Transactions on Systems, Man and Cybernetics, 1, 296–297.

R. R. Iyer, I. E. Grossmann, 1998, A Bilevel Decomposition Algorithm for Long-Range Planning of Process Networks, Ind. Eng. Chem. Res., 37, 474-481.

J. R. Jackson, I. E. Grossmann, 2002, High-level optimization model for the retrofit planning of process networks, Ind. Eng. Chem. Res., 41, 3762-3770.

N. V. Sahinidis, I. E. Grossmann, R. E. Fornari, M. Chathrathi, 1989, Optimization model for long range planning in the chemical industry, Comput. Chem. Eng., 13, 1049-1063.

N. V. Sahinidis, I. E. Grossmann, 1991, Multiperiod investment model for processing networks with dedicated and flexible plants, Ind. Eng. Chem. Res., 30, 1165.

N. Shah, 2005, Process industry supply chains: Advances and challenges, Comput. Chem. Eng., 29, 1225-1235.

L. C. Norton, I. E. Grossmann, 1994, Strategic planning model for complete process flexibility, Ind. Eng. Chem. Res., 33, 69-76.

Jiří Jaromír Klemeš, Petar Sabev Varbanov and Peng Yen Liew (Editors)
Proceedings of the 24th European Symposium on Computer Aided Process Engineering – ESCAPE 24
June 15-18, 2014, Budapest, Hungary. Copyright © 2014 Elsevier B.V. All rights reserved.

Combining Supplier Selection and Production-Distribution Planning in Food Supply Chains

Pedro Amorim[a,*], Bernardo Almada-Lobo[a], Ana P.F.D. Barbosa-Póvoa[b], Ignacio E. Grossmann[c]

[a]INESC TEC, Faculdade de Engenharia, Universidade do Porto, Rua Dr. Roberto Frias, s/n, 4600-001 Porto, Portugal
[b]CEG-IST, Instituto Superior Técnico, Universidade de Lisboa, Av. Rovisco Pais, 1049-101 Lisboa, Portugal
[b]Department of Chemical Engineering, Carnegie Mellon University, Pittsburgh, PA 15213, USA
amorim.pedro@fe.up.pt

Abstract

This work addresses an integrated framework for deciding about the supplier selection in processed food supply chains that accounts for tactical production and distribution planning. We are especially concerned with the option of producing with local or mainstream raw materials. The contribution of this paper is two-fold. Firstly, it proposes a new multi-objective two-stage stochastic mixed-integer programming model for the supplier selection that maximizes the profit and minimizes the risk of a low customer service. Secondly, the main complexities of processed food supply chains management are considered: perishability of raw materials and final products, uncertainty at downstream and upstream parameters, and customer willingness to pay. Results indicate that dual sourcing is a strategy to be pursued across several scenarios. The multi-objective approach shows that a small decrease in the expected value of profit results in a significant increase in the customer service. Acknowledging the increase in customers willing to pay for local products is also fundamental.

Keywords: supplier selection; production-distribution planning; perishability

1. Introduction

The present work addresses the joint decision of choosing which suppliers to subcontract, and of planning the procurement, production and distribution in a medium-term planning horizon. We focus on companies that process a main perishable raw material and convert it into perishable final food products. These conditions happen for instance in the dairy, fresh juices and tomato sauce industries. Within this scope we integrate strategic and tactical decisions in a common framework. We consider a setting in which companies have their plants and distribution channels well implanted and, therefore, the supply chain design decisions that are considered address the supplier selection. These decisions are crucial to influence the key food supply chain drivers: profit, risk, demand and freshness. In this research we classify the suppliers as local or mainstream. This differentiation has already been made for the agri-business (Ata et al., 2012), but not for the food processing industry. Nevertheless, there are several practical examples of the incorporation of local sourcing in the current business practices as a way of increasing customer willingness to pay for food processed products (Martinez, 2010). Hence, we acknowledge that branding a given product as local has a positive effect on the perception of this product by customers. Therefore, customer willingness to pay will be higher for fresh products that are produced with local raw materials. We model this overall planning problem with a multi-objective two-stage stochastic mixed-integer programming model. In the first-stage we decide on which suppliers to contract and the quantities to be procured in advance. In the second-stage, we decide on the quantities to produce and transport as well as on the quantities to procure in the spot market. The uncertainties relate to the suppliers' raw material availability, suppliers' lead time, suppliers' spot market prices and demand for final products. Figure 1 gives an overview of the scope of this research.

Most of the approaches to tackle solely the supplier selection problem are based on the analytic hierarchy process (AHP) method to help decision makers in dealing both with uncertainty and subjectivity (Deng et al., 2014). When coupling decisions about supplier selection and ordering quantities, there are several analytical approaches that incorporate uncertainty in different forms, such as with different probability distributions or focusing on different uncertainty sources. More recently, researchers have started to address other relevant aspects that could be studied under this general problem. Chen and Guo (2013) studied the importance of supplier selection in competitive markets and concluded that besides the more evident conclusion that dual sourcing can help to mitigate supply chain risks, strategic sourcing can also be an effective tool in approaching retail competition. Qian (2014) develops an analytical approach that incorporates extensive market data when determining the supplier selection in a make-to-order production strategy setting. With a more practical emphasis, Hong and Lee (2013) lay the foundations of a decision support system for effective risk-management when selecting suppliers in a spot market using measures similar to the Conditional Value-at-Risk, such as the Expected Profit-Supply at Risk. Another aspect that has received attention from researchers has to do with disruption management, especially in the suppliers' availability. Silbermayr and Minner (2013) develop an analytical model based on Markov decision processes in which suppliers may be completely unavailable at a given (stochastic) interval of time. Due to the complexity of the optimal ordering policies, they also derive a heuristic to the same end. Sawik (2013) proposes a model similar to the one in this paper as it is able to deal with multiple periods and it accounts for uncertainty through stochastic programming. The

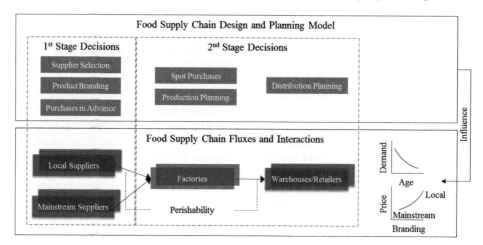

Figure 1. Overview of the research problem scope.

main differences relate to the fact that in this paper we acknowledge different types of uncertainty, such as in the lead time, and we consider distribution decisions as well as the emphasis on food products by incorporating perishability.

2. Mathematical Formulation

This section presents a multi-objective two-stage stochastic model to deal with supplier selection and production-distribution planning in food supply chains of processed goods that are subject to perishability both in the raw materials and final products. Let $k = 1,\dots,K$ be the products that are produced in the different factories ($f \in F$). To produce these products the factory has to procure raw materials from the different suppliers ($s \in S$) available. These raw materials are classified either as mainstream ($u = 0$) or local ($u = 1$) depending on the supplier. The planning horizon is divided into periods $t = 1,\dots,T$. These periods correspond to months as we are dealing with tactical plans. After production, products are transferred to retailers($r \in R$), which face an uncertain demand (D_{ktr}^{av}) that also depends on products' age$a \in A_k = \{0,\dots,(SL_k - 1)\}$, where SL_k corresponds to the shelf-life of product k. Notice that raw materials have also their age limited to$a \in A_u = \{0,\dots,(\widehat{SL}_u - 1)\}$, where $\widehat{SL}_u$ corresponds to the shelf-life of raw material u. The stochastic data is initially given by continuous distribution and it is then modelled on some probability space, where V is a set of discrete scenarios with corresponding probabilities of occurrenceϕ_v, such that $\phi_v > 0$ and $\sum_v \phi_v = 1$. This discretization relates to the sampling strategy used in the computational experiments. In our two-stage stochastic program, we define the quantities to procure in advance from each supplier (s_{tsf}) and the branding strategy for each product: local ($\chi_k = 1$) or mainstream($\chi_k = 0$) as first-stage decisions. Procured quantities in the spot market ($\bar{s}_{tsf}^v$), production quantities in regular and in overtime ($p_{kuft}^{av}$and$\dot{p}_{kuft}^{av}$), transportation flows (x_{ktfr}^v), inventory levels of both raw materials ($\widehat{w}_{utf}^{av}$)and final products (w_{ktr}^{av}), and demand satisfaction (ψ_{kutr}^{av}) are the second-stage decisions. In the remainder of this section we present the main highlights of the formulation.

The first objective function maximizes the profit of the producer over the tactical planning horizon. Expected revenue, which depends on the products' branding is subtracted by supply chain related costs: purchasing costs of raw materials both when bought in advance and or in the spot market, holding costs for raw materials and final products, transportation costs between the supply chain nodes, and production related costs. Eq.(1) is the second objective function that maximizes the $(1 - \alpha) \cdot 100$ scenarios that yield the lowest customer service. Parameter$\alpha$is usually set to 0.95. This is an adaptation of the Conditional Value-at-Risk (Rockafellar and Uryasev, 2000) focusing on customer service. Similar concepts, such as the supply-at-risk (SaR) were developed in a similar context (Hong and Lee, 2013). The main advantages of this type of metrics (against more conventional risk-averse measures) is that they are less influenced by very seldom uncertain scenarios that could steer the whole solution structure to a very conservative behaviour.

$$\max \eta - \frac{1}{1 - \alpha} \sum_v \phi_v \cdot \delta_v \qquad (1)$$

Decision variable η retrieves an approximation of the customer service value-at-risk, and auxiliary variable δ_v is defined using Eq.(2). The equation defines variable

δ_v making it zero when the customer service in a given scenario is higher that the customer servicevalue-at-risk. Otherwise, variable δ_v determines the difference between the customer service value-at-risk and the corresponding mean customer service of the scenario.

$$\delta_v \geq \eta - \sum_{k,u,t,r,a \in A_u} \psi_{kutr}^{av} \quad \forall v \in V \tag{2}$$

Eq.(3) translates the first stage decision that defines the quantity and the arrival time of raw material from each supplier (s_{tsf})to a second stage decision variable (τ_{tsf}^{av}) that is affected by the uncertainty on the lead time (LT_{ts}^v) and by the available quantity (AQ_{ts}^v). Lead time uncertainty offsets both the arrival time and the age of the product. Therefore, say a product that was supposed to arrive on $t = 2$ with age 0, will arrive on $t = 4$ with age 2, if $LT_{ts}^v = 2$. The availabilityAQ_{ts}^v is defined between 0 and 1 and it just affects the amount of the arriving quantity. It is also important to enforce over the entire planning horizon that the amount of product arriving with different ages is equal to what we have ordered discounted by the availability and arrivals outside the planning horizon.

$$\tau_{t+LT_{ts}^v,sf}^{LT_{ts}^v,v} = AQ_{ts}^v s_{tsf} \quad \forall t \in T, s \in S, f \in F, v \in V \tag{3}$$

Eq.(4) indicates that the amount of raw material$u$ available to process at factory f with age 0, is equivalent to the amount bought and transported from the different suppliers that deliver raw material u (S_u).

$$\sum_{s \in S_u} \left(\tau_{tsf}^{0v} + \bar{s}_{tsf}^v \right) = \widehat{w}_{utf}^{0v} \quad \forall u \in U, t \in T, f \in F, v \in V \tag{4}$$

Eqs.(5)-(6) relate the consumption of raw material into the production of final products. While Eq.(5) acts as an inventory balance constraint that updates also the age of the raw material stock, and that takes into account the raw materials arriving with older ages (bigger than 0), Eq.(6) forces the utilization of local raw material in case of marketing the product as local.

$$\widehat{w}_{utf}^{av} = \widehat{w}_{u,t-1,f}^{a-1,v} + \sum_{d \in S_u} \tau_{tsf}^{av} - \sum_k \left(p_{ku,t-1,f}^{a-1,v} + \dot{p}_{ku,t-1,f}^{a-1,v} \right) \quad \forall u \in U, t$$

$$\in \{1, \dots, T+1\}, f \in F, a \in A_u : a \geq 1, v \in V \tag{5}$$

$$p_{k,0,tf}^{av} + \dot{p}_{k,0,tf}^{av} \leq M(1 - \chi_k) \quad \forall k \in K, t \in T, f \in F, a \in A_k, v \in V \tag{6}$$

Both normal and extra production are limited to the available plant capacity. After production, all products made in the different factories flow to retailers within the same planning period. Therefore, the amount of final products entering each retailer corresponds to the inventory available with age 0 to satisfy demand. Eqs.(7)-(8) link the choice on the product branding as local or mainstream to the type of demand profile that will determine the customer willingness to pay. Therefore, choosing to produce a local product will give access to a higher customer willingness to pay.

$$\psi_{k0tr}^{av} \leq 1 - \chi_k; \psi_{k1tr}^{av} \leq \chi_k \quad \forall k \in K, t \in T, r \in R, a \in A_k, v \in V \tag{7); (8}$$

Eq.(9) is another inventory balancing constraint, but this time in the retailers' premises. This constraint updates the age of final products' inventory throughout the horizon.

$$w_{ktr}^{av} = w_{k,t-1,r}^{a-1,v} - \sum_u \psi_{ku,t-1,r}^{a-1,v} D_{k,t-1,r}^{0v} \quad \forall k \in K, t \in \{1,\dots,T+1\}, r$$
$$\in R, a \in A_k \colon a \geq 1, v \in V \tag{9}$$

Eq.(10) keeps the demand fulfilled at different inventory ages below the respective demand profile. It is also important to ensure that the demand fulfilled with different ages is always below the demand that the customer would be willing to pay for the product in the fresher state.

$$\sum_u \psi_{kutr}^{av} D_{ktr}^{0v} \leq D_{ktr}^{av} \quad \forall k \in K, t \in T, r \in R, a \in A_k, v \in V \tag{10}$$

3. Computational Experiments

The results for the model presented in Section 2 were obtained by solving an adaptation of the data set described in Amorim et al (2013). We further characterized the local supplier as having a lower and more uncertain yield and a smaller and more certain lead time than the mainstream supplier. Regarding the raw material price we considered that the mainstream supplier was cheaper than the local one and that both had a similar variance of their spot prices. In our experiment design we have done a sensitivity analysis varying the shelf-life (SL) of the raw materials between 3 and 9 months (the planning horizon is 12 months) and the premium price that customers are willing to pay for local products (Premium) between 0 % and +10 %. In order to obtain solutions from the Pareto front we have used the ε-constraint method embedded in a sample average approximation scheme, limiting the minimum customer service conditional value at risk (cscVaR) to be above 90 % and 95 %.We sampled 81 scenarios and solved 50 instances of the approximating stochastic programming. We then evaluated the objective function by solving 1,296 independently sampled scenarios. In Table 1 we report several metrics: the profit, the cscVaR, the quantity of local procured raw material over the total procured raw material (% local), the amount of spoiled raw material over the total procured raw material (% spoiled), the total procured raw material over the total demand (% raw) and the number of products that the model chose to be branded as local (# local), which has a maximum value of 6.

Preliminary results shown that the integrated approach is relevant compared to a decoupled one has it is able to grasp the advantages of having a product branded as local in order to dilute key supply chain costs. These costs may arise, for example, from producing in overtime. From Table 1 we notice that a dual sourcing strategy is used in all solutions and that a 10 % increase in the revenue obtained by selling local products

Table 1. Results of the sensitivity analysis.

Premium	0 %				+10 %			
SL	3 months		9 months		3 months		9 months	
Profit	32801	32496	33064	32866	32966	32734	33151	32919
cscVaR	90 %	95 %	90 %	95 %	90 %	95 %	90 %	95 %
% local	3.4%	3.8%	2.5%	2.9%	56.3%	66.8%	64.1%	78.5%
% spoiled	0.1%	0.1%	6.9%	6.5%	0.0%	0.0%	3.8%	3.9%
% raw	104%	106%	106%	107%	112%	117%	116%	121%
# local	0	0	0	0	3	4	4	5

results in an increase of more than 50 % on local sourcing. Regarding the trade-off between profit and cscVaR, it seems that small losses in the average profit may lead to substantial shift in cscVaR. Also, both higher service levels and lower shelf-lives of raw materials lead to an increase in the amount of spoiled material and an increase of the quantities purchased from suppliers in relation to the actual demand.

4. Conclusions

In this paper, we have proposed a novel multi-objective two-stage stochastic mixed-integer programming model to tackle the integrated decision of supplier selection and production-distribution planning for food supply chains. Uncertainty is present in the suppliers' processes namely in lead time, availability and spot price, and it is also present in customers' demand that, furthermore, is dependent on the age of the sold product. Results show that a dual sourcing is used across several different settings. Local sourcing increases drastically with an increase in the price premium paid by customer for products branded as local. Moreover, results indicated that a slight decrease in the expected profit (~1 %) results in a substantial increase in the cscVaR (~5%).Future work should expand the computational experiments and derive more managerial insights as well as investigate if tighter formulations could be proposed for this problem.

Acknowledgements

This work is financed by the ERDF – European Regional Development Fund through the COMPETE Programme (operational programme for competitiveness) and by National Funds through the FCT – Fundação para a Ciência e a Tecnologia (Portuguese Foundation for Science and Technology) within project «EXPL/EMS-GIN/1930/2013».

References

P. Amorim, A. Costa, B. Almada-Lobo, 2013, Influence of consumer purchasing behaviour on the production planning of perishable food, OR Spectrum, DOI 10.1007/s00291-013-0324-9, 1-24.

B. Ata, D. Lee, M.H. Tongarlak, 2012, Got Local Food?, Harvard Business School Working Paper, 12-058, Boston, USA.

J. Chen, Z. Guo, 2013, Strategic Sourcing in the Presence of Uncertain Supply and Retail Competition, Production and Operations Management, DOI 10.1111/poms.12078.

X. Deng, Y. Hu, Y. Deng, S. Mahadevan, 2014, Supplier selection using AHP methodology extended by D numbers, Expert Systems with Applications,41, 1, 156-167.

Z. Hong, C. Lee, 2013, A decision support system for procurement risk management in the presence of spot market, Decision Support Systems, 55, 1, 67–78.

S. Martinez, 2010, Local Food Systems: Concepts, Impacts, and Issues, ERR 97, U.S. Department of Agriculture, Economic Research Service, Washington, USA.

L. Qian, 2014, Market-based supplier selection with price, delivery time, and service level dependent demand, International Journal of Production Economics, 147, 697–706.

R.T.Rockafellar, S. Uryasev, 2000, Optimization of conditional value-at-risk, Journal of Risk, 2, 21-41.

T. Sawik, 2013, Integrated selection of suppliers and scheduling of customer orders in the presence of supply chain disruption risks, International Journal of Production Research, 51, 23-24, 7006-7022.

L. Silbermayr, S. Minner, 2013, A multiple sourcing inventory model under disruption risk, International Journal of Production Economics, 149, 37-46.

Jiří Jaromír Klemeš, Petar Sabev Varbanov and Peng Yen Liew (Editors)
Proceedings of the 24th European Symposium on Computer Aided Process Engineering – ESCAPE 24
June 15-18, 2014, Budapest, Hungary. Copyright © 2014 Elsevier B.V. All rights reserved.

Embedding of Timed Automata-based Schedule Optimization into Recipe Driven Production

Christian Schoppmeyer[a], Stephan Fischer[a], Jochen Steimel[a], Vinh Quang Do[b], Nan Wang[c], Sebastian Engell[a*]

[a]*Process Dynamics and Operations Group, Department of Biochemical and Chemical Engineering, TU Dortmund University, Emil-Figge-Str. 70, 44221 Dortmund, Germany*
[b]*Department of Automation Technology, Can Tho University, Can Tho City, Vietnam*
[c]*China Nuclear Control System Engineering Co., Ltd., No.8 Kechuang 3rd Rd., Beijing Economic-Technological Development Area, Beijing (100176), China*
christian.schoppmeyer@bci.tu-dortmund.de, s.engell@bci.tu-dortmund.de

Abstract

In this contribution, we discuss the conceptual idea of a hierarchical control system with an integration of schedule optimization and process control. We propose to embed timed automata (TA)-based schedule optimization into recipe driven production based on sequential control logic combined with interlocks in order to handle uncertainties in the operation on the different levels of the control hierarchy, depending on the type and on the impact of the uncertainty. The efficiency and robustness of the proposed operations management system is evaluated on a lab-scale multiproduct pipeless batch plant using different scenarios of uncertainties.

Keywords: Process operations, integration of scheduling and control, robust control logic, timed automata, reactive scheduling.

1. Introduction

The increasing demand for customized products with short life-cycles and the pressure to produce cheaper, faster, and more flexibly call for an efficient scheduling and a robust operation of multiproduct batch plants (Engell and Harjunkoski, 2012). In such plants, an optimized scheduling of the recipe operations enables to economically utilize the scarce resources of the plant. A robust operation enables the execution of recipe operations as planned in the schedule while preventing the plant from reaching unsafe states which could lead to delays in the production, off-spec products, or in the worst-case to a shut-down of the plant. Usually, the planning of the production is done for the next months and a detailed scheduling is performed for each day. The resulting optimized production schedule for the next day is forwarded to the lower level process control layer for execution. From the process control level upwards, only condensed information is provided (end-times of recipe operations or batches, quality information). In case of disturbances in the execution, e.g. actuator malfunctions or varying raw material quality, the calculated schedule gets obsolete quickly. In the event of such a disturbance, either the process control is able to handle it, e.g. by repeating a step of a recipe operation or by delaying parts of the production, and the execution can continue as planned but with a certain delay, or the error cannot be handled within an appropriate time by the process control layer only, e.g. in case of a machine breakdown, and hence rescheduling is required or preferred. Since the upward information flow in current production systems is condensed, in most cases an explicit rescheduling cannot be triggered by the process control layer. Moreover, in the majority of the plants the scheduling is performed by plant operators or plant managers (Engell and Harjunkoski, 2012). Hence, the system cannot directly respond to uncertain events in an efficient and automated way and thereby time and economic performance are lost. Grossmann (2005) identified the enterprise-wide optimization (EWO) which combines supply-chain management with optimal operation, the integrated optimization of major operational decisions, of a plant as the next frontier to remain competitive in the global market place. Several integrated methods for scheduling and dynamic optimization have emerged in the recent decade whose mainly focus on deterministic problems due to computational complexity (Nie et al., 2012). Deviations in the production process make those solutions obsolete quickly. Only a few methods consider uncertainties in the process (Chu and You, 2013). To the best knowledge of the authors, in none of the contributions an integration of the lower process control level with uncertainties was considered.

In this contribution, we discuss the conceptual idea of an operations management system with an integration of scheduling and process control by embedding TA-based schedule optimization into recipe driven production based on sequential control logic combined with interlocks. Subsequently, the performance of the proposed approach for a lab-scale multiproduct pipeless batch plant using different scenarios of uncertainties is compared and discussed.

2. Operations management system

The conceptual idea of an operations management system with an integration of scheduling and process control is shown in Figure 1. The integrated system has two hierarchical levels: an upper scheduling level and a lower process control level. Based on the production targets and the current state of the plant, the upper scheduling level calculates optimized production schedules of the recipe operations. Start signals of the recipe operations of these schedules are passed to the lower process control level. The process control layer executes the scheduled sequence of operations by sending the corresponding control signals to the actuators of the plant and reading the sensor measurements. The current status of the plant and of the schedule execution and detected errors are fed back to the scheduling level. The scheduling is executed in a moving window approach where a new overlapping schedule is calculated if either a predefined set of recipe operations of the current schedule are finished or if an error-based rescheduling request is sent by the process control layer. The process control layer executes in real-time an "as-fast-as-possible" strategy taking sensor feedback from the plant into account.

To realize the integrated operations management system it is proposed to embed TA-based schedule optimization into the sequential control logic, e.g. Sequential Function Charts (SFC), combined with interlocks, e.g. Function Block Diagrams (FBD).

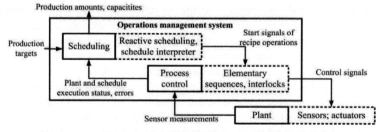

Figure 1. Schematic diagram of the structure of the proposed operations management system.

2.1. Timed Automata-based scheduling

On the scheduling level, the scheduling problem is solved by modelling it using TA and applying the technique of reachability analysis for TA to compute the schedules (Subbiah et al., 2011). The TA-based approach is capable of calculating optimal or at least very good schedules in a short period of time. Thus, the schedule can be adapted quickly to the current state of the system and to new information (Subbiah et al., 2013). The schedule optimization is performed in a moving window approach that starts with calculating an initial schedule for a predefined set of recipe operations - usually, all recipe operations of a small set of orders, called the prediction set. The optimized schedule of the prediction set is passed to the process control layer and is executed for a certain time, called the control horizon, e.g. 75 % of the makespan of the prediction set. During the execution, all newly revealed information, e.g. the arrival of new orders or delays in the execution, is collected. When the end of the control horizon is reached, a rescheduling is triggered for a shifted prediction set based on the current state of the plant, the recipe operations, and the collected information. Since the calculation of a new schedule requires a certain amount of time, the response time, the rescheduling is not triggered at the end of control horizon, but it is based on a predicted state of the plant at the end of the control horizon instead of the current state. Within the response time, the old schedule is still executed as planned, if possible.

2.2. Robust control logic

On the process control level, a combination of sequential control logic and interlocks is used. For each of the possible recipe operations on the scheduling level, a so-called elementary sequence is defined on the process control level in the SFC formalism.

The execution of the elementary sequence is triggered by an appropriate start signal sent by the scheduler. However, the sequence will not be started if an error is detected. Each of the elementary sequences consists of one or more sequential sub-operations that are usually executed one after the other until the end step is reached as depicted in Figure 2. In case of small errors, these are handled by means of alternative branches which consist of an error-handling procedure and a jump to an appropriate restart step within the nominal sequence. The error handling and the restarting step can depend on the error or

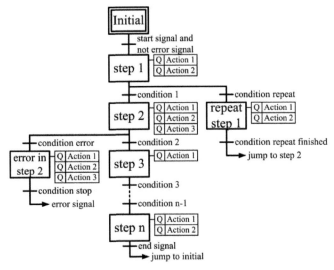

Figure 2. Schematic diagram of an elementary sequence in the SFC formalism.

on the operation phase it is detected in. This low level error-handling is limited to small errors e.g. an actuator malfunction which can be handled by repetition of a part of the task. When the operation has finished successfully, the elementary sequence sends the end signal to the scheduler, switches back into the waiting mode and waits for a new start signal. Larger errors, which in general cannot be handled within the low level control layer, are handled by means of alternative branches which consist of an error-reporting procedure to safely shutdown the affected part of the plant, block this part for further execution, and report the error back to the scheduler. All output signals of the elementary sequences are filtered by a set of interlocks.

2.3. Integration of scheduling and sequence control

The two levels of control are integrated by a feedback structure where the scheduling level passes start signals to the corresponding elementary sequences of the process control level which in turn reports end and error signals to the scheduling level. Figure 3 shows the hierarchical integration of the system, in particular the flow of information when operation op1_2 is started (marked with arrows) at time point "Start op1_2": the scheduling level determines the start time and sends the start signal to the elementary sequences of the recipe operation, sequence op1_2. The sequential control logic in the sequence is executed by sending control inputs via the interlocks to the plant and reading sensor feedback. Once the sequence finished its execution, an end signal is fed back to the scheduling level, marked as "Finish op1_2" on the time line of the schedule.

This execution procedure leads to an "as-fast-as-possible" strategy while adhering to the exact timing and sequence of the calculated schedule where required. During the execution of a schedule, the scheduler is responsible for checking the dependencies of the recipe operations regarding the resources, resource-based dependencies, and the other operations of the same recipe, recipe-based dependencies. A recipe operation has a resource-based dependency on all other recipe operations which are allocated to the same resource as required for the chosen recipe operation, but which are scheduled to be executed before it, e.g. in Figure 3 op3_3 is dependent on op2_1 and op1_2. A recipe operation has a recipe-based dependency on all recipe operations which belong to the same recipe and are scheduled before it, e.g. in Figure 3 op3_3 is dependent on op3_1 and op3_2. If all "upstream" operations of a recipe operation finished their executions, the scheduler is allowed to send the start signal for the recipe operation, if no strict tim-

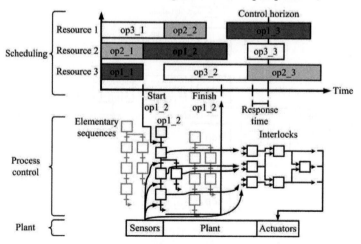

Figure 3. Schematic diagram of the hierarchical integration.

ing conditions have to be met. Recipe operations cannot overtake "upstream" operations in the execution, as the order of operations and thus their dependencies can only be changed by rescheduling.

3. Case study – Multiproduct pipeless batch plant

As a case study, a lab scale multiproduct pipeless batch plant which produces coloured substances from three different raw materials, yellow, blue and red, is considered. In contrast to traditional multiproduct batch plants, the connection between the different processing stations is realized by a centralized bidirectional rotary gripping arm which transports the materials in mobile vessels, instead of using pipes. A schematic diagram of the plant is shown in Figure 4. The materials are transported in ten vessels which are stored in the storage station, which is implemented as a turntable to allow the gripping arm to access all vessels. The arm transports the vessels between the storage station and the six processing stations. The processing stations implement four basic process operations: filling, cleaning, mixing, and dosing. Station 2 provides a stirrer to mix the fluid. Stations 3, 4 and 6 are connected to pumps feeding raw materials into the vessels. Station 5 is equipped with water and detergent feeds as well as a waste pump in order to clean a vessel. Station 7 and 8 transfer a determined amount of liquid from one vessel to another.

The integrated operations management system was implemented for this case study. On the process control level, for each of the basic process operations of the processing stations, for the rotation of the storage station, and for the basic operations of the gripping arm (grab, release, rotate) a separate elementary sequence in the SFC formalism was designed. Additionally, safety related interlocks were created in Function Block Diagrams (FBD) in order to prevent the controller from sending unsafe commands to the plant. On the scheduling level, the scheduling problem is modelled using TA and the nominal schedule calculation using reachability analysis is implemented in a moving window approach (Subbiah et al., 2013). The operations management system supports the handling of several identified uncertain events. These events can be grouped into two classes: the first class covers small, non-critical events like the unsuccessful release of a vessel to a station. Such events are handled by repeating the operation in the control logic. The second class encompasses critical events like the breakdown of one of the three raw material pumps, and a malfunction of the mixing, cleaning or dosing. In these cases, a rescheduling is performed. While the new schedule is calculated, all tasks, which are not affected by the breakdown, continue, e.g. if the filling station for material red is unavailable, a mixing task scheduled for the same time can still be finished. If a breakdown cannot be handled by a maintenance operation, no rescheduling is triggered and the plant is shut down in a controlled fashion.

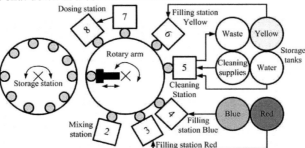

Figure 4. Schematic diagram of the multiproduct pipeless batch plant.

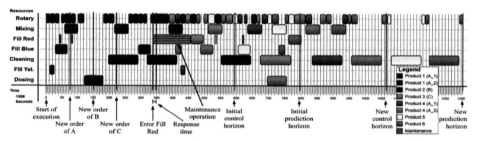

Figure 5. Gantt chart of the resulting schedule for the defined uncertainty scenario.

4. Results and conclusion

Figure 5 shows the resulting Gantt chart for the production of five products in the multiproduct pipeless plant. In the beginning, three initial orders are given and scheduled (prediction set: all available orders). During the execution of the initial schedule, two additional orders arrive at different points in time. These new orders are collected for the planned rescheduling of the next window at the end of the initial control horizon. At the time point "Error Fill Red" an error of the pump at station 3 is reported to the scheduler by the corresponding elementary sequence of the process control layer. At this point in time, a rescheduling based on the current state of the production and with a predefined response time of ten seconds is triggered and a new schedule including the maintenance operation on the station 3 and the changed production demand is calculated in less than two seconds. The result shows that the proposed approach is able to handle uncertain events in the production in an efficient and robust way.

In the scope of this work, a hierarchical integrated control system which combines the effective approach of TA-based schedule optimization with robust sequential control logic was proposed and applied to a multiproduct pipeless batch plant. The realized integrated execution system turned out to be effective and flexible. It is able to react to a broad range of uncertain events in the operation leading to an efficient use of the scare resources. The implementation of the proposed control approach benefits from the modular nature of the models on the different levels and can be adapted to growing needs at later stages, e.g. when a new product is introduced, the TA model can be extended by an additional recipe automaton and the control logic by the elementary sequences for the corresponding recipe operations.

References

Y. Chu, F. You, 2013, Integration of scheduling and dynamic optimization of batch processes under uncertainty, Industrial and Engineering Chemistry Research, 52, 16851-16869.

S. Engell, I. Harjunkoski, 2012, Optimal operation: Scheduling, advanced control and their integration, Computers and Chemical Engineering, 47, 121-133.

I.E. Grossmann, 2005, Enterprice-wide optimization: A new frontier in process systems engineering, AIChE Journal, 51, 1846-1857.

Y.S. Nie, L.T. Biegler, J.M. Wassick, 2012, Integrated scheduling and dynamic optimization of batch processes using state equipment networks, AIChE Journal, 58, 3416-3432.

S. Subbiah, C. Schoppmeyer, S. Engell, 2011, An intuitive and efficient approach to process scheduling with sequence-dependent changeovers using timed automata models, Industrial & Engineering Chemistry Research, 50, 5131-5152.

S. Subbiah, C. Schoppmeyer, J.M. Valdes, C. Sonntag, S. Engell, 2013, Optimal management of shuttle robots in a high-rise warehouse using timed automata models, Proc. IFAC Conference on Manufacturing Modelling, Management, and Control, Saint Petersburg, Russia.

Jiří Jaromír Klemeš, Petar Sabev Varbanov and Peng Yen Liew (Editors)
Proceedings of the 24th European Symposium on Computer Aided Process Engineering – ESCAPE 24
June 15-18, 2014, Budapest, Hungary. Copyright © 2014 Elsevier B.V. All rights reserved.

Life-cycle Modelling for Fault Detection - Extraction of PCA Models from Flowsheeting Simulators

Barbara Farsang*, Sandor Nemeth, Janos Abonyi

University of Pannonia, Department of Process Engineering, Egyetem Street 10. Veszprém, H-8200, Hungary
farsangb@fmt.uni-pannon.hu

Abstract

The operation of chemical processes is often supported by flowsheeting simulators and process monitoring systems. In many practical applications simulators used for planning, scheduling or operator training are often too complex for direct usage in real-time process monitoring; the structure of the related non-linear models does not support low-cost and rapid implementation of process monitoring systems. In this paper we present a novel method that effectively utilizes these first principle models for the development, maintenance and validation of multivariate statistical models. We demonstrate that the performance of Principal Component Analysis (PCA) models used for process monitoring can be improved by model based data reconciliation. The applicability of developed method is demonstrated in the Tennessee Eastman benchmark problem.

Keywords: fault detection, life-cycle modelling, PCA, data reconciliation, Tennessee Eastman problem

1. Introduction

Today's chemical companies are faced with intense competition and rising energy/material costs. Cost reduction and quality/productivity improvement have now become key levers for gaining competitive advantage. Three pillars of operational excellence are production planning & control; manufacturing execution and operational effectiveness of people; processes and assets. Tight coordination among these three pillars is required in order to achieve overall operational excellence. In this paper we focus on the development of model based tools for fault detection that could contribute significantly to the improvement of operational excellence. Multivariate statistical models are powerful tools for fault detection. The most commonly used model is the PCA. Ralston et al (2001) published a detailed description of the PCA technique along an in-depth case study on a chemical process. PCA model based fault detection techniques are continuously in the focus of process engineering research. Dobos and Abonyi (2012) combined and integrated recursive and dynamic PCA into time series segmentation techniques, Du (2007) improved PCA with joint angle analysis method, Liu et al (2013) showed how an improved version of PCA detects and isolates faults in case of Tennessee Eastman Process. The performance of the model based process monitoring system highly depends on the quality of the model. Hence, for a good PCA based solution requires accurate and validated historical process data with high information content. The synergy between data reconciliation and PCA has already been realized (Amand et al. 2001).

The aim of our research is to develop a method that can be applied in industrial environment and includes advantages of a priori knowledge based models and data-driven multivariate statistical process monitoring tools. Although detailed first principle models cannot be applied directly for process monitoring. As we will show, in some cases it is possible to extract useful information from these simulators to support the development of PCA models. This is a novel example for the important model life-cycle concept, as experts of main process engineering companies believe that the "model integrates the whole organization" (Krieger, 1995) and the extensive use of models is the way how data, information, and knowledge should be conveyed from research to manufacturing (Bayer et al., 2000).

2. Improved PCA with data reconciliation

Our method combines first-principle model, data reconciliation and PCA to improve the sensitivity of fault detection. These models are used for pre-processing and reconciliation of historical process data and augmenting this data by simulated operating variables used for the identification of the PCA model. Flowsheeting simulator is used for generating the projection matrix of PCA. In other words, the PCA model acts as a local linear approximation of the process (or the flowsheeting simulator). Data reconciliation can reconcile the measured data to filter random noise. Data reconciliation can be used easily in case of simple stationer linear models, e.g. in case models representing material balances, but complex technology requires more complex solution: extraction information from flowsheeting simulators (Farsang et al. 2013), when Monte-Carlo simulation is used to sensitivities to define a linear process monitoring oriented PCA model.

The procedure of the proposed methodology is summarized in Figure 1. The manifold of the process variables has lower local dimension than their embedding dimension since these variables are correlated thanks to balance equations represented by the laws of physics and chemistry. Hence, projection of process data into the low dimensional manifold (of model equations) can be considered as a data reconciliation task. When this manifold is approximated by a PCA model, this projection error (Q-type error in PCA based process monitoring) can be effectively used for as model based fault detection.

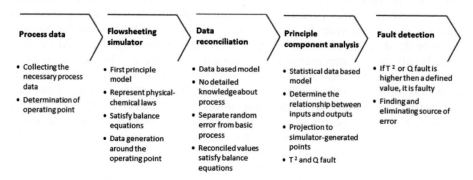

Figure 1. Proposed algorithm for fault detection

The Q projection error can be calculated as

$$Q = (I - PP^T)\tilde{x} \qquad (1)$$

where $\tilde{x}$ is a vector of raw measurements (in case of data reconciliation) or scaled measurements (in case of PCA), P is the projection matrix, and I is identity matrix.

The key question is how we should calculate the P projection matrix to get informative Q signal for fault detection. We will analyse three approaches. (1) P will be calculated based on the concept of data reconciliation; using linear balance equations, (2) we extract PCA models from the process simulator or (3) we combine these methods as we firstly reconcile the raw process data and then apply PCA for its projection.

Data reconciliation takes minimal correction of measured variables to make them satisfy a set of model constraints thereby improves the accuracy of the measurement results and verifies the acceptability of measurements. These model constraints are mostly linear and defined in the following form:

$$Ax = b \qquad (2)$$

where A is the coefficient matrix, x process variables of the balance equations and b represents the source terms in the equations.

The aim of data reconciliation to minimize the difference between the measured and reconciled values taking into account the variance of the variables and it ensures that reconciled parameters satisfy balance equations. When the expected value of measurement errors is zero and measurement errors follow normal (Gaussian) distribution, the optimal projection of the raw data can be calculated by the following equation:

$$\hat{x} = (I - V_{\tilde{a}}A^T(AV_{\tilde{a}}A^T)^{-1}A)\tilde{x} + V_{\tilde{a}}A^T(AV_{\tilde{a}}A^T)^{-1}b \qquad (3)$$

where $\hat{x}$ is a vector of estimates (reconciled values), $\tilde{x}$ is a vector of raw measurements, I is identity matrix (its size depends on the number of variables), $V_{\tilde{a}}$ is covariance matrix of the measurements error and A is the coefficient matrix.

As the previous equation shows the data reconciliation based projection matrix is the following:

$$P_{DR} = I - V_{\tilde{a}}A^T(AV_{\tilde{a}}A^T)^{-1}A \qquad (4)$$

PCA is based on the singular value decomposition of covariance matrix.

$$F = \frac{1}{N-1}X^TX = USW \qquad (5)$$

The eigenvalues of covariance matrix of the available normalised data X are the squares of the singular values in S. The number of principle components is determined based on eigenvalues. We calculate their contribution to variance and we select which have got the greatest impact. U matrix contains the eigenvectors of covariance matrix (F) and it will be the projection matrix (P), its size depends on the number of principal components.

3. Results and discussion

The proposed concept has been applied to a well-known Tennessee Eastman Process. The gaseous reactants fed to reactor where four gas-phase reactions occur: two major and two sides. Then the mixture is cooled to products can condense. Unreacted feedstock is separated from the liquid product in vapor-liquid separator and recirculated to the reactor. Purge stream removes the inert component and byproducts from the system. The separator underflow goes to the stripper because the products stream contains dissolved reactants. Product stream is the bottom streams of stripper. The benchmark problem is defined by 41 measured, 12 control variables and 20 disturbances (Downs and Vogel, 1993). Among these disturbances five were applied to test fault detection performance of the projections Table 1.

Data reconciliation is applied to ensure that input and output mass flows satisfy the mass balance of the technology:

$$Feed\ A + Feed\ D + Feed\ E + Feed\ C - Purge - Product = 0 \qquad (6)$$

Figure 2 shows the projection error of data reconciliation (see Eq. (4)). In area between dashed lines shows when disturbance affects the system, while dotted lines indicate set point changes. As the figure shows, this method can identify some disturbances, changes that are not affect the mass balance are not detected (e.g. stripper set point change is invisible). As a further step of life-cycle modelling we utilized the flowsheeting simulator to determine the projection matrix of PCA. With the use of the simulator we generated an informative dataset that can describe the behaviour of system. In this case external disturbances do not affect the process; there is no measurements noise, so data pairs satisfy the balance equations. After we determined the optimal number of principal components, we designed the process monitoring system based on projection of the measured raw process values (A.1 case).

Table 1. Disturbance in system

Time-interval (h)	Type of disturbance
75-100	Change A/C feed ratio (IDV(1))
400-470	Unknown disturbance (IDV(16))
850-920	Unknown disturbance (IDV(18))
530-1000	Purge valve set point changes from 0 to 10 %
700-1000	Stripper level set point changes from 50 to 45 %

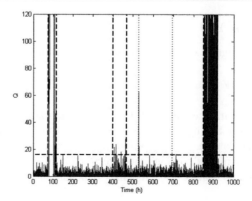

Figure 2. Data reconciliation based fault detection

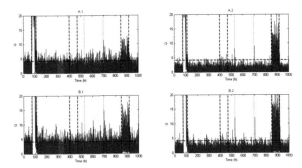

Figure 3. Effect of data reconciliation to the sensitivity of PCA (A) Simulator based PCA (B) Data driven PCA

We also studied a combined approach as reconciled process variables were projected (A.2 case). Figure 3 shows the difference between the two approaches. In first case (Figure 3 A.1) we get a lot of alarm and the real disturbances cannot be separated, so we cannot identify all faults and set point changes (similarly to the case when only data reconciliation is applied). If we pre-processed the measured values by data reconciliation we get perfect alarming, signals related to faults are generated only when real disturbances affect the process (Figure 3 A.2). To demonstrate the benefit of the proposed approach we compare the result obtained by the classical data-driven PCA model. In this case the projection matrix is identified based on measured - erroneous - data. If we used this matrix to project the measured values (Figure 3 B.1) we get alarms almost all the time, so we are not able to detect differences among the different faults. However, when we use data reconciliation to filter out the random noise (case B.2), we get much less false alarms and real disturbances appear.

This result shows that the combined method can improve the application of data reconciliation and PCA in fault detection and this algorithm gives a more sensitive model to determine faults from the changes of process. The reason is that data reconciliation filter the random noise so we should determine the systematics error using PCA. Comparison of A.2 and B.2 cases shows that model driven projection has significant benefits, it is worth to extract PCA model from flowsheeting simulators. The drawback is that this approach assumes available and accurate process simulator. Data-driven PCA has also drawbacks, the bottleneck of this approach is that the quality of the data used for the identification of PCA significantly affects the performance of the projection, and PCA model is defined in a narrow operating regime, so it is difficult to select accurate yet informative data for multivariate statistical modelling, contrary to the simulation based approach.

4. Conclusions

Efficient fault detection is essential in process industry to ensure product quality and operational excellence. We presented a fault detection method by combining the concept of model life-cycle and data reconciliation with PCA. We found that first principle model and data reconciliation can be utilized for the development and validation of principal component analysis models used in process monitoring systems. We developed model based techniques to improve both the projection matrix and the quality of the projected data. The combined application of these improvements significantly increases the sensitivity of PCA in fault detection.

The acceptability of proposed algorithm is analysed in a detailed case study. We show PCA and data reconciliation are independently suitable for fault detection. However, when the effect of fault to monitored process variable is comparable to the variation of process, data-driven PCA models are not able to isolate these faults. Data reconciliation based process monitoring can identify faults only having effect for balance equations.

PCA models extracted from well-designed experiments preformed on process simulators show superior performance. Further performance improvement can be achieved when reconciled data is used for process monitoring. This combined approach significantly improves the sensitivity of fault detection. The drawback of this approach is that it assumes available and accurate process simulator. The bottleneck of data-driven PCA is that quality of data significantly affects the performance of the projection, and PCA model is defined in a narrow operating regime, so it is difficult to select accurate yet informative data. In case of only historical data are available for fault detection, data reconciliation still improves the accuracy of projection, and also allows the reduction of the number of principal components.

Acknowledgements

The research of Janos Abonyi was realized in the frames of TÁMOP 4.2.4.A/2-11-1-2012-0001 "National Excellence Program – Elaborating and operating an inland student and researcher personal support system convergence program". The infrastructure of research is supported by the frame of the TÁMOP 4.2.4.A/11/1-KONV-2012-0071 project. The projects were subsidized by the European Union and cofinanced by the European Social Fund.

References

T. Amand, G. Heyen, B. Kalitventzeff, 2001, Plant monitoring and fault detection: Synergy between data reconciliation and principal component analysis, Computers and Chemical Engineering, 25, 501-507.

B. Bayer, W. Marquardt, L. von Wedel, 2000, Perspectives on lifecycle modeling, AIChE Symposium Series, 96, 323, 192-214.

L. Dobos, J. Abonyi, 2012, On-line detection of homogeneous operation ranges by dynamic principal component analysis based time-series segmentation, Chemical Engineering Science, 32, 1303-1308.

J.J. Downs, E.F. Vogel, 1993, A plant-wide industrial process control problem, Computers and Chemical Engineering, 17, 3, 245-255.

Z. Du, X. Jin, L. Wu, 2007, Fault detection and diagnosis based on improved PCA with JAA method in VAV systems, Building and Environment, 42, 9, 3221-3232.

B. Farsang, Z. Gomori, G. Horvath, G. Nagy, S. Nemeth, J. Abonyi, 2013, Simultaneous Validation of Online Analyzers and Process Simulators by Process Data Reconciliation, Chemical Engineering Transactions, 32, 1303-1308.

J. Liu, S.J. Liu, D.S.H. Wong, 2013, Process Fault Diagnosis Based on Bayesian Inference, Computer Aided Chemical Engineering, 32, 751-756.

J.H. Krieger, 1995, Process simulation seen as pivotal in corporate information flow, Chemical and Engineering News, <pubs.acs.org/cen/hotarticles/cenear/950327/art08.html>, accessed on 28/01/2014

P. Ralston, G. DePuy, J.H. Graham, 2001, Computer-based monitoring and fault diagnosis: a chemical process case study, ISA Transactions, 40, 85-98.

Jiří Jaromír Klemeš, Petar Sabev Varbanov and Peng Yen Liew (Editors)
Proceedings of the 24th European Symposium on Computer Aided Process Engineering – ESCAPE 24
June 15-18, 2014, Budapest, Hungary. Copyright © 2014 Elsevier B.V. All rights reserved.

Integration of Scheduling and ISA-95

Iiro Harjunkoski*

ABB Corporate Research Germany, Wallstadter Str. 59, 68526 Ladenburg, Germany
iiro.harjunkoski@de.abb.com

Abstract

Collaboration between production systems and scheduling is often cumbersome, partly due to the difficulty of sharing problem data. This paper presents the ISA-95 standard and its role as a neutral data platform. Typical industrial requirements are highlighted together with insights on how to systematically provide production data from a production facility to mathematical models. This can also foster the collaboration between Academia and Industry by making realistic problem instances easier available.

Keywords: Scheduling, standards, ISA-95, integration, re-usability

1. Motivation

Enterprise-wide optimization (Grossmann, 2005) comprising supply-chain management and production planning and scheduling (P&S), gain nowadays more importance and attention also from the industry at the same time as it implies larger problem instances, more complex models and a more complex solution landscape. Short- or mid-term production targets are often set by enterprise resource planning (ERP) systems and the activity of creating a detailed schedule for achieving the targets through a detailed and realistic production plan is given to production management systems, e.g. manufacturing execution systems (MES) or collaborative production management (CPM) solutions. These systems host normally the activities necessary for performing short-term scheduling tasks. It is thus important to efficiently transfer the data between a production system environment and the scheduling engine. The topic of integrating a scheduling solution - even though not widely discussed - is a very important issue in helping to deploy solutions for real problems in the process industries. The gap between industry and academia has been identified (Henning, 2009) and the way how to plug-in a scheduling solution into a production management environment must be well defined in order to ensure the practical usability of best research results. Framinan et al. (2012) addresses successful strategies for its development and deployment. In this paper, we discuss the role of the ISA-95 standard in overcoming some of the integration challenges.

2. System components and the functional hierarchy

As depicted in Fig. 1 (adapted from Engell and Harjunkoski, 2012), the system landscape is complex and there are many decision layers. Each layer has well defined input/output data that is processed within the six main functionalities. The information is shared mainly between neighboring layers: The planning layer sets the production targets and in return gets the total amount of realized production. The scheduling layer generates the detailed schedule defining the sequence of production, equipment assignments and main timings. The feedback to scheduling comprises a.o. the production progress (necessary for tracking purposes), equipment availability and capability data. An approved schedule is dispatched to the production area and a recipe

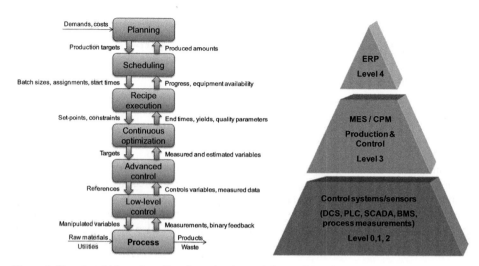

Figure 1. Functional hierarchy of batch production and the traditional automation pyramid

execution layer governs the batch- or production recipes defining the detailed production steps, control set-points and other production-related constraints. The lower layers may comprise a continuous optimization layer optimizing the trajectories during the production phases and an advanced control layer for defining the optimal trajectory e.g. through model-predictive control (MPC). Finally, the low-level or regulatory control layer is directly connected to the process. The more commonly used automation pyramid (right side of Fig. 1) divides the functions in three main layers: ERP, MES/CPM and control, each of which is composed of industrial system components to manage the vertical integration of production.

There has been an increasing research focus on the integration of control and scheduling (Engell and Harjunkoski, 2012) and many of the discussed approaches aim at a closed-loop implementation where the main focus is on the mathematical models and algorithms, e.g. in the closed-loop approach in Zhuge and Ierapetritou (2012). These approaches can for instance work iteratively or by pre-generating a number of alternative control schemes, the most suitable of which is then selected by the scheduler (Chu and You, 2012). The commonly reported application is to minimize the off-spec quality during product-grade transitions, e.g. in polymer production. The integration done as a monolithic model is much too complex for larger process instances and managing the number of system components makes the data handling difficult.

3. Scheduling and the standard ANSI/ISA-95

In order to enable efficient collaboration schemes it must be ensured that the information and data can be accessed and exchanged smoothly, e.g. information such as equipment availability and capability is transmitted through this functional hierarchy up to the scheduling layer. The Instrumentation, Systems, and Automation Society (ISA) has created an ISA-95 standard (ANSI/ISA-95.00.03-2005, 2005) with the main aim of systematizing the data exchange between enterprise resource planning (ERP) and control systems, enabling in a larger context a plug-ability of various production system components. The standard contains all main elements for processing orders, including scheduling and production control and defines the type of data that need to be exchanged between each of the modules. The XML-implementation of ISA-95 is called

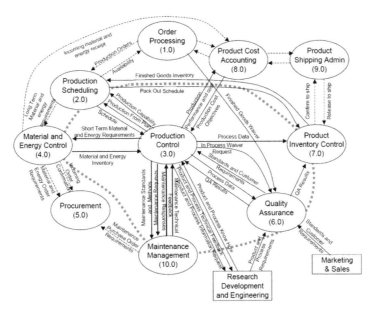

Figure 2. Purdue Reference model (ISA-95)

business-to-manufacturing-markup-language (B2MML). It contains several complex XML-elements comprising various production equipment and product aspects and provides a generic, common and extendable platform for data exchange. A systems view of the ISA-95 standard is provided in the Purdue Reference Model (Fig. 2). It shows that scheduling interacts closely with production control. Typical information flows are: Planned orders (schedule) are passed to the control layer and the control system returns the production response and information about the plant capability, which is also part of the standard. The standard comprises material, personnel, equipment and other information required when defining a scheduling model.

The ISA-95 standard does not dictate exactly how to use the standard but provides good guidelines and a structure for hosting the data exchange between production systems in a neutral, systematic and standardized manner that can reduce significantly the efforts in designing a scheduling system SW-architecture. Even if it is still far from perfect, the B2MML implementation can be adapted to various production environments by using the provided flexibility. If all necessary input data for solving a scheduling problem is provided in a well-defined and jointly agreed format, the exchange, testing and collaboration of various mathematical scheduling methods becomes much easier and more efficient to implement. This can significantly enhance the collaboration, not only between industrial solutions but also between industry and academia – or even between different academic groups, as the data representation is completely disconnected from the solution approach. This should allow faster and fairer testing of alternative approaches. In the following we discuss some concrete examples where ISA-95 is used to formulate the necessary input/output data to enable a smooth data exchange across the system landscape.

Figure 3 shows the most important B2MML-elements. The "operations definition" block contains the production recipes, i.e. which production stages are needed and which equipment may be used, as well as their respective processing times. The "opera-

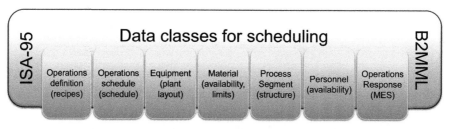

Figure 3. Main components of B2MML v5 (ISA-95) that are relevant for scheduling

tions schedule" can be used both as input (including production requests and their references to a production recipe) and output (resulting schedule information). The sections "equipment", "material" and "personnel" contain information about existing production resources and their restrictions and "process segment" defines the process flow of the production site. The rightmost block, "operations response" is used to transfer status information about a running production order from the MES-system to the scheduling, e.g. actual start/end times or status of a processing stage.

In order to concretely illustrate the data hosted by ISA-95, an example of the hierarchical structure of the "Operations Schedule" element is shown in Fig. 4. Each schedule contains basic information and all orders to be scheduled are located under the sub tree "OperationsRequest". Here, no release/due date properties can be seen but the StartTime/EndTime tags can be used for these. The production stages are defined under "SegmentRequirement", which contains references to equipment, duration, material (including energy) and all other relevant information. For handling multiple- equipment

Figure 4. "Operations Schedule" component of B2MML v5 (ISA-95)

Figure 5. ISA-95 as a data exchange platform

choices with deviating processing times (duration), it is possible to define nested segment requirements, one for each equipment option. Similarly, each batch operation can be divided into sub-steps. In the case of variable processing times, min/max limits can be provided as segment parameters. Other challenges of scheduling such as exponential problem size growth, disturbances in the process (communicated via "OperationsResponse"), conflicting targets between optimization module and data availability, as well as need for manual interaction are left out of focus here. Nevertheless, these are all crucial factors that must be kept in mind when trying to integrate an off-line scheduling solution into an at least partly online-control system.

4. Example

As it is not possible to provide a complete example, in the following some aspects are illustrated to show how a standard can concretely be implemented and reflected in a model formulation. In Fig. 5, we see the possible role of an ISA-95 model. Implemented as a database, memory-resident or file-based it can act as a logical data platform that hosts all relevant information within a production system and shares it online ensuring that each application has access to up-to-date and valid information. A concrete example to illustrate the relation between an XML-file and corresponding mathematical models is shown in Fig. 6, where dependencies in "operations definition" between reaction and succeeding packaging stage are displayed.

In the example one can see that the XML-file covers information to define the type of inequality, the required time between the operations considered. Note that this segment dependency is located in the recipe definition of the packaging stage of product i. Both

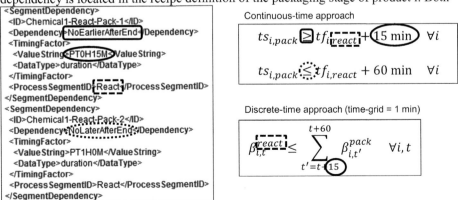

Figure 6. B2MML-example and corresponding constraints on the right (connections highlighted)

Figure 7. Example of scheduling timing (B2MML & Gantt chart)

the XML representation as well as the mathematical constraints enforce the packaging stage to start within 15-60 mins after the finishing time of the reaction stage. An example of scheduling results is shown in Fig. 7, where the mix timing from the left XML-file is in a corresponding simple Gantt chart. Elements such as material consumption, availability times can also be expressed in B2MML as parameters. The above example shows that B2MML goes beyond providing only data as also the type of inequality can be defined in the XML-files. Disconnecting models from data makes it possible to easily test given problems on different solution methods, once an interface to reading the B2MML information is at hand. This could motivate e.g. a B2MML-GAMS wrapper, in which case all sets and parameters be fully defined in XML format and the chosen modeling approach implemented as before in the GAMS language. The main benefit of this is that exchanging problem instances between industry and academia becomes significantly easier and standardized.

5. Conclusions

It has been shown that low-level process data and high-level business data need to be combined in real-time for optimal decisions of complex systems. ISA-95 provides a vehicle: A neutral, systematic and standardized structure for data exchange. Apart from data, also model aspects can be transferred (e.g. dependencies) as well as relevant dynamically changing information from the process. This can help reducing the efforts in designing a scheduling system SW-architecture, as B2MML can be adapted to various production needs. If all necessary input data for solving a scheduling problem is provided in a well-defined and jointly agreed format, the exchange, testing and collaboration of various methods becomes much easier and efficient to implement, enhancing the collaboration, not only between industrial solutions but also between industry and Academia. Standards are here to stay and B2MML (ISA-95) – when further improved – has the potential of becoming an established part of scheduling.

References

ANSI/ISA-95.00.03-2005, 2005, Enterprise-Control System Integration, Part 3: Activity models of manufacturing operations management, Research Triangle Park, NC, USA

S. Engell, I. Harjunkoski, 2012, Optimal Operation: Scheduling, Advanced Control and their Integration, Computers and Chemical Engineering, 47, 121-133

I. Grossmann, 2005, Enterprise-wide optimization: A new frontier in process systems engineering, AIChE J., 51, 7, 1846–1857.

G.P. Henning, 2009, Production Scheduling in the Process Industries: Current Trends, Emerging Challenges and Opportunities, Computer Aided Chemical Engineering, 27, 23-28.

J.M. Framinan, R. Ruiz, 2012, Guidelines for the deployment and implementation of manufacturing scheduling systems, International Journal of Production Research, 50, 7, 1799-812

Y. Chu, F. You, 2012, Integration of scheduling and control with online closed-loop implementation: Fast computational strategy and large-scale global optimization algorithm, Computers and Chemical Engineering, 47, 248-268

J. Zhuge, M.G. Ierapetritou, 2012, Integration of scheduling and control with closed loop implementation. Industrial and Engineering Chemistry Research, 51, 25, 8550-8565

Jiří Jaromír Klemeš, Petar Sabev Varbanov and Peng Yen Liew (Editors)
Proceedings of the 24th European Symposium on Computer Aided Process Engineering – ESCAPE 24
June 15-18, 2014, Budapest, Hungary.

Stochastic Price/Cost Models for Supply Chain Management of Refineries

Rafael Rasello,[a,b] Davide Manca[b,*]

[a]Process and Informatics Engineering Department, ENSIACET, Toulouse, FRANCE
[b]PSE-Lab, CMIC Department, Politecnico di Milano, ITALY
davide.manca@polimi.it

Abstract

The paper focuses on crude oil refineries and presents a methodology to determine dynamic models of prices of different oils and the derived distillates. It shows how to take into account stochastic fluctuations of quotations due to market volatility. These dynamic models can be used to forecast possible economic scenarios in supply chain problems. They allow removing the rather limiting hypothesis of fixed prices, which is often present in the literature. Indeed, the paper shows how even on short-term horizons the historical fluctuations of prices of crude oil and distillates can be quite significant. Eventually, it proposes a methodology to simulate the fan of distinct dynamic scenarios that apply to the solution of the supply chain problem. The proposed methodology is appropriate for both short-term (i.e. planning) and medium-term (i.e. scheduling) problems, which may cover time horizons from few weeks up to some months.

Keywords: Supply Chain Management; Crude oil quotations; Distillates price; Market demand; Stochastic models.

1. Introduction

The scientific literature on supply chain management (SCM) applied to refineries has progressively switched from a deterministic description of the problem to its stochastic modeling and solution (Tong et al., 2012). Overall, the stochastic feature focuses on the volatility of supply and demand. The supply element refers to crude oil, which changes in terms of both quality and quantity subject to the geographical origin and obtainable profit. The demand element refers to oil distillates and their distribution in time and space according to end-user requirements (Tong et al., 2012). If one focuses the attention on the transport sector, which is the most important user of refined products (up to 70 % of oil usage)it is possible to observe from consumption data of different countries that SCM solutions should be tailored to specific markets and geopolitical backgrounds. The literature on refinery SCM focused mainly on both the optimal supply sources and optimal blending of crudes to fulfill a given demand (Pitty et al., 2008); such demand being either assigned or variable according to either predefined tendencies or stochastic fluctuations (Robertson et al., 2011). Conversely, the volatility of prices and costs of crude oil and by-products has been repeatedly neglected due to two main reasons. Firstly, the volatility is often regarded as an economic/financial feature, whose forecast is difficult to model and distant from the process-engineering knowledge. Secondly, the time horizon of supply chain problems is frequently rather short and this allows assuming the prices/costs constant. This manuscript shows how these assumptions are null since the modeling, as previously discussed in Manca (2013a), is not a prerogative of high finance, and because even short-term supply chains (e.g., spanning few weeks; You and Grossmann, 2008) may experience rather significant fluctuations of oil and distillates prices (Yuan et al., 2014). Figure 1 shows how crude oil quotations can see a 50 % reduction in only a 10-week period (for instance from 80 to 40 US$/bbl in October-November 2008). Similar reductions of 28 % from 140 to 100 US$/bbl and of 42 % from 60 to 35 US$/bbl took respectively 10 and 7 weeks across the second semester of 2008.

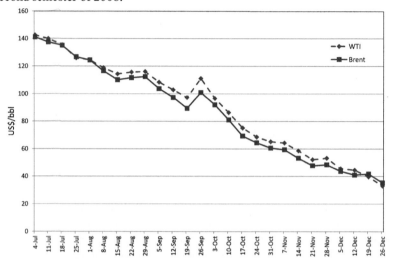

Figure 1. Weekly quotations of WTI and Brent oils in the second semester of 2008.

Even if that semester was a quite peculiar period, with a tremendous financial and economic crisis, which was triggered by the US subprime mortgage crisis, other similar periods, either bearish or bullish, marked the oil quotations of last years (Moya-Martínez et al., 2014). This point shows how the fluctuations in raw materials, products, by products, and utilities should be accounted for when designing and solving SCM problems for refinery processes/plants (Pitty et al., 2008). Specifically, the manuscript focuses on proposing candidate models, and identifying their adaptive parameters, to describe stochastically the quotations of different typologies of crude oils and their distillates.

2. Crude oil

The quotations of WTI and Brent, which are two of the most important crude oils in the world, orbit respectively around the US and Europe markets. Such quotations have been tightly interwoven for years up to 2010. From 2011 on, they took apart and lost their mutual consistency. The reason for WTI and Brent quotations following rather independent paths depends on a number of distinct but correlated reasons. Shale gas, shale oil, international crises, embargos, available infrastructures, industrial and transport accidents, natural calamities, and weather variability played a major role in the fluctuations of quotations even over short periods with a further influence from complex geopolitical backgrounds.

2.1. Quotation models for crude oil

The development of price/cost models for both commodities (Manca, 2013a) and utilities (Manca, 2013b) starts from identifying a reference component. Such a component plays a primary role (either direct or indirect) on the process/plant under study. In refinery plants/processes, the reference component corresponds naturally to crude oil, which is also the raw material. It is rather evident that the features, which were listed and discussed above, influence the choice of the specific crude oil that plays the role of reference component. Consequently, it is advisable to conduct a preliminary analysis so that the choice of the specific crude oil is done by considering the features of the SCM structure under study. In addition, depending on the location of the process/plant and mainly on the SCM market (which comprises both suppliers and consumers), it is advisable adopting values of the oil quotations that include taxes and therefore allow describing more realistic scenarios. For the sake of consistency, a straightforward selection criterion consists in choosing WTI quotations for North American refineries and Brent quotations for European refineries. A simple analysis of time-series of oil prices shows scenarios with non-periodic and difficult to foresee fluctuations. Since the causes are based on unpredictable contributes, the fluctuations are modeled as random events by introducing a stochastic term in the problem. The hypothesis of Markovian process sets up the crude oil forecasting model and introduces a stochastic noise as reported in the following equations (Manca, 2013a):

$$WTI_i = WTI_{i-1}\left(1 + RANDN \cdot \sigma_{WTI} + \overline{X}_{WTI}\right) \tag{1}$$

$$WTI_i = WTI_{i-1}\left(1 + RANDN \cdot \sigma_{WTI}\right) \tag{2}$$

with: $\overline{X}_{WTI} = 0.0020$, $\sigma_{WTI} = 0.0318$. Eqs. (1) and (2) may be used respectively for short-/medium- and long-term horizon problems and are specifically tailored to WTI crude oil quotations in US\$/bbl. The mean trend of weekly prices, $\overline{X}_{WTI}$, is representative of short- and medium-term periods as it quantifies the behavior of recent quotations. Conversely, Eq. (2) suggests neglecting that term as it would add a systematic drift to price forecasts over long-term horizons.

3. Refined products

The most important products obtained from crude oil distillation are liquefied petroleum gas, gasoline, diesel fuel, kerosene, naphtha, heating oil, and asphalt base. For the sake of space, the paper focuses on SCM in refineries of North America where a subset of the aforementioned products plays a major role in planning and scheduling the production (EIA, 2013). Specifically, the focus is given to gasolines with 90 and 93 RON, diesel, and fuel oil (as extensively discussed in Tong et al., 2012). Three of the four products are the most important fuels representative of the transport sector. The last one is characterized by the highest boiling temperature among the four fuels and epitomizes the byproduct and heavy components of refineries. Figure 2 shows the dynamic evolution of quotations of the refined products in the 2010-2016 time interval. Actually, the 2010-2013 (up to August 2013) period is based on past quotations, whilst the 2013-2016 (from September 2013) period is based on a specific scenario (among the infinite ones that the forecasting model can produce) where future values are obtained through the equations described in Sections 3.1 and 4. It is worth observing how the price trends are similar though they display peculiar fluctuations that occur asynchronously with different magnitudes. The rate of change and the relative variability in prices resemble qualitatively the ones observed for crude oil. The highs and lows of price trends depend on the stochastic contribute of the model whose properties will be discussed in the following sections. As already illustrated in the crude oil case study, the rapidly evolving horizon of distillate quotations shows how even short term SCM problems cannot rely on fixed prices. Therefore, it is advisable to take into account the fluctuations of distillate quotations and implement proper models that are capable of describing this complex evolution.

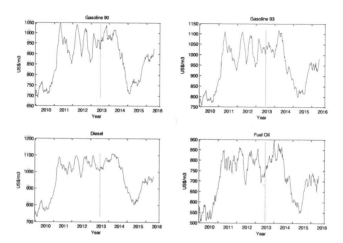

Figure 2. Weekly prices of four oil distillates over the 2010-2016 period. Real past quotations on the left of vertical dashed line; future forecast prices on the right of vertical dashed line.

3.1. Price models for crude oil distillates

Mazzetto et al. (2013) proposed a number of alternative models to describe possible dynamic trends for prices of refined products. Among those models, the autoregressive with distributed lag (ADL) model occupied a prominent position thanks to its structure, simplicity, and reduced number of parameters (Ghaffari and Zare, 2009). ADL models, applied to the economic assessment of industrial processes, allow determining future prices of commodities as a function of previous quotations of both commodities and a reference component. A correlogram analysis (Manca, 2013a) allows determining the optimal number of elements that the ADL model should include to reach a compromise between the description capability and its complexity, while avoiding the over parameterization risk. For all the four representative distillates the correlogram analysis showed that the ADL(1,0) formulation is the optimal one even if it works with only one previous value of the dependent variable and the contemporary value of the independent one. A multidimensional linear regression routine determined the parameters of the four ADL models:

$$G90_i = a_1 + a_2 \cdot WTI_i + a_3 \cdot G90_{i-1} \qquad a_1 = -21.975 \quad a_2 = 0.1983 \quad a_3 = 0.8984 \qquad (3)$$

$$G93_i = b_1 + b_2 \cdot WTI_i + b_3 \cdot G93_{i-1} \qquad b_1 = -16.795 \quad b_2 = 0.1904 \quad b_3 = 0.9051 \qquad (4)$$

$$Diesel_i = c_1 + c_2 \cdot WTI_i + c_3 \cdot Diesel_{i-1} \qquad c_1 = -11.640 \quad c_2 = 0.1462 \quad c_3 = 0.9276 \qquad (5)$$

$$FO_i = d_1 + d_2 \cdot WTI_i + d_3 \cdot FO_{i-1} \qquad d_1 = -31.454 \quad d_2 = 0.1844 \quad d_3 = 0.9005 \qquad (6)$$

$G90$, $G93$, and FO refer respectively to gasolines with 90 and 93 RON and to fuel oil. The prices are for weekly quotations in US$/m^3.

4. Applications to refinery SCM problems

Once both sets of models for the prices of raw material and final products have been developed, it is possible to produce different economic scenarios based on the dynamic quotations of crude oil and its distillates. Since fluctuations and uncertainty are intrinsic to quotations of crude oil and refined products, it is necessary to introduce stochasticity in the ADL models presented in Section 3.1. Indeed, Eqs. (7-10) include both a deterministic and a stochastic term. The deterministic term describes the functional dependency of present quotations from previous ones whereas the stochastic term allows simulating the unexpected and unforeseen issues that were presented in Section 2. In analogy with Eqs. (1) and (2), Eqs. (3-6) can be adapted to account for the stochastic contribute as follows:

$$G90_i = \left(a_1 + a_2 \cdot WTI_i + a_3 \cdot G90_{i-1}\right) \cdot \left(1 + RANDN \cdot \sigma_{G90}\right) \tag{7}$$

$$G93_i = \left(b_1 + b_2 \cdot WTI_i + b_3 \cdot G93_{i-1}\right) \cdot \left(1 + RANDN \cdot \sigma_{G93}\right) \tag{8}$$

$$Diesel_i = \left(c_1 + c_2 \cdot WTI_i + c_3 \cdot Diesel_{i-1}\right) \cdot \left(1 + RANDN \cdot \sigma_{Diesel}\right) \tag{9}$$

$$FO_i = \left(d_1 + d_2 \cdot WTI_i + d_3 \cdot FO_{i-1}\right) \cdot \left(1 + RANDN \cdot \sigma_{FO}\right) \tag{10}$$

where the standard-deviation values, which are calculated over the 2010-2013 (up to August) time interval, are: $\sigma_{G90} = 0.0134$, $\sigma_{G93} = 0.0117$, $\sigma_{Diesel} = 0.0102$, $\sigma_{FO} = 0.0242$ (see also Manca 2013a for further details).

Eqs. (1-2) together with Eqs. (7-10) allow simulating different scenarios of prices for refinery SCM problems. The call for creating several distinct scenarios comes from the necessity of solving both planning and scheduling problems, which share comparable features projected on time horizons that span from short-term to medium-term intervals. These economic scenarios play a significant role in taking the final decisions on how and when allocate resources to produce refined distillates as a function of market demand, crude oil quality and availability, and products/byproducts price.

By solving the same SCM model subject to different economic scenarios, it is possible to assess the resiliency of the refinery respect to either low-trend or high-trend quotations of oil and distillates. In addition, it is possible to assess the flexibility of the production schedule as a function of price fluctuations even over short-term problems. By running a large number of economic scenarios based on the stochastic contribute of Eqs. (1-2) and (7-10) it is finally possible to determine the distribution of the achievable

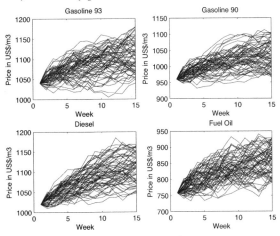

Figure 3. Different economic scenarios of refinery distillates over a 15-week time horizon.

profits and determine a suitable feasibility threshold below which production should be either suspended or better rescheduled. For instance, Figure 3 shows four sets of 50 economic scenarios over a typical short-term planning of 15 weeks for a SCM problem in a North American refinery as described in Tong et al. (2012).

Instead of parameterizing the decision variables according to some stochastic distribution as often done in SCM problems, it is possible to solve a set of deterministic SCM problems based on single stochastic economic scenarios as shown in Figure 3.

At each discretization time of the SCM problem, the corresponding values of crude oil and distillate prices can be evaluated through the aforementioned equations thus obtaining a set of solutions based on a large number of scenarios. A further processing of the SCM solutions allows extracting the bits of information that are most important to finalize the decisions and (re)schedule the real production activity.

5. Conclusions

Starting from the complexity of solving refinery SCM problems that are afflicted by uncertainty of market prices (EIA, 2013) the paper proposed some economic models to simulate the dynamic evolution of prices for both crude oil and distillates. A case study based on a reference North American refinery focused the attention on WTI and some of its distillates: G90, G93, Diesel, and FO. A rather simple ADL linear model coupled with stochastic contributes, whose dimensions are inferred from available quotations, allowed grasping the complex behavior of prices. Eventually, a set of distinct scenarios simulated from the proposed models enable testing the resiliency of both the refinery and SCM solutions respect to stochastic fluctuations of quotations and market demand.

References

EIA - U.S. Energy Information Administration, 2013, Short-Term Energy Outlook - Market Prices and Uncertainty Report, U.S. Energy Information Administration, Washington, US.
A. Ghaffari, S. Zare, 2009, A novel algorithm for prediction of crude oil price variation based on soft computing, Energy Economics, 31, 4, 531–536.
D. Manca, 2013a, Modeling the Commodity Fluctuations of Opex Terms, Comput. Chem. Eng., 57, 3–9.
D. Manca, 2013b, A Methodology to Forecast the Price of Electric Energy, Computer Aided Chemical Engineering, 32, 679–684.
F. Mazzetto, R.A. Ortiz, D. Manca, F. Bezzo, 2013, Strategic Design of Bioethanol Supply Chains Including Commodity Market Dynamics, Ind. Eng. Chem. Res., 52, 10305–10316.
P. Moya-Martínez, R. Ferrer-Lapeña, F. Escribano-Sotos, 2014, Oil price risk in the Spanish stock market: An industry perspective, Economic Modelling, 37, 280–290.
S.S. Pitty, W. Li, A. Adhitya, R. Srinivasan, I.A. Karimi, 2008, Decision support for integrated refinery supply chains. Part 1. Dynamic simulation, Comput. Chem. Eng., 32, 11, 2767–2786.
G. Robertson, A. Palazoglu, J.A. Romagnoli, 2011, A multi-level simulation approach for the crude oil loading/unloading scheduling problem, Comput. Chem. Eng., 35, 5, 817–827.
C. Sung, H. Kwon, J. Lee, H. Yoon, Il Moon, 2012, Forecasting Naphtha Price Crack Using Multiple Regression Analysis, Computer Aided Chemical Engineering, 31, 145–149.
K. Tong, Y. Feng, G. Rong, 2012, Planning under demand and yield uncertainties in an oil supply chain, Industrial and Engineering Chemistry Research, 51, 2, 814–834.
F. You, I.E. Grossmann, 2008, Design of responsive supply chains under demand uncertainty, Comput. Chem. Eng., 32, 12, 3090–3111.
Y. Yuan, X. Zhuang, Z. Liu, W. Huang, 2014, Analysis of the temporal properties of price shock sequences in crude oil markets, Physica A, 394, 235–246.

Jiří Jaromír Klemeš, Petar Sabev Varbanov and Peng Yen Liew (Editors)
Proceedings of the 24th European Symposium on Computer Aided Process Engineering – ESCAPE 24
June 15-18, 2014, Budapest, Hungary. Copyright © 2014 Elsevier B.V. All rights reserved.

Integrating Planning and Scheduling in an Oil Refinery with a Rolling Horizon Approach

Edwin Zondervan,[*] Michiel Kaland, Martijn A.H. van Elzakker, Jan C. Fransoo, Jan Meuldijk

Eindhoven University of Technology, Den Dolech 2, Eindhoven 5600 MB, The Netherlands
e.zondervan@tue.nl

Abstract

Decisions in an oil refinery are made at three levels: planning, scheduling and control. Existing facilities have to be operated close to their maximum capacity, while continuously responding to cost fluctuations. In many of the currently reported planning models each decision level has its own model and is used separately. Integration of these models will lead to solutions closer to the optimum than modeling the decision levels separately. However, simply combining the levels into one model would lead to very large models that yet cannot be solved within reasonable time. To overcome the computational time issue a rolling horizon approach is proposed in this work.

Keywords: Scheduling, Planning, MILP, Rolling horizon, oil refinery

1. Introduction

Historically, the scheduling of crude oil unloading, blending and charging in a refinery has been done manually by a scheduler (Kelly et al., 2003). This is a very time consuming process and often the manual scheduler will not find the optimal schedule. Systematic optimization could dramatically improve the quality of the schedules.

Secondly, while the scheduler can create a feasible schedule, it is almost never the optimal schedule. Optimizing the schedule can reduce costs in many ways. For example, cheaper crudes can be used more intelligently and crude changeovers can be minimized (Chandra et al., 2004).

Because of the disadvantages of manual scheduling, it is desirable to automate the optimization of the scheduling process. This optimization can be performed by utilizing mixed integer (non) linear programming (MILP/MINLP) models. Ideally these models would comprise the complete oil refinery. Unfortunately this would lead to intractably large problems (Jia et al., 2003)

Therefore a decomposition of this problem was proposed in various articles. The decomposition proposed by Jia et al. (2003) is commonly used. The first part of this decomposition comprises the unloading of the oil from the vessels to the storage tanks, the loading of the charging tanks and the charging of the crude distillation units (CDU's).

Various models that describe this part of the decomposition have been proposed. In Chandra et al. (2003) and Jia et al. (2003) continuous time formulations for short term oil refinery scheduling problems are proposed. In Lee et al. (1996) and Li et al. (2002) additions are proposed that allow also the optimization of crude oil loading and unloading. In Karrupiah et al. (2002) the models are coded such that a global optimimum can be found. Besides model improvements also new algorithms to solve the resulting models have been formulated (Chandra et al., 2004; Li et al., 2007)

The most suitable model proposed for this problem is the model by Li et al. (2007). This model has several advantages. First it uses an algorithm that prevents composition discrepancy (the difference between the concentration inside a tank and the concentration of the flow leaving this tank). Second, the model that Li et al. propose, uses a discrete time model that incorporates part of the beneficial features of a continuous time model Third, Li et al. propose an improved algorithm to ensure that the model will always give a feasible solution.

In earlier work (van Elzakker et al., 2010) we have worked out an oil refinery scheduling model on the basis of the model by Li et al. (2007) and introduced an improved feasibility algorithm that is based on the application of integer cuts to parcel-tank combinations, instead of tank-period combinations. The problem formulation was further improved by addition of the inventory costs to the models.

In a follow up contribution (Zondervan et al., 2012) we setup a planning model and identified the information flow between the scheduling and planning models. We have subsequently integrated the models in a straight-forward fashion using run modes and a rolling horizon. Although the method worked properly, extending the time horizon above 26 weeks gave rise to computational issues.

However, in this paper we have endeavoured to merge the planning and scheduling models into a single model that optimizes a production plan over a longer time horizon using a rolling horizon, up to 52 weeks.

2. Problem statement
In this work we have merged our earlier developed scheduling model and planning model, where we will consider a refinery where the number of parcels, tanks, CDUs, crudes, fractions and products are known, see Figure 1.

We also know the inventory levels, the production levels and the allowed connections between the different units. We have to decide on a production plan that maximizes the profit.

We have also added the possibility of a time variable demand, crude parcel availability and run mode selection to overall model.

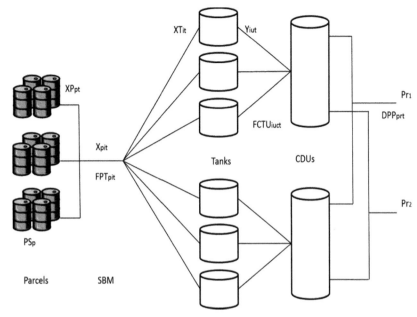

Figure 1. Topology of the oil refinery

3. Rolling horizon method

The rolling horizon method is based on iteratively solving an integrated planning-scheduling problem. In each iteration of the solution procedure, the detailed scheduling requirements are imposed only for the current or several recent planning periods depending on the horizon length. As the iterations proceed, planning decisions are updated with all the previously executed decisions fixed from the scheduling. This mode is repeated until all the planning periods are calculated.

The above idea is supported by the fact that planning decisions for far future cannot be accurate enough due to the unpredicted future uncertainty. Start from what has the highest certainty, which is the current scheduling situation, and work from there to the future, i.e. the planning level. Based on the calculation time, it is reasonable to consider a relative simple model. Ergo, the rolling horizon approach results in reduced size models and computation cost.

Although the rolling horizon framework has received a lot of attention in the literature, a major drawback of most existing methods is that they often rely on the simplistic or rather poor representation of the scheduling problem. Within such modeling framework, the rolling horizon method is generally efficient in the computational manner. However, the method only generates feasible planning –scheduling decisions and the quality (optimality) of the solution cannot be ensured. (Peng and Gang, 2009 and Li and Ierapetritou, 2010)

The length of the scheduling horizon and step size are variables. The best solution will be given when the scheduling length is the same length as the planning horizon. This solution is unattractive because the computational time is very long. By variation of the length of the scheduling horizon and the step size, a solution can be found which is close to the optimal solution, but faster. When the scheduling horizon is chosen too short, the solution will not be the best solution. When the step size has the same length as the scheduling, the model will be an iterative model without a rolling horizon.

The advantage of a rolling horizon approach is that the computational time can be controlled to reasonable level and that the model is continuously updated. The rolling horizon approach is illustrated in figure 2.

4. Numerical example

The problem under investigation runs over a planning period of 52 weeks (with a rolling horizon that moves at intervals of 5 weeks), where we evaluate 12 parcels, 4 crudes, 6 tanks and 2 CDU's (with each 2 run modes) and 2 products. The number of constraints of this MILP is 26,239, with 28,688 variables (of which 3,520 are binary). Solving this problem on a standard desktop computer with CPLEX 12.4 as solver requires a CPU time of 33 minutes.

As an example we show in Figure 3 the total inventory levels of the tanks feeding CDU's 1 and 2 per week. Also the limits of the inventory levels in the tanks are shown.

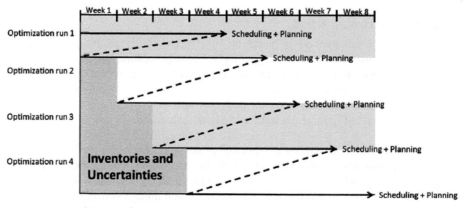

Figure 2. Rolling horizon method

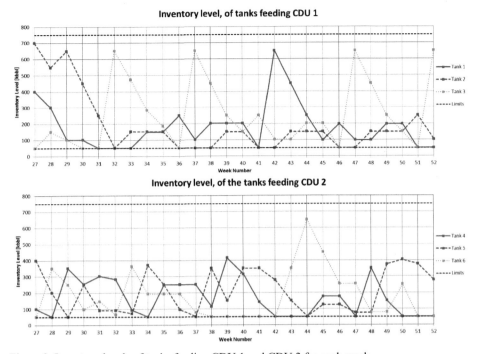

Figure 3. Inventory levels of tanks feeding CDU 1 and CDU 2 for each week.

Figure 3 shows that the tanks are almost filled to their maximum and only then feed the CDU1 until the inventory level is at the minimum level. This is caused by the fact that changeovers in the supply of the CDU's are translated into costs.

In figure 3 also the inventory profiles for CDU 2 are shown, which have a less pronounced behavior as compared to CDU 1 This suggests that the focus of the model is on unloading the large parcels as efficiently as possible and to use the small parcels to meet the specific demands for the production.

5. Conclusions

In this contribution we have merged the scheduling and planning models developed in earlier work (van Elzakker et al., 2010, Zondervan et al., 2012) for the scheduling of crude unloading, blending and charging in an oil refinery to a planning model. With this new model and implementation of a rolling horizon we can optimize over a longer time span where CPU time remained manageable and the solution integrity of was maintained. In addition to the implementation of a rolling horizon we have also added the possibility of a time variable demand, crude parcel availability and run mode selection to the planning and scheduling models, which we have tested and compared to the example case.

References

P. Chandra Prakash Reddy, I.A. Karimi, R. Srinivasan, 2004, A new continuous-time formulation for scheduling crude oil operations, Chemical Engineering Science, 59, 6, 1325-1341.

P. Chandra Prakash Reddy, I.A. Karimi and R. Srinivasan, 2004, Novel Solution Approach for Optimizing Crude Oil Operations, American Institute of Chemical Engineers Journal, 50, 6, 1177-1197.

M.A.H. van Elzakker, E. Zondervan, J.C. Fransoo, A.B. de Haan, 2010, An improved feasibility algorithm for the optimization of crude unloading, blending and charging in an oil refinery, Computer Aided Chemical Engineering, 20, 1805.

Z. Jia, M. Ierapetritou, J.D. Kelly, 2003, Refinery Short-Term Scheduling Using Continuous Time Formulation: Crude-Oil Operations, Ind. Eng. Chem. Res.,42,13, 3085-3097.

R. Karuppiah, K.C. Furman, I.E. Grossmann, 2008, global optimization for scheduling refinery crude oil operations, Computers and Chemical Engineering, 32, 11, 2745-2766.

J.D. Kelly, J.L. Mann, 2003, Crude Oil Blend Scheduling Optimization: an Application with Multimillion dollar benefits, Hydrocarbon Processing, 82, 6, 47-53.

H. Lee, J.M. Pinto, I.E. Grossmann, S. Park, 1996, Mixed-Integer Linear Programming Model for Refinery Short-Term Scheduling of Crude Oil Unloading with Inventory Management, Ind. Eng. Chem. Res., 35, 5, 1630-1641.

J. Li, W. Li, I. A. Karimi , R. Srinivasan, 2007, Improving the robustness and efficiency of crude scheduling algorithms, American Institute of Chemical Engineers Journal, 53, 10, 2659-2680.

Z. Li, M.G. Ierapetritou, 2010, Rolling horizon based planning and scheduling integration with production capacity consideration, Chem. Eng. Sc., 65, 22, 5887-5900.

C. Peng, R. Gang, 2009, A strategy for the Integration of Production Planning and Scheduling in Refineries under Uncertainty, Chinese Journal of Chemical Engineering, 17, 1, 113-127.

L. Wenkai, C.-W. Hui, B. Hua, Z. Tong, 2002, Scheduling Crude Oil Unloading, Storage and Processing, Ind. Eng. Chem. Res., 41, 26, 6723-6734.

E. Zondervan, T.P.J. van Boekel, J.C. Fransoo, A.B. de Haan, 2012, Simultaneous Optimization of Planning and Scheduling in an Oil Refinery, Computer Aided Chemical Engineering, 21, 925-929.

Jiří Jaromír Klemeš, Petar Sabev Varbanov and Peng Yen Liew (Editors)
Proceedings of the 24th European Symposium on Computer Aided Process Engineering – ESCAPE 24
June 15-18, 2014, Budapest, Hungary. Copyright © 2014 Elsevier B.V. All rights reserved.

Improving the Energy Management of a Building Complex through Utility System Modelling

Michal Touš[a,]*, Vítězslav Máša[a], Martin Pavlas[a], Valentýn Avramov[b]

[a] *Institute of Process and Environmental Engineering, Brno University of Technology, Technická 2896/2, 616 69 Brno, Czech Republic*
[b] *ENESA a.s., U Voborníků 852/10, 190 00 Praha 9, Czech Republic*
tous@fme.vutbr.cz

Abstract

According to Escrivá-Escrivá (2011), utility systems are often managed by non-specialised technicians who need understandable and cost-effective actions to be implemented. Therefore, we can assume that tools for simulation and optimization may further improve operation of utility systems. However, a good model is essential for these purposes. The paper deals with complex utility system modelling using operational data. Our experience shows that data acquisition in common utility system of a municipal building is sometimes poor. Usability of a model based on data of lower quality is discussed and demonstrated on the case of the utility system of The National Theatre building complex in Prague, the capital of the Czech Republic. It shows that even model based on poor data may be useful for some energy management improvements.

Keywords: utility system, energy management, regression model

1. Introduction

The share of services in the total consumption of energy is not negligible. Fourcroy et al. (2012) demonstrates that energy consumption is even underestimated. Modernization and optimization of heating, ventilation and air conditioning (HVAC) can significantly contribute to reducing energy use. But the modernization of utility systems is not the only part of energy efficiency improvements. The system has to be operated efficiently as well. For instance, Ndlovu and Majozi (2013) showed that optimization of a plant utility system operation can bring significant increase of revenues. Efficient operation of utility systems is very extensive topic, including demand forecasting and subsequent operation planning, based on the model of the system.

Basically, there are three ways of modelling – analytical, data-based and combination of both. Data-based models should be preferred (if possible) because they better describe real operation. In the scientific papers, data used for data-based modelling of utility systems is either provided by the manufacturer or it is obtained using well-managed (data measurement and acquisition) processes. However, a measurement in common utility system of a building is often not well-managed and contains many errors. Data-based modelling is then very difficult. Our literature search has shown that data-based model of a utility system of a municipal building with poor data acquisition (i.e. operational data with many errors) has not been presented in scientific papers yet.

This article involves real utility system providing heating and cooling for a building complex (four buildings) of the National Theatre in Prague in the Czech Republic. It was modernized in 2008 using energy performance contracting method. The current heating and cooling system includes a wide range of interconnected units (multi-fuel boilers, condensing boilers, heat pumps). It has total annual Natural gas (NG) consumption reaching 500,000 m^3 and power consumption reaching 900 MWh. The system is now very effective. The modernization brought significant financial savings (up to 450,000 EUR/y). These savings may be further increased by cost-effective control and operation planning. However, due to the complex nature of the system, it is a difficult task. The development of a utility system model and its practical use, which should support further improvements, is the objective of this article.

2. Utility system in National Theatre in Prague

The utility system provides heating and cooling for four buildings of the National Theatre in Prague. The simplified flow-sheet is shown in Figure 1.

Two highly efficient condensing gas boilers (B3-G, B4-G) were installed. These boilers replaced one older multi-fuel boiler. There are two more multi-fuel boilers (B1-MF, B2-MF) remaining. The condensing boilers are able to satisfy almost 100 % of heating demand. About one third of return water can be subcooled by reverse water-cooled chiller to enhance the condensation effect. The older boilers run only occasionally (peak demand, gas boiler outage). Hot water is heated by a heat pump (HP) utilizing waste heat from hydraulic oil in a stage system (HEX3).

The cooling system consists of two water-cooled chillers (CH1, CH2) cooling sun-exposed facades. This extracted heat is then rejected to river water via cooling circuit (HEX1). Direct cooling by river water without CH1 and CH2 being in operation is possible as well.

The key unit of the modernization is the reverse water-cooled chiller (RCH). It can also run in a heating mode and combined cooling and heating mode (the low-grade heat from the cooling may be utilized for heating). In addition to heat from sun-exposed facades cooling, river water and waste heat from the cooling of return water (HEX2) for B3-G and B4-G (enhancement of condensing effect) are other sources of low-grade-heat. The design parameters of the key units are summarized in Table 1.

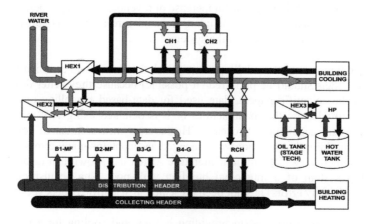

Figure 1. Simplified flow sheet of the utility system

Table 1. Design parameters of the key units

Unit	Heat output (kW)	Cooling output (kW)
Multi-fuel boilers (B1-MF, B2-MF)	3,120	
Gas boilers (B3-G, B4-G)	1,440	
Water-cooled chillers (CH1, CH2)		826
Water-cooled reverse chiller (RCH)	1,422	470
Heat pump (HP)	30	

3. Utility system model

The purpose of the model is prediction of NG, oil and power consumption in different operational regimes based on estimated heating and cooling demand (estimation based on weather forecast). Operational data for most of the key units were available for model development. In the majority of research papers on data-based modelling, data is either provided by the manufacturer or it is obtained using well-managed processes (e.g. in the case of an experimental utility system). Based on our experience, the situation is more complicated in case of daily operated utility systems due to systematic measurement errors and poor data acquisition system, e.g. varying delay in acquisition. Especially delay in acquisition makes data-based modelling tricky and exactly this problem was indicated during the analysis of operational data from the objective utility system. The relations between dependant variable and independent variables may be distorted in such case.

Modelling approach should be chosen considering the purpose of a model and data nature. Based on our literature search in the field of data-based modelling, linear regression (LR) models and neural network (NN) models seem to be the most frequently used. NN models can successfully identify nonlinear relations. On the other hand, LR models show a lower level of complexity. A review of NN applications for chillers and heat pumps was presented by Mohanraj et al. (2012). It shows that NN models are widely applied in this field. For example, Khan et al. (2012) developed NN model to predict performance of a multi-stream heat exchanger. Kusiak et al. (2010) modelled HVAC energy consumption by several data-mining algorithms (C&RT trees, support vector machine, etc.) and NN showed the best accuracy. Swider (2003) concludes that NN models give better results for complex vapour-compression liquid chillers without more detailed knowledge about a system. On the other hand, when further information is available, extended LR models are almost equally accurate. We decided for LR models because NN cannot identify proper relations between variables due to data quality discussed before and thus more complex model is useless.

Simple energy balance equation (assuming constant efficiency) was used to calculate NG/oil consumption in case of B1-MF and B2-MF due to lack of operational data. Balance equations were applied also for mixers, dividers and heat exchangers. Models of NG consumption for B3-G and B4-G and power consumption for RCH, CH1 and HP were developed using operational data. The models will be presented later. Now, let us discuss aforementioned delays in acquisition. Due to them, we are not able to assess goodness of fit from residuals. Let us prove it on the example of B3-G. Looking at Figure 2a, the heat output is fluctuating (due to delay), however observed NG consumption is smoother (obvious at 18:00). The model responds to the heat output by fluctuating NG consumption (predicted values). So residuals are significant but it makes misleading conclusion that the model is useless. Comparing cumulative sum of

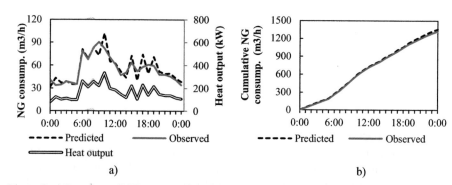

Figure 2. a) line chart of NG consumption (B3-G); b) cumulative NG consumption (B3-G)

observed and predicted values (Figure 2b), we can see that the model is able to predict NG consumption accurately for a longer period. We can conclude that the model can provide sufficient support in operation planning or in other long-term problems. This conclusion is valid for the other models as well.

NG consumption for B3-G and B4-G is described by two equations – one for the case with cooled return water (Eq.(1)) and the other for the case without cooled return water (Eq.(2)).

$$m_{gas,B3} = 0.87 \cdot t_{in,B3} + 0.081 \cdot P_{B3} - 24.93, \quad m_{gas,B4} = 0.65 \cdot t_{in,B4} + 0.079 \cdot P_{B4} - 15.49, \qquad (1)$$

$$m_{gas,B3} = 0.58 \cdot t_{in,B3} + 0.088 \cdot P_{B3} - 16.00, \quad m_{gas,B4} = 0.58 \cdot t_{in,B4} + 0.083 \cdot P_{B4} - 15.50, \qquad (2)$$

where $m_{gas,B3/B4}$ (m³/h) is NG flow rate, $t_{in,B3/B4}$ (°C) is return water temperature, $P_{B3/B4}$ (kW) is boiler output. Temperature of cooled return water is not included in Eq.(1) because it is in strong correlation with $t_{in,B3/B4}$.

In case of RCH, we need two regression functions to predict power consumption. One describes relation between heat output and power consumption (Eq.(3)) and one describes relation between cooling output and power consumption (Eq.(4)).

$$P_{pow,RCH} = 0.57 \cdot t_{out,co,RCH} - 0.36 \cdot t_{in,ev,RCH} + 0.25 \cdot P_{heat,RCH} - 12.46, \qquad (3)$$

$$P_{pow,RCH} = 0.75 \cdot t_{out,co,RCH} - 0.31 \cdot t_{in,ev,RCH} + 0.41 \cdot P_{cool,RCH} - 29.25, \qquad (4)$$

where $P_{pow,RCH}$ (kW) is power consumption, $P_{heat,RCH}$ (kW) is heat output, $P_{cool,RCH}$ (kW) is cooling output, $t_{out,co,RCH}$ (°C) is water temperature at condenser side and $t_{in,ev,RCH}$ (°C) is water temperature at evaporator side.

Heat output in not important in case of CH1/CH2 and therefore only one regression function is needed, Eq.(5).

$$P_{pow,CH1} = 5.34 \cdot t_{in,co,CH1} - 0.17 \cdot t_{in,ev,CH1} + 0.153 \cdot P_{cool,CH1}, \qquad (5)$$

where $P_{pow,CH1}$ (kW) is power consumption, $P_{cool,CH1}$ (kW) is cooling output, $t_{in,co,CH1}$ (°C) is water temperature at condenser side and $t_{in,ev,CH1}$ (°C) is water temperature at evaporator side. The same function is considered for CH2 (no data available).

Table 2. Goodness of fit for data-based models

Unit consumption	MAE	MRAE	Sum observed	Sum of predicted
B3-G (NG)	52.3 m³/d	2.8 %	47,877 m³	47,660 m³
B4-G (NG)	37.7 m³/d	2.1 %	46,570 m³	46,826 m³
RCH (power).	19.6 kWh/d	0.0 %	39,054 kWh	38,159 kWh
CH1 (power)	22.2 kWh/d	0.0 %	23,838 kWh	23,955 kWh
HP (pow)	8.7 kWh/d	3.3 %	3,784 kWh	3,832 kWh

Data analysis showed that heat output and power consumption of HP are nearly constant all the time (when put into operation). Therefore very simple model is applied, Eq.(6).

$$P_{pow,HP} = 8 \text{ for } P_{heat,HP} > 0 \text{ and } P_{pow,HP} = 0 \text{ otherwise}, \tag{6}$$

where $P_{pow,HP}$ (kW) is power consumption and $P_{heat,HP}$ (kW) is heat output.

Table 2 shows goodness of fit for the models. Mean absolute error (MAE) and mean relative absolute error (MRAE) were calculated from daily cumulative consumptions; sum of observed and sum of predicted are cumulative consumptions per selected month.

4. Model application

An illustrative example will be used to demonstrate the application of the model in an optimization problem. The practical goal can be to find the optimum value of the daily NG limit and by this to reduce the NG price in a contract. The costs of NG consumption may be structured into variable and fixed costs. Variable cost is determined by NG consumption. Fixed cost is related to payment for the amount of NG per day guaranteed by supplier (daily NG limit), which is fixed for the whole year. There are high penalties when it is exceeded but also a higher daily NG limit means higher fixed cost. Let us assume that we have perfect information (prediction) about demand during the heating period (hourly data), which needs to be satisfied with B-MF and/or B-G (RCH excluded). Further, we have perfect information about return water temperature (equitherm regulation based on the actual demand and ambient temperature), which is needed to simulate the boilers performance properly. The energy management needs to know how to set the daily NG limit in a contract with this perfect information. The objective function to be minimized is given by Eq. (7).

$$z = \sum_{\substack{heating \\ period}} m_{gas} \cdot c_{gas} + \sum_{\substack{heating \\ period}} m_{oil} \cdot c_{oil} + m_{gas,day} \cdot c_{gas,day} + \sum_{\substack{heating \\ period}} m_{gas,pen} \cdot c_{pen}, \tag{7}$$

where m_{gas} is NG consumed, c_{gas} is unit costs of NG consumed (0.38 €/m³), m_{oil} is oil consumed, c_{oil} is unit costs of oil consumed (1 €/kg), $m_{gas,day}$ is the amount of NG in daily limit, $c_{gas,day}$ is unit costs of NG in daily limit (5.6 €/m³), $m_{gas,pen}$ is NG consumed over the daily limit and c_{pen} is unit penalty costs (20 €/m³). Let us further assume that the heating period lasts 109 days and heat demand corresponds to real operational data obtained in the period from 23/12/2011 to 11/4/2012.

The minimal value of the objective function is 140,423 EUR; the optimal daily NG limit is 5,712 m³/d. The operation, or more precisely, the NG and oil consumption are showed in Figure 3. There are only three days (43, 45 and 49) with a higher heat demand, in which NG is on its daily limit and therefore it is partially replaced by oil.

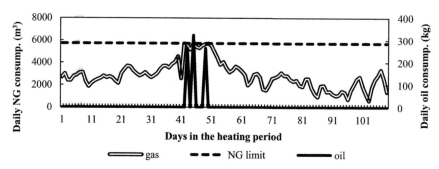

Figure 3. Optimal operation of boilers regarding minimum costs

This was illustrative case of perfect information about future. In real life, we are able to predict one or few days based on weather forecast. However, long-term predictions are very uncertain and it is better to use stochastic methods (Monte Carlo simulation or two-stage stochastic programming).

5. Conclusion

In addition to modernization of a utility system guarantying better efficiency, there is also potential for "soft" improvements such as better control, better operation planning, etc. These soft improvements are based on a model of a system. Considering data-based modelling, quality of a model depends on operational data quality. We presented the case where delay in data acquisition was detected. However, it was demonstrated that the model based on these data may be successful in cumulative predictions and therefore it can be useful in long-term problems.

Acknowledgement

The authors gratefully acknowledge financial support provided within the projects No. CZ.1.07/2.3.00/30.0039 "Excellent young researchers at Brno University of Technology", CZ.1.07/2.3.00/20.0020 "Science for practice" and CZ.1.05/2.1.00/01.0002 "NETME Centre – New Technologies for Mechanical Engineering".

References

G. Escrivá-Escrivá, 2011, Basic actions to improve energy efficiency in commercial buildings in operation, Energy and Buildings, 43, 11, 3106–3111.

C. Fourcroy, F. Gallouj, F. Decellas, 2012, Energy consumption in service industries: Challenging the myth of non-materiality, Ecological Economics, 81, 155–164.

M.S. Khan, Y.A. Husnil, M. Getu, M. Lee, 2012, Modeling and Simulation of Multi-stream Heat Exchanger Using Artificial Neural Network, Computer Aided Chemical Engineering, 31, 1196-1200.

A. Kusiak, M. Li, F. Tang, 2010, Modeling and optimization of HVAC energy consumption, Applied Energy, 87, 10, 3092–3102.

M. Mohanraj, S. Jayaraj, C. Muraleedharan, 2012, Applications of artificial neural networks for refrigeration, air-conditioning and heat pump systems—A review, Renewable and Sustainable Energy Reviews, 16, 2, 1340–1358.

M. Ndlovu, T. Majozi, 2013, Overall optimization of a comprehensive utility system, Computer Aided Chemical Engineering, 32, 439-444

D.J. Swider, 2003, A comparison of empirically based steady-state models for vapor-compression liquid chillers, Applied Thermal Engineering, 23, 5, 539–556.

Jiří Jaromír Klemeš, Petar Sabev Varbanov and Peng Yen Liew (Editors)
Proceedings of the 24th European Symposium on Computer Aided Process Engineering – ESCAPE 24
June 15-18, 2014, Budapest, Hungary. Copyright © 2014 Elsevier B.V. All rights reserved.

Operation and Modeling of RO Desalination Process in Batch Mode

Marta Barello[a,b], Davide Manca[a], Raj Patel[b], Iqbal M. Mujtaba[b, *]

[a]*PSE-Laboratory – Dipartimento di Chimica Industriale e Ingegneria Chimica, Politecnico di Milano, Piazza Leonardo da Vinci 32, 20133 Milan, Italy*
[b]*School of Engineering, University of Bradford, West Yorkshire BD7 1DP, UK*
I.M.Mujtaba@bradford.ac.uk

Abstract

In this work, a reverse osmosis (RO) desalination process operating under batch mode is considered experimentally. The effect of operating parameters, such as pressure and feed salinity on the permeate quantity and salinity is evaluated. In addition, the water permeability constant, K_w, which is one of the main parameters that affect the optimal design and operation of RO processes is evaluated as a function of changing feed salinity and pressure using the experimental data and two literature models. A strong pressure dependence of the water permeability constant is observed in line with earlier observations. Interestingly, a strong concentration dependence of the water permeability constant is also observed which has always been neglected or ignored in the literature. Finally, for a given pressure, concentration dependent correlations for K_w are developed and are used in the full process model (described by a system of ordinary differential and algebraic equations) for further simulation studies and to validate the experimental results.

Keywords: Reverse osmosis; Batch system; Permeability; Modelling; Performance.

1. Introduction

Desalination via RO is a separation process for making fresh water from seawater. While continuous RO and nanofiltration (NF) processes received considerable attention in the past (Sassi and Mujtaba, 2013), the batch RO system, shown schematically in Figure 1, has received very little attention (Stover, 2011). In batch system, the brine feed is recirculated to the feed tank till the target permeate recovery level has been reached. In this work, a batch RO desalination process is characterized in terms of permeate flow and its salinity, concentration polarization, salt transport and influence of the operating conditions on the water permeability constant. In addition, a system of differential and algebraic equations is proposed to model the system and it is solved using a MATLAB program.

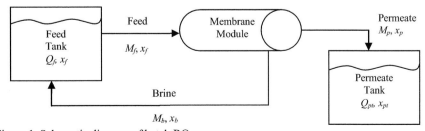

Figure 1. Schematic diagram of batch RO process.

2. Experiments

The saline feed is pumped through two tubular membranes coupled in series and housed in the membrane module (Figure 1) (Armfield FT18). Experiments are carried out at two different levels of pressure and three different initial feed salinities. Experimental settings are x_{f0} = 15-25-35 g/L, M_f = 18 L/min, A = 0.024 m^2, ΔP = 40-45 bar, L = 30 cm, d = 0.01635 m. Figure 2(a) shows plots of permeate flux trend and Figure 2(b) plots the corresponding feed tank salinity. The increase in permeate flux is due to the fact that higher pressure means higher driving force. As the feed salinity increases, the corresponding permeate flux decreases because the separation is more difficult (Figure 3a). This behavior confirms the findings of Shamel and Chung (2006). Figure 3(b) shows the change in salinity with time for pressures of 40 and 45 bar. The permeate salinity increases gradually and at the same rate for both pressures, with the gradual increase in feed salinity (see Figure 2(b)) until about 250 mins. Then, the increase in the rate of permeate salinity for 45 bar pressure is greater than that at 40 bar. This may be due to the fact that beyond this point higher pressure takes over the effect of concentration polarization. These results confirm the findings of Shamel and Chung (2006) and Voros et al. (1996).

Figure 4(a) illustrates the variation of permeate salinity against the feed salinity and Fig. 4(b) shows the corresponding M_p trend. In an ideal case, it would have been expected to obtain only one line joining all the points. However, beyond x_f = 25, the rate of increase in x_p is higher for x_{f0} = 15 compared to that for x_{f0} = 25. This is due to the fact that with x_{f0} = 15, the *CP* effect becomes increasingly more pronounced. Processes that start with x_{f0} = 25 achieve higher Mp values if compared to those with x_{f0} = 15 (see Figure 4(b)). To the best of authors' knowledge, these types of observations have not been reported in literature.

3. Water permeability

3.1. El-Dessouky and Ettouney model, 2002
According to the solution-diffusion model, the water flux through the membrane is:

$$M_p = K_w A (\Delta P - \Delta \pi) \tag{1}$$

Where, K_w is the water permeability, A the membrane area and ΔP and $\Delta \pi$ the hydraulic and osmotic pressure difference between the feed and permeate sides of the membrane respectively.

Results are plotted in Figure 5(a) and it is possible to see how water permeability increases with pressure due to a higher driving force. This trend is not in accord with the results of Voros et al. (1996). Figure 5(b) shows a very important result. It was not possible to find evidence in literature of the feed salinity effect on the water permeability constant. Some authors studied the dependence of K_w only from the pressure (Voros et al., 1996) or its decay with the time due to fouling. Conversely, we observed that K_w values depend also on feed salinity (Barello et al., 2013). Higher feed salinity corresponds to lower values of K_w coefficient. This trend confirms the dependence found between the permeate flux and initial feed salinity.

3.2. Meares model, 1976
Meares (1976) based his RO studies on an irreversible thermodynamic treatment of the system. The model assumes turbulent flow with, osmotic pressure represented by the

Van't Hoff equation. A tubular configuration is used with isothermal conditions, and the reflection coefficient approximately equal to the intrinsic salt rejection R_j, and the Nerst film model to describe polarization phenomenon. The permeate flux is given by:

$$M_p = K_w A \left(\Delta P - R_j^2 \alpha R T x_w \right) \tag{2}$$

Where α is the number of ions produced on complete dissociation of one molecule of electrolyte, R the universal gas constant, T the absolute temperature and x_w the concentration at the wall. Figure 6(a) and 6(b) show K_w as a function of time for different conditions. The trends confirm the various dependencies found with the El-Dessouky model.

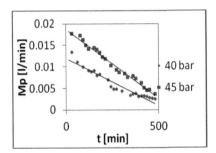 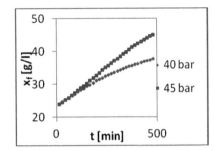

Figure 2. (a) Permeate flux trend with x_{f0}=25 g/L. (b) Feed salinity trend with x_{f0}=25 g/L.

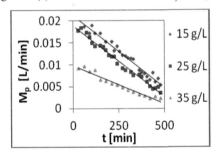 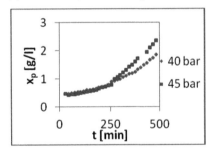

Figure 3. (a) Permeate flux trend with P=40 bar. (b) Permeate salinity trend with x_f=35 g/L.

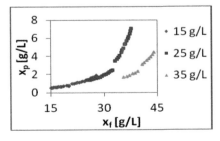 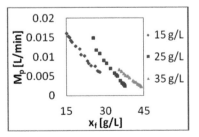

Figure 4. (a) Permeate salinity variation with the feed salinity. (b) Permeate flux variation with the feed salinity

4. Concentration polarization

The term concentration polarization refers to the concentration gradient of salts on the high-pressure side of the RO membrane surface. This phenomenon increases the osmotic pressure at the membrane's surface leading to reduced flux, increased salt leakage, and it favours scale development. As suggested by Kennedy et al. (1974), a material balance within the mass-transfer boundary layer near the membrane wall, between the solute carried to the membrane by convection and the solute carried away by diffusion, gives an expression that quantifies concentration polarization (CP):

$$CP = \frac{x_w - x_p}{x_w - x_b} = \exp\left(\frac{M_p}{k}\right) \tag{3}$$

Figure 7(a) shows the variation of CP with feed tank salinity for different initial feed salinity. In an ideal case, one would expect all the data points to fall on a single line. However, in processes starting with $x_{f0}=25$, the CP value is higher compared to CP with $x_{f0}=15$. Again, to the best of authors' knowledge, these results have not been reported in the literature.

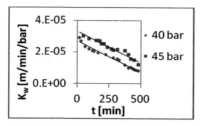 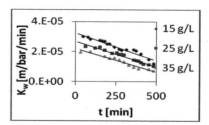

Figure 5. (a) K_w profile with $x_{f0}=25$ g/L (b) K_w profile with $P=45$ bar. (El-Dessouki and Ettouney model)

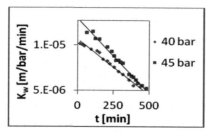 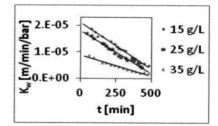

Figure 6. (a) K_w profile with $x_{f0} = 15$ g/L. (b) K_w profile with $P = 45$ bar. (Mares model)

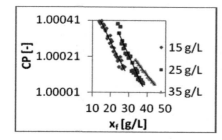 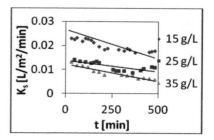

Figure 7. (a) Concentration polarization trend with permeate flux at $P = 45$ bar (b) K_s profile with $P = 40$ bar.

5. Salt permeability

As suggested by El-Dessouky and Ettouney (2002), the rate of salt flow through the membrane can be defined by:

$$J_S = K_S (\bar{x} - x_p) A \tag{4}$$

where K_s is the salt permeability coefficient and $\bar{x}$ the average salinity. In Figure 7(b) it can be observed that higher values of x_{f0} corresponds to lower K_s values. This behavior confirms the results of Voros et al. (1996).

6. Process modelling

With reference to Figure 1, the overall mass and salt balances for the feed tank and the permeate tank can be written:

$$\frac{d(Q_f)}{dt} = -M_p \tag{5}$$

$$\frac{d(x_f)}{dt} = \frac{M_p}{Q_f}(x_f - x_p) \tag{6}$$

$$\frac{d(Q_{pt})}{dt} = M_p \tag{7}$$

$$\frac{d(x_{pt})}{dt} = \frac{M_p}{Q_{pt}}(x_p - x_{pt}) \tag{8}$$

If K_w and K_s values (for a non-fouled membrane) are taken from Voros et al. (1996) (Table 1), it is possible to observe a mismatch between the experimental results and the calculated ones (Figure 8). This is partly due to some measurement errors, and use of constant values for K_w and K_s. From our experimental results, a linear regression is made in order to obtain two expressions for K_w and K_s as a function of x_f. Table 1 shows the correlations used and Figure 9 shows that there is a better fit, especially with El-Dessouky and Ettouney model, when both water and salt permeability correlations are implemented in the model. Note the K_w and K_s correlations could have been presented as a function of time as shown in Figures 5, 6 and 7(b).

7. Conclusions

This work studied, characterized and modelled a reverse osmosis desalination process. Experimental data was collected for different initial feed salinities and operating

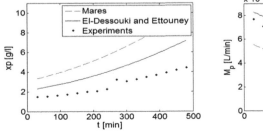
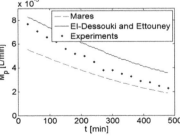

Figure 8. (a) Permeate salinity trends. (b) Permeate flux trends.

Table 1. Water and salt permeability correlations

	Voros et al. literature values	Based on El-Dessouki and Ettonuey model	Based on Meares model
K_w [l/min/kPa/m^2]	0.00024	$-10^{-6}x_f + 6 \times 10^{-5}$	$-5 \times 10^{-7}x_f + 3 \times 10^{-5}$
K_s [l/min/m^2]	0.0237	$-0.0003x_f + 0.0224$	$-0.0003x_f + 0.0224$

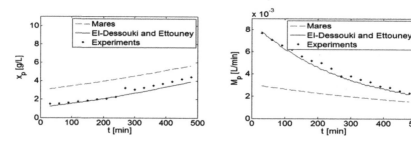

Figure 9. (a) Permeate salinity trends (b) Permeate flow trends (feed salinity dependence on water and salt permeability)

pressures. One of the most important observations is that the concentration polarization phenomena can influence the permeate salinity trends so that for different initial conditions the values at same feed salinity are different. Interestingly, strong salinity dependence of water permeability constant was also observed although it has been ignored in the literature. Finally, the batch process was modeled as a differential-algebraic system and solved using MATLAB. When water and salt permeability constants are introduced in the model as functions of feed salinity, results are found to be in good agreement with other researchers , especially with the El-Dessouky and Ettouney model.

References

M. Barello, 2013, Neural network based correlation for estimating water permeability constant in RO desalination process under fouling, Internal Report, School of Engineering, University of Bradford, UK.

H.T. El-Dessouky, H.M. Ettouney, 2002, Fundamentals of sea water desalination, Elsevier Science, Amsterdam, Netherlands.

T.J. Kennedy, R.L. Merson, B.J. McCoy, 1974, Improving permeation flux by pulses reverse osmosis, Chemical Engineering Science, 29, 1927-1931.

P. Meares, 1976, Membrane separation process, Elsevier Scientific, Oxford, UK.

K.M. Sassi, I.M. Mujtaba, 2013, Optimal Operation of RO System with Daily Variation of Freshwater Demand and Seawater Temperature, Computer and Chemical Engineering, 59, 101–110

M.M. Shamel, O.T. Chung, 2006, Drinking water from desalination of seawater: optimisation of reverse osmosis system operating parameters, Journal of Engineering Science and Technology, 203-211.

R. Stover, 2011, CCD Starts a New Generation for RO, Desalination and Water Reuse, November-December, 34 – 35.

N.G. Voros, Z.B. Maroulis, D. Marinos-Kouris, 1996, Salt and sea water permeability in reverse osmosis membranes, Desalination, 104, 141-154.

Jiří Jaromír Klemeš, Petar Sabev Varbanov and Peng Yen Liew (Editors)
Proceedings of the 24th European Symposium on Computer Aided Process Engineering – ESCAPE 24
June 15-18, 2014, Budapest, Hungary. Copyright © 2014 Elsevier B.V. All rights reserved.

Simultaneous Nonlinear Reconciliation and Update of Parameters for Online Use of First-Principles Models: An Industrial Case-Study on Compressors

Matteo Cicciotti[a,b,]*, Dionysios P. Xenos[c], Ala E. F. Bouaswaig[a], Ricardo F. Martinez-Botas[b], Flavio Manenti[d], Nina F. Thornhill[c]

[a]BASF SE, Automation Technology, Advanced Process Control, 67056 Ludwigshafen, Germany
[b]Imperial College London, Department of Mechanical Engineering, Turbomachinery Research Group, SW7 2AZ London, UK
[c]Imperial College London, Department of Chemical Engineering, Centre for Process Systems Engineering, SW7 2AZ London, UK;
[d]Politecnico di Milano, Dipartimento di Chimica, Materiali e Ingegneria Chimica 'Giulio Natta', Piazza Leonardo da Vinci 32, 20133 Milano, Italy;
matteo.cicciotti@basf.com

Abstract

Online uses of first-principles models include nonlinear model predictive control, soft-sensors, real-time optimization, and real-time process monitoring, among others. The industrial implementation of these applications needs accurate adaptive models and reconciled data. The simultaneous reconciliation and update of parameters of a first-principles model can be achieved using an optimization framework that exploits physical and analytical redundancy of information. This paper demonstrates this concept by means of an industrial case-study. The case-study is a multi-stage centrifugal compressor for which a first-principles model was recently developed. The update of the model parameters is necessary to capture slowly progressing mechanical degradation (e.g. due to fouling and erosion). The reconciliation of the data is necessary for reducing downtime of the online model-based applications caused by gross errors. Two industrial cases including sensor failures were analysed. Applying the proposed framework, it was possible to reconcile the measurements for both cases.

Keywords: data reconciliation, compressor first-principles model, online monitoring

1. Introduction

Many applications for online uses in the process industry, such as performance monitoring and real-time optimization, employ first-principles models. To ensure that these models represent the process accurately, measurements are collected from the operation and are subsequently used to update the model. The measurements typically contain random errors, and less frequently may also contain gross errors. The role of the data reconciliation is to properly identify and correct these errors, and therefore provide reliable information for updating the parameters of the model. There is a broad literature of data reconciliation techniques for different applications. Özyurt and Pike (2004) presented a review of the available methods and discussed the comparison of different objective functions for efficient and robust data reconciliation and gross errors detection. Faber et al. (2003) suggested solving the estimation of parameters and the data reconciliation problem for large-scale nonlinear models with a sequential approach.

In Faber et al., (2004) the sequential method was applied to an industrial coke-oven-gas purification process. Martinez-Maradiaga et al. (2013) applied a similar method, however considering only the data reconciliation problem for a test bench single-effect ammonia-water absorption chiller. Prata et al. (2009) reported the simultaneous data reconciliation and update of parameters for an industrial polymerization reactor. Additionally, Prata et al. presented a literature review of data reconciliation techniques in real industrial applications. It was reported that only few applications were nonlinear data reconciliation problems and even fewer considered also the simultaneous update of the parameters. This paper reports an industrial application of the simultaneous steady-state nonlinear data reconciliation and update of parameters problem for a multistage centrifugal compressor, which is modelled by first-principles. To the best of the authors' knowledge, research-works employing aerodynamic first-principles models of compressors for online applications have not yet been published. However, there is a growing interest for a more synergic integration of turbomachinery and process system engineering knowledge, e.g. for real-time performance monitoring and optimization of networks of compressors. The following section contains a description of: the compressor under analysis, the modelling approach, an analysis for the degree of freedoms, the implemented algorithm, and finally the results of two industrial cases.

2. Case-study

A compressor is a machine that increases the pressure of a gas. A centrifugal compressor stage realizes this increase of pressure in two consecutive steps. At first, the gas flow is accelerated by a rotating component (i.e. impeller). Secondly, the gas flow is slowed down by a stationary component (i.e. diffuser: divergent duct) that converts the kinetic energy of the gas into pressure increase. The performance of the compressor stage depends on the aerodynamic profile of the rotating and stationary components. Hence, the performance will degrade if these components deteriorate (e.g. fouled or eroded). The following case-study shows that the health condition of the compressor stage and that of its measuring system can be monitored simultaneously. This is done exploiting the physical redundancy of sensors and the analytical redundancy provided by the first-principles model.

2.1. Compressor description

The compressor described in this section is a multistage intercooled air centrifugal compressor operated in the network of compressors of the BASF SE air separation plant. This compressor has five closed impellers mounted on a single shaft. As can be seen from Fig.1 the flow enters the impellers axially and leaves them radially. At the exit of each impeller the flow is divided into four streams. Each stream is directed towards a dedicated diffuser channel and then cooled in a dedicated intercooler block allocated in the same casing. After the streams have been cooled they are remixed and redirected to the inlet of the successive impeller by means of return channels. The suction static temperature and pressure sensors are placed after the filtering system for the first stage and in proximity of the impeller eye for the others. The four discharge static temperature and two pressure sensors are placed right after the diffuser channels (physical redundancy). The volumetric flow in standard conditions is measured at the exit of the last stage.

2.2. Compressor first-principles model

The proposed modelling approach considers a fluid mean streamline to be representative of the total flow through the gas-paths (Figure 2(a)).

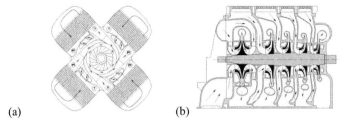

(a)   (b)

Figure 1. Compressor axial and longitudinal view.

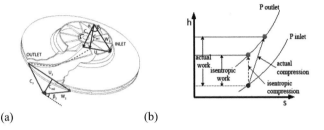

(a)   (b)

Figure 2. Velocity vectors for the impeller (a), and h-s diagram (b).

For convenience, two different reference systems (one rotating and one stationary) are considered for modelling the thermodynamic transformations that the mean streamline experiences from the inlet to the outlet of the impeller and then in the diffuser channel. Figure 2(a) demonstrates the flow velocity vectorial decomposition in the absolute velocity components c, which refer to the stationary frame of reference, and the relative velocity components w, which refer to the frame of reference rotating with the impeller (with linear velocity u. The velocity vectors modules can be calculated imposing the continuity of momentum, mass and energy (Cicciotti et al., 2013). However, information regarding: the dimensions of the hub radius and inlet tip radius, the blade angles, the number of revolutions per minute of the axle, the mass flow rate, and its suction conditions (pressure and temperature) have to be available. Finally, from the velocity vectors, all the other intermediate and outlet intensive variables (enthalpies, temperatures, and pressures) can be estimated. Figure 2(b) can be used to show the effect of compression on the gas. This diagram shows the enthalpy of the gas versus the entropy. The transformation is assumed to happen in adiabatic conditions. Hence, mechanical energy is transferred from the impeller to the fluid without dissipation of heat into the surrounding environment. The dotted line represents the ideal/isentropic path from the isobaric curve P_{inlet} to the isobaric curve P_{outlet}. The isentropic path represents the minimum work that is needed for the increase of pressure. However, due to turbulent vortices and flow separations upstream to the exit of the impeller, the thermodynamic transformation is bound to happen with an increase of entropy (continuous line). Consequently, the required actual work will be higher. This nonideality is accounted for in the model by mechanical loss correlations with adaptive parameters.

In summary, the proposed model is a nonlinear algebraic model, based on fundamental physics with the inclusion of empirically derived parts. The relation between input and output for one steady-state operative point is written as:

$$0 = f(\boldsymbol{y}_i, \boldsymbol{u}_i, \boldsymbol{\Theta}, \boldsymbol{\Omega}) \tag{1}$$

where: i is one operative point, f is the algebraic system of equations representing the first-principles model (e.g. mass and energy balances, equations of state, 1D flow models, and mechanical loss correlations), y_i is the vector of output variables (e.g. outlet temperature and pressure), u_i is the vector of input variables (e.g. mass flow), Θ is the vector of fixed parameters (e.g. main geometrical dimensions and fluid properties), Ω is the vector of adaptive empirical parameters (i.e. these are used to model the effect of degradation). The adaptive parameters Ω are not measurable directly. These parameters have to be, at first, estimated during off-line calibration of the model and then updated online to capture the slowly progressing mechanical degradation.

2.3. Degrees of freedom for a compressor

A qualitative analysis of the degrees of freedom of the system can be carried out considering the thermodynamics (Figure 2(b)). The proposed first-principles model represents the relationship between the conditions of the flow (h and P) at the inlet and at the outlet, i.e. continuous line representing the actual compression in Figure 2(b). The slope of this line represents the deviation from the ideal isentropic compression. This deviation depends from the aerodynamic performance which is related to the geometry of the components and the mass flow rate. Therefore, considering inlet and outlet enthalpy and pressure, and the mass flow rate, it is possible to univocally determine two out of these five variables provided any combination of the remaining three. Hence, when measurements for more than three of these variables are available, these can be used to reconcile the data and update the model parameters.

2.4. Simultaneous data reconciliation and update of parameters

The simultaneous data reconciliation and updated of parameters results from the minimization of the deviation between the estimated values $\tilde{y}$ and $\tilde{u}$ of the variables and the corresponding actual measurements y^m and u^m, for a window of time where the readings are in steady-state. Figure 3 shows the optimization framework. The implementation follows the physical structure of the problem. For each steady-state window, the optimization problem is initialized using the actual measured values and the parameters updated at the previous steady-state window. At each iteration, the optimizer provides the values of Ω^k and u^k, thus the values of the output variables y^k are obtained by finding the roots of the nonlinear implicit algebraic model.

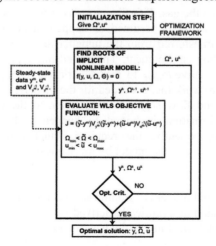

Figure 3. Optimization framework for simultaneous data reconciliation and parameter estimation

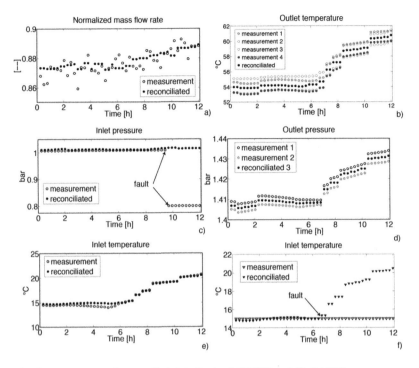

Figure 4. Measurements and reconciled data for (a-e) CASE1 and (f) CASE2.

Hence, the Weighted Least Squares (WLS) objective function J is evaluated and the optimizer decides whether a new iteration is needed or a local optimum is found. $V_{y^m}^{-1}$ and $V_{u^m}^{-1}$ are the covariance matrix for the measured variables, these are estimated using the historical data. The values of $\tilde{u}$ and Ω are bounded between linear constraints. In particular, the values of Ω are allowed to vary only for a small percentage of Ω^0, because they represent the slow degradation dynamics due to the compressor aging. The values for $\tilde{u}$ are bounded between physical meaningful constraints e.g. the true value of the inlet temperature to the first stage (ambient) can range from -10 °C to 40 °C. Finally, the values of the $\tilde{y}$ are implicitly bounded through the nonlinear model.

2.5. Results

This section presents the results of the simultaneous data reconciliation and update of the parameters for the first stage of the compressor. For this stage: five temperatures, three pressures, and one mass flow are reconciled, while two model parameters are updated Two cases are shown here CASE1 and CASE2, for an operative window of 12 hours. CASE1 presents data from the field. In CASE1, the sensor for the inlet pressure failed during operation. CASE2 was produced by altering the data to simulate another fault for testing the algorithm. In CASE2 all the measurements are as in CASE1 apart for the inlet temperature, which was set to 15 °C. Figure 4(a-e) presents the results for CASE1 and Figure 4(f) presents the results for CASE2. The results for the mass flow are plotted in Figure 4(a). The measurements for the mass flow rate are noisy and and have the largest variance. The data reconciliation increases the signal to noise ratio for this variable and reduces its variance. Figure 4(b) shows the readings coming from the four temperature sensors placed at the outlet. The four readings have a small variance, show all the same trend and deviate only slightly from each other, the reconciled value is close to the mean of the four readings, similarly, for the outlet pressure Figure 4(d) and for the inlet temperature Fig. 4(e). Figure 4(c) shows the measured and reconciled values for the inlet pressure. At the start of the monitored period the sensor started slowly drifting, and then failed abruptly around the 9th working hour. The pressure indicated by the sensor deviates from the reconciled value by more than 20 %. From the comparison of Figure 4(e) with Figure 4(f), it can be observed that also for CASE2 the algorithm is able to reconcile the inlet temperature producing reasonable results. For all the other variables, the reconciled values differed only slightly for CASE1 and CASE2. These results demonstrate that modelling the compressor by first-principles, it is possible to reconcile the data also when one or two measurements are strongly biased. In this situation, the algorithm relies on the model predictions for reconciling the values of the biased variables. However, the parameters have to be tightly constrained, to adapt only to slow changes in the system (i.e. caused by mechanical degradation).

3. Conclusions

This work studied the simultaneous data reconciliation and update of parameters for nonlinear steady-state first-principles models. A case-study for an air centrifugal compressor operating in an industrial plant examines the problem of reconciling data containing sensors malfunctions. The proposed approach involves the consecutive solution of a root-finding problem and WLS objective function evaluation within an optimization framework. The application of this framework to two cases yielded encouraging results which motivate future research into the direction of sensor faults detection, particularly for applications were safety is an issue (e.g. surge control for highly loaded compressors).

Acknowledgements

The authors would like to thank BASF SE for providing a case study and technical support. The research leading to these results has received funding from the Marie Curie FP7-ITN project "Energy savings from smart operation of electrical, process and mechanical equipment - ENERGY-SMARTOPS", Contract No: PITN-GA-2010-264940.

References

M. Cicciotti, R. F. Martinez-Botas, A. Romagnoli, N. F. Thornhill, S. Geist and A. Schild, 2013, Systematic one zone meanline modelling of centrifugal compressors for industrial online applications, Proceedings of ASME Turbo Expo 2013, GT2013, San Antonio, Texas, USA.

R. Faber, P. Li, G. Wozny, 2003, Sequential parameter estimation for large-scale systems with multiple data sets 1: Application to an industrial coke-oven-gas purification process, Industrial Engineering and Chemistry Research, 42, 5850-5860.

R. Faber, P. Li, G. Wozny, 2004, Sequential parameter estimation for large-scale systems with multiple data sets 2: Application to an industrial coke-oven-gas purification process, Industrial Engineering and Chemistry Research, 43, 4350-4362.

D. Martinez-Mariaga, J. C. Bruno, A. Coronas, 2013, Steady-state data reconciliation for absorption refrigeration systems, Applied Thermal Engineering, 51, 1170-1180.

D. Martinez Prata, M. Schwaab, E. Luis Lima, J. Carlos Pinto, 2010, Simultaneous robust data reconciliation and gross error detection through particle swarm optimization for an industrial polypropylene reactor, Chemical Engineering Science, 65, 4943-4954.

D. B. Özyurt, R.W. Pike, 2004, Theory and practice of simultaneous data reconciliation and gross error detection for chemical processes, Computers and Chemical Engineering, 28, 381-402.

Jiří Jaromír Klemeš, Petar Sabev Varbanov and Peng Yen Liew (Editors)
Proceedings of the 24th European Symposium on Computer Aided Process Engineering – ESCAPE 24
June 15-18, 2014, Budapest, Hungary. Copyright © 2014 Elsevier B.V. All rights reserved.

Data-Based Tiered Approach for Improving Pharmaceutical Batch Production Processes

Lukas G. Eberle[a,*], Hirokazu Sugiyama[b], Stavros Papadokonstantakis[a], Andreas Graser[c], Rainer Schmidt[c], Konrad Hungerbühler[a]

[a]Institute for Chemical and Bioengineering, ETH Zurich, Wolfgang-Pauli-Strasse 10, 8093 Zurich, Switzerland
[b]The University of Tokyo, 7-3-1, Hongo, Bunkyo-ku, 113-8656 Tokyo, Japan
[b]Parenterals Production, F.Hoffmann-La Roche Ltd., Grenzacherstrasse 124, 4070 Basel, Switzerland
lukas.eberle@roche.com

Abstract

Enhancing yield in production is paramount for success in the increasingly competitive pharmaceutical industry, especially for manufacturers of costly biopharmaceutical products. Effort and complexity of implementing enhancements are forcing decision makers to first identify and quantify potentials and opportunities and then trigger process reviews efficiently. Data for supporting such quantifications have been traditionally recorded in the industry; the trend towards better accessibility of production data now facilitates consulting them and the need for developing appropriate tools gets evident. We present a four-level approach to convert production data into serviceable information, supporting the prioritization of processes and assisting real-life changes based on information from analysing production conditions. The approach was applied at a drug product manufacturing plant on a sample of 43 batches; main loss causes were identified and quantified. The three dominant loss sources account for nearly two-third of losses and are largely batch-size independent.

Keywords: Pharmaceutical Production, Industrial Application, Decision-making, Statistical Process Control, Multivariate Data Analysis.

1. Introduction

Cutting costs of drug product manufacturing becomes a key element in the historically "spoiled" pharmaceutical industry to meet the public longing for cheaper medicinal treatments. Production of such drug products is performed by a chain of value-adding processes as shown in Figure 1, including Drug Substance Manufacturing, Drug Product Manufacturing, Drug Product Bulk Packaging and finally the Drug Product Distribution. The presented approach defines a generic tool for yield enhancements that is adoptable to any element of the value chain and applies it to the Drug Product Manufacturing of sterile drug products, so-called Parenterals. Parenterals production consists of the processes Compounding, Filling, Visual Inspection and the concluding Batch Record Review (BRR). Compounding blends Active Pharmaceutical Ingredient (API) with water-for-injection and excipients. Filling includes the sterile and particle-free filling of syringes or vials. Visual Inspection performs an extensive screening for imperfections and BRR conducts a review of production records to assure quality.

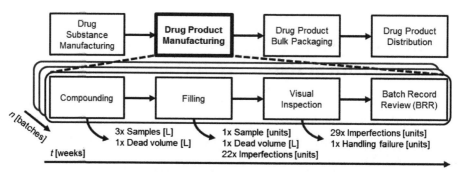

Figure 1. Overview of the value-adding chain for Parenterals, adapted from Gernaey et al. (2012). The upper elements represent the overall Supply Chain, the lower indicate the main activities in Drug Product Manufacturing. In Compounding three different samples are taken for the validation of the process, microbiological burden and in-process control. Also the difference between material-in and -out unit is calculated (dead volume). In Filling, besides sampling and dead volume calculation, vials are rejected due to imperfections (e.g., under-filled products, unsealed products, etc.). In Visual Inspection further screening for imperfections and product handling is performed.

Losses may arise at any point during Parenterals production and appear in a variety of patterns. They can be caused inter alia by sampling, dead volumes or imperfect products, for instance scratched vials. Hence, losses emerge in multiple forms and are measured in various units ([g], [L], [#vials]), which makes it hard to establish an overview over the losses arisen in a facility. To make it even worse, losses are caused at multiple time points within one batch, possibly spread over weeks, which calls for a sophisticated pooling and extraction of loss data to standardize this error-prone process. Moreover, when performing an inter-batch comparison, additional obstacles have to be overcome with respect to batch size variability and fine-tuning of equipment. On the top of that, various performance indicators can be used in these comparisons. For instance, besides the two most established indicators, that is cost impact and mass of API lost, (Sugiyama and Schmidt, 2012) also implied GMP-risks should be considered.

The mentioned factors impede drawing the overall picture about loss causes. Hence, prioritizing improvement efforts cannot be performed reasonably without applying a systematic data-based approach. The work of Schoot et al. (2007) on root causes of quality variability includes a differentiation of critical and noncritical disturbances and it was advanced by the efforts of Gins et al. (2011) with additional input parameters. Further efforts in this direction are, for example, those of Sugiyama and Schmidt (2012), which solely considered mass as a target parameter. Troup and Georgakis (2013) summarize the currently available process systems engineering tools for the pharmaceutical industry and present an optimisation approach, which is based on additional experimental data, hence, very costly for biopharmaceutical drug products. Latest efforts by Muñoz et al. (2014) align the varying quality of several reactor inputs to achieve enhanced overall product quality and thereby reducing the risk of batch rejections. However, conclusive research studies proposing pragmatic methodologies for pharmaceutical production are still missing (Kontoravdi et al., 2013). In this work, we first present a data-based, hierarchical four-level model tailored to batchwise production and then apply it to real-life production data to derive managerial implications.

2. Methodology

The 1st level of the methodology conducts a cross-product comparison of the end-to-end yield, namely the performance indicators API yield ([g-API/batch], Y_{API}), financial yield ([monetary units/batch], Y_F), and GMP-risk ([-/batch], Y_{GMP}) are determined for every product. Products are distinguished from each other by differing in at least one of the following key features: API identity, API concentration, filling volume or product type (e.g., prefilled syringes). Y_{API} is calculated as defined by Eq.(1).

$$Y_{API} = \left(\sum_{k=1}^{n} \frac{O_k \times \rho \times v}{I_k} \right) \times n^{-1} \tag{1}$$

where n is the amount of batches for a product [-], O_k is the output resulting from production [number of vials] per batch, ρ is the density of the solution [kg/L], v is the volume of solution filled into each vial [L/vial] and I_k is the quantity of all input materials of a drug solution [kg] per batch. As shown in Figure 2, the costs per vial accumulate during production and can be doubling between Compounding and BRRfor small-volume products. Y_F accounts for this trend and is determined according to Eq.(2).

$$Y_F = \left(\sum_{k=1}^{n} \frac{O_k \times C_g}{O_k \times C_g + \sum_{i=1}^{m} L_{k,i} \times C_i} \right) \times n^{-1} \tag{2}$$

where m are the loss sources (e.g. samples, scratched or under-filled vials), $L_{k,i}$ is the quantity lost per loss source and batch [L or vial], C_g the cost of a vial that is released to the market and C_i the cost of losses per loss source [monetary units/(l or vial)]. The third indicator, Y_{GMP}, accounts for the fact that losses with low implied GMP-risks are to be treated differently than losses more likely to have an impact on the therapeutic effect, if they would pass Visual Inspection, and is defined by Eq.(3).

$$Y_{GMP,i} = \left(\sum_{k=1}^{n} \frac{O_k}{O_k + \sum_{i=1}^{m} G_i \times L_{k,i}} \right) \times n^{-1} \tag{3}$$

where G_i is the GMP-factor [-/vial] of a loss source i based on the categorization of loss sources detected in Visual Inspection for the hypothetical negative impact on the health of a patient. The categorization is influenced by collaboration with pharmaceutical industry and includes critical losses with a weighting factor of 9 (e.g. for underfilled or imperfectly sealed products), a factor of 3 for major losses (e.g., empty or overfilled vials) and a factor of 1 for minor losses (e.g., scratches or abrasion at the glass body). Y_{GMP} and Y_F are both aggregations of information from the second level of our method, as opposed to Y_{API} which is calculated with top level information.

By managerial decision and based on the findings from the 1st level, the manufacturing review on the 2nd level focuses on the product with highest priority and the corresponding production is split into processes. The contribution of processes to the overall loss is investigated as L_{API} [g-API/batch], L_F [monetary units/batch] and L_{GMP} [-/batch]; Eq.(4) shows the calculation of $L_{X,i}$ for these three performance indicators.

$$L_{x_i} = \left(\sum_{k=1}^{n} L_{k,i} \times F_i\right) \times n^{-1} \tag{4}$$

L_X is determined as an average of n batches by multiplying quantity $L_{k,i}$ [L] and impact factor F_i (i.e., grams of API lost per unit for L_{API} [g/L], C_i for L_F [monetary units/L] and G_i for L_{GMP} [-/L]). These performance indicators quantify the impact of loss sources and facilitate Fault Tree Analyses (FTA) to list possible root causes for the most important loss factors, as described for Drug Product Bulk Packaging by Rivero et al. (2008). The FTA allows to disaggregate a parameter that cannot be controlled directly, such as share of scratched vials, into elements that can be controlled (e.g. stirring velocity, temperatures, etc.). The branches of the FTA are then either starched or dropped with respect to the information gained on the 3rd and 4th level. Reducing the scope of the FTA on the 3rd and 4th level is crucial, since the amount of information available per level is increasing while progressing in the approach.

On the 3rd level, tools of Statistical Process Control (SPC) are applied (e.g., Chopra et al., 2012) for eliminating some of the root causes listed by FTA. To achieve that goal, trends are associated to production conditions, mechanisms triggering outliers are investigated and production parameters that are found to be constant are neglected as causes of production variation. In this way, whole clusters of potential loss causes can be discarded and further efforts can be directed towards identified decisive production parameters.

The concluding 4th level of our approach is presented conceptually and will exercise multivariate data analysis to further investigate and reveal non-trivial dependencies of root causes from multiple data sources (Rathore, 2011). The concept is to consolidate the plant information (PI) recordings and similar data recording systems, and to correlate losses to equipment parameters. A detailed description of the 4th level and the application to real-life production challenges will be presented in a next publication.

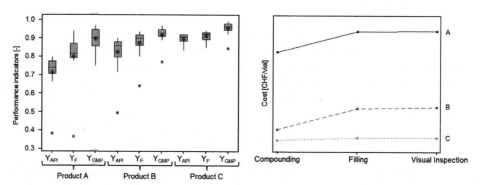

Figure 2. Left: Comparison of Y_{API}, Y_F and Y_{GMP} for products A, B and C. The grey boxes indicate the location of the central 50 % of values from a sample of batches, the horizontal line within a box represents the median and the crosshairs the mean. The vertical line is 1.5 times the heights of the respective box-half. All performance indicators show highest improvement potential for product A. Right: Cost comparison within Parenterals production for products A, B and C(e.g., indicating an increase in costs per vial by about 30 % for product A).

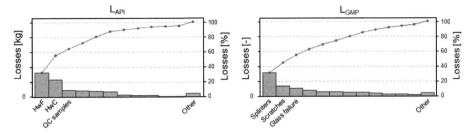

Figure 3. Left: L_{API} for product A, highlighting hardware losses (HwF, HwC) and samples as most decisive. Right: L_{GMP} highlights three challenges associated with container of Product A.

3. Case Study

The data-based approach was applied at a Parenterals manufacturing facility of Roche in Switzerland, which produces injectables with biopharmaceutically produced API for the fight against deadly diseases such as cancer. The study is based on 43 batches from commercial production of three drug products with a total of 2.3 million units and considers 58 loss causes.

As indicated on the left side of Figure 2, three products were compared by their Y_{API}, Y_F and Y_{GMP} on the 1st level of our approach. All indicators rank the products in the order A, B and C, that is the same ascending order as their batch-sizes. The manufacturing of product A, identified as the process with the highest improvement potential was selected for further examination. The cost development within manufacturing of products A, B and C is reported on the right half of Figure 2, indicating that costs for a unit of product A are increasing roughly by 30 % from the ready-to-fill product solution to the inspected ready-to-inject drug product.

Then, on the 2nd level, the indicators L_{API}, L_F and L_{GMP} were determined for product A. As shown in Figure 3, the loss sources Hardware: Filling (HwF) and Hardware: Compounding (HwC) are the two most important loss causes in terms of L_{API}. Both are not measured values but calculated as the difference of material in- and output from the Filling and Compounding unit, respectively. For enhancing the yield, the hardware setting will have to be modified, for instance tubes have to be shortened and diameters reduced. Furthermore, a request for increased batch-sizes was submitted to relevant health authorities and will take effect shortly after this study. Further data analysis will be executed after the production of product A in the updated setting.

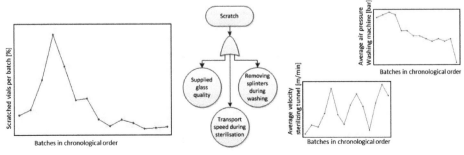

Figure 4. The appearance of scratches (left) was associated to production parameters (right) to investigate root causes for the creation of scratches.

As sketched in Figure 4, the 3rd level of the methodology was performed on scratches, the second most decisive GMP-loss because the most dominant loss source (i.e. glass splinters) was caused to a very large extent by a single event. An initial screening of production parameters that are associated by expert knowledge to scratches was performed graphically. Hence, a more rigorous data analysis with tools of multivariate data analysis is needed, which will be performed by executing the 4th level of the presented approach.

4. Conclusions

In this work we present a data-based four-level approach for efficient yield enhancement in drug product manufacturing. Based on three performance indicators, first product and second loss sources are prioritized in the order of their improvement potential. Possible root causes are then listed by performing a Fault Tree Analysis before reducing the root cause list with statistical analysis. The case study identified the product with the highest improvement potential in manufacturing processes and quantified the most decisive loss sources. For financial and API yield, hardware losses during pumping processes and quality control samples cause nearly two-thirds of losses, which are largely batch-size independent. In terms of implied GMP-risks, the three dominant factors are associated to the glass container of the drug product (i.e. glass splinters, scratches and glass failures). For future research, the third and fourth level of our approach will be advanced and applied to more production data. Also the GMP indicator can be further developed to support the mitigation of GMP-risks in pharmaceutical production.

References

V. Chopra, M. Bairagi, P. Trivedi, M. Nagar, 2012, A case study: application of statistical process control tool for determining process capability and sigma level, PDA J. Pharm. Sci. Tech., 66, 2, 98-115.

K. Gernaey, A. Cervera-Padrell, J. Woodley, 2012, A perspective on PSE in pharmaceutical process development and innovation, Comput. Chem. Eng., 42, SI, 15-29.

G. Gins, J. Valaer, J. Van Impe, 2011, Discriminating between Critical and Noncritical Disturbances in (Bio)Chemical Batch Processes Using Multimodel Fault Detection and End-Quality Prediction, Ind. Eng. Chem. Res., 51, 38, 12375-12385.

C. Kontoravdi, N. Samsatli, N. Shah, Development and design of bio-pharmaceutical processes, Curr. Opin. Chem. Eng., 2, 4, 435-441.

S. Muñoz, V. Padovani, J. Mercado, 2014, A computer aided optimal inventory selection system for continuous quality improvement in drug product manufacture, Comput. Chem. Eng., 60, 396-402.

A. Rathore, 2011, Quality by Design for Biologics and Biosimilars, Pharm. Technol., 35, 3, 64-68.

A. Rivero, N. Prado, Y. Molina, I. de Zayas, 2008, Packing-Line Improvement Based on a Fault-Tree Analysis Approach, Pharm. Technol., 3, 32, 106-126.

S. Schoot, B. Nuijen, A. Huitema, J. Beijnen, 2007, Assessment of Performance of Manufacturing Procedures in a Unit for Production of Investigational Anticancer Agents, Using a Mixed Effects Analysis, Pharm. Res., 24, 3, 605-612.

H. Sugiyama, R. Schmidt, 2012, Model-based Optimization in Pharmaceutical Technical Operations – Yield Measurement and Increase in Roche's Parenterals Production Kaiseraugst, Comput. Aided Chem. Eng., 30, 577-581.

G. Troup, C. Georgakis, 2013, Process systems engineering tools in the pharmaceutical industry, Comput. Chem. Eng., 51, 157-171.

Jiří Jaromír Klemeš, Petar Sabev Varbanov and Peng Yen Liew (Editors)
Proceedings of the 24th European Symposium on Computer Aided Process Engineering – ESCAPE 24
June 15-18, 2014, Budapest, Hungary. Copyright © 2014 Elsevier B.V. All rights reserved.

Plug Flow vs. Discontinuous Modelling Approaches for Plasma – Based Depollution of Exhausts

Valentina Gogulancea*, Vasile Lavric

University Politehnica of Bucharest, Polizu 1-7, Bucharest RO-011061, Romania
v.gogulancea@gmail.com

Abstract

The non-thermal plasma treatment of exhausts using electron beams is an innovative, highly effective process, which can simultaneously remove sulphur and nitrogen oxides as well as a variety of volatile organic compounds. The main objective of this paper is to introduce the plug flow approach to the modelling of the physico-chemical phenomena occurring in the irradiation chamber, followed by a comparison of its results with the classical discontinuous model outcome. The plug flow approach is more versatile, the model being able to consider local mixing influence (axial dispersion), axially varying dose magnitude and the addition of a non-irradiated working volume (polishing length). The results obtained using both mathematical models are in good agreement with published data from laboratory experiments and pilot installations.

Keywords: electron beam, plug flow, flue gas, plasma exhaust depollution

1. Introduction

Demonstrated at industrial level in Europe and Asia, the electron beam flue gas treatment (EBFGT) is based upon the interactions of accelerated electrons with the flue gas, stimulating the transformation of SO_2 and NO_x, in the presence of NH_3, into their corresponding ammonia salts. Contrary to classical methods for flue gas treatment, the EBFGT process can attain high efficiencies for small pollutant concentrations, has relatively small space requirements and can remove simultaneously several gaseous pollutants.

The advantages of the electron beam process have prompted numerous investigations into the mechanisms of non-thermal plasma treatment of exhausts, which have revealed the occurrence of over 700 gas phase chemical reactions, with approximately 450 of them involving only nitrogen and oxygen (Matzing, 1991). However, due to the huge computational effort required, most researchers have designed simplified models that can still account for the irradiation associated phenomena: either considering in their modelling only a portion of these reactions, or by neglecting the contributions of some of the flue gases' components or by employing empirical models. To add to the complexity of the modelling process, experiments have indicated that a dispersed liquid phase is formed inside the reactor during the irradiation treatment. Even though early modelling studies (Li et al., 1998) have stressed the importance of the liquid phenomena, more recent papers (Zhang et al., 2009) neglect them, stating that the ratio of liquid to gas in the irradiation chamber is extremely low.

In recent years, with the notable exception of Schmitt and Dibble (2011), who developed an extensive chemical kinetic model only for the gas phase, the interest in finding a mathematical model for the irradiation of SO_2 and NO_x containing flue gases using electron beams has stagnated. Current efforts are focusing on reducing the energy consumption of the EBFGT by employing hybrid irradiation methods, using catalytic coupling for combined pollutant removal or by dispersing fine water droplets into the irradiation chamber (Calinescu et al., 2013). The results obtained using the latter technique show that intensification of the liquid phase chemical phenomena plays a beneficial role in the yield of the pollutants' removal, improving the method's overall energy efficiency. Thus, the mathematical modelling of EBFGT proposed in this paper, that takes into account the liquid aerosols, provides not only a better understanding of the process but also the means for reducing the energy requirements for the irradiation treatment.

1.1. General aspects

The frequency of the interactions between the electron beam and the components of the flue gas depends upon the mass fractions of the latter. These components undergo ionization, excitation and dissociation reactions due to irradiation; a series of highly reactive intermediates thus emerge. These reactive species (secondary electrons, ions, excited atoms and molecules, and free radicals) are responsible for the removal of SO_2 and NO_x, through a complex series of chemical and physical transformations.

1.2. Liquid phase phenomena

Due to the nucleation of H_2SO_4 in the presence of water vapours, a dispersed liquid phase is formed in which other gas components are absorbed, mainly SO_2, NH_3, hydroxyl and peroxyl radicals. It was experimentally proven by Li et al. (1998) that as SO_2 enters the liquid droplets it undergoes dissociation, being oxidized by the hydroxyl radicals through chain propagation reactions to hexavalent sulphur compounds.

2. Mathematical modelling

The present mathematical model improves our previous work (Gogulancea and Lavric, 2013), quantifying the main physico – chemical phenomena occurring in the irradiation chamber.

2.1. Irradiation

The concept of radiochemical yields, expressed as stoichiometric coefficients, describes the effect of the accelerated electrons collisions with the main components of the flue gas; e.g., the radiolysis equation for nitrogen reads (Gogulancea and Lavric, 2013):

$$4.14\,N_2 \rightarrow 0.885\,N^2D + 0.295\,N^2P + 1.87\,N^4P + 2.27\,N_2^+ + 0.69\,N^+ + 2.96\,e^- \qquad (1)$$

The liquid droplets are subject to irradiation too, with the same effects:

$$4.1\,H_2O \rightarrow 2.7OH + 0.6H + 0.45H_2 + 0.7\,H_2O_2 + 2.6\,H^+ + 2.6\,e^- \qquad (2)$$

2.2. Gas and liquid phase chemical reactions

The most complex kinetic model proposed for flue gas irradiation include over 200 chemical species contributing to more than 850 chemical reactions in the gas phase (Schmitt and Dibble, 2011). Our kinetics consider, for the gas phase, 100 chemical reactions and 53 ionic, molecular and radical species selected from different sources and assembled after rigorous testing. For the liquid phase, the kinetics of Li et al. (1998) was embedded in our model, which employs 20 chemical species and 35 chemical reactions.

2.3. Nucleation phenomena

The nucleation of H_2SO_4 was modelled using Eq. (3), where J_{nucl} is the nucleation rate, RH represents the relative humidity and $[H_2SO_4]_g$ is the sulfuric acid concentration in gas phase (Seinfeld et al., 1998).

$$J_{nucl} = \exp\left(7 - 64.24 - 4.7 \cdot RH + (6.13 + 1.95 \cdot RH)\log[H_2SO_4]_g\right) \quad (3)$$

2.4. Absorption in the liquid

The species absorbed in the liquid phase (SO_2, NH_3, HNO_3, HNO_2, OH•, HO_2•, O_3 and NO_3) reach thermodynamic equilibrium instantaneously and the partition between the gas and liquid phases can be described using Henry's law, taking into account the increase of the liquid volume caused by the absorption phenomena.

2.5. Reactor modelling

While the traditional approach assumes the irradiation chamber as a discontinuous (DC) perfectly mixed reactor, the new one considers the gas being in plug flow (PF) through the chamber. For the DC approach, the mass balance for a component i is written using Eq. (4), where N_i represents the number of molecules and D^* is the irradiation rate (the ratio between the absorbed dose D and the irradiation time τ).

$$N_i + \left(D^* \rho G_i X_i + \text{formation rate}\right)dt = N_i + dN_i + \text{decomposition rate} \cdot dt \quad (4)$$

X_i is the mass fraction of the species i and G_i is the corresponding radiochemical yield, while ρ represents the density of the gas phase, while the rates of formation and disappearance are associated with the chemical reactions involving the reactive species.

For the steady–state PF modelling approach, Eqs. (5) and (6) represent the mass balances, where the volume fraction of liquid (f_l) changes at every integration step.

$$\frac{dN_{Gi}}{(1-f_L) \cdot dV} = D_G^* \rho G_i X_i + \text{formation rate} - \text{decomposition rate} \quad (5)$$

$$\frac{dN_{Li}}{f_L \cdot dV} = D_L^* \rho G_i X_i + \text{formation rate} - \text{decomposition rate} \quad (6)$$

Both models result in a system of differential algebraic equations embedding mass and charge balances for the "in–situ" chemical species. The systems, stiff due to the multiple time–scales of the different physico-chemical processes, are solved with an in-house written routine based on Gear's method for stiff differential equations.

3. Results and discussion

The white experiment was conducted using the initial conditions and pollutant concentrations detailed in the paper of Chmielewski et al. (2000), who was in search for an empirical experimentally based model for the electron beam treatment's performance. The composition of the flue gas as well as the operating parameters are presented in Table 1; the flue gas mixtures were subjected to double stage irradiation.

The results of the simulation show that the removal efficiency for the sulfur dioxide is 95.7 % using the PF model and 96.1 % using the DC approach. The experimental value given for the SO_2 removal in the original work is 93.2 %, while the proposed empirical model gives a removal efficiency of 98.6 %.

Table 1. Initial conditions

Component	Concentration (volume)	Operating parameter	Value
Sulfur dioxide	383 ppm	Dose	10 kGy
Nitrogen oxide	127 ppm	Irradiation time	14.43 s
Oxygen	7.5 %	Humidity	12 %
Carbon dioxide	8 %	Temperature	58.6 °C
Nitrogen	Up to 100 %	Volume flow	4216 m³/h
Ammonia ratio	0.92	Pressure	1 atm

The concentration profile of SO_2, presented in Figure 1, reveals an exponential decrease in both the PF and DC cases, which is normal taking into account that formally, the performance of isothermal PF and DC are quite similar. The relatively high humidity percent promotes the formation of liquid droplets, which enhance the removal of SO_2. Moreover, the water in the vapour phase undergoes irradiation and generates hydroxyl radicals with a strong oxidative capacity, promoting the radio–chemical removal pathway for the pollutants. On the other hand, the reduced temperature of the process increases both the solubility of the gaseous compounds in the liquid and the rates for the $SO_2 - NH_3$ thermo–chemical reactions.

The small initial concentration of the NO and the humidity percent have a positive influence on the removal rate for nitrogen monoxide (see Figure 2). The irradiation dose has a high value that ensures successful removal of nitrogen monoxide and balances the detrimental effect of the reduced temperature. The removal efficiency of the nitrogen oxide is 81.3 % using the DC modelling approach and 79.8 % using the PF model. The experimental value for the removal efficiency is 77.9 %, while the empirical model developed predicts only 76.4 % efficiency.

The concentration profile of NO_2 is shown in Figure 3, behaving similarly for both the plug flow and the discontinuous model. With no initial nitrogen dioxide supplied, the pollutant is formed through the oxidation of nitrogen oxide and nitrogen in the presence of hydroxyl and peroxyl radicals. However, its concentration is one order of magnitude smaller than the concentration of NO as it is rapidly consumed in the reaction with water to form nitric acid.

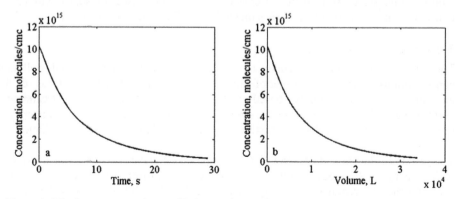

Figure 1. SO_2 time concentration profile in gas phase using a. DC and b. PF approaches

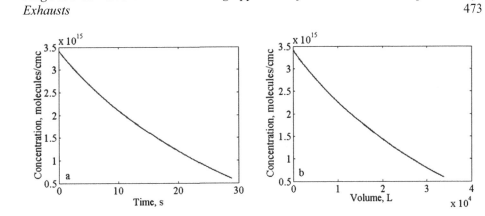

Figure 2. NO concentration profile in gas phase using a. DC and b.PF approaches

The profile of NO_2 shows a steep increase for the two-third of the irradiation treatment and then decreases as the NO is removed from the gas phase.

The profiles of sulfuric acid in the gas and droplets, as seen in Figure 4, are complementary. In the liquid phase, sulphuric acid is dissociated almost completely to form the bisulfate anion, which participates in the chain propagation reactions. Its concentration profile shows an exponential increase followed by a stagnation period as the nucleation rate approaches zero with decreasing sulfuric acid gas phase concentration.

4. Conclusions

The models proposed can predict in a consistent manner the overall efficiency of the electron beam treatment for exhausts, while the sulphur and nitrogen oxides concentrations follow the trends presented in literature in what regards the influence of the main operating parameters: irradiation dose, humidity content and temperature.

The simulation results are in very good agreement with the experimental data: the relative deviation for the DC model in the case of SO_2 is -3.1 % while for NO it gives -4.3 % compared to -5.8 % and 1.9 %, respectively, for the empirical model.

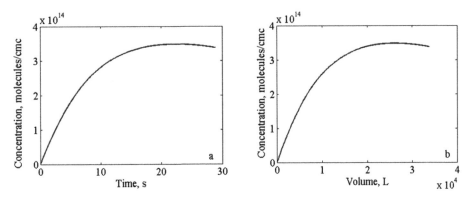

Figure 3. NO_2 concentration profile in gas phase using a. DC and b. PF approaches

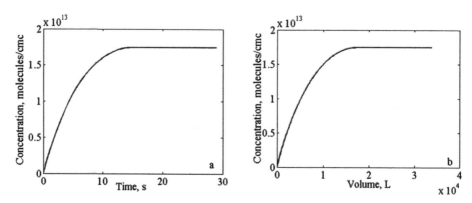

Figure 4. HSO_4^- concentration in liquid phase a. DC and b.PF approaches

The PF approach gives slightly better results compared with the DC model (relative deviation of -2.7 % and -2.4 %, respectively), being able to account for the volume variation occurring during the irradiation treatment. This approach, although utilized in modelling other plasma-based depollution techniques was, to the best of the authors' knowledge, for the first time successfully applied in connection with the EBFGT.

The novelty of our work originates in proposing a complex reaction model, comprising over 130 radio-chemical reactions, that takes into account the liquid phase phenomena in addition to the gas phase chemistry and implementing this model for discontinuous and plug flow configurations. The successful mathematical modelling of both gas and liquid phenomena occurring during irradiation provides an important aid to a wider market penetration of the EBFGT technology. Moreover, using for the first time the PF approach brings the mathematical model results closer to the experimental values and offers new possibilities for the optimization of the irradiation profiles and reactor configurations, resulting in an increase of the overall efficiency of the process.

References

I. Calinescu, D. Martin, A. Chmielewski, D. Ighigeanu, 2013, E-Beam SO2 and NOx removal from flue gases in the presence of fine water droplets, Radiation Physics and Chemistry, 85, 130-138.

A. G. Chmielewski, B. Tyminski, A. Dobrowolski, E. Iller, Z. Zimek, J. Licki, 2000, Empirical models for NO_x and SO_2 removal in a double stage flue gas irradiation process, Radiation Physics and Chemistry, 57, 527-530.

V. Gogulancea, V. Lavric, 2013, Flue gas cleaning by high energy electron beam – enhancement effects due to water droplets generation, Chemical Engineering Transactions, 35, 697-702.

R. N. Li, K. P. Yan, J. S. Miao, X. L. Wu, 1998, Heterogeneous reactions in non-thermal plasma flue gas desulfurization, Chemical Engineering Science, 53, 1529-1540.

H. Matzing, 1991, Chemical Kinetics of Flue Gas Cleaning by Irradiation with Electrons, Advances in Chemical Physics Volume LXXX, John Wiley & Sons, Inc., Hoboken, NJ, USA, 315-402.

K. L. Schmitt, T. S. Dibble, 2011, Understanding OH Yields in Electron Beam Irradiation of Humid N2, Plasma Chemistry and Plasma Processing, 31, 41-50.

J. H. Seinfeld, F. W. Lurmann, P. M. Roth, 1998, Grid - based aerosol modeling: A tutorial. In: ENVAIR, ed., San Joaquin Valley Air Quality Study, Fresno, CA, USA.

J. Zhang, J. Sun, Y. Gong, D. Wang, T. Ma, Y. Liu, 2009, A scheme for solving strongly coupled chemical reaction equations appearing in the removal of SO2 and NOx from flue gases, Vacuum, 83, 133-137.

Jiří Jaromír Klemeš, Petar Sabev Varbanov and Peng Yen Liew (Editors)
Proceedings of the 24th European Symposium on Computer Aided Process Engineering – ESCAPE 24
June 15-18, 2014, Budapest, Hungary. Copyright © 2014 Elsevier B.V. All rights reserved.

Application of Pricing Policies for Coordinated Management of Supply Chains

Kefah Hjaila, Miguel Zamarripa, Ahmed Shokry, Antonio Espuña*

Chemical Engineering Department, Universitat Politècnica de Catalunya, ETSEIB, Diagonal Avenue 647, 08028 Barcelona, Spain.
antonio.espuna@upc.edu

Abstract

An optimization approach is proposed to coordinate multi-site multi-product SC networks taking into account the cooperation between suppliers and production/ distribution SCs. For this purpose, all the interacting entities are integrated into the optimization model as full SCs, so any production/distribution echelon/SC can work as supplier for any other echelon/SC and so on. Financial issues based on price elasticity of demand, usually considered in these models just at the final SC echelon (end product), are incorporated in the proposed model at all interacting levels, so cost is subject to the trade-off between the price and the quantity demanded. Different approximations to model this demand elasticity have been tested, and the resulting NLP/MINLP models have been applied to a case study where the coordination of service (energy generation) SCs and production/distribution SCs is proposed. The results prove that pricing policies management add to PSE an additional instrument towards improving decision making.

Keywords: coordinated management, SC planning, pricing, demand elasticity.

1. Introduction

Coordinated Supply Chain Management (SCM) has been studied in the last years with different perspectives. One of them intends to integrate different decision making levels within a single SC, as in the works of Varma et al. (2007), who proposed enterprise-wide cross-functional coordination approach integrating both strategic and tactical processes, or Cóccola et al. (2013), who studied the integration between production and distribution models for multi-echelon SCs. Coordinated management also appears when different SCs are expected to work together, being one of the most studied situations such appearing in closed loop SCs, where the coordination between forward and reverse channels is required (Zeballos et al., 2012). In the general case, although typical planning models contemplate information and material flows in multiple directions (information from customers to suppliers and material from suppliers to customers), the detailed behaviour of third parties participating in the resources and information flows of the SC of interest is usually neglected. Consequently, each entity within the global SC network seeks to pursue its own objective, disregarding the impact of the external entities on its decisions and vice versa, leading to sub-optimal decisions.

In this context, economic issues are usually considered as the main driving force for decision making and, since demand is a price sensitive variable (Viswanathan and Wang, 2003), it is clear that an adequate pricing policy is determinant for a proper decision making: Using price discounts may lead to higher demands which, in turn, will probably allow to negotiate lower raw material prices and thus higher profits for the SC.

But so far, only few PSE literature models consider demand elasticity and price discounts: Weng (1995a) started to use the demand elasticity as a cost reduction methodology to provide decisions for a single buyer SC; Shapiro (2004) extended the model to include revenue functions based on price elasticity; Iida (2012) studied the effect of the production cost reduction in a decentralized SC with one production plant and multiple suppliers; or Liu et al. (2012) proposed a MILP planning model for multiproduct SC considering price fluctuations based on demand elasticity. But the aforementioned literature only considers price variations at the final markets, disregarding the pricing behaviour of raw/intermediate materials; so much information is lost affecting the efficiency of the global tactical decisions.

This work aims to provide a robust decision making tool able to integrate the information of the resource flows as full SCs within the global SC network based on different pricing policies (fixed, piecewise, and polynomial). The resulted coordinated optimization NLP/MINLP models are solved to find the optimal discount pricing policy that provides the best planning decisions of the coordinated SC network comply with the global objective function (minimize total cost).

2. Problem statement

2.1 SC coordinated management

A general coordinated SC is characterized as composed by several multi-site multi-product SC networks. These SCs receive, transform, store and deliver resources from/to other entities belonging to its organization (same SC) or to third party's entities (external SCs: resource suppliers, clients, waste & recovery systems, etc.). The planning model incorporates all information of the global SC, including the third parties SC's.

2.2 Mathematical model

The general SC coordination problem has been formulated as a NLP model following the planning model described by Zamarripa et al. (2013), which has been modified for this purpose: a set of SCs (s= 1, 2, ..., SC) and their new subsets linking the entities (suppliers, plants, markets, etc.) to their corresponding SCs have been considered along the generated model. Within the coordinated management, any echelon/SC can act as internal market for other echelons SCs. Eq. (1) represents the coordination where the internal demand $Dmi_{r',e,t}$ is calculated as a function of production levels *PRD*.

$$Dmi_{r',e,t} = \sum_{\substack{r \in R \\ r \neq r'}} prf_{r,r',e} \cdot PRD_{r',e,t} \qquad \forall\, r' \in R;\, e \in E;\, t \in T \qquad (1)$$

Where, *prf* is a production factor which depends on the resources required by the utilized recipe; *E* is the set of echelons, and *R* is the set of resources produced and demanded internally or externally (intermediate/final products). The total external demand (*dmd*) may be satisfied from any of the echelons/SCs as stated by Eq. (2), where M represents the external markets,

$$\sum_{\substack{e \in E \\ e \neq e'}} DLV_{r,e,e',t} \geq dmd_{r,e',t} \qquad \forall\, e' \in M;\, r \in R;\, t \in T \qquad (2)$$

The objective function Eq. (3) used in this study corresponds to the minimization of the total cost of the entire SC along the considered planning horizon *T* (external resources purchase, transport, storage, and production total cost, respectively).

$$Cost = \sum_{t \in T}(CRM_t + CTRtr_t + CST_t + TCpr_t) \qquad (3)$$

The external resources acquisition cost (*CRM*) is calculated as function of the quantity demanded (*DLV*) and price (*val*), Eq. (4), which depends on the selected pricing model.

$$CRM_t = \sum_{r \in R} \sum_{e \in N}(val_{r,e,t} \cdot DLV_{r,e,t}) \quad \forall \ t \in T \tag{4}$$

2.3 Pricing models

Three pricing models (fixed, piecewise, and polynomial) have been considered as alternatives to adjust the resource prices depending on the supplied quantities, and incorporated to a general coordinated optimization model:

i) *Fixed price vs. demand:* $val_{r,e,t}$ = a fixed cost is assumed, regardless the demand.

ii) *Polynomial price vs. demand:* Based on the information on the price elasticity of the demand, a polynomial trend is adjusted (Figure 1) and the resource price is calculated as in Eq. (5)

$$val_{r,e,t} = a \cdot \left(DLV_{r,e,t}\right)^4 + b \cdot (DLV_{r,e,t})^3 + c \cdot (DLV_{r,e,t})^2 + d \cdot DLV_{r,e,t} + f \tag{5}$$

$$\forall \ r \in R; e \in N; t \in T$$

Where: *a, b, c, d, f* are constants; *N* corresponds to the set of external suppliers.

iii) *Piecewise price vs. demand:* Three resource pricing possibilities are offered by the supplier: initial price (val_{in}), elastic price ($val_{r,e,t}$), and minimum price (val_{min}), depending on the quantity demanded each time period, as illustrated in Figure 2.

In this later case, the price elasticity coefficient (*PE*) is considered constant (Eq. 6). When the resource demand is whithin the DLV_2 interval (Figure 2), *val* is calculated as in Eq.(7); otherwise, it is equal constant as in the fixed price case. In order to allocate the resource to its pricing interval (*DLV1/DLV2/DLV3*), binary variables are introduced in the developed MINLP model.

$$PE = \frac{\% \ \Delta DLV}{\% \ \Delta val} \tag{6}$$

$$val_{r,e,t} = val_{in(r,e,t)}\left(\frac{DLV_{r,e,t} - DLVin_{r,e,t}}{PE \cdot DLVin_{r,e,t}} + 1\right) \quad \forall \ r \in R; e \in N; t \in T \tag{7}$$

In all cases, the model has been solved to minimize the cost of the global system, so decisions are to be taken at each time node such as resource purchase levels and prices, inventory levels, production levels, distribution levels, transportation flows and directions, etc.

3. Case study

The resulting NLP/MINLP models have been solved for a case study (Figure 3) modified from the one proposed by Zamarripa et al. (2013). The entire SC network

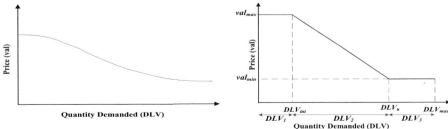

Figure 1. Polynomial price vs. demand   Figure 2. Piecewise price vs. demand

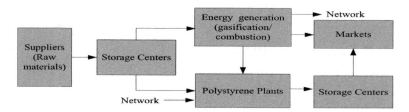

Figure 3. The Entire SC network

integrates an energy generation SC (EGSC) and a polystyrene production/distribution SC (PDSC). One supplier of wood pellets, petcock, marc waste, and coal feeds 6 energy plants (*P1,P2,…,P6*). Four raw material suppliers provide the PDSC plants (*pl1,pl2,pl3*) with alternative resources (*rm1,rm2,rm3,rm4*) in order to produce two products: *ps1*, and *ps2*. The final products are stored in (*dc1, dc2*) and later distributed to the final polystyrene markets (*mk1, mk2,mk3*).

4. Results

The results show how the planning decisions are affected by the quality of the pricing policy modeling. For example, Figure 4 shows how *rm1* and *rm2* dominate the purchase levels in the fixed pricing scenario, while *rm2* and *rm4* dominate in the piecewise and polynomial scenarios. The trend was to buy high amounts of *rm2* and *rm4* at the minimum price to gain the highest discount and then to store these amounts to be used later for polystyrene production; that's why the polynomial model leads to the highest inventory levels (Figure 5). It is also worth to note that the total quantity purchased by the PDSC is the same in all pricing scenarios (5,522 Tons), but the total cost is different, in favor of the decisions made using the polynomial model (Figure 5). As a result, the polynomial model allows improving the entire SC total cost by 8.06 % and 0.24 % when compared with the use of fixed and piecewise pricing models (Table 1).

Due to the high number of binary variables in the piecewise scenario, some heuristics have been proposed to accelerate the computing process by fixing the binary variables and solving the relaxed problem (Table 2). Iteration 3 has been the one considered in the analysis, as it shows the lowest cost along the different iterations.

Figure 6 shows the economic breakdown of the planning decisions for all pricing policies. In order to satisfy the same market demand, the fixed pricing model leads to the most expensive decision making as its management does not take into account the benefits associated to the demand/price elasticity. Some additional savings in the total cost of the purchased resources (k€ 39.27) are also found using the polynomial approach in comparison with the piecewise approach.

Table 1. Economic Summary

	Fixed price	Polynomial	Piecewise
EGSC Cost (M€)	6.89	6.82	6.82
PDSC Cost (M€)	10.79	9.44	9.48
Total Cost (M€)	17.68	16.26	16.30
Sales (M€)	29.76	29.76	29.76
Total Profit (M€)	12.07	13.50	13.46

Table 2. Piecewise results – iterative process

Total SC Cost (k€)					
Iteration 0	Iteration 1	Iteration 2	Iteration 3	Iteration 4	Iteration 5
16,522	16,644	17,404	16,299	16,608	16,721

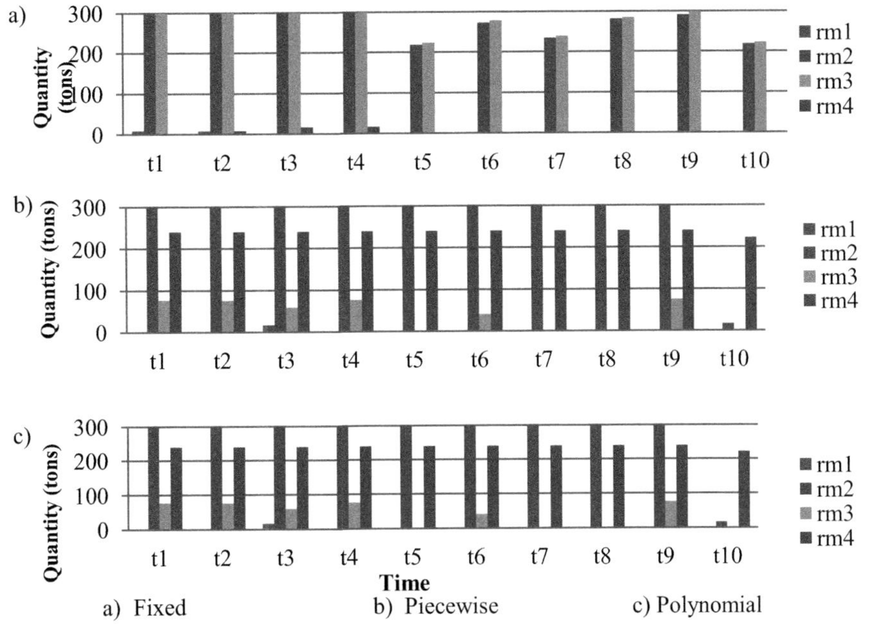

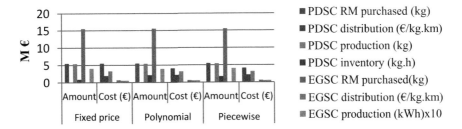

a) Fixed   b) Piecewise   c) Polynomial

Figure 4. PDSC resource purchase levels

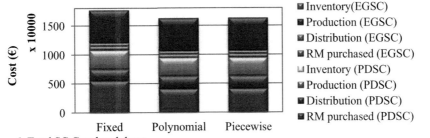

Figure 5. The entire SC decision profiles

Figure 6. Total SC Cost breakdown

5. Conclusions

The price elasticity theory has been considered in the frame of a coordinated optimization model built to integrate a set of multi-site multi-product SCs within an entire/global SC network. Different approaches (fixed, pricewise, and polynomial) of a certain pricing policy have been proposed, leading to multiple model implementations, which have been used to determine the decisions which minimize the resulting global SC cost required to fulfill the same external requirements. The results show that the pricing approximation used significantly affects the planning decisions and the economic behavior of the whole system. To achieve the same market demand, the same total amounts of RM are proposed to be purchased, but with different time patterns, resulting in different economic performance. The trade-off between the inventory and the RM purchasing cost drives the producer to buy different amounts at different prices and to store different quantities for the later productions. The best approximation to the real pricing policy (polynomial approach) allows to identify better solutions, leading to significant cost improvements (in the presented case study, more than 8 % in terms of total cost, compared with the fixed pricing model) although its use may require much larger computational effort. From another perspective, these results indicate that coordination management may be used to identify appropriate pricing policies to give suppliers enough freedom to participate and control their financial flows and thus to compete in a global market; in this sense, integrating the resources information flows is a good start towards a global resource management.

Acknowledgements

Financial support received from the "Agència de Gestió d'Ajuts Universitaris i de Recerca AGAUR", and the Spanish "Ministerio de Economía y Competitividad" and the European Regional Development Fund, both funding the SIGERA research project (DPI2012-37154-C02-01) are fully appreciated.

References

J.D. Gwartney, R.L. Stroup, R.S. Sobel, D. MacPherson, 2012, Economics: Private and Public Choice, Cengage Learning Custom Publishing, Mason, USA.

L.J. Zeballos, M.I. Gomes, A.P. Barbosa-Povoa, A.Q. Novais, 2012, Addressing the uncertain quality and quantity of returns in closed-loop supply chains, Comput. Chem.Eng.,47,237–247.

M. Cóccola, M. Zamarripa, C.A. Méndez, A. Espuña, 2013, Toward integrated production and distribution management in multi-echelon supply chains, Comp. and Chem. Eng., 15, 78–94.

M. Zamarripa, K. Hjaila, J. Silvente, A. Espuña, 2013, Simplified model for integrated Supply Chains Planning, Computer Aided Chemical Engineering, 32, 547-552.

S. Liu, N. Shah, L.G. Papageorgiou, 2012, Multiechelon Supply Chain Planning with Sequence-Dependent Changeovers and Price Elasticity of Demand under Uncertainty, American Institute of Chemical Engineers (AIChE) J., 58, 11, 3390–3403.

S. Viswanathan, Q. Wang, 2003, Discount pricing decisions in distribution channels with price-sensitive demand, European J. of Operational Research, 149, 3, 571–587.

T. Iida, 2012, Coordination of cooperative cost-reduction efforts in a supply chain partnership, European J. of Operational Research, 222, 180–190.

V.A.Varma, G.V. Reklaitis, G.E. Blau, J.F. Pekny, 2007, Enterprise-wide modelling and optimization—An overview of emerging research challenges and opportunities, Computers and Chemical Engineering, 31, 692–711.

Jiří Jaromír Klemeš, Petar Sabev Varbanov and Peng Yen Liew (Editors)
Proceedings of the 24th European Symposium on Computer Aided Process Engineering – ESCAPE 24
June 15-18, 2014, Budapest, Hungary. Copyright © 2014 Elsevier B.V. All rights reserved.

Energy from Lignocellulosic Biomass: Supply Chain Modeling to Maximize Net Energy Production

Helena Paulo[a,b*], Ana Paula F.D. Barbosa-Póvoa[a], Susana Relvas[a]

[a]CEG-IST, Instituto Superior Técnico, Universidade de Lisboa, Av. Rovisco Pais, 1049-001, Lisboa, Portugal
[b]ISEL, IPL, Rua Conselheiro Emídio Navarro, 1959-007 Lisboa, Portugal
hpaulo@deq.isel.ipl.pt

Abstract

Renewable energy systems are complex systems where the high energy expenditure in all supply chain stages strongly affects the overall system performance. In this paper supply chain design is explored in order to maximize the global net energy of the system emphasising the increased energy efficiency required to attain viable economic and environmental solutions in renewable energy production. A mixed integer linear programming (MILP) model is developed for the optimal design with the objective of minimizing supply chain total energy input. The model is applied to a real world case study in Portugal. The results show that to satisfy a global demand of 2.95 PJ of electricity and 1.55 PJ of bioethanol for fuel purposes, 2.68 PJ are required as energy input to perform all supply chain operations.

Keywords: Supply Chain, MILP model, Design, Net energy.

1. Introduction

Lignocellulosic biomass for energy production has attracted an increased interest in recent years. Work has been performed, namely research on scientific and technological areas in order to develop efficient industrial processes that can produce energy in one of its final forms (electricity, heat or fuels) through biomass conversion (Faaij, 2006). However, despite the recognized benefits on the use of renewable sources for energy production, some questions concerning economic, environmental and social issues related with renewable energy are still under debate. One of them is related to the need of developing significant contributions on the design of effective renewable energy supply chains. The cost and the complexity of the logistic operations of these systems have been studied by several authors. Gold and Seuring (2011) provide a review paper where the main contributions are described. Current literature mainly focuses on i) cost minimization/profit maximization, or environmental aspects regarding greenhouse gas emissions minimization and on ii) the supply chain design for a single energetic product from biomass. Dunnett et al. (2007) provides the design and operational scheduling in the biomass to heat supply chain, using a state-task-network approach. The design of a biomass based supply chain for electricity generation using a MILP approach is presented by Pérez-Fortes et al. (2012). Concerning biofuel production the optimal design and planning of a biofuel supply chains was analyzed by You (2013). Energy inputs and outputs from a biomass biorefinery are presented by Zhu and Zhuang (2012) based on published literature data to evaluate the process performance. To the best of our knowledge, none of the existing work has taken into account the maximization of net energy production on the supply chain design, which consists in our goal.

Biomass to energy supply chain encompasses a large portfolio of decisions to be made under the scope of strategic decisions. The highly geographic dispersion, the low bulk density and seasonality of biomass supply introduces increased complexity to the system, as well as the different alternatives regarding the establishment of intermediate biomass storage units and the large portfolio of technologies available for energy production. To address these issues, it is requested the development of customized supply chain designs. The present work explores possible alternatives in each supply chain node in order to establish an efficient supply chain. Knowing in advance that considerable energy consumption exists in each one of the operations the supply chain design is performed in order to maximize the net energy output.

A MILP model is developed to identify the supply chain best configuration regarding the maximization of net energy production satisfying the total demand of energy products, in order to establish the most energy efficient supply chain. The model handles the supply chain critical factors to create an adequate logistics of supply, with the capacity of dealing with several sources of residual lignocellulosic biomass, with different compositions, characteristics and highly geographically dispersed. It also deals with the capability of defining more centralized or decentralized structures using intermediate units for biomass storage. Regarding biomass storage locations, pre-processing technologies can be included in order to reduce biomass deterioration, improve the performance of transport operations and convert biomass into more useful forms that can assure appropriate conditions for biomass processing. A wide variety of technologies are available for energy production from biomass. The model identifies the best technology to install in order to satisfy the market demand for energy. Lastly, all the transportation operations required to move the material between the supply chains nodes are considered. A sensitivity analysis is performed on the most uncertain parameters as: required energy for biomass collection, transportation and handling. The applicability of the model is demonstrated with a Portuguese case study where residual lignocellulosic biomass is used to produce electricity and liquid fuels.

2. Problem statement and model formulation

The problem addressed in this work is defined as follows: Given are a set of sources of the biomass feedstock, a set of energy products, a set of available locations to install the storage units and the facilities to energy production and a set of transportation modes to biomass and to products transportation. The problem aims at determining the optimal supply chain configuration to yield the solution with the maximum total net energy production. The total net energy production is attained considering the difference between output energy (electricity, fuel and heat) and the energy input required in all stages of the biomass to energy supply chain. The energy input required reflects the energy input for biomass collection, biomass transport, biomass processing into energy products and for the products transport to the markets. The supply of feedstock is limited per location and the products' demand is to be satisfied.

The problem for the optimal design of the biomass based supply chain to energy production is formulated as a MILP model. The notation used in the formulation is as follows. Sets/indices: B set of biomass types, P set of products, I set of biomass source sites, J set of storage sites, K set of potential candidates to facility location, V set of markets, C set of storage facilities capacities, Q set of energy facility capacities, N set of preprocessing technologies available to include on storage units, R set of transportation modes for biomass and S transportation modes for produced products. A subset $MP=\{(m,p):m \in M \wedge p \in P\}$ as each technology is related to a type of product and $PT=\{(s,p):s \in S \wedge p \in P\}$ as each product is related with a specific transport mode. Parameters: BA_{bit} the amount of available biomass, $EIBC_b$ the energy input required for biomass collection, $EIBS_n$ energy input required to biomass storage, $EIBT1_r$ the energy input to transport wet and bulk biomass, $EIPT2_r$ the energy input to transport dense and dry biomass, $EIPP_m$ the energy input for biomass processing into energy products, $EIPT_{ps}$ the energy input for products transport, EIS_{nc} the energy input related with a storage unit installation, EIF_{mq} the energy input of an energy production facility installation, DIK_{ik}, DIJ_{ij}, DJK_{jk}, DKV_{kv} are the distances between locations reflected by the indices, CB_n the conversion factor in storage, CF_{mp} the conversion factor in energy facility, SC_{nc} the storage facility, FPC_{mq} is the energy production facility capacity and D_{pvt} is the maximum demand of product p in the market v at time t. Non-negative variables: B_{bit}^C the collected biomass b from location i at time t, X_{bikrt}^A, X_{bijrt}^B, X_{bjkrt}^C the biomass flow b using transport mode r at time t from de locations reflected by the indices i, j, k, U_{bjcnt}^S the biomass type b at storage location j with capacity c, pre-processing technology n at time t, U_{bkqmt}^B the biomass b consumed at energy facility k with capacity q and processing technology mat time t, S_{bjt} the stock level of biomass type b at location j at time t, X_{pkvst}^P amount of product p produced at energy facility k for market v using transport mode s at time t. Binary variables: Y_{kqm} equals 1 if an energy facility is located in k with capacity q and technology m and Y_{jcn}^S equals 1 if a storage unit is located in j with capacity c and pre-processing technology n. Taking into account the above sets, parameters and variables, the model is formulated below:

$$\text{MIN} \quad \sum_b \sum_i \sum_t B_{bit}^C \, EIBC_b + \sum_b \sum_j \sum_c \sum_n \sum_t U_{bjcnt}^S \, EIBS_n + \tag{1}$$

$$\sum_b \sum_i \sum_j \sum_r \sum_t X_{bijrt}^B \, EIBT1_r \, DIJ_{ij} + \sum_b \sum_j \sum_k \sum_r \sum_t X_{bjkrt}^C \, EIBT2_r \, DJK_{jk} +$$

$$\sum_b \sum_i \sum_k \sum_r \sum_t X_{bikrt}^A \, EIBT1_r \, DIK_{ik} + \sum_b \sum_k \sum_q \sum_m \sum_t U_{bkqmt}^B EIPP_m +$$

$$\sum_p \sum_k \sum_v \sum_s \sum_t X_{pkvst}^P DKV_{kv} EIPT_{ps} + \sum_j \sum_c \sum_n Y_{jcn}^S \, EIS_{nc} + \sum_k \sum_q \sum_m Y_{kqm} EIF_{mq}$$

Subject to:

$$B_{bit}^C \le BA_{bit} \quad \forall b \in B, \forall i \in I, \forall t \in T \tag{2}$$

$$B_{bit}^C = \sum_j \sum_r X_{bijrt}^B + \sum_k \sum_r X_{bikrt}^A \quad \forall b \in B, \forall i \in I, \forall t \in T \tag{3}$$

$$S_{bjt} + \sum_c \sum_n U_{bjcnt}^S = (S_{bjt})|_{t=1}; (ISL_{bjt-1})|_{t>1} + \sum_i \sum_r X_{bijrt}^B \quad \forall b \in B \; \forall j \in J, \forall t \in T \tag{4}$$

$$\sum_b \sum_c \sum_n U_{bjcnt}^S CB_n = \sum_b \sum_k \sum_r X_{bjkrt}^C \quad \forall j \in J, \forall t \in T \tag{5}$$

$$\sum_i \sum_r X_{bikrt}^A + \sum_j \sum_r X_{bjkrt}^C = \sum_m \sum_q U_{bkqmt}^B \quad \forall b \in B, \forall k \in K, \forall t \in T \tag{6}$$

$$\sum_b \sum_{m:(m,p) \in MP} CF_{mp} \, U_{bkqmt}^B = \sum_v \sum_{s:(s,p) \in SP} X_{pkvst}^P \quad \forall p \in P, \forall k \in K, \forall t \in T \tag{7}$$

$$\sum_k \sum_{s:(s,p) \in SP} X_{pkvst}^P = D_{pvt} \quad \forall p \in P, \forall v \in V, \forall t \in T \tag{8}$$

$$\sum_{c}\sum_{n} Y_{jcn}^{S} \leq 1 \quad \forall j \in J \tag{9}$$

$$\sum_{b} U_{bjcnt}^{S} \leq SC_{nc} \, Y_{jcn}^{S} \qquad \forall j \in J, \forall c \in C, \forall n \in N, \forall t \in T \tag{10}$$

$$\sum_{q}\sum_{m} Y_{kqm} \leq 1 \qquad \forall k \in K \tag{11}$$

$$\sum_{b} U_{bkqmt}^{B} \leq FPC_{mq} \, Y_{kqm} \qquad \forall k \in K, \forall q \in Q, \forall m \in M, \forall t \in T \tag{12}$$

$$B_{bit}^{C}, X_{bikrt}^{A}, X_{bijrt}^{B}, X_{bjkrt}^{c}, U_{bjcnt}^{S}, U_{bkqmt}^{B}, X_{pkvst}^{P} \geq 0 \tag{13}$$

$$Y_{kqm}, Y_{jcn}^{S} \in \{0,1\} \tag{14}$$

The objective is the minimization of the total energy input for all supply chain operations which consists of the energy input for biomass collection, biomass transport, storage and pre-processing operations, for biomass processing into biofuel, electricity and heat and energy input required for products transport to the market. The objective function, Eq.(1), is minimized subject to the material balance on each node of the supply chain. Eqs.(3), (4) and (6) define the mass balance on biomass collection site, on storage site and on energy production facility, respectively. Eq.(2) assures that collected biomass does not exceed the available biomass in each site. On Eq.(5) the biomass that arrives at a storage facility with pre-processing operation multiplied by the conversion factor equals to the pre-processed biomass transported to the energy production facility. Eq.(7) sets that the total amount of each product produced will be equal to biomass used to produce it multiplied by the conversion factor. The demand of each product on each market that must be satisfied is defined on Eq.(8). Only one storage facility with pre-processing technology n and capacity c can be open in each location as defined in Eq.(9) and the amount of biomass processed cannot surpass its capacity in Eq.(10). Only one processing facility with technology m and capacity q can open in each location and the amount of biomass processed cannot surpass its capacity is defined in Eqs.(11) and (12) respectively. Eqs.(13) and (14) define the domain of the model variables.

3. Case study and results

The described model has been applied to a case study to electricity generation and to cellulosic ethanol production in Portugal. Given that 38 % of Portuguese territory is covered by forest, producing at least 3.5 Mton of residual forestry on a yearly basis, forest residues are considered as feedstock resource. Availability of forest residues at the 278 Portuguese municipalities is identified and these are potential candidates to biomass supply. The same 278 municipalities are potential candidates to storage units and energy production facilities location. Different alternatives can be considered to technological transformation of biomass into electricity, fuel and heat. Mature technologies with reasonably high yields are chosen. For lignocellulosics ethanol production, hydrolysis and fermentation conversion technology with dilute acid pre-treatment process are selected for the case study. For electricity generation from biomass, combustion direct-firing is used. Given that the heat production for commercial use through district heating is not used in Portugal and the use of heat for industrial purpose is not known this product is not considered. Regarding storage facilities, particle size reduction and drying are the available technologies to transform biomass into more useful form to transport and processing operations. The demand for each product is estimated in order to satisfy the targets imposed by the government for energy production from renewable sources, namely from biomass. 100 MWe of electricity are still needed to install to attain the 250 MWe of bio-electric capacity. The target for ethanol production has been settled to 57,567 t by 2016. That is roughly 2.95 PJ of electricity and 1.55 PJ of ethanol. The capitals of the 18 Portugal regions are defined as representing the demand points. The demand is estimated based on population density. Despite the presence of railroad infrastructure the lack of data regarding energy issues lead to a train option dropdown and only truck is considered. The model has been implemented using GAMS version 24.0, and solved using CPLEX 12.5.0.0. An Intel Core i5, 2.4 GHz and 4.0 GB of RAM was used to run the model. The problem formulation resulted in 247,977 variables (2,780 binary) with 5,319 constraints. A MILP gap tolerance of 0.02 % was obtained in 2,293 CPU seconds. For this case study, the results show a net energy balance of 1.82 PJ. That means, for the production of the 4.5 PJ are required as energy input 2.68 PJ of energy to accomplish all supply chain operations. Storage and pre-processing technologies were not selected, 42 small capacity production facilities (2 and 5 MW) are installed in order to satisfy the electricity demand and 2 bioethanol production facilities of 50 ML capacity to satisfy the bioethanol demand. Electricity production is, therefore, a more decentralized network due to the high energy consumption for biomass transport when compared to electricity transport, associated with the high geographic dispersion of biomass and the low energy input to install a small electricity production facility. Energy input breakdown is presented on Figure 1. As can be seen, energy input to biomass processing into energy product represents the largest contribution to the global supply chain energy input. In order to improve energy efficiency, it is necessary to continue with the efforts that have been developed to improve the performance of conversion processes. While technology improvement is focus of many researchers, the facility itself it also should be designed for better energy efficiency given that also represents heavy energy expenditure. Biomass collection operations have a significant impact on overall process efficiency.

Having established the case base scenario for energy inputs to all supply chain operations, a sensitivity analysis was undertaken to investigate how changes in energy input parameters affect the net energy produced as well as the supply chain structure. Taking into account that improvements are expected on the energy efficiency as a result of all research involvement, the variations on the parameters reflect the expected reduction of energy input in all supply chain operation. So, variations of -15 %, -10 % and -5 % on energy input for biomass collection (EIBC), biomass processing (EIP) and production facility installation (EIF) were performed. The results of the sensitivity analysis to energy input parameters are illustrated in Figure 2. As expected when energy input decreases the net energy input will increase. However, taking for example the analysis for the 15 % reduction on energy input, larger achievements are obtained when the reduction respect on energy input for biomass processing, with the increase of 13 %

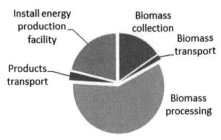

Figure 1. Energy Input Breakdown

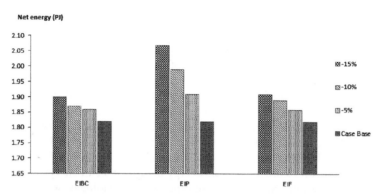

Figure 2. Sensitivity Analysis Results

for the supply chain net energy. For all cases the supply chain does not suffer major changes. Slight changes are found on the number of electricity production facilities, except for the case of the reduction on the energy input for biomass transportation where only 36 facilities for electricity production are installed.

4. Conclusions

This paper presents a MILP model for the optimal design of biomass to energy supply chains. The model is able to determine storage and energy facility locations as well as production technologies to install in each location, flows of biomass and energy products, transportation modes for biomass and for products to determine de maximum net energy production. Case study results illustrate that a positive balance of energy production can be attained, by installing decentralized supply chains as well as the need to achieve more efficient processing technologies for biomass processing into energy products. Sensitivity analyses demonstrate the importance of production processes energy input to attain more effective biomass based to energy supply chains. Being the example solved as a first attempt to solve such problem, some data assumptions had to be made. These should be further analyzed so as to get closer to the optimal solution, concerning net energy, as much as possible. Also as a future work it would be interesting to investigate the result of the proposed model applied to cost minimization objective and even building a trade-off curve for decision support.

References

A. Dunnett, C. Adjiman, N. Shah, 2007, Biomass to heat supply chains applications of process optimization, Process Safety and Environmental Protection, 85, 419-429.

A. P. C. Faaij, 2006, Bio-energy in Europe: changing technology choices, Energy Policy, 34, 322-342.

S. Gold, S. Seuring, 2011, Supply chain and logistics issues of bio-energy production, Journal of Cleaner Production, 19, 32-42.

M. Pérez-Fortes, J. M. Laínez-Aguirre, P. Arranz-Piera, E. Velo, L. Puigjaner, 2012, Design of regional and sustainable bio-based networks for electricity generation using a multi-objective MILP approach, Energy, 44, 79-95.

F. You, 2013, Design of Biofuel Supply Chains under Uncertainty with Multiobjective Stochastic Programming Models and Decomposition Algorithm, Computer Aided Chemical Engineering, 32, 493-498.

J. Y. Zhu, X. S. Zhuang, 2012, Conceptual net energy output for biofuel production from lignocellulosic biomass through biorefining, Progress in Energy and Combustion Science, 38, 583-598.

Jiří Jaromír Klemeš, Petar Sabev Varbanov and Peng Yen Liew (Editors)
Proceedings of the 24th European Symposium on Computer Aided Process Engineering – ESCAPE 24
June 15-18, 2014, Budapest, Hungary. Copyright © 2014 Elsevier B.V. All rights reserved.

SPIonWEB – Ecological Process Evaluation with the Sustainable Process Index (SPI)

Khurram Shahzad *, René Kollmann, Stephan Maier, Michael Narodoslawsky

Institute for Process and Particle Engineering, Graz University of Technology, Inffeldgasse13/3, A-8010 Graz/Austria
k.shahzad@tugraz.at

Abstract

Chemical engineers however need quick and reliable cradle-to-grave evaluations, conforming to the ISO norm 14040, already at the design stage in order to assess the ecological performance of their design compared to design alternatives as well as to identify ecological hot spots in order to decrease the ecological impact of the process in question.

The Sustainable Process Index methodology has been particularly developed for this purpose and has been widely applied to the measurement of the ecological performance in production systems. Ecological performance is expressed in aggregate form as Ecological Footprint per service unit, thus allowing the engineer to take decisions. De-aggregation into different environmental pressure categories that this methodology allows as well helps the engineer to understand, what causes the engineer to pinpoint the process steps that are critical to the overall performance of the ecological pressure in a certain process step. For the modelling of these problems the software tool SPIonExcel has been in use in the last decade.

SPIonWeb is a web browser based software tool substituting SPIonExcel, which allows to model industrial processes on a thoroughly revised data base and a still more encompassing methodological base. Basic processes like electricity, transport, base chemical production chains are provided in a life cycle based database. Dynamic modelling allows creating process loops which allows simulating changes in the final product ecological performance if sub-process modification are assumed. Besides the Ecological Footprint (calculated with the SPI method) the program also features process visualization, detailed material balance for inputs and emissions, CO_2 and GWP life cycle emissions.

The paper provides examples of ecological process evaluation for different chemical engineering applications, in particular processes providing energy from different renewable sources and bio-chemical processes, e-g. bio-plastic production. Analysing these thoroughly different process chains will be used to highlight the information that can be gleaned from ecological process evaluation during chemical engineering design.

Keywords: Ecological Footprint, Ecological Performance, Sustainable Process Index on Web, Dynamic Lifecycle Impact Assessment

1. Introduction

A wide variety of assessments methods are available, depending on the goal and context of the studies (Mayer, 2008). The ultimate need to measure the pressure exerted by humanity on the environment required an appropriate set of indicators. Similarly increased awareness about environmental issues, life cycle impact assessment has become an important issue for access to consumer as well as international market. As a result processes that provide products or service has to be ecologically optimized (Sandholzer and Narodoslawsky, 2007). Life cycle assessment (LCA) is an important assessment method which helps to successful execution of product or process development under environmental sustainability framework. It is an assessment technique which measures environmental performance of a process, product or service unit along its life cycle (Khan et al., 2004), including resources extraction until waste handeling (Harst and Potting 2013). In the recent times footprint indicators have become important tools for researchers, consultants and policy makers, in order to assess different aspects of sustainability (Fang et al. 2014). The SPI is a member of the ecological footprint family and is compatible with the procedure of the life cycle analyses described in the EN ISO 14,000. It provides the opportunity to describe the relevant ecological pressures of a process including process chain and product usage and disposal.

2. Methodology

2.1. Sustainable Process Index (SPI)

The Sustainable Process Index (SPI) is a tool for the evaluation of environmental impacts of processes. It was developed by Krotscheck and Narodoslawsky based on the assumption that a sustainable economy builds only on solar radiation as natural income (Krotscheck and Narodoslawsky, 1995). The Sustainable Process Index is calculated by using material and energy flows of a product or service extracted from and dissipated to the ecosphere and compares them to natural flows. The sum of total area A_{tot} i.e. ecological footprint of a process or service, required for sustainable embedding of it into the ecosphere is calculated as:

$$A_{tot} = A_R + A_E + A_I + A_S + A_P \qquad [m^2] \qquad (1)$$

According to equation 1, A_{tot} is the sum of partial areas. A_R, is area required for raw material production. A_E, Area required to provide process energy (heat and electricity). A_I, area required for infrastructure facility or Installations. A_S, area required for staff support and A_P is the area required for sustainable disposal of wastes and emissions to the ecosphere (Gwehenberger and Narodoslawsky, 2007). For technological optimization calculation of impact per unit product, good or service is of importance. It is known as the overall footprint of the product a_{tot} and calculated as:

$$a_{tot} \left(\frac{m^2}{unit} \right) = A_{tot}/NP \qquad (2)$$

NP represents the number of products or services provided by the process under observation for a reference period, which is 1 year in general, practice. This per service unit area itself is a relative sustainability measure. To make it more prominent it is further divide by available area per inhabitant (a_{in}) in the region which is relevant to the process. It is theoretical mean area (per capita) available per inhabitant for goods and energy supply to each person.

$$SPI = \frac{a_{tot}}{a_{in}} \; cap/unit \qquad (3)$$

SPIonWeb is built on basic SPI methodology following sustainability principles. The only difference between SPIonExcel and SPIonWeb methodology is calculation of dissipation emission areas. The dissipation areas for emissions into different compartments were used to sum up in SPIonExcel, while SPIonWeb uses eq. 4 to define the dissipation area for emission flow. The largest area among these partial dissipation areas is identified as key emission area and it is assumed that if area is provided for the key area, loading of impacts in all other replenished compartments will take place safely below natural concentrations.

$$a_p = \max(a_{ew}, a_{es}, a_{ea}) \qquad\qquad [m^2] \qquad\qquad (4)$$

SPIonWeb is an online web based free software tool, which can be used on any computing device (computer, smartphone or tablet), equipped with a browser regardless of operating system (windows, Linux, Mac, IOS etc.). It helps the user to assess life cycle of a product or service and estimates its SPI footprint, life cycle CO_2 emissions and GWP (global warming potential). It provides the opportunity of making quick scenarios for comparison and evaluation of recycled material (making loops). It's more user friendly and addresses to students, engineers and experts in LCA modelling.

This paper deals with ecological evaluation of PHA production from animal slaughtering waste utilizing SpionWeb. A basic scenario (PHA_EU27) was executed producing PHA utilising conventional energy resource (electricity EU27 mix and natural gas for process energy). In the next scenario (PHA_biogas_conventional), energy (electricity and process energy) is provided by burning conventional biomethane (produced from 50 % mixture of conventional corn and manure) in the combined heat and power (CHP) unit. In the final scenario (PHA_biogas loop) biomethane produced from biomass (50 % mixture of biological corn silage and manure) cultivated using purified biogas as fuel in the agricultural machinery (Kettl and Narodoslawsky, 2013).

Biopolymer Polyhydroxyalkanoate (PHA)

The results discussed in this study are based on the data acquired during ANIMPOL project, it studies production of biopolymers "polyhydroxyalkonates (PHA)", utilising slaughtering waste as starting material. The overall process consists of following sub-process: hydrolysis, rendering, biodiesel production and fermentation process. The process inventory data for 1 Ton (t) PHA production, obtained from different project partners is shown in Table 1 (Shahzad et al., 2013).

Table 1: Inventory inputs for PHA_EU27_natural gas process

Input	Unit	Inventory
Ammonium Hydroxide	t	0.0770
Glycerol production	t	0.2370
Inorganic Chemicals	t	0.0060
Iron Sulfate	t	0.0001
Net electricity EU-27, medium voltage	MWh	0.3214
Phosphoric acid (H3PO4)	t	0.0524
Process energy, natural gas, industrial heater > 100 kW	MWh	0.2921
Sodium Chloride	t	0.0002
Sodium Sulfate	t	0.0192

Waste water treatment, average	m3	8.1178
Biodiesel_EU27	t	1.8588
Nitrogen from hydrolysis_EU27	t	0.0043
Process water (Europe) m3	m3	8.1178

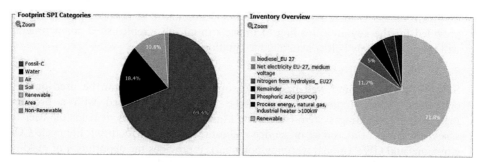

Figure 1. Screen snapshot of graphical inventory overview of PHA_EU27_natural gas process

The electricity consumption (Net electricity EU27, medium voltage) includes stirring, transfer of media and downstream processing. The process energy (process energy, natural gas, industrial heater > 100 Kw) consumption constitutes sterilisation of the media and maintenance of media temperature at 37 °C (Shahzad et al., 2013).

Figure 1 is a snapshot of automatically generated graph, which shows the distribution of foot print in SPI categories and share of different inventory Inputs.

The SPIonWeb also automatically generates process hotspots to figure out optimisation potentials as shown in Figure 2. In the current study, optimisation potential are in electricity consumption, biodiesel production, process heat consumption and PHA production (fermentation process). Biodiesel production has shown the highest potential, due to highly energy intensive production from tallow and maximum consumption as a raw material in the fermentation process.

In the light of hotspot results it is decided to evaluate the whole process using renewable energy resources. In PHA_biogas_conventional scenario, energy system is replaced with electricity and heat produced from conventional biogas using combined heat and power (CHP) unit. In PHA_biogas loop scenario, energy provision in the PHA production process is replaced with energy obtained from biogas produced using mixture of 50 % biological corn silage and manure. In this case biomass is produced using biogas fuelled machinery in agricultural practice (for ploughing, harvesting and transportation), creating a loop of biogas and purified biogas used in the machinery (Kettl and Narodoslawsky, 2013).

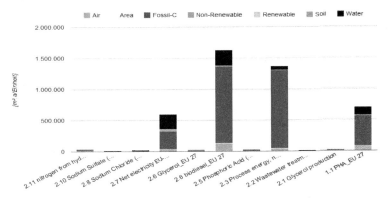

Figure 2. Screen shot of SPI hot spot graph for PHA_EU27_natural gas

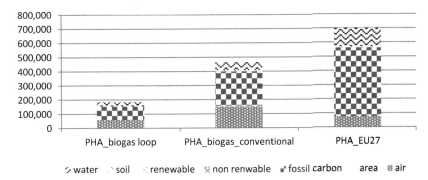

Figure 3. Comparison of overall SPI footprint in different scenarios

In the light of hotspot results it is decided to evaluate the whole process using renewable energy resources. In PHA_biogas_conventional scenario, energy system is replaced with electricity and heat produced from conventional biogas using combined heat and power (CHP) unit. In PHA_biogas loop scenario, energy provision in the PHA production process is replaced with energy obtained from biogas produced using mixture of 50 % biological corn silage and manure. In this case biomass is produced using biogas fuelled machinery in agricultural practice (for ploughing, harvesting and transportation), creating a loop of biogas and purified biogas used in the machinery (Kettl and Narodoslawsky, 2013).

Figure 3 represents the comparison of SPI footprints for 1 (t) of PHA production in different scenarios based on ANIMPOL process. SPIonWeb also calculates SPI footprint, CO2 life cycle emissions out of fossil carbon category, as well as global warming potential (GWP) as shown in Table 2. PHA_biogas_conventional scenario has 33 % lower ecological pressure than PHA_EU27 (normal industrial practice) production scenario, while PHA_biogas loop scenario has 73 % reduction in ecological pressure. Similarly life cycle CO2 emissions comparison show a maximum reduction of 81 % for PHA_biogas loop scenario and 50 % reduction for PHA_biogas_conventional scenario. The GWP results show similar trend for PHA_EU27 and PHA_biogas loop scenarios while PHA_biogas_conventional have highest GWP. The higher GWP values are related to NOX (nitrogen oxides) emissions in the agricultral practises. The highest GWP value for PHA_biogas_conventional is due to the usage of diesel fuel in the agricultural machinery input and application of synthetic fertilizers and pesticides in conventional agriculture.

Table 2: Comparison of footprint, CO_2 emissions and GWP in PHA production processes

Comparison of footprint, CO_2 emissions and GWP			
	Footprint (m^2)	CO_2 emissions (kg)	GWP (kg CO_2 e.)
PHA_EU27	697,769	3,556	63,323
PHA_biogas_conventional	462,269	1,766	101,373
PHA_biogas_biogas loop	184,207	671	61,856

3. Conclusions

SPI provides the opportunity to include ecological assessment in technology selection as well as planning of regional development. It can be computed utilising basic input-output flow (mass and energy balances, prices for installations and raw material) data. It computes clear, understandable and meaningful results which allow comparative analysis of alternative technologies in the process industry and regional optimization. Similarly it is very useful tool for process design, development and optimisation, using early stage ecological assessment for decision making.

References

A. Niederl-Schmidinger, M. Narodoslawsky, 2008, Life Cycle Assessment as an engineer's tool?, Journal of Cleaner Production, 16, 245-252.
A. L. Mayer, 2008, Strengths and weaknesses of common sustainability indices for multidimensional systems, Environment International, 34, 2, 277–29.
D. Sandholzer, M. Narodoslawsky, 2007, SPIonExcel-Fast and easy calculation of the Sustainable Process Index via Computer, J Resources, Conservation and Recycling, 50,130-142.
E. van der Harst, J. Potting, 2013, A critical comparison of ten disposable cup LCAs, Environmental Impact Assessment Review, 43, 86–96.
G. Gwehenberger, M. Narodoslawsky, B. Liebmann, A. Friedl, 2007, Ecology of scale versus economy of scale for bioethanol production, Biofuels, Bioproducts and Biorefining, 1, 4, 264–269.
K. Fang, R. Heijungs, G. R. de Snoo, 2014, Theoretical exploration for the combination of the ecological, energy, carbon, and water footprints: Overview of a footprint family, Ecological Indicators, 36, 508–518.
F.I. Khan, R. Sadiq, B. Veitch, 2004, Life cycle iNdeX (LInX): a new indexing procedure for process and product design and decision-making, Journal of Cleaner Production, 12, 59–76.
K.-H. Kettl, M. Narodoslawsky, 2013, SPIonWeb – Dynamic Life Cycle Impact Assessment (LCIA) process modelling based on Sustainable Process Index (Ecological Footprint), Journal of Environmental Accounting and Management, 1, 1, 1-5.
K. Shahzad, K.-H. Kettl, M. Titz, M. Koller, H. Schnitzer, M. Narodoslawsky, 2013, Comparison of ecological footprint for biobased PHA production from animal residues utilizing different energy resources, Clean Techn Environ Policy, 15, 3, 525-536.
M. Narodoslawsky, C. Krotscheck, 1995, The sustainable process index (SPI): evaluating processes according to environmental compatibility, Journal of Hazardous Materials, 41, 2-3, 383-397.

Jiří Jaromír Klemeš, Petar Sabev Varbanov and Peng Yen Liew (Editors)
Proceedings of the 24th European Symposium on Computer Aided Process Engineering – ESCAPE 24
June 15-18, 2014, Budapest, Hungary. Copyright © 2014 Elsevier B.V. All rights reserved.

Reactive Scheduling for the Coordination of Energy Supply and Demand Management in Microgrids

Javier Silvente[a], Georgios M. Kopanos[b], Efstratios N. Pistikopoulos[b], Antonio Espuña[a],*

[a]Chemical Engineering Department, ETSEIB, Universitat Politècnica de Catalunya, 647 Diagonal Avenue, 08028 Barcelona, Spain.
[b]Imperial College London, Department of Chemical Engineering, Centre for Process Systems Engineering, SW7 2AZ London, United Kingdom.
antonio.espuna@upc.edu

Abstract

This work focuses on the development of scheduling strategies for the coordination of energy production and consumption tasks in microgrids through the management of flexible demand profiles. Delays in the nominal energy demands are allowed under associated penalty costs. The basic microgrid structure studied consists of renewable energy generators (photovoltaic panels, wind turbines) and energy storage units that alleviate the main drawback of such systems which is the mismatch between energy production and demand. A mathematical formulation is presented and used in a rolling horizon scheme that periodically updates input data information.

Keywords: rolling horizon; scheduling; mathematical programming; microgrid.

1. Introduction

The pressure to extend the use of renewable energy resources has led to an increasing use of microgrids, which are decentralized energy networks that integrate several energy generators of limited capacity (Wang and Singh, 2009) with the purpose of distributing the generated energy locally, in order to reduce energy losses and to improve the responsiveness to demand fluctuations. The operations management of microgrids is affected by several types of uncertainty, such as energy demand variations and weather conditions which affect the availability and production capacity of renewable energy generators.

A major drawback of renewable energy systems is the apparent mismatch of energy production and energy demand (Kopanos et al. 2013a). The use of energy storage systems is a common way to alleviate this mismatch effect and appropriately tackle the energy demand uncertainty, and also to schedule the energy demand according to time-of-use market base pricing, introducing enough operational flexibility to efficiently exploit periods of low prices, avoiding pick prices and reducing energy costs. In any case, the consideration of uncertainty is essential to ensure the operability and the reliability of microgrids. Therefore, an energy scheduling tool is required to properly manage energy production, consumption, and storage tasks.

1.1. Rolling-horizon approach

The consideration of uncertainty in microgrids is crucial to ensure the generation of feasible solutions of good quality and practical interest. One of the main challenges is the incorporation of the presence of variability in the parameters characterizing process scenario (energy demand, prices and availability of resources, etc.), but variability in process parameters (task duration, reaction conditions, etc.) should be also considered. In general, scheduling approaches under uncertainty can be classified into reactive and proactive (Li and Ierapetritou, 2008). Typically, reactive approaches modify a nominal plan, obtained by a deterministic (or stochastic) approach, to adjust it to the updated system data. Proactive approaches (e.g., stochastic or robust optimization) generate a plan that satisfies all possible scenarios. Proactive scheduling has the advantage that the solution found will be feasible for all considered scenarios; however it may be too conservative.

The rolling horizon approach is a reactive scheduling method that solves iteratively the deterministic problem by moving the optimization horizon in every iteration (Li and Ierapetritou, 2010); assuming that the status of the system is updated as soon as the different uncertain or not accurate enough parameters became to be known, the optimal schedule for the new resulting scenario (and optimization horizon) may be found. This approach considers: a prediction horizon, in which all the uncertain parameters related to this time horizon are assumed to be known with certainty, due to the fact that the system under study receives feedback related to the unknown parameters, and a control horizon, where the decisions of the optimization for the prediction horizon are.

To the best of the authors' knowledge, the coordinated scheduling of energy consuming operations and energy production in microgrids has received limited attention. In this work, a mathematical model is presented to cope with the underlying uncertainty through a rolling horizon approach to optimally manage a microgrid (i.e., schedule the energy production and consumption tasks).

2. Problem statement

The problem formulation takes into account not only the production and storage levels to be managed by the microgrid, but also the possibility to modify the timing of the energy consumption. The proposed formulation considers energy selling to the main power grid as well as all the involved costs, including generation and storage costs, as well as penalty costs to be applied in case of deviations from the energy consumers' target, in order to maximize the profit. The mathematical model includes not only the energy balance constraints required to describe the energy flows (generation, storage and consumption), but also the constraints associated to the equipment and technologies involved in the microgrid. Consequently, the problem under study is described in terms of the following items:

(i)   A given planning horizon, which is divided into a set of equal-size time intervals $t \in T$. Also, a given Prediction Horizon (PH) and a Control Horizon (CH).

(ii) A set of energy generators $i \in I$, characterized by a minimum and maximum energy generation capacity and a given operational cost.

(iii) A set of energy storage systems $k \in K$, having a minimum and a maximum energy storage capacity and cost.

(iv) A given energy demand, given by the amount of energy required by a set of energy consuming tasks (j, f), where $f \in F_j$ denotes the fth time that the consumer j is active.

For any energy consuming task, its duration and a target starting time are established although, as indicated, tasks can be delayed within certain limits generating a penalty cost. All tasks which might be active during each iteration of the rolling horizon approach are included in the dynamic set F_jRH.

(v) A given set of power grids($r \in R$), which can buy the excessive energy produced, or sell additional energy if required.

The main decisions to be made in order to maximize the profit of the microgrid, are:

(i) The amount of power ($P_{i,t}$) produced by generator i at time interval t.

(ii) The energy storage level ($SE_{k,t}$) at the end of each time interval t.

(iii) The specific (nominal) time to execute an energy consuming task (Dem_t).

The main equations of the mathematical formulation are briefly described (Silvente et al., 2013). Energy production bounds for every energy generator are specified by eq 1. For each source (i) and time interval (t) included in the prediction horizon the binary variable ($X_{i,t}$) indicates if this source is being used or not. Eq. 2 represents the links among energy flows at a specific storage system and time (k,t), where the storage level ($SE_{k,t}$), the energy requirements covered by the storage ($SP_{k,t}$), the supply flows arriving to the storage ($Ld_{k,t}$) and the efficiency of the energy storage system (η) are represented. The energy required by each consumption task(j,f) is calculated with Eq. 3, while Eq. 4 establishes the overall energy balance of the microgrid, considering the production, the consumption, the charge and discharge of the storage unit (i.e., battery), and the energy sales to the power grids.

$$P_{i,t}{}^{min} \cdot X_{i,t} \le P_{i,t} \le P_{i,t}{}^{max} \cdot X_{i,t} \qquad \forall i,t \qquad (1)$$

$$SE_{k,t} = \eta \cdot SE_{k,t-1} + Ld_{k,t} - SP_{k,t} \qquad \forall k,t \qquad (2)$$

$$Dem_t = \sum_{j=1}^{J} \sum_{f \in F_j} Cons_{j,f} \cdot DT \cdot TDem_{j,f,t} \qquad \forall t \qquad (3)$$

$$\sum_{i=1}^{I} P_{i,t} \cdot DT - Dem_t + \sum_{k=1}^{K} SP_{k,t} - \sum_{k=1}^{K} Ld_{k,t} - \sum_{r=1}^{R} Pg_{r,t} \cdot DT = 0 \qquad \forall t \qquad (4)$$

Eq. (5) gives the bounds for the starting times ($Ts_{j,f}$). Moreover, following Eq. (6), the final time ($Tf_{j,f}$) of each energy consumption is given by the starting time plus its duration.

$$Ts_{j,f}{}^{min} \le Ts_{j,f} \le Ts_{j,f}{}^{max} \qquad \forall j,f \in F_jRH \qquad (5)$$

$$Tf_{j,f} = Ts_{j,f} + Dur_{j,f} \qquad \forall j,f \in F_jRH \qquad (6)$$

Equations (7-10) locate the start consumption time ($Ts_{j,f}$) and the final consumption time ($Tf_{j,f}$) at the beginning and at the end of each consumption task (j,f). The binary variable ($Y_{j,f,t}$) is active when energy consumption (j,f) starts at time period t of the prediction horizon. Accordingly, ($Z_{j,f,t}$) is active when the consumption task(j,f) finishes at time period t. These logical restrictions can be reformulated as a set of big-M constraints:

$$\left(t - Ts_{j,f}\right) - \left(1 - Y_{j,f,t}\right) \cdot M \le 0 \qquad \forall j,f \in F_jRH \qquad (7)$$

$$\left(t - Ts_{j,f}\right) + \left(1 - Y_{j,f,t}\right) \cdot M \ge 0 \qquad \forall j,f \in F_jRH \qquad (8)$$

$$(t + 1 - Tf_{j,f}) - (1 - Z_{j,f,t}) \cdot M \leq 0 \qquad\qquad \forall j, f \in F_j RH \qquad (9)$$

$$(t + 1 - Tf_{j,f}) + (1 - Z_{j,f,t}) \cdot M \geq 0 \qquad\qquad \forall j, f \in F_j RH \qquad (10)$$

The total benefit of the microgrid, which is the objective function, is calculated considering incomes and costs in Eq. (11), subject to the previous constraints. Note that production and storage costs will depend on the use of the different available energy production/storage systems, and the penalization cost is determined by the delay in satisfying each energy demand.

$$Benefit = Incomes - (CostProduction + CostStock + CostPenalty) \qquad (11)$$

In order to use the proposed model in a rolling horizon scheme, the following set of variables and equations are used to link past decisions with the current prediction horizon:

$$\hat{Y}_{j,f} + \sum_{t \in RH} Y_{j,f,t} = 1 \qquad\qquad \forall j, f \in F_j, t \qquad (12)$$

$$Ts_{j,f}{}^{min} = Ts_{initial,j,f}{}^{min} - CH \cdot it \qquad \forall j, f \in F_j \qquad (13)$$

$$Ts_{j,f}{}^{max} = Ts_{initial,j,f}{}^{max} - CH \cdot it \qquad \forall j, f \in F_j \qquad (14)$$

$$Dur_{j,f} = Dur_{initial,j,f} - (CH \cdot it - Ts_{j,f}) \cdot \hat{Y}_{j,f} \qquad \forall j, f \in F_j \qquad (15)$$

$$SE_{k,t-1} = \widehat{SE}_{k,t,it} \qquad\qquad \forall k, t, it = CH + t - 1 \qquad (16)$$

The binary variable $Y_{j,f,t}$ indicates if the consumption task (j,f) will start at time (t) (parameter $\hat{Y}_{j,f}$ indicates if the consumption task (j,f) started before the beginning of the current prediction horizon), so Eq. (12) establishes that all consumption tasks must start in the scheduling horizon. Minimum and maximum starting times for these tasks at each iteration are given by Eq. (13) and (14), considering the minimum/maximum starting time of the previous iteration and the duration of the control horizon (*CH*). The duration of the consumption tasks is updated at each iteration, as indicated by Eq.(15). And finally, the energy storage level of the previous control horizon is linked to the initial energy storage level of the current prediction horizon by Eq.(16).

Then, the rolling horizon algorithm can be applied as follows:
- To establish the first planning period and to solve the scheduling problem.
- To solve again the scheduling problem using data from the last optimization.
- If this re-scheduling corresponds to the last period of time, stop. Otherwise, fix the values obtained in the optimization problem for that iteration, re-schedule and update the period of time until the last planning period is reached.

The proposed formulation allows to upload or modify the different parameters related to the uncertainty, such as the variability in weather conditions (which affects the energy production) or the variability of the duration of the consumption tasks (which affects the energy demand).

3. Case study

The microgrid under study consists of a photovoltaic panel, a wind turbine, and a system of electric batteries. The microgrid is connected to the main power grid (Silvente et al. 2012). The scheduling horizon considered is 24 h, and the duration of each time interval is 15 min (i.e., 96 time intervals in total). Prediction Horizons (PHs) of 10, 20, and 30 time intervals have been considered. Several energy consumption tasks (j,f) are considered and a limited starting time delay is allowed subject to a penalty cost. It has been considered that input data (e.g., energy demands, weather conditions, etc.) will be updated at the beginning of every time interval, so the control horizon has been established also as 15 min.

3.1. Results and discussion

The MILP problem was solved in GAMS 24.1/CPLEX 12. Figure 1 displays the daily schedule for energy production and consumption tasks; for a PH=20 time intervals. Some consumption tasks have been delayed (i.e., energy demand has shifted). Figure 2 shows the aggregated objective value for the rolling horizon approach under different prediction horizons in comparison with the perfect information case. Not surprisingly, as the length of the prediction horizon increases, the total objective is improved and closes the gap from the perfect information solution.

4. Conclusions

In this work, a mathematical programming model applicable to the simultaneous optimization of energy production and consumption (i.e., demand) tasks in microgrids has been presented. A rolling horizon approach has been used to address the energy demand uncertainty. As expected, longer prediction horizons favor the generation of better solutions, under the assumption of accurate demand predictions.

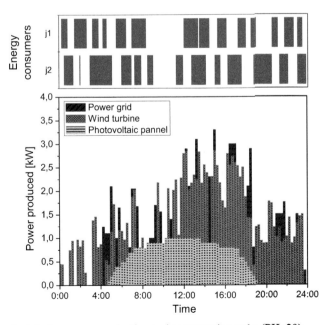

Figure 1. Daily schedule for energy production and consumption tasks (PH=20).

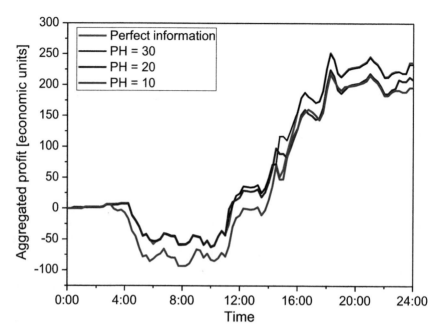

Figure 2. Aggregated objective value for different PHs and the perfect information case.

Acknowledgements

The authors thank the financial support received from the Spanish "Ministerio de Economía y Competitividad" and the European Regional Development Fund (both funding the research Project SIGERA, DPI2012-37154-C02-01), from the "Ministerio de Economía y Competitividad" (Subprograma de Formación de Personal Investigador, BES-2010-036099), and the ERC-Mobile Project (num. 226462).

References

G.M. Kopanos, M.C. Georgiadis, E.N. Pistikopoulos, 2013, Energy production planning of a network of micro combined heat and power generators, Applied Energy, 102, 1522-1534.

Z. Li, M.G. Ierapetritou, 2008, Reactive scheduling using parametric programming, AIChE Journal, 54, 2610-2623.

Z. Li, M.G. Ierapetritou, 2010, Rolling horizon based planning and scheduling integration with production capacity consideration, Chemical Engineering Science, 65, 5887-6000.

J. Silvente, M. Graells, A. Espuña and P. Salas, 2012, An optimization model for the management of energy supply and demand in smart grids, IEEE, 424-429.

J. Silvente, A. Aguirre, G. Crexells, M. Zamarripa, C. Méndez, M. Graells, A. Espuña, 2013, Hybrid time representation for the scheduling of energy supply and demand in smart grids, Computer Aided Chemical Engineering, 32, 553-558.

L. Wang, C. Singh, 2009, Multicriteria design of hybrid power generation systems based on a modified particle swarm optimization algorithm, IEEE Trans. Energy Conversion, 24, 163-172.

Jiří Jaromír Klemeš, Petar Sabev Varbanov and Peng Yen Liew (Editors)
Proceedings of the 24th European Symposium on Computer Aided Process Engineering – ESCAPE 24
June 15-18, 2014, Budapest, Hungary. Copyright © 2014 Elsevier B.V. All rights reserved.

Robust Production Planning and Scheduling of a Pulp Digester and a Paper Machine

Gonçalo Figueira*, Bernardo Almada-Lobo

INESC TEC - Faculty of Engineering, University of Porto, Rua Dr. Roberto Frias, s/n 4200-465 Porto, Portugal
goncalo.figueira@fe.up.pt

Abstract

Disturbance Management is a major issue in process industries like the pulp and paper (P&P) case and is mostly performed in the execution/control level. That approach is confined to the amendment of plans sent by upper levels and can thus be problematic. This paper moves towards the integration of planning and control, starting from the planning's point of view. The application of Simulation-Optimization (S-O) allows considering uncertainty, but keeping a deterministic tractable optimization model. Indeed, it is the simulation model that incorporates more complex elements such as stochastic variables, as well as integrates (with more or less detail) the execution/control behaviour. In this work, we present a case study of a P&P mill, focusing on the two most critical production resources (the digester and the paper machine). The feedback obtained by simulating their interaction is used to adjust the slacks introduced in the intermediate tank. In this way, we are able to generate plans that are not only optimized concerning company's indicators, but also robust against disturbances.

Keywords: Production planning and scheduling; Disturbance management; Pulp and paper industry; Simulation-optimization.

1. Introduction

The pulp and paper (P&P) industry converts fibrous raw materials into pulp, paper and paper-board. In a first step wood chips are processed into pulp (in the digester) and in a second step different paper grades are produced out of this pulp (in the paper machine). These two steps can be processed on separate plants or combined into an integrated mill. Figure 1 illustrates the production process of an integrated P&P mill.

According to CEPI (2013), 65 % of European's pulp consumption occurs in integrated plants. In these plants, stages tend to be more tightly integrated, with limited intermediate storage space, in order to operate efficiently. Therefore, the interdependencies between stages can result in multiple and shifting bottlenecks. In addition, the system is subject to process variability (e.g. in production yield, pulp mixture) and disturbances (e.g. paper breaks, equipment failures). Disturbances in one process tend to propagate to other processes, resulting in production losses, unnecessary rate changes (which further cause quality disturbances and undesired wear on equipment) and increase of the environmental load of the mill. It is clear that all these factors can cause considerable economic losses.

Disturbance management is mostly performed in the execution/control level. Model Predictive Control (MPC) is one of the most popular methods to address these types of

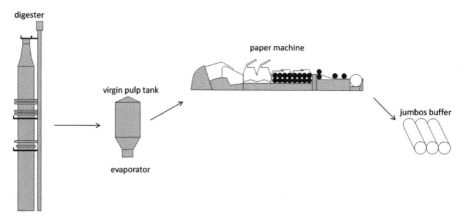

Figure 1. Pulp digester and paper machine in an integrated P&P mill.

problems. Ledung et al. (2004) and Mercangöz and Doyle (2008) developed MPC-based approaches that apply process simulation to predict the state of the system. Nevertheless, these approaches do not optimize production plans, but rather their execution. The optimization criteria are thus related to the minimization of deviations from the production plan. Therefore, if those plans are not robust, their implementation can be problematic, since the sequence of paper grades may require major changes. Some efforts were made in order to integrate planning and control. Harjunkoski et al. (2009) review some contributions in this context. Still, the authors conclude that the integrated approaches essentially start from the control's point of view and have only been able to address smaller instances of the planning problem. Engell and Harjunkoski (2012) discuss the challenges of integrating scheduling and control. Lindholm et al. (2013) apply hierarchical scheduling and control in a rolling-horizon scheme, where the lower levels update the schedule of upper levels. However, their approach is simply reactive.

At the planning level, there are three main approaches to obtain robust solutions and thus mitigate the effects of variability and disturbances:

- accommodate uncertainty, considering buffers in the form of (predefined) safety stocks or safety times;
- incorporate uncertainty, in the so called Stochastic Programming or Robust Optimization;
- consider uncertainty in a lower level, simulating the execution (and possible adaptation) of plans.

The first approach is the most simplistic and results in plain deterministic models. The buffers are however blindly defined. Hence, they may result in too conservative or too risky plans. The second approach, on the other hand, can increase drastically the complexity and scale of the original problems, if a large set of scenarios is considered (possibly in multiple stages). The last one, which corresponds to the well-known Simulation-Optimization (S-O), has the most potential in terms of detail and accurate representation of reality. Indeed, it may even allow integrating the control problem within the simulation framework. Still, it can easily require a prohibitive computational time. Therefore, the combination of simulation and optimization has to be carefully designed, so that the method can achieve a reasonable efficiency.

In this paper, we propose an S-O method, where simulation is used to implement just particular plans and the obtained feedback is employed in the enhancement of our (deterministic) analytical model. In this way, we are able not only to save a large amount of simulations, but also to keep the linearity of the problem. This method is used in the generation of production plans for a P&P mill.

The remaining paper is organized as follows. First, we describe the production process and the challenges posed by the planning activities. Then, we present our methodology, including the interaction between simulation and optimization. At the end, preliminary results show how this approach behaves in practice and some perspectives on this work are given.

2. Production and planning processes

The whole process begins with the wood being debarked and reduced to small chips, which are later cooked inside the digester. The virgin pulp is then stocked in tanks and later pulled by the paper machine, where it is mixed with recycled pulp, in different proportions according to the desired paper receipts. The final paper is characterized not only by the pulp mixture, but also by the paper grammage (measured in g/m^2). For the sake of simplicity, the term "grade" is used for the combination of both (e.g. KLB115, which means receipt KLB and 115 g/m^2). The time and paper loss in a changeover of grades is sequence-dependent.

In many companies, the short-term production planning process is completely manual and typically follows a hierarchical scheme. The top-level focuses on the paper machine, dealing with the sizing and scheduling of paper campaigns, which are programmed to occur in cycles, in order to balance resources. The base-level tries to schedule and control all the other production resources, subject to the input from the top-level. Various iterations between the two levels may be needed to find a feasible solution. Indeed, the pulp quality strongly depends on the digester's stability and thus, its synchronization with the paper machine is crucial. In fact, different paper grades pull more or less pulp from the digester, forcing the change of its rate. The rate is constrained to a maximum variation, due to technological limitations of the equipment. Therefore, the close interrelation between these two stages must be carefully managed.

Facing several constraints, conflicting objectives and eventually multiple and shifting bottlenecks, planners are led to place feasibility over optimality. In addition, the production system is subject to disturbances, such as: paper breaks in the paper machine (which are particularly frequent in lower grades and changeovers), process delays, unsteady productivities (due to unstable pulp quality) and various types of breakdowns. Therefore, planners need also to consider slacks in their plans, in order to accommodate those disturbances and avoid tanks overflow. However, those slacks are arbitrarily defined, instead of being included in the optimization process.

In short, there is the need for decision support systems that can on the one hand optimize integrated P&P mills, correctly weighting the different company's KPIs (key performance indicators) and on the other hand, generate robust production plans that can accommodate a variety of disturbances.

3. Methodology

3.1. General approach

In our approach, we combine simulation and optimization, where optimization generates production plans and simulation implements them. However, simulation does not serve as a simple evaluation function of the optimization. That would not only result in tremendous inefficiency, given the vast amount of solutions to evaluate, but also all the linear structure of our problem would be lost. Therefore, we use simulation to implement just particular plans and the obtained feedback is employed in the enhancement of our (deterministic) analytical model.

This refinement procedure is performed while the optimization problem is being solved. Therefore, an iterative process where the problem needs to be solved multiple times is avoided. The idea of our Progressive Model Refinement framework is thus converging to a solution with increasing accuracy.

3.2. Optimization

The analytical model is a discrete time model, where macro-periods of fixed length (in this case, days) are subdivided in micro-periods of variable length, allowing the continuous definition of paper campaigns. The model also considers sequence-dependent setup times and costs and is based on that presented by Santos and Almada-Lobo (2012). Our solution method combines a variable neighbourhood search (VNS), which manages the setup-related variables, with an exact solver, focusing on the continuous variables. The method provides good quality solutions (beating both pure exact methods and MIP-based heuristics) for real-world instances in feasible time (Figueira et al., 2013a).

3.3. Simulation

The implementation of production plans is performed by a discrete event simulator, which uses probability distributions for stochastic parameters, approximated by real data gathered from the company. Figure 2 presents the distributions of two of those parameters, one related to process variability and the other to disturbances. For each type of disturbances, we estimated not only the time between failures (TBF), but also the time to repair (TTR).

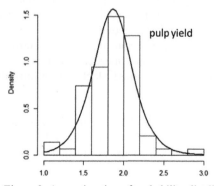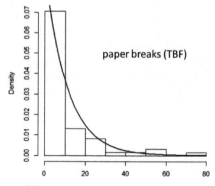

Figure 2. Approximation of probability distributions to real data.

3.4. Parameters refinement

The essential part of an S-O method of this type is the way the analytical model is enhanced. Indeed, the parameters to be refined are not necessarily the stochastic parameters considered in simulation or in a possible stochastic analytical model. In fact, Figueira et al. (2013b) chose to penalize the deviations of tank levels to their corresponding targets, in order to avoid under and overflow (the ultimate impact of disturbances). Although it allowed improving the robustness of the generated plans, its effectiveness was not very high, since a small average deviation did not avoid some large (and hence problematic) deviations. Therefore, here we impose slacks in the tank limits, so that there is always a buffer to accommodate possible disturbances. This is actually the way practitioners manage their systems. The difference is that with an S-O method, those slacks are not blindly defined, but determined based on the feedback from simulation. A similar approach was used by Jung et al. (2008) for safety stocks.

4. Results

Our S-O approach proved to be effective in generating plans with good KPIs and, at the same time, robust against several disturbances. In our simulation tests, this new approach was able to reduce the amount of tank levels violation (measured in t · h) by 89 %, when compared to the deterministic optimization method.

Figure 3 exhibits two production plans, each generated by these two methods. As it can be seen, the deterministic method creates a shorter cycle of paper grades and that requires a sharper variation in the virgin tank level. The new S-O approach, on the other hand, extends the grades cycle, resulting in smoother variations. Therefore, the system is able to accommodate possible disturbances that may occur either upstream (in the digester) or downstream (in the paper machine).

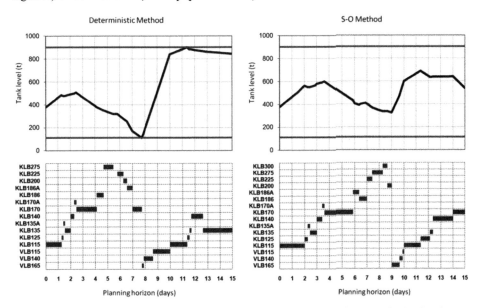

Figure 3. Comparison between plans generated by the deterministic and S-O methods, showing the synchronization between the tank level and the paper grades schedule.

5. Conclusions

With our S-O framework we expect to be able to manage disturbances in both preventive and reactive perspectives. Our algorithm can generate solutions of reasonable quality very quickly (in a few minutes). Therefore, in a disturbance situation reactions can be prompt and even preventive, regarding other parts of the mill that are not currently affected. The framework proposed here can also be applied to a variety of problems, in particular to other process industries (such as the chemical industry), where there is limited storage capacity at intermediate production stages.

As future research, this study could be extended to a more complex system, with more than two stages. That extension may require a more elaborated scheme in the way the various parameters (related to various tanks) are refined in the analytical model, since the individual impact of each parameter has to be assessed.

Acknowledgement

The first author is grateful to the Portuguese Foundation for Science and Technology (FCT) for awarding him the Ph.D. Grant SFRH/BD/80109/2011. This work is partially financed by the European Regional Development Fund (ERDF) through the COMPETE Programme (operational programme for competitiveness), by national funds through the FCT within project "FCOMP-01-0124-FEDER-037281" and by the Project "NORTE-07-0124-FEDER-000057", supported by the North Portugal Regional Operational Programme (ON.2 – O Novo Norte), under the National Strategic Reference Framework (NSRF).

References

CEPI, Confederation of European Paper Industries, 2013, Key statistics 2012, June, 2013.
S. Engell, I. Harjunkoski, 2012, Optimal operation: Scheduling, advanced control and their integration, Computers and Chemical Engineering, 47, 121–133.
G. Figueira, M. Santos, B. Almada-Lobo, 2013a, A hybrid VNS approach for the short-term production planning and scheduling: A case study in the pulp and paper industry, Computers and Operations Research, 40, 7, 1804–1818.
G. Figueira, M. Furlan, B. Almada-Lobo, 2013b, Predictive production planning in an integrated pulp and paper mill, Proceedings of the IFAC Conference on Manufacturing Modelling, Management, and Control, 7, 1, 371–376.
I. Harjunkoski, R. Nyström, A. Horch, 2009, Integration of scheduling and control – theory or practice?, Computers and Chemical Engineering, 33, 12, 1909–1918.
J. Y. Jung, G. Blau, J. F. Pekny, G. V. Reklaitis, D. Eversdyk, 2008, Integrated safety stock management for multi-stage supply chains under production capacity constraints, Computers and Chemical Engineering, 32, 11, 2570–2581.
L. Ledung, P. Sahlin, U. Persson, T. Lindberg, 2004, P3 pulp production planning, Journal ABB, 4, 39–43.
A. Lindholm, C. Johnsson, N-H. Quttineh, H. Lidestam, M. Henningsson, J. Wikner, O. Tang, N-P. Nytzén, K. Forsman, 2013, Hierarchical scheduling and utility disturbance management in the process industry, Proceedings of the IFAC Conference on Manufacturing Modelling, Management and Control, 7, 1, 140–145.
M. Mercangöz, F. J. Doyle, 2008, Real-time optimization of the pulp mill benchmark problem, Computers and Chemical Engineering, 32, 4-5, 789–804.
M. Santos, B. Almada-Lobo, 2012, Integrated pulp and paper mill planning and scheduling, Computers and Industrial Engineering, 63, 1, 1–12.

Jiří Jaromír Klemeš, Petar Sabev Varbanov and Peng Yen Liew (Editors)
Proceedings of the 24th European Symposium on Computer Aided Process Engineering – ESCAPE 24
June 15-18, 2014, Budapest, Hungary. Copyright © 2014 Elsevier B.V. All rights reserved.

Modelling Cobalt Solvent Extraction using Aspen Custom Modeler

Heather A. Evans[a], Parisa A. Bahri[a*], Linh T.T. Vu[a], Keith R. Barnard[b]

[a]School of Engineering and Information Technology, Murdoch University, South Street, Murdoch 6150, Australia
[b]CSIRO Process Science and Engineering, PO Box 7229 Karawara, WA 6152, Australia
P.Bahri@murdoch.edu.au

Abstract

The cobalt solvent extraction system using Cyanex 272, a phosphinic acid based extractant, has been modelled using the Aspen Custom Modeler mathematical modelling software. The principle advantage of this method is that the model can easily be imported into Aspen Plus and run as part of an integrated flowsheet containing other unit operations. The cobalt solvent extraction circuit operates on a counter-current basis, with the barren organic entering the final stage and the aqueous feed entering at the first stage. Since the metal extraction efficiencies were dependent on the conditions of the outlet streams, a solver must be selected to simultaneously solve a set of algebraic nonlinear model equations. Initial sensitivity analysis for a single stage Aspen Custom Modeler model has shown that increasing pH or the organic to aqueous (O:A) ratio significantly increases individual metal extraction efficiencies. To achieve the ultimate aim of maximising cobalt extraction while minimising magnesium and nickel co-extraction and reagent consumption, an economic objective function has been formulated within the optimisation problem to solve for the optimum pH setpoint and O:A ratio. The optimised single stage results indicate operating at pH 4.5 and O:A of 0.78 to achieve 95 % cobalt extraction, while limiting nickel extraction to <1%

Keywords: Aspen Custom Modeler, Cobalt Solvent Extraction, modelling, Cyanex 272

1. Introduction

Cobalt has a range of uses from colouring agents to alloys designed for enhanced wear resistance and batteries for use in electric and hybrid electric vehicles, mobile phones and other electronic devices (CDI, 2012). Cobalt is usually recovered as a by-product of other metal ore bodies, typically nickel and copper. One common method for recovering cobalt and other metals is using a hydrometallurgical process whereby the metal ore is dissolved into an aqueous solution via acid addition. Cobalt can then be recovered from the resulting mixed metal aqueous pregnant leach solution (PLS) via solvent extraction (SX) using Cyanex 272 containing the active component bis (2,4,4 trimethlylpentyl) phosphinic acid as the organic extractant (Bacon and Mihaylov, 2002). The use of SX for cobalt and other metal recovery was thoroughly discussed in a review of modern hydrometallurgical flowsheets (Sole, 2008). In recent years this system has been modelled by Cytec, the manufacturer of Cyanex 272 (Soderstrom et al., 2010). A simulation software package named MINCHEM used in copper SX, has recently been expanded to allow evaluation of more complex metal/ligand interactions, such as those pertaining to cobalt SX (Bourget et al., 2011). However, this is a standalone, in-house model not currently compatible with existing flowsheeting packages used by engineering companies. Currently, the client provides potential feed scenarios to Cytec who model the system and return the results to the client. The principle advantage of this current project is that the Aspen Custom Modeler (ACM) cobalt solvent extraction (CoSX) model can potentially be exported as a .msi package into Aspen Plus and run as part of an integrated flowsheet containing other unit operations.

The CoSX system was studied experimentally to generate data for subsequent modelling work (Evans et al., 2008). Equilibrium constants (k) for cobalt, nickel and magnesium were previously calculated using least squares regression techniques, from experimentally determined pH extraction isotherms for a given set of operating conditions (Evans et al., 2012).These k values were then used in the modelling equations to predict the extraction extents of cobalt, nickel and magnesium under a range of conditions in order to determine the optimal set of conditions to maximise cobalt extraction whist minimising the co-extraction of the other metals.

2. Model development

Like most commercial SX circuits (incluing cobalt SX), the CoSX model routinely operates on a counter-current basis, with the barren organic entering the final stage and the aqueous feed entering at the first stage. The input variables are the initial concentration of the extractant, metal tenors of the aqueous feed and organic feed, temperature, aqueous feed flow, organic to aqueous ratio (O:A) and pH setpoint. Fixed parameters include the constants A and B determined from prior experimental work, which are used to calculate the equilibrium constant for each metal. The model uses a series of mass balance equations to calculate the extraction extent for each metal and hence the tenors of the organic and aqueous streams leaving each stage for a given set of operating conditions.

The model was initially designed as a single stage with three inlet streams (aqueous feed(PLS), barren organic (BOrg) and alkali (Alk) for pH control) and two outlet streams (aqueous raffinate (Raff) and loaded organic (LOrg)) as shown in Figure 1. The metal concentrations to two significant figures and flowrates are shown for the aqueous and organic phases with the addition of the uncomplexed extractant concentration [RH] shown at the bottom of the organic streams.

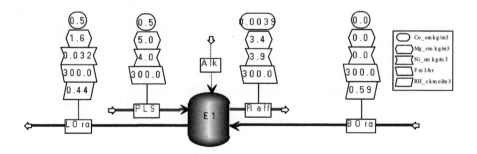

Figure 1. Single stage CoSX ACM model, using Cyanex 272 (0.59M RH) at 35 °C, pH 5.0.

Phosphinic acid extractant RH exists in the dimeric form $(RH)_2$ in non-polar solutions such as kerosene. The extraction reactions for Co, Mg and Ni with the dimer are given in Eqs.(1) - (3), respectively (Manksi et al. 2002). The individual metal extraction efficiencies ($Xeff_M$) (where M = Co, Ni or Mg), are given by Eq.(4).

$$Co^{2+}{}_{(aq)} + 2(RH)_{2\ (Org)} \leftrightarrow Co(R_2H)_{2\,(org)} + 2H^+{}_{(aq)} \tag{1}$$

$$Mg^{2+}{}_{(aq)} + 2(RH)_{2\ (Org)} \leftrightarrow Mg(R_2H)_{2\,(org)} + 2H^+{}_{(aq)} \tag{2}$$

$$Ni^{2+}{}_{(aq)} + 3(RH)_{2\ (Org)} \leftrightarrow NiR_2(RH)_{4\,(org)} + 2H^+{}_{(aq)} \tag{3}$$

Since the individual metal extraction efficiencies were dependent on the conditions of the outlet streams, specifically the available extractant concentration [RH] (in kmol/m³) following extraction (as expressed in Eq.(5))as well as the k_M value and pH setpoint, a solver must be selected to simultaneously solve a set of algebraic nonlinear model equations. This is typically done using a mathematical modelling software such as ACM or MATLAB.

$$Xeff_M = \frac{k_M.[RH]^z}{k_M.[RH]^z+[H]^2} \qquad \text{where } z = 2 \text{ for Co, Mg and } z= 3 \text{ for Ni} \tag{4}$$

$$[RH] = [RH]_{In} - \frac{RH\,(n_{Co}+n_{Mg}+n_{Ni})}{F_{Org}} \tag{5}$$

In the above equations, $(RH)n_M$ is the amount of RH reacted in kmol/h during the extraction reaction for each metal, F_{Org} is the organic flowrate in m³/h and $[RH]_{In}$ is the initial concentration in kmol/m³ of extractant entering the extractor vessel.

More complex models incorporating multiple stages have been built based on the principles used in the initial single stage model. The single stage model was first modified by the addition of a splitter and a mixer to allow for the recycle of the organic phase back to the mixer to reflect typical operating conditions to manage losses due to entrainment. However there is minimal variation to the unit extraction once equilibrium has been obtained. The next step was to add additional extraction units as shown schematically in Figure 2.

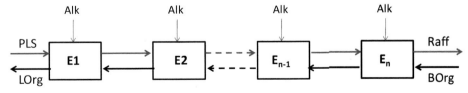

Figure 2. Schematic of a CoSX model with n stages. The multi-stage counter-current system presents its own unique challenges due to the co-dependency of the metal extraction efficiency and the amount of available extractant in each stage.

3. System optimisation

An optimisation problem was set up for a single stage extraction model using a baseline set of conditions, namely 20 % Cyanex 272 in kerosene as the organic extractant and a PLS with flowrate of 300 m³/h containing 0.5 g/L cobalt, 5.0 g/L magnesium and 4.0 g/L nickel in a sulfate system at 35°C. The optimisation variables were the O:A ratio and the pH setpoint. The objective function was formulated using an economic model Eq.(6) based on the selling price (SP) of cobalt and an assumed penalty price (PP) for co-extracted magnesium and nickel, where m represents the mass of metal extracted and reagent costs (RC) including extractant, kerosene, alkali, acid.

$$\text{Maximise} \qquad Profit = SP_{Co}m_{Co} - PP_{Mg}m_{Mg} - PP_{Ni}m_{Ni} - RC \qquad (6)$$

Subject to:
- The set of equality constraints represented by Eq.(4) and Eq.(5);
- The set of inequality constraints including:
  - $0 \leq Xeff_M \leq 1$;
  - $4 \leq \text{pH setpoint} \leq 5.5$;
  - $0 \leq [RH]$; and
  - $0.5 \leq O:A \leq 1.1$

4. Results and Discussion

The results for cobalt, magnesium and nickel extraction from the sensitivity analysis on O:A ratio and pH setpoint using the baseline single stage ACM model (20 % Cyanex 272 in kerosene as the organic extractant and a PLS with flowrate of 300 m³/h containing 0.5 g/L cobalt, 5.0 g/L magnesium and 4.0 g/L nickel in a sulfate system at 35 °C) are shown in Figures 3 and 4.

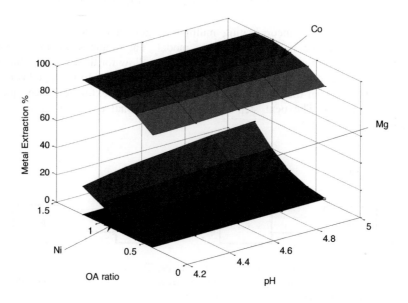

Figure 3. Effect of O:A ratio and pH setpoint for a single stage CoSX model, using 20 % v/v Cyanex 272 (0.59M RH) at 35 °C with a PLS of 300 m³/h containing 0.5 g/L Co, 5.0 g/L Mg and 4.0 g/L Ni.

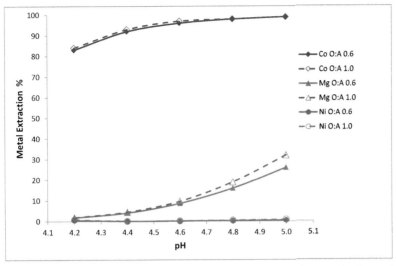

Figure 4. Effect changing of O:A ratio from 0.6 to 1.0 on extraction results for various pH setpoints for a single stage CoSX model, using 20 % v/v Cyanex 272 (0.59M RH) at 35 °C.

These results show that while cobalt extraction is consistently high (83-99%) across the range of O:A and pH setpoints modelled, and nickel co-extraction is consistently <1 %, a better (more selective) separation between cobalt and magnesium can be achieved by lowering the pH and O:A ratio. This limits the magnesium extraction, while still achieving acceptable cobalt recoveries. Magnesium is a common impurity element in CoSX that can consume the active sites on Cyanex 272, limiting the availability of the reagent for cobalt extraction. Limiting the magnesium extraction has additional cost benefits as the amount of reagents used for pH control in the extraction and subsequent stripping of the loaded magnesium can be reduced.

The sensitivity analysis is a first stage approach to determining the optimal operating conditions for this system. However this can be improved by using optimisation techniques. For instance, applying the optimisation problem in Eq.(6)suggests the optimum conditions for a single stage of CoSX under these base line conditions to be an O:A ratio of 0.78 and a pH setpoint of 4.5. This produces a raffinate grade of 0.025 g/L Co, 4.7 g/L Mg and 4.0 g/L Ni corresponding to extractions of 95 % Co, 6.4 % Mg and 0.14 % Ni.

The cobalt metal price is currently ~USD 27,000 /t for 99.9 % Co. Depending on the end market of the cobalt product, certain impurities may be tolerated although penalties will be imposed for them. To determine if changing the cobalt price had any impact on the optimal operating conditions, the cobalt price was normalised to 1 and incrementally changed in the optimisation problem, while keeping the magnesium and nickel penalties and reagent costs constant.

Initial results indicate that the pH setpoint is relatively independent of cobalt price with the setpoint only changing by < 0.2 pH units during a doubling of the price. The O:A ratio was more sensitive but the optimisation point stayed within the range 0.5 to 0.8.

5. Future work

If lower cobalt raffinate grades are required, it is suggested that multiple stages be employed to achieve a better separation of cobalt from the impurity elements. For example using multiple stages of counter-current extraction allows for higher extraction extents in the final stage, as lower tenor solutions are contacted with barren organic (i.e. more available RH) thereby increasing extraction efficiencies. In a multistage model, changing the pH profile across the extraction circuit can result in some scrubbing of the loaded magnesium by new cobalt entering the circuit. This needs to be addressed by the inclusion of additional equilibrium equations representing the exchange reaction between cobalt, magnesium and nickel complexes.

6. Conclusions

Initial sensitivity analysis for a single stage ACM model has shown that increasing pH or the O:A ratio significantly increases individual metal extraction efficiencies. Using an optimisation economic function based on the cobalt price and penalty rates for impurities, the optimum operating conditions were determined to be an O:A 0.78 and pH setpoint of 4.5 to achieve 95 % cobalt extraction, while limiting magnesium coextraction to 6.4 % and nickel coextraction to <1 %.

Acknowledgement

The authors would like to thank the Parker Centre for the initial project funding, CSIRO and the Minerals Down Under National Research Flagship for the provision of laboratory facilities and Murdoch University for ongoing support.

References

G. Bacon, I. Mihaylov, 2002, Solvent extraction as an enabling technology in the nickel industry, ISEC 2002: International Solvent Extraction Conference, Johannesburg, South Africa, South African Institute of Mining and Metallurgy, 1-13.

C. Bourget, M. Soderstrom, B. Jakovljevic, J. Morrison, 2011, Optimization of the design parameters of a Cyanex 272 circuit for recovery of nickel and cobalt, Solvent Extraction and Ion Exchange, 29,823-836.

Cobalt Development Institute, <www.thecdi.com>, Accessed on 1/10/2013.

H. A. Evans, P. A. Bahri, J. A. Rumball, K. R. Barnard, 2008, Modelling cobalt extraction with Cyanex 272, ISEC 2008: International Solvent Extraction Conference,Tucson, AZ, United States, Canadian Institute of Mining, Metallurgy and Petroleum, 459-466.

H. A. Evans, L. T. T. Vu, P. A. Bahri, K. R. Barnard, 2012, Development of an integrated model for cobalt solvent extraction using Cyanex 272, Computer Aided Chemical Engineering, 31, 550-554.

R. Manski, H.-J. Bart, A. Görge, M. Traving, J. Strube, W. Bäcker, 2002, Solvent extraction as an enabling technology in the nickel industry, ISEC 2002: International Solvent Extraction Conference, 161-166.

M. Soderstrom, C. Bourget, B. Jakovljevic, T. Bednarski, 2010, Development of Process Modelling for Cyanex 272, ALTA Nickel-Cobalt 2010.

K. C. Sole, 2008, Solvent Extraction in the Hydrometallurgical Processing and Purification of Metals : Process Design and Selected Applications, Solvent Extraction and Liquid Membranes Fundamentals and Applications in New Materials, CRC Press,USA.

Jiří Jaromír Klemeš, Petar Sabev Varbanov and Peng Yen Liew (Editors)
Proceedings of the 24th European Symposium on Computer Aided Process Engineering – ESCAPE 24
June 15-18, 2014, Budapest, Hungary.

Hierarchical Production Scheduling – A Case Study at Perstorp

Anna Lindholm[a], Helene Lidestam[b*], Nils-Hassan Quttineh[b]

[a]Lund University, Lund 221 00, Sweden
[b]Linköping University, Linköping 581 83, Sweden
helene.lidestam@liu.se

Abstract

Planning and scheduling are functions that have large economic impact in the chemical process industry. For integrated sites with many interconnected production areas, obtaining production schedules that respect all production-related constraints is a complex task. One important issue is the constraints due to disturbances in utilities, such as steam and cooling water. These are often site-wide disturbances that may make it impossible to maintain desired production rates in several production areas at a site. In this study, scheduling at two levels of the functional hierarchy at a site of a world lead chemical industry, Perstorp, is handled. The activities are denoted production scheduling (PS) and detailed production scheduling (DPS). Real data of incoming orders and utility disturbances are used to produce a production schedule and detailed production schedule for one month. The PS and DPS problems are formulated as optimization problems, where production-related constraints such as production rate constraints, inventory limitations, and start-up costs are included. The objective functions of the PS and DPS problems are formulated to reflect the importance of different issues at the site. The procedure aims to show how the hierarchical optimization framework may be used to provide decision support for how to operate the production at a site in order to maximize profit while minimizing the effects of site-wide disturbances.

Keywords: production scheduling, utility disturbances, chemical industry, optimization

1. Introduction

To remain competitive, process industrial companies must continuously improve the operational efficiency and profitability (Bansal et al., 2005). The planning and scheduling activities are thus of great importance for these companies, and the functions can yield both for the nearest future and for decades ahead. Different planning strategies and their importance are described in Stadtler and Kilger (2008). Today, use of optimization for planning and scheduling is uncommon at industrial sites, and the tools are mainly spreadsheet based. Furthermore, disturbances in utilities are often not considered directly together with the planning and scheduling problems. The aim of this study is to use optimization methods for solving scheduling problems at two different levels of the functional hierarchy of a site. The solutions from the upper level (time step of days) will be used as input to the lower level (time step of hours), and the solutions from the lower level will in turn be used as feedback for the upper level. A general version of this hierarchical structure has been suggested previously in Lindholm (2013). In the current study, the structure is utilized to perform an industrial case study. To our knowledge, this is the first real industrial case study that is performed using this model structure. A similar two-level planning case study at an oil refinery can be found in

Zondervan et al. (2011). The models in the current study have been constructed using information on site structure, production and inventory limitations, utility usage, etc. from the industrial site. Simulation results for one month are produced with real input data, and are compared to actual plant operation during the same time period. The case study is performed at a site in Stenungsund, Sweden, that is operated by Perstorp. Perstorp produces chemical intermediates such as aldehydes and organic acids, which are delivered to industrial customers to be added to other products used in daily life, for example protective glass and windscreens in cars.

2. Problem description

In the case study, eight products at site Stenungsund that are produced in different production areas are considered, where each area has a separate inventory tank. The interconnection of the production areas and the inventories is shown in Figure 1. In this study, scheduling at two levels of the functional hierarchy at site Stenungsund is handled. The activities are denoted production scheduling (PS) and detailed production scheduling (DPS), in line with the definition in the standard ISA-95 (2005). The hierarchical structure for production scheduling that is presented in Lindholm (2013) is used. A brief description of the structure is given below.

2.1. Hierarchical scheduling

The PS activity produces a production schedule for one month ahead, which suggests how much to produce and sell of each product each day of the month, and how the inventories of the products at the site should be used. The PS activity aims to maximize profit, by minimizing the backlog of orders while considering production and inventory limitations. The schedule is updated each day in receding horizon, based on incoming orders and the actual production the previous day. The production schedule serves as a reference for the DPS activity, which produces a detailed production schedule for one day ahead. The DPS activity determines how the production should be controlled to handle disturbances on a time-scale of hours in an economically optimal way. In the current case study, the response to disturbances in the steam utility is studied. Steam is used by several of the production areas at site Stenungsund and disruptions in the steam supply thus give rise to site-wide disturbances. The detailed production schedule consists of trajectories that suggest how much to produce and sell each hour during the day, and how the buffer tanks at the site should be utilized. The schedule is updated each hour in receding horizon, based on predictions of the operation of the steam utility.

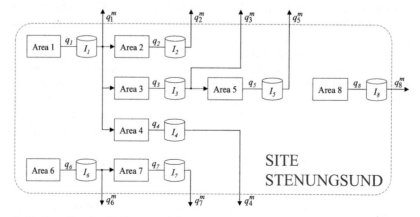

Figure 1. Product flow at site Stenungsund.

2.2. Model inputs and simulation parameters

In the case study, real data from two months during the previous year are used to produce production schedules and detailed production schedules for one month. Data used as input to the models are information on order quantities (i.e. the amount of each product that should be delivered from the site each day), and utility disturbance data (i.e. steam pressure of high and middle pressure steam). Furthermore, information about production-related constraints such as production rate constraints, inventory limitations, and start-up costs is gathered from the site to adapt the models for the PS and DPS. The objective functions of the PS and DPS are formulated to reflect the importance of different issues at the site.

3. Models

The models for the PS and DPS problems consist of constraints related to production, sales, and inventory limitations, and objective functions that aim to maximize the overall profit. Examples of constraints are the limitations due to maximum- and minimum production rates, inventory limitations and limitations due to start-up and shutdown of areas. There are also limitations due to utility disturbances. A simple model of utilities that was presented in Lindholm (2013) is used, that assumes a linear relationship between the amount of a utility that is available and the achievable production rates in the areas that use the utility. The constraints that make the scheduling problem complex are the mass balance constraints and the utility constraints, since these constraints define connections between different areas at the site. Areas are connected both by the flow of products through the site, and by sharing of utilities.

The objective functions of the PS and DPS problems reflect the trade-off between different issues at the site, such as minimizing late delivery of products, keeping the level of the inventories between reference intervals, minimizing variations in production rate, and avoiding shutdown and start-up of areas. For the DPS problem, it also has to be considered how important it is to follow the reference values for sales, production rates, and inventories that are given by the PS, in comparison to avoiding shutdowns and avoiding to change the production rate rapidly. A linear objective function is used for the PS, and a quadratic objective function for the DPS. The full models with all parameters and variables cannot be printed here due to space limitations, but can be found in Lindholm (2013).

4. Results and discussion

The scenario that is studied is the operation of the eight areas at site Stenungsund during one month the previous year. Real input data have been used both for the incoming orders and utility disturbances. The optimization for the PS level is performed each day in receding horizon with a horizon of one month, and the optimization for the DPS level is performed each hour in receding horizon with a horizon of one day. This means that for each optimization, input data (orders and utility disturbance trajectories) for one month/day ahead are needed. In the simulation, the DPS solution is given as feedback to the PS each day. The real data for sales, production rates and inventory usage are only used as initial conditions for the simulation. The utilities that are studied are middle-pressure (MP) steam and high-pressure (HP) steam, where there has been one major disturbance for each of them at day 17 of the month. During this day, MP steam operated at approximately 30 % of its maximum capacity for about 3 h, and HP steam operated at approximately 40 % of its maximum capacity for about 3 h. MP steam is required at areas 1, 2, 3, 4, 6 and 8, and HP steam is required only at area 1. In addition to the utility disturbances, there has also been a planned production disruption during the month. This is a planned shutdown of area 7 at day 11 for 20 h, which is also simulated.

Given the input data and the PS and DPS models according to Lindholm (2013), the hierarchical scheduling is performed for the eight areas at site Stenungsund. The resulting sales, production, and inventory trajectories after one month are shown in Figure 2-4. The notation can be found in Figure 1. As can be seen in Figure 2-4, the suggested sales, production and inventory trajectories given by the PS and DPS are similar to the actual operation of the site during the month, even if no feedback from the measurement data is performed during the simulation. The DPS solution follows the reference values from the PS very closely, which is why the PS solution is rarely visible in the figures. In Figure 2 it can be seen that the ordered volumes of each product are delivered on time most days, even in the presence of disturbances. If the ordered volumes are not delivered on time, they are delivered one or a few days later. In Figure 3 it can be seen that the available HP and MP steam is divided among the areas that require the utilities at the disturbance, day 17. All areas require steam except for area 5, but this area is also indirectly affected due to the area interconnections. Area 2, 3, 4, and 8 are run at the minimum rate during the disturbance, to avoid the high cost of shutting areas down. Area 1 is prioritized during the disturbance since this area provides raw material for several other areas in the network, and area 7 is prioritized because this is one of the most profitable products at the site.

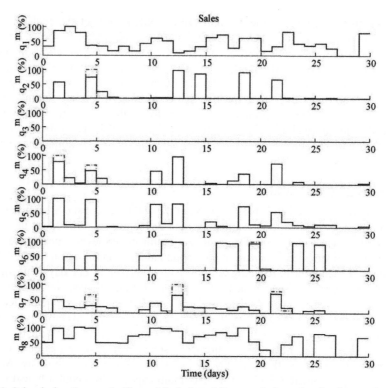

Figure 2. Sales during the month. The red dash-dotted lines mark the ordered volumes, the green dashed lines the PS solution and the blue solid lines the DPS solution.

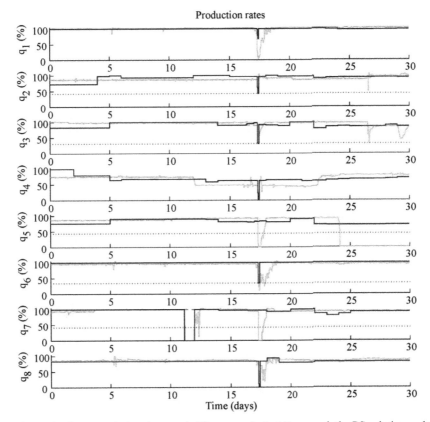

Figure 3. Production rates during the month. The green dashed lines mark the PS solution and the blue solid lines the DPS solution. The actual production rates are plotted in cyan in the same figure. Red dotted lines indicate the minimum production rates.

During the planned production disturbance at day 11, area 7 is forced being shut down. Since the start-up time of this area is 0 days, it can start up again directly after the disturbance. Figure 4 shows that the inventory usage according to the simulation is similar to the actual usage. The inventories are utilized to deliver orders on time and at the same time avoid changing the production rates rapidly. The levels are maintained within the reference intervals when possible, but when needed, they are allowed to deviate outside these intervals.

In the real data in Figures 2-4 it can be seen that the correspondence of the production rates and sales to the change of inventory does not always seem to be perfect for all products at all times. The reason for differences could be e.g. that there are other inventories or product flows of the same products that are not included in the measurements available to us. This indicates that the comparison of the real and simulated trajectories has to be taken with a grain of salt. A more thorough look at the measurement data together with Perstorp would probably make it possible to give a more fair comparison of the trajectories. Nevertheless, we believe that including the measurement data in the figures give some intuition on how well the model captures reality. When performing the scheduling online, this is not a problem since measurements are given as feedback to the DPS level.

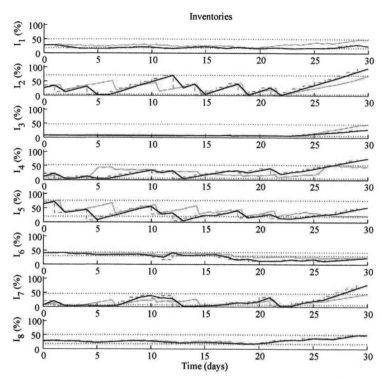

Figure 4. Inventory usage during the month. The green dashed lines mark the PS solution and the blue solid lines the DPS solution. The actual inventory usage is plotted in cyan in the same figure. Red dotted lines mark the reference intervals.

5. Conclusions

The presented case study shows that the suggested hierarchical scheduling procedure may be used as decision support for how to control the production at industrial sites at the occurrence of utility disturbances, or at planned production disturbances. Simulation results imply that the procedure should work well for monthly and daily production scheduling, using the hierarchical structure that is suggested.

Acknowledgement

The research is performed within the Process Industry Centre (PIC) supported by the Swedish Foundation for Strategic Research (SSF).

References

M. Bansal, A. Adhitya, R. Srinivasan, I.A. Karimi, 2005, An online decision support framework for managing abnormal supply chain events, Comput. Aided Chem. Eng., 20, 985-90.

ISA-95.00.03, 2005, Enterprise-Control System Integration, Part 3: Models of Manufacturing Operations Management, Standard, Instrument Society of America, US.

A. Lindholm, 2013, Hierarchical scheduling and utility disturbance management in the process industry, PhD thesis, Lund University, Sweden.

H. Stadtler, C. Kilger, 2008, Supply Chain Management and Advanced Planning, Springer, New York, US.

E. Zondervan, T.P.J. van Boekel, J.C. Fransoo, A.B. de Haan, 2011, Simultaneous optimization of planning and scheduling in an oil refinery, Computer Aided Chemical Engineering, 29, 925-9.

Jiří Jaromír Klemeš, Petar Sabev Varbanov and Peng Yen Liew (Editors)
Proceedings of the 24th European Symposium on Computer Aided Process Engineering – ESCAPE 24
June 15-18, 2014, Budapest, Hungary.

An Extended Comparative Study of Two- and Three-Way Methodologies for the On-line Monitoring of Batch Processes

Raquel D. Moita, Véronique M. Gomes, Pedro M. Saraiva, Marco S. Reis*

CIEPQPF, Chemical Engineering Department, University of Coimbra, Polo II – Pinhal de Marrocos, 3030-790 Coimbra, Portugal

marco@eq.uc.pt

Abstract

Last decades witnessed a significant increase in the production of high-valued products from industrial batch processes. Dynamic (non-stationary) behavior is an intrinsic characteristic of this class of processes. In this work the performance of several 2- and 3-way multivariate statistical methods able to cope with these features in on-line batch process monitoring are compared, along with the use of different control limits and data infilling methods. PCA, combined with leave-one-out control limits and current deviation or zero deviation infilling methodologies, shows the best overall performance.

Keywords: Batch process monitoring, MPCA, Tucker3, PARAFAC, Comparison study

1. Introduction

During a batch run several process variables are measured along time, generating potentially valuable information about the process. The data structure generated by a batch process consists of a 3-way data array, $\underline{\mathbf{X}}$, of size $(I \times J \times K)$, where I is the number of batches, J the number of variables and K the number of time intervals. Several multivariate statistical methodologies were developed for the monitoring and diagnosis of batch processes. These include 2- and 3-way approaches. As well as studies accounting for different durations or unsynchronized batches trajectories. For instance, González-Martínez et al. (2011) recently analyzed the batch synchronization problem.

Despite the extensive reference to the good performance of 2-way and 3-way methods in the literature, the pros and cons of each class of methodologies is still not well established for on-line methods. Therefore, with the purpose of evaluating the mentioned methodologies, we have devised an extensive and rigorous comparison study involving the leading 2-way and 3-way batch process monitoring methodologies. It is extensive, because we compared the main representatives by taking into account the several options available for data filling of future observations during on-line monitoring, as well as different methodologies to establish the control limits for the statistics. It is also rigorous, because the comparison was made in terms of objective and robust performance metrics regarding detection ability, namely by computing the receiver operating characteristic curve, ROC. The monitoring performance of all the studied methodologies was compared and evaluated through a simulated batch process, in which several faults take place, with different magnitudes and starting times. Built upon those results and analysis, general guidelines can be provided, acting as a decision supporting strategy for the proper selection of the batch process monitoring approaches, to be applied according to the specific scenario under analysis.

In the following section we will present the methods used in this analysis. Section 3 presents the case study used in the simulations. In section 4 we present the results, and in section 5 we summarize our main conclusions.

2. Methods

In this section we present the monitoring methods that will be considered in the extensive comparison study along with the several alternative ways to address the estimation of future data (data infilling, which is a common trace among all 2-way and 3-way methodologies) and to establish the control limits for the monitoring statistics.

2.1. Monitoring methods

The proper monitoring of the dynamic profiles found in batch processes raise important challenges to process monitoring activities, leading to the proposal of a variety of multivariate statistical process control methods. These approaches have in common the typical 2-phase process: Phase 1 for analysing process stability and estimating the normal operation conditions (NOC) model and control limits; Phase 2 for monitoring future incoming batches. Several multivariate statistical methodologies have been proposed for monitoring and diagnosing batch processes. These include both 2-way and 3-way approaches. Here we present a brief description of the monitoring methods used in the extended comparison study, which represent the variety of current state of the art approaches.

2-way approaches. Based on Multiway Principal Component Analysis (MPCA) proposed by Nomikos and MacGregor (1995). The MPCA technique corresponds to unfolding the 3-dimensional array $\underline{\mathbf{X}}$ ($I{\times}J{\times}K$) slice by slice, rearranging the slices into a large 2-dimensional matrix $\mathbf{X}$ and then applying regular PCA. The unfolding operation results in a two dimensional matrix preserving the batch mode, $\mathbf{X}$ ($I{\times}JK$), with the first slice corresponding to the first time interval situated on the left side. The data are then mean centered and scaled prior to performing PCA, ensuring that the global dynamic trends or mean trajectories for each variable are removed before applying PCA. The $\mathbf{X}$ data is decomposed into a summation of products of scores vectors (t) and loadings matrices (p), plus residuals (E), which are as small as possible in the (orthogonal) least square sense. The scores vectors are orthogonal and the loadings matrices are orthonormal.

3-way approaches. This class of approaches consists of different trilinear decompositions of $\underline{\mathbf{X}}$ ($I{\times}J{\times}K$) performed by several chemometric methods (Louwerse and Smilde, 2000), such as PARAFAC and Tucker3, both constituting a generalization of principal component analysis to 3-way data structures. Tucker3 provides a decomposition of the 3-way array into three orthogonal loadings (A, B and C) and a core matrix (G) plus a residual matrix (E). The PARAFAC model is written in terms of the product of the three loading matrices (A, B and C) plus a matrix of residuals (E). This last 3-way method differs from Tucker3, mainly because each of its three dimensions cannot be flexibly combined as occurs in the Tucker3 model, due to the nature of its core matrix. Furthermore, PARAFAC also requires that all loading matrices share the same number of components.

2.2. Infilling future observations

A common problem to both 2-way and 3-way approaches for on-line batch process monitoring, regards the need to have access to the full length of the batch in order to estimate the scores associated with each method. As this is not possible during batch operation, some scheme must be adopted to infill such future data and allow the monitoring statistics to be computed. In this context, several methods were proposed (Nomikos and MacGregor, 1995), namely: the current deviation (CD) approach, which assumes that future data maintain the same deviation regarding the reference trajectory as observed in the current time; zero deviation (ZD) approach, where no deviations are considered to exist in future data; and projection data (PD) approach, consisting on estimating future measurements as missing data values using a PCA projection operation.

2.3. Control Limits

As referred before, NOC models are estimated during Phase 1 for all methods, using a reference dataset with normal operation data. Then, using such dataset and the estimated NOC models, the statistical control limits for the several monitoring statistics are finally established, which will be used to monitor on-line the new profiles during Phase 2. Two types of monitor statistics are used in each method (2-way or 3-way): one involving the method's scores, T^2 or D, Eq. (1) (for monitoring the variability in the latent variables subspace) and another statistic involving the residuals, Q, Eq. (2) (for monitoring the variability around the latent variable space).

Different methodologies to establish the control limits for the statistics have been applied and in this paper we also propose a comparison between them.

<u>Current control limits I</u>: Eqs. (1) and (2) define the D and Q statistics (these formulas hold for the 3-way methods, but those for the 2-way methods are similar). a_{new} are the scores of the new sample at time k, $\overline{a}_{I,k}$, is the mean of scores at time k for the reference samples, and S is the covariance matrix of the reference scores. m and v are the estimated mean and variance for the Q-statistic obtained from reference samples. The control limits for the D statistic are obtained from an F-distribution with $(L,I-L)$ degrees of freedom, $F_{L,I-L,a}$, and, in an approximate way through the moments of the $g.\chi^2$ distribution for the Q statistic.

$$D_k = \left(a_{new,k} - \overline{a}_{I,k}\right)^T S^{-1} \left(a_{new,k} - \overline{a}_{I,k}\right) \sim \frac{I(I-L)}{L(I^2-1)} \tag{1}$$

$$Q_{i,k} = \sum_{j=1}^{J}\sum_{k=1}^{K} e_{ijk}^2 \sim g \cdot \chi_{h,\alpha}^2 \,, \quad g = v/2m\,, \quad h = 2m^2/v \tag{2}$$

<u>Current control limits II</u>: are the same as above, except that a time window of k-1 to k+1 is considered in the computation of the Q-statistic at each time k.

<u>Leave-One-Out control limits</u>: one batch is removed from the reference set of NOC data and a model is estimated with the remaining ones. This NOC batch is treated as a new batch and projected onto the model estimated by the other ones, leading to profiles for the D and Q statistics. The limits are computed using all profiles obtained through this procedure where each batch was left out once, and the monitoring statistics computed for each one of them.

3. Case study

The studied system, adapted from Ingham et al. (2007), consists of a semi-batch non-stationary reactor in which an exothermic reaction between two reactants takes place: $A + B \rightarrow C$. The reactor is fitted with a cooling jacket and includes a PI control system to maintain the reactor temperature (T_R) within its target value (~25 °C), by controlling the jacket fluid volumetric flow rate (F_C). The performance of the control unit was optimized by determining the best parameters values of the mentioned PI control system. The model developed was simulated in the Matlab platform. Its 6 output variables were used for on-line statistical monitoring. Variability was added into the simulations through different dynamic time profiles for the input variables (loads), different initial batch conditions and noise in the measured variables.

4. Results and discussion

The proposed monitoring methods along with the three infilling approaches (CD, ZD, PD) and the three alternatives for establishing the control limits for the monitoring statistics described before (current control limits I, current control limits II and leave-one-out), were applied to on-line batch process monitoring. In our study, a total of 200 batches representing normal operation conditions were simulated to estimate the two and 3-way models and to develop their control limits. Seven different types of faults were simulated with six different magnitudes each, from the lower (1) to the highest (6). Each combination of fault/magnitude contains ten batches runs replicates. The test datasets, with dimensions $\underline{X}_{new}$ (60×6×601) and representing a given fault, are projected onto the estimated model subspace and the several control charts constructed.

The performance of the different on-line monitoring statistics was carefully compared, in such a way that one can appreciate the relative merits of the type of monitoring method, infilling approach and the different ways to compute the control limits. In order to compare all the methodologies and evaluate the monitoring performance of each combination (method/in-filling/control limits), the ability to detect a fault occurrence was analyzed through the receiver operating characteristic curve, ROC curve. This curve is obtained by varying the control limits and computing the associated true positive rate (TPR) and false positive rate (FPR), Eq.(3). This analysis allows for the evaluation of the sensitivity and specificity performances of all the models. The area under curve (AUC) is registered as the outcome based on which the several methods are compared at the lowest level. An AUC close to one indicates a high sensitivity and specificity of the associated approach, and therefore a good performance of the methodology combination.

$$TPR = \frac{TP}{TP+FN}, \quad FPR = \frac{FP}{FP+TN} \tag{3}$$

TP and *FN* are the number of true fault detections and undetected faults, respectively. *FP* and *TN* are the number of false alarms and correctly detected NOC observations.

The performance for a given combination of faults and magnitude ($P_{f/M,i}$) is based on the relative performance of each different approach, regarding the AUC values obtained in the 10 replicates.

Table 1. Global procedure for the comparison of all combinations of methodologies.

A. For each combination *i*: method (2-way, 3-way approach), in-filling (current deviation, zero deviation, projection data) and control limit (current control limit I, current control limit II, leave-one-out), perform the following steps:

Step 1. Compute AUC for each statistic, *D* and *Q*, for method *i=1,...,n* over the dataset containing the replicates *j=1,...,p*, for all faults *f=1,...,F* and all magnitudes *m=1,...,M*;

$$\left\{AUC_{i,j}^{D}\right\}, \ \left\{AUC_{i,j}^{Q}\right\} \tag{4}$$

Step 2. Determine the performance of each method *i* for each fault/magnitude combination, $P_{f/M,i}$; (see description in table 2);

B. Evaluate the global performance relative to each methodology, i, in a global ranking tanking into accounting all faults and magnitudes. Find the:

B.1 Best method (comparison between 2-way and 3-way approaches);

B.2 Best control limit (comparison between control limits described before);

B.3 Best in-filling (comparison between current dev., zero dev. and projection data).

For each method, *i*, the performance indices are used to compare and rank the methods (two and 3-way), the in-filling methods and the three different techniques of control limits, from the best (1) to the worst (3). The global steps of the comparison are described in Table 1. The computation of the $P_{f/M,i}$ for a given combination of method, in-filling and control limit is detailed in Table 2.

The global ranking was computed taking into account all faults and magnitudes by counting the number of times that a given combination appears in first, second and third place in a decreasing ordering of performance. To compare the 2- and 3-way approaches, all combinations for infilling and control limits were counted and a ranking of the position, from the best (1) to the worst (3), was created. The same procedure was followed for comparing the in-filling methods and control limits.

Table 2. Algorithm for the computation of the performance for a combination fault/magnitude, for a given method (*i* is the methods' index, and *j* the replicate index).

---

a) For each method *i=1:n*, pick the best AUC for the monitoring statistics (D or Q):

$$best_{i,j} = \max\left\{AUC_{i,j}^{D}, AUC_{i,j}^{Q}\right\} \tag{5}$$

b) Compute the relative performance of method *i=1,...,n* in the *j*th replicate:

$$RP_{i,j} = \frac{best_{i,j} - m_j}{M_j - m_j} \times 100 \tag{6}$$

Where m_j and M_j are the performances for the worst and best methods in replicate *j*,

$$m_j = \min\left\{best_{i,j}\right\}, \ M_j = \max\left\{best_{i,j}\right\} \tag{7}$$

c) Compute the $P_{f/M,i}$ for each fault/magnitude based on average performance:

$$P_{f/m,i} = \frac{\sum\limits_{j=1}^{p} RP_{i,j}}{p} \tag{8}$$

Table 3. Global ranking of all methodologies presented in this study.

		First	Second	Third
Methods:	PCA (2-way)	319	30	29
	Tucker3 (3-way)	37	226	115
	PARAFAC (3-way)	22	122	234
In-filling approaches:	Current deviation	160	87	131
	Zero deviation	145	150	83
	Projection data	73	141	163
Control limits:	Current control limit I	107	182	79
	Current control limit II	103	43	232
	Leave-One-Out	168	153	57

Table 3 summarizes all the results obtained in the extensive comparison between all the metrics proposed. Analysing the results, we can verify that the 2-way model occupies a better position in the ranking followed by the 3-way Tucker3 model. In what concerns to the in-filling methods for predicting future observations, we can conclude that current deviation is the best approach followed closely by zero deviation. Regarding the control limits alternatives, the technique leave-one-out presents the best overall ranking. The comparison results suggest that the 2-way approach, PCA, when combined with leave-one-out control limits and current deviation or zero deviation filling methodologies, tends to present the best overall performance for on-line batch process monitoring.

5. Conclusions

In this work, we have conducted a thorough comparison study of the performance of different multivariate statistical methodologies for on-line batch process monitoring, which also includes three different ways to establish control limits and different in-filling methods for predicting future observations. PCA, when combined with leave-one-out control limits and current deviation or zero deviation infilling methodologies, shows the best performance.

In future work we will extend the study in order to also include the analysis of the speed of detection, through the evaluation of the so called conditional expected delay, CED.

Acknowledgements

The authors acknowledge financial support through projects PTDC/EQU-ESI/108597/2008 and PTDC/EQU-ESI/108374/2008 co-financed by the Portuguese FCT and European Union's FEDER through "Eixo I do Programa Operacional Factores de Competitividade (POFC)" of QREN (with ref. FCOMP-01-0124-FEDER-010398 and FCOMP-01-0124-FEDER-010397, respectively).

References

J.M. González-Martínez, A. Ferrer, J. Westerhuis, 2011, Real-time synchronization of batch trajectories for on-line multivariate statistical process control using dynamic time warping, Chemometrics and Intelligent Laboratory Systems, 105, 196-205.

J. Ingham, I.J. Dunn, E. Heinzle, J.E. Prenosil, J.B. Snape, 2007, Chemical engineering dynamics: an introduction to modelling and computer simulation, Wiley-VCH, Weinheim, Germany.

D.J Louwerse, A.K. Smilde, 2000, Multivariate statistical process control of batch processes based on three-way models, Chemical Engineering Science, 55, 1225-1235.

P. Nomikos, J.F. MacGregor, 1995, Multivariate SPC charts for monitoring batch process, Technometrics, 37, 41-59.

Jiří Jaromír Klemeš, Petar Sabev Varbanov and Peng Yen Liew (Editors)
Proceedings of the 24th European Symposium on Computer Aided Process Engineering – ESCAPE 24
June 15-18, 2014, Budapest, Hungary.

Integrated Scheduling and Dynamic Optimization for Network Batch Processes

Yunfei Chu, Fengqi You[*]

Department of Chemical & Biological Engineering, Northwestern University, Evanston, IL 60208 USA.
you@northwestern.edu

Abstract

We address the integration of scheduling and dynamic optimization for batch processes that have complex network structures, allowing material splitting and mixing. The integrated problem is formulated into a mixed-integer nonlinear programming (MINLP) problem. To reduce the computational complexity, we develop a tailored and efficient decomposition method based on the framework of generalized Benders decomposition by exploiting the special structure of the integrated problem. The decomposed master problem is a scheduling problem with variable processing times and processing costs, as well as the Benders cuts. The primal problem comprises a set of separable dynamic optimization problems for the processing units. In comparison with the simultaneous method which solves the integrated problem by a general-purpose MINLP solver, the proposed method can reduce computational times by orders of magnitude, although global optimality of the solutions cannot be guaranteed for non-convex problems.

Keywords: Scheduling, dynamic optimization, generalized Benders decomposition

1. Introduction

In traditional production hierarchy, scheduling and dynamic optimization problems are usually solved separately in a sequential way. Though widely applied, the sequential method only returns a suboptimal solution for the entire batch process. To improve the performance of the entire process, the two problems should be solved in an integrated way (Wassick et al., 2012). However, solving the integrated problem is much more challenging than solving the subproblems sequentially. The complexity arises from the coupling of binary variables in the scheduling problem with differential equations characterizing the dynamic models. The integration results in a complicated mixed-integer dynamic optimization (MIDO) problem (Engell and Harjunkoski, 2012). Due to the complexity, most integrated scheduling and dynamic optimization approaches are restricted to continuous processes (Flores-Tlacuahuac and Grossmann, 2006). An integration framework with PI controllers is proposed by Chu and You (2012). An efficient method for solving the integrated problem of a polymerization process is developed based on the generalized Benders decomposition (Chu and You, 2013c). However, relatively few methods, e.g. Chu and You (2013a), are developed for batch processes. Nie et al. (2012) formulates the integrated problem using state equipment networks. Chu and You (2013b) extends the generalized Benders decomposition method to sequential batch processes. The integrated problem under uncertainties is solved by a two-stage stochastic programming method (Chu and You, 2013d). Recently, Chu and You (2014) proposed a moving horizon approach for the integrated scheduling and control of sequential batch processes.

Even for the batch process, the complexity of the integrated problem depends on the process structure. Generally, there are two types of batch processes: the sequential process where material splitting and mixing are not allowed, and the network process where these operations are allowed (Mendez et al., 2006). In a sequential process, the batch integrity is preserved and the batch size is fixed. Taking advantage of these special features, an efficient integrated method can be developed for the sequential process. However, a network batch process is intrinsically much more complex than a sequential batch scheduling problem (Chu et al., 2014). Consequently, methods applicable to a sequential process generally cannot be extended to a network process.

This work proposes an efficient and effective method to solve the challenging integrated problem for batch processes with a general network structure. We first formulate the integrated problem as an MINLP by discretizing the differential equations into algebraic equations using a collocation method. Then, we develop a tailored solution method based on the framework of generalized Benders decomposition (GBD) (Floudas, 1995) to solve the formulated MINLP problem. A case study demonstrates advantages of the proposed method. The proposed method finds the optimal solution in about 6 minutes while the simultaneous method only finds a suboptimal one within 24 hours.

2. Problem statement

The problem statement of the integrated scheduling and dynamic optimization for batch processes is given below.

Production model
    Batch process with general network structures where material splitting and mixing are allowed
Given
    Process structure
    Processing units and their usages
    Production horizon
    Order demands and unit price of products
    Unit cost of raw materials and utilities
    Fixed and variable processing costs for performing a task
    Lower and upper bounds on batch sizes and processing times
    Storage policies and capacities of storage tanks
    Species concentrations in all states
    Differential equations describing a dynamic model
    Safety and quality constraints
    Expression of the processing costs
Determine
    Unit assignment for performing a task
    Production sequence of tasks in a unit
    Starting time of each task
    Processing time, processing cost, and batch size for each task
    Dynamic trajectories of operating variables, e.g. flowrates, temperatures, and concentrations
Objective
    Maximize the profit within the production horizon

---

3. Model formulation and solution algorithm

The detailed mathematical formulation can be seen in (Chu and You, 2013a). The integrated problem can be expressed in a compact form as

$$
\max \left\{ \varphi\left(\xi, \{VPT_{ijk}\}_{\forall j,\, i\in I_j^{dyn},\, k<n_k}, \{B_{ijk}\}_{\forall j,\, i\in I_j^{dyn},\, k<n_k}\right) - \sum_{i\in I_j^{dyn},j,k<n_k} \Phi_{ijk}\left(\omega_{ijk}, T_{ijk}^{final}, V_{ijk}\right) \right\} \tag{1}
$$

s.t.

$$
g^{Sch}\left(\xi, \{VPT_{ijk}\}_{\forall j,\, i\in I_j^{dyn},\, k<n_k}, \{B_{ijk}\}_{\forall j,\, i\in I_j^{dyn},\, k<n_k}\right) \le 0 \tag{2}
$$

$$
g_{ijk}^{Dyn}\left(\omega_{ijk}, T_{ijk}^{final}, V_{ijk}\right) \le 0,\ \forall j,\, i\in I_j^{dyn},\, k<n_k \tag{3}
$$

$$
T_{ijk}^{final} = VPT_{ijk},\ \forall j,\, i\in I_j^{dyn},\, k<n_k \tag{4}
$$

$$
V_{ijk} = B_{ijk},\ \forall j,\, i\in I_j^{dyn},\, k<n_k \tag{5}
$$

where VPT_{ijk} is the processing time of stage k for job j executed in unit i, B_{ijk} is the batch size. These variables correspond T_{ijk}^{final} and V_{ijk} in the dynamic models. The remaining scheduling variables are stacked into ξ and the remaining variables in the dynamic models are stacked into ω_{ijk}. In the objective function (1), the last term of the total processing cost is the sum of those over the dynamic models. The constraints in the vector g^{Sch} in Eq.(2) represent the scheduling model while the constraints in the vector g_{ijk}^{Dyn} in Eq.(3) represent the dynamic models. The last two Eqs.(4) and (5) are linking constraints.

Based on the compact formulation of the integrated problem, we develop a GBD method. The primal problem is

$$
\eta_{ijk}\left(\overline{VPT}_{ijk}^{(l)}, \overline{B}_{ijk}^{(l)}\right) = \min\ \Phi_{ijk}\left(\omega_{ijk}, T_{ijk}^{final}, V_{ijk}\right) \tag{6}
$$

s.t.

$$
g_{ijk}^{Dyn}\left(\omega_{ijk}, T_{ijk}^{final}, V_{ijk}\right) \le 0 \tag{7}
$$

$$
T_{ijk}^{final} = \overline{VPT}_{ijk}^{(l)} \tag{8}
$$

$$
V_{ijk} = \overline{B}_{ijk}^{(l)} \tag{9}
$$

The master problem is formulated as

$$
v^* = \max \left\{ \varphi\left(\xi, \{VPT_{ijk}\}_{\forall j,\, i\in I_j^{dyn},\, k<n_k}, \{B_{ijk}\}_{\forall j,\, i\in I_j^{dyn},\, k<n_k}\right) - \sum_{i\in I_j^{dyn},j,k<n_k} \eta_{ijk} \right\} \tag{10}
$$

s.t.

$$
g^{Sch}\left(\xi, \{VPT_{ijk}\}_{\forall j,\, i\in I_j^{dyn},\, k<n_k}, \{B_{ijk}\}_{\forall j,\, i\in I_j^{dyn},\, k<n_k}\right) \le 0
$$

$$
\eta_{ijk} \ge \overline{\Phi}_{ijk}^{(l')} - \overline{\lambda}_{ijk}^{(l')}VPT_{ijk} - \overline{\gamma}_{ijk}^{(l')}B_{ijk},\ \forall j,\, i\in I_j^{dyn},\, k<n_k,\, l'\le l \tag{11}
$$

The Benders cut constraints are appended sequentially to the master problem as expressed in Eq.(11) where l' and l denote the iteration step. The coefficients in the constraints are calculated as

$$
\overline{\Phi}_{ijk}^{(l')} = \Phi_{ijk}^* + \lambda_{ijk}^* T_{ijk}^{final*} + \gamma_{ijk}^* V_{ijk}^*,\ \lambda_{ijk}^{(l')} = \lambda_{ijk}^*,\ \gamma_{ijk}^{(l')} = \gamma_{ijk}^* \tag{12}
$$

where Φ^*_{ijk}, T^{final*}_{ijk}, V^*_{ijk}, λ^*_{ijk}, and γ^*_{ijk} are the optimal function value, solution and dual variables from solving the primal problem in the l'-th iteration.

The flow chart of the GBD method is shown in Figure 1. The master problem and the primal problem only provide the upper and lower bounds for the optimal value. We need to iterate between the two subproblems to reduce the gap between the upper bound and the lower bound. We initialize the method by fixing the complicating variables at some value. Since they are variables in the scheduling model, we can simply fix them at the optimal solution of the scheduling problem solved by the sequential method. Then the primal problem is solved with the fixed complicating variables. It is a separable dynamic optimization problem where each dynamic model can be optimized independently. The solution of the primal problem is used to update the lower bound and generate the Benders' cut constraints for the master problem. The master problem is solved to update the upper bound. The iteration terminates when the gap is less than a threshold value.

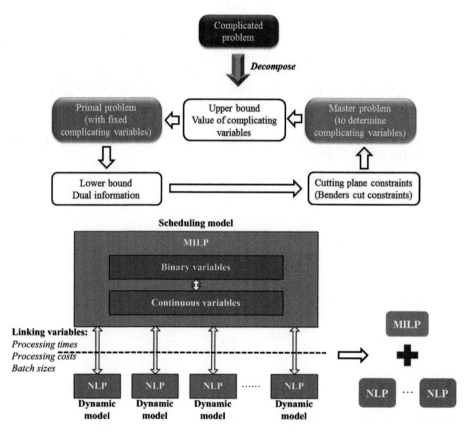

Figure 1. Flow chart of generalized Benders decomposition algorithm for the integration problem.

4. Case study

The batch plant consists of 5 processing units, including one mixing tank, two reactors (one large and one small), one separation unit and one packing unit. Among the five units, we model the dynamics of the two reactors. The process diagram is displayed in Figure 2. The model and solution statistics are listed in Table 1. By using the integrated optimization approach, a complicated MINLP problem has to be solved. The MINLP problem is solved by SBB which is the common solver for the integrated problems. After 24 h, the optimality gap still remains as large as 27.5 %. To reduce the complexity of the integrated problem, we apply the proposed method.

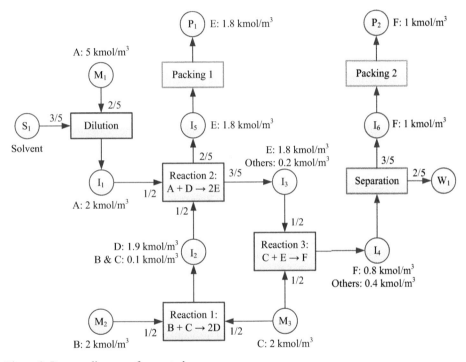

Figure 2. Process diagram of case study

Table 1. Model and solution statistics

Method	Simultaneous	Proposed
Obj. (m.u.)	2,191.7	2,650.5
CPU (s)	86,400	385.6
Gap	27.5 %	1.0 %
Equations	–	1,509×54
Variables	–	1,436×54
Type	MINLP	MILP
Equations	88,338	2,471
Variables	83,772	2,030
Binary var.	145	145
Solver	SBB with CONOPT 3	CPLEX 12

With gap of 1 % set as the same as the simultaneous method, the computational time is 385.6 s, which is much shorter by 2 orders of magnitude than the simultaneous method. More importantly, the proposed method solves the integrated problem to the 1.0 % optimality gap. As a result, it returns a much higher profit by 21.0 % than the simultaneous method.

5. Conclusion

The integrated scheduling and dynamic optimization on a batch process is formulated into a large-scale MINLP, which is challenging to solve. To overcome the computational complexity, we propose an efficient and effective decomposition method based on the GBD framework. In the case study, the simultaneous method only returns a suboptimal solution within the resource limit of 24 h. The remaining gap is as large as 27.5 %. The suboptimal solution is further improved by 21.0 % using the proposed method, which solves the problem to 1.0 % optimality gap in about 6.5 minutes. When the integrated problem is non-convex, the decomposition method as well as the simultaneous method may fail to find the global optimal solution.

References

Y. Chu, F. You, 2012, Integration of scheduling and control with online closed-loop implementation: Fast computational strategy and large-scale global optimization algorithm, Computers and Chemical Engineering, 47, 248-268.

Y. Chu, F. You, 2013a, Integrated scheduling and dynamic optimization of complex batch processes with general network structure using a generalized Benders decomposition approach, Industrial and Engineering Chemistry Research, 52, 7867-7885.

Y. Chu, F. You, 2013b, Integrated scheduling and dynamic optimization of sequential batch processes with online implementation, AIChE Journal, 59, 2379-2406.

Y. Chu, F. You, 2013c. Integration of production scheduling and dynamic optimization for multi-product CSTRs: Generalized Benders decomposition coupled with global mixed-integer fractional programming, Computers and Chemical Engineering, 58, 315-333.

Y. Chu, F. You, 2013d. Integration of scheduling and dynamic optimization of batch processes under uncertainty: Two-stage stochastic programming approach and enhanced generalized Benders decomposition algorithm, Industrial and Engineering Chemistry Research 52, 16851–16869.

Y. Chu, F. You, 2014. Moving horizon approach of integrating scheduling and control for sequential batch processes. AIChE Journal, Accepted. DOI: 10.1002/aic.14359

Y. Chu, F. You, J.M. Wassick, 2014. Hybrid method integrating agent-based modeling and heuristic tree search for scheduling of complex batch processes. Computers and Chemical Engineering, 60, 277-296.

S. Engell, I. Harjunkoski, 2012, Optimal operation: Scheduling, advanced control and their integration, Computers & Chemical Engineering, 47, 121-133.

A. Flores-Tlacuahuac, I. E. Grossmann, 2006, Simultaneous cyclic scheduling and control of tubular reactors: Parallel production lines, Industrial and Engineering Chemistry Research, 45, 6698-6712.

C. A. Floudas, 1995, Nonlinear and mixed-integer optimization: fundamentals and applications, Oxford University Press, New York, USA.

C. A. Mendez, J. Cerda, I. E. Grossmann, I. Harjunkoski, M. Fahl, 2006, State-of-the-art review of optimization methods for short-term scheduling of batch processes, Computers and Chemical Engineering, 30, 913-946.

Y. Nie, L. T. Biegler, J. M. Wassick, 2012, Integrated scheduling and dynamic optimization of batch processes using state equipment networks, AIChE Journal, 58, 3416-3432.

J. M. Wassick, A. Agarwal, N. Akiya, J. Ferrio, S. Bury, F. Q. You, 2012, Addressing the operational challenges in the development, manufacture, and supply of advanced materials and performance products, Computers and Chemical Engineering, 47, 157-169.

Jiří Jaromír Klemeš, Petar Sabev Varbanov and Peng Yen Liew (Editors)
Proceedings of the 24th European Symposium on Computer Aided Process Engineering – ESCAPE 24
June 15-18, 2014, Budapest, Hungary.

Integration of Scheduling and Control Using Internal Coupling Models

Jungup Park[a], Juan Du[a], Iiro Harjunkoski[b], Michael Baldea[a],*

[a]*McKetta Department of Chemical Engineering, The University of Texas at Austin, 200 East Dean Keeton St., Stop C0400, Austin, TX 78712, USA*
[b]*ABB AG Corporate Research, Wallstadter Str. 59, 68526 Ladenburg, Germany*
mbaldea@che.utexas.edu

Abstract

In this paper, we present a novel framework for the integration of scheduling and control of process systems. We introduce internal coupling models (ICMs), defined as (low-order) representations of the closed-loop input-output behaviour of the process under supervisory control. We explore the derivation of ICMs for a specific class of input-output linearizing nonlinear controllers. Then, we formulate the scheduling problem as a mixed-integer dynamic optimization under the constraints imposed by the ICM, aimed at finding the optimal setpoint trajectory for the supervisory controller. We illustrate these concepts with a case study, demonstrating that ICM-based scheduling has comparable performance to other scheduling approaches in the absence of plant-model mismatch, and vastly outperforms them when mismatch is present.

Keywords: Short-term Scheduling, Control, Integrated Scheduling and Control

1. Introduction

Scheduling and control are essential components of the operation of chemical process systems, and it is anticipated that a closer interaction and integration of these operational layers can lead to important economic benefits (Harjunkoski et al., 2009). As the scheduling and control problems are closely related at the fundamental mathematical level, one would expect this integration process to be seamless, and to be supported by recent advances in communication technology, which simplify enterprise-wide sharing of the relevant data and information. Yet, and in spite of industrial efforts and academic interest, the development of a comprehensive and rational framework for integrating scheduling and control continues to be confronted several theoretical (Harjunkoski et al., 2009) and organizational challenges (Shobrys and White, 2002), and remains an important open problem in process systems engineering.

In this paper, we propose the use of an explicit low-order model of the closed-loop input-output behaviour of a process under supervisory control as the internal coupling model for integrating short-term scheduling and supervisory control. Within this novel framework, the scheduling layer relies on the closed-loop process model to perform *dynamic* scheduling in a computationally efficient fashion. The result of the scheduling calculation is a sequence of *setpoint* changes, which are then imposed in the process by the supervisory controller, with the latter being designed to produce a well-defined closed-loop behaviour which is captured by the low-order model. This is possible owing to, i) the time scale separation between supervisory control and distributed control in a process, (i.e., the supervisory controller acts over a longer time horizon), as well as, ii) the proximity in time scale between supervisory control and short term scheduling (see, e.g., Baldea and Daoutidis, 2012). Our approach allows scheduling and control calculations to be performed transparently and independently using a decomposition-based strategy, increasing solution speed as well as the robustness and resilience of the integrated system. The proposed concepts are illustrated using a case study concerning a four-product reactor with highly nonlinear behaviour.

2. Internal Coupling Models for Integration of Scheduling and Control

2.1. Scheduling Problem Formulation

We rely on the developments in (Flores-Tlacuahuac and Grossmann, 2006) to formulate the cyclical process scheduling problem as described below. The objective is to maximize overall production profit (Eq.(1)).

$$\max \left(\sum_{i=1}^{N_P} C_i^P W_i / T_c - \sum_{i=1}^{N_P} \left\{ C_i^{inv} \left(G_i - W_i / T_C \right) \sum_{k=1}^{N_S} tp_{i,k} / 2 \right\} \right) \tag{1}$$

where the first term represents profit and the second term stands for inventory cost. Index i represents the product number and index k represents the time slots for the production cycle. N_P is the total number of products and C_i^P is the product price. The decision variables are the total production time (T_c), the production time for product i in time slot k ($tp_{i,k}$) and the optimal production sequence ($z_{i,k}$). Eq.(2) enforces that only one product can be manufactured in each time slot. Eq.(3) states that within one production cycle, the product can be manufactured only once. $z_{i,k}$ is a binary variable that determines the production of product i in time slot k. N_S represents the number of time slots, which is the same as the total number of products.

$$\sum_{i=1}^{N_P} z_{i,k} = 1, \ \forall k \tag{2}$$

$$\sum_{k=1}^{N_S} z_{i,k} = 1, \ \forall i \tag{3}$$

Eq.(4) defines the amount of the product i (W_i) produced as a product of the production time ($\sum_k tp_{i,k}$) and the production rate (G_i). Eq.(5) enforces that the manufactured amount is greater than the demand rate of the product (D_i) times the total production time (T_c).

$$W_i = G_i \sum_{k=1}^{N_S} tp_{i,k}, \ \forall i \tag{4}$$

$$W_i \geq D_i T_C, \ \forall i \tag{5}$$

The timing relation in Eq.(6) computes the time at the end of slot k (t_k^e) as the sum of the start time (t_k^s), the processing time ($\sum_i tp_{i,k}$) and the transition time (τ_k). Eq.(7) states that the start time of each slot is the end time of the previous slot. Eq.(8) enforces that the end time of each slot is not greater than the total production time.

$$t_k^e = t_k^s + \tau_k + \sum_{i=1}^{N_P} tp_{i,k}, \ \forall k \tag{6}$$

$$t_k^s = t_{k-1}^e, \ \forall k \neq 1 \tag{7}$$

$$t_k^e \leq T_c, \quad \forall k \tag{8}$$

2.2 Internal coupling model (ICM)

We note that the formulation of the scheduling problem above depends on the *dynamics* of the process through the transition times τ_k. Intuitively, there are two ways to determine τ_k: i) via process experiments, after which the transition times become part of a transition table, which makes the problem static MI(N)LP and, ii) via a rigorous dynamic simulation of the process. Here, the full dynamic model of the process must be included as a set of model constraints (Flores-Tlacuahuac and Grossmann, 2011) and the scheduling problem becomes a mixed-integer dynamic optimization (MIDO).

Both approaches have advantages and drawbacks. The static scheduling formulation is easier to solve but is agnostic to process dynamics and control performance. On the other hand, the second approach, which we will refer to as "full dynamic scheduling" presents the advantage of rigorously accounting for the process dynamics in calculating the transition times and the corresponding control moves. On the downside, it is computationally intensive. Further, computing the control moves offline for the entire makespan leaves the system vulnerable to disturbances and plant-model mismatch.

In order to mitigate the aforementioned challenges, we propose a novel approach based on an internal coupling model (ICM), which captures the closed-loop, input-output behaviour of the process. The process is now assumed to be under a supervisory control system (potentially part of a hierarchical control structure including a distributed/base layer of control). We define the ICM as the explicit function relating the setpoints of the supervisory controller to the measured process outputs that are of interest to scheduling (e.g., product grade, production rate), of the form:

$$y(t) = f\left(y_{sp}(t)\right) \tag{9}$$

Previous research (Baldea and Daoutidis, 2012) suggests that this overall input-output behaviour of process systems evolves over a longer time horizon, which is in the order of magnitude of the scheduling time horizon. It is thus this behaviour that should be accounted for in scheduling calculations. ICM-based scheduling therefore proceeds similar to full dynamic scheduling, with the exception that the full process model is replaced with the ICM, and the decision variables that are related to process manipulated variables are replaced by the setpoints y_k^{sp} of the supervisory controller. The solution thus consists of the optimal *setpoint* sequence that imposes, via the supervisory controller, the optimal production sequence for the original problem, i.e.,

$$y_k^{sp} = \sum_{i=1}^{N_p} y_i^{ss} z_{i,k}, \quad \forall k \tag{10}$$

where y_k^{sp} represents the setpoint to be tracked by the state variable y in each time slot k. y_i^{ss} is the operating condition for producing product i.

Using the ICM presents several important advantages. First, scheduling becomes aware of the process dynamics. Second, the process operates in closed loop and is thus robust to disturbances and plant-model mismatch. Third, the scheduling and control calculations are performed independently and using a low-order ICM can significantly ease the computational burden of scheduling. Evidently, the above are dependent on the availability of a closed-form expression for the closed-loop input-output behaviour of the process. In the present work, we rely on using input-output linearizing controllers with integral action (see, e.g., Daoutidis and Kravaris, 1994) for imposing a well-defined (multivariable) linear closed loop behaviour of the form $\sum_{i=1}^{r} \tau_r \frac{d^r y}{dt^i} = y_{sp}$ (where r is the relative order and τ_r are tunable time constants), which will be used as the ICM for scheduling. In what follows, we illustrate these concepts with a case study.

3. Case Study

We consider a non-isothermal multiproduct CSTR with four products manufactured at different operating conditions. Our goal is to maximize overall production profit while meeting the manufacturing demand for each product. The scheduling problem thus consists of determining the total production time, the optimal production sequence and the processing times for each product. We solve this problem following the three approaches described above, i.e., static scheduling, full dynamic scheduling, and dynamic scheduling using an internal coupling model. The full dynamic scheduling problem for this system has been formulated and solved by Flores-Tlacuahuac and Grossmann (2006) and we follow closely their developments in that direction, as well as using the same model parameters as in their paper. The static scheduling problem is solved assuming a constant transition time $\tau = 10$ h for all transitions.

Let us now focus on the development of the ICM for this process. The process model is given in Eq.(11) and (12), where y_1 is the dimensionless concentration, and y_2 stands for the dimensionless temperature.

$$\frac{dy_1}{dt} = \frac{1-y_1}{\tau} - k_{10} e^{-N/y_2} y_1 \tag{11}$$

$$\frac{dy_2}{dt} = \frac{y_f - y_2}{\tau} + k_{10} e^{-N/y_2} y_1 - \alpha u (y_2 - y_c) \tag{12}$$

In Eq.(12), τ represents reactor residence time, k_{10} is the pre-exponential factor, and N is the activation energy. In Eq.(13), y_f denotes the dimensionless feed temperature, y_c is the dimensionless coolant temperature, α is the dimensionless heat transfer area. The coolant flow rate u is the manipulated variable available for changing the output of interest, which in this case is the composition y_1. The relative order of this system is r = 2. We design a nonlinear input-output linearizing controller with integral action to impose a critically damped second-order input-output behaviour:

$$\tau_{CM}^2 \frac{d^2 y_1}{dt^2} + 2\tau_{CM} \frac{dy_1}{dt} + y_1 = y_1^{sp} \tag{13}$$

with $\tau_{CM} = 2$ h (note that this value was chosen so that the step response of the closed-loop system reaches steady state in about 10 h, which is the same as the transition time used for static scheduling. ICM-based scheduling is thus formulated using the above equation as a constraint, aiming to determine the optimal setpoint profile in Eq.(10).

4. Results and Discussion

4.1. Optimal Solutions to Scheduling Problem Formulations

The static, full dynamic and ICM-based scheduling problems were solved using GAMS/CPLEX. The dynamic optimization problems were reformulated as MINLPs using a full-discretization approach as described in (Flores-Tlacuahuac and Grossman, 2006). The optimal solutions are shown in Tables 1–4. The optimal solution for ICM-based scheduling was validated via simulation on the closed-loop system using the derived input-output linearizing controller.

4.2. Performance in the Presence of Model Uncertainty

The aforementioned results were obtained assuming no plant-model mismatch, i.e., that the dynamic model used is perfect. Here, we assume that the reaction rate constant has been overestimated in the model by 10 % compared to the plant. The control actions computed using full dynamic scheduling were imposed on the mismatched plant. Clearly, in the absence of feedback control, most of the products are off-spec. Then, we imposed the setpoint sequence computed from IBO-based scheduling on the closed-loop

Table 1. Optimal Solutions to Three Different Scheduling Formulation Problems

Case	Profit	Production Sequence	Total Production Time
Proposed Method	36.615	4→2→3→1	119.585 h
Static	36.615	2→3→4→1	119.585 h
Full dynamic	34.218	2→1→3→4	124.016 h

Table 2. Optimal Solution for IBO-based Scheduling

k (Time Slot)	1	2	3	4
τ_k	10	10	10	10
i (Product)	1	2	3	4
W_i	35.100	21.525	20.330	27.526
$tp_{i,k}$	($i = 4$, $k = 1$) 18.35	($i = 2$, $k = 2$) 16.064	($i = 3$, $k = 3$) 15.171	($i = 1$, $k = 4$) 30

Table 3. Optimal Solution for Static Scheduling

k (Time Slot)	1	2	3	4
τ_k	10	10	10	10
i (Product)	1	2	3	4
W_i	35.100	21.525	20.330	27.526
$tp_{i,k}$	($i = 2$, $k = 1$) 16.064	($i = 3$, $k = 2$) 15.171	($i = 4$, $k = 3$) 18.350	($i = 1$, $k = 4$) 30

Table 4. Optimal Solution for Full Dynamic Scheduling

k (Time Slot)	1	2	3	4
τ_k	10	10	12.291	10.937
i (Product)	1	2	3	4
W_i	35.100	22.323	21.083	27.594
$tp_{i,k}$	($i = 2$, $k = 1$) 16.659	($i = 1$, $k = 2$) 30	($i = 3$, $k = 3$) 15.733	($i = 4$, $k = 4$) 18.396

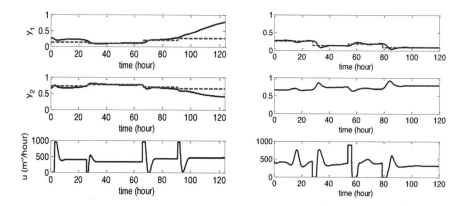

Figure 1. Process response using full dynamic (left) and IBO-based (right) scheduling in the presence of plant-model mismatch. Dashed lines represent the target values of the variables.

system using the input-output linearizing controller. While each of the products is initially off-spec, feedback control with integral action compensates for plant-model mismatch and helps recover product purity (Figure 1, right).

5. Conclusions

In this paper, we proposed a novel path for integrating short term scheduling and supervisory process control. We defined the internal coupling model (ICM) as a low-order model that describes the closed-loop input-output behaviour of the process, and derived ICMs for a specific class of supervisory controllers. We then formulated the scheduling problem as a MIDO, in terms of identifying the optimal sequence of setpoints for the supervisory controller, subject to the closed loop dynamics described by the ICM. Using a case study, we showed that ICM-Based scheduling is comparable to full dynamic scheduling in the nominal cases, and outperforms it in terms of on-spec production when plant-model mismatches are present.

Acknowledgements

Financial support from ABB Corporate Research is gratefully acknowledged.

References

M.Baldea, P. Daoutidis, 2012, Dynamics and Nonlinear Control of Integrated Process Systems, Cambridge University Press, Cambridge, UK.

P. Daoutidis, K. Kravaris, 1994, Dynamic output feedback control of minimum-phase multivariable nonlinear processes, Chem. Eng. Sci., 49, 433–447.

A. Flores-Tlacuahuac, I. Grossmann, 2006, Simultaneous cyclic scheduling and control of a multiproduct CSTR, Ind. Eng. Chem. Res., 45, 6698–6712.

A. Flores-Tlacuahuac, I. Grossmann, 2011, Simultaneous cyclic scheduling and control of tubular reactors: Parallel production lines, Ind. Eng. Chem. Res., 50, 8086–8096.

I. Grossmann, 2005, Enterprise-wide optimization: A new frontier in process systems engineering, AIChE J., 51, 7, 1846–1857.

I. Harjunkoski, R. Nystrom, A. Horch, 2009, Integration of scheduling and control – Theory or practice?, Comput. Chem. Eng., 33, 12, 1909–1918.

D. Shobrys, D. White, 2002, Planning, scheduling and control system: why cannot they work together, Comput. Chem. Eng., 26, 2, 149–160.

Jiří Jaromír Klemeš, Petar Sabev Varbanov and Peng Yen Liew (Editors)
Proceedings of the 24th European Symposium on Computer Aided Process Engineering – ESCAPE 24
June 15-18, 2014, Budapest, Hungary.

Supervisory Control of a Drop on Demand Mini-manufacturing System for Pharmaceuticals

Elcin Icten, Zoltan K. Nagy, Gintaras V. Reklaitis[*]

School of Chemical Engineering Purdue University, West Lafayette, IN, 47906, USA
reklaiti@purdue.edu

Abstract

A mini-manufacturing process for the production of personalized pharmaceutical products has been developed using drop on demand printing technology. A supervisory control system including online monitoring has been implemented on the process to achieve the desired dosage amount and drug morphology, consistently. A PCE based surrogate model has been developed to predict the dissolution profiles.

Keywords: supervisory control, temperature control, process development, drug delivery, polynomial chaos expansion

1. Introduction

There are a number of characteristics of conventional pharmaceutical manufacturing processes that provide significant challenges for the industry, including high production costs, long manufacturing times, scale-up difficulties and recurring quality issues (Lainez et al., 2012). In recent years, the FDA has encouraged innovation in production technologies, such as on-line measurement and process control and their exploitation in the development of more efficient pharmaceutical production processes. As part of this renewed emphasis on improvement of manufacturing, the pharmaceutical industry has begun the selective transition from traditional batch processing to continuous manufacturing. Continuous production processes offer the potential for reduced production costs, faster product release, reduced variability, increased flexibility and efficiency, and improved product quality (Gernaey et al., 2012).

As a part of the research agenda of the NSF Engineering Research Center for Structured Organic Particulate Systems, a mini-manufacturing process for solid oral drug product has been under development. The process utilizes the drop-on-demand (DoD) printing technology for predictable and highly controllable deposition of active pharmaceutical ingredients (API) onto an edible substrate, such as a polymeric film or placebo tablet, using a semi-continuous operation suitable for low volume production of personalized dosage forms (Hirshfield et al., 2014).

Implementation of a supervisory control system on the mini-manufacturing process, including on-line monitoring, automation and closed-loop control, is essential for producing individual dosage forms with the desired properties. This paper presents such a system which assures precise control of formulation composition, drop size, and deposit morphology.

2. Drop on Demand Mini-manufacturing Process Description

The DoD mini-manufacturing system consists of a precision positive displacement pump, xy-staging, a hot air based heating system, online imaging and sensing, and temperature, pump and stage controllers, as shown in Figure 1. A supervisory control system with the features described next has been implemented on the mini-manufacturing process. The drop volume is monitored using a moderate speed camera based imaging system, to ensure consistent drop size. An image of each drop is taken after it is ejected from the nozzle. The volume of each drop is calculated based on the image using arbitrary rotational symmetric shape model. The xy-staging and synchronization logic allows creating precise drop positioning on the substrate while printing and enables layering of different drugs. The interested reader is invited to refer to Hirshfield et al. (2014) for more detailed process description.

Using this process, different drug formulations including polymer-API systems, i.e. co-melts, and solvent-polymer-API systems can be produced. Polymers are added to the printing material to help control drug morphology, material rheological properties and the formulation composition (Trasi and Taylor, 2012). In order to produce melt-based dosage forms reproducibly, the complete system must be, maintained at suitable temperature. Therefore temperature control on each process component, including reservoir, pump, tubing and nozzle, is implemented. Since crystallization temperature will have an effect on product morphology, influencing the dissolution properties and hence the bioavailability of the drug, precise control of the drop solidification process once the drop is deposited on the substrate is important (Fujiwara, et al., 2005). This is achieved indirectly by manipulating the substrate temperature profile using varying temperature gradients.

3. Supervisory Control Framework

As with any process for producing a drug product, the desired critical quality attributes (CQA), which are its essential physical, chemical and biological characteristics, must be within the appropriate limits defining the desired product quality (FDA, 2009). In order to achieve the desired CQA's, i.e. dosage amount and product morphology, the critical process parameters (CPP) should be controlled. For this mini-manufacturing system, the CPP's, whose variability has an impact on the CQA's, are the drop size, product and process temperatures.

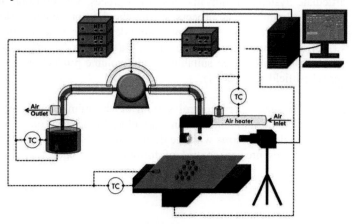

Figure 1. Drop on Demand Mini-manufacturing System

The supervisory control strategy for the mini-manufacturing process is shown in Figure 2. Automation of the on-line monitoring and control systems is implemented using the LabVIEW program. The program executes pump, camera and xy-stage, simultaneously. The dosage amount of each drop is monitored using the corresponding drop volume calculated by the image analysis. The product morphology depends on the formulation composition, on the selection of the substrate and on the CPP's, i.e. product temperature and drop size. The selection of the polymer used in the formulation can change the morphology by promoting or inhibiting crystallization of the drug (Trasi and Taylor, 2012). The surface properties of the substrate onto which the drops are deposited also can have an effect on product morphology (Hsu et al., 2013). The product temperature corresponds to the crystallization temperature after the drop is deposited on the substrate. By manipulating the substrate temperature profile using varying temperature gradients, the drop solidification process can be controlled. The drop size also affects the drop solidification process by changing the heat transfer dynamics.

The printability and reproducibility of co-melt formulations depends on the process temperature, which is maintained above the melting temperature and within the desired operating limits. Therefore temperature control is implemented on reservoir, pump, and tubing and nozzle using heating tape, built-in pump heater and air-heater, respectively.

4. Temperature Control on Co-melts

In order to study the effects of critical process parameters on the product morphology, dosage forms of co-melts are produced using two different drop sizes, and different substrate temperature profiles are applied. The model formulation of co-melts is a mixture of naproxen and polyethylene glycol 3350 (PEG 3350) with the composition of (15:85), at which they form a eutectic. Dosage forms containing 15 mg of API were produced by either with large drops of size 24 mg or with small drops of size 19 mg. The dosage forms were printed onto HPMC films at 60 °C and cooled down to 30 °C using one of the three temperature profiles shown in Figure 3. The points marked on the fast cooling and slow cooling temperature profile curves represent the induction times. The differences in the induction points show that applying different cooling profiles changes the crystallization behavior. For fast cooling the induction occurs at 36 °C in 4.4 min. For slow cooling the induction temperature is 44 °C occurring in 18 min.

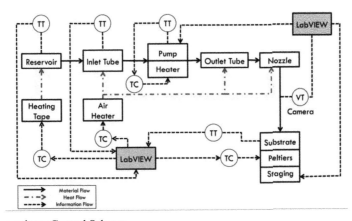

Figure 2. Supervisory Control Scheme

Raman spectra of the dosage forms confirm that naproxen present in the dosage forms is crystalline. Thus the crystallization temperature does not have an effect on the crystallinity of the dosage forms. However, using optical microscopy with a hot stage, morphological differences are observed between the dosage forms solidified at different temperature profiles.

Dissolution testing was performed to show the effect of the drop size and the substrate temperature profile on the dissolution behaviour of the drug. In Figure 4, the dissolution profiles of the dosage forms printed with different drop sizes and solidified using different cooling rates are shown. For the dosage forms printed either with small or large drop sizes, faster dissolution is observed when fast cooling rate of 10 °C/min is applied. During fast cooling, more nucleation sites are created which result in higher surface area and therefore in faster dissolution of the dosage forms.

When the dosage forms created with small or large drops are deposited onto the substrate at a constant temperature of 30 °C, high variation of the dissolution profile is observed within the same drop size, as well as between the small and large drops. When the substrate temperature is constant, the cooling profile within the droplets is significantly influenced by their volume, yielding to large variations in the crystallization conditions. This variation can be seen in terms of the error bars in Figure 5.a. In the case of solidification of the dosage forms by applying a fast cooling rate of 10 °C/min, the differences within the same drop size decrease, which is represented by the reduced error bars, Figure 5.b. When the dosage forms are solidified by applying a slow cooling rate of 1 °C/min, the differences both within the same drop size and between different drop sizes decrease, Figure 5.c. Applying slow cooling profile, mini-

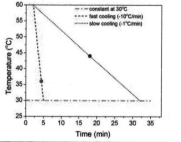

Figure 3. Temperature profiles applied on the substrate

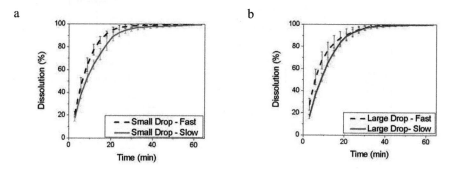

Figure 4.a. Dissolution profiles of the dosage forms printed with small drops which are solidified with fast and slow cooling rates. b. Dissolution profiles of the dosage forms printed with large drops which are solidified with fast and slow cooling rates.

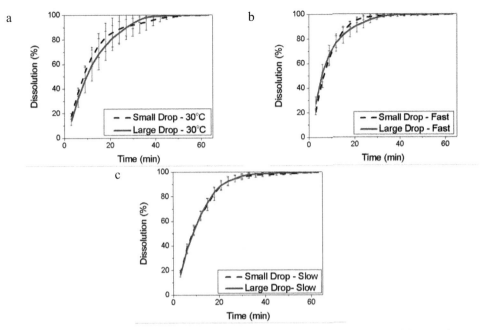

Figure 5. Dissolution profiles of the dosage forms created with two different sizes of drops and a. constant temperature 30 °C, b. fast cooling 10 °C/min, c. slow cooling 1 °C/min is applied.

mizes the differences due to the drop size by enabling better heat transfer and eliminating the differences due to the spatial distribution on the substrate. With this model formulation, the amorphous form of naproxen is not exhibited in the presence of PEG 3350, which promotes crystallization of naproxen. However amorphous forms can be produced with alternative choices of operating conditions and polymers, which inhibit crystallization. Amorphous drug forms can offer improved dissolution performance thus higher bioavailability.

5. Polynomial Chaos Expansion

Due to the nonlinear behaviour of the solidification and crystallization processes occurring within the co-melt drops and due to the presence of disturbances, the use of typical linear data driven modeling approaches cannot yield models to relate the crystallization temperature profiles to the dissolution profile with acceptable accuracy. Therefore, a methodology based on polynomial chaos expansion (PCE) containing orthogonal basis with respect to the Gaussian probability measure is used to develop a nonlinear surrogate model. (Nagy and Braatz, 2004) The input data of temperature profiles can be represented as the temperature values at the discretized times or as the linear cooling rate applied to the drops, depending on the number of input data required to describe the system. The output data is calculated as the time constant of the first order function defining the dissolution profile.

As a case study, using fast and slow cooling temperature profiles and corresponding dissolution profiles, 1st and 2nd order PCE were tested with 1, 3 and 5 input parameters. The simplest parameterization is achieved with the single input single output case and the experimental dissolution time constants versus the PCE predicted time constants are shown in Figure 6, for illustrative purposes. By using more experimental data points to

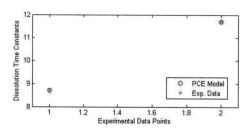

Figure 6. Experimental vs PCE predicted dissolution time constants for 1st order PCE with SISO

build a PCE model, the dissolution profile of the solidified drug deposition can be predicted given the temperature profile applied on the substrate.

6. Conclusions

In this work, a supervisory control strategy for the DoD mini-manufacturing system is reported. Using the imaging system, the drops sizes and therefore the dosage amounts are monitored. Using the proposed substrate temperature control strategy, the crystallization behavior can be tailored and consistent drug morphology achieved. We show that a PCE based nonlinear model can be built to predict the dissolution profile of the solidified drug deposition given the temperature profile applied on the substrate. Using this model, a hierarchical control system is being implemented by monitoring the drop size online and predicting a temperature profile to achieve the desired dissolution profile for the dosage forms created.

Acknowledgement

This work was funded by the National Science Foundation under grant EEC-0540855 through the Engineering Research Center for Structured Organic Particulate Systems.

References

Food and Drug Administration, 2009, Guidance for Industry Q8(R2) Pharmaceutical Development, ICT, USA.

M. Fujiwara, Z. K. Nagy, J. W. Chew, R. D. Braatz, 2005, First-principles and direct design approaches for the control of pharmaceutical crystallization, Journal of Process Control, 15, 5, 493–504.

K. V. Gernaey, A. E. Cervera-Padrell, J. M. Woodley, 2012, A perspective on PSE in pharmaceutical process development and innovation, Computers and Chemical Engineering, 42, 15–29.

L. Hirshfield, A.Giridhar, L. Taylor, M. Harris, G. V. Reklaitis, 2014, Dropwise Additive Manufacturing of Pharmaceutical Products for Solvent-based Dosage Forms, Journal of Pharmaceutical Sciences, 103, 2, 496-506.

H. Hsu, S. J. Toth, G. J. Simpson, L. Taylor, M. Harris, 2013, Effect of substrates on naproxen-polyvinylpyrrolidone solid dispersions formed via the drop printing technique, Journal of Pharmaceutical Sciences, 102, 2, 638-648.

J. M. Laíne, E. Schaefer, G. V. Reklaitis, 2012, Challenges and opportunities in enterprise-wide optimization in the pharmaceutical industry, Computers and Chemical Engineering, 47, 19-28.

Z. K. Nagy, R. D. Braatz, 2004, Open-loop and closed-loop robust optimal control of batch processes using distributional and worst-case analysis, Journal of Process Control, 14, 411-422.

N. S. Trasi, L. S. Taylor, 2012, Effect of Additives on Crystal Growth and Nucleation of Amorphous Flutamide, Crystal Growth and Design, 12- 6, 3221–3230.

Jiří Jaromír Klemeš, Petar Sabev Varbanov and Peng Yen Liew (Editors)
Proceedings of the 24th European Symposium on Computer Aided Process Engineering – ESCAPE 24
June 15-18, 2014, Budapest, Hungary. Copyright © 2014 Elsevier B.V. All rights reserved.

Simultaneous Multi-Parametric Model Predictive Control and State Estimation with Application to Distillation Column and Intravenous Anaesthesia

Ioana Nascu, Romain S.C Lambert, Alexandra Krieger, Efstratios N. Pistikopoulos[*]

Dept. of Chemical Engineering, Centre for Process Systems Engineering (CPSE), Imperial College London SW7 2AZ, London, U.K.
e.pistikopoulos@imperial.ac.uk

Abstract

The objective of this paper is to implement simultaneous multi-parametric model predictive control (mp-MPC) and moving horizon estimation (MHE). The approach is tested on two different processes: the control of a high dimensional chemical process, the distillation column and the regulation of the depth of anaesthesia (DOA). Due to the high dimensionality of the distillation column, model order reduction techniques were used together with the simultaneous mp-MPC and MHE. The methods show good performances and a good behavior in dealing with the effect of noise and the presence of constraints.

Keywords: Moving horizon estimation, model predictive control, multi-parametric/explicit control, Model Order Reduction.

1. Introduction

Explicit/multi-parametric model predictive control (mp-MPC) solves the online optimization problem using multi-parametric programming and derives the control inputs as a set of explicit functions of the system states to obtain the governing control laws for the system. The main advantage of mp-MPC is that it replaces the online optimization-based implementation of traditional MPC with simple function evaluations, which are faster, more robust and reliable than solving the optimization problem on line (Pistikopoulos et al., 2002). One of the key limitations of this method is computational complexity due to nonlinearity and dimensionality. A possible way to address this issue is model order reduction. mp-MPC has successfully been combined with various model order reduction techniques with an in-sillico test on relatively complex mathematical models (Lambert et al., 2013). While Kalman Filters and extended Kalman Filters are efficient to build observers on a reduced order model (Singh and Hahn, 2005), dealing with system constraints favors the simultaneous use of MHE, which can be implemented in a multi-parametric fashion (Darby and Nikolaou, 2007), with recent enhancement addressing robustness against estimation error (Voelker et al., 2013).

The main aim of this study is to design and implement mp-MPC simultaneously with MHE for two different processes: distillation column and the regulation of the DOA. The paper is structured as follows. The patient model, theoretical framework regarding mp-MPC, MHE, model approximation methodologies and the estimation and control algorithms are described in Section II. The simulation results are presented in Section III and the conclusions are summarized in Section IV.

2. Theoretical Background

2.1. Framework

The presented framework is leading to a closed loop control design in four steps: step 1 - model reduction, step 2 - model linearization, step 3 - state estimation and step 4 - mp-MPC and is applied to two examples in process engineering distillation and anaesthesia. Consider a nonlinear system of ODEs of the following form:

$$\dot{x}(t) = f(x(t), u(t), \theta(t))$$
$$y(t) = h(x(t), u(t), \theta(t))$$
(1)

2.1.1. Step 1 - Nonlinear model reduction

Due to current the limitations and requirements of mp-MPC methodologies, it is necessary to reduce high fidelity and non-linear models to linear low order models in a systematic way. The applied approach is nonlinear balanced truncation, which is a snapshots based technique and an empirical extension of the linear balanced truncation technique (Singh and Hahn, 2005). The method consists of finding a transformation matrix T in order to project the state vector on a lower order subspace $\bar{x} = Tx$. Using a Garlekin projection $P = [I, 0]$ matrix with the same rank as the reduced system, the unimportant states may be set to a nominal steady state value and the nonlinear reduced order model (Xiao et al., 2013):

$$\dot{\bar{x}}_1(t) = PTf(T^{-1}P^T\bar{x}(t), u(t))$$
$$\dot{\bar{x}}_2(t) = \bar{x}_{2ss}(0)$$
$$y = g(T^{-1}\bar{x}, u)$$
(2)

2.1.2. Step 2 – Model linearization

mp-MHE and mp-MPC routines require a linear model. The system is firstly reduced via empirical model order reduction and subsequently linearized around the steady state of the reduced order model $\bar{x}_{ss}$. The analytical Jacobians of the original and reduced order systems are used.

2.1.3. Step 3 – Moving Horizon Estimation

MHE is an state estimation method based on optimization. Contrary to Kalman filters, MHE only considers a limited amount of past data. One of the main advantages of MHE is the possibility to incorporate system knowledge such as constraints in the estimation. In MHE the system states are derived by solving following optimization problem:

$$\min_{\hat{x}_{T-N/T}, \hat{W}_T} \left\| \hat{x}_{T-N/T} - \underline{x}_{T-N/T} \right\|_{P_{T-N/T-1}^{-1}} + \left\| Y_{T-N}^{T-1} - O\hat{x}_{T-N/T} - \bar{c}bU_{T-N}^{T-2} \right\|_{P-1}^2 + \sum_{k=T-N}^{T-1} \|\hat{w}_k\|_{Q_k^{-1}} + \sum_{k=T-N}^{T-1} \|\hat{v}_k\|_{R_k^{-1}}$$

s.t.:
(3)

$$\hat{x}_{k+1} = A\hat{x}_k + Bu_k + G\hat{w}_k$$
$$y_k = C\hat{x}_k + \hat{v}_k$$
$$\hat{x}_k \in X, \hat{w}_k \in \Theta, \hat{v}_k \in V$$

where T is the current time, $Q_k \succ 0, R_k \succ 0, P_{T-N/T-1} \succ 0$ are the covariances of w_k v_k x_{T-N} assumed to be symmetric, N is the horizon length of the MHE, Y_{T-N}^{T-1} is a vector containing the past $N+1$ measurements and U_{T-N}^{T-1} is a vector containing the past N inputs. x, v, w denote the variables of the system and $\hat{x}, \hat{v}, \hat{w}$ denote the estimated variables of the system and $\hat{x}_{T/T-N}$ and $\hat{W}_T = W_{T-N}^{T-1}$ denote the decision variable of the optimization problem, the estimated state variable and the noise sequence respectively. In mp-MHE, the matrices Q_k R_k $P_{T-N/T-1}$ are constant. In particular $P_{T-N/T-1} = P_{ss}$ which corresponds to the steady state Kalman covariance matrix.

To obtain an mp-MHE formulation, the problem in Eq.(3) is reformulated as a multi-parametric programming problem:

$$\min_{\hat{x}_{T-N/T}, \hat{W}_{T-N/T}^{T-1}} \frac{1}{2} \left[\hat{x}_{T-N/T}^T, \hat{W}_{T-N/T}^{T-1} \right]^T H \begin{bmatrix} \hat{x}_{T-N/T} \\ \hat{W}_{T-N/T}^{T-1} \end{bmatrix} + O.f \begin{bmatrix} \hat{x}_{T-N/T} \\ \hat{W}_{T-N/T}^{T-1} \end{bmatrix}$$

$$st\ K \begin{bmatrix} \hat{x}_{T-N/T} \\ \hat{W}_{T-N/T}^{T-1} \end{bmatrix} \le k \tag{4}$$

The parameters of the multi-parametric programming problem in (4) are the past and current measurements and inputs and the initial guess for the estimated states.

2.1.4. Step 4 – Multi-parametric Model Predictive Control
Multi-parametric programming is a technique to solve an optimization problem, where the objective is to minimize or maximize a performance criterion subject to a given set of constraints where some of the parameters vary between specified lower and upper bounds. The most important characteristic of mp-MPC is its ability to obtain the objective and optimization variable as a function of the varying parameters, and the regions in the space of the parameters where these functions are valid (critical regions) (Pistikopoulos et al., 2007). For the mp-MPC, the generic optimization problem solved is:

$$\min_{x,y,u} J = x'_N P x_N + \sum_{k=1}^{N-1} x_k Q_k x_k + \sum_{k=1}^{N-1} (y_k - y_k^R)' Q R_k (y_k - y_k^R) + \sum_{k=0}^{M-1} u_k' R_k u_k + \sum_{k=0}^{M-1} \Delta u_k R1_k \Delta u_k \tag{5}$$

where x are states, y outputs and u controls, all (discrete) time dependent vectors. The time dependent set points of the subsets of tracked output variables are denoted with y^R. The step changes in control variables are defined as $\Delta u(k) = u(k) - u(k-1)$. The control action in the first interval u_0 is an optimization variable. The prediction horizon is denoted by N and control horizon by M.

2.2. Controller design
For the control design of the distillation process step 1 to 4 will be applied, for the intravenous anaesthesia only steps 3-4 are used.

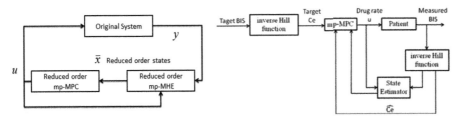

Figure 1. Schematic of simultaneous reduced MHE/MPC – distillation process

Figure 2. Simultaneous mp-MPC order mp-and MHE - anaesthesia process.

2.3. Controller design – distillation process

Using the model approximation techniques described previously, simultaneous reduced order mp-MPC/MHE is applied. The main advantages of this approach is the reduction in computational complexity since both the controller and estimator no longer operate based on full state information. Another advantage is related to the case of extended Kalman filters (Singh et al., 2005). The use of reduced order observers avoids an estimation error due to poor observability of part of the states. The methodology is applied to a distillation column example and the control scheme is described in Figure1.

2.4. Controller design – anaesthesia process

For the implementation of the mp-MPC, the problem is reformulated as a model predictive control problem by considering the states as the parameters and the control inputs as the continuous decision variable. The controller is implemented using two different state estimation techniques: Kalman filter and MHE. The structure of the control scheme is presented in Figure 2.

The Patient block is composed of the pharmacokinetic part (linear) and the pharamacodynamic part, the Hill curve (nonlinear). Since the controller is designed only using the linear part of the process and the Hill curve is highly nonlinear, a parameter scheduling technique is used (Nascu et al., 2012). To compensate the nonlinearity, the inverse of the Hill curve is implemented with the nominal patient model parameters. The closed loop control tests are performed on a set of 12 virtually generated realistic patients (Ionescu et al., 2008). A *nominal* patient model is defined using the mean of virtual biometric values. A Kalman filter and mp-MHE are used to estimate the current states of the patients using the A, B, C and D matrices of the nominal patient, the online BIS measurement and the drug rate.

3. Results

3.1. Controller design – distillation process

The distillation column benchmark example considers the design of a controller for a simplified model of a distillation column (Benallou et al., 1986). The control problem consists of regulating the product purity to a fixed set-point, using the constrained reflux ratio as the manipulated variable. Here, the inlet concentration is the main source of uncertainty of the system and is included as noise for the MHE. A Gaussian distribution centred in 0.5 and with a 3 % standard deviation is assumed. The system is mostly linear, with nonlinearities arising from the equilibrium relations. The control problem consists of regulating the product purity to a fixed set-point of $y = 0.935$, using the reflux ratio as the manipulated variable. Figure 5 shows the closed-loop simultaneous mp-MHE and mp-MPC simulations. This was performed to evaluate the performance of the methodology.

The estimator is able to provide accurate information to the parametric controller so the system will reach the desired set point based only on measurement information. For high order chemical process the combination of two reduced order parametric maps is sufficient to operate a control policy. There is a small offset around the set-point given by the noise or uncertainty of the inlet concentration of the column. Even under high measurement noise, as shown in Figures 8 and 9, the simultaneous implementation of mp-MPC and mp-MHE shows good performances and achieve the desired set-point change despite the control profiles being more erratic.

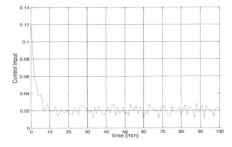 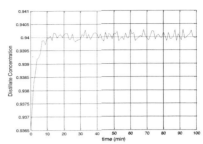

Figure 3. Close loop simulation of simultaneous MHE/mp-MPC - high measurement noise.

Figure 4. control input variable - high measurement noise

3.2. Controller design – anaesthesia process

For the automatic DOA the intravenous agent Propofol is the input and the Bispectral Index (BIS) the output of the system. Due to its pharmacological profile, Propofol is used as one of the drugs of choice for induction and maintenance of hypnosis during anaesthesia. A BIS value of 0 equals EEG silence, while a BIS value of 100 is the value of a fully awake and conscious adult, 60 - 70 and 40 - 60 range represents light and moderate hypnotic condition, respectively. The target value during surgery is 50, giving us a gap between 40 and 60 to guarantee adequate sedation, (Absalom et al., 2011). The PK –PD blocks denote compartmental models, used to represent the distribution of drugs in the body, i.e. mass balance. The PK-PD models most commonly used for Propofol are the 4th order compartmental model described by Schnider (1999) and Minto (1997) respectively.

The controllers are tested against each other for different patients to compare their performances by means of the BIS index and the corresponding Propofol infusion rates. Ideally, the induction of the patient is performed as fast as possible, such that little time is lost before the surgeon can start operating. It is therefore desirable that the patient reaches the BIS = 50 target and remains within the target value without much undershoot or overshoot. Figure 5 and Figure 6 show the simulation results of the controllers using different estimators for patient 2. As it can be the output is strongly influenced by noise. Even so, the controllers manage to have good performances, with no significant undershoot and fast settling time. It can be observed from the figures that the controller using mp-MHE has better results than the one using the Kalman filter, no undershoot and a settling time of 240 s.

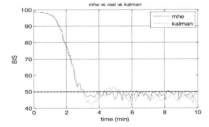 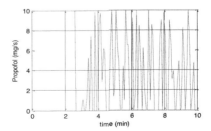

Figure 5. BIS response – patient 2

Figure 6. Control input variable patient 2

4. Conclusions

Using simultaneous multi-parametric moving horizon state estimation and model predictive control has proven to be of great importance. In both examples, the distillation column which is a high dimensional chemical process and the regulation of the depth of anaesthesia, a highly nonlinear process, the designed methodologies show better performances even under the influence of noise and constraints. The estimators provide sufficiently accurate information to the parametric controllers to drive the systems to the desired set points based only on the measured information. The distillation column process underlines the importance of using nonlinear model order reduction for simultaneous mp-MHE and mp-MPC. Future work will focus on robust controllers used simultaneously with model order reduction and moving horizon estimation.

Acknowledgements

Financial support from EPSRC (EP/G059071/1, EP/I014640), the European Research Council (MOBILE, ERC Advanced Grant, No: 226462) and the European Commission (OPTICO/G.A. No.280813) is gratefully acknowledged.

References

A. Absalom, R. De Keyser, M.R.F. Struys, 2011, Closed loop anaesthesia: are we getting close to finding the Holy Grail?, AnesthAnalg, 112, 3, 516-518.

A. Benallou, D. Seborg, D. Mellichamp, 1986, Dynamic compartmental models for separation processes, AIChE Journal, 32, 7, 1067–1078.

M.L. Darby, M. Nikolaou, 2007, A parametric programming approach to moving-horizon state estimation, Automatica, 43, 5, 885–891.

C.M. Ionescu, R. De Keyser, B.C. Torrico, T. De Smet, M. Struys, J.E. Normey-Rico, 2008, Robust Predictive Control Strategy Applied for Propofol Dosing using BIS as a Controlled Variable during Anaesthesia, IEEE Trans Biomed Eng, 55, 2161-2170.

R.S.C. Lambert, P. Rivotti, E.N. Pistikopoulos, 2013. A Monte-Carlo based model approximation technique for linear model predictive control of nonlinear systems, Computers & Chemical Engineering, 54, 60-67.

C.F. Minto, T.W. Schnider, T.D. Egan, E. Youngs, H.J. Lemmens, P.L. Gambús, V. Billard, J.F. Hoke, K.H. Moore, D.J. Hermann, K.T. Muir, J.W. Mandema, S.L. Shafer, 1997, Influence of age and gender on the pharmacokinetics and pharmacodynamics of reminfetanil. I. Model development, Anesthesiology, 86, 10-23.

I. Nascu, C. M. Ionescu, R. De Keyser, 2012, Adaptive EPSAC predictive control of the hypnotic component in anesthesia, 2012 IEEE International Conference on Automation Quality and Testing Robotics (AQTR), 103–108.

E. Pistikopoulos, V. Dua, N. Bozinis, A. Bemporad, M. Morari, 2002, On-line optimization via off-line parametric optimization tools, Computers and Chemical Engineering, 26, 2, 175–185.

E. Pistikopoulos, M. Georgiadis, V. Dua, 2007, Multi-parametric Programming: Theory, Algorithms and Applications, 1, Wiley-VCH.

T.W. Schnider, C.F. Minto, S.L. Shafer, P.L. Gambús, C. Andresen, D.B. Goodale, E.J. Youngs, 1999, The influence of age on Propofol pharmacodynamics, Anesthesiology, 90, 1502-16.

A.K. Singh, J. Hahn, 2005, State Estimation for High-Dimensional Chemical Processes, Computers and Chemical Engineering, 29, 11-12, 2326-2334.

A. Voelker, K. Kouramas, E.N. Pistikopoulos, 2013, Moving horizon estimation: Error dynamics and bounding error sets for robust control, Automatica, 49, 4, 943-948

D. Xiao, F. Fang, J. Du, C.C. Pain, I.M. Navon, A.G. Buchan, A.H ElSheikh, G.Hu, 2013, Non-linear Petrov-Galerkin methods for reduced order modelling of the Navier-Stokes equations using a mixed finite element pair, Computer Methods in Applied Mechanics and Engineering, 255, 147-157

Jiří Jaromír Klemeš, Petar Sabev Varbanov and Peng Yen Liew (Editors)
Proceedings of the 24th European Symposium on Computer Aided Process Engineering – ESCAPE 24
June 15-18, 2014, Budapest, Hungary. Copyright © 2014 Elsevier B.V. All rights reserved.

Controller Design for Nonlinear Hammerstein and Wiener Systems Based on VRFT Method

Jyh-Cheng Jeng,* Yi-Wei Lin

Department of Chemical Engineering and Biotechnology, National Taipei University of Technology, Taipei 106, Taiwan
jcjeng@ntut.edu.tw

Abstract

This paper presents a novel data-based controller design for nonlinear Hammerstein and Wiener systems based on the VRFT design framework. In the proposed method, identification of a complete dynamic model of the nonlinear system is not required, whereas only the static nonlinearity has to be estimated. Furthermore, the nonlinearity estimation and the controller design are performed simultaneously without the needs of iterative procedures or nonlinear optimization. Simulation study of a pH neutralization process confirms the effectiveness of the proposed controller design method.

Keywords: Nonlinear process control; Hammerstein system; Wiener system; VRFT.

1. Introduction

Most dynamical systems can be better represented by nonlinear models, which are able to describe the global behavior of the system over wide ranges of operating conditions. One of the most frequently studied classes of nonlinear models is the so-called block-oriented nonlinear model, which involves a cascade combination of a linear dynamic block and a nonlinear static (memoryless) one. Two typical block-oriented model structures are the Hammerstein and Wiener models. In the Hammerstein structure, the linear dynamic element is preceded by the static nonlinearity. The order of connection is reversed in the Wiener structure. In the last decades, a considerable amount of research has been carried out on modeling and control of Hammerstein/Wiener systems. Traditional control design approaches are often based on mathematical models that approximate the behavior of the physical process. There are two steps in the model-based controller design: an empirical model of the process is identified first, which is subsequently used together with certain algorithms to design the controller. The identification process, however, usually relies on some prior assumptions such as model structure and order, which are often unavailable or subject to uncertainties. Hence, the complexity and errors associated with such models increase the difficulty of the control design task, and may lead to degradation of control performance.

Data-based control design methods are very useful in many practical control applications, where obtaining a suitable model is a very difficult task. The virtual reference feedback tuning (VRFT) method (Campi et al., 2002) allows to directly design controllers using a set of process input-output data, without resorting to any process model. Most existing results on the VRFT design are however restricted to linear systems. Campi and Savaresi (2006) explored the extension of VRFT to nonlinear systems, which requires iterative procedure. Adaptive version of the VRFT design (Yang et al., 2012) was proposed for adaptive PID controller parameter tuning. Unlike the linear VRFT, the extended versions of VRFT to nonlinear systems are not one-shot methods so that a significant advantage of VRFT method is lost. This study aims to design controllers for nonlinear Hammerstein and Wiener systems based on the VRFT design framework. A simple linearizing control scheme for Hammerstein/Wiener systems using the inverse of nonlinearity and a PID controller is adopted. The control scheme results in an equivalent linear control system that enables the application of one-shot VRFT design method. Therefore, model identification of the linear dynamics is not required. In addition, the nonlinearity estimation and the PID controller design are performed simultaneously without the needs of iterative procedures or nonlinear optimization.

2. Controller design for Hammerstein systems

The control scheme for Hammerstein system is as shown in Figure 1 where f, G, f^{-1}, and G_C denote the static nonlinear element, linear dynamics, inverse of nonlinearity, and controller, respectively. This linearizing control scheme results in an equivalent linear control system shown in Figure 2(a). It is assumed that the static nonlinear function can be represented by the B-spline series expansion as

$$v_k = f(u_k) = \sum_{i=1}^{r} a_i B_i(u_k)$$

(1)

where B_i are B-splines, and a_i are unknown coefficients. The B_i can also be other basis functions, but the B-splines are used in this study because the B-spline series is a local basis which has more flexibility in signal (function) representation, compared with using a global basis such as Laguerre functions. Because the gain of a Hammerstein system can be arbitrarily distributed in nonlinear and linear blocks, it is assumed, without loss of generality, that $a_1 = 1$. In addition, to meet the condition of $f(0) = 0$, the following relation holds when the 3rd-order B-splines with 0 as one of its knots are used.

$$a_s B_s(0) + a_{s+1} B_{s+1}(0) = 0 \quad \text{or} \quad a_s = -\frac{B_{s+1}(0)}{B_s(0)} a_{s+1} \triangleq \alpha\, a_{s+1} \quad \text{for some (known) } s$$

(2)

Consequently, the inaccessible intermediate variable v_k can be expressed as

$$v_k = B_1(u_k) + \sum_{i=2}^{s-1} a_i B_i(u_k) + a_{s+1}\big[\alpha B_s(u_k) + B_{s+1}(u_k)\big] + \sum_{i=s+2}^{r} a_i B_i(u_k)$$

(3)

The controller G_C is a PID controller with discrete transfer function given by

$$G_C(z) = K_P + \frac{K_I}{1 - z^{-1}} + K_D\left(1 - z^{-1}\right)$$

(4)

where K_P, K_I, and K_D are the PID parameters. The problem of controller design is to determine the PID parameters and the unknown coefficients a_i ($i = 2,\dots,r$), from an N-point data set $\{u_k, y_k\}_{k=1\sim N}$ of observed input-output measurements.

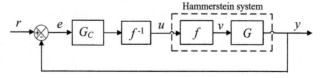

Figure 1. Linearizing control scheme for Hammerstein system.

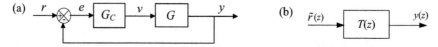

Figure 2. Equivalent linear control system for Hammerstein system and (b) its reference model.

This study applies the VRFT method to the equivalent linear control system shown in Figure 2(a), so that a model-reference problem, as depicted in Figure 2(b), is to be solved. In Figure 2(b), the reference model $T(z)$ describes the desired behavior of the closed-loop system, which is typically specified by the following first-order dynamics:

$$T(z) = \frac{(1-A)z^{-1}}{1-Az^{-1}} \tag{5}$$

where A is a tuning parameter related to the speed of response. The design goal is to determine the PID parameters and the unknown coefficients a_i, such that the control system in Figure 1 behaves as similarly as possible to the prespecified reference model $T(z)$. Based on the virtual reference signal $\tilde{r}(z) = T(z)^{-1} y(z)$, the virtual output of controller G_C is calculated as

$$\tilde{v}(z) = G_C(z)\left[\tilde{r}(z) - y(z)\right] = \left[K_P + \frac{K_I}{1-z^{-1}} + K_D\left(1-z^{-1}\right)\right] \frac{1-z^{-1}}{(1-A)z^{-1}} y(z) \tag{6}$$

When the linear block is fed by v_k, it generates y_k. Therefore, a PID controller that shapes the closed-loop behavior to the reference model generates v_k when the error signal is given by $\tilde{r}_k - y_k$. The task of controller design then becomes minimizing the difference between v_k (Eq.(3)) and $\tilde{v}_k$ (Eq.(6)), or equivalently, minimizing the difference between $B_1(u_k)$ and x_k, where

$$x_k = \tilde{v}_k - \sum_{i=2}^{s-1} a_i B_i(u_k) - a_{s+1}\left[\alpha B_s(u_k) + B_{s+1}(u_k)\right] - \sum_{i=s+2}^{r} a_i B_i(u_k) \tag{7}$$

Eq.(7) can be written as $x_k = \psi_k \theta$, where

$$\psi_k = \left[\psi_{P,k} \quad \psi_{I,k} \quad \psi_{D,k} \quad -B_2(u_k) \quad \cdots \quad -B_{s-1}(u_k) \quad -(\alpha B_s(u_k) + B_{s+1}(u_k))\right.$$
$$\left. -B_{s+2}(u_k) \quad \cdots \quad -B_r(u_k)\right] \tag{8}$$

$$\theta = \left[K_P \quad K_I \quad K_D \quad a_2 \quad \cdots \quad a_{s-1} \quad a_{s+1} \quad a_{s+2} \quad \cdots \quad a_r\right]^T$$

$$\psi_{P,k} = \frac{1}{1-A}(y_{k+1} - y_k); \quad \psi_{I,k} = \frac{1}{1-A}y_{k+1}; \quad \psi_{D,k} = \frac{1}{1-A}(y_{k+1} - 2y_k + y_{k-1})$$

Now, the parameter θ is computed by solving the following minimization problem:

$$\min_{\theta} \sum_{k=2}^{N-1}\left[B_1(u_k) - \psi_k\theta\right]^2 = \min_{\theta}\left\|\varphi - \Psi\theta\right\|_2^2 \tag{9}$$

where

$$\Psi = \left[\psi_2^T \quad \psi_3^T \quad \cdots \quad \psi_{N-1}^T\right]^T; \quad \varphi = \left[B_1(u_2) \quad B_1(u_3) \quad \cdots \quad B_1(u_{N-1})\right]^T \tag{10}$$

The solution can be calculated using the least-squares technique given by

$$\hat{\theta} = \left(\Psi^T\Psi\right)^{-1}\Psi^T\varphi \tag{11}$$

The PID parameters and estimates of the coefficients a_i ($i = 2,\ldots,s-1,s+1,\ldots,r$), can be obtained by partitioning the estimate $\hat{\theta}$, according to the definition of θ in Eq.(8). The coefficient a_s is then computed from Eq.(2). With the estimated nonlinear function, its inverse function f^{-1}, also represented by the B-spline series, can be readily obtained.

3. Controller design for Wiener systems

The control scheme for Wiener system is as shown in Figure 3, which results in an equivalent linear control system shown in Figure 4(a). It is assumed that the inverse function of the static nonlinearity can be represented by the B-spline series expansion as

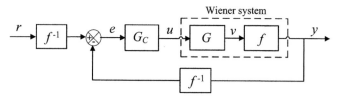

Figure 3. Linearizing control scheme for Wiener system.

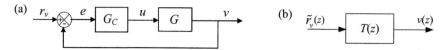

Figure 4. (a) Equivalent linear control system for Wiener system and (b) its reference model.

$$v_k = f^{-1}(y_k) = \sum_{i=1}^{r} a_i B_i(y_k) \tag{12}$$

Eq.(2) is required to meet the condition of $f^{-1}(0) = 0$. Consequently, the inaccessible intermediate variable v_k can be expressed as

$$v_k = \sum_{i=1}^{s-1} a_i B_i(y_k) + a_{s+1}\left[\alpha B_s(y_k) + B_{s+1}(y_k)\right] + \sum_{i=s+2}^{r} a_i B_i(y_k) \tag{13}$$

The problem of controller design is to determine the PID parameters and the unknown coefficients a_i ($i = 1,\ldots,r$) from an N-point input-output data set $\{u_k, y_k\}_{k=1\sim N}$.

The VRFT method is applied to the equivalent linear control system shown in Figure 4(a), so that a model-reference problem, as depicted in Figure 4(b), is to be solved. The design goal is to determine the PID parameters and the unknown coefficients a_i, such that the control system in Figure 3 behaves as similarly as possible to the prespecified reference model $T(z)$. Based on the virtual reference signal $\tilde{r}_v(z) = T(z)^{-1}v(z)$, the virtual output of controller G_C is calculated as

$$\tilde{u}(z) = G_C(z)\left[\tilde{r}_v(z) - v(z)\right] = \left[K_P + \frac{K_I}{1-z^{-1}} + K_D\left(1-z^{-1}\right)\right]\frac{1-z^{-1}}{(1-A)z^{-1}}v(z) \tag{14}$$

When the linear block is fed by u_k, it generates v_k. Therefore, a PID controller that shapes the closed-loop behavior to the reference model generates u_k when the error signal is given by $\tilde{r}_{v,k} - v_k$. The task of controller design then becomes minimizing the difference between u_k and $\tilde{u}_k$. Substituting Eq.(13) into Eq.(14) yields $\tilde{u}_k = \psi_k\theta$, where

$$\begin{aligned}
\psi_k &= \left[\psi_{P1,k}\ \psi_{I1,k}\ \psi_{D1,k} \cdots \psi_{P(s-1),k}\ \psi_{I(s-1),k}\ \psi_{D(s-1),k}\ \alpha\psi_{Ps,k} + \psi_{P(s+1),k}\ \alpha\psi_{Is,k} + \psi_{I(s+1),k}\right.\\
&\qquad \left. \alpha\psi_{Ds,k} + \psi_{D(s+1),k}\ \psi_{P(s+2),k}\ \psi_{I(s+2),k}\ \psi_{D(s+2),k} \cdots \psi_{Pr,k}\ \psi_{Ir,k}\ \psi_{Dr,k}\right]
\end{aligned}$$

$$\begin{aligned}
\theta &= \left[K_P a_1\ K_I a_1\ K_D a_1 \cdots K_P a_{s-1}\ K_I a_{s-1}\ K_D a_{s-1}\ K_P a_{s+1}\ K_I a_{s+1}\ K_D a_{s+1}\right.\\
&\qquad \left. K_P a_{s+2}\ K_I a_{s+2}\ K_D a_{s+2} \cdots K_P a_r\ K_I a_r\ K_D a_r\right]^T
\end{aligned} \tag{15}$$

$$\psi_{Pi,k} = \frac{1}{1-A}\left[B_i(y_{k+1}) - B_i(y_k)\right]; \quad \psi_{Ii,k} = \frac{1}{1-A}B_i(y_{k+1});$$

$$\psi_{Di,k} = \frac{1}{1-A}\left[B_i(y_{k+1}) - 2B_i(y_k) + B_i(y_{k-1})\right]$$

Now, the parameter θ is computed by solving the following minimization problem:

$$\min_{\theta} \sum_{k=2}^{N-1}\left[u_k - \psi_k\theta\right]^2 = \min_{\theta}\left\|\varphi - \Psi\theta\right\|_2^2 \tag{16}$$

where

$$\mathbf{\Psi} = \begin{bmatrix} \psi_2^T & \psi_3^T & \cdots & \psi_{N-1}^T \end{bmatrix}^T; \quad \mathbf{\varphi} = \begin{bmatrix} u_2 & u_3 & \cdots & u_{N-1} \end{bmatrix}^T \tag{17}$$

The solution can be calculated using the least-squares technique given by Eq.(11). The problem is how to obtain the PID parameters and estimates of the unknown coefficients a_i $(i=1,\ldots,s-1,s+1,\ldots,r)$ from the estimate $\hat{\theta}$. Define

$$\mathbf{\Theta} = \begin{bmatrix} K_P a_1 & \cdots & K_D a_{s-1} & K_D a_{s+1} & \cdots & K_D a_r \\ K_I a_1 & \cdots & K_D a_{s-1} & K_D a_{s+1} & \cdots & K_D a_r \\ K_D a_1 & \cdots & K_D a_{s-1} & K_D a_{s+1} & \cdots & K_D a_r \end{bmatrix} = \mathbf{K} \cdot \mathbf{a}^T \tag{18}$$

where

$$\mathbf{K} = \begin{bmatrix} K_P & K_I & K_D \end{bmatrix}^T; \quad \mathbf{a} = \begin{bmatrix} a_1 & \cdots & a_{s-1} & a_{s+1} & \cdots & a_r \end{bmatrix}^T \tag{19}$$

An estimate $\hat{\mathbf{\Theta}}$ of the matrix $\mathbf{\Theta}$ can then be obtained from the estimate $\hat{\theta}$. Let the economy-size SVD of $\hat{\mathbf{\Theta}}$ be given by

$$\hat{\mathbf{\Theta}} = \mathbf{U}\mathbf{\Sigma}\mathbf{V}^T = \begin{bmatrix} U_1 & U_2 & U_3 \end{bmatrix} \cdot \operatorname{diag}\begin{bmatrix} \sigma_1 & \sigma_2 & \sigma_3 \end{bmatrix} \cdot \begin{bmatrix} V_1 & V_2 & V_3 \end{bmatrix}^T \tag{20}$$

Then, the closest, in the 2-norm sense, estimates of the parameter vectors $\mathbf{K}$ and $\mathbf{a}$ can be computed as (Gómez and Baeyens, 2004)

$$\hat{\mathbf{K}} = U_1; \quad \hat{\mathbf{a}} = \sigma_1 V_1 \tag{21}$$

The coefficient a_s is then computed from Eq.(2).

4. Simulation example: pH neutralization process

The proposed controller design method for Wiener systems was applied to a pH process (Palancar et al., 1998), which involves the neutralization of acetic acid (AcH), propionic acid (PrH), and sodium hydroxide (NaOH) in a single tank. Without buffering, the process exhibits a high degree of nonlinearity. The governing equations are

$$\frac{dC_{AcH}}{dt} = \frac{1}{V}\left[q_a C_{0AcH} - (q_a + q_b)C_{AcH}\right]; \quad \frac{dC_{PrH}}{dt} = \frac{1}{V}\left[q_a C_{0PrH} - (q_a + q_b)C_{PrH}\right]$$

$$\frac{dC_{NaOH}}{dt} = \frac{1}{V}\left[q_b C_{0NaOH} - (q_a + q_b)C_{NaOH}\right] \tag{22}$$

$$\frac{C_{AcH}}{1 + 10^{pK_{AcH} - pH}} + \frac{C_{PrH}}{1 + 10^{pK_{PrH} - pH}} + 10^{pH-14} - C_{NaOH} - 10^{-pH} = 0$$

where q_a and q_b are the flow rates of acidic and alkaline streams, V is the tank volume, and C denotes the concentration. The nominal operating conditions are $q_a = 14.2$ mL/s, $V = 1.0$ L, $C_{0AcH} = 1$ M, $C_{0PrH} = 1$ M, $C_{0NaOH} = 2$ M, $pK_{AcH} = 4.75$, $pK_{PrH} = 4.87$. The objective is to control the pH of the effluent solution by manipulating the base flow rate q_b. At the steady-state of $q_b = 14.2$ mL/s and pH $= 9.407$, a uniform random signal, with a maximum amplitude of $\pm 50\%$ of the nominal value, was introduced to the base flow q_b and the resulting pH was simulated with a sampling time of 0.1 s, as shown in Figure 5. To simulate a more realistic condition, measurement noise has been added to the output data. A set of 1000 data points were used for the proposed controller design, with a tuning parameter $A = 0.82$. The resulting PID parameters are $K_P = -0.897$, $K_I = -0.005$, and $K_D = 0.442$, and the estimated inverse of the nonlinearity is plotted in Figure 6. For the purpose of comparison, the conventional PID controller was also designed based on the (linear) VRFT method using the same process data. Figure 7 shows the closed-loop performance of the proposed nonlinear control system and the conventional PID controller to successive set-point changes. The nonlinear control system shows better

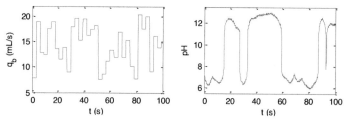

Figure 5. Input-output data used for controller design.

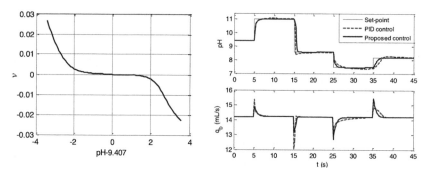

Figure 6. Estimated inverse of nonlinearity.   Figure 7. Closed-loop response.

and almost the same control performance for the set-point changes because it effectively compensates the process nonlinearity. However, the conventional PID controller shows different dynamic behaviors for the different set-point values due to the nonlinearity.

5. Conclusions

In this paper, VRFT-based methods for controller design of Hammerstein and Wiener systems have been presented. The PID parameters and process nonlinearity are simultaneously obtained based directly on a set of plant data. This is in sharp contrast to the model-based design methods that require identifying an approximate process model, which is often difficult and subject to modeling errors, before controller design. In the proposed algorithms, combining the B-splines representation of the nonlinearity with the VRFT framework allows putting the system in linear regressor form, so that least-squares techniques can be used to design the controller, which avoids implementation problems due to computational limitations. The superiority of the proposed nonlinear control design over linear control has been illustrated using a pH neutralization process.

References

M.C. Campi, A. Lecchini, S.M. Savaresi, 2002, Virtual Reference Feedback Tuning: A Direct Approach for the Design of Feedback Controllers, Automatica, 38, 1337–1346.

M.C. Campi, S.M. Savaresi, 2006, Direct Nonlinear Control Design: The Virtual Reference Feedback Tuning (VRFT) Approach, IEEE Trans. Automatic Control, 51, 14–27.

X. Yang, Y. Li, Y. Kansha, M.S. Chiu, 2012, Enhanced VRFT Design of Adaptive PID Controller, Chem. Eng. Sci., 76, 66–72.

J.C. Gómez, E. Baeyens, 2004, Identification of Block-Oriented Nonlinear Systems Using Orthonormal Bases, J. Process Control, 14, 685–697.

M.C. Palancar, J.M. Aragon, J.S. Torrecilla, 1998, pH-Control Systems Based on Artificial Neural Networks, Ind. Eng. Chem. Res., 37, 2729–2740.

Jiří Jaromír Klemeš, Petar Sabev Varbanov and Peng Yen Liew (Editors)
Proceedings of the 24th European Symposium on Computer Aided Process Engineering – ESCAPE 24
June 15-18, 2014, Budapest, Hungary. Copyright © 2014 Elsevier B.V. All rights reserved.

Time-Optimal Control of Batch Multi-Component Diafiltration Processes

Martin Jelemenský[a,*], Radoslav Paulen[a,b], Miroslav Fikar[a], Zoltán Kovács[c,d]

[a]*Faculty of Chemical and Food Technology, Slovak University of Technology in Bratislava, Slovakia*
[b]*Process Dynamics and Operations Group, Technische Universität Dortmund, Germany*
[c]*Department of Food Engineering, Corvinus University of Budapest, Hungary*
[d]*Institute of Bioprocess Engineering and Pharmaceutical Technology, University of Applied Sciences Mittelhessen Giessen, Germany*
martin.jelemensky@stuba.sk

Abstract

This paper studies the time-optimal operation of batch multi-component diafiltration processes. We employ the technique of Pontryagin's minimum principle to derive the candidates for optimal operation. Simulations and numerical optimizations are applied to define the time-optimal solution. The obtained results are evaluated on a case study, a typical multi-component diafiltration process. A comparison is provided between standard operational approaches and the newly derived optimal one.

Keywords: optimal control, multi-component systems, Pontryagin's minimum principle

1. Introduction

Over the past decades, many energy-intensive (conventional) separation processes have been replaced by the membrane separation techniques mainly because of their reduced energy usage. Diafiltration (DF) stands for a membrane process with a unique potential of simultaneous concentration of high-value components and washing-out of the impurities of the liquid solution (Cheryan, 1998). This processing technique is traditionally applied for the treatment of multi-component mixtures (Cheang and Zydney, 2004), for example in biotechnology applications, where it can serve to purify the solution (e.g. containing valuable proteins), by removing the salts or by exchanging the solution buffer. It can equally be designed to fulfill both the salt removal and buffer exchange goals in case of treatment of complex solutions (Marchetti et al., 2013).

In recent years, several published works dealt with the optimization of the DF process (Foley 1999). These addressed mainly the paramount issue of efficient run of the DF processes in minimum time. Several analytical (Paulen et al., 2012) and numerical (Takači et al., 2009) approaches were exploited therein where the solutions were presented with respect to time-optimal DF processes of various complexity. None of these studies, however, attempted to solve the problem of minimization of the processing time of DF with multi-component mixtures. In this paper, we approach the problem of time-optimal control of multi-component DF using an analytical approach of optimal control theory, Pontryagin's minimum principle (PMP). We first analyze the process with regard to the differences between two-solute DF and multi-component DF. Next, we derive the necessary conditions for optimality and we define the generalized optimal control procedure. We also compare the time-optimal operation to several traditionally used control strategies on a small-scale case study.

2. Problem Formulation

2.1. Process Description

We study the batch DF process which processes a liquid solution that consists of a solvent and N solutes. The solution is continuously brought to the membrane from the feed tank. The membrane is designed to retain the components with higher molecular sizes (macro-solutes) and to allow the micro-solutes (impurities with lower molecular sizes) to pass through. The permeate, that leaves the system at flow rate q, is often found to be a function of concentrations of all solutes. The retentate stream (rejected by the membrane) is introduced back to the feed tank where its flow rate is adjusted to maintain the set point on transmembrane pressure. The process control is achieved via adjusting the flow rate of diluant into the feed tank.

The control variable α is defined as a ratio between the inflow of diluant into the feed tank and the outflow of the permeate q. There are several types of control strategies which differ by the rate of diluant utilization: (a) concentration (C) mode with $\alpha = 0$; (b) variable-volume diafiltration (VVD) with $\alpha \in (0,1)$ taking a constant value; (c) constant-volume diafiltration (CVD) with $\alpha=1$; (d) dilution (D) mode with $\alpha \in (1,\infty)$ where $\alpha \to \infty$ represents an instantaneous dilution that maintains the ratio of solutes concentrations. The traditional control strategies for achieving the dual goal of concentration and purification of the solution consider various arbitrarily predefined combinations of these modes (e.g. C-CVD).

Based on the description above, a dynamic mathematical model of the process can be derived for N-component solution in the following form

$$\frac{dc_i}{dt} = \frac{c_i}{V}q(R_i - \alpha), \qquad c_i(0) = c_{i,0}, \qquad \forall i \in \{1, \dots, N\}, \tag{1a}$$

$$\frac{dV}{dt} = (\alpha - 1)q, \qquad V(0) = V_0, \tag{1b}$$

where c_i represents the concentration of the i-th solute with initial condition $c_{i,0}$, V stands for the volume of the processed solution with an initial value V_0, and R_i is the rejection coefficient of the i-th solute which can be a function of solute concentrations.

2.2. Separation Goal

As stated above, the goal of the DF process is to increase the concentrations of valuable components (macro-solutes) and to wash-out the impurities, i.e. to decrease the concentrations of micro-solutes. This implies that the overall goal of the process can be expressed as driving the system from its initial volume V_0 and initial concentrations $x_0 = (c_{1,0}, \dots, c_{N,0})$ to the point where desired concentrations are reached for the species present in the solution, $x_f = (c_{1,f}, \dots, c_{N,f})$.

Let us now study the process evolution by considering the concentrations of k-th and l-th solute and the volume. We can rewrite the process model (1) as

$$\frac{dc_k}{dt} = \frac{c_k}{V}\frac{R_k - \alpha}{\alpha - 1}, \qquad \frac{dc_l}{dt} = \frac{c_l}{V}\frac{R_l - \alpha}{\alpha - 1}, \qquad \frac{dc_k}{dc_l} = \frac{c_k}{c_l}\frac{R_k - \alpha}{R_l - \alpha}. \tag{2}$$

From the above equations, control variable α can be eliminated in order to obtain the quantitative behavior of the system. When other two solutes (m and n) are considered, we can arrive at the control-invariant expression

$$\frac{R_l-1}{R_k-R_l}\frac{dc_k}{c_k} - \frac{R_k-1}{R_k-R_l}\frac{dc_l}{c_l} = \frac{R_n-1}{R_m-R_n}\frac{dc_m}{c_m} - \frac{R_m-1}{R_m-R_n}\frac{dc_n}{c_n}. \tag{3}$$

Several conclusions can be drawn at this point. When the rejection coefficients are constant the expression (3) can be integrated until the final time of the operation yielding

$$\left(\frac{c_{k,f}}{c_{k,0}}\right)^{\frac{R_l-1}{R_k-R_l}}\left(\frac{c_{l,f}}{c_{l,0}}\right)^{\frac{R_k-1}{R_l-R_k}} = \left(\frac{c_{m,f}}{c_{m,0}}\right)^{\frac{R_n-1}{R_m-R_n}}\left(\frac{c_{n,f}}{c_{n,0}}\right)^{\frac{R_m-1}{R_n-R_m}} \tag{4}$$

Hence, once the final concentrations of any two solutes are specified, the concentrations of remaining solutes are fixed. This result states that it is not possible to reach the separation goal (point x_f) exactly but the over-concentration or over-purification of the process liquor will take place. In this respect, the design of optimal operation of DF process can be simplified to specification of final concentrations of two solutes whose increase or decrease stand for the limit factors of the separation. Although it is not possible to analytically solve (3) for arbitrarily varying solute rejections, it is reasonable to expect the same conclusions.

2.3. Optimization Problem Formulation

The mathematical formulation of finding the time-optimal operation of N-component DF can be formulated as an optimal control problem. We focus here on the case with three solutes which is chosen since: (a) it maintains certain level of lucidity of the presented results w.r.t. the standard two-solute DF; (b) based on the analysis provided in Section 2.2, the general conclusions can still be provided as implied by (3); (c) it represents a typical setup when micro-solute removal and solvent exchange are desired simultaneously. We will assume a system with product (of the concentration c_1), micro-solute (of the concentration c_2), and solvent to be washed-out (of the concentration c_3). The rejection coefficients of solutes are assumed to be concentration-dependent whereas rejection of macro-solute is absolute. The optimization problem reads as:

$$min_{\alpha\in[0,\infty)}\ t_f \tag{5a}$$

$$s.t.\ \frac{dc_1}{dt} = c_1^2\frac{q}{c_{1,0}V_0}(1-\alpha), \qquad c_1(0) = c_{1,0}, \qquad c_1(t_f) \geq c_{1,f}, \tag{5b}$$

$$\frac{dc_i}{dt} = c_1 c_i\frac{q}{c_{1,0}V_0}(R_i - \alpha), \qquad c_i(0) = c_{i,0}, \qquad c_i(t_f) \leq c_{i,f}, \tag{5c}$$

where $i = 2,3$ and we used $V = c_1/(c_{1,0}V_0)$ since $R_1 = 1$. We assume the required final concentrations to be defined accordingly w.r.t. the preceding analysis so that the later presented optimal operation will hold true even if some of the inequality constraints are tightened to equalities.

3. Optimal Operation

Pontryagin's minimum principle (Bryson, Jr. and Ho. 1975) is used to identify the solution candidates of (5). The process differential equations are affine in control and, hence, can be rearranged as

$$\dot{x} = f(x) + g(x)\alpha, \tag{6}$$

where $x = (c_1, c_2, c_3)^T$. The Hamiltonian function can be then written as

$$H(x,\lambda,\alpha) = 1 + f^T(x)\lambda + g^T(x)\lambda\alpha = H_0(x,\lambda) + H_\alpha(x,\lambda)\alpha \tag{7}$$

where $\lambda = (\lambda_1,\lambda_2,\lambda_3)^T$ is the vector of adjoint variables which are defined from

$$\dot{\lambda} = -\frac{\partial H}{\partial x} = -(f_x + g_x \alpha)\lambda, \quad \text{with} \quad f_x(x) = \frac{\partial f^T(x)}{\partial x}, \quad g_x = \frac{\partial g^T(x)}{\partial x}. \tag{8}$$

According to Pontryagin's minimum principle the optimal solution to (5) minimizes the Hamiltonian function. Since Hamiltonian is affine in α, its minimum is attained with α on its boundaries based on the sign of the switching function H_α. If $H_\alpha = 0$ then the Hamiltonian is singular and does not depend on α. We use the fact that the condition $H_\alpha = 0$ implies the derivatives of H_α w.r.t. time to be equal to zero. Then we obtain a set of equations linear in λ

$$H_\alpha(x,\lambda) = g^T\lambda = 0, \quad \dot{H}_\alpha(x,\lambda) = h^T\lambda = (g_x f - f_x g)^T\lambda = 0, \tag{9a}$$

$$\ddot{H}_\alpha(x,\lambda,\alpha) = k^T\lambda = \left(\frac{\partial h^T(x)}{\partial x}f - f_x h + \left(\frac{\partial h^T(x)}{\partial x}g - g_x h\right)a\right)\lambda = 0. \tag{9b}$$

We are now ready to present the main theoretical results and to define the time-optimal operation of multi-component DF process. We will distinguish two cases.

3.1. Optimal Operation with Constant Solute Rejections

In this case, it is possible to eliminate the adjoint variables from the conditions (9a) which results in the expression for singular surface in the state space

$$S(c_1, c_2, c_3) = det(g,h) = q + c_1(\partial q/\partial c_1) + c_2(\partial q/\partial c_2) + c_3(\partial q/\partial c_3) = 0. \tag{10}$$

Note that Eq. (3) is used to evaluate the determinant. A physical interpretation of this optimality condition is that the flux of micro-solutes is maximized along this surface. It can be generalized for systems with constant rejections to solutes (even if $R_1 \neq 1$) in the similar form

$$S(c_1, \dots, c_N) = det(g,h) = q + \sum_{i=1}^{N} c_i(\partial q/\partial c_i) = 0. \tag{11}$$

The corresponding singular control that keeps the states on singular surface by differentiation of the singular surface (10) w.r.t. time

$$\alpha_{sing}(c_1, \dots, c_N) = \left[\sum_{i=1}^{N} c_i R_i(\partial S/\partial c_i)\right] / \left[\sum_{i=1}^{N} c_i(\partial S/\partial c_i)\right]. \tag{12}$$

The optimal operation consists of three arcs and it is defined by

- In the first step, the control is saturated on minimum (concentration mode) or maximum (pure dilution mode) until the condition $S(c_1, \dots, c_N) = 0$ is met.
- In the second step, the condition (11) is kept with a singular control (12).
- The last step uses again saturated control to satisfy the terminal constraints.

Note that any of these three steps can be missing in the optimal solution due to particular setup of the process. The duration of the steps is fully determined from the initial and final conditions on concentrations.

3.2. Optimal Operation with Constant Solute Rejections

In this case, it is no longer possible to obtain singular state surface from the conditions (9a). However, the expression for the singular control can still be derived via elimination of adjoint variables from (9). This step uses

$$det(g,h,k) = 0 \quad \Rightarrow \quad \alpha_{sing} = \alpha_{sing}(c_1, \dots, c_N). \tag{13}$$

The optimal structure is not changed in this case w.r.t. the above stated one. The only difference to the preceding case is given by the fact that it is not anymore possible to decide when to switch between the individual phases. On the other hand, the order and the duration of the arcs of the solution can be decided based upon a resolution of simple nonlinear programming problem. Note that the control on these arcs is completely

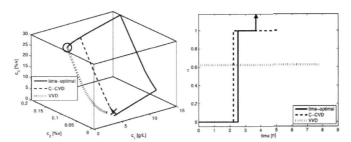

Figure 1. Comparison of different control strategies (left - state space, right - control profiles).

characterized by PMP. Optimized time intervals can be initialized based on their counterparts obtained via approximation of rejection coefficients with constant values and the subsequent utilization of procedure described in Section 3.1.

4. Case Study

We consider the separation of peptide (of the concentration c_1 in g/L) from trifluoroacetic acid (of the concentration c_2 in %v) and acetonitrile (of the concentration c_3 in %v) (Marchetti et al., 2013). The goal is to drive the concentrations from the initial point $[c_{1,0}, c_{2,0}, c_{3,0}] = [1, 0.1, 30]$ to the final point $[c_{1,f}, c_{2,f}, c_{3,f}] = [5, 0.02, 3]$. The volume of the processed solution is 5L and the employed nanofiltration membrane has an area A = 0.0522m^2. The experimentally obtained permeate flux was found to obey

$$q(c_1, c_2, c_3) = Ae^{3.22 - 0.16c_1 + 0.04c_2 + 9.03x10^{-4}c_3 + 0.048c_1 c_2 + 3.77x10^{-4}c_1 c_3}, \tag{14}$$

and the rejection coefficients for the solutes were found to be

$$R_1 = 1, \qquad R_2(c_1, c_2, c_3) = 23.61 + 3.29c_1 - 16.39c_2 + 0.05c_3, \quad R_3 = 0 \tag{15}$$

In order to determine the optimal operation, we first determine the nature of control arcs. When R_2 is approximated with the constant value, an expression for the singular surface in state space is obtained. This optimality condition predicts the concentration c_1 to be much greater than 15 g/L which represents a limiting value recommended in (Marchetti et al., 2013). Based on this observation we need to restate the optimal operation without a use of singular arc. As this predicts to over-concentrate the solution initially, we will use the control $\alpha = 0$ from the beginning of the operation in order to arrive at maximum attainable concentration $c_1 = 15$ g/L. Then, the CVD operation will be used which will maintain the constraint active. Finally, a pure dilution of the solution will be performed in order to satisfy the final conditions. Hence, the optimal control strategy is found to consist of basic operational modes of DF process. The derived optimal operation is justified by numerical optimization and simulation. Figure 1 shows the evolution of the concentrations and the profiles of control variable for time-optimal control compared to other traditionally used control strategies. The initial and final concentrations are denoted in the state space by a circle and by a cross, respectively.

Table 1 summarizes the comparison of final processing times, the final concentrations for all solutes and the rate of optimality loss δ^* for different control strategies. Using the time-optimal operation the solution is processed in 3.69 h. We can observe that the final concentrations of peptide and trifluoroacetic acid represent the limiting factors of the separation as they reach their desired values exactly at the final time of the operation. The comparison with traditional control strategies shows that the C-CVD strategy, which uses C until $c_1 = c_{1,f}$, finishes the operation in substantially longer time

Table 1. Comparison of different control strategies in terms of final processing time, reached final concentrations for solutes and the rate of suboptimality.

Operation	$t_f[h]$	$c_1(t_f)[g/L]$	$c_2(t_f)[\%v]$	$c_3(t_f)[\%v]$	δ^*
Time- optimal	3.69	5	0.02	1.05	0%
C-CVD	5.08	5	0.02	2.08	38%
VVD	8.69	5	0.02	2.11	136%

compared to the optimal one. The VVD operation, which character is determined by numerical optimization here, runs the process more than twice longer as the time-optimal strategy.

Another interesting observation is made when comparing the reached final concentrations of the acetonitrile. The time-optimal strategy reaches the smallest concentration of $c_3 = c_{3,f}$ among all the other strategies. As this case study was originally formulated to achieve a solvent (acetonitrile) exchange, we can recommend to use time-optimal control strategy as derived in this paper with a subsequent purification/diafiltration of the final solution using DF with the membrane of the smaller cut-off.

5. Conclusions

In this paper, we studied the problem of time-optimal control of a batch diafiltration process with multi-component solution. We provided an analysis of the operation of the process. Based on Pontryagin's minimum principle, we derived the conditions for optimality and we identify the candidates for the optimal control profiles. The developed theory was applied on an example of multi-component separation including concentration of macro-solute, removal of a micro-solute and exchange of a solvent. The results indicate that the time-optimal operation is a three-step strategy which might not be necessarily complicated to apply using modes of traditional operations.

Acknowledgements

The authors thank to Patrizia Marchetti for the discussions. The authors gratefully acknowledge the contribution of the Scientific Grant Agency of the Slovak Republic under the grant 1/0053/13 and the Slovak Research and Development Agency under the project APVV-0551-11. ZK is grateful to the Hessen State Ministry of Higher Education, Research and Arts (LOEWE-Program), the MEMFIDA2 program (EUREKA HU 08-1-2010-0010), and the European Commission for the Marie Curie FP7 Integration Grant (PCIG11-GA-2012-322219).

References

A. E. Bryson, Jr., Y. C. Ho, 1975, Applied Optimal Control: Optimization, Estimation and Control, Taylor & Francis Group, New York, USA.

B. Cheang, A. L. Zydney, 2004, A two-stage ultrafiltration process for fractionation of whey protein isolate, Journal of Membrane Science, 231, 1-2, 159–167.

M. Cheryan, 1998, Ultrafiltration and Microfiltration Handbook, CRC Press, Florida, USA.

G. Foley, 1999, Minimisation of process time in ultrafiltration and continuous diafiltration: the effect of incomplete macrosolute rejection, Journal of Membrane Science, 163, 1–2, 349–355.

P. Marchetti, A. Butté, A. G. Livingston, 2013, Quality by design for peptide nanofiltration: Fundamental understanding and process selection, Chem. Eng. Sci., 101, 200–212.

R. Paulen, M. Fikar, G. Foley, Z. Kovács, P. Czermak, 2012, Optimal feeding strategy of diafiltration buffer in batch membrane processes, J. Membr. Sci., 411-412, 160–172.

Jiří Jaromír Klemeš, Petar Sabev Varbanov and Peng Yen Liew (Editors)
Proceedings of the 24th European Symposium on Computer Aided Process Engineering – ESCAPE 24
June 15-18, 2014, Budapest, Hungary.

Novel Domain-Specific Language Framework for Controllability Analysis

Afshin Sadrieh*, Parisa A. Bahri

Murdoch University, Perth, 6150, Australia
afshin.sadrieh@ murdoch.edu.au

Abstract

Controllability is one of the most important aspects of process systems' operability. Failure to achieve a standard controllable process may lead to environmental disasters and economical difficulties. Therefore, the need for highly standard specific software tool for this area is now visible more than any time. However, this category of problems varies significantly from case to case, which makes providing software tools an inefficient task. In this study, a new methodology to develop software tool for controllability analysis is proposed and the maintainability of the software in terms of number of lines of code and time spent to apply a particular new request is discussed. Moreover, a controllability case study is applied to this software and the results are presented.

Keywords: Domain-Specific Language, Maintainability, Controllability analysis, CAPE

1. Introduction

Among three aspects of operability (controllability, switchability and flexibility), controllability is an important factor to achieve strict safety and economical standards in process systems. As research shows, the Chernobyl catastrophe could have been avoided if controllability issues of that plant were taken into consideration (Salge and Milling 2006).

The first article published on controllability was back in 1943, where Ziegler and Nichols defined it for the first time. Since then, it has been defined and used in different areas and applications. Moreover, since the first article, it has been emphasised that controllability of a system is inherited form its design and not the controller. Therefore, it should be taken into consideration at the design stage.

On the other hand, during the last few decades, computer hardware and software have grown rapidly and influenced almost every aspect of process engineering. Many software systems, both commercial and open-source (e.g., gPROMS, ASPEN, Hysys and ASCEND) were developed specifically to address modelling and computational issues in this field.

However, although the need for controllability evaluation of process systems at design stage was bolded out decades ago, surprisingly, there is no software tool available for this purpose. This may be due to the fact that these problems vary significantly from case to case, and therefore, implementing software tools specific to each case becomes inefficient. A proper software must be modifiable, be able to adopt to the changes and cover a wider range of problems.

In this study, a new methodology to develop a software for controllability analysis is proposed. The software is then tested through a process case study. Finally, the results of evaluating both the controllability of the case study and the effort needed for developing the software, are presented.

2. Background

There have been breakthroughs in software developing methodologies in recent years. Domain Specific Language (DSL) is a new term defined as "a computer programming language of limited expressiveness focused on a particular domain" (Fowler 2013). The main idea behind developing a DSL is to provide a programming language for a narrowed down, specific domain. As a result, DSLs are easy to learn programming languages. Providing its user with notations and symbols to write scripts that are familiar, DSLs fill the gap between programmers and domain experts. Using meaningful symbols also makes the resulting script to be modifiable for domain experts. Moreover, DSLs are easy to learn, due to their bounded domain. Apart from that, due to level of abstraction that their structure provides, compared to General-Purpose Language (GPL), using DSL boosts up maintainability of the product (Kan, 2002).

Although DSL benefits both programmers and end users in different aspects, it has some drawbacks. Like any other programming language, DSL needs to be developed and implemented. Also end users have to learn DSL. The impact of these costs is taken into consideration especially when DSL is applied to a reasonably small domain.
However, one of the solutions to address overhead cost of using DSL is to use its extensive tool support that eases the process of language defining, implementing and modification. Language work-bench is the general name for this category of softwares. According to Fowler, "Language workbenches could change the game of DSLs significantly".

3. Methodology

In this study the language workbench, MetaEdit+ is used, to generate the DSL based framework (Tolvanen and Kelly 2009) This framework evaluates the controllability of process design based on the interaction between control loops of a process system design using the Relative Gain Array (RGA) index (Hovd and Skogestad 1991) The RGA matrix is calculated based on Eq.(1):

$$\Lambda(s) = G(s) \times (G^{-1}(s))^T \tag{1}$$

Where G(s) is the gain matrix calculated from the transfer function of the process system.

In this work the R value calculated through (Eq. 2) is used for each RGA matrix as the basis of comparison.

$$R = \sum (\lambda_i - 1)^2 \text{ for each positive } \lambda_i \tag{2}$$

Where λ_i is each element of Λ matrix.

3.1. Software Structure

This framework consists of four elements, each of them loosely coupled. In other words, they behave independent of each other. This characteristic benefits the framework in two ways: 1) developing the whole framework takes less effort (Sadrieh and Bahri 2013) and 2) adding new features is a considerably easier task. This is mainly

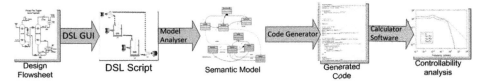

Figure 1. Structure of the Software

because changing each element does not affect others. In the following section through an example it is explained how adding new features would affect different parts of the framework.

The elements of the framework are described as follows (Figure 1):

3.1.1. DSL Graphical User Interface (GUI)

GUI is part of the framework through which it interacts with the end user; also it is the GUI that fits the framework into the definition of a DSL. Moreover, not only the notations and symbols defined in the GUI should be familiar to process engineers (domain expert), but also they are limited into a specific area; i.e., controllability problem.

The input into this element is the flow sheet of the process system and the output is a file in XML format which contains essential information about the process system design.

3.1.2. Model Analyzer

After getting the process model data from the domain expert, it is now essential to store them in a well-defined data structure, so it can be accessed through the evaluation process. This data structure is called "semantic model". Basically, all information entered into GUI by domain expert, is now interpreted into objects and connections inside the semantic model. Due to high level of abstraction that it provides, semantic model plays a crucial role in any DSL system structure. It helps with the data entry from model evaluation, which makes the tasks of development and maintenance considerably easier. To generate the semantic model, the model analyzer would parse the XML file from the previous step.

3.1.3. Code Generator

So far the semantic model of process system design is generated. The environment within which this happens is a general purpose programming language (C#), which provides tools and data structure support for previous steps. However, from now on, the main task is to deal with the mathematical model of the process system design. Therefore, a new implementation environment which supports mathematical calculation is preferred. In this case study MATLAB is selected. However, before taking advantage of the new environment, the semantic model must interpret the new environment syntax.

This issue is addressed by Code Generator element of the framework in three phases:

1) Calculating the steady state: From the mathematical model and the topology of the flow sheet, a script containing the non-linear equations of each element of the system (e.g. CSTR, mixer, splitter) is generated. By solving these equations, the steady state conditions are calculated and saved in the semantic model future references.

2) Generating the state space model: After calculation of the steady state conditions, another script is generated, which contains the necessary information for producing the state space model and the process transfer function matrix.

3) Evaluating controllability: Using the process transfer function matrix, it is now possible to generate the code to evaluate the controllability index of each design. The controllability index used in this case is RGA.

3.1.4. Calculator Software

This part of the framework is responsible for performing the linear and non-linear calculations, which are necessary to assess the controllability index of the process system design. In the previous step, the mathematical model of process was generated in the form of code scripts, which are valid for this part of the framework. However, high performances as well as covering wide range of mathematical operations are the essential characteristics of this part of the framework. The result that is generated from this element is the final result showing how controllable each design configuration is.

3.2. Adding new features

As was mentioned in section 1, controllability of a process system is an inherent characteristic of process itself and it should be evaluated during design stage. In some cases the designer can alter the order of the units in the flowsheet to gain better controllability. This leads to the idea of superstructure selection, in which the designer declares all possible configurations first and the framework would subsequently suggest the best design based on the controllability index.

4. Illustrative example

The case study (adapted from [6]) consists of two stirred tank reactors, which could be configured in various ways and the interaction between the loops is measured using RGA index.

The reaction occurring (A→B) is Arrhenius temperature dependent. In this example there are four states (the concentration and temperature in each reactor: C_1, T_1, C_2 and T_2), two manipulated variables (the cooling water flows to the two reactors: M_{C1} and M_{C2}), five disturbance variables (concentration, temperature and flow rate of the feed, T_f, Q_f and C_f, along with two input cooling water temperatures: T_{ci1} and T_{ci2}) and two controlled variables (temperature and concentration of the process output: T_m and C_m).

A DSL based framework was generated for this case study. A superstructure was then created by adding splitter and mixer elements into the DSL (Figure 2). The splitters split the flow that comes to their inlet into two flows, outlet one and outlet two, while the portion of the flows can change automatically. This makes it possible to have more than one design in a flowsheet. The ratio between the outlet flow rates is either zero, half, equal, twice or infinity, with the last one having all of the input flow rate directed to outlet one. The mixer elements act as normal mixers, enabling the additional flows created through splitters to be managed in the system.

Based on the structure of the framework, if the splitter and mixer features are to be added, each software element is modified as follows: DSL GUI is altered so it would be possible to use a notation for the new element. Semantic model is changed to store the

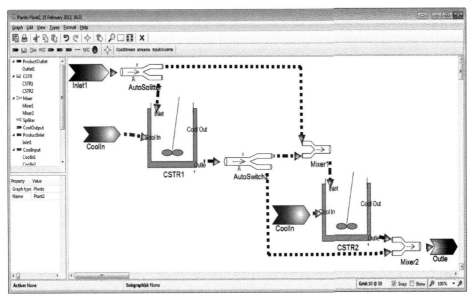

Figure 2. Superstructure of the two CSTRs case study

order of the elements of the design. The most changes will apply to code generator, which has to produce a different code script for each configuration. Calculator software remains unchanged.

5. Results

Through the application of the framework to the case study, 25 different configurations were observed (Figure 3.a). Among these, six were irrelevant (marked with "NaN"), and the best one from the controllability point of view was the one where all of the flow from the first splitter goes through the lower output (into CSTR1) and the flow of the second splitter is divided equally between the two outputs (Figure 3.b)

1	Splitter 1 State	Splitter 2 State	λ	R
2	zero	zero	NaN	NaN
3	half	zero	1.6	0.3844
4	equal	zero	7.6	43.56
5	twice	zero	2	1.0404
6	infinity	Zero	NaN	NaN
7	zero	half	1.2	0.0256
8	half	half	3.3	5.2441
9	equal	half	14	174.24
10	twice	half	2.7	2.8561
11	infinity	half	NaN	NaN
12	zero	equal	1.1	0.0196
13	half	equal	5.8	22.5625
14	equal	equal	25	593.4096
15	twice	equal	3.3	5.3361
16	infinity	equal	NaN	NaN
17	zero	twice	1.2	0.0225
18	half	twice	14	178.4896
19	equal	twice	122	14733.1
20	twice	twice	4.4	11.4921
21	infinity	twice	NaN	NaN
22	zero	Infinity	1.8	0.6241
23	half	Infinity	18	283.2489
24	equal	Infinity	19	338.56
25	twice	Infinity	14	179.0244
26	infinity	Infinity	NaN	NaN

a

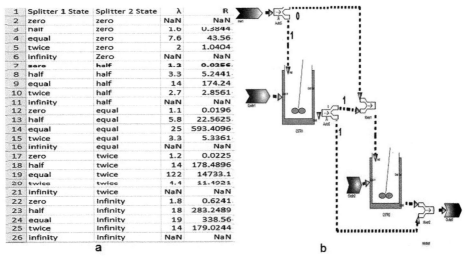

b

Figure 3. Results of evaluating the case study: a) Controllability index of 25 configurations, b) The best configuration from controllability perspective

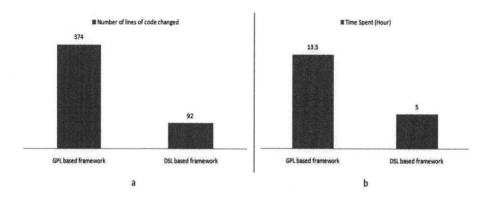

Figure 4. Comparing the efforts needed for applying changes to DSL and GPL based softwares: a) Number of lines of code changed or added to each software and b) The time needed to apply modification

The framework was also evaluated with respect to the modification effort. A software tool typically used in process engineering domain (based on GPL) was employed to solve the same problem. Requirements for both GPL and DSL based softwares were the same. Similar modifications were applied to both softwares and the efforts needed for each tool were measured (Figure 4).

As illustrated in Figure 4, using this methodology can reduce the time needed for modification more than 2.5 times compared to the methodologies currently used. Additionally, the number of lines of codes which has to be modified is more than four times less.

6. Conclusion

This research presents a new framework for controllability analysis based on a novel software development methodology. The maintainability of this product is verified and compared from two perspectives: 1) The time that is needed to apply changes is reduced by about 27 times (from 135 to 5 hour) and 2) the number of lines of codes which is needed to be changed through the process of modification is reduced by approximately 4 times (from 374 to 92). This study shows that using DSL to develop software for process engineering applications, makes future modification of the software product simpler and easier compared to current methods.

References

M. Fowler, R. Parsons, 2010, Using Domain-Specific Languages, Domain-Specific Languages, Addison Wesley, Massachusetts, USA, 27-42.

S.R. De Hennin, J.D. Perkins, 1993, Structural decisions in on-line optimization, Technical Report, Imperial College, London, UK, B93-37.

M. Hovd, S. Skogestad, 1991, Controllability analysis for the fluid catalytic cracking process, AIChE annual meeting, 17-22.

A. Sadrieh, P.A. Bahri, 2013, A Novel Graphical Method for Controllability Analysis of Chemical Process Designs, Computer Aided Chemical Engineering, 32, 655-660.

M. Salge, P. Milling, 2006, Who is to blame, the operator or the designer? Two stages of human failure in the Chernobyl accident, System Dynamics Review, 22, 2, 89–112.

J. Tolvanen, S. Kelly, 2009, MetaEdit+: defining and using integrated domain-specific modeling languages, OOPSLA '09 Proceedings of the 24th ACM SIGPLAN conference companion on Object oriented programming systems languages and applications, 819-820

Jiří Jaromír Klemeš, Petar Sabev Varbanov and Peng Yen Liew (Editors)
Proceedings of the 24th European Symposium on Computer Aided Process Engineering – ESCAPE 24
June 15-18, 2014, Budapest, Hungary. Copyright © 2014 Elsevier B.V. All rights reserved.

Polynomial Chaos Expansion (PCE) Based Surrogate Modeling and Optimization for Batch Crystallization Processes

Nahid Sanzida,[a] Zoltan K. Nagy, [a,b,]*

[a]*Department of Chemical Engineering, Loughborough University, Loughborough, LE11 3TU, United Kingdom*
[b]*School of Chemical Engineering, Purdue Univesity, West Lafayette, IN, USA*
z.k.nagy@lboro.ac.uk.

Abstract

The paper presents a computationally efficient approach to represent a nonlinear data-driven input/output model between the finite-time control trajectories and the quality index at the end of the batch, based on the approximate representation of the full process model via polynomial chaos expansion (PCE). A batch cooling crystallization system of Paracetamol in water was used to estimate the dependence of output mean length of crystals at the end of the batch on the temperature trajectory applied during the crystallization. The surrogate model was then validated for its performance. Later, the surrogate model was used to determine the optimal temperature profile needed to maximize the mean length of crystals at the end of the batch. The validation and optimization results prove that the experimental data based PCE can provide a very good approximation of the desired outputs, providing a generally applicable approach for rapid design, control and optimization of batch crystallization systems based on experimental optimization.

Keywords: Polynomial Chaos Expansion, Surrogate Modeling, Optimization, Crystallization Process.

1. Introduction

Many high value products such as pharmaceuticals, batteries, microelectronic devices, and artificial organs are manufactured using finite-time processing steps, which are generally represented by complex distributed parameter systems, making the development of first-principles models difficult and often impractical. Because of the inherent nonlinearity of these processes the use of typical linear data-driven modeling approaches cannot yield models with acceptable accuracy and robustness. In addition, due to the limited availability of robust on-line sensors, often only off-line quality measurements are widely available. As a result, there is a growing demand for the development of relatively simple data-driven and computationally efficient nonlinear models that can be applied for robust model based optimization or the robust optimal control of these processes. Crystallization from solution is an inherently nonlinear distributed parameter system mostly carried out in batches. It is estimated that more than 80 % of the active pharmaceutical ingredients (APIs) involve at least one crystallisation step in their manufacturing process (Reutzel-Edens, 2006). The control of the crystal size distribution (CSD) is important for efficient downstream operations (i.e. filtration, drying, and formulation) and better product performance (i.e. dissolution rates, bioavailability and shelf life).

One general trend is to state a nonlinear system as a finite sum of orthogonal polynomials to accurately approximate the function of interest (Kim and Braatz, 2012). Different orthogonal functions are optimal for different parameter probability density functions (PDFs) (e.g. Gaussian, Gamma, Beta, Uniform, Poisson, Binomial). Since PCE contains orthogonal basis with respect to the Gaussian probability measure, it is stated as an expansion of multidimensional Hermite polynomial functions of the uncertain parameters. PCE can be used to replace a nonlinear system with surrogate model that accurately describes the input-to-state and input-to-output behaviour within the trajectory bundle (Braatz, 2010). After Wiener introduced the PCE in late thirties (Wiener, 1938) only relatively recently PCE has been widely accepted and applied in different disciplines, e.g. climate modeling, hurricane prediction, computational fluid dynamics (CFD), biochemical networks (Streif et al., 2013) and batch process control for uncertainty propagation (Huan and Marzouk, 2013). Researchers have also demonstrated that use of PCE promises to be a computationally efficient and cheap alternative to Monte Carlo approaches for analysis and controller design of uncertain systems (Kim and Braatz, 2012). However, despite their potential to capture the systems nonlinear behavior until now only a few studies have been done towards the application of PCE in the field of chemical process control (Kim et al., 2013).

In this paper, PCE is used to develop a nonlinear surrogate model of a batch crystallization process. Performance analysis was also performed on the surrogate model to evaluate its accuracy. Later this model was used to optimise the temperature profile required to obtain a desired mean length of crystal (L_n) at the end of the batch for analysing the robustness of the developed surrogate model.

2. Polynomial Chaos Expansions (PCE)

If the input variable is described in terms of standard normal random variables, the polynomial chaos expansion (PCE) can describe the model output ψ as an expansion of multidimensional Hermite polynomial functions of the input parameters θ (Nagy and Braatz, 2007) as shown in Eq. (1), in terms of the standard random normal variables $\{\theta_i\}$ using an expansion of order d,

$$\psi^{(d)} = \underbrace{a_o^{(d)}\Gamma_o}_{\text{constant}} + \underbrace{\sum_{i_1=1}^{n_\theta} a_{i_1}^{(d)}\Gamma_1(\theta_{i_1})}_{\text{first-order terms}} + \underbrace{\sum_{i_1=1}^{n_\theta}\sum_{i_2=1}^{i_1} a_{i_1 i_2}^{(d)}\Gamma_2(\theta_{i_1},\theta_{i_2})}_{\text{second-order terms}} + \underbrace{\sum_{i_1=1}^{n_\theta}\sum_{i_2=1}^{i_1}\sum_{i_3=1}^{i_2} a_{i_1 i_2 i_3}^{(d)}\Gamma_3(\theta_{i_1},\theta_{i_2},\theta_{i_3})}_{\text{third-order terms}} + \dots \tag{1}$$

where n_θ is the number of parameters, the $a_{i_1}^{(d)}, a_{i_1 i_2}^{(d)}$, and $a_{i_1 i_2 i_3}^{(d)}$ are the deterministic coefficients in $\mathbf{R}$ to be estimated, Γ_1, Γ_2, and Γ_3 are the successive polynomial chaoses of their arguments, the subscripts denote the order of the expansion which is convergent in the mean square. An expression for deriving the multi-dimensional Hermite polynomials of degree $m = i_1, i_2, \dots i_{n_\theta}, \Gamma_m(\theta_{i_1}, \dots \theta_m)$ is shown in below,

$$\Gamma_m(\theta_{i_1}, \dots \theta_m) = (-1)^m e^{(1/2)\theta^T\theta} \frac{\partial^m e^{-(1/2)\theta^T\theta}}{\partial\theta_1 .. \partial\theta_m}$$

The polynomial chaos terms are random variables, since they are functions of the random variables, and terms of different order are orthogonal to each other (with respect to an inner product defined in Gaussian measures as the expected value of the product of the two random variable, i.e. $\varepsilon[\Gamma_i\Gamma_j]=0$ for $\Gamma_i \neq \Gamma_j$. The number of coefficients (N) in the PCE depends on the number of uncertain parameters (n_θ) and the order of expansion (m).For engineering applications, to adequately represent fairly large levels of random fluctuations the recommended order of expansion is not higher than four (Ghanem and Spanos, 1991). Since, the PCE is convergent in the mean-square sense it is beneficial to calculate the coefficients using least-square minimization (LSM) considering sample input/output pairs from the model. The optimization is performed until the best fit is achieved between the surrogate PCE and the nonlinear model (or experimental data).

3. PCE Based Surrogate Modeling and Validation of a Batch Cooling Crystallization System

In this study an unseeded batch cooling crystallization system of Paracetamol in water with a batch time of 300 mins was considered. The kinetics of the system is given by the following set of ordinary differential equations (Fujiwara et al., 2002),

$$d\mu_0/dt = B \tag{2}$$

$$d\mu_i/dt = iG\mu_{i-1} + Br_0^i \qquad i=1,2,.... \tag{3}$$

$$dC/dt = -k_v\rho(3G\mu_3 + Br_0^3) \tag{4}$$

where, B and G are the nucleation and growth rates respectively, $S = C - C_S(T)$ is the absolute supersaturation, C is concentration, C_S is the solubility as a function of the temperature T, μ_0, μ_1, μ_2, and μ_3 are the moments defining total number, length, area, and volume of crystals in the system respectively, r_0 is the size of the nuclei. The initial and final temperatures were 314.13 K and 294.15 K respectively. With the density of crystal, $\rho = 1.296$ g/cm^3; volumetric shape factor, $k_v = 0.24$; initial concentration, $C_0 = 0.0254$ g/g solvent. Other model parameters are shown below,

Solubility in water (T in K) $\qquad C_S = 1.58 \times 10^5 T^2 - 9.057 \times 10^3 T + 1.31 \qquad (5)$

Growth rate (cm/sec)
$$G = \begin{cases} 1.64(S)^{1.54} & if \ S > 0 \\ -1.64(S)^{1.54} & if \ S \leq 0 \end{cases} \tag{6}$$

Nucleation rate
$$B = \begin{cases} 7.8529 \times 10^{19}(S)^{6.23} & if \ S > 0 \\ -7.8529 \times 10^{19}(S)^{6.23} & if \ S \leq 0 \end{cases} \tag{7}$$

A simulation program was developed using MatLab to be treated as the real process. The batch length was divided into $N = 10$ equal stages. For this study, thirty sets of historical data were used as training data. The training data was generated so as to span the behavior of the states as much as possible so that they can capture the system's response. The inputs were the temperature trajectories over the batch duration. The output was the corresponding L_n at the end of the batch (i.e. a single parameter). The system was then re-identified by the nonlinear PCE using these data. Both 2nd and 3rd order PCE was tested. For 2nd and 3rd order PCE with 10 parameters, the numbers of coefficients are 66 and 286 respectively. To initiate the calculation of the PCE coefficients by the LSM method, a set of initial coefficients were assumed randomly in the beginning and then these were finalized through successive trials, i.e. the simulation were continued from one trial to another using the coefficients calculated by the previous trial as the initial guess for the next trial until there was no further progress in prediction accuracy. The surrogate model was then subject to validation by selecting validation data as such that some input profiles lead to L_n within the range of training data and some were outside the range to check extrapolation ability too. The results of the 2nd order and 3rd order PCE predictions have been shown in Fig. 1(a) and Fig. 1(b). Table 1 gives the overall sum squared error (SSE) values between actual L_n and L_n from the surrogate models. These values reveals that the validation results were better for the within limit tests than the extrapolation one. Also, the SSEs of validation were greater than that of model identification which indicates the reasonable presence of overfitting. These results show that the 3rd order PCE captured the system more closely than the 2nd order PCE.

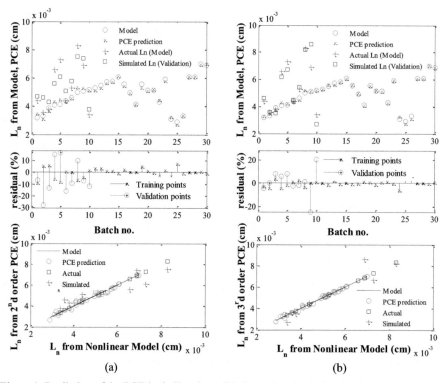

Figure 1. Prediction of the PCE including the validation points (a) 2nd order (b) 3rd order.

Table 1. SSE Values for the Validation of 2nd and 3rd Order PCE.

	2nd Order SSE	3rd Order SSE
Surrogate Model Identification	2.5338×10^{-8}	9.8300×10^{-9}
Validation: Input trajectories within the limit of the training data	4.4894×10^{-7}	3.2950×10^{-8}
Validation: Input trajectories outside the limit of the training data	1.1014×10^{-6}	2.1501×10^{-7}

4. Optimization of PCE Based Surrogate Model

To optimize the temperature profile by the surrogate models that corresponds to the maximum L_n determined by the first principle model, the theoretical model was first subject to optimize its performance. The objective was to maximize L_n. The system was subjected to the constraints of maximum and minimum allowable temperatures, the rate of cooling, and also maximum allowable final concentration to ensure minimum yield. The surrogate model was then used to determine the optimal temperature profile needed to obtain the crystals with desired theoretical optimal L_n. The objective function is shown in Eq. 8. The same linear temperature profile was used in all three cases to initiate the optimization. For the optimal temperature profiles to be determined by the surrogate models, the initial and final temperature was kept fixed at 314.07 K and 294.15 K respectively, which were the terminal temperatures from the theoretical optimization. The optimization problem is solved through sequential quadratic programming (SQP) approach applied in the MATLAB® function fmincon.

$$\min_{T(1),T(2),\ldots.T(N)} \left(\frac{L_n^{\text{target}} - L_{n,\text{PCE}}}{L_n^{\text{target}}} \times 100 \right)^2 \tag{8}$$

Subject to,

$$T_{\min} \le T(k) \le T_{\max} \text{ and } R_{\min} \le dT/dt \le R_{\max}.$$

These inequality constraints ensure that the optimised temperature profile is implementable. Figure 2(a)-(d) shows the optimal results from the model based optimization and the surrogate models. The computation time for surrogate model optimization was much less than the first principle model based optimization. The target L_n by the theoretical model was 102 μm which was quite far from the maximum limit used in the training data while identifying the surrogate model. Due to this extrapolation, the L_n produced by the optimal temperature profiles by 2nd and 3rd order surrogate models were quite far from the desired 102 μm. The 2nd order PCE produced an actual L_n of 67 μm at the end of the batch with SSE of 1.225×10^{-5} and the 3rd order PCE produced an actual L_n of 71 μm at the end of the batch with SSE of 9.61×10^{-6}. The SSE value for the 2nd order PCE optimization was greater than that of extrapolation during validation. However, the 3rd order SSE is quite closer to the SSE values of the extrapolation during validation (Please see Table 1). In addition, the linear initial profile produced an L_n of 59 μm which was far from the desired 102 μm, hence, the surrogate models suffered to capture the nonlinearity of the system properly. Also, the 2nd and 3rd order optimal temperature profiles were not the same as the theoretical optimal profile. Since this study was aimed at the mean length at the end of the batch, it is possible to arrive at the same final L_n from multiple temperature trajectories. Overall, the results

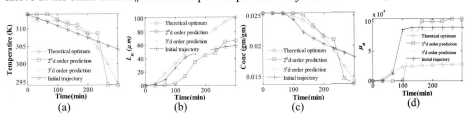

Figure 2. Optimum profiles (a) temperature (b) L_n (c) concentration (d) μ_o.

for the optimization are in perfect harmony with the previous validation results. From these figures and the SSE values, it is evident that the performance of the third order surrogate model was also better in terms of better yield and nucleation point of view. This coherency indeed suggests the choice of 3rd order PCE over 2nd order PCE.

5. Conclusions

Whilst PCE is mostly used for uncertainty analysis, in this work, a novel PCE based operating data-driven nonlinear surrogate modeling approach was developed for batch cooling crystallization system. The performance of the surrogate model was first validated and later optimized to generate the required temperature profile to obtain desired L_n of crystals at the end of the batch. The initial assumption of the PCE coefficients played a vital role during developing the surrogate model. So, the overall bottleneck of the PCE based nonlinear surrogate modeling can be identified to be the initial guess of coefficients to avoid being entrapped in local minima. The developed surrogate model showed reasonable overfitting during validation and optimization. However, the findings confirm that as the order of expansion was increased the nonlinear system can be identified more precisely, e.g. residual error was on average 15 % and 10 % for 2nd and 3rd order prediction respectively (Figure 1(a-b)). The validation and optimization results prove that the experimental data based PCE can provide a significant approximation of the desired outputs, providing a generally applicable approach for rapid design, control, and optimization of batch crystallization systems.

References

R.D. Braatz, 2010, Robust Optimal Control of Finite-time Distributed Parameter Systems. <sites.uclouvain.be/inma/reddot/slides/Braatz2009.pdf>, accessed on 17/2/2014.

M. Fujiwara, P.S. Chow, D.L. Ma, R.D. Braatz, 2002, Paracetamol crystallization using laser backscattering and ATR–FTIR spectroscopy: metastability, agglomeration, and control, Crystal Growth and Design, 2, 363-370.

R. Ghanem, P. Spanos, 1991, Spectral Stochastic Finite Element Formulation for Reliability Analysis, J. Eng. Mech., 117, 10, 2351-2372.

X. Huan, Y.M. Marzouk, 2013, Simulation-based optimal Bayesian experimental design for nonlinear systems, Journal of Computational Physics, 232, 288-317.

K-K K. Kim, R.D. Braatz, 2012, Generalized polynomial chaos expansion approaches to approximate stochastic receding horizon control with applications to probabilistic collision checking and avoidance, Proc. of the IEEE Conference on Control Applications, Croatia, 350-355.

K-K K. Kim, D.E. Shen, Z.K. Nagy, R.D. Braatz, 2013, Wiener's Polynomial chaos for the analysis and control of nonlinear dynamical systems with probabilistic uncertainties, IEEE Control Systems Magazine, 33, 5, 58-67.

Z.K. Nagy, R.D. Braatz, 2007, Distributional uncertainty analysis using power series and polynomial chaos expansions, Journal of Process Control, 17, 229–240.

S.M. Reutzel-Edens, 2006, Achieving polymorph selectivity in the crystallization of pharmaceutical solids: Basic considerations and recent advances, Current Opinion in Drug Discovery and Development, 9, 6, 806–815.

S. Streif, K-K K. Kim, P. Rumschinski, M. Kishida, D.E. Shen, R. Findeisen, R.D. Braatz, 2013, Robustness Analysis, Prediction and Estimation for Uncertain Biochemical Networks, Preprints of the 10th IFAC DYCOPS, December 18-20, Mumbai, India, 1-20.

N. Wiener, 1938, The homogeneous chaos, Amer. J. Math., 60, 897-936.

Jiří Jaromír Klemeš, Petar Sabev Varbanov and Peng Yen Liew (Editors)
Proceedings of the 24th European Symposium on Computer Aided Process Engineering – ESCAPE 24
June 15-18, 2014, Budapest, Hungary. Copyright © 2014 Elsevier B.V. All rights reserved.

Multi-Objective and Robust Optimal Control of a CVD Reactor for Polysilicon Production

Mattia Vallerio, Daan Claessens, Filip Logist, Jan Van Impe*

KU Leuven, BioTeC& OPTEC, Department of Chemical Engineering, Willem de Croylaan 46, 3001 Leuven, Belgium
jan.vanimpe@cit.kuleuven.be

Abstract

Traditionally, high-grade polysilicon is produced in the so-called "Siemens" reactor. The process is based on the Chemical Vapor Deposition (CVD) of silicon from a gaseous mixture of silanes and hydrogen on silicon rods. To obtain the crystal growth on the rod surface high temperatures are needed. The rods are heated internally by the Joule effect, i.e., an electrical current induces heating due to the electrical resistance of the silicon material. The Joule effect allows for a tight temperature control but, it also makes this process extremely energy intensive. In this work an existing model is improved by accounting for the reflectivity of the wall and the radiative absorption of the bulk. Additionally, the uncertainty on the thermal conductivity parameter of the silicon rods is taken into account. Hence, a robust optimal control problem is formulated and solved based on the evaluation of Lyapunov equations. Finally, the trade-off among productivity and energy cost is studied via a multi-objective (MO) scalarization method.

Keywords: multi-objective, robust optimization, crystal grade silicon, CVD

1. Introduction

The market for purified silicon (polysilicon) used to be mainly devoted to microelectronics. However, during the last decade, the photovoltaic industry expanded enormously. This led to a significant increase in silicon demand and production. In 2007, 80,000 t of silicon were produced, whereas in 2012 the production has increased to 260,000 t of which 94 % designated to the solar industry (Ramos et al., 2013).The classic way to produce crystal-grade polysilicon is via CVD. A thin high-purity silicon bar is placed inside the reactor and it is used as a seed for the crystal growth. The deposition reaction is endothermic. Higher temperatures enhance the thermodynamics and the kinetics of the process leading to higher productivity. The rods are heated by the Joule effect, i.e., an electrical current induces a heating effect due to the electrical resistance of the silicon. The Joule effect enables for a fine temperature control but excessive temperatures in the center of the rod must be avoided at all times. This work exploits a detailed reactor model and advanced optimization algorithms to enhance the operation of this industrially relevant case study. Specifically, a robust (ROCP) and a multi-objective optimal control problem (MOOCP) are defined and solved. The ROCP deals with the uncertainty on the thermal conductivity parameter of the silicon rods. It is assumed that the uncertainty on the considered parameter lays in a bounded set. Hence, a hard-to-solve robust counterpart problem is formulated, i.e., a worst-case scenario or min-max optimal control problem. The approximation approach used is based on linearization strategies of the model with respect to the uncertainty (Diehl et al., 2006). Additionally, the robust counterpart problem is solved with the use of Lyapunov functions (Bittanti et al., 1984). The MOOCP is formulated to quantify the underlying trade-off between (i) maximizing productivity (i.e., the radius of the rods) and (ii) minimize energy consumption. The aim is to reduce the excessive electricity consumption due to the Joule heating. The resulting MO problem is tackled via the scalarization approach Normal Boundary Intersection (NBI) (Das and Dennis, 1998). It has been shown that the integration of direct optimal control methods with advanced scalarization ones leads to an efficient solution of MOOCPs (Logist et al., 2012). The article unfolds as follows: Section 2 introduces the dynamic model of the CVD reactor. Sections 3 and 4 introduce the ROCP and the MOOCP formulation and present the corresponding results. Section 5 reports the main conclusions.

2. An extended version of the "Siemens" CVD reactor model

The first contribution is an extension of the model as introduced by Viganò et al. (2004). In particular the following features were added: (i) a direct link between the rod surface temperature, the rod core temperature and the applied current intensity, (ii) the reflectivity of the external wall and (iii) the thermal radiative absorption of the gaseous bulk. The resulting model accounts for 9 differential Eqs.(1-9) and 1 algebraic equation Eq.(10). In particular, $\dot{F}_{IN}$ is the inlet volumetric flow rate, $\dot{F}_{OUT}$ is outlet volumetric flow rate and C_i^{IN}, C_i^V and C_i^S are the species concentration in the inlet, the vapor-phase and on the surface. The ideal gas law is used, given the composition and temperature of the system. V and V_R are the vapor-phase reaction and the rod volume. A is the outer rod surface area, R is the rod diameter and A_W the inner wall surface. k_1 is the vapor-phase kinetics constant, while k_2 and k_3 are the surface kinetics constants. $h_{m,i}$ and h_T are the mass and heat transfer coefficient, σ is the Stefan-Boltzmann constant. NRS = 2 and NRV = 1 are the number of surface and vapor-phase reactions respectively. $\Delta H_{R,i}$ and $H_{f,i}$ represent the molar reaction and molar formation enthalpy. Cp_i are the specific heats. ρ_{Si} is the density of the silicon rod, λ_e and λ_T are the electrical and thermal conductivity of the rod, I the current intensity flowing in the rod. T, T_S, T_W and T_C are the vapor-phase, the rod surface, the external wall and the core rod temperatures. Finally, F is the fraction of radiation absorbed by the bulk. For this work, a laboratory-scale reactor with one rod is considered. Parameter values used in the model are reported in Table 1. For the sake of brevity the sensitivity analysis performed on the introduced parameters is not reported here.

$$\frac{dC_{SiH4}^V}{dt} = \frac{\dot{F}_{IN}}{V}C_{SiH4}^{IN} - \frac{\dot{F}_{OUT}}{V}C_{SiH4}^V - h_{m,SiH4}\frac{A}{V}\left(C_{SiH4}^V - C_{SiH4}^S\right) + k_1 C_{SiH4}^V \tag{1}$$

$$\frac{dC_{SiH4}^S}{dt} = h_{m,SiH4}\frac{A}{V}\left(C_{SiH4}^V - C_{SiH4}^S\right) - k_3 C_{SiH4}^S\frac{A}{V} \tag{2}$$

$$\frac{dC_{SiH2}^V}{dt} = \frac{\dot{F}_{IN}}{V}C_{SiH2}^{IN} - \frac{\dot{F}_{OUT}}{V}C_{SiH2}^V - h_{m,SiH2}\frac{A}{V}\left(C_{SiH2}^V - C_{SiH2}^S\right) + k_1 C_{SiH2}^V \tag{3}$$

$$\frac{dC_{SiH2}^S}{dt} = h_{m,SiH2}\frac{A}{V}\left(C_{SiH2}^V - C_{SiH2}^S\right) - k_2 C_{SiH2}^S\frac{A}{V} \tag{4}$$

$$\frac{dC_{H2}^V}{dt} = \frac{\dot{F}_{IN}}{V}C_{H2}^{IN} - \frac{\dot{F}_{OUT}}{V}C_{H2}^V - h_{m,H2}\frac{A}{V}\left(C_{H2}^V - C_{H2}^S\right) + k_1 C_{H2}^V \tag{5}$$

$$\frac{dC_{H2}^S}{dt} = h_{m,H2}\frac{A}{V}\left(C_{H2}^V - C_{H2}^S\right) + k_2 C_{SiH2}^S\frac{A}{V} + 2k_3 C_{SiH4}^S\frac{A}{V} \tag{6}$$

$$\frac{dc_{Si}^S}{dt} = k_2\, C_{SiH2}^S \frac{A}{V} + 2k_3 C_{SiH4}^S \frac{A}{V} \tag{7}$$

$$\sum_{i=1}^{NC} Cp_i V \frac{dT}{dt} =$$
$$\dot{F}_{IN} \sum_{i=1}^{NC} C_i^{IN} \left(H_{f,i}(T_{ref}) + \int_{T_{ref}}^{T_{IN}} Cp_i dT \right) - \dot{F}_{OUT} \sum_{i=1}^{NC} C_i^V \left(H_{f,i}(T_{ref}) + \int_{T_{ref}}^{T_{IN}} Cp_i dT \right) + \sum_{i=1}^{NRV} r_i V \left(-\Delta H_{R,i}(T) \right) + h_T A(T_S - T) + h_T A(T_W - T) + F\sigma A(T_S^4 - T_W^4) \tag{8}$$

$$(\rho_{Si} V_R Cp_{Si}) \frac{dT_S}{dt} = \sum_{i=1}^{NRS} r_i A \left(-\Delta\tilde{H}_{R,i}(T_S) \right) - h_T A(T_S - T) + \frac{\lambda_T}{R} \sigma A(T_C - T_S) - (1 - F)\sigma A(T_S^4 - T_W^4) \tag{9}$$

$$T_C = T_S + \left(\frac{I^2}{\lambda_e} \right) \frac{R^2}{4\lambda_T} \tag{10}$$

3. Robust optimal control: formulation and results

The thermal conductivity parameter λ_T of the silicon rods are of key importance in the model, since it is responsible for the heat dispersion from the inside of the rods to theirs surfaces. Moreover, the cross section area of the rods increases leading to higher deposition rate and heat dispersion. To keep the temperature of the rod surface above the deposition limit the Joule effect must be increased. However, overheating can occur at the core of the rods, achieving local melting. An internal melting of the rods must be avoided at all times, since it means a complete loss of the batch. Hence, the uncertainty on the thermal conductivity parameter λ_T is taken into account.

3.1. Robust optimal control method

The numerical technique employed here assumes that the uncertainty on the considered parameter λ_T lays in a bounded set, the dimensions of which are defined through the robust parameter γ. Hence, an increase of γ increases also the uncertainty on the parameter adding safety margin. A robust counterpart problem, i.e., a worst-case scenario or min-max optimal control problem is formulated. No efficient algorithm to solve this class of problems is known. The proposed approach is based on a heuristic method centered on linearization strategies (Houska and Diehl, 2009). The linearization is justified if the uncertainty is small in respect to the curvature of the equations leading to negligible higher-order terms. This method splits up the states into reference trajectories y_{ref} and a deviation δy such that $y = y_{ref} + \delta y$. The original dynamic system equations:

$$\frac{d}{d\xi} = f\big(u(\xi), p, y(\xi), q(\xi)\big) \tag{11}$$

can be split into dynamics for the reference trajectory, if the uncertainties q are small:

$$\frac{d}{d\xi} y_{ref}(\xi) = f\big(u(\xi), p, y_{ref}(\xi), q_{ref}(\xi)\big) \, with \, \delta y_{ref}(0) = y_0^{ref} \tag{12}$$

and the approximate linearization based dynamics of the uncertainty affected deviation:

$$\frac{d}{d\xi} y(\xi) = A(\xi)\delta y(\xi) + B(\xi)\delta q(\xi) \, with \, \delta y(0) = B_0 \delta q_0 \tag{13}$$

$$A(\xi) = \frac{\partial f(u(\xi),p,y_{ref}(\xi),q_{ref}(\xi))}{\partial y} \; ; B = \frac{\partial f(u(\xi),p,y_{ref}(\xi),q_{ref}(\xi))}{\partial q} \tag{14}$$

where represents the independent variable, $zy(\xi)$, $u(\xi)$, p and $w(\xi)$ are the vectors of states, controls, parameters and disturbances. The evaluation of the robust control problem is performed with the use of Lyapunov equations (Kalman, 1960):

$$\frac{d}{d\xi}P(\xi') = A(\xi')P(\xi') + A^T(\xi')P(\xi') + B(\xi')B^T(\xi'); P(0) = B_0 B_0^T \tag{15}$$

where P is a 9x9 diagonal matrix, whose 81 elements $p_{i,j}$ are additional Lyapunov differential states that are added to the original model for this case study. This allows us to impose the following robustified constraints on T_C.

$$T_S + \left(\frac{I^2}{\lambda_e}\right)\frac{R^2}{4\lambda_T} + \gamma\lambda_T\sqrt{p_{9,9}} \le 1687.0 \text{ K} \tag{16}$$

More details about the ROCP method can be found in Logist et al.(2011) and references therein.

3.2. Results
The reformulation adopted for the robust counterpart problem introduces 81 additional differential states to the original problem. The problem was discretized with the orthogonal collocation approach resulting in more than 180,000 inequality, 90,000 equality constraints and more than 90,000 variables. Figure 1 and 2 report the results obtained when the robust technique is applied to the CVD reactor. It can be seen that the current intensity gets more conservative with the increase of the robust parameter γ. This is due to the enlargment of the bounded uncertainty set on the parameter λ_T. As a consequence the rod core temperature moves away from the upper constraints of 1,687 K. Moreover, the control action decreases over time due to the increasing rod radius.

4. Multi-objective optimal control problem and results

High temperatures mean high productivity, but also excessive energy costs. A trade-off between productivity and energy cost is therefore inherently present. Consequently, a MOOCP with the two conflicting objectives is formulated.

4.1. Multi-objective optimal control method
The MO methods used belong to the class of scalarization methods. These methods reformulate the MOOCP to a parametric single objective optimization problem. By consistently varying the scalarization parameters an approximation of the Pareto Front (PF) is obtained. This work exploits Normal Boundary Intersection(NBI) (Das and Dennis, 1998) as the classic Weighted Sum presents some intrinsic drawbacks, i.e., it is highly scale dependent, an even spread of weights does not yield an even spread of solutions along the PF and it fails to find points in non convex part of the PF. The NBI method overcomes these drawbacks. For the sake of brevity, the description of the NBI method is omitted. The reader is referred to Logist et al. (2012) and references therein.

4.2. Results
The solution of the MOOCP with the NBI method generated the Pareto front reported in Figure3. The trade-off between the objectives is clearly visible. Maximizing the growth of the rod causes the total cost of operation to increase and vice versa. Moreover, as expected a uniform distribution of solutions is achieved on the Pareto front. Figure 4 illustrates the effect of the objectives on the current intensity profile. Maximizing the

rod growth causes a higher current intensity to ensure a high temperature for fast deposition, while minimizing the total cost of operation leads to the opposite.

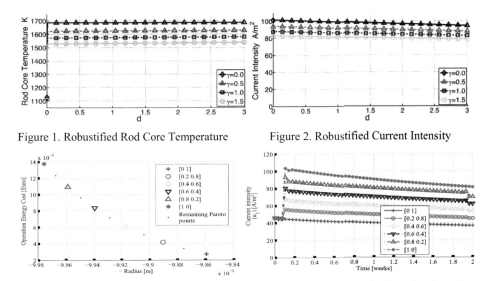

Figure 1. Robustified Rod Core Temperature   Figure 2. Robustified Current Intensity

Figure 3. Pareto Front for the CVD reactor   Figure 4. Current intensity for points in the PF

Table 1. Paremeter values for the CVD reactor models

Parameter	Value	Units	Parameter	Value	Unitss
V	480	cm^3	λ_e	$2.5 \times 10{-}3$	$1/(\Omega.m)$
A	120	cm^2	λ_T	7.167	$cal/(m.K)$
v	10	cm/s	D_{SiH2}	$0.59 \cdot (T[K]/300)^{1.8}$	cm^2/s
x^{IN}_{H2}	0.998	%	$S_{f,H2};\ S_{f,Si}$	31.2; 4.5	$cal/(mol.K)$
x^{IN}_{SiH4}	0.001	%	$S_{f,SiH4}$	48.8	$cal/(mol.K)$
x^{IN}_{SiH2}	0.001	%	$S_{f,SiH2}$	49.5	$cal/(mol.K)$
T^{IN}	373.15	K	$k_2;\ k_3$	$1.9 \cdot 104;\ 5.4$	cm/s
T_S	1,100	K	Cp_{SiH4}	$4.9 + 0.018 \cdot T[K]$	$cal/(mol.K)$
A_W	512	cm^2	Cp_{SiH2}	$6. + 0.001 \cdot T[K]$	$cal/(mol.K)$
ρ_{Si}	0.19	mol/cm^3	Cp_{H2}	$6.5 + 0.0016 \cdot T[K]$	$cal/(mol.K)$
$H_{f,SiH2}$	64,590	cal/mol	Cp_{Si}	5.4	$cal/(mol.K)$
$H_{f,SiH4}$	8,100	cal/mol	k_1	$2.7 \cdot 10^{14} \cdot \exp(-57000/R/T[K])$	$1/s$
$H_{f,H2};\ H_{f,Si}$	0; 0	cal/mol	k_T	$1.3 \cdot 10^{-4} + 3.45 \cdot 10^{-4} \cdot T[K]/300 - 2.9 \cdot 10^{-5} \cdot (T[K]/300)^2$	$cal/(cm.s.K)$

5. Conclusions

Modern solution methods for optimal control theory are well suited to handle complex nonlinear dynamic systems such as the CVD reactor. In this work two advanced optimal control techniques are applied to an industrially relevant case study: (i) ROCP and (ii)

MOOCP. First, an ROCP is formulated and solved taking in consideration the uncertainty on a key model parameter. The resulting solution of the problem guaranties an additional safety margin on the temperature control. Then, a MOOCP is formulated and solved via the NBI method. This approach systematically evaluates the trade-off between maximizing production and minimizing energy consumption. Additionally, the reactor mode has been extended to account for the reflectivity of the external wall, the bulk radiative adsorption and to directly evaluate the core temperature of the silicon rod.

Acknowledgements

M. Valleriohas a PhD grant of the Agency for Innovation through Science and Technology in Flanders (IWT). J. Van Impe holds the chair Safety Engineering sponsored by the Belgian Chemistry and Life Sciences Federation essenscia. The research was supported by the KU Leuven Research Fund: PFV/10/002 (OPTEC), OT/10/035; the Research Foundation Flanders (FWO): FWO KAN2013 1.5.189.13, FWO-G.0930.13 and the Belgian Federal Science Policy Office: IAP VII/19 (DYSCO).

References

S. Bittanti, P. Bolzern, P. Colaneri, 1984, Stability analysis of linear periodic systems via the Lyapunov equation, Proc. of the 9th IFAC World Congres, Budapest, 169–172.

I. Das, J.E. Dennis, 1998, Normal-Boundary Intersection: a new method for generating the Paretosurface in nonlinear multicriteria optimization problems, SIAM Journal on Optimization, 8, 631–657.

M. Diehl, H. Bock, E. Kostina, 2006, An approximation technique for robust nonlinear optimization,Mathematical Programming, 107, 213–230.

B. Houska, M. Diehl, 2009, Robust nonlinear optimal control of dynamic systems with affine uncertainties, IEEE Conference on Decision and Control, 2274–2279.

F. Logist, B. Houska, M. Diehl, J. Van Impe, 2011, Robust multi-objective optimal control of uncertain (bio)chemical processes, Chemical Engineering Science, 37, 191–199.

F. Logist, M. Vallerio, B. Houska, M. Diehl, J. Van Impe, 2012, Multi-objective optimal control of chemical processes using acado toolkit, Computers & Chemical Engineering, 37, 191–199.

A. Ramos, C. del Cañizo, J. Valdehita, J. C. Zamorano, A. Luque, 2013, Radiation heat savings in polysilicon production: Validation of results through a CVD laboratory prototype. Journalof Crystal Growth, 374, 5-10

L. Vigano, M. Vallerio, F. Manenti, N. Lima, L. Linan, G. Manenti,2010, Model predictive control of a CVD reactor for production of polysilicon rods, Chemical Engineering Transactions, 21, 523–528.

Jiří Jaromír Klemeš, Petar Sabev Varbanov and Peng Yen Liew (Editors)
Proceedings of the 24th European Symposium on Computer Aided Process Engineering – ESCAPE 24
June 15-18, 2014, Budapest, Hungary.

On the Modeling of C_{7+} Fractions with Real Components in Plant Simulations

Marcella Porru[a], Andrea Saliu[b], Roberto Baratti[a,*]

[a] *Dip. Ingegneria Meccanica, Chimica e dei Materiali,via Marengo, 2. 09123 Cagliari, Italy.*
[b] *SARLUX S.R.L. SS195 Sulcitana Km 19. 09018 Sarroch (CA), Italy*
roberto.baratti@dimcm.unica.it

Abstract

Motivated by the need to reconstruct blends properties and their behavior in industrial distillation columns for control and monitoring purposes, the problem of the C_{7+} fractions modeling is addressed with substitute mixture of real components. The reliability of the proposed approach (comparable with the employment of hypothetical component as made in commercial simulators) is demonstrated in the context of the steady state simulation of an industrial debutanizer (located at SARLUX refinery, Italy).

Keywords: process modeling, feed characterization, refinery processes.

1. Introduction

In refineries and petrochemical industries, plant simulations play an important role in units' design or revamping, in prediction of the unit functioning, in optimization of performances, and in development of dynamic models for monitoring and control purposes. Since complex mixtures of hydrocarbons (HCs) are mostly treated, the knowledge of the influent and effluent composition is not available. Indeed, hardware analyzers can commonly measure the concentration of light HCs, no molecules with more than six carbons are detected, while an HC mixture can be composed of hundreds of different species with seven or more carbons, which is usually called the C_{7+} fraction. In order to obtain the complete blend characterization, more expensive analyses (e.g., *the crude oil assay reports* for petroleum) have to be provided from the petroleum companies research institutes. To identify a petroleum-derived blend, the techniques normally employed are based on the distillation curve, with the true boiling point (TBP) analysis according to ASTM D-2892 standard or the simpler/cheaper ASTM D-86 standard, used for routine analysis.

In industry, the plant functioning is usually reproduced with commercial simulators (e.g., Aspen Plus and Aspen HYSYS) which handle the real mixture characterized from the distillation curve as a substitute mixture of hypothetical components (named pseudo- or hypo-components). Hypo-components are artificial components for which it is necessary to deliver a set of physical properties calculated with the TBP curve by simplifying correlations (Technical API, 1989). However, a substituting mixture of hypo-components cannot properly describe the chemical nature of the mixture, and it cannot be employed as reactive mixture in the field of the reactor modeling.

An alternative approach can be the modeling of the real blend with a simplified mixture of real components. Practitioners in dynamic plant simulation (e.g., for control or monitoring purposes) know that a compromise between number of real components to be modeled and unit behavior reconstruction must be found, because (i) if on one hand the behavior tracking increase with the number of real components, on the other hand (ii) the tractability in dynamic simulations dramatically decrease, (iii) and chemical and physical properties of high HCs could not be available in the data bases. However, the advantage is that the properties of real components can be easier estimated than the ones of hypo-components. The pioneer of this approach is Eckert and Vaněk (2005) who proposed an algorithm based on the partition of the TBP in non-overlapping temperature intervals. Each interval represents a component with normal boiling point (NBP) given by the integral mean temperature over the corresponding interval of fraction distillate. The same authors tested the proposed method on petroleum C_{7+} fractions for few systems (Eckert et al., 2012). The main disadvantage of this method is the need of TBP curve, preferably accompanied by one or more additional curves describing the dependency of the density, molecular weight, API gravity, or viscosity on the volume or mass fraction. Albahry (2006) employed a similar method for predicting the properties of light petroleum fractions. The Albahry's algorithm has the advantage to start from ASTM D-86 but a step of its conversion to TBP curve is required.

In this work, a method to evaluate the concentration of the real components in a substitute mixture starting from the ASTM D-86 is proposed. It must be pointed out that the target of the proposed approach is its employment in that case where the operation involves mixture with relative low final boiling point for which the ASTM D-86 is a routine analysis. Concentration of real HCs in the substitute mixture are evaluated using the HYSYS packages for a debutanizer located at SARLUX refinery (Sarroch, Italy), and assessed comparing the fitting of the experimental data for mixtures of real and hypo- components.

2. C_{7+} fraction characterization

A C_{7+} fraction is a mixture that contains molecules with seven or more carbons and hundreds of different species. C_{7+} fractions have the feature that the analyzers typically available in plant laboratory cannot (i) distinguish the species present in there, and consequently, (ii) determine the composition. For this reason, to identify a petroleum-derived blend, the techniques normally employed are based on the distillation curve, with the TBP analysis according to ASTM D-2892 standard, or the cheaper ASTM D-86 standard.

The ASTM D-2892 test method (ASTM Int., 2003) employs a batch-fractionating column having an efficiency of 14 to 18 theoretical plates operated at a reflux ratio of 5:1 under the atmospheric pressure. From the application of the test procedure the TBP graph of temperature versus % of mass or volume distilled can be produced. Since the high reflux ratio and number of stage (that means high separation level), the TBP curve is the locus of NBPs of the HCs in the blend. The ASTM D-86 (ASTM Int., 2006) is the standardization of the basic test method of determining the boiling range of a petroleum product by performing a simple, one theoretical stage, batch distillation which is in use since the petroleum industry has existed. This standard is cheap, simple, quick, and normally used for routine analysis. In ASTM D-86 the initial and the final boiling point (IBP and FBP) are not accurately detected because the low separation level and the normal boiling temperature of the lightest and heaviest HCs are missed. Although the ASTM D-86 fails in the correct determination of the IBP and FBP, it remains the most employed characterization technique for the C_{7+} fractions in plant laboratories while the ASTM D-2892 apparatus in not generally presents for its cost and time consumption.

3. The problem of the C_{7+} fraction modeling

Consider the debutanizer located at SARLUX refinery (Sarroch, Italy). The debutanizer is a multicomponent distillation column that separates the GPL and a light gasoline cut with the prescribed composition specification in distillate (i-pentane max 0.3 StdVol %) and bottom (i-butane + n-butane max 1 StdVol %). The column has 39 stages, a kettle reboiler (39-th stage), total condenser (first stage), temperature measurement at 13 and 35 stages, and feed at the 26-th stage. The feed is mainly constituted by a flow that directly arrives from the topping plus a GPL stream. It is characterized by the ASTM D-86 distillation curve depicted in Figure 1.

In a preliminary analysis of the unit functioning we are interested in the study of the steady state in order to obtain (i) the temperature and composition stage-to-stage gradients, and (ii) the liquid-vapor equilibrium properties, for the design of a model based composition estimator with the methodology proposed in Porru et al., (2013). Under this point of view, the feed modeling with a mixture of real components becomes a key step in estimation design.

4. Choice of real components to be modeled

Components in the substitute mixture have to be chosen according to the ASTM D-86 range of temperatures, the PNA (paraffins, naphthenes, aromatics) analysis, the context where the unit is placed, and the composition specifications for effluents (e.g., composition control targets) remembering that a compromise between number of real component to be modeled and unit behavior reconstruction must be found.

In particular, for the proposed case study it is known that the debutanizer feed directly arrives from the topping, so no olefins are expected. Moreover, the topping feed is a paraffinic-naphthenic crude oil, so that aromatics are in low concentration in the light naphtha. For the sake of brevity, among all possible mixtures, we choose to present the result obtained for the test mixture composed by the HCs listed in Table 1. This mixture is designed including (i) all n-paraffins present in the boiling range; (ii) a naphthenic compound both in the first and in the second half of the distillation curve; (iii) the toluene as unique aromatic knowing from other analysis that the amount of benzene is

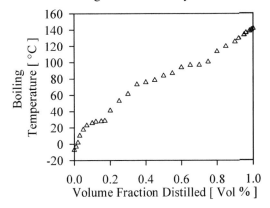

Figure 1. Debutanizer feed characterization with ASTM D-86.

Table 1. Real hydrocarbons for the modeling of the debutanizer feed.

Real HCs	NBP [°C]	Real HCs	NBP [°C]
propane	-42.05	n-hexane	68.75
i-butane	-11.75	3,3-dimethylpentane	86.05
n-butane	-0.45	n-heptane	98.45
i-pentane	27.85	toluene	110.65
n-pentane	36.05	n-octane	125.65
cyclopentane	49.25	ethyl-cycloexane	131.75
2,3-dimethylbutane	57.95	2-methyloctane	143.25

considerably low; (iv) i-, n-butane, and i-pentane since they are components for which a control target is established, (v) preferring methyl and dimethyl i-paraffins.

5. Concentration evaluation

Concentration of real HCs in the substitute mixture can be evaluated with regressive methods that find the optimal composition that minimize the gap between the experimental ASTM D-86 and the calculated one. Commercial simulator such as Aspen HYSYS can help in the composition determination offering the possibility to regress the ASTM D-86 boiling curve using a mixture of real components up to the high limit of 90 % in terms of molar fraction. On the other hand, the behavior of the heaviest HCs is tracked with hypo-components. It is possible to set the final cuts on the curve in such a way that the hypo-components have the same NBP as that the heaviest HCs initially chosen. Alternatively, the simulator automatically cuts the remaining part of the curve and then the initial decision have to be modified selecting heavy HCs with NBP similar to the one of the hypo-components generated by the simulator. The subsequent step consists of imposing the equality between the concentrations of the heavy HCs and their corresponding hypo-components. In order to assess the results, it must be finally evaluated whether the blend of real components fits the ASTM D-86 under the prescribed uncertainty.

6. Composition Assessment

The assessment step is made simulating the ASTM D-86 experimental apparatus by a dynamic model. The one stage, batch, and atmospheric distillation of a mixture of NC components under the hypothesis of (i) time constant heat duty, (ii) ideal thermodynamics for both liquid and vapor phases, (iii) no vapor loss, it is modeled with the system (1) of two ODEs.

$$\partial(Hx_i)/\partial t = -Vy_i; \quad \partial(H)/\partial t = -V \tag{1}$$

where H is the liquid hold up in the flask; x_i is the concentration (in terms of molar fraction) of the i-th HC in the liquid mixture, and y_i is the concentration of the i-th HC in the vapor flow with $i=1,..,NC$; V is the molar vapor flow rate. Other algebraic equation employed are

$$V(t) = Q/\lambda_H(t); \quad D(t) = (H_o - H(t))/[\rho_D(t)] \tag{2,3}$$

$$y_i = Ps_i x_i / P_{atm}; \quad f_T = \sum_{i=1}^{NC} Ps_i(T)x_i - P_{atm} \tag{4},(5)$$

where the time varying molar vapor flow rate V is computed on the basis of the heat duty Q and the heat of vaporization λ_H of the boiling mixture; the volume of the distillate D (named also volume recovered) at time t is computed in Eq.(3) on the difference between the initial H_o and actual H molar hold up in the flask and converting by using its molar density ρ_D. Since the analysis is conducted under atmospheric pressure the thermodynamics can be well approximated with the Raoult's law Eq.(4) where P_{si} is the vapor pressure of the i-th component and P_{atm} is the atmospheric pressure; according to the prescribed description of the liquid-vapor equilibrium, the initial boiling point of the blend is the zero of the implicit bubble point function Eq.(5). Finally, the distillation curve is obtained plotting the percent volume recovered versus corresponding temperature. Physical properties are computed according to Reid et.al. (1988).

7. Modeling results

In order to give a comparison with the approach mainly employed in industry, in Table 2 the compositions of a mixture of hypo-components (auto-selected by the simulator plus propane and butanes as light ends) and the molar fraction of the proposed blend of HCs (obtained with the HYSYS simulation according to the methodology previously described) are reported.

The fitting of the real (continue line) and hypothetical (circles) mixture with the experimental ASTM D-86 (triangles) is displayed in Figure 2a. It can be noticed that (i) the hypothetical mixture perfectly fits the experimental behavior, and that the real mixture (ii) approximates well the experimental curve, and (iii) the small deviations in the initial and final portion of the curve can be related both with the assumption of ideal thermodynamic conditions and with the already discussed uncertainty that affects the experimental determination of the IBP and FBP.

As it can be appreciated in Figure 2b, the static simulation of the debutanizer fed with the mixture of real (continue line) and hypo- (circles) components according to a typical operative condition leads to the same results in terms of column temperature profiles. The two profiles are also in agreement with the available (condenser, first, 13-th, 35-th, 38-th stages, and reboiler) temperature measurements (triangles).

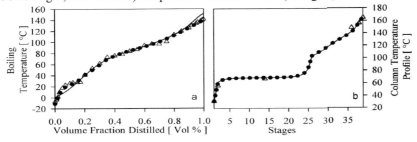

Figure 2. a) Fitting of the mixture of real (continue line) and hypo- (circles) components with the experimental ASTM D-86 (triangles). b) Debutanizer temperature measurements (triangles) and temperature profiles obtained with feeds of real HCs (continue line) and hypo-components (circles).

582   *M.Porru et al.*

Table 2. Composition of the mixtures of hypo-, and real components.

Hypo-components	[mole frac.]	Real HCs	[mole frac.]
propane	0.0461	propane	0.0461
i-butane	0.0605	i-butane	0.0605
n-butane	0.1257	n-butane	0.1257
i-pentane	0.0858	i-pentane	0.0654
NBP_37	0.212	n-pentane	0.0152
NBP_52	0.0714	cyclopentane	0.0972
NBP_68	0.1064	2,3-dimethylbutane	0.0184
NBP_81	0.1071	n-hexane	0.0945
NBP_96	0.1566	3,3-dimethylpentane	0.1347
NBP_114	0.0648	n-heptane	0.0991
NBP_128	0.0901	toluene	0.0387
NBP_144	0.0643	n-octane	0.0559
		ethyl-cycloexane	0.0852
		2-methyloctane	0.0635

8. Conclusions

The problem of the modeling of the C_{7+} fractions with substitute mixture of real component under the point of view of industrial plant simulation has been addressed. The proposed methodology is motivated by the need to provide chemical and physical properties or reconstruct the behavior of specific HCs. Results are presented for a case study (feed modeling of an industrial debutanizer located at SARLUX refinery, Italy), and they prove that the proposed approach is a valid alternative to the classical one (modeling with hypothetical components) since the simulated column steady state in the two cases was in agreement with the available plant data.

Acknowledgement

M. Porru thankfully acknowledges SARLUX refinery for the fellowship support.

References

T. A. Albahri, 2006, Advanced method for predicting the properties of light petroleum fractions, Fuel, 85, 748-754.

ASTM Int., 2003, Standard test method for distillation of crude petroleum (15-Theoretical Plate Column), ASTM Book of Standards, ASTM, West Conshohocken, PA, USA.

ASTM Int., 2006, Standard test method for distillation of petroleum products at atmospheric pressure, ASTM Book of Standards, ASTM, West Conshohocken, PA, USA.

E. Eckert, T. Vaněk, 2005, New approach to the characterisation of petroleum mixtures used in the modelling of separation processes, Computer and Chemical Engineering, 30, 343–356.

E. Eckert, T. Vaněk, Z. Bělohlav, P. Zamostný, 2012, Effective characterization of petroleum C7+ fractions, Fuel, 102, 545-553.

M. Porru, J. Alvarez, R. Baratti, 2013a, Composition estimation design for industrial multicomponent distillation column, Chemical Engineering Transaction, 32, 1975-1980.

R. C. Reid, J. M. Prausnitz, B. E. Poling, 1988, The properties of gases & liquids, 4th Ed, McGraw-Hill, New York, US.

Technical API, 1989, Technical data book on petroleum refining. In: Daubert, Danner, editors, API, Washington, DC.

Jiří Jaromír Klemeš, Petar Sabev Varbanov and Peng Yen Liew (Editors)
Proceedings of the 24th European Symposium on Computer Aided Process Engineering – ESCAPE 24
June 15-18, 2014, Budapest, Hungary. Copyright © 2014 Elsevier B.V. All rights reserved.

Towards Model-Based Diagnosis of von Willebrand Disease

Federico Galvanin[a], Andrea Monte[a], Alessandra Casonato[b], Roberto Padrini[c], Massimiliano Barolo[a], Fabrizio Bezzo[a,*]

[a]CAPE-Lab – Computer Aided Process EngineeringLaboratory, Department of Industrial Engineering, University of Padova, via Marzolo 9, 35131, Padova PD (Italy)
[b]Department of Cardiologic, Thoracic and Vascular Sciences, University of Padova Medical School, via Ospedale Civile 105, 35128, Padova PD (Italy)
[c]Department of Medicine, University of Padova Medical School, via Ospedale Civile 105, 35128, Padova PD (Italy)
fabrizio.bezzo@unipd.it

Abstract

Von Willebrand disease (VWD) is the most common inherited coagulation disorder to be seen in humans. It originates from a deficiency and/or dysfunction of the von Willebrand factor (VWF), a large multimeric glycoprotein playing a central role in the hemostasis process. Diagnosing VWD may be complicated because of the heterogeneous nature of the disorder. A new mechanistic model of VWD, identified from clinical data, is presented in this paper. The model allows for the automatic detection of VWD variants, elucidating the critical pathways involved in the disease recognition and characterisation.

Keywords: Von Willebrand disease, model identification, clinical data.

1. Introduction

Von Willebrand disease (VWD) is the most common inherited coagulation disorder described in humans, with an estimated prevalence in the population of approximately 1 % (Werner et al., 1993). The disease is related to a deficiency and/or abnormality of the von Willebrand factor (VWF), a large multimeric glycoprotein mediating the adhesion and aggregation of platelets to the subendothelium and carrying factor VIII (FVIII) in the blood circulation. The clinical symptoms of VWD include nosebleeds, menorrhagia, bleeding from small lesions in skin and excessive bleeding after traumas, surgical interventions or childbirth (Lillicrap, 2007). VWD is a very heterogeneous disease occurring in a large variety of forms whose precise diagnosis strongly relies on the clinician's skill and expertise (N.H.L.B.I, 2007). However, rather frequent repetitions of preliminary and advanced diagnostic tests are required because of the poor reproducibility of clinical trials and the significant inter-individual variability of VWD, thus making the precise recognition of the disease a very long and complicated task. Pharmacokinetic (PK) tests have been proposed for measuring VWF plasma concentrations after the subcutaneous administration of 1-desamino-8-d arginine vasopressin (DDAVP) (Casonato et al., 2010), forcing the release of VWF from endothelial cells. These tests provided the basis for the development of semi-empirical PK models providing useful indications in the characterisation of the VWD types by means of pharmacokinetic indices. However, these simple models do not allow for the characterisation of the complex physiological patterns involved on VWF multimer distribution in time, and do not cover the large variety of VWD types and the high intra-subject variability observed during the hemostatic laboratory findings.

In this paper a physiologically-based PK model (Galvanin et al., 2014) is presented in order to provide a valid support to VWD diagnosis and a quantitative description of the biochemical pathways, which is required for the characterization of VWD. The availability of clinical data from PK experiments related to individuals affected by VWD permits the model identification and a faster and objective diagnosis of VWD from clinical data, allowing for the discrimination between several known VWD types by using standard PK indices. The model, properly tuned-up and adapted to the specific response of an individual subject, allows describing the VWF multimer distribution in time and can be used to perform in-silico experiments suggesting which mechanisms should be aimed at for intervention in the therapeutic process, and possibly to assess the effectiveness of highly customised therapies.

2. Model development

Laboratory tests for VWD diagnosis are carried out once a subject's history evidences a bleeding disorder or abnormal coagulative activity. Preliminary tests usually include the measurement of plasma VWF/FVIII levels and function; however, advanced VWD laboratory tests are usually required to identify VWD sub-types. These tests may include the analysis of multimer distribution, ristocetin-induced platelet aggregation, the binding of FVIII to VWF (VWF:FVIIIB), or the execution of even more oriented studies (DDAVP test and DNA sequencing). Hence, VWD diagnosis is the result of a complex procedure where the crucial role of the clinician is to analyse signs and symptoms of the disease as well as the amount of quantitative data provided by these clinical tests. A reliable PK model of VWD would represent a valuable support for data analysis and in-silico experimentation.

2.1 Model formulation

Clinical measurements of VWF antigen (VWF:Ag) and collagen binding (VWF:CB) concentrations following the subcutaneous administration of DDAVP at a dose of 0.3 µg/kg of body weight were available for distinct pools of subjects of variable age and body weight, including healthy subjects (O and non-O blood group) and subjects affected by VWD (types 2A, 2B and Vicenza). VWF:Ag and VWF:CB measurements were taken during a daily test at fixed times (0, 15, 30, 60, 120, 180, 240, 360, 480, 1440 min) with a standard deviation on the readings of $\sigma^{Ag} = \sigma^{CB} = 2$ U/dL. An example of VWF:Ag and VWF:CB measurements is given in Figure 1a for healthy (O) subjects and subjects affected by VWD types 2A and Vicenza. After DDAVP administration, a three-step mechanism is known to occur:

1. release of super ultra large multimers (SUL); the release rate and amount are subject-dependent;
2. proteolysis of SUL to smaller species by means of a specific enzyme (ADAMTS13): SUL multimers are cleaved to ultra large (UL), high (H) and low (L) molecular weight multimers;
3. clearance (i.e. multimer elimination from plasma), taking place at the liver level and largely independent of the multimer size.

VWF:Ag measures the overall VWF amount (i.e. independently from multimer size), while VWF:CB measure only high molecular weight multimers. Healthy subjects show a balance between high and low molecular weight multimers (similar VWF:Ag/CB values), while 2A subjects show an increased proteolytic activity (low VWF:CB values). Vicenza subjects show lower VWF levels and an increased clearance without apparent anomalies on multimer distribution.

The model identification procedure for the development of a PK model for the description of VWD followed the approach described in Galvanin et al. (2013). The available data were used *i*) to formulate alternative mechanisms representing reasonable approximations of the physiological behaviour of the subject affected by VWD; *ii*) to perform a preliminary model discrimination using statistical indices to assess model adequacy. In this study the commercial software gPROMS® was used in each step of the identification procedure. A suitable model structure (Figure 1b) was obtained by performing a preliminary discrimination between rival model structures by using average population data. The compartmental model was developed under the following physiological assumptions:

1. at the basal state, only H and L multimers are present;
2. SUL multimers cannot be measured directly from VWF measurements, and their release (D) is a consequence of DDAVP administration;
3. the sum of UL and H multimer units can generate L multimers.

Furthermore, it is assumed that VWF:Ag measurements (y^{AG}) are related to the sum UL+H+L, while VWF:CB measurements (y^{CB}) are related to UL+H amount.

The model is described by the following set of differential and algebraic equations:

$$\frac{dx^{SUL}}{dt} = k_0 D \exp^{-k_0(t-t_{max})} - k_1\left(x^{SUL} - x_b^{SUL}\right) - k_2\left(x^{SUL} - x_b^{SUL}\right) \tag{1}$$

$$\frac{dx^{UL+H}}{dt} = k_1\left(x^{SUL} - x_b^{SUL}\right) - k_3\left(x^{UL+H} - x_b^{UL+H}\right) - k_e\left(x^{UL+H} - x_b^{UL+H}\right) \tag{2}$$

$$\frac{dx^L}{dt} = k_2\left(x^{SUL} - x_b^{SUL}\right) + k_3\left(x^{UL+H} - x_b^{UL+H}\right) - k_e\left(x^L - x_b^L\right) \tag{3}$$

where x^{SUL}, x^{UL+H} and x^L are the number of SUL, UL+H and L multimer units (respectively) present in the plasma, and subscript b is used to define the variables at the basal state. The release of SUL multimers is characterised by k_0 and the release

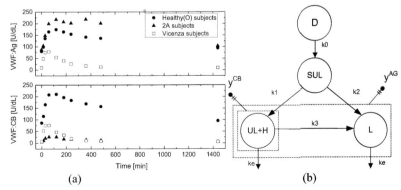

Figure 1. (a) VWF:Ag and VWF:CB measurements obtained after DDAVP administration for healthy (O) subjects and subjects affected by VWD type 2A and Vicenza; (b) Model structure.

parameters D and t_{max} (here fixed to 3.3 min). The measured responses are y^{AG} (antigen concentration [U/dL]) and y^{CB} (collagen binding concentration [U/dL]):

$$y^{AG} = \left(x^{UL+H} + x^L\right)/V_d \tag{4}$$

$$y^{CB} = x^{UL+H}/V_d. \tag{5}$$

The initial conditions for the integration of the differential system are defined by $\mathbf{x}^0 = \mathbf{x}(0) = [\, x_b^{SUL} \quad x_b^{UL+H} \quad x_b^L \,]^T = [\, 0 \quad y_b^{CB}V_d \quad y_b^{AG}V - y_b^{CB}V_d \,]^T$; $V_d = 40$ mL/kg body weight is the approximated distribution volume following Menache et al. (1996). A correction is introduced in the definition of the collagen binding measurements in order to account for the different affinity of multimers to collagen observed in distinct VWD types:

$$y^{CB'} = ky^{CB} \frac{y_b^{AG}}{y_b^{CB}} = ky^{CB}\left(1 + \frac{x_b^L}{x_b^H}\right). \tag{6}$$

A reparametrisation was carried out in order to guarantee the model structural identifiability. Vector $\theta = [\,k_0 D/k_e \quad k_1 \quad k_2 \quad k_3 \quad k_e \quad D\,]$ is the set of parameters to be estimated, with the additional correction parameters k and y_b^{CB} of Eq.(4,5). Pharmacokinetic indices, i.e. clearance (CL, [mL/kg/h]) and amount of released VWF (Q, [U/kg]), are defined in order to discriminate between subjects affected by VWD:

$$CL = k_e V_d \tag{7}$$

$$Q = BW^{-1}\int_0^\tau k_0 D \exp^{-k_0(t-t_{max})} dt \tag{8}$$

where τ is the test duration (here fixed to 24 hours) and BW is the body weight [kg].

2.1. Results from parameter estimation

A preliminary parameter estimation was obtained from VWF:Ag/CB data available for healthy O/non-O subjects and subjects affected by VWD type 2A, 2B and Vicenza.For each measured response (y^{AG} or y^{CB}), the variability within each available pool of subjects was characterised by adopting a heteroscedastic variance model in the form

$$\sigma^2 = \omega^2(y)^\gamma \tag{9}$$

where ω and γ are parameters estimated by regression from average data allowing one to build a time-dependent uncertainty region for the model response. Results from parameter estimation are shown in Table 1 in terms of estimated values and a-posteriori statistics including χ^2 test (χ^2 must be less than the reference value χ^2_{Rif} evaluated from a tabulated chi-square distribution). Results show that a good fitting is achieved for all the subjects' conditions, allowing to quantify some important physiological patterns, which are known to exist in the clinical practice: *i*) non-O subjects present a reduced elimination of VWF from plasma (k_e) if compared to O subjects, while subjects affected by VWD type Vicenza show an increased elimination; *ii*) subjects 2A and 2B show an increased UL+H to L pathway (k_3) related to a more intense proteolytic activity operated by ADAMTS13 (type 2A) or induced by a greater affinity to platelets (type 2B); *iii*) while for healthy O/non-O subjects the pathway SUL-(UL+H) is preferred (k_1), for 2A and 2B subjects the SUL-L is preferential; *iv*) for Vicenza subjects SUL to (UL+H) and SUL to L pathways are fast (high values for k_1 and k_2) and multimer elimination is prevailing if compared to(UL+H) cleavage (i.e. $k_e \gg k_3$).

Table 1. Parameter estimation results from clinical tests for distinct classes of subjects: estimated values and results from χ^2 test.

Parameter	Subjects				
	Healthy (O)	Healthy (non-O)	2A	2B	Vicenza
$k_0 D/k_e$	8,566.88	2,0059.80	11,716.60	4,158.79	1,343.30
k_1	0.0350	0.0326	0.0035	0.0094	0.1013
k_2	0.0025	0.0056	0.0219	0.0145	0.1048
k_3	0.0003	0.0001	0.0050	0.0017	0.0007
k_e	0.0015	0.0007	0.0011	0.0028	0.0076
D	100.00	100.00	133.74	143.55	173.51
k, y_b^{CB}	1.04, 53.97	0.95, 75.65	0.07, 4.26	0.28, 18.3	0.69, 2.93
χ^2 (χ^2_{Rif})	6.7 (24.9)	1.3 (25.0)	12.3 (23.7)	4.4 (23.7)	1.7 (23.7)

Table 2. Model-based diagnosis results in terms of SSWR (the lowest value is indicated in boldface).

Subject	Healthy O	Healthy non-O	2A	2B	Vicenza
A	5,350	3,409	7,268	8,311	9,148
B	92	87	50	20	177

3. Model-based diagnosis

The model allows for a quantitative description of the VWF levels, and can be used as a support tool for VWD diagnosis. Once new measurements are available, the pathophysiological condition of a subject can be determined by exploiting: *i*) the individual measurements including VWF:Ag/VWF:CB data; *ii*) the VWF:Ag/VWF:CB historical data related to each pool of subjects. Given average VWF:Ag/VWF:CB data and the variance model (Eq. 9),a model-based VWD classification is realised by comparing the relative statistics obtained after parameter estimation in terms of sum of squared weighted residuals (SSWR):

$$SSWR = \sum_{i=1}^{N}\sum_{j=1}^{M}\sum_{k=1}^{N_{sp}} r_{ijk}^2 \,/\, \sigma_{ijk}^2 \qquad (10)$$

where r_{ijk} is the residual for sampling point k of measured response j in experiment I with standard deviation σ_{ijk}, N is the total number of experiments, M is the number of measured responses, and N_{sp} is the number of sampling points per experiment.

As a case study, two new subjects (subject A and subject B), whose diagnosis is supposed unknown, are considered for the validation of the procedure for model-based diagnosis. The preliminary estimates reported in Table 1were used as a starting guess for the identification of the model parameters for single subjects. Results in terms of SSWR are given in Table 2.The lowest value of SSWR is obtained when the individual VWF:Ag/CB measurements are coupled with the data from the healthy non-O pool of subjects (subject A) and with the 2B pool (subject B). The diagnosis is therefore unambiguous and the result is consistent with the medical evaluation of these subjects obtained from the analysis of advanced laboratory tests. A good representation of the VWF levels is also achieved, as can be observed from VWF profiles after identification (Figure 2a), thus allowing for a clear distinction between the two subjects in terms of *CL* and *Q* pharmacokinetic indices (Figure 2b).

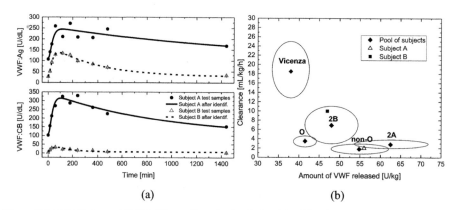

Figure 2 (a) VWF:Ag and VWF:CB profiles obtained after identification for subject A and B (the test samples are indicated by symbols); (b) Clearance and amount of VWF released: results for subjects A and B (each pool of subjects is indicated by a diamond and 95 % confidence ellipse).

4. Conclusions

A mechanistic model for the description of VWD has been presented in this paper. The model, identified from clinical data, can be used to describe the mechanisms of release, distribution and elimination of VWF from the blood stream and represents a starting point for a procedure of model-based diagnosis, where data are exploited to define the unknown pathophysiological condition of a subject. Future work will be required to extend the model applicability to other VWD types and to apply the model-based diagnosis procedure in order to discriminate among VWD subtypes.

Acknowledgments

The authors gratefully acknowledge the financial support granted to this work by the University of Padova under Projects CPDA127585/12 and CPDR110403-2011.

References

A. Casonato, L. Gallinaro, M.G. Cattini, E. Pontara, R. Padrini, A. Bertomoro, V. Daidone, A. Pagnan, 2010, Reduced Survival of Type 2B von Willebrand Factor, Irrespective of Large Multimer Representation or Thrombocytopenia, Haematologica, 95, 1366-1372.

F. Galvanin, C.C. Ballan, M. Barolo, F. Bezzo, 2013, A General Model-Based Design of Experiments Approach to Achieve Practical Identifiability of Pharmacokinetic and Pharmacodynamic Models, J. Pharmacokinet. Pharmacodyn., 40, 451-467.

F. Galvanin, M. Barolo, R. Padrini, A. Casonato, F. Bezzo, 2014, A Model-Based Approach to the Automatic Diagnosis of von Willebrand Disease, AIChE J., doi: 10.1002/aic.14373.

D. Lillicrap, 2007, Von Willebrand Disease-Phenotype Versus Genotype: Deficiency Versus Disease, Thrombosis Research, 120, S11-S16.

D. Menache, D.L. Aronson, F. Darr, R.R. Montgomery, J.C. Gill, C.M. Kessler, J.M. Lusher, P.D. Phatak, A.D. Shapiro, A.R. Thompson, G. White, 1996, Pharmacokinetics of von Willebrand Factor and Factor VIIIC in Patients with Severe von Willebrand Disease (type 3VWD): Estimation of the Rate of Factor VIIIC Synthesis, Br. J. Haematol., 94, 740-745.

N.H.L.B.I., 2007,The diagnosis, Evaluation and Management of von WIllebrand disease, NIH Publication No. 8-5832, U.S. Department of Health and Human Services, Bethesda, MD, U.S.A.

E.J.Werner, E.H. Broxson, E.L. Tucker, D.S. Giroux, J. Shults, T.C. Abshire, 1993, Prevalence of von Willebrand Disease in Children: a Multiethnic Study, J. Pediatr.,123, 893–898.

Jiří Jaromír Klemeš, Petar Sabev Varbanov and Peng Yen Liew (Editors)
Proceedings of the 24th European Symposium on Computer Aided Process Engineering – ESCAPE 24
June 15-18, 2014, Budapest, Hungary.

Control of Cyclic Distillation Systems

Costin Sorin Bildea,[a,*], Cătalin Pătruț,[a] Anton A. Kiss[b]

[a] *University Politehnica of Bucharest, Department of Chemical Engineering, Str. Gh. Polizu 1-7, 011061 Bucharest, Romania*
[b] *AkzoNobel Research, Development & Innovation, Process Technology ECG, Zutphenseweg 10, 7418 AJ Deventer, The Netherlands.*
s_bildea@upb.ro

Abstract

Cyclic distillation is a process intensification technique that allows key benefits such as increased column throughput, lower energy requirements and higher separation performance. Despite these advantages, the application to industrial processes is limited, mainly due to serious controllability concerns. To address this challenge, this study is the first to prove that cyclic distillation is also well controllable, hence being able to provide in practice the expected key economic benefits. In this work we developed a dynamic model which consists of two non-linear functions that map the initial conditions to the system state at the end of vapor and liquid periods, respectively, by solving the dynamic mass balance together with equilibrium relationships. A periodic state is reached when the initial condition is attained after successive application of the two maps. A discrete-time controller is used, with the temperatures in the lower and upper parts of the column as controlled variables and the vapor flow rate and the amount of liquid reflux as manipulated variable. A case study is presented, proving that the discrete PI algorithm in the velocity form gives excellent performance. Thus, the system is able to cope with changes in the feed flow rate and composition.

Keywords: cyclic distillation, dynamics, modelling, control

1. Introduction

Process intensification in distillation systems received much attention during the last decades, aiming to increase energy and separation efficiency. Various techniques, such as internal heat-integrated distillation, dividing-wall columns and reactive distillation were studied (Yildirim et al., 2011). Cyclic operation (Cannon, 1961) is considered as an innovative method for operating existing distillation columns (Flodman and Timm, 2012), leading to key benefits, such as: increased column throughput, lower energy requirements (Bausa and Tsatsaronis, 2001) and higher separation performance (Maleta et al., 2011). The cyclic operation is achieved in distillation by alternating two steps: a) Vapor period, when vapor flows upwards through the column and liquid is stationary; b) Liquid period, when vapor flow is stopped, reflux and liquid feed are supplied and the liquid holdup is dropped from each plate to the one below (Gaska and Cannon, 1961). This mode of operation can be easily achieved by using perforated trays, without downcomers, combined with sluice chambers located under each tray (Maleta et al., 2011). If the vapor velocity exceeds the weeping limit, the liquid does not overflow from tray to tray during the vapor-flow period. When the vapor supply is interrupted, the liquid drops down by gravitation to the sluice chamber. When the vapor supply is started again, the sluice chambers open and the liquid is transferred to the tray below. The principle of cyclic operation is schematically illustrated in Figure 1.

Vapour-flow period   Liquid-flow period

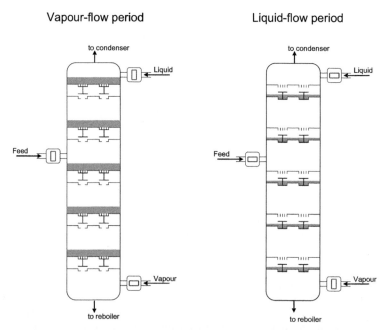

Figure 1. Schematics illustrating the working principle of cyclic distillation

Although the advantages of cyclic operation have been demonstrated experimentally, the information about control of cyclic distillation columns is rather limited. Matsubara et al. (1985) used both computer simulation and experiments to study the controllability of a cyclic distillation column stripping ammonia from an aqueous solution. For this particular system, the product composition was easy to be determined by conductivity measurements. However, for most practical systems, composition measurements are not available and inferential control is needed.

2. Problem statement

The literature review clearly proves the advantages of cyclic operation as compared to conventional, steady state operation of distillation. Several models are available to simulate the behavior of the cyclic distillation columns. When the assumption of linear equilibrium is employed, it is indeed possible to derive analytical solutions of the model equations. However, the accuracy of the results is limited. Moreover, these models are not applicable for control studies, as they do not take into account the nonlinearity of the system, the non-ideal vapor-liquid equilibrium, the dependence of the pressure versus the vapor and liquid flows and the dynamics of the temperature measurements. This paper fills this gap by presenting a rigorous model of cyclic distillation systems which is further used for a controllability study.

3. Mathematical model

The model of the cyclic distillation column is derived under the following assumptions: ideal stages (vapor-liquid equilibrium is reached); equal heat of vaporization (implying constant molar holdup and vapor flow rate); Perfect mixing on each stage; negligible vapor holdup; saturated liquid feed. Note that in contrast to the previously cited papers, no assumptions are made here with regard to the linearity of vapor-liquid equilibrium, negligible or constant pressure drop, infinite reboiler holdup or zero condenser holdup.

The vapor-flow period: For each component, $j = 1$, NC, the following equations describe the evolution of tray holdup:

Condenser:
$$\frac{dM_{1,j}}{dt} = V \cdot y_{2,j} \tag{1}$$

Trays:
$$\frac{dM_{k,j}}{dt} = V\left(y_{k+1,j} - y_{k,j}\right); \quad k = 1, NT - 1 \tag{2}$$

Reboiler:
$$\frac{dM_{NT,j}}{dt} = -V \cdot y_{NT,j} \tag{3}$$

For each tray, $k = 1, NT$, the following relationships describe the liquid-vapor equilibrium:

$$P_k \cdot y_{k,j} - x_{k,j} \cdot \gamma_{k,j}\left(x_1, \ldots x_{NC}, T_k\right) \cdot P_j^{vap}\left(T_k\right) = 0 \tag{4}$$

$$x_{k,j} = \frac{M_{k,j}}{\sum_j M_{k,j}}; \quad \sum_j y_{k,j} - 1 = 0 \tag{5}$$

For each tray, $k = 3$, NT, the pressure is calculated based on the **vapor flow rate** and the amount of liquid on the tray above:

$$P_2 = P_{cond} + \Delta P_{cond}; \quad P_k = P_{k-1} + \Delta P\left(M_{k-1,j}, V\right) \tag{6}$$

The state of the system at the beginning of the vapor-flow period is the same as the state at the end of the liquid-flow period:

$$\mathbf{M}(t = 0) = \mathbf{M}^{(L)} \tag{7}$$

The state of the system at the end of the vapor flow period is found by integrating the Eqs.(1)-(7)

$$\mathbf{M}^{(V)} = \mathbf{M}\left(t = t_{vap}\right) \tag{8}$$

The liquid-flow period: for each component, $j = 1$, NC, the following equations give the stage holdup at the end of the liquid-phase period:

Condenser:
$$M_{1,j}^{(L)} = M_{1,j}^{(V)} - (D + L) \cdot x_{1,j}^{(V)} \tag{9}$$

Trays, rectifying section:
$$M_{2,j}^{(L)} = L \cdot x_{1,j}^{(V)}; \quad M_{k,j}^{(L)} = M_{k-1,j}^{(V)}, \quad k = 2, NF \tag{10}$$

Feed tray:
$$M_{NF+1,j}^{(L)} = M_{NF,j}^{(V)} + F \cdot x_{F,j} \tag{11}$$

Trays, stripping section:
$$M_{k,j}^{(L)} = M_{k-1,j}^{(V)}, \quad k = NF + 2, NT - 1 \tag{12}$$

Reboiler:
$$M_{NT,j}^{(L)} = M_{NT,j}^{(V)} - B \cdot x_{NT,j}^{(V)} + M_{NT-1,j}^{(V)} \tag{13}$$

Eqs.(1) - (6) and (9) - (13) can be written in the following condensed form, where $\Phi^{(V)}$ and $\Phi^{(L)}$ are mappings relating the state at the start and the end of the vapor- and liquid-flow periods, respectively.

$$\left(M^{(V)}, x^{(V)}\right) = \Phi^{(V)}(M, x) \qquad \left(M^{(L)}, x^{(L)}\right) = \Phi^{(L)}(M, x) \qquad (14)$$

Periodicity condition requires:

$$\left(M^{(L)}, x^{(L)}\right) = \Phi^{(L)} \circ \Phi^{(V)}\left(M^{(L)}, x^{(L)}\right) \qquad (15)$$

A straight forward solution of Eq.(15) can be obtained by considering an initial state and applying relationships (14) until the difference between two iterations becomes small. However, the convergence can be accelerated (Toftegard and Jørgensen, 1989) by applying algebraic equations numerical methods (for example Newton).

4. Results and discussion

The design procedure described in our earlier work (Lita et al., 2012) was applied to the separation of an equimolar mixture of ethanol and propanol. The feed flow rate was set to 0.833 kmol/cycle, while the distillate and bottoms purities were set to 0.995. The cyclic distillation column has 21 stages of 1 m diameter, with the feed located on stage 11. The required vapor and liquid flows are V = 3.06 kmol/min and L = 0.417 kmol/cycle, respectively. The duration of vapor- and liquid-flow periods are 25 s and 5 s, respectively. The total pressure drop is 0.24 bar. Hydrodynamic calculations showed that, under these conditions, no weeping occurs.

Figure 2 presents results of dynamic simulation, as the composition of the top and bottom products at the end of the vapor-flow period. After 20 liquid-vapor cycles, the feed amount (left) and composition (right) are changed by 10 % and 0.1, respectively. Large deviations of the product purities from the desired values can be observed, the need for control being obvious.

The control strategy measures two temperatures, at the top and bottom of the distillation column (stages 5 and 17), at the end of the vapor-flow period. The model was extended by including the dynamics of the temperature measurements as first-order elements with a time constant of 0.5 min. Figure 3 shows the dynamics of composition, temperature and temperature measurements during several vapor-liquid cycles, on the trays chosen for control. The lag of the temperature measurement is obvious.

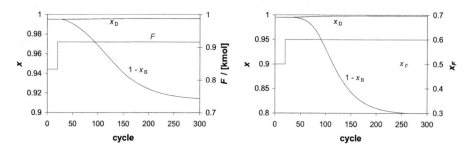

Figure 2. Distillate and bottoms purities for feed rate (left) and composition (right) disturbances

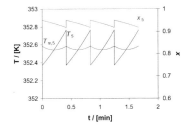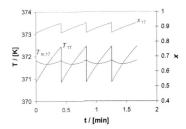

Figure 3. Dynamics of composition, temperature and temperature measurements during several vapor-liquid cycles (left – stage 5; right – stage 17).

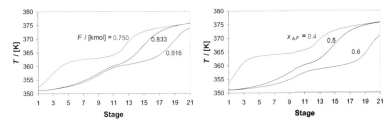

Figure 4. Stationary temperature profiles for different feed rate (left) and composition (right)

Figure 4 shows the stationary temperature profiles which are established after a new stationary state is reached. The temperature profile is sensitive therefore it can be used for inferential control. Taking into account their sensitivities, temperatures on tray 5 and 17 are chosen for control purposes.

A discrete PI-algorithm adjusts the values of the vapor flow rate and reflux amount, for the next vapor-liquid cycle:

$$u_{k+1} = u_k + \alpha \cdot \varepsilon_{k+1} + \beta \cdot \varepsilon_k \tag{16}$$

where u and are the manipulated and control errors, respectively, while α and β are the control tuning parameters.

The performance of the control system was tested for +/- 10 % change of the feed flow rate, as well as for a change of the feed composition from $x_F = 0.5$ to 0.6 and 0.4. The results presented in Figure 5 and Figure 6 show that the product purities can be indeed kept to their set points. The disturbances in the feed flowrate and composition are rejected successfully with short settling times, low overshooting and small changes of the manipulated variables, proving the good controllability of cyclic distillation.

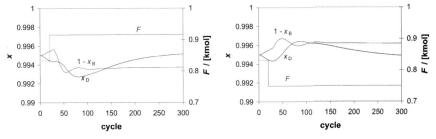

Figure 5. Performance of the control system for feed rate disturbances

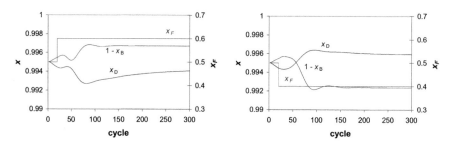

Figure 6. Performance of the control system for feed composition disturbances

5. Conclusions

Cyclic distillation can bring new life in old distillation columns, providing key benefits, such as: high column throughput, low energy requirements and high separation performance. This study presents a detailed model of cyclic distillation column, applicable to multicomponent mixtures and including nonlinear vapor-liquid equilibrium, tray pressure drop relationships and temperature sensor dynamics. Dynamic simulation results suggest that cyclic distillation columns can be easily controlled by adjusting the reflux and the vapor flow rate, in order to keep temperatures in the top and bottom sections close to their setpoints. For the ethanol – propanol separation considered in this paper, disturbances in the feed flow rate and composition are successfully rejected with low settling times, low overshooting and small control action.

References

J. Bausa, G. Tsatsaronis, 2001, Reducing the energy demand of continuous distillation processes by optimal controlled forced periodic operation, Comput. Chem. Eng., 25, 359-370.

M. R. Cannon, 1961, Controlled cycling improves various processes, Ind. Eng. Chem., 53, 629-629.

H. R. Flodman, D. C. Timm, 2012, Batch distillation employing cyclic rectification and stripping operations, ISA Transactions, 51, 454-460.

R.A. Gaska, M. R. Cannon, 1961, Controlled cycling distillation in sieve and screen plate towers, Ind. Eng. Chem, 53, 630-631.

A. A. Kiss, C. S. Bildea, 2011, A control perspective on process intensification in dividing-wall columns, Chemical Engineering and Processing, 50, 3, 281-292.

I. Lita, C. S. Bildea, A. A. Kiss, 2012, Modeling, design and control of cyclic distillation dystems, Procedia Engineering, 42, 1311 - 1322.

V. N. Maleta, A. A. Kiss, V. M. Taran, B. V. Maleta, 2011, Understanding process intensification in cyclic distillation systems, Chem. Eng. Process., 50, 655-664.

M. Matsubara, N. Watanabe, H. Kurimoto, 1985, Binary periodic distillation scheme with enhanced energy conservation I - Principle and computer simulation, Chem. Eng. Sci., 40, 715-721.

M. Matsubara, N. Watanabe, H. Kurimoto, K. Shimizu, 1985, Binary periodic distillation scheme with enhanced energy conservation II - Experiment, Chem. Eng. Sci., 40, 755-758.

B. Toftegard, S. B. Jørgensen, 1989, An integration method for dynamic simulation of cycled processes, Comput. Chem. Eng., 13, 927-930.

O. Yildirim, A. A. Kiss, E. Y. Kenig, 2011, Dividing wall columns in chemical process industry: A review on current activities, Sep. Pur. Tech., 80, 403-417.

Jiří Jaromír Klemeš, Petar Sabev Varbanov and Peng Yen Liew (Editors)
Proceedings of the 24th European Symposium on Computer Aided Process Engineering – ESCAPE 24
June 15-18, 2014, Budapest, Hungary. Copyright © 2014 Elsevier B.V. All rights reserved.

On the Stability of Set-Valued Integration for Parametric Nonlinear ODEs

Mario E. Villanueva[a], Boris Houska[b], Benoît Chachuat[a,*]

[a]*Centre for Process Systems Engineering, Department of Chemical Engineering, Imperial College London, South Kensington Campus, London SW7 2AZ, UK.*
[b]*Department of Automation, School of Electronic Information and Electrical Engineering, Shanghai Jiao Tong University, Shanghai 200240, China.*
b.chachuat@imperial.ac.uk

Abstract

This paper is concerned with bounding the reachable set of parametric nonlinear ordinary differential equations using set-valued integration methods. The focus is on discrete-time set-propagation algorithms that proceed by first constructing a predictor of the reachable set and then determine a step-size for which this predictor yields a valid enclosure. For asymptotically stable systems, we give general conditions under which the computed bounds are stable, at least for small enough parametric variations. We also propose a strategy accounting for possible invariants of the dynamic system in order to further enhance stability. These novel developments are illustrated by means of numerical examples.

Keywords: ordinary differential equations, set-valued integration, stability, invariants

1. Introduction

Enclosing the reachable set of uncertain dynamic systems, also known as set-valued integration, finds applications in many research fields, including reachability analysis for control systems (Blanchini and Miani, 2008), robust optimal control (Houska et al., 2012), and global optimization of dynamic systems(Chachuat et al., 2006). This paper considers parametric nonlinear ordinary differential equations (ODEs) of the form:

$$\forall t \in [0,T], \quad \dot{x}(t,p) = f(x(t,p),p) \quad \text{with} \quad x(0,p) = x_0(p), \tag{1}$$

where the state $x : [0,T] \times P \to \mathbb{R}^{n_x}$ is regarded as a function of the parameter vector $p \in P \subseteq \mathbb{R}^{n_p}$ along $[0,T]$; f and x_0 are sufficiently often continuously differentiable.

The focus is on algorithms that compute a time-varying enclosure $Y(t)$ of the actual reachable set $X(t) := \{x(t,p) \mid p \in P\}$ of (1). Existing approaches for set-valued integration can be broadly classified into either continuous-time or discrete-time set-propagation methods. The emphasis here is on the latter methods, which discretize the integration horizon into finite steps and typically proceed in two phases (Nedialkov et al., 1998): (i) obtain a step-size and an a priori enclosure of the ODE solutions over the current step; then, (ii) propagate a tightened enclosure until the end of the step. In particular, the second phase relies on a high-order Taylor expansion of the ODE solutions in time, for instance evaluated using interval arithmetic or Taylor model arithmetic with interval remainder bounds (Lin and Stadtherr, 2007; Sahlodin and Chachuat, 2011). Even though care is taken to minimize the over-estimation of the enclosures and to mitigate the wrapping effect, bounds computed with these approach typically explode after a finite time, even when the solution of the original system does not.

In fact, a natural requirement for a consistent set-valued integrator would appear to be that, for a stable ODE system, the computed enclosures should themselves be stable, at least for small enough parametric variations. Recently, we proposed a reversed, two-phase algorithm that starts by constructing a predictor of the reachable set and then determines a step-size for which this predictor yields a valid enclosure (Houska et al., 2013a). Moreover, we introduced a new type of bounder for vector-valued functions, namely Taylor model with ellipsoidal remainder. The main objective of this paper is to present general conditions under which this algorithm generates stable enclosures. A second principal contribution concerns the development of strategies accounting for possible invariants of the ODEs in order to further improve the enclosure stability.

The paper is organized as follows. In Sect. 2 we recall the set-valued integration algorithm. The main contributions of the paper, namely providing stability conditions and incorporating invariants, are presented in Sects. 3 and 4, respectively, and these developments are illustrated with numerical examples. Finally, Sect. 5 concludes the paper.

2. Set-Valued Integrator

Notations and concepts are introduced first in order to present the set-valued integration proposed by Houska et al. (2013a). To keep our considerations general, we consider affine set-parameterizations, a particular class of computer-representable sets in the form

$$\forall Q \in \mathbb{D}_{n,\ell}, \quad \mathrm{Im}_{\mathbb{E}_\ell}(Q) := \left\{ Q[b\,1]^\mathsf{T} \mid b \in \mathbb{E}_\ell \right\},$$

where $\mathbb{E}_\ell \subseteq \mathbb{R}^\ell$, $\ell \geq 1$, is the so-called basis set; and $\mathbb{D}_{n,\ell} \subseteq \mathbb{R}^{n \times (\ell+1)}$, $n \geq 1$, the associated domain set. Usual convex sets such as intervals, ellipsoids or zonotopes can all be characterized using affine set-parameterizations on convex basis sets. For instance, choosing $\mathbb{E}_\ell^{\mathrm{ball}} := \{ \xi \in \mathbb{R}^\ell \mid \|\xi\|_2 \leq 1 \}$ and the associated domain $\mathbb{R}^{\ell \times (n+1)}$ allows representation of ellipsoids in $\mathbb{R}^n$. Nonconvex sets too can be represented in terms of affine set-parameterizations. For instance, qth-order polynomial models with ellipsoidal remainder terms can be constructed using the basis set $\mathbb{E}_\ell^{\mathrm{pol}(q)} \times \mathbb{E}_\ell^{\mathrm{ball}}$, where $\mathbb{E}_\ell^{\mathrm{pol}(q)} := \{ M_{\ell,q}(\xi) \mid \xi \in [-1,1]^\ell \}$ and $M_\ell^{(q)}(\xi) \in \mathbb{R}^{\alpha_\ell^{(q)}}$ is the vector containing the first $\alpha_\ell^{(q)}$ monomials in ξ in lexicographic order.

Now, given a function $g : \mathbb{R}^n \to \mathbb{R}^m$ as well as an affine set-parameterization on the basis set $\mathbb{E}_\ell$ with associated domains $\mathbb{D}_{n,\ell}$ and $\mathbb{D}_{m,\ell}$, we call the function $g^{\mathbb{E}_\ell} : \mathbb{D}_{n,\ell} \to \mathbb{D}_{m,\ell}$ an $\mathbb{E}_\ell$-extension of g if

$$\forall Q \in \mathbb{D}_{n,\ell}, \quad \mathrm{Im}_{\mathbb{E}_\ell}\left(g^{\mathbb{E}_\ell}(Q) \right) \supseteq \left\{ g(z) \mid z \in \mathrm{Im}_{\mathbb{E}_\ell}(Q) \right\}.$$

Moreover, we say that the extension $g^{\mathbb{E}_\ell}$ has Hausdorff convergence order $q \geq 1$, if

$$\forall Q \in \mathbb{D}_{n,\ell}, \quad d_{\mathrm{H}}\left(\mathrm{Im}_{\mathbb{E}_\ell}\left(g^{\mathbb{E}_\ell}(Q) \right), \left\{ g(z) \mid z \in \mathrm{Im}_{\mathbb{E}_\ell}(Q) \right\} \right) \leq \mathscr{O}(\mathrm{diam}(\mathrm{Im}_{\mathbb{E}_\ell}(Q))^q),$$

where d_{H} denotes the usual Hausdorff distance. The construction of extensions on the set of intervals or Taylor models with interval remainders can be automated for tree-decomposable (factorable) functions using interval analysis and Taylor model arithmetic, respectively, yet such extensions enjoy linear Hausdorff convergence only. On the other hand, a procedure for constructing extensions on the set of Taylor models with ellipsoidal remainders that enjoys quadratic Hausdorff convergence is detailed in (Houska et al., 2013a).

Discrete-time approaches for set-valued integration of parametric ODEs such as (1) typically consider a Taylor expansion in time of the solutions as

$$\exists \tau \in [t, t+h]: \quad x(t_j + h_j, p) = \sum_{i=0}^{s} h_j^i \phi_i(x(t,p), p) + h_j^{s+1} \phi_{s+1}(x(\tau,p), p), \tag{2}$$

Input: ODE (1) with factorable right-hand side and initial value functions f, x_0; tolerance TOL > 0; affine parameterization Q_p of the parameter set P on the basis $\mathbb{E}_{n_p}$; maximum and minimum step-sizes $h_{\max} \geq h_{\min} > 0$; step-size reduction parameter $0 < \rho < 1$.

Initialization:

1. Set $j = 0$, $t_0 = 0$, and $Q_x(0) = x_0^{\mathbb{E}_{n_p}}(Q_p)$

Repeat:

2. Construct predictor $Q_x(t_j + h)$ for all $h \in [t_j, T - t_j]$ as in (2) with extensions $\phi_0^{\mathbb{E}_{n_p}}, \ldots, \phi_s^{\mathbb{E}_{n_p}}$

3. Set step-size guess $\bar{h} = \min \left\{ \rho \left(\frac{\text{TOL}}{\|\Phi(0)\|} \right)^{\frac{1}{s}}, h_{\max} \right\}$

   While $\bar{h}^s \Phi(\bar{h}) \not\subseteq \text{TOL}\, \mathbb{I}(Q_{\text{unit}})$, **Repeat** $\bar{h} \leftarrow \rho \bar{h}$, where $\Phi(h) := \phi_{s+1}^{\mathbb{I}}(\mathbb{I}(Q(t_j + h)), \mathbb{I}(Q_p))$

4. **If** $\bar{h} < h_{\min}$, **Return** with an error message

5. **If** $t_j + \bar{h} \geq T$, **Return** with an indication of success; Otherwise, set $t_{j+1} \leftarrow t_j + \bar{h}$, increment $j \leftarrow j + 1$, and **Return** to Step 2

Output: Enclosure function $Q_x : [0, t_j] \to \mathbb{D}_{n_x, n_p}$ such that $\text{Im}_{\mathbb{E}_{n_p}}(Q_x(t)) \supseteq X(t)$ for all $t \in [0, t_j]$

Figure 1. Algorithmic procedure for the set-valued integrator.

with s the expansion order; and $\phi_0, \ldots, \phi_{s+1}$, the Taylor coefficients of the ODE solution. Given parameterizations Q_p of the parameter set and $Q_x(t_j)$ of the reachable set at t_j, so that $\text{Im}_{\mathbb{E}_{n_p}}(Q_p) \supseteq P$ and $\text{Im}_{\mathbb{E}_{n_p}}(Q_x(t_j)) \supseteq X(t_j)$, a predictor of the reachable set is given by:

$$\forall h \in (0, T - t_j], \quad Q_x(t_j + h) := \bigoplus_{i=0}^{s} h^i \phi_i^{\mathbb{E}_{n_p}}(Q_x(t_j), Q_p) \oplus h\, \text{TOL}\, Q_{\text{unit}}, \tag{3}$$

where $\oplus$ denotes the extension of the addition operator; TOL > 0 is a user-defined tolerance; $Q_{\text{unit}} \in \mathbb{D}_{n_x, n_p}$; and $\phi_i^{\mathbb{E}_{n_p}}$ are extensions of the Taylor coefficients ϕ_i. In turn, a step-size $\bar{h} > 0$ can be computed such that the parameterization $Q_x(t_j + h)$ yields an enclosure of the reachable set, $\text{Im}_{\mathbb{E}_{n_p}}(Q_x(t_j + h)) \supseteq X(t_j + h)$, for all $\bar{h} \in [0, h]$.

An algorithmic procedure applying these two phases repeatedly in order to compute a matrix-valued enclosure function $Q_x : [0, T] \to \mathbb{D}_{n_x, n_p}$ is summarized in Fig. 1.

3. Stability of the Set-Valued Integrator

Conditions under which the set-valued integration algorithm outlined previously inherits the stability properties of the underlying dynamic system are now discussed. Due to space limitations, these conditions are given without a proof; see, e.g., (Houska et al., 2013b).

The focus is on those asymptotically stable systems that have a unique (stable) equilibrium point $\bar{x}(p)$ for every initial value $x(0, p)$ in the set $\{x_0(p) \mid p \in P\}$ and for all $p \in P$. In particular, let us denote by $\bar{X}(P) := \{\bar{x}(p) \mid p \in P\}$ the set of all equilibrium points and by $Y(t, P) := \{\text{Im}_{\mathbb{E}_{n_p}}(Q_x(t)) \mid p \in P\}$ the parameterized reachable set enclosures for $t \geq 0$. We say that a set-valued integrator itself is locally asymptotically stable if the following conditions are satisfied for all sufficiently small tolerances TOL > 0 and all sufficiently small maximum step size $h_{\max} > 0$:

$$\exists M < \infty \text{ such that: } \forall t \geq 0, \ d_{\text{H}}(Y(t, P), \bar{X}(P)) < M + \mathcal{O}(\text{TOL}) + \mathcal{O}(h_{\max}^s),$$

for all parameter set P with sufficiently small diameter, and

$$\forall p \in P, \quad \limsup_{t \to \infty} d_{\mathrm{H}}(Y(t, \{p\}), \bar{x}(p)) < \mathcal{O}(\mathrm{TOL}) + \mathcal{O}(h_{\max}^s) \,.$$

It can be shown that the local asymptotic stability of the proposed set-valued integrator depends essentially on the way the enclosures are constructed; that is, on the underlying set arithmetic used to construct the extensions of the Taylor coefficients $\phi_0, \ldots, \phi_s$ and of the initial value function x_0. More specifically, the key requirement is that these extensions must exhibit at least quadratic Hausdorff convergence in order for the set-valued integrator to be locally asymptotically stable. This is the case for instance when Taylor models with ellipsoidal remainders are used, as illustrated in the following example.

Case Study: Anaerobic Digestion   Consider the two-reaction model of an anaerobic digester with self-regulated pH, as developed in (Bernard et al., 2001):

$$\begin{aligned}
\dot{X}_1 &= (\mu_1(\xi) - \alpha D)X_1 \\
\dot{X}_2 &= (\mu_2(\xi) - \alpha D)X_2 \\
\dot{S}_1 &= D(S_1^{\mathrm{in}} - S_1) - k_1 \mu_1(S_1)X_1 \\
\dot{S}_2 &= D(S_2^{\mathrm{in}} - S_2) + k_2 \mu_1(S_1)X_1 - k_3 \mu_2(S_2)x_2 \\
\dot{Z} &= D(Z^{\mathrm{in}} - Z) \\
\dot{C} &= D(C^{\mathrm{in}} - C) - q_{\mathrm{C}} + k_4 \mu_1(S_1)x_1 + k_5 \mu_2(S_2)x_2
\end{aligned}$$

with:
$$\begin{aligned}
\mu_1(S_1) &:= \frac{\mu_1 S_1}{S_1 + K_{S_1}} \\
\mu_2(S_2) &:= \frac{\mu_2 S_2}{S_2 + K_{S_2} + S_2^2/K_{I_2}} \\
\phi &:= C + S_2 - Z + K_{\mathrm{H}}P_{\mathrm{T}} + \frac{k_6 \mu_2(S_2)X_2}{k_{\mathrm{L}}a} \\
P_{\mathrm{C}} &:= \frac{\phi - \sqrt{\phi^2 - 4K_{\mathrm{H}}P_{\mathrm{T}}(C+S_2-Z)}}{2K_{\mathrm{H}}} \\
q_{\mathrm{C}} &:= k_{\mathrm{L}}a(C + S_2 - Z - K_{\mathrm{H}}P_{\mathrm{C}})
\end{aligned}$$

where X_1, X_2 and S_1, S_2 denote biomass and organic substrate concentrations for the two reactions, respectively; C and Z denote inorganic carbon concentration and total alkalinity, respectively. We consider a dilution rate of $D = 0.4 \ \mathrm{day}^{-1}$ and the values for all the other parameters are the same as in (Bernard et al., 2001).

Enclosures of the reachable set obtained with 2nd- and 3rd-order Taylor models with ellipsoidal remainders are shown in Fig. 2, for uncertain initial values given by $X_1(0) \in 0.5 \times [0.98, 1.02]$, $X_2(0) \in [0.98, 1.02]$, $S_1(0) = 1$, $S_2(0) = 5$, $Z(0) = 50$, and $C(0) = 40$. 3rd-order (or higher-order) Taylor models successfully stabilize the reachable set enclosure here, whereas 2nd-order Taylor models fail to do so for this level of uncertainty. In the latter case, stabilizing the enclose would require reducing the uncertainty set further.

4. Accounting for ODE Invariants

In order to improve the stability of the enclosures as well as to tighten them further, suppose now that an invariant for the parametric ODE system is known, namely a function $h : \mathbb{R}^{n_x} \times \mathbb{R}^{n_p} \to \mathbb{R}$

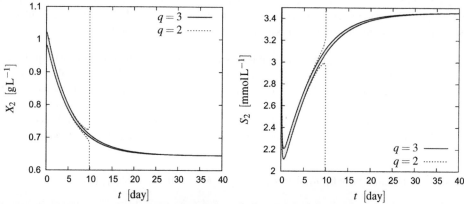

Figure 2. Reachable set enclosure projections for the variables X_2 and S_2.

such that $h(x(t,p),p) = 0$ for any solution $x(t,p)$ of (1). Given an affine-parameterization basis $\mathbb{E}_{np}$, it follows that an extension $h^{\mathbb{E}_{np}}$ of h should satisfy

$$\forall t \geq 0, \quad \mathrm{Im}_{\mathbb{E}_{np}}\left(h^{\mathbb{E}_{np}}(Q_x(t),Q_p)\right) = \{0\},$$

for given parameterizations Q_p and $Q_x(t)$ of the parameter and reachable sets.

Consider the special case of qth-order Taylor models with ellipsoidal remainders, such that $[\mathscr{P}_x(t),\mathscr{R}_x(t)] := Q_x(t)$ and $[\mathscr{P}_h(t),\mathscr{R}_h(t)] := h^{\mathbb{E}_{np}^{\mathrm{pol}(q)} \times \mathbb{E}_{np}^{\mathrm{ball}}}(Q_x(t),Q_p)$. The polynomial part $\mathscr{P}_h(t)$ is trivially equal to zero by construction. On application of Algorithm 1 in (Houska et al., 2013a), the ellipsoidal remainder is constructed such that:

$$\mathrm{Im}_{\mathbb{E}_{np}^{\mathrm{ball}}}\left(\mathscr{R}_h(t)\right) \supseteq \mathrm{Im}_{\mathbb{E}_{np}^{\mathrm{ball}}}\left(A_h(t)\mathscr{R}_x(t)A_h(t)^{\mathrm{T}}\right) \oplus N_h(t),\tag{4}$$

where $A_h(t)$ is the Jacobian matrix of h evaluated along the solution trajectory for some $\hat{p} \in P$, and $N_h(t)$ is an interval nonlinearity bounder. For linear invariants in particular, we have $N_h(t) = \{0\}$ and the ellipsoidal remainder $\mathrm{Im}_{\mathbb{E}_{np}^{\mathrm{ball}}}\left(\mathscr{R}_h(t)\right)$ can be thus be safely intersected with the hyperplane $\mathscr{H}_h(t) := \{x \in \mathbb{R}^{n_x} \mid A_h(t)^{\mathrm{T}}x = 0\}$. This intersection is simply repeated multiple times when several invariants are known.

Case Study: Reversible Chemical Reactions   Consider the reversible reactions $A + B \rightleftharpoons C$ and $A + C \rightleftharpoons D$ in a batch reactor, as described by the following dynamic model:

$$\begin{aligned}
\dot{x}_A &= -r_1(x_A,x_B,x_C) \\
\dot{x}_B &= -r_1(x_A,x_B,x_C) \\
\dot{x}_C &= r_1(x_A,x_B,x_C) - r_2(x_A,x_C,x_D) \\
\dot{x}_D &= r_2(x_A,x_C,x_D)
\end{aligned}$$

with:
$$\begin{aligned}
r_1(x_A,x_B,x_C) &:= k_1^{\mathrm{f}}x_Ax_B - k_1^{\mathrm{r}}x_C \\
r_2(x_A,x_B,x_C) &:= k_2^{\mathrm{f}}x_Ax_B - k_2^{\mathrm{r}}x_C
\end{aligned}$$

Based on mass-conservation considerations, it is not hard to see that the functions $h_1(x) := x_B + x_C + x_D$ and $h_2(x) := x_A - x_B + x_D$ are both linear solution invariants for the ODE system, i.e., $\dot{h}_1(x) = \dot{h}_2(x) = 0$ for all $t \geq 0$. Such invariants are typical in chemical reaction systems (e.g., Scott and Barton, 2010; Srinivasan et al., 1998). Mixed uncertainty in the initial values and kinetic parameters is considered here, with $x_A(0) = 1$, $x_B(0) \in [0.95, 1.05]$, $x_C(0) = x_D(0) = 0$, $k_1^{\mathrm{f}} \in [50,60]$, $k_2^{\mathrm{f}} = 20$, and $k_1^{\mathrm{r}} = k_2^{\mathrm{r}} = 1$.

Enclosures of the reachable set obtained with 3rd-order Taylor models with ellipsoidal remainders are shown in Fig. 3, with and without accounting for the invariants. On account of the invariants the set-valued integrator is able to stabilize the reachable set enclosure, whereas it fails to do so for this level of uncertainty when the invariants are ignored.

5. Conclusions

This paper was concerned with discrete-time, set-valued integration for computing parameterized enclosures of the reachable set of nonlinear parametric ODEs. Special emphasis has been on the stability properties of the enclosures, giving conditions under which the set-valued integrator inherits the asymptotic stability property of the original dynamic system. The key requirement here is that the underlying set arithmetic constructs extensions of factorable functions that are at least quadratically convergent. This stability property has been illustrated with the case study of an anaerobic digester, using Taylor model arithmetic with ellipsoidal remainders. Another contribution has been incorporating ODE invariants in order to further improve the stability of the

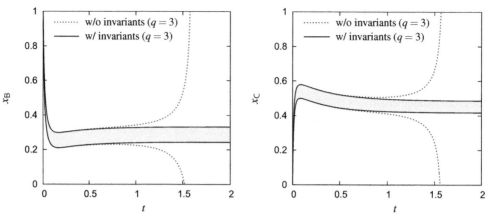

Figure 3. Reachable set enclosure projections for the variables x_A and x_B.

algorithm. Future work will focus on taking into account a priori enclosures derived from physical insight, and applying this generic bounding capability in global and robust dynamic optimization.

Acknowledgments

Financial support from Marie Curie grant PCIG09-GA-2011-293953 and from EPSRC under Grant EP/J006572/1 is gratefully acknowledged. MEV thanks CONACYT for doctoral scholarship.

References

O. Bernard, Z. Hadj-Sadok, D. Dochain, A. Genovesi, J. P. Steyer, 2001, Dynamic model development and parameter identification for an anaerobic wastewater treatment process, Biotechnol. Bioeng., 75, 844–438.

F. Blanchini, S. Miani, 2008, Set-Theoretic Methods in Control, Birkhäuser.

B. Chachuat, A. B. Singer, P. I. Barton, 2006, Global methods for dynamic optimization and mixed-integer dynamic optimization, Ind. Eng. Chem. Res., 45, 8373–8392.

B. Houska, F. Logist, J. Van Impe, M. Diehl, 2012, Robust optimization of nonlinear dynamic systems with application to a jacketed tubular reactor, J. Process Contr., 22, 1152–1160.

B. Houska, M. E. Villanueva, B. Chachuat, 2013a, A validated integration algorithm for nonlinear ODEs using Taylor models and ellipsoidal calculus, Proc. 52th IEEE Conference on Decision and Control (CDC), pp. 484–489, Florence, Italy.

B. Houska, M. E. Villanueva, B. Chachuat, 2013b, Stable validated integration algorithm for nonlinear ODEs using affine set parameterization, to appear on www.optimization-online.org.

Y. Lin, M. A. Stadtherr, 2007, Validated solutions of initial value problems for parametric ODEs, Appl. Numer. Math., 57, 1145–1162.

N. S. Nedialkov, K. R. Jackson, G. F. Corliss, 1998, Validated solutions of initial value problems for ordinary differential equations, Appl. Math. Comput., 105, 21–68.

A. M. Sahlodin, B. Chachuat, 2011, Convex/concave relaxations of parametric ODEs using Taylor models, Comput. Chem. Eng., 35, 844–857.

J. K. Scott, P. I. Barton, 2010, Tight, efficient bounds on the solutions of chemical kinetics models, Comput. Chem. Eng., 34, 717–731.

B. Srinivasan, M. Amrhein, D. Bonvin, 1998, Reaction and flow variants/invariants in chemical reaction systems with inlet and outlet streams, AIChE J., 44, 1858–1867.

Jiří Jaromír Klemeš, Petar Sabev Varbanov and Peng Yen Liew (Editors)
Proceedings of the 24th European Symposium on Computer Aided Process Engineering – ESCAPE 24
June 15-18, 2014, Budapest, Hungary. Copyright © 2014 Elsevier B.V. All rights reserved.

Statistical Control of Commercial Detergents Production through Fourier Transform Infra-Red Spectroscopy

Alessandra Taris[a], Massimiliano Grosso[a*], Fabio Zonfrilli[b], Vincenzo Guida[b]

[a]*Dipartimento di Ingegneria Meccanica, Chimica e dei Materiali, Università degli Studi di Cagliari, Via Marengo 2, 09123, Cagliari, Italy*
[b]*Procter & Gamble, Pomezia R&D Research Center, Via Ardeatina 100, 00040 Pomezia (RM), Italy*
massimiliano.grosso@dimcm.unica.it

Abstract

Multivariate statistical control in conjunction with mid-infrared spectroscopy was implemented to monitor the quality of commercial detergents. The approach was developed by estimating the Hotelling T^2 and Square Prediction Error Q statistics. A joint analysis of these two scalars has led to the introduction of a bivariate probability density function, which brings to the proposal of a novel normal operating region for the process. The sensitivity to detect abnormal processes is shown to be improved, with a correct identification of the detergent samples out of specifications.

Keywords: Fourier Transform Infrared Spectroscopy, statistical control, on-line monitoring

1. Introduction

Quality control of industrial products requires fast and simple procedures in order to ensure efficient on-line process monitoring. With this regard, one might be interested on the implementation of not invasive methodologies devoted to fast detection of out of control conditions. A proper experimental tool might be the classical attenuated total reflectance (ATR) coupled with Fourier transform infrared (FTIR) spectrometers that are capable to measure in very fast times the infrared spectra of aqueous samples and characterize materials in a really efficient way.

Here, we tackle the issue of the on-line monitoring of detergent mass production through a method based on a multivariate statistical process control approach applied on FTIR measurements of detergent samples. For these purposes, two different sets of detergent samples are taken into account and compared: a set of samples following standard production (hereafter referred as the in-control set) and an out-of-control set with a higher concentration value for one component of the mixture. In all the samples, small variations in the components are introduced in order to mimic typical fluctuations unavoidably present in the standard mass production.

The procedure is summarized in the following. First, a PCA linear model is carried out by analysing the in-control multivariate data set. Then, the T^2 and Q statistics pertaining all the samples are estimated with the PCA model. These scalars are a useful tool to reveal abnormalities occurring in the process (Qin, 2003). Traditionally, the approach is to analyse T^2 and Q on separate scalar charts (see e.g. Borin and Poppi, 2004 for an application on FTIR measurements). Recently, Chen et al. (2004) proposed a joint estimation of these two statistics by resorting to a nonparametric evaluation of the bivariate probability density function estimated from the observed values for the scalars T^2 and Q. Along this line of investigation, we propose an alternative, simple approach based on a nonlinear transformation $\mathbf{z}^*=[T^{2*},Q^*]$ of the original scalars. The objective is to achieve new statistics following a Gaussian dispersion. Eventually, it is thus possible to (i) evaluate the joint probability density function of these two new scalars and (ii) estimate the bounded region where the $[T^{2*},Q^*]$ values are expected to occur. The final goal is to assess whether it is possible or not to correctly detect the anomalies introduced in the blend composition and properly classify the samples.

2. Experimental section

2.1. Samples
The detergents used for the preparation were commercial solutions used for the mass production. The composition of the samples was varied in order to mimic typical fluctuations occurring in the manufacturing system. In more detail, 71 different samples were considered with fluctuations generated from their nominal values for the following species: sodium hydroxide, pH, chelating agents, anphoteric surfactant, ethanol, fatty acid, non ionic surfactant ($\pm$ 10 %); anionic surfactant ($\pm$ 5 %); sodium carbonate ($\pm$ 12 %); perfume ($\pm$ 15 %); polymer additive ($\pm$ 20 %). Other 44 samples were generated with the same average values and fluctuations, but with a concentration of the anionic surfactant 10 % greater than the maximum value assumed in the first data set. Therefore, these latter samples may be regarded as an out-of-control dataset when compared with the former one.

2.2. Experimental setup
The infrared measurements were performed on a Thermo Scientific Nicolet™iS™10 FT-IR Spectrometer with a deuterated triglycine sulfate (DTGS) detector and a KBr/Ge mid-infrared optimized beamsplitter. The spectra cover the range from 3000 to 800 cm^{-1} with a wavenumber resolution equal to 1.928 cm^{-1} and they are reported in Figure 1.

3. Methods

The FTIR spectra are analyzed by resorting to a principal component analysis: PCA is a well consolidated statistical modelling technique that exploits the singular value decomposition (SVD) for the treatment of a set of multivariate samples (Hada et al., 2012). The data are represented as a matrix $\mathbf{Y} \in \mathbb{R}^{J \times L}$ where J refers to the number of observations and L is the number of variables. Unity variance standardization is usually performed, i.e. the variables are mean centred and scaled to unity variance. The proce-

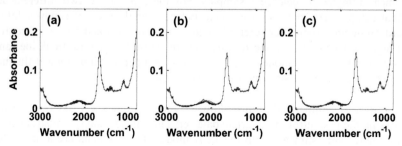

Figure 1. FTIR spectra for the: (a) training data (53 samples); (b) test data (18 samples); (c) out-of control data (44 samples)

dure is accomplished referring to the training data set, that is usually achieved under normal operating conditions of the process. The PCA decomposition can be therefore written as (see e.g. Jackson, 1991):

$$\mathbf{Y} = \hat{\mathbf{Y}} + \mathbf{E} \tag{1}$$

where

$$\hat{\mathbf{Y}} = \mathbf{T}_m \cdot \mathbf{P}_m^T \tag{2}$$

is the prediction of $\mathbf{Y}$ obtained by retaining the first m principal components (PCs) and $\mathbf{E} \in \mathbb{R}^{J \times L}$ is the residual matrix. $\mathbf{T}_m$ is the matrix of the first m scores accounting for the significant data variation whereas $\mathbf{P}_m$ is the loading matrix, which is an orthogonal rotation matrix. A generic multivariate sample $\mathbf{x}_k \in \mathbb{R}^{1 \times L}$ can be projected onto the space spanned by the first m principal components through the relationship:

$$\mathbf{t}_k = \mathbf{x} \cdot \mathbf{P}_m \tag{3}$$

Eqs.(1) and (2) permit the evaluation of two scalar statistics for the generic sample $\mathbf{x}_k$, known as T^2 and Q statistics:

$$T_k^2 = \mathbf{t}_k^T \cdot \mathbf{S}^{-1} \cdot \mathbf{t}_k \tag{4}$$

$$Q_k = \mathbf{e}_k^T \cdot \mathbf{e}_k, \qquad \mathbf{e}_k = \mathbf{x}_k - \mathbf{t}_k \cdot \mathbf{P}_m \tag{5}$$

where, in Eq.(4), $\mathbf{S}$ is the covariance matrix of the $\mathbf{t}_k$ scores. In practice, the T^2 statistic represents an overall measure of the process variation related to $\mathbf{x}_k$ as it was captured by the PCA model, whilst the Q statistic describes how well the PCA model predicts the $\mathbf{x}_k$ vector (Jackson, 1991).

To implement a PCA based on-line process monitoring, the following steps are required: first, a PCA model, based on the reference data of the process, has to be identified. For on-line monitoring, the new data points $\mathbf{x}_k$ are projected onto the model space defined by the PCA model, spanned by the retained m loading vectors as reported in Eq.(2). Then, the associated values of the T^2 and Q statistics are calculated by means of Eqs.(4) and (5). The occurrence $Q_k > Q_{lim}$ and/or $T^2_k > T^2_{lim}$ may be indicative of abnormal process behaviour (MacGregor and Kourti, 1995). The limiting values can be calculated by exploiting the expressions available in the literature (see e.g. Jackson, 1991). Eventually, one defines the normal operating region (NOR) of the regular process conditions as the square region: $[T^2, Q] \in [0 - T^2_{lim}] \times [0 - Q_{lim}]$ (Romagnoli and Palazoglou, 2012). From a theoretical point of view the T^2 and the Q statistics are independent of each other (Chen et al., 2004): T^2 follows a generalized Student t-distribution and the Q statistic a Chi-Squared distribution (Jackson, 1991). In practice, these statistics seldom follow the distributions assumed in the theory, as it was found in the current case (not reported in detail because of space limitations).

In the present work, we address a Box-Cox transformation for the statistics:

$$z_i^* = \begin{cases} \left(z_i^\gamma - 1\right)/\gamma & \gamma \neq 0 \\ \log z_i & \gamma = 0 \end{cases} \qquad i = 1,2, \quad z_i = T^2, Q \tag{6}$$

The goal is to approximate the data as much as possible to a Gaussian variable. The value of γ in Eq.(6) was found maximizing the Akaike Information Criterion (Akaike, 1974). The normality assumption for the transformed data is finally tested performing a Lilliefors goodness-of-fit test (Lilliefors, 1967). Thus, the bivariate samples of the statistic $\mathbf{z}^*$ can be regarded as outcomes of the multidimensional Gaussian random variable:

$$f_Z\left(\mathbf{z}^*\right)=\frac{1}{\left(\sqrt{2\pi}\right)^2 \sqrt{\det \mathbf{V}}}\exp\left(-\frac{1}{2}(\mathbf{z}^* -\bar{\mathbf{z}}^*)^T \cdot \mathbf{V}^{-1}\cdot(\mathbf{z}^* -\bar{\mathbf{z}}^*)\right) \tag{7}$$

where the term:

$$g\left(\mathbf{z}^*\right)=(\mathbf{z}^* -\bar{\mathbf{z}}^*)^T \cdot \mathbf{V}^{-1}\cdot(\mathbf{z}^* -\bar{\mathbf{z}}^*)=const \tag{8}$$

represents isolevel curves identified in the $\mathbf{z}^*$ space. The $\mathbf{V}$ matrix is the covariance matrix estimated by the samples. Eq. (8) allows to define a recipe for the calculation of a new normal operating region that can be adopted for the statistical control: in detail we will refer to the ellipse in the $[T^2,Q^*]$ space including the most of the observed $\mathbf{z}^*$ values (e.g. the 95 % of the date). Hereafter this region will be referred as the Elliptical Normal Operating Region (ENOR).

4. Results

For the case at hand, the PCA model was identified using a training data set of 53 spectra (75 % of the original dataset measured under normal operating conditions). The remaining 18 spectra were subsequently used as test set for the model validation. The appropriate number of principal components in the PCA model was found to be $m=6$, explaining more than the 90 % of the total data variance. The samples of the T^2 and Q statistics were then generated by applying Eqs.(4) and (5). It was found that the best choice for the nonlinear transformation was $\gamma=1$ for the Hotelling statistic (i.e. $T^{2*}\equiv T^2$) and $\gamma=0$ for the *SPE* statistic (i.e. $Q^*=\log Q$). The Lilliefors tests give a p-value equal to 0.193 and 0.123, for the two transformations, respectively. Incidentally, it should be mentioned that normality assumption for Q was rejected with a p-value=0.021. Therefore the bivariate sample of statistics $\mathbf{z}^*=[T^2,Q^*]$ can be reasonably approximated as an outcome of a multidimensional Gaussian random variable.

A summary of the results is reported in Figure 2, that reports the scatter points of the T^2 and Q^* statistics as they were estimated for the different data set here taken into account: white circles, grey squares and black triangles correspond to the training set, test set, and out-of-control set, respectively. For the sake of completeness it is shown in the figure: (i) the ENOR calculated with Eq.(8) and including the 95 % of the training data set (dotted line) and (ii) the threshold values (dashed-dotted line) estimated for the statistics $T^2{}_{lim}=15.61$ and $Q^*{}_{lim}=5.11$ as they were evaluated through the expressions available in the literature. Some comments are in order. Both the traditional NOR and the ENOR correctly classify almost all the samples of both the training (NOR: 96 %; ENOR: 92 %) and the test set (NOR: 89 %; ENOR: 89 %) as true negative (i.e. $0<Q^*<Q^*{}_{lim}$ and $0<T^2<T^2{}_{lim}$). It should be remarked that the successful classification of the test set further confirms the properness of the PCA model with $m=6$ principal components (at least for the parameter variations here explored). Furthermore, the additional samples obtained at the higher level of anionic surfactant concentration are

almost completely out of both the operating regions and they are correctly classified as abnormal process conditions. An effective separation between the in-control (both training and test set) and out-of-control data is again observed. As a final remark, one can appreciate from visual inspection that the Q^* statistic is also able to successfully discriminate the two data sets, at least for the case at hand.

The efficiency of the protocol here introduced is confirmed by representing the Receiver Operating Characteristic (ROC) curves (Scheipers et al., 2005), that are two-dimensional graphs of the true positive rates (TPs; i.e., successes) versus the false positive rates (FPs; i.e., false alarms). To perform the ranking statistical test, a scalar metric is required. In this work we consider two scalars for the three datasets: (i) the Q^* statistic and (ii) the distance d_e for the ENOR defined in Equation (9).

$$d_e = (\mathbf{z}^* - \bar{\mathbf{z}}^*)^T \cdot \mathbf{V}^{-1} \cdot (\mathbf{z}^* - \bar{\mathbf{z}}^*) \tag{9}$$

The results are reported in Figure 3. The area under the ROC curve is the so-called AUC index, which is a scalar measure of the overall performance of a classifier, averaging across different thresholds that can be used to generate a classifier. In general, a model with a larger AUC is preferred to a model with a smaller one. The AUC of a random classifier is 0.5, whereas AUC=1 corresponds to perfect classification.

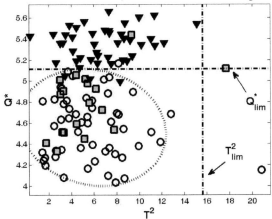

Figure 2. Scatter plot of the statistics T^2 and Q^*. White circles represent the observations for the training data set, gray squares the observations for the test set, black triangles the out-of-control data set. Dashed dotted lines are the limiting values calculated for the statistics. The dotted ellipse is the NOR evaluated with Eq.(8).

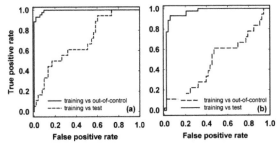

Figure 3. Roc curves resulting from the comparison of the training with out-of-control data (solid line) and the training with test data (dashed line) for (a) the Q^* statistic and (b) the d_e scalar.

Table 1. AUC scalars for the Q^* statistic and the d_e scalar.

		AUC	AUCmin	AUCmax
Q^* statistic	Out of control	0.994	0.974	0.999
	Test set	0.696	0.553	0.826
d_e scalar	Out of control	0.962	0.881	0.988
	Test set	0.482	0.339	0.656

The AUC values determined are shown in Table 1, where it is reported the comparison among the three different data sets, together with the related coefficient intervals estimated with a bootstrap technique. The ideal picture would be: (i) an AUC value as close as possible to 1, when comparing the training set with out-of-control set (thus meaning a perfect separation between the two classes) and (ii) an AUC value close to 0.5 when comparing the training set with the test set. It is further confirmed how the proposed procedure shows a high capability to distinguish the in-control from the out-of-control data.

5. Conclusions

A PCA based model in conjunction with mid-infrared spectroscopy was implemented to monitor the control quality of the mass production of a commercial detergent. To this end, a novel approach based on the definition of a joint pdf for the T^2 and Q statistics is proposed. This statistic leads to the definition of a novel region of normal operating condition. It was found, at least for the case under investigation, that the proposed protocol correctly classifies the samples with a performance, at least comparable, with the state of art approaches, but with a much higher specificity. As a final remark, it should be noticed that, up to our knowledge, a PCA based statistical control has been seldom implemented in the framework of infrared spectroscopy measurements.

References

H. Akaike, 1974, A new look at the statistical model identification, IEEE Trans Auto Contr, AC-19, 716–723.

A.Borin, R.J.Poppi, 2007, Multivariate Quality Control of Lubricating Oils Using Fourier Transform Infrared Spectroscopy, J. Braz.Chem.Soc., 15, 4, 570-576.

Q. Chen, U. Kruger, M. Meronk, A.Y.T. Leung, 2004, Synthesis of T2 and Q statistics for process monitoring, Control Eng. Practice, 12, 745-755.

S.Hada, N.G. Chemmangattuvalappil, C.B. Roberts, M.R. Eden, 2012, Product and Mixture Design in Latent Variable Space by Chemometric Techniques, Computer Aided Chemical Engineering, 30, 147-151.

J. E. Jackson, 1991, A Users Guide To Principal Components, John Wiley & Sons, Inc.,NY, USA.

H.W. Lilliefors, 1967, On the Kolmogorov-Smirnov test for normality with mean and variance unknown, Journal of the American Statistical Association, 62, 399–402.

J.F. MacGregor, T. Kourti, 1995, Statistical process control of multivariate process, Control Eng. Practice, 3, 3, 403-414.

J.F. Padilha, R. W.S. Pessoa, J. G.A. Pacheco, P. R.B. Guimarães, 2009, Evaluation of Alternative Methods for the Determination of Gasohol Fuel Properties when Compared to Standard Methods, Computer Aided Chemical Engineering, 27, 753-758.

S.J. Qin, 2003, Statistical process monitoring: basics and beyond, J. Chemometrics, 17, 480–502.

J. Romagnoli, A.Palazoglou, 2012, Introduction to process control, CRC Press, Boca Raton, Italy.

U. Scheipers, C. Perrey, S. Siebers, C. Hansen, H. Ermert, 2005, A tutorial on the use of ROC analysis for computer-aided diagnostic systems, Ultrasonic Imaging, 27, 3, 181-198.

Jiří Jaromír Klemeš, Petar Sabev Varbanov and Peng Yen Liew (Editors)
Proceedings of the 24th European Symposium on Computer Aided Process Engineering – ESCAPE 24
June 15-18, 2014, Budapest, Hungary. Copyright © 2014 Elsevier B.V. All rights reserved.

A Self-Optimizing Strategy for Optimal Operation of a Preheating Train for a Crude Oil Unit

Johannes Jäschke, Sigurd Skogestad

Department of Chemical Engineering, Norwegian University of Science and Techology (NTNU), 9471 Trondheim, Norway
skoge@ntnu.no

Abstract

We apply a recently developed approach for optimizing heat exchanger networks with stream splits to the case study of a preheating train of the crude oil unit at the Mongstad Refinery in Norway. To maximize heat transfer, we adjust the split such that the "Jäschke Temperatures" assume equal values for each branch. For a branch with one heat exchanger, the Jäschke Temperature is calculated as $T_J = \frac{(T-T_0)^2}{T_h-T_0}$, where T is the temperature of the split stream at the heat exchanger exit, and T_h and T_0 are inlet temperatures of the hot and cold stream, respectively. Controlling the Jäschke Temperatures to equal values gives near-optimal operation despite varying flow rates, stream temperatures, and heat transfer coefficients. We fitted a model to plant data obtained from the refinery, and consider two cases with decentralized PI control, and one case where the Jäschke Temperatures are controlled by a model predictive controller. Our paper demonstrates that controlling the Jäschke Temperatures of each branch to equal values is a simple alternative to online real-time optimization methods. Moreover, it is significantly cheaper to implement as an online optimizer, and it is easier to maintain.

Keywords: Heat exchanger networks, Self-optimizing control, Real-time optimization, Jäschke Temperature

1. Introduction

Energy costs contribute a large portion of the total operating costs in a refinery, and limited global resources and strong competition are forcing plant owners and operators to find ways of operating their plants close to the optimum. Often, as in the case presented here, optimizing the heat exchanger network of the preheating train of a crude oil unit not only makes the process more energy efficient, but also allows for an increased throughput, which directly translates to higher revenues.

For optimizing operation of such a process, there are two common approaches. In the first one, online optimization (Marlin and Hrymak, 1997), a model is repeatedly optimized online during plant operation, and the computed optimal inputs are implemented in the plant. Here the plant measurements are used to update model parameters, and are not directly used for control purposes. With the recent rise in computing power, this method has become more and more attractive, and is used increasingly in the process industries. However, it is still an expensive method because of the high costs of developing and maintaining a good process model.

A different approach is based on using a model off-line to find a good set of controlled variables, which when held constant at their setpoints, indirectly leads to near-optimal operation in spite of varying disturbances. This approach is followed e.g. in self-optimizing control (Skogestad, 2000), or when tracking the necessary conditions for optimality (Srinivasan et al., 2003). For heat exchanger networks without splits and with single bypasses, optimal operation can be described by a linear program, and a self-optimizing control strategy is to determine and control the active constraints (Aguilera and Marchetti, 1998). However, in networks with

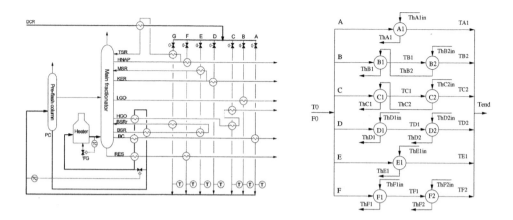

Figure 1. Preheating train of the Mongstad refinery (the left Figure is taken from Lid et al. (2001))

stream splits there are unconstrained degrees of freedom, and in addition to the active constraints also self-optimizing variables must be controlled.

Previously, there existed only methods for systematically finding linear measurement combinations as self-optimizing controlled variables (e.g. Alstad et al. (2009)). Recently there has been some advance towards finding controlled variables which are polynomial functions of measurements (Jäschke and Skogestad, 2012a). This allows more flexibility to handle nonlinear plants and has been successfully applied to heat exchanger networks with parallel flow paths, where the objective is to adjust the split such that the total heat transfer is maximized. Under assumption of the arithmetic mean temperature difference driving force (AMTD), a set of nonlinear measurement combinations, the "Jäschke Temperatures", of all branches must be equal under optimal operation. The optimal control policy is thus to control the differences between all Jäschke Temperatures to zero. Although the Jäschke Temperatures were derived using the AMTD, they give good performance on systems with a logarithmic mean temperature difference as driving force (Jäschke and Skogestad, 2014). The approach has been submitted for a patent (Jäschke and Skogestad, 2012b), and the objective of this paper is to present some results for an industrial size case study.

2. Process Description and Modelling

We apply our approach to the preheating train of a model of the Mongstad refinery in Norway, Figure 1, for which an online-RTO was developed by Lid et al. (2001). A cold feed is split into parallel branches, which are heated by hot product streams from the crude oil unit. Under operation, the flow rates and temperatures vary, and the optimization objective is to optimally adjust the split such that a maximum amount of heat is recovered. This minimizes the fuel required in the heater. Moreover, since the heater used to be the bottleneck of the process, optimizing the transferred heat directly translates into increased throughput and revenues.

The hot and the cold path of the heat exchangers in the preheating train are modelled as a series of 10 ideally mixed tanks, which are exchanging heat with each other. This results in an approximation of the logarithmic mean temperature difference. No phase change takes place in the heat exchangers, and the heat transfer properties were fitted to data from the refinery. The heat capacities of the streams were fitted to temperature data from the plant. All branches are assumed to have the same pressure drop, such that the flow F_i through branch i is proportional to the valve opening z_i, i.e. $F_i = \frac{z_i}{z_A + z_B + z_C + z_D + z_E + z_F} F_0$ with $z_i \in [0, 1]$ for $i \in \{A, B, C, D, E, F\}$. A detailed model description is found in Leruth (2012).

3. Controlled variables for parallel heat exchanger systems

Consider the system on the right-hand side of Figure 1. The optimization objective is to distribute the feed F_0 between the lines $A - F$ such that the total heat transfer P is maximized, i.e. the optimization problem can be written as

$$\max P = \sum_{i=A,\dots,F} Q_i \quad \text{subject to} \quad \sum_{i=A,\dots,F} F_i = F_0, \tag{1}$$

where Q_i denotes the heat transferred in branch i (e.g $Q_B = Q_{B1} + Q_{B2}$), and F_i denotes the flow through the branch. Note that maximizing P is equivalent to maximizing T_{end}. For such a system of parallel heat exchangers, the optimality condition can be expressed in terms of the marginal costs $\frac{\partial Q_i}{\partial F_i}$ (e.g. Downs and Skogestad (2011)):

$$\frac{\partial Q_A}{\partial F_A} = \dots = \frac{\partial Q_i}{\partial F_i} = \dots = \frac{\partial Q_F}{\partial F_F}. \tag{2}$$

If the marginal costs $\frac{\partial Q_i}{\partial F_i}$ could be measured, then one could easily adjust the split such that the marginal costs are equal for all branches. However, in practice the marginal costs are not measured, as they are functions of unmeasured disturbances and parameters, such as heat capacities, stream temperatures and heat transfer properties UA. Instead of estimating all unknown parameters to evaluate the marginal costs online, Jäschke and Skogestad (2014) have derived a simple approximation of the marginal costs in terms of temperatures only.

To simplify notation, we define the "shifted temperature" ΔT, where the Δ-operator denotes a shift in the reference temperature to the feed stream temperature T_0. For example, the shifted temperature of the exit temperature of stream A is $\Delta T_{A1} = T_{A1} - T_0$. Using the shifted temperatures, the marginal costs are approximated by the Jäschke Temperature, which is defined for a line with N heat exchangers with N hot streams as

$$T_J = \sum_{j=1}^{N} a_j, \tag{3}$$

where the contributions corresponding to the individual heat exchangers $j = 1 \dots N$ are calculated as

$$a_j = \frac{(\Delta T_j - \Delta T_{j-1})(\Delta T_j + \Delta T_{j-1} - a_{j-1})}{\Delta T_{hj} - \Delta T_{j-1}} \quad \text{for } j \geq 1 \quad \text{with } a_0 = 0, \text{ and } \Delta T_0 = 0. \tag{4}$$

In the simple case of only one heat exchanger per line, as for line A in Figure 1, this formula reduces to

$$T_{J,A} = \frac{(T_{A1} - T_0)^2}{T_{h,A1} - T_0} = \frac{\Delta T_{A1}^2}{\Delta T_{h,A1}}. \tag{5}$$

The configuration on branch B and C, where there are two heat exchangers which are connected in counter-current configuration, can be considered as one large heat exchanger. Therefore, the Jäschke Temperatures for branch B is calculated as $T_{J,B} = \frac{\Delta T_{B2}}{\Delta T_{h,B2}}$, and the Jäschke Temperature for branch C is calculated in the same way. When two heat exchangers on a line are connected to different hot streams, as in line D, the Jäschke Temperature becomes

$$T_{J,D} = \frac{\Delta T_{D1}}{\Delta T_{h,D1}} + \frac{(\Delta T_{D2} - \Delta T_{D,1})(\Delta T_2 + \Delta T_{D1} - \frac{\Delta T_{D1}}{\Delta T_{h,D1}})}{\Delta T_{h,D2} - \Delta T_{D1}}, \tag{6}$$

and the Jäschke Temperature for line F is calculated the same way.

Table 1. Steady state simulation results

Outlet temperature	Optimized	Equal T_J
Branch A	228.45 °C	222.98 °C
Branch B	211.78 °C	214.69 °C
Branch C	217.49 °C	208.49 °C
Branch D	201.44 °C	202.41 °C
Branch E	200.39 °C	206.03 °C
Branch F	203.55 °C	202.93 °C
Total network T_{end}	207.79 °C	207.61 °C

Surprisingly, as shown by Jäschke and Skogestad (2014), the Jäschke Temperatures correspond to the exact marginal costs when the arithmetic mean temperature is the driving force in the heat exchangers. Then we have $T_{J,i} = \frac{\partial Q_i}{\partial F_i}$. However, if the arithmetic mean temperature difference assumption does not hold, the Jäschke Temperatures can be used as approximations of the marginal costs. The resulting near-optimal control policy is then to control the Jäschke Temperatures of all branches to equal values.

4. Results

4.1. Steady state simulation

In Table 1, we compare the optimized steady state operation point with the results obtained from our method. Controlling the Jäschke Temperatures to equal values gives slightly different end temperatures for the different branches, but we observe that the finally obtained end temperature after merging the branches again is very similar to the optimized end temperature. This indicates that the overall heat transfer in the different branches is almost identical to the optimized case. Because the Jäschke Temperatures are derived based on the arithmetic mean temperature assumption, our approach does not give the exact optimum. However, the performance is still very good. The reason for this is that the optimum in such a system is very flat, so that the stream split ratios can be off the optimal value, while still resulting in very close to optimal performance.

4.2. Dynamic simulations

To test the dynamic performance of our approach on the heat exchanger network, we consider three scenarios. In the first two scenarios we use a decentralized control structure, and in the third scenario we use model predictive control to control the Jäschke Temperatures to equal values. The temperature sensor dynamics are modelled as first order dynamics with a time constant of 5s and a delay of 1s.

In all three cases we use the difference between the Jäschke Temperature of branches $A - E$ and branch F, i.e. $c_i = T_{J,i} - T_{J,F}$ for $i = A, B, C, D, E$, as controlled variables. The reason all controlled variables are taken relative to T_{JF} is that branch F has the largest heat capacity, and thus we expect this to mitigate interactions when controlling the system.

4.2.1. Scenario 1 and 2: Decentralized control

The Jäschke Temperatures contain temperature measurements of inlet and outlet streams of the heat exchangers. A temperature change in an inlet stream, e.g. T_0, will have a direct effect on the value of the Jäschke Temperature. The effect of the exit temperature, however, will be on a slower time-scale, and therefore there will be competing dynamic effects in the disturbance response of the controlled variables. In Scenario 1 we will use the Jäschke Temperatures

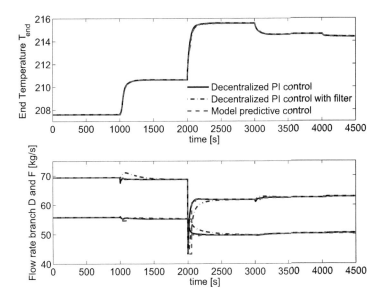

Figure 2. Comparison of control strategies. Top: Final outlet temperature T_{end}, Bottom: Flow rate through branches F and E

directly as controlled variables, while in Scenario 2, to mitigate undesired dynamic lead-lag effects on the response of the controlled variables, we add first order filters to the inlet temperature measurements. This ensures that all variables in the Jäschke Temperatures change at a similar rate, and avoids direct feed-forward of temperature disturbances from the feed streams to the controlled variables. Overall we expect this to results in smoother operation.

4.2.2. Scenario 3: Model predictive control (MPC)

Since the system is interactive, we also try using model predictive control to control the Jäschke Temperatures to equal values. The MPC was implemented using the Matlab™ and the model predictive control toolbox (Bemporad et al., 2012). We used a sample time of 60s, which corresponds to the residence time in the smallest heat exchanger, and the prediction horizon was set to 10. The control horizon was set to 1 sample time, which is quite typical for many industrial MPC implementations and results in little computation time. Note that the MPC does not work on filtered incoming temperature measurements, because we expect the MPC to handle the lead-lag effects.

4.2.3. Results

All three approaches keep the controlled variables at their setpoints, and the performance looks quite similar. In the top of Figure 2 we have plotted the end temperature (objective function to maximize). The steady state value is very close (<0.5 K) to the optimal value for the disturbances:

- At 5,000s step in feed temp (+10 °C)
- At 6,000s step in feed flowrate (-10 %)
- At 7,000s step in hot stream inlet temperature branch C (-10 °C)
- At 8,000s step in hot stream flow rate on branch E (-10 %)

All three control structures give excellent performance, as can be seen from the temperature profiles of the end temperature in Figure 2. For comparing the input usage, we show the flow rates to line D and F. Here we see that the unfiltered decentralized approach and the MPC give a more aggressive control action, while the filtered decentralized approach gives a smother, slower performance. The difference is, however, not reflected in the end temperature. From this point of view, it seems that the filtered decentralized control structure works best, because it does not require as much input usage as the other approaches. However, de-tuning the MPC controller may also result in smoother control action.

5. Conclusions

We have applied the Jäschke Temperature approach to a large heat exchanger network for preheating the feed stream of a crude oil unit. This resulted in a very simple control structure, which gave very close to optimal performance. The main advantage of our approach is that it requires no optimization at all. Neither off-line, to find the optimal nominal split, nor on-line, to re-optimize when disturbances occur.

Although the Jäschke Temperatures were derived using the arithmetic mean temperature, it is found that controlling them to equal values also gives good performance when this assumption is not satisfied, and the logarithmic mean temperature is the driving force (or some approximation, as in this work). The optima of these kind of systems are typically very flat, so if the split is not 100 % correct, the loss is still very small.

We applied a filter to mitigate the effects on different time scales. This resulted in an overall smoother control action. Note that the controllers need not be tuned aggressively, since because the goal is to optimize the energy consumption over a larger time-scale. From our simulations, it seems that using MPC and a decentralized control scheme give a practically identical performance in terms of the objective function (end temperature).

Acknowlegements

The authors would like to thank Alexandre Leruth for performing the simulations.

References

N. Aguilera, J. L. Marchetti, 1998. Optimizing and controlling the operation of heat-exchanger networks. AIChE Journal 44 (5), 1090--1104.

V. Alstad, S. Skogestad, E. S. Hori, 2009. Optimal measurement combinations as controlled variables. Journal of Process Control 19 (1), 138--148.

A. Bemporad, M. Morari, N. L. Ricker, 2012. Model predictive control toolbox. Tech. rep., Mathworks.

J. J. Downs, S. Skogestad, 2011. An industrial and academic perspective on plantwide control. Annual Reviews in Control 35 (1), 99 -- 110.

J. Jäschke, S. Skogestad, 2012a. Optimal controlled variables for polynomial systems. Journal of Process Control 22 (1), 167 -- 179.

J. Jäschke, S. Skogestad, 2012b. Parallel heat exchanger control, EU/UK patent application pct/ep2013/059304 and gb1207770.7.

J. Jäschke, S. Skogestad, 2014. Optimal operation of heat exchanger networks with stream split: Only temperature measurements are required. Sumbitted to Computers & Chememical Engineering, available as internal report at www.nt.ntnu.no/users/skoge/publications/2014/jaschke-hen-paper-cce-morari-issue.

A. Leruth, 2012. Heat exchanger network self-optimizing control -- application to the crude unit at Mongstad refinery. Master's thesis, Norwegian University of Science and Technology.

T. Lid, S. Strand, S. Skogestad, January 2001. On-line optimization of a crude unit heat exchanger network. In: Proceedings of the 6th Conference on Chemical Process Control (CPC VI), Tucson Arizona, AIChE Symposia Series No. 326. pp. 476 -- 480.

T. E. Marlin, A. Hrymak, 1997. Real-time operations optimization of continuous processes. In: Proceedings of CPC V, AIChE Symposium Series vol. 93. pp. 156--164.

S. Skogestad, 2000. Plantwide control: The search for the self-optimizing control structure. Journal of Process Control 10, 487--507.

B. Srinivasan, S. Palanki, D. Bonvin, 2003. Dynamic optimization of batch processes: I. characterization of the nominal solution. Computers & Chemical Engineering 27 (1), 1 -- 26.

Jiří Jaromír Klemeš, Petar Sabev Varbanov and Peng Yen Liew (Editors)
Proceedings of the 24th European Symposium on Computer Aided Process Engineering – ESCAPE 24
June 15-18, 2014, Budapest, Hungary.

Sugar Crystallization Benchmark

Rogelio Mazaeda[a*], Luis F. Acebes[a], Alexander Rodríguez[a], Sebastian Engell[b], César de Prada[a]

[a]*Systems Engineering and Automatic Control Group, University of Valladolid, c/ Real de Burgos s/n, Valladolid 47011, Spain*
[b]*Process Dynamics and Operation Group, Technische Universität Dortmund, Emil-Figge-Str. 70, Dortmund 44227, Germany*
rogelio@cta.uva.es

Abstract

The design of scalable and efficient plant-wide optimal control and operation schemes in process industries is an important research topic. Most promising strategies approach the problem by subdividing overall large optimization problems into local, more manageable tasks. The solutions for sub-tasks need to collaborate with each other in driving the process near the optimal operation of the overall plant. This paper describes a benchmark model of the evaporation and crystallization sections of a beet sugar factory that provides a test-bed for this kind of approach.

Keywords: process models, plant-wide control, simulation, hierarchical control, distributed control.

1. Introduction

This paper describes a model that was designed to experiment with plant-wide control and optimization strategies. It corresponds to a process of the sugar industry that combines units of continuous and semi-batch type, which are highly integrated, so that its operation and control requires taking into account continuous and discrete decisions. At the same time, the model is been used as a benchmark in the FP7, EU Network of Excellence "Highly-complex and Networked Control Systems" (HYCON2). This work has been also partially funded by the project CICYT DPI2012-37859.

The plant-wide control job can be approached by trying to optimize a profit related performance index, stating and solving a large mixed integer non-linear mathematical programming problem. However, this kind of monolithic strategy scales poorly with the size of the problem, so that a distributed or hierarchical approach offers a reasonable and more practical course of action.

In what follows, a description of the plant and the benchmark model is given in section 2, while in section 3 the proposed overall optimal control problem is discussed, along with a possible decomposition in lower level local sub-tasks.

2. Benchmark description

A sugar factory constitutes a complex hybrid plant with two main sections that interchange mass and energy. The first one, related to beets and juice processing, is of a continuous nature and provides a concentrated syrup and steam to the second one, whe-

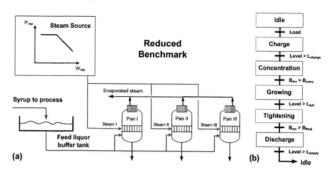

Figure 1. Sugar benchmark (a). Crystallizer recipe (b).

re the sugar crystals are manufactured in a set of semi-batch vacuum pans, which operate in semi-batch mode.

The benchmark proposed here (Fig.1a) represents some of the most important challenges that need to be faced in the operation of a sugar plant. The set of three identical crystallizers receives a continuous flow of syrup from the upstream continuous plant. The syrup arrives with a given flow-rate, concentration and purity and is provisionally stored in a buffer tank. The crystallizers (vacuum pans) are important consumers of steam, which is also delivered by the evaporation section. In the benchmark, this fact is represented by a simple model that tries to capture the limited availability of this resource.

The sugar crystallizer is the more complex unit represented in the model. The model used is a simplified version of a previous one developed for an operator training simulator project presented in Mazaeda et al. (2011). The complete mathematical description of the benchmark, including the simulation code, which has been implemented in the object oriented simulation package EcosimPro$^©$ (ESA International, 2011), can be accessed from the HYCON 2 webpage (HYCON2/WP5 sugar show case, 2013). In what follows, the main assumptions and some key equations are briefly described, along with a succinct description of the main trade-offs involved in the operation of the units.

$$s = \frac{Pur_{ml} B_{ml}}{y_{sat} \cdot C_{sol\_i}} \tag{1}$$

$$w_{cris} = K(s-1)^\alpha \tag{2}$$

The crystallization process consists of growing an initial seed of sugar crystals in the environment provided by a super-saturated sucrose solution. The key element for obtaining a uniform population of sugar grains is to keep the sucrose super-saturation (s), in the metastable zone, avoiding the dissolution that would occur if super-saturation goes below unity, or the creation of false grain by spontaneous nucleation if the labile zone is reached for high values of that variable (Fig.2a). Super-saturation, which is the excess of the actual dissolved sucrose over the solubility of the impure solution (C_{sol_i}), depends, as shown in Eq. (1), on the temperature (through the parameter y_{sat}) and on the characteristics of the mother liquor of the slurry or massecuite and ultimately of the feeding syrup: the concentration of all dissolved substances or Brix (B_{ml}) and the purity (Pur_{ml}). The correct super-saturation can be enforced during the processing of the batch by adequately combining the rate of evaporation of water with the inflow of syrup. The syrup input compensates the mass flow of dissolved sucrose (W_{cris}) that migrates to the growing crystals as shown in Eq.(2). Quality specifications demand that the crystallization is conducted at vacuum pressure. Each crystallizer consumes steam which provides the energy that is needed for the evaporation of water from the mass contained in the pan chamber. This steam is drawn from the evaporation section.

The control of industrial sugar crystallizers has to be performed under considerable uncertainties. The key super-saturation variable, for example, can only be inferred from other measurements and the influence of the impurities has to be found for each specific case. The scheme followed in practice is to define a configurable recipe that consists of a number of stages, as shown in Figure 1.b. The recipe is used for steering the sequential execution of the crystallization: the initial charge with syrup, the concentration to achieve the required super-saturation previous to the introduction crystal seed, the main growing stage, and the final step of mass discharge which occurs after a required further concentration or tightening phase. The recipe also establishes the profiles of the heating steam pressure for the pan heat exchanger and of the vacuum pressure to be enforced in the chamber at each point. In the important stage of grain growing, the syrup intake is adjusted by means of a control loop as the one shown in Fig. 2.b. The objective is to guarantee a specified concentration of the massecuite (B_{mc}) at each point in the evolution of the strike. The B_{mc} variable, which is measured, weighs not only the presence of solute in the mother liquor but also the amount of suspended sugar. So, to take it as an indirect indicator of the super-saturation, the progress of crystallization should be approximately assessed, and for doing that, the level of the mass in the pan is used. So, an adjustable Brix vs. level curve is used to provide the set-point for the mentioned Brix or massecuite concentration controller.

The first principles model of the crystallizer makes the assumption that there is no mass interchange between the impurities and any other component, so as the strike progresses and the relative amount of sugar crystals grows (Fig. 3.c), the purity of the mother liquor decreases (Fig. 3.d). So the concentration of the massecuite must be increased towards the end of the strike, an effect that is obtained by the reduction of the syrup intake (Fig. 4.d). It is known that there is a severe reduction of the heat transfer coefficient between the heating steam and the massecuite as the level in the pan and the viscosity increases, so that it gets harder to attain the needed super-saturation as the batch evolves (Fig 4.c). For a fixed Brix vs. level curve, the batch duration is highly dependent on the purity (Fig. 3.a) and concentration (Fig. 3.b) of the feed syrup.

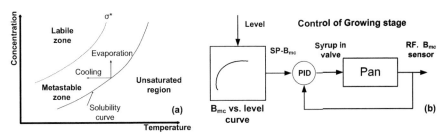

Figure 2. (a). Solubility curve (b). Mass concentration control loop in growing stage (b).

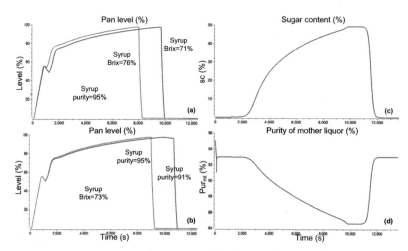

Figure 3. (a). Evolution of the level inside the pan for a change in the syrup purity obtained from validated model (a) and in the syrup Brix (b). Typical evolution of the sugar crystal content (c) and of the purity of the mother liquor (d).

3. The proposed optimal operation problem

The objective of the benchmark is to serve as a test bed for plant-wide control strategies. The problem that is put forward (see OT in Table 1) is that of minimizing the consumption of heating steam (of unitary price p_{st}) by the three crystallizers in the entire exercise, complying with the restriction that all incoming syrup is processed in time, or equivalently, that the level in the buffer tank is always kept in safe limits (L_{min}, L_{max}).

In order to keep the complexity of the problem manageable, we postulate here that the recipe based control of the individual crystallizer is given; the recipes can be changed only by manipulating the pressure to each heat exchanger of the pans by means of a multiplying factor (P_F) in order to accelerate the strike as depicted in Figure 4.a. A greater than unity factor P_F implies an acceleration of the strike (Fig. 4), as it moves up the complete profile of the heating steam pressure set-point that is established by the nominal recipe, making the concentrations, stipulated by the Brix vs. level curve, being arrived at earlier. But the process cannot be rushed up without limits: the crystallization

Table 1. Overall and local optimization problems.

Overall problem (OT)	Local problems (LT)
$\min_{u} J_{cost\_all} = \min_{P_{f_i}, Load_i} p_{st} W_{st}$	$\max_{P_f} J_{single} = \max_{P_f} P_{sug} - C_{st} - C_{syp}$
s.t.	$= \max_{P_f} \dfrac{1}{T_{Batch}} \left[p_{sug} \int_0^{T_{Batch}} W_{cris} - p_{st} \int_0^{T_{Batch}} W_{st} - p_{syp} \int_0^{T_{Batch}} W_{feed} \right]$
$f_{overall}(\dot{x}, x, u, p, t) = 0$	
$L_{min} \le L_{Buf}(t) \le L_{max}$	*s.t.*
$s_{min,i}(t) \le s_i(t) \le s_{max,i}(t)$	$f_{single}(\dot{x}, x, u, p, t) = 0$
$P_{f\,min,i} \le P_{f_i}(t) \le P_{f\,max,i}$	$s_{min}(t) \le s(t) \le s_{max}(t)$
$Load_i \in \{0,1\} \quad i \in \{1,2,3\}$	$P_{f\,min} \le P_f(t) \le P_{f\,max}$

kinetics has its own pace, decided mainly by the syrup purity, so a greater evaporation rate could result in the super-saturation entering the labile zone (Fig. 4.c). So, there is an additional constraint on the value of super-saturation, s(t), here considered to be a directly measured variable for the sake of simplicity. Evidently, the solution found has to comply with the dynamic equations of the complete model ($f_{overall}$), including those of each crystallizer. The decision variables are: the above mentioned factor P_F for each crystallizer and the discrete command for initiating the batch in each unit ($Load_i$). Summing up, an optimal strategy is one that minimizes the steam consumption from the common source and is able of processing all incoming syrup, with a flowrate, concentration and purity that varies between known limits. For doing that, the plant-wide controller must schedule the batches and can, up to a point, influence each batch duration, provided that the super-saturation remains between safe limits.

A centralized monolithic plantwide optimization as the one posed in OT is sound but does not scale satisfactorily with the size of the problem. In the case at hand, the fact that we are dealing with a hybrid, discrete-continuous model, calling for the use of mixed integer non-linear, computationally demanding, mathematical programming algorithms, aggravates the situation. There is a growing interest on exploring non-centralized optimization strategies to better manage this kind of problems (Scatollini, 2009). The use of a hierarchical or distributed optimization approaches which are more in accord with the usual way in which automation projects evolve in the process industries, strives for the design of local optimal solutions at the level of the individual units and then the coordination of those individual controllers to drive the process near the optimum of the plantwide problem.

In conformity with this kind of approach, we propose to optimally solve the problem LT (see Table 1) for each crystallizer unit. The local problem is to maximize the sugar production profit per unit of time, taking into account the unitary prices of sugar (p_{sug}), of steam (p_{st}) and of feed syrup (p_{syp}). The decision variable, in this case, is the individual acceleration factor (P_F) and the solution must comply, obviously, with the dynamic equations defining the crystallizer workings (f_{single}) but also with the restriction imposed on the super-saturation. The solution to LT will likely tend to increase each unit throughput by reducing the batch cycle time (T_{Batch}). But each individual crystallizer is not, by itself, directly in the bottleneck of the entire process, but rather the sum of the three crystallizers that are operated in parallel is. The set of pans considered share the common resources represented by the feed syrup and the heating steam. So this kind of "greedy" individual strategy should be arbitrated, by exchanging information or by using some kind of coordinating algorithm at a higher hierarchical level

For example, for the sake of concreteness, we can assume the existence of a high level arbiter. Its task would be to use its vantage point of having access to the overall structure of the plant and to on-line measurements giving information on the current state of each unit, in order to coordinate the individual crystallizer controllers. In this case, the coordinator would have to manipulate the scheduling of pans ($Load_i$ commands) and, possibly, to modify the cost index of the LT sub-problems, to comply with the global restriction of keeping the buffer tank level within bounds, driving, at the same time the whole process to the minimum steam consumption objective of the original OT task. A promising coordinating paradigm, for example, is to assign prices to the common resources, using a market metaphor (Martí et al., 2012). This benchmark

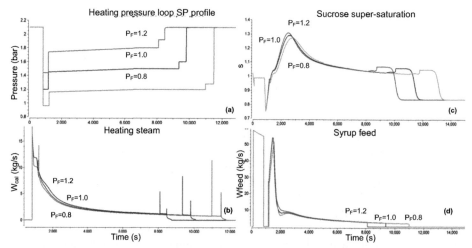

Figure 4. Impact of heating steam pressure as the P_F parameter is modified.

lends naturally such an approach: the coordinator could tune the prices in each individual LT problem.

It should be noticed that there is much to be gained by tightly integrating the short-time scheduling of the pans with the control of the individual processes. The scheduling needs can change drastically in the face of the disturbances represented in particular by the characteristics of the arriving syrup. While the acceleration policy implemented in the lower layer can help in coping with the inertia represented by this kind of batch processes, giving the scheduler an extra flexibility for accommodating the load represented by the need of processing all the incoming syrup. In Engell and Harjunkoski (2012), there is an in-depth discussion of these issues.

4. Conclusions

The sugar benchmark previously described represents a realistic plant-wide control problem. It lends itself naturally to a hierarchical or distributed approach by introducing a physically motivated decomposition. The novelty of the proposed problem resides in the need that it poses for a tight integration between the control decisions and the short time scheduling of the batch crystallizers.

References

S. Engell, I. Harjunkoski, 2012, Optimal operation: Scheduling, advanced control and their integration, Computers and Chemical Engineering, 47, 121-133.

ESA International, 2011. EcosimPro User Manual, EL Modelling Guide. EA International.

HYCON2 /WP5 sugar show case, 2013, <hycon.isa.cie.uva.es/home>, accessed on 23/01/2014.

R. Martí, D. Navia, D. Sarabia, C. de Prada, 2012, Shared Resources Management by Price Coordination, Computer Aided Chemical Engineering, 30, 902-906.

R. Mazaeda, A. Merino, C. de Prada, L.F. Acebes, 2011, Sugar End Training Simulator, International Sugar Journal, 114, 42-49.

R. Scatollini, 2009, Architectures of distributed and hierarchical Model Predictive Control-a review, Journal of Process Control, 19, 723-731.

Jiří Jaromír Klemeš, Petar Sabev Varbanov and Peng Yen Liew (Editors)
Proceedings of the 24th European Symposium on Computer Aided Process Engineering – ESCAPE 24
June 15-18, 2014, Budapest, Hungary.

Dynamic Simulation and Control of Post-combustion CO_2 Capture with MEA in a Gas Fired Power Plant

Evgenia D. Mechleri[a,] *, Chechet Biliyok[b], Nina F. Thornhill[a]

[a]Centre for Process System Engineering (CPSE), Department of Chemical Engineering, Imperial College London, South Kensington Campus, SW7 2AZ, UK
[b]Energy and Power Engineering Division, School of Engineering, Cranfield University, Bedfordshire MK43 0AL, UK
e.mehleri@imperial.ac.uk

Abstract

This paper presents a dynamic model of a post combustion CO_2 capture plant via chemical absorption using monoethanolamine (MEA) for natural gas combined cycle (NGCC) power plants. Insight regarding the process dynamics due to various disturbances caused by the operation of the power plant is presented and a control structure is proposed, based on heuristics. The performance of the proposed control scheme was evaluated by changing the flue gas flow rate which is commonly induced in the operation of power plants such as during start-up, shutdown and cyclic loading. Consideration has also been given to the variations to the control tuning due to the lower composition of CO_2 in NGCC plant compared to coal fired power plants. The results have shown that with the implementation of the proposed control scheme, the flexible operation of the power plant in combination with the capture plant can be maintained.

Keywords: Dynamic modelling, Process control, post combustion, flexible operation, NGCC plant

1. Introduction

Carbon capture and storage (CCS) is one family of technologies that could be used to reduce CO_2 emissions from power plants. Chalmers et al. (2009) have identified that post-combustion capture with aqueous solutions of MEA is getting close to commercial deployment, however to date no commercial CO_2 capture plant has been built to capture CO_2 from a natural gas power plant. The energy required to operate the reboiler, which leads to a reduction in power generation, is one of the main reasons.

To control the MEA system, Ziaii et al. (2009) proposed adjusting the ratio between the rich amine flow rate and the reboiler heat duty to maintain the CO_2 removal at a given level, while keeping the lean loading constant, during the period of high electricity demand. The proposed control strategy resulted in higher CO_2 capture than that obtained from the regeneration of the whole rich solvent in the stripper. However, this study only focused on the stripper as a standalone unit and not on the whole capture process.

In recent years, several studies which focused on the control of the complete CO_2 capture have been published. Lin et al. (2011) simulated the CO_2 capture process using the equilibrium column model in Aspen Dynamics. A control structure is proposed in order to maintain the CO_2 removal at a specific value by manipulating the lean solvent flow rate in the top of the absorber column. In order to achieve the optimal operation of the whole process the liquid level in the reboiler and the lean loading are controlled by the water make-up and the reboiler duty, respectively. In their study (Nittaya et al., 2014), provided an insight regarding the dynamic operation of a CO_2 capture plant in closed loop in the presence of several scenarios that may reflect the true operating conditions for this process. The above survey shows that a control structure design for the complete CO_2 capture plant for natural gas turbines has not been explicitly addressed in the literature. The majority of the papers is based on coal fired power plants. This work will focus on NGCC power plants and will show the dynamic performance of these plants with the capture plants. The control loops implemented in the NGCC plants do not differ from these applied on coal plants since the capture units are the same. What changes is the tuning of the controllers since the composition and the flowrate of the flue gas and MEA will change.

The aim of this work is to identify the main factors that are affected when a disturbance is applied. Moreover this work is a benchmark study for the Gas-Facts project, that will underpin the future work of the project. (Gas-Facts, 2012).

This work is undertaken with the aim of presenting an alternate control structure of a post combustion CO_2 capture plant using MEA absorption. The control structure proposed in this study was developed using a heuristic approach. A dynamic model of the capture plant is implemented in Aspen HYSYS Dynamics (Luyben, 2002). As the amine solution is an electrolytic system and comprises chemical reactions, the VLE models of MEA and CO_2 were described using the Kent-Eisenberg thermodynamic model. Aspen HYSYS has an Amines property package and the thermodynamic properties related to the CO_2 absorption are calculated. The dynamic closed-loop performance of the plant was evaluated by changing the flue gas flow rate, which reflects on different operating conditions of the power plant.

2. Base case operating condition

The typical CO_2 plant is illustrated in Figure 1. The flue gas carrying the CO_2 from the 200 MW NGCC power plant flows to the bottom of the absorber, whereas the lean amine solution of 30 % MEA is fed at the top. The low temperature in the absorber enhances the exothermic reaction between the CO_2 and the MEA solution. Treated gas is vented to the atmosphere from the top of the absorber. The rich amine solution is sent to a heat exchanger before entering the stripper where it is preheated to 100 °C. The capture plant design parameters and nominal stream conditions are given in Table 1.

Table 1. Capture Plant Parameters

Design Specs		**Initial Conditions**	
Absorber diameter (m)	15.80	Flue gas rate (kg/h)	$1.397 \cdot 10^6$
Absorber packing height (m)	28.30	CO_2 content (mol %)	3.73
Stripper diameter (m)	5.029	Lean Solvent rate (kg/h)	$2.997 \cdot 10^6$
Stripper packing height (m)	8.117	Lean loading	0.2747
Packing type	Mellapak 250X	Rich loading	0.3898

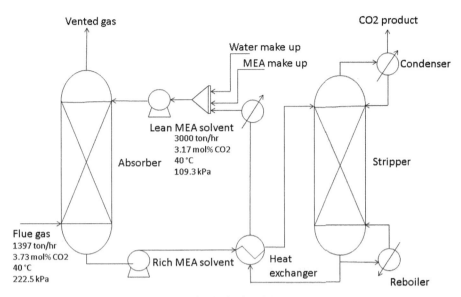

Figure 1. Process flowsheet of the absorption/stripping CO_2 capture process

Due to the relatively high temperature in the stripper, CO_2 releases from the Rich solvent and produces a rich CO_2 vapour stream and a liquid stream (lean MEA) with low CO_2 content. The CO_2 vapour stream passes through a condenser where some water and most MEA is removed prior to entering a compression train. The lean MEA leaves the reboiler and enters the heat exchanger, a cooler and a mixer thereafter. The sorbent concentration of the entire CO_2 absorption system is maintained by two makeup streams of water and MEA. Then the lean MEA is recycled back to the absorber.

3. Control analysis on the CO_2 capture plant

This section presents the methodology in order to specify the control structure proposed for the CO_2 capture process.

In dynamic mode, in order to optimally operate the CO_2 capture plant some operational constraints need to be taken to account. One constraint is the % of the CO_2 captured which is defined as the amount of the CO_2 captured per total CO_2 entering the plant. This metric is widely used to measure the performance of the CO_2 removal process (Nittaya et al., 2014). In this study it is to be maintained around 90 %. The operating temperature in the reboiler needs to be maintained in the range of 110-120 °C in order to avoid MEA degradation (Nittaya et al., 2014). The temperature of the lean MEA entering the absorber needs to be maintained around 40 °C in order to achieve high removal efficiency (Aroonwilas et al., 2000). The condenser temperature is kept around 40 °C in order to achieve a high concentration of CO_2 in the product stream and therefore reduce the compression costs. In this study the condenser temperature is kept at 42 °C, to keep a purity of 99 % in the CO_2 existing from the stripper and also minimise the duty of the condenser.

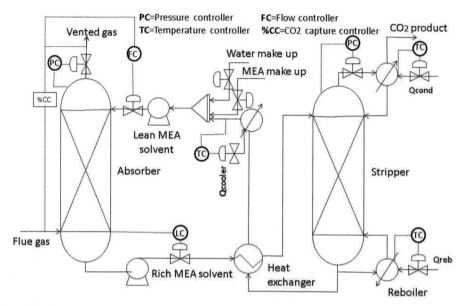

Figure 2.The proposed control scheme

In order to design a basic control scheme for a given process the following steps are implemented: i) specification of the process control goals, (ii) identification of the manipulated and controlled variables, (iii) identification of the basic control scheme. The process control objectives are the high level of CO_2 capture and the purity of the CO_2 leaving the condenser. Figure 2 illustrates the control structure designed for the capture process.

Apart from the operational constraints there are other process variables that have significant effect on the efficiency of the system and therefore need to be controlled. These are the amine concentration in the lean sorbent, the lean loading and the MEA flowrate in the lean stream. The MEA concentration and the lean loading depend indirectly on the temperature in the reboiler. As illustrated in Figure 2 several controllers were installed including pressure, temperature, flow and level controllers. A flow controller adjusts the mass flow rate of the lean amine entering the absorber in order to maintain the removal rate.

4. Performance evaluation of the control structure

The control structure proposed in this study for the CO_2 capture process was evaluated under the scenario of changing the flue gas flow rate. This is a common disturbance in the operation of power plants, e.g. changes in flue gas flow rate during plant start-up, shutdown, or cyclic loading. In this study a step increment of 10 % in the flue gas flowrate with respect to its nominal operating point was introduced to the plant at the first hour of operation. The responses to this disturbance in the operation of the plant are presented in Figure 3.

Figure 3 shows that, due to the increase in the flue gas flowrate and in order to maintain the capture level at 90 %, the lean solvent flow rate is increased and then stabilised in a new steady state. The reboiler temperature remains almost stable as the temperature controller implemented in the reboiler shoed a fast recovery to the disturbance, while the reboiler duty increases slowly then stabilises to account for the increased solvent circulation that requires regeneration.

In Figure 4, the responses in a decrease of 10 % in the flue gas flow rate are illustrated. After a decrease in the lean amine flow rate in order to maintain the capture rate, the responses of the temperature controller showed fast disturbance rejection and after a small temperature increase the new steady state was reached.

In both disturbances (increase/decrease in flue gas flow rate), the actions proposed by the control scheme rejected the disturbance effectively, as shown by the very small deviation in the % capture level.

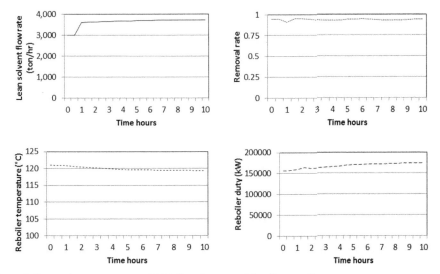

Figure 3. Dynamic responses to +10 % disturbance to inlet flue gas flow

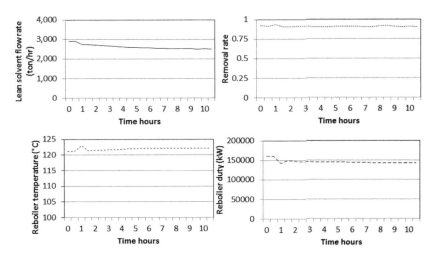

Figure 4. Dynamic responses to -10 % disturbance to inlet flue gas flow

5. Conclusions

This paper presented a dynamic model of a post combustion CO_2 capture plant via chemical absorption using MEA for natural NGCC power plants. The control structure proposed in this study was developed using a heuristic approach. A dynamic model of the capture plant is implemented in Aspen HYSYS Dynamics. The dynamic closed-loop performance of the plant was evaluated by changing the flue gas flow rate, which reflects on different operating conditions of the power plant.

The control scheme presented, comprises of several controllers in order to maintain a capture level of 90 %. A flow controller adjusts the mass flow rate of the lean amine in order to maintain the removal rate. A temperature controller in the reboiler controls apart from the temperature of the reboiler, the lean MEA concentration and the lean loading of the amine.

A disturbance in the flue gas flow rate was implemented and the dynamic responses of the system were recorded. The results showed that with the proposed control scheme the capture rate of the CO_2 was kept almost constant, with a very small deviation, while the controllers responded quite fast in the disturbance and moved the system to a new steady state. This work is a benchmark study for the Gas-Facts project.

Acknowledgement

The authors gratefully acknowledge the financial support of the ABB Chair of Process Automation and of EPSRC through grant EP/J020788/1 Gas-FACTS: Gas - Future Advanced Capture Technology Options.

References

A. Aroonwilas, P. Tontiwachwuthikul, 2000, Mechanistic model for prediction of structured packing mass transfer performance in CO_2 absorption with chemical reactions, Chemical Engineering Science, 55, 3651-3663.

H. Chalmers, M. Lucquiaud, J. Gibbins, M. Leach, 2009, Flexible Operation of Coal Fired Power Plants with Postcombustion Capture of Carbon Dioxide, Journal of Environmental Engineering, 135, 449-458.

Gas-Facts project, 2012, <www3.imperial.ac.uk/processautomation/research/gasfacts> accessed on 30/01/2014.

T. Nittaya, P.L. Douglas, E. Croiset, L.A. Ricardez-Sandoval, 2014, Dynamic modelling and control of MEA absorption processes for CO_2 capture from power plants, Fuel, 116, 672-691.

Y. Lin, T. Pan, D.S. Wong, S. Jang, Y. Chi, C. Yeh, 2011, Plantwide control of CO2 capture by absorption and stripping using monoethanolamine solution, Industrial and Engineering Chemistry Research, 50, 1338-1345.

Luyben W.L., 2002, Plantwide Dynamic Simulators in Chemical Processing and Control, Marcel Dekker, New York, United States.

S. Ziaii, G.T. Rochelle, T.F. Edgar, 2011, Optimum design and control of amine scrubbing in response to electricity and CO_2 prices, Energy Procedia, 4, 1683–1690.

Jiří Jaromír Klemeš, Petar Sabev Varbanov and Peng Yen Liew (Editors)
Proceedings of the 24th European Symposium on Computer Aided Process Engineering – ESCAPE 24
June 15-18, 2014, Budapest, Hungary.

A Methodology for Experimental Determination of Stability Boundaries with Application to Fluidized Bed Spray Granulation

Stefan Palis[a,*], Christian Dreyschultze[a], Achim Kienle[a,b]

[a]Institute for Automation Engineering, University of Magdeburg, Universitätsplatz 2, 39104, Magdeburg, Germany
[b]Max-Planck Institute Magdeburg, Dynamics of Complex Technical Systems, Sandtorstr. 1, 39106, Magdeburg, Germany
stefan.palis@ovgu.de

Abstract

This paper is concerned with the experimental determination of stability boundaries for fluidized bed spray granulation processes with external product classification. In order to cope with the problems of an implementation on the real plant a closed loop strategy consisting of a simple tuning controller, a closed loop identification procedure and a step size control algorithm is proposed.

Keywords: Closed loop system identification, determination of stability boundaries, granulation.

1. Introduction

Granulation is an important class of production processes in food, chemical and pharmaceutical industries. It is used to produce granules from liquid products, e.g. solutions or suspensions. More and more frequently, granulation is combined with fluidized bed technology. The process dynamics are typically very complex involving different types of micro processes (e.g. Alaathar et al. (2013) and Dosta et al. (2013)).

In order to guarantee a stable process operation a precise knowledge of stability boundaries is needed. Their determination in open loop operation can be critical from an operation point of view and rather time consuming, since oscillations are usually weakly damped in the neighborhood of the stability boundary. To overcome these problems we propose a strategy complementary to the one presented in Barton and Sieber (2013) based on closed loop operation.

2. Continuous fluidized bed spray granulation

The granulator consists of a granulation chamber, where the particle population is fluidized through an air stream with predefined pressure, temperature and humidity. Then a liquid solution or suspension is injected, which settles on the particles. Due to the low humidity and increased temperature the liquid fraction, i.e. the solvent or the external phase, is evaporated. The remaining solid forms a new layer on the particle surface. Typically, nucleation due to spray drying, particle agglomeration and breakage are in this configuration negligible. As one is in general interested in product particles with a defined particle size distribution withdrawn granules have to be sieved, which results in two additional fractions. The fine particles are directly sent back to the granulation chamber, whereas

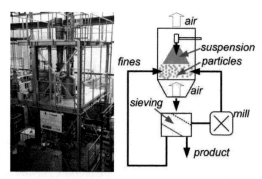

Figure 1. Pilot plant operated by NaWiTec at the University of Magdeburg (left) and process scheme of fluidized bed spray granulation with external product classification (right)

the oversized granules are send to a mill. There they are grinded to a specific size and then send back to the granulation chamber. It should be mentioned that due to this sieve-mill cycle a permanent generation of new particles is guaranteed, which hence allows a continuous process operation. The associated pilot plant and process scheme is depicted in Figure 1 (left and right). In Heinrich et al. (2002) a population balance model for the fluidized bed spray granulation with external product classification has been presented. There, it was assumed that the particles are almost spherical and can hence be described by one internal coordinate L, the particle diameter, giving rise to the particle size distribution $n(t, L)$. The associated particle growth can be described by

$$G = 2\frac{\dot{m}_e}{\rho\pi\mu_2} \tag{1}$$

where μ_2 is the second moment of the particle size distribution $n(t, L)$ and $\dot{m}_e$ is the mass suspension injection rate.

In the continuous configuration of the fluidized bed spray granulation particles are continuously removed in order to achieve a constant bed mass, which correlates to a constant third moment of the particle size distribution. The particle flux being removed from the granulator is

$$\dot{n}_{out}(t, L) = K\, n(t, L) \tag{2}$$

where K is the drain, which has to be controlled such that the bed mass is constant. The removed particles $\dot{n}_{out}(t, L)$ are then sieved in two sieves and separated into three classes: fines fraction Eq. (3), i.e. particles which are smaller than the desired product, product fraction Eq. (4), i.e. particles with the desired size and oversize fraction Eq. (5), i.e. particles being bigger than the desired product.

$$\dot{n}_{fines}(t, L) = (1 - T_2(L))(1 - T_1(L))\, \dot{n}_{out}(t, L) \tag{3}$$

$$\dot{n}_{prod}(t, L) = T_2(L)(1 - T_1(L))\, \dot{n}_{out}(t, L) \tag{4}$$

$$\dot{n}_{oversize}(t, L) = T_1(L)\dot{n}_{out}(t, L) \tag{5}$$

The separation functions $T_1(L)$ and $T_2(L)$ for the two screens are

$$T_{1,2}(L) = \frac{\int_0^L exp\left(\frac{(L'-\mu_{1,2})^2}{2\,\sigma_{1,2}^2}\right)dL'}{\int_0^\infty exp\left(\frac{(L'-\mu_{1,2})^2}{2\,\sigma_{1,2}^2}\right)dL'}. \tag{6}$$

The particle flux from the mill is given by

$$\dot{n}_{mill}(t,L) = \frac{n_M(L)}{\int_0^\infty L^3 n_M(L) dL} \int_0^\infty L^3 \dot{n}_{oversize}(t,L) dL \tag{7}$$

where

$$n_M(L) = \frac{6 exp\left(\frac{(L-\mu_M)^2}{2\sigma_M^2}\right)}{\sqrt{2\pi}\pi\rho\sigma_M}. \tag{8}$$

The overall population balance equation thus reads

$$\frac{\partial n}{\partial t} = -G\frac{\partial n}{\partial L} - \dot{n}_{prod} - \dot{n}_{oversize} + \dot{n}_{mill}. \tag{9}$$

Assuming an ideal mass controller the drain K can be directly calculated.

$$K = -\frac{\int_0^\infty L^3 G\frac{\partial n}{\partial L} dL}{\int_0^\infty L^3 \dot{n}_{prod} dL} \tag{10}$$

As has been shown in Radichkov et al. (2006) the qualitative dynamical behavior of the fluidized bed spray granulation with external product classification strongly depends on the process parameters especially the mill grade μ_M. For sufficiently high mill grade, transition processes decay and the particle size distribution reaches as table steady state (Figure 2 left). Decreasing the mill grade below a critical value gives rise to nonlinear oscillations (Figure 2 right). Using the population balance model the critical mill grade, i.e. the mill grade where the qualitative change in the stability behavior occurs, can be derived by a one-parameter bifurcation analysis as depicted in Figure 3. It is important to mention that this qualitative behavior is not induced by the specific model formulation but is directly connected to the presented process configuration.

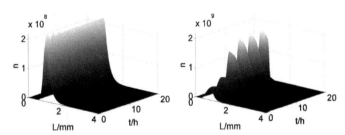

Figure 2. Dynamical behavior of the particle size distribution $n(t,L)$ for a sufficiently high mill grade (left) and for a sufficiently low mill grade (right)

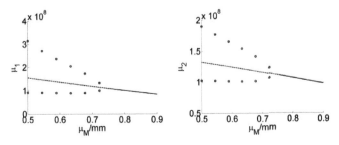

Figure 3. Bifurcation diagrams – first moment μ_1 (left) and second moment μ_2 (right)

3. Experimental determination of stability boundaries

As has been presented earlier the critical mill grade can be derived by a model based bifurcation analysis. However, due to model simplifications, uncertainties in process parameters and operation conditions the critical mill grade typically greatly differs on the real plant. Therefore, in the following a new strategy for the experimental derivation of stability boundaries in the space of the operational parameters will be derived.

A precise experimental determination of stability boundaries in open loop operation, which can also be used for model validation or model discrimination, can be rather time consuming, since oscillations are usually weakly damped in the vicinity of the stability boundary (Figure 4 left). Further process behaviour in this region can be rather critical and therefore prohibitive for an open loop strategy. To overcome these problems we propose a strategy based on closed loop operation. The main advantages of closed loop operation are

- increased process stability due to stabilizing control,
- considerable speed up of experiments as open loop transients are typically very slow (Fig. 4 left)
- enhanced reproducibility as the controller compensates for unforeseen disturbances, which may strongly influence the experiment.

In order to experimentally determine the open loop stability boundaries with respect to a parameter u the iterative algorithm depicted in Fig. 4 (right) is proposed

4. Closed loop system identification

System identification in closed loop operation (Figure 5 (left)) may cause serious problems for several identification methods due to signal correlation and non-informative measurement information even if the input is persistently exciting. In order to overcome these problems several approaches (direct, indirect and joint input-output) in combination with a prediction error method have been proposed (e.g. Forssell and Ljung, 1999).

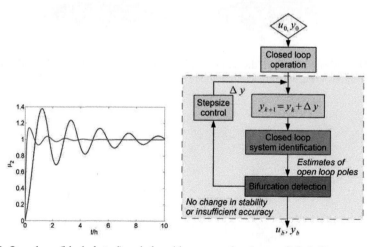

Figure 4. Open loop (black dotted) and closed loop operation (gray solid) (left), strategy for experimental determination of open loop stability boundaries (right)

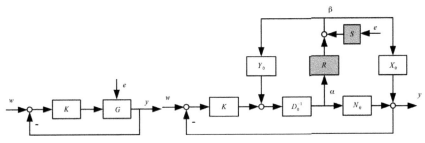

Figure 5. Closed loop system identification (left) – dual Youla parameterization (right)

In this contribution the dual Youla parameterization approach will be applied. Here, the given controller $K(s)$ and nominal plant $G_0(s)$ are both represented by their coprime factorization.

$$K(s) = \frac{X_0(s)}{Y_0(s)} \text{ and } G_0(s) = \frac{N_0(s)}{D_0(s)} \tag{11}$$

Using this coprime representation the set of all plants being stabilized by the given controller $K(s)$ is given by

$$G(s) = \frac{N_0(s) + Y_0(s)R(s)}{D_0(s) - X_0(s)R(s)} \tag{12}$$

where $R(s)$ is an arbitrary stable proper transfer function. The problem of identifying a process model for a plant in stable closed loop operation, which has to be in the set of all plants $G(s)$, can hence be restated as an open loop identification problem for $R(s)$ as depicted in Fig. 5 (right). Here, the signals α and β have to be calculated from the transfer functions $X_0(s), Y_0(s), N_0(s)$ and $D_0(s)$ and the measured signals u and y.

$$\alpha(s) = Y_0(s)U(s) + X_0(s)Y(s) \tag{13}$$

$$\beta(s) = D_0(s)Y(s) - N_0(s)U(s) \tag{14}$$

With the input/output signals α and β the transfer function $R(s)$ can be estimated using a standard prediction error method. From our previous work (Palis and Kienle, 2012) it is known that stabilization of the described process, at least in a certain region, is possible applying simple PI control. The initial controller has therefore been derived using a simple tuning rule

$$K(s) = \frac{1}{K_s}\left(k_0 + \frac{k_1}{s}\right) \tag{15}$$

where $1/K_s$ is the plant open loop gain and $k_0 = 20$, $k_1 = 10^{-5}$ are tuning factors.

5. Step size control

In order to control the step size Δy three strategies are applied
1. $\Delta y = const.$, resulting in equidistant steps of the parameter y_k.
2. Bisection. Starting with a constant step size $\Delta y = const.$ a crossing of the stability boundary is detected. By further bisecting the crossing interval the method converges linearly.
3. Secant method. Here, the step size Δy_k is calculated using the secant between y_{k-2} and y_{k-1}, i.e. $\Delta y_k = -\frac{y_{k-2} - y_{k-1}}{f(y_{k-2}) - f(y_{k-1})} f(y_{k-1})$.

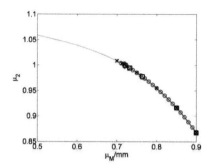

Figure 6. Determination of the critical mill grade - $\Delta y = const.$(gray circles), bisection (black crosses), secant method (black squares) and critical mill grade (red diamond)

6. Results and Conclusion

Applying the presented step size control to the described process yields the result presented in Figure 6. As can be seen all three strategies succeed in finding the critical mill grade μ_M. However, the number of steps differs greatly. Starting from a mill grade $\mu_M = 0.9\,mm$ the strategy using a constant step size of 0.01 mm takes 20 steps, whereas the bisection and secant method converge in 8 and 5 steps, respectively ($\Delta y_0 = 0.01 mm$).

In this contribution a closed loop strategy for experimental determination of stability boundaries has been proposed and successfully tested on the fluidized bed spray granulation process. Future work will be concerned with experiments on the real plant.

Acknowledgement

This work was supported by the Deutsche Forschungsgemeinschaft (DFG) in the framework of the Priority Programme "DynSim-FP – Dynamische Simulation vernetzter Feststoffprozess" by a grant (KI 417/3-1).

References

D.A.W. Barton, J. Sieber, 2013, Systematic experimental exploration of bifurcations with non-invasive control, Phys Rev E Stat Nonlin Soft Matter Phys, 87, 5, 052916.

I. Alaathar, E.-U. Hartge, S. Heinrich, J. Werther, 2013, Modeling and flowsheet simulation of continuous fluidized bed dryers, Powder Technology, 238,132-141.

M. Dosta, S. Antonyuk, S. Heinrich, 2013, Multiscale simulation of agglomerate breakage in fluidized beds, Ind. Eng. Chem. Res., 52,11275–11281.

S. Heinrich, M. Peglow, M. Ihlow, M. Henneberg, L. Mörl, 2002, Analysis of the start-up process in continuous fluidized bed spray granulation by population balance modeling, Chem. Eng. Sci., 57, 4369-4390.

R. Radichkov, T. Müller, A. Kienle, S. Heinrich, M. Peglow, L. Mörl, 2006, A numerical bifurcation analysis of continuous fluidized bed spray granulation with external product classification, Chem. Eng. Proc., 45, 826-837.

S. Palis, A. Kienle, 2012, Stabilization of continuous fluidized bed spray granulation with external product classification, Chem. Eng. Sci., 70, 200-209.

U. Forssell, L. Ljung, 1999, Closed-loop identification revisited, Automatica, 35, 1215-1241.

Jiří Jaromír Klemeš, Petar Sabev Varbanov and Peng Yen Liew (Editors)
Proceedings of the 24th European Symposium on Computer Aided Process Engineering – ESCAPE 24
June 15-18, 2014, Budapest, Hungary. Copyright © 2014 Elsevier B.V. All rights reserved.

Control Strategy Designs and Simulations for a Biological Waste Water Treatment Process

Linh T.T. Vu*, Mitchell S.J. Williams, Parisa A. Bahri

School of Engineering and Information Technology, Murdoch University, South Street Campus, Murdoch WA 6150, Australia
linh.vu@murdoch.edu.au

Abstract

A new and more appropriate continuous recycled system for aBiological Nutrient Removal process has been developed based on a sequencing batch reactor. This system comprises a Continuously Stirred Tank Reactor, a surge tank and a settling tank, from which a fraction of treated water is recycled back to the reactor. To design the control system for the whole plant, step tests have been conducted and Relative Gain Array analysis performed. Six control loops with the Process Variables including dissolved oxygen and nitrate concentrations, and volume holdups have been formed. Two designed control strategies Proportional Integral controllers and Generic Model Control have been implemented. The simulated results will be presented for comparison.

Keywords: Biological Nutrient Removal process, Relative Gain Array, Proportional Integral controllers, Generic Model Control

1. Introduction

The importance of recycling water has become a large issue in modern society especially in dry countries like Australia, due to the shortage of available water and the growing demand for more usable water. One of the most common sources of water recycling these days is through the treatment of brackish water or Waste Water Treatment (WWT). The treatment process is generally split up into four stages. The first two stages are mainly involved with the physical removal of large then fine material. The last two stages are typically involved with the biological treatment.

The use of a Biological Nutrient Removal (BNR) system in a WWT process is more economical in terms of nutrient removal than many other types of biological treatments. There are a few different types of BNR, but this work will focus on the nitrification and denitrification processes, which involve in the removal of the main contaminants in WW such as ammonium, nitrites and nitrates (Jeyanayagam et al.,2005).

In brief nitrification and denitrification are biological processes carried out by autotrophic and heterotrophic bacteria, to maximize the cell growth of the microorganism whilst consuming the contaminants in the water to be treated.In the nitrification process ammonia oxidizing bacteria are responsible for the oxidation of ammonium (NH_4^+) to nitrite (NO_2^-) and then further to nitrate (NO_3^-). The conditions, which favour the oxidation reaction are a high hydraulic retention time due to the slow growth of microorganism, the maximum reaction temperature below 30 °C, a Dissolved Oxygen (DO) level above 2 g/L and a pH level within from 6.8 to 7.4. In the denitrification process the heterotrophic bacteria consume nitrate with other Readily Biodegradeable Organic Matter (RBOM) to produce N_2. The Microorganism will strip oxygen from the nitrite and nitrate; therefore the presence of DO is not needed. However a steady supply of RBOM and a constant reaction temperature above 20 °C are necessary to maintain the biological activity.

Countless journal articles on WWT especially with the BNR system can be found in the literature. Most of the models used to represent the system were derived from the same original IAWQ (International Association on Water Quality) No.1 Model (Henze et al., 1987; cited in Coelho et al., 1999). Amongst these papers a few dealt with basic control strategies (Stahl et al., 2013) or plant-wide control (Jeppsson et al., 2006) but very few involved with advanced process control. The aim of this work is to derive a suitable mathematical dynamic model for the BNR process and design, implement and simulate two control strategies (i) Proportional Integral (PI) controllers to be compared with (ii) Generic Model Control (GMC).

2. Model development

2.1. System description and model equations

A simplified biological WWT processcomprisesan aerated continuous flow Continuously Stirred Tank Reactor (CSTR), followed by an aerated surge tank and a settling tank, from which the under flow stream is recycled back to the CSTR. Figure 1 shows the BNR Process Flow Diagram (PFD).

Many assumptions were made to ensure that the models could more accurately describe the complexity of the biological reactions. For example to derive the mass balance of DO, the concentration of DO was assumed to be strongly affected by the oxygen consumption of the autotrophic and aerobic heterotrophic bacteria and the aeration rate supplied for the reaction. To develop the mass balance for Particulate Organic Nitrogen (PON), it was assumed that a generation of this PON occurred from the cell decay of the bacterium, but the PON concentration could also be reduced by the hydrolysis in the biofloc. Many other assumptions can be found in Coelho et al. (1999). Yet the mathematical dynamic models developed by the mentioned authors for the BNR process in a sequencing batch reactor are still complex, comprising a set of 8 algebraic equations and a set of 11 Ordinary Different Equations (ODEs). The first set is used for the calculation of the constants and the variables required before solving the ODE set. For the continuous system shown in Figure 1, more material balances, Eqs.(1)-(3) have been added and the original models have been modified accordingly. Some ODEs used for the control purpose in this work are shown below. Other ODEs with the constants and parameters required for solving the ODEs can be found in Coelho et al. (1999).

Total mass balances are shown for the reactor Eq.(1), surge tank Eq.(2) and settler Eq.(3). Component balances for DO (O_{Re}), nitrate (NO_{Re}) ammonium (NH_{Re}) concentrations in the reactor are presented in Eqs.(4)–(6).Similar sets of ODEs can be written for the surge tank and the settler tank assuming no metabolic activity of microorganism in the settler tank. In these equations and in Figure 1, additional symbols used include: F_i, F_r, F_p, F_{o1} and F_{o2} for flowrates of the inlet, recycle, and outlet (from the settler, reactor and surge tank, respectively) streams; V_R and V_S for holdup volumes of the reactor and surge tank; i_{XB} for ratio of biomass nitrogen/Chemical Oxygen Demand (COD);RA for system aeration rate; r_{AG} for aerobic growth rate of the autotrophic microorganisms; r_{HG} for growth rate of the heterotrophic bacteria; r_{HG}^{aero} and

r_{HG}^{anoxic} for the aerobic and anoxic growth rates of the heterotrophic microorganisms; Y_A for the autotrophic yield; Y_H for the heterotrophic yield. Values of these were given or pre-calculated using the set of algebraic equations before solving the ODE model equations.

$$\frac{dV_R}{dt} = F_i + F_r - F_{o1}, \text{ where } F_r = \beta F_p; \text{ and } \beta: \text{recycle ratio} \tag{1}$$

$$\frac{dV_S}{dt} = F_{o1} - F_{o2} \tag{2}$$

$$\frac{dV_{ST}}{dt} = F_{o2} - F_p - F_r = F_{o2} - (1+\beta)F_p \tag{3}$$

$$\frac{dO_{Re}}{dt} = \frac{F_i}{V_R}(O_{Re,f} - O_{Re}) - \frac{1-Y_H}{Y_H} r_{HG}^{aero} - \frac{4.57 - Y_A}{Y_A} r_{AG} + RA_{Re} \tag{4}$$

$$\frac{dNO_{Re}}{dt} = \frac{F_i}{V_R}(NO_{Re,f} - NO_{Re}) + \frac{1}{Y_A}(r_{AG} + r_{HG}) - \frac{1-Y_H}{2.86Y_H} r_{HG}^{anoxic} \tag{5}$$

$$\frac{dNH_{Re}}{dt} = \frac{F_i}{V_R}(NH_{Re,f} - NH_{Re}) - \left(i_{XB} + \frac{1}{Y_A}\right) r_{AG} + r_{NH} - i_{XB} r_{HG} \tag{6}$$

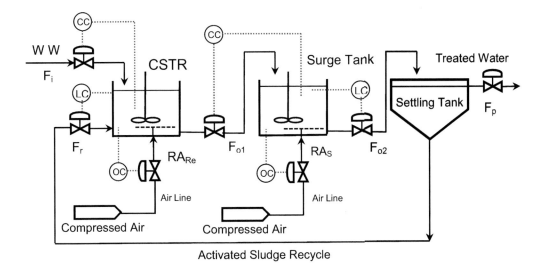

Figure 1. Flow diagram of a biological nutrient removal process.

2.2. Control strategy designs

As mentioned before, the process as a whole is an extremely complicated interacting system described by a set of more than 20 ODEs. The codes of these models were generated in MATLAB. Dynamic simulations were performed at steady state conditions with constants, parameters and initial values of variables found in the literature to ensure free of coding errors and correct model validations.

Step tests were conducted on each of possible Manipulated Variables (MVs).The disturbance effects of each stepped MV on each of the Process Variables (PVs) were recorded. The above task is very tedious and time consuming but essential for Relative Gain Array (RGA) analysis (Ogunnaike and Ray, 1994) and loop-pairing later.

Within the limit of the manuscript, the control strategy design for the reactor is presented in this work. The surge tank and settler are assumed to be well controlled. Biological reaction rates are temperature and pH dependent. To enhance the nitrification process the DO, nitrate and ammonium concentrations, temperature, pH and hold-up volume or level should be measured and controlled in the reactor. Additionally there are six PVs in the surge tank to be monitored and at least another two in the settler. The number of MVs available however is much less than the number of PVs. As a result the following control strategy is proposed for investigation. The DO levels in the reactor and surge tank are measured and independently controlled by the aeration ratessupplied by compressed air lines. Temperature, pH and ammonium concentration are monitored but not controlled. Further discussions on the control of these PVs will be shown elsewhere. Possible PVs and MVs in this work are:

- 4 PVs: holdup level and nitrate concentration of reactor, holdup level and nitrate concentration of surge tank;
- 4 MVs: inlet flowrate F_i, recycle flowrate F_r, outlet from reactor F_{o1} and outlet from surge tank F_{o2}.

The steady-state gain matrix K and the RGA for the above four-by-four system was calculated. The results presented in Table 1 lead to the loop-pairing recommendation shown in Table 2. The control loops are drawn in Figure 1 as well.

Eq.(7) shows a common mathematical model for a PI controller, where $c(t)$, K_c, τ_I, c_s are controller action, controller gain, integral time and steady-state controller action, respectively. The error $\varepsilon(t)$ represents the subtraction of PV measured from the setpoint.

The GMC strategy (Ogunnaike and Ray, 1994) is more sophisticated than the PI strategy. The controller model, shown in Eq.(8) can be equated to the model equation, for example, Eq.(4) to control the DO concentration in the reactor.

Table 1. Gain matrix [K] and RGA [Λ].

K-Λ	F_i	F_{o1}	F_{o2}	F_r	F_i	F_{o1}	F_{o2}	F_r
NO_{Re}	114	-155	66	76	3	0	0	-2
NO_S	123	∞	102	82	0	1	0	0
V_R	0.33	-0.2	0	0.33	-2	0	0	3
V_S	0	0.2	0.33	0	0	0	1	0

Table 2. Loop-pairing recommendation.

MV	PV
F_i	NO_{Re}
F_{o1}	NO_S
F_r	V_R
F_{02}	V_S

$$c(t) = K_c \left[\varepsilon(t) + \frac{\int_0^t \varepsilon(t')dt'}{\tau_i} \right] + c_s \qquad (7)$$

$$\frac{dO_{Re}}{dt} = k_1 \varepsilon(t) + k_2 \int_0^t \varepsilon(t')dt' \; ; \; k_1 \text{ and } k_2 \text{ are controller parameters.} \qquad (8)$$

From Eq.(4) and Eq.(8), the reactor aeration rate in the reactor RA_{Re} can be calculated.

3. Results and discussions

Table 3 shows the controller parameters designed for the PI controllers and GMC strategy to control volume holdup of the reactor, DO and NO concentrations. Figure 2 compares responses of the DO concentration in the reactor to a set point change of DO concentration and a disturbance change caused by a set point change of the volume of the reactor.

For the reactor volume setpoint tracking, both responses of GMC and PI controllers are very much similar. The corresponding MVs of these controllers are almost the same. As a result the PI controllers are more favourable to control the liquid holdup in the reactor since their implementation is much easier.

For the DO setpoint tracking shown in the graphs on the left of Figure 2, both responses of GMC and PI controllers first time reach the new setpoint at the same time but the PI response exhibits a much higher overshoot. In terms of MVs, the aeration rate of the PI controller varies more than that of the GMC. For the DO disturbance rejection shown in the graphs on the right of Figure 2, the GMC response returns and remains at the setpoint at time 25 hours; meanwhile it takes more time for the PI response to reject the same disturbance. The GMC performance is therefore more favourable as it can deal with non-linear multivariable control. The implementation of GMC is however much more difficult due to the requirement of the exact mathematical models. The NO responses corresponding to the changes of DO setpoint tracking and disturbance rejection are very much slower. Further investigations are presented elsewhere.

Table 3. Controller parameters designed for the reactor.

	PI		GMC	
	K_c	τ_i	k_1	k_2
Volume	1	0.02	2	0.04
DO concentration	0.5	0.26	0.51	0.0026
NO concentration	0.55	$2*10^{-4}$		

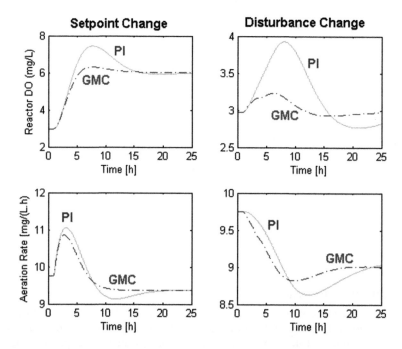

Figure 2. Responses of DO concentrations and aeration rates in the reactor to setpoint and disturbance changes.

4. Conclusions

A new and more appropriate continuous recycled mathematical model has been developed to test two designed control systems: conventional PI and non-linear GMC. As a whole the BNR is an extremely complicated interacting process, therefore the GMC strategy is more favourable in controlling one of the most important PVs, the DO concentrations in the reactor. The PI controllers can still be used for liquid holdups due to their simple implementation. Further work will be done for additional PVs such as ammonium concentration, pH and temperature for the CSTR and surge tank and for a more advanced control strategy like dynamic matrix control.

References

B. A. Ogunnaike, W. H. Ray, 1994, Process Dynamics, Modeling, and Control, Oxford University Press, USA.

M. A. Z. Coelho, C. Russo, O. Q. F. Araujo, 1999, Optimization of a Sequencing Batch Reactor for Biological Nitrogen Removal, Water Research, 34, 10, 2809-2817.

M.Henze, C. P. L.Grady, W.Gujer, G. V. R. Marais,T. Matsuo, 1987, A General Model for Single-Sludge Wastewater Treatment Systems, Water Research, 2, 15, 505-515.

S. Jeyanayagam, 2005, True Confessions of the Biological Nutrient Removal Process, Florida Water Resourses Jounal, January, 38-46.

T. Stahl, G. Duffy, S. Kestel, M. Gray, 2013, Dissolved Oxygen Control Based in Real-Time Oxygen Uptake Rate Estimation, Florida Water Resourses Jounal, 50-53.

U. Jeppsson, C. Rosen, J. Alex, J. Copp, K. V. Gernae, M.-N Pons, P. Vanrolleghem, 2006, Towards a Bench Mark Simulation Model for Plant-Wide Control Strategy Performance Evaluation of WWTPs, Water Science Technology, 53, 3, 287-295.

Jiří Jaromír Klemeš, Petar Sabev Varbanov and Peng Yen Liew (Editors)
Proceedings of the 24th European Symposium on Computer Aided Process Engineering – ESCAPE 24
June 15-18, 2014, Budapest, Hungary. Copyright © 2014 Elsevier B.V. All rights reserved.

Optimal Integrated Operation of a Sugar Production Plant

Reinaldo Hernández[a], Lars Simora[a], Radoslav Paulen[a], Sven Wegerhoff[a],

Rogelio Mazaeda[b], Cesar de Prada[b], Sebastian Engell[a]*

[a]*Process Dynamics and Operation Group, Technische Universität Dortmund, Emil-Figge-Straße 70, Dortmund 44227, Germany*
[b]*Systems Engineering and Automatic Control Group, University of Valladolid, c/Real de Burgos s/n, Valladolid 47011, Spain*
sebastian.engell@bci.tu-dortmund.de

Abstract

In this work an integrated approach to the operation of the evaporation and crystallization sections of a sugar refinery is proposed. The objective is the minimization of the fresh steam consumption and of its variance, while several process constraints must be satisfied. The employed model is taken from the sugar plant benchmark of the EU Network of Excellence HYCON2-Highly-Complex and Networked Control Systems. A dynamic optimization problem is formulated for computation of optimal trajectories of the manipulated variables. Significant savings in the amount of steam consumed in comparison to the traditional operation were obtained for one cycle time. In order to keep the levels in the buffer tanks (connecting the continuous and discontinuous sections of the plant) within safe values, a hierarchical coordination structure based on a temporal decomposition of the problem is implemented, which ensures a continuous and safe operation in the long term.

Keywords: Sugar refinery, dynamic optimization, hierarchical control structure, hybrid systems, scheduling.

1. Introduction

The decline in world sugar prices together with an increase in the cost of production (as a consequence of the rise in the price of energy) motivates the improvement of the efficiency in sugar production. Specifically the evaporation and crystallization sections in a sugar refinery represent energy-intensive processes that are tightly integrated by exchange of material and energy (Figure 1). In the evaporation section, fresh steam is used as the heat source for the concentration of thin juice with a solid content (Brix) of 15 % to concentrated juice with a solid content in the range of 65-72 %.

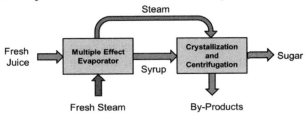

Figure 1. Integrated operation of evaporation and crystallization sections

_----

The concentrated juice (syrup) is delivered to the crystallization section where supersaturation conditions are realized by evaporation of water at a low temperature (under vacuum) using the excess of steam produced in the evaporation section. The sugar crystals produced are separated by centrifugation from the saturated solution and are sent to the drying and packing section for commercialization. Additional complexity arises in the system as a consequence of its hybrid character: the evaporation section operates continuously while the operation of the crystallizers is semi-batch (following a predefined recipe). For smooth operation of the process, the level in the buffer tanks (connecting the continuous and discontinuous sections of the plant) should be kept within safe limits.

Significant achievements have been reported in the literature regarding the optimal control and operation of the crystallization section in sugar refining. Multivariable linearizing control has been used in sugar cane crystallization for the tracking of crystal content (Damour et al., 2011). Sarabia et al. (2005) reported the application of Model Predictive Control (MPC) using a black-box model of the crystallizers. Furthermore, a modification of nonlinear MPC has been proposed and using a Recurrent Neural Network (RNN) predictive model (Paz Suárez et al., 2011). Dynamic optimization has been performed in which the objective was to produce sugar crystals with a desired quality, described by the average crystal size and its coefficient of variation (Galvanauskas et al, 2006). Nonetheless, to our best knowledge there is no work reported in recent literature concerning the integrated operation of the system with the goal of the minimization of the consumption of energy.

2. Process and Model Description

In this work, the employed model corresponds to the sugar benchmark of the EU-Network of Excellence HYCON2 (see www.hycon2.eu for detailed explanation) which is a first principles model based on material and energy balances with a simplified representation of the crystallizer operation. This benchmark model is provided along with a reference case of a plant operation.

2.1. Evaporation Section
This section consists of a three-effect co-current evaporation system which operates continuously. It is assumed that vapor and the juice are in equilibrium in each evaporator, with the liquid phase perfectly mixed. Fresh steam is fed to the first effect of the evaporator and the steam generated in each effect is partially used by the subsequent effect. The Brix in the syrup stream is controlled in the third effect by adjusting the flow of steam to a barometric condenser.

2.2. Crystallization Section
A simplified representation of the crystallization section is shown in Figure 2. Syrup from the evaporation section is mixed continuously with sugar crystals coming from the recovery stages and a bypass stream of thin juice; the resulting stream is sent to the storage tank which feeds three crystallizers (vacuum pans) that are operating in parallel. The operation of the crystallizers is semi-batch, according to a predefined recipe which includes six steps: idle, charging, crystallization (that involves concentration, growing and tightening) and discharging. Once the crystallization process has been finished, the mixture of crystals and saturated solution is sent to the strike receiver, which buffers the operation of the crystallizers and the centrifuge.The model of the evaporation and crystallization sections corresponds to an index-one differential-algebraic (DAE) equation system, involving 1,114 algebraic variables and 102 differential variables.

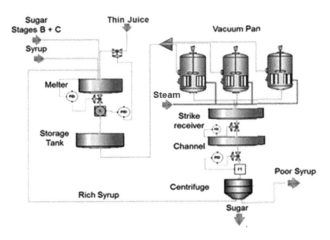

Figure 2 . Simplified flow diagram of the crystallization section of the sugar factory

3. Problem Formulation

3.1. Cost Function

The goal is to minimize a cost function (see Eq. (1)) which includes two terms: (a) the mean fresh steam consumption and (b) its variance. The coefficients c_1 and c_2 determine the relative weight of these terms in the cost function. Their values are chosen such that both terms have about the same magnitude. Therefore, the energy consumption is minimized as well as disturbance introduced in the process by changes in the input variables. The cost function is determined by the mass flow of fresh steam w_{steam} to the first evaporator and it is evaluated over a finite time horizon T equivalent to a cycle time, i.e. the time in which the operation of the whole crystallization section (the three crystallizers) is started and finished once, and the crystallizers are in the same condition as at the initial state.

3.2. Manipulated Variables

The manipulated variables are the pressure of the fresh steam, the set point of the Brix controller at the outlet of the evaporation section and the set point of the pressure controller in the heating system in each crystallizer. The pressure of the fresh steam P can be adjusted by throttling a valve upstream the evaporation section; it can vary in the range of 1.8-2.4 bar and is fixed at 2.1 bar in the reference case. In the case of the Brix set point at the outlet of the evaporation section (Bx), the lower and upper bounds correspond to 68 % and 72 %.

The set point of the pressure in the heating system of each crystallizer is adjusted indirectly by means of a single variable called Pressure Factor Pf. This variable multiplies the values of the set points of the reference operation case in the different stages of the recipe; it can vary from 0.8 to 1.2 (in reference case the value is 1). This variable is related to the heat flow rate to the crystallizers.

3.3. Process Constraints

There are different constraints within the process. Firstly, the levels in the buffer tanks L_{st} and L_{sr} should be kept within safe limits (20-80 %). The specified crystal size distribution is obtained if the mechanism of growing is the only one that takes place and no additional nucleation occurs (Asadi, 2007). In order to achieve this objective, the supersaturation values S should be kept below a predefined maximum S^U of 1.32.

3.4. Formulation

The mathematical formulation of the dynamic optimization problem is:

$$\min_{Bx(t),P(t),Pf(t)} \quad c_1 \frac{1}{T} \int_0^T w_{steam}(t)\, dt + c_2 \frac{1}{T} \int_0^T \left(w_{steam}(t) - \overline{w_{steam}(t)} \right)^2 dt$$

$$\text{s. t.} \qquad\qquad f(\dot{x}, x, y, u, p, t) = 0, \tag{1}$$

$$L_{st}^L \leq L_{st}(t) \leq L_{st}^U, \quad L_{sr}^L \leq L_{sr}(t) \leq L_{sr}^U, \quad S^L \leq S(t) \leq S^U,$$

$$Bx^L \leq Bx(t) \leq Bx^U, \quad P^L \leq P(t) \leq P^U, \quad P^Lf \leq Pf(t) \leq Pf^U,$$

Where the vectors *f, x, y, u,* and *p* stand for the set of model equations, state variables, algebraic variables, manipulated variables, and time-independent model parameters. Superscripts ^{L} and ^{U} denote lower and upper bounds.

4. Dynamic Optimization

4.1. Optimization Method

The model has been implemented in gPROMS 3.5.3 in order to use the optimization capabilities of this software, specifically the dynamic optimization tool gOPT. This tool implements the control vector parameterization method to solve the problem (1). For a time horizon equivalent to a cycle time (12,050 s), a piece-wise constant discretization of the control profiles was implemented. In this work the control horizon is discretized in time into eight intervals of equal lengths.

4.2. Optimal Integrated Operation for a Cycle Time

In the optimal solution, the pressure of the fresh steam is kept constant for the entire horizon at the lower bound of 1.8 bar. This is expected since at this value, the vaporization enthalpy per unit of mass of steam is the highest attainable. For the set point of the Brix controller at the outlet of the evaporation section, the optimal solution corresponds to a constant value at the upper bound of 72 %. This means that the optimal process uses evaporation section to increase the sugar content in the syrup more in comparison to the reference case (where the Brix set point is set to 70 %).

Figure 3 depicts the optimal profiles obtained for the Pressure Factor (*Pf*). In the optimal solution the crystallizers should be operated in almost all the intervals at the lower bound *Pf*=0.8 or 80 % of the pressure set point of the reference case. However, there are jumps to the upper bounds in some intervals which compensate the fluctuations in the steam flow that occur when the crystallization stage is started in another crystallizer. Hence minor local fluctuations in the individual crystallizers are introduced to minimize the global variance of the fresh steam flow.

Because of this operational policy the batch time is increased as shown in Figure 4 for the vacuum pan I. The lower the steam pressure, the slower the crystallization process, as a consequence of running the crystallization with a lower heat input. Furthermore, the total amount of sugar processed per cycle time (the productivity of the batch) increases without hitting the limits at the scheduling level. The increase in the batch time is compensated by the reduction of the waiting time of the reference case operation. In Figure 5, the optimal fresh steam consumption is compared to the reference case. A reduction of 5 % in the amount of fresh steam required per mass of sugar produced is achieved.

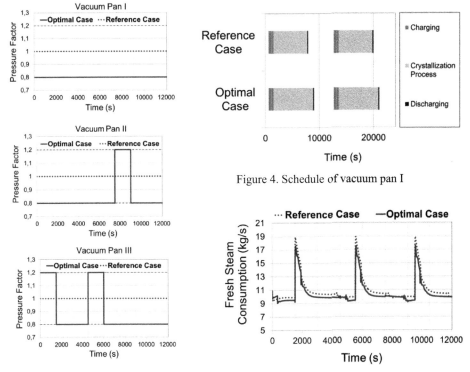

Figure 4. Schedule of vacuum pan I

Figure 3. Optimal profiles of Pressure Factor   Figure 5. Fresh steam consumption

5. Optimal Integrated Operation and Proposed Hierarchical Structure

As it was stated above, the optimal solution leads to an increase in the brix of the concentrated juice from 70 to 72 % (and therefore a decrease in its flow rate) as well as an increase in productivity of the batch. As a consequence there is a continuous decline in the inventory of the juice in the buffer tank of the crystallizer which can be only detected after a long period of time, representing a potential limitation to the continuity of the process. Figure 6 shows the trajectory of the level of the storage tank before the crystallizers for a simulation time of 96 h (345,600 s). Due to its size and complexity, it is computationally prohibitive to solve problem (1) on such a long horizon.

One possibility for overcoming emptiness is by addition of an additional constraint on the minimum level (we consider 40 %) for the start of the charging stage of the crystallizers (Figure 7). This simple methodology is limited and cannot address the problems of overflowing. Another possible approach that ensures the operation in the long term involves the use of a hierarchical coordination multilevel structure (see Figure 8). The upper layer performs the recalculation of scheduling of the crystallizers and it determines the set point of the flow controller for the outflow of the strike receiver to the centrifuges using a simplified model. A temporal decomposition of the problem is then practically established. The dynamic optimization is performed in the lower layer in order to find the best possible operation of the next cycle, while a static model of the plant is then employed in the upper layer, in order to close the mass sugar balance in the system in the long term, as a result potential bottlenecking produced by emptiness or overflow in the buffer tank is avoided.

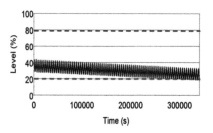

Figure 6. Level in storage tank

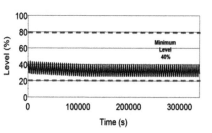

Figure 7. Level in the storage tank
(imposing a minimum level of 40%)

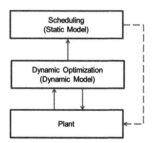

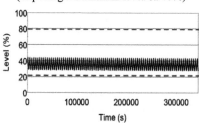

Figure 8. Hierarchical coordinator

Figure 9. Level in the storage tank
(with hierarchical coordinator)

Figure 9 shows that the level in the storage tank is kept within the safe limits after application of the methodology proposed here, while the minimization of the steam consumption has been addressed by the lower layer. Note that the presented control scheme is also capable of handling disturbances in the production.

6. Conclusions

In this work, an integrated approach to the operation of the evaporation and the crystallization sections of a sugar factory has been considered with the objective to minimizing the fresh steam consumption and its variance. The reduced model of the sugar factory benchmark was implemented in gPROMS environment and optimal trajectories of the manipulated variables were obtained for one cycle time. The results show significant savings in the amount of consumed fresh steam. Stability of long term operation is ensured by the use of a hierarchical coordination structure which considers the scheduling coordination (higher level) and the dynamic optimization (lower level).

References

M. Asadi, 2007, Beet-Sugar Handbook, John Wiley & Sons, Inc, New Jersey, U.S.

C. Damour, M. Benne, L. Boillereaux, B. Grondin-Perez, J. Chabriat, 2011, Multivariable Liniearizing Control of an Industrial Sugar Crystallization Process, Journal of Process Control, 21, 46-54.

V. Galvanauskas, P. Georgieva, S. feyo de Azevedo, 2006, Dynamic Optimization of Industrial Crystallization Process Based on a Hybrid (Mechanistic+ANN) Model, International Join Conference on Neural Network, 5035-5042.

HYCON2, Highly-coplex and networked control systems, <www.hycon2.eu> Accessed 15/07/ 2013.

L.A. Paz Suárez, P.Georgieva, S. Feyo de Ayevedo, 2011, Nonlinear MPC for Fed-batch Multiple Stage Crystallization, Chemical Engineering Research and Design, 89, 735-767.

D. Sarabia, C. de Prada, S. Cristea, R. Mazaeda, W. Colmenarez, 2005, MPC of a Sugar House, International Worshop on Assesment and Future Directions of NMPC, Freudenstadt, 26-30.

Jiří Jaromír Klemeš, Petar Sabev Varbanov and Peng Yen Liew (Editors)
Proceedings of the 24th European Symposium on Computer Aided Process Engineering – ESCAPE 24
June 15-18, 2014, Budapest, Hungary. Copyright © 2014 Elsevier B.V. All rights reserved.

Sensitivity Enhancing Transformations for Large-Scale Process Monitoring

Tiago J. Rato, Marco S. Reis[*]

CIEPQPF, Department of Chemical Engineering, University of Coimbra, Rua Sílvio Lima, 3030-790, Coimbra, Portugal
marco@eq.uc.pt

Abstract

A new pre-processing methodology is proposed for improving the detection capability to changes in process structure. It is named sensitivity enhancing transformation (SET), and uses information of the causal network topology underlying the measured process variables in order to construct a set of uncorrelated transformed variables around which the detection of changes in the variables correlation structure is maximized. A new group of monitoring statistics, based on partial correlations, is also presented that take full advantage of the SET features. The use of partial correlations as an association measure provides a finer map of the connectivity between process variables even without attributing any causal directionality. The availability of such a finer association map potentiates the development of more sensitive schemes for detecting structural changes, such as the ones proposed in this work. The results obtained in the comparison study involving other current methodologies for monitoring the correlation structure, show that the proposed methods are able to effectively detect changes in the systems structure and presented higher sensitivity when compared to the current monitoring statistics tested.

Keywords: Process monitoring; Multivariate dynamical processes; Variable transformation; Partial correlation; Marginal correlation.

1. Introduction

Most of the multivariate statistical process control schemes proposed in the last decades intent to detect deviations on the process mean levels. Very few methodologies have been proposed that explicitly address the detection of changes in variables correlation structure. Moreover, the monitoring of the process correlation is usually done by monitoring statistics based solely on the marginal correlation, which is unable to discern local changes in the process structure. This happens because process variables may present a significant marginal covariance even though they do not directly interact in a causal way (as long as they are affected by some common variation sources). Therefore, monitoring procedures based on this quantity are unable, by design, to effectively detect and discern changes in the local causal correlation structure.

Most of the procedures to monitor the process covariance proposed in the literature, are still based on the generalised variance (GV) or the likelihood ratio test (LRT) introduced by Alt et al. (1988). Improvements to such control charts were made by Aparisi et al. (2001), who developed an adaptive sample size method to compute the GV, and by Djauhari (2005), who proposed unbiased limits for the GV. Other approaches, such the one suggested by Guerrero-Cusumano (1995), which considers the conditional entropy, or by Djauhari et al. (2008), based on the vector variance (i.e., the sum of the squares of all eigenvalues of the sample covariance matrix), are also focused on the analysis of the marginal correlation. Even more recent developments, as for instance the control chart proposed by Yen et al. (2012), designed to detect both increases and decreases in process dispersion, and the control chart for monitoring the covariance matrix computed from fewer observations than variables developed by Maboudou-Tchao et al. (2013), remain based on the LRT. The online versions of these procedures (i.e., the ones based on individual observations) are also subject to similar constrains, since they usually update the covariance matrix trough an EWMA recursion and then monitor it by use of cumulative deviations from the target value (Yeh et al., 2005), covariance's trace (Huwang et al., 2007) or LRT (Hawkins et al., 2008). Thus, none of the previous proposals actually explore the variables inner associations, since they are all based on the marginal correlation.

In order to address this issue, we propose new monitoring statistics based on partial correlation network reconstruction techniques and assess them against the methodologies currently available. The choice of partial correlations as a measurement of the process correlation structure is based on their ability to retain, to a larger extent, local information regarding the direct association between process variables, thus providing a finer map of the correlation structure. Therefore, statistical process monitoring based on them should be able to detect changes in the local structure of variables in a more effective way. Moreover, throughout this work, it was found out that the detection of changes in correlation is dependent on its nominal value. Therefore, in order to promote the detection capabilities of the monitoring statistics to small changes in the process structure, a pre-processing stage is considered, based on a sensitivity enhancing transformation (SET).

The proposed SET eliminates the variables causal contribution in a similar manner as suggested by Hawkins (1993). However, in such work the transformation applied aims to improve the detection of mean deviations, without any reference to its application in structure monitoring. In fact, the use of variables transformation in the context of monitoring procedures for the dispersion are just for the sake of simplifying the exposition and not for the purpose of improving the methods' sensitivity. Moreover, they tend to be based on the inverse of the covariance matrix, which may be ill-conditioned, or triangularization methods, such as the Cholesky decomposition, which may not efficiently decorrelate the data. Other methods exist that lead to uncorrelated variables, but are not driven by the inner process structure and therefore do not contribute to such an increase in the faults detection capability. An example of such methods is Principal Component Analysis (PCA), which is extensively used to describe and monitor multivariate process variability. However, PCA ends up with a linear combination of variables that may not be directly related, and consequently the final sensitivity to structural changes is significantly lower than that obtained with a proper transformation, such as the one proposed here. Thus, to our knowledge, the effects of transformed variables on the detection of correlation changes and the subsequent study of the most adequate transformations to adopt have not been properly addressed yet.

In this context, we propose in this work several methodologies for monitoring changes in the process structure through the use of partial correlation information. Moreover, a SET based on the process causal network is proposed in order to increase the detection of structural changes. The suggested statistics methods, based on partial correlation information, are applied to multivariate systems and their performances compared with marginal-based approaches available in the literature. The results obtained showed that partial correlation based statistics combined with the SET were indeed able to detect changes in the systems structure and presented higher sensitivity when compared to the current monitoring statistics tested.

2. Methods

2.1. Sensitivity enhancing transformations

The detection of changes on correlation coefficients is highly dependent of their normal operation condition levels. This situation happens, because some correlation coefficients are more sensitive to changes than others. For instance, when the intrinsic relationship between two highly correlated variables suffer a small deviation, their correlation coefficient remains almost unchanged. On the contrary, whenever two initially unrelated variables become related, their correlation changes more abruptly than in other situations. This feature is illustrated in Figure 1 for the correlation between x and z (r_{xz}), where $x = kz + w\varepsilon$ and both z and ε follow an *i.i.d.* $N(0,1)$. This situation motivates the construction of variables transformations that produce uncorrelated variables in order to increase the detection of structural changes.

To obtain such a set of uncorrelated variables, a variable transformation that removes the relevant variables relationships by application of linear regressions only on the causally related variables is proposed. For such, information about the causal relationship between the variables is required. This information can be either obtained by *a priori* knowledge of the process or through network reconstruction techniques, as for instance, the one proposed by Pellet et al. (2007). The knowledge of the casual network can then be used to fit a regression model for each variable by considering as regressors only its causal parents. Thus, the final regression model produces a new set of residual variables that are uncorrelated among each other. To ensure that these new variables are uncorrelated, an additional Cholesky decomposition can also be applied to the residuals.

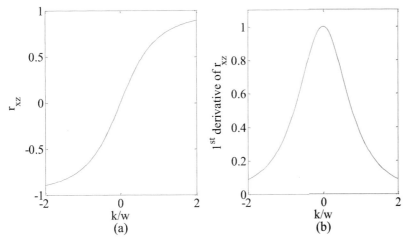

Figure 1. Graphical representation of (a) the effect of k/w on the correlation (r_{xz}) and (b) the first derivative of r_{xz}. The maximum sensitivity is attained for $k/w = 0$, which corresponds to $r_{xz} = 0$.

2.2. Monitoring statistic for the correlation

To detect changes on the process structure, hypothesis tests can be applied in order to verify if the partial correlations remain close to their values obtained under common cause variability sources. This is the basic idea applied on network reconstruction methodologies, where partial correlation coefficients are tested for the hypothesis H_0: $\rho = 0$ *vs* H_1: $\rho \neq 0$ in order to identify relationships between the variables. Based on this principle, each partial correlation is tested against the null hypothesis of being equal to their in-control values. To simplify this procedure, it is desirable that all partial correlations have the same distribution, something that can be done through a simple normalization procedure. Instead of constructing a single control chart for each correlation coefficient, we only evaluate their maximum, in absolute value. This is justified because, after normalization, all correlations will have the same symmetric distribution. This normalization function can be obtained by considering that when the number of observations (n) is large, the distribution of the q-th order partial correlation coefficients (r), transformed according to Eq.(1), tend to be Gaussian with zero mean and unit variance (Anderson, 2003).

$$w_1 = \frac{\sqrt{n-q-1}(r-\rho)}{1-\rho^2} \tag{1}$$

Another useful normalization function is based on the Fisher's z transformation (Anderson, 2003), which tends to normality more rapidly, and results in,

$$w_2 = \frac{\sqrt{n-q-1}}{2}\left[\ln\left(\frac{1+r}{1-r}\right) - \ln\left(\frac{1+\rho}{1-\rho}\right)\right] \tag{2}$$

In cases where it cannot be assume that partial correlation follow a normal distribution, an estimation of the density function can be applied to perform the normalization.

After applying a suitable transformation to all the partial correlations, they are monitored by the maximum of the normalized partial correlation, in absolute value, defined as,

$$R0MAX = \left\|w(\mathbf{r}_0)\right\|_\infty = \max\left\{\left|w(\mathbf{r}_0)\right|\right\} \tag{3}$$

$$R1MAX = \left\|w(\mathbf{r}_1)\right\|_\infty = \max\left\{\left|w(\mathbf{r}_1)\right|\right\} \tag{4}$$

where $w(\cdot)$ is a normalization function based on the partial correlations distribution, $\mathbf{r}_0$ is the $(p(p-1)/2)\times1$ column vector containing all distinct correlation coefficients (0th order partial correlations) and $\mathbf{r}_1$ is the $(p(p-1)(p-2)/2)\times1$ column vector of 1st order partial correlation coefficients.

3. Results

A linear stationary system composed by 16 variables based on the artificial network originally presented by Tamada et al. (2003) provide the basis for the assessment of the process monitoring statistics and sensitivity enhancing transformations proposed in this work. In each fault considered in this case study, 1,000 sample covariance matrices were determined with 3,000 observations each, taken at regular intervals of time.

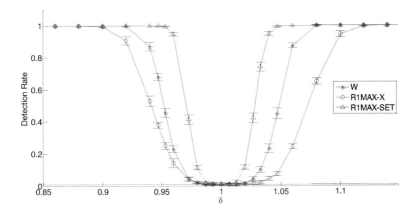

Figure 2. Detection rate curve for changes of δ times the slope on the causal relationship between two variables of the linear stationary system.

The sample covariance matrices were then used to determine the monitoring statistics and to compute the corresponding fault detection rates (true detection rate and false alarm rate). The same procedure was repeated 10 times in order to estimate the confidence levels of the detection rates. The control limits for all the monitoring statistics were preliminarily adjusted, by trial and error, so that all monitoring statistics present the same false detection rate of 1 % under normal operation conditions (NOC).

The results obtained, show that the combined use of the proposed RMAX monitoring statistics and SET (*R1MAX-SET*) lead to noticeable improvements in the detection of small deviations on the process structure as can be seen in Figure 2. For illustration purposes, the LRT proposed by Alt et al. (1988) is represented as *W* and the proposed R1MAX statistic applied to the original data is represented as *R1MAX-X*. These results clearly show a significant improvement in the detection capability when *R1MAX-SET* is used, proving the importance of the RMAX scheme, since *W* is invariant to linear transformations, as well as the critical role of the SET, as the same statistic when applied to the original variables show a significantly lower performance.

The previous results were obtained for a linear stationary system, where all the current monitoring statistics are expected to perform well. For more complex systems, the difference in performance becomes even more evident, especially because the SET allows for better description of the process dynamics. Therefore, the results suggest that the proposed RMAX statistics and SET are capable to detect small deviations on the process structure and to cope with the dynamics of complex systems, making them suitable approaches for detecting structural changes. Moreover, their close connection to network reconstruction techniques also gives them the potential to improve the fault diagnostic stage.

4. Discussion and Conclusions

In this work we addressed the statistical process monitoring of the process structure by means of partial correlations and using a sensitivity enhancing transformation (SET). The use of SET allows a better description of the systems dynamics and non-linearity and highlights structural deviations as a result of a higher sensitivity to changes on correlation when the monitored correlation is originally close to zero. For instance, while a small fault produces changes of only 2.6 standard deviations in the original variables correlation, the SET variables show changes of 24 standard deviations. This situation favours the monitoring statistics based on partial correlations, leading to an increase in the fault detection capability. Moreover, since more localized information is being used, the proposed methodology also presents a great potential for fault diagnosis. Additionally, it is observed that partial correlation and the SET are closely related: the marginal correlation of the transformed variables can be interpreted as partial correlations of the original set of variables. We have also found out that, for more complex systems (with non-linear and/or dynamic characteristics), the improvements obtained by using a SET based on the process causal network are even more noticeable. However, the proposed method is rather insensitive to changes in variance alone, a feature that is currently being addressed.

5. Acknowledgements

Tiago J. Rato acknowledges the Portuguese Foundation for Science and Technology for his PhD grant (grant SFRH/BD/65794/2009). Marco S. Reis acknowledges financial support through project PTDC/EQU-ESI/108374/2008 co-financed by the Portuguese FCT and European Union's FEDER through "Eixo I do Programa Operacional Factores de Competitividade (POFC)" of QREN (with ref. FCOMP-01-0124-FEDER-010397).

References

F. B. Alt, N. D. Smith, 1988, Multivariate process control, Handbook of Statistics, 7, 333-351.
T. W. Anderson, 2003, An Introduction to Multivariate Statistical Analysis, Wiley, New Jersey, U.S.
F. Aparisi, J. Jabaloyes, A. Carrión, 2001, Generalized Variance Chart Design With Adaptive Sample Sizes. The Bivariate Case, Communications in Statistics - Simulation and Computation, 30, 4, 931–948.
M. A. Djauhari, 2005, Improved Monitoring of Multivariate Process Variability, Journal of Quality Technology, 37, 1, 32-39.
M. A. Djauhari, M. Mashuri, D. E. Herwindiati, 2008, Multivariate Process Variability Monitoring, Communications in Statistics - Theory and Methods, 37, 11, 1742-1754.
J.-L. Guerrero-Cusumano, 1995, Testing variability in multivariate quality control: A conditional entropy measure approach, Information Sciences, 86, 1–3, 179-202.
D. M. Hawkins, 1993, Regression Adjustment for Variables in Multivariate Quality Control, Journal of Quality Technology, 25, 3, 170-182.
D. M. Hawkins, E. M. Maboudou-Tchao, 2008, Multivariate Exponentially Weighted Moving Covariance Matrix, Technometrics, 50, 2, 155-166.
L. Huwang, A. B. Yeh, C.-W. Wu, 2007, Monitoring Multivariate Process Variability for Individual Observations, Journal of Quality Technology, 39, 3, 258-278.
E. M. Maboudou-Tchao, V. Agboto, 2013, Monitoring the covariance matrix with fewer observations than variables, Computational Statistics and Data Analysis, 64, 99-112.
J.-P. Pellet, A. Elisseeff, 2007, A partial correlation-based algorithm for causal structure discovery with continuous variables, Proceedings of the 7th international conference on Intelligent data analysis, Ljubljana, Slovenia, Springer-Verlag, 229-239.
Y. Tamada, S. Kim, H. Bannai, S. Imoto, K. Tashiro, S. Kuhara, S. Miyano, 2003, Estimating gene networks from gene expression data by combining Bayesian network model with promoter element detection, Bioinformatics, 19, 1, ii227-ii236.
A. B. Yeh, L. Huwang, C.-W. Wu, 2005, A multivariate EWMA control chart for monitoring process variability with individual observations, IIE Transactions, 37, 11, 1023-1035.
C.-L. Yen, J.-J. H. Shiau, A. B. Yeh, 2012, Effective Control Charts for Monitoring Multivariate Process Dispersion, Quality and Reliability Engineering International, 28, 4, 409-426.

Jiří Jaromír Klemeš, Petar Sabev Varbanov and Peng Yen Liew (Editors)
Proceedings of the 24th European Symposium on Computer Aided Process Engineering – ESCAPE 24
June 15-18, 2014, Budapest, Hungary.

Data-driven Self-optimizing Control

Salihu Adamu Girei[a], Yi Cao[a*], Alhaji Shehu Grema[a], Lingjian Ye[b], Vinay Kariwala[c]

[a]*School of Engineering, Cranfield University, Bedford UK MK43 0AL*
[b]*Ningbo Institute of Technology, Zhejiang University 315100, Ningbo, Zhejiang, China*
[c]*ABB Global Industries and Services Ltd, Mahadevpura, Bangalore 560048, India*
Y.Cao@cranfield.ac.uk

Abstract

Selection of controlled variables (CVs) plays a crucial role in overall operational performance. Existing approaches for CV selection based on the self-optimizing control (SOC) strategy are model-driven. Selection of CVs using rigorous nonlinear process models requires linearization around nominal operating point. Inevitably, these approaches not only result in large losses as a result of linearization errors, but also are difficult to be adopted for practical applications due to the requirement of a rigorous model. In this paper, a novel data-driven approach, where the necessary conditions of optimality (NCO) are directly approximated by CVs using operational data in a single regression step is proposed for selecting CVs based on SOC. The new approach does not require evaluation of derivatives so that process models associated with commercial simulators can be directly used for CV selection. The effectiveness of the proposed approach is demonstrated using a 3-stream heat exchanger network (HEN) case study.

Keywords: Control variables, Data-driven, Heat exchanger networks, Necessary condition of optimality, Self-optimizing control.

1. Introduction

Selection of controlled variables (CVs) based on the concept of self-optimizing control (SOC) has recently received a lot of attention due to its ability in achieving optimal or near optimal operation by maintaining CVs at constant setpoints in spite of the presence of various uncertainties and disturbances (Skogestad, 2000). In the SOC approach, feedback controllers are used to achieve optimal operation through appropriately selected CVs (Ye et al., 2013). The main challenge, however, is to select the appropriate CVs which will provide acceptable loss without the need to reoptimize the setpoint when the disturbances occur (Skogestad, 2004).

Several authors have proposed different methods for CV selection based on SOC strategy. Halvorsen et al. (2003) proposed singular value and exact local method. Cao (2005) suggested direct and indirect gradient methods. Kariwala (2007) proposed exact local method with worst-case loss minimization using singular value and eigenvalue decompositions. Alstad and Skogestad (2007) proposed null space method based on loss incurred due to disturbances. However, all these methods depend heavily on process models, the ability to solve the optimization problem offline and linearization of nonlinear process model, which results in local solution. These factors render the SOC method unsuitable for practical situations, where a model is not available.

A different but complementary approach to SOC strategy is CV selection based on the concept of necessary condition of optimality (NCO) approximation (Ye et al., 2013). The NCO approximation technique can be used to overcome the localness associated with linearization required by existing approaches. Particularly, CVs are selected to approximate unmeasured NCO over the entire operation region with zero setpoint to achieve near optimal operation globally. Furthermore, Ye et al. (2012) recently proposed a two-step data-driven CV selection approach using regression to approximate the NCO or reduced gradient using measurement function, which is able to achieve near optimal control in a much wider operational range. However, large regression errors arising in both regression steps are a limitation of this approach.

In this paper, we present a novel one step regression procedure for data-driven SOC based on finite difference method to determine the CVs as a function of measurements without evaluating the gradient function. This method does not require rigorous process model to select the CVs, as is the case with other available SOC procedures. The new method has the advantage that it entirely relies on measurements to achieve near optimal control with minimum loss in the objective cost function. To demonstrate the effectiveness of the proposed approach, a 3-stream heat exchange network (HEN) which has been used as a benchmark by several researchers, such as Glemmestad et al. (1999) and Lersbamrunsuk et al. (2008), is used. The case study shows that the proposed methodology is capable of achieving optimal operation of HEN with uncertainties in operational parameters.

The rest of the paper is structured as follows: next section presents some basic concepts of SOC for CV selection. In Section three, the new finite difference based data-driven SOC is introduced. Section four presents the HEN case study. Finally, some conclusions are presented in Section five.

2. Self-optimizing control and CV selection

Self-optimizing control is said to occur when acceptable operation is achieved with constant setpoints for CVs (Skogestad, 2004). The general optimization problem is formulated as

$$\min_{u} J(u, d)$$

$$s.t. \, g(u, d) \leq 0 \tag{1}$$

where J is the objective function (or cost function), $u \in \mathbb{R}^{n_u}$, are the manipulated variables and $d \in \mathbb{R}^{n_d}$, are the uncertain disturbances, $g: \mathbb{R}^{n_u} \times \mathbb{R}^{n_d} \rightarrow \mathbb{R}^{n_g}$ are the constraints including the process model. The CVs are selected as a linear combination of measurements

$$c = Hy \tag{2}$$

where H is the measurement combination matrix with full row rank, n_u and y denotes n_y dimensional measurment vector. The worst case and the average case losses resulting from the given control structure represented by H are derived by assuming fixed active constraints in Halvorsen et al. (2003) and Kariwala et al. (2008), respectively, as

$$L_{worst} = \frac{1}{2}\sigma^2_{max}(M)$$

$$L_{average} = \frac{1}{6(n_d + n_y)} \|M\|^2_F \tag{3}$$

The matrix M is defined as $M = \left[J^{\frac{1}{2}}_{uu}(J^{-1}_{uu}J_{ud} - G^{-1}G_d)W_d \quad J^{\frac{1}{2}}_{uu}G^{-1}HW_n \right]$, where $G = HG_y$, $G_d = HG_{yd}$, $J_{uu} = \frac{\partial J^2}{\partial u^2}$ and $J_{ud} = \frac{\partial J^2}{\partial u \partial d}$ are the steady state gain and disturbance matrices, the second order partial derivatives with respect to manipulated variables u and disturbances d, respectively. A recent review on available different expressions for H, is available in Umar et al. (2012).

3. Regression based CV Selection

The aim is to find sets of measurement functions as CVs such that if they are maintained at constant setpoints, the overall process operation is optimal or near optimal. For this purpose, assume that the required CVs to be measurement functions, either linear or nonlinear, such as polynomial or even a neural network, defined as $C = C(y, \theta)$ with parameters, θ to be determined through regression. Recall that the optimal operation is realized by maintaining dJ/du = 0 in presence of disturbances. Accordingly, we can find θ such that,

$$\frac{dJ}{du} = C(y, \theta) \tag{4}$$

This is equivalent to

$$dJ = C(y, \theta)du \tag{5}$$

This can further be approximated using finite-difference,

$$J_k = J_0 + C(y_0, \theta)(u_k - u_0) \tag{6}$$

where the subscript 0 indicates a reference point and subscript k represents a neighbourhood point. For cases with degrees of freedom (DOF) larger that one, the vector form of the equation is

$$J_k = J_0 + C^T(y_0, \theta)(u_k - u_0) \tag{7}$$

Therefore, for a set of data, u_i, y_i, J_i, and d_i(unknown), $i = 1, \ldots, N$, the regression problem can be expressed as follows:

$$min_\theta \sum^N_{i=1} \sum^{i_k}_{j=i_1} (J_j - J_i - C^T(y_i, \theta)(u_j - u_i))^2 \tag{8}$$

where $i_1, \ldots, i_k$ are k neighbourhood points of point i and k may depend on i.

4. Heat Exchanger Network (HEN) case study

The simple HEN comprises of two exchangers, one hot utility and one cold utility exchangers, as shown in Figure 1. Each process exchanger is fitted with a single bypass line for manipulation.

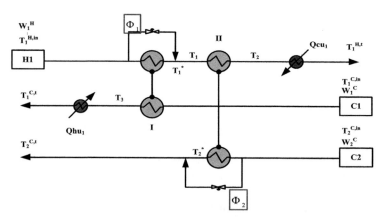

Figure 1. 3-Streams HEN model taken from Glemmestad et al. (1999)

The inlet (supply) and the outlet (target) temperatures of each stream are denoted as $T_1^{H,in}$, $T_1^{C,in}$, $T_2^{C,in}$ and $T_1^{H,t}$, $T_1^{C,t}$, $T_2^{C,t}$, respectively, while the exchanger duty, utility duty and bypass split on each exchanger are denoted as Q_1, Q_2, Qcu_1, Qhu_1 and Φ_1, Φ_2.

The classification of manipulative variables u, available measured variables y and disturbances d is given as

$$u = [\Phi_1] \tag{9}$$

$$y = [\Phi_1, T_1, T_2, T_3,]^T \tag{10}$$

$$d = [T_1^{H,t}, w_2^c]^T \tag{11}$$

Although there are four manipulative variables (Qcu_1, Qhu_1, Φ_1 and Φ_2) in the network, Qcu_1, Qhu_1, Φ_2 are used for maintaining the target temperatures at their setpoint values, hence only Φ_1 is available for SOC.

The objective is to minimize the costs C_{Qhu_1} of heating and C_{Qcu_1} of cooling utilities while satisfying the target temperatures.

$$J = C_{Qhu_1} Qhu_1 + C_{Qcu_1} Qcu_1 \tag{12}$$

There are two disturbances with magnitude ± 10 ^{0}C in the supply stream H1 and ± 0.05 kW/^{0}C in the heat capacity flowrate (CP) of stream C2 as show in Table 1. Using factorial design method, the disturbances are divided into 10 equal parts and $11^2 = 121$ pairs of disturbances were generated. Exchanger I & II design parameters UA_1 and UA_2 are given as 0.523 kW/^{0}C and 1.322 kW/^{0}C.

Table 1. HEN Process stream data

Stream Number	T_S (^{0}C)	T_T (^{0}C)	CP (kW/^{0}C)
H1	190±10	30	1.0
C1	80	160	1.5
C2	20	130	0.5±0.05

4.1. HEN operation and data sampling procedure

Suppose that the HEN model equations are not readily available for CV selection and only process data can be collected from the plant. The network interconnection temperatures T_1, T_2, T_3 and bypass split Φ_1 are the available measurements. Simulation results (data samples) were collected by manipulating the bypass fraction Φ_1 over the specified range of disturbances in hot stream H1 inlet temperature $T_1^{H,t}$ and cold stream C2 heat capacity flowrate w_2^c as shown in Table 1. It is assumed that utility exchangers Qcu_1, and Qhu_1 have sufficient duties to maintained the stream targets $T_1^{H,t}$ and $T_1^{C,t}$ for all ranges of bypass fractions. Furthermore, the bypass split Φ_2 is used to maintain the stream outlet temperature $T_2^{C,t}$ at its target value.

Data samples are collected for measurements T_1, T_2, T_3 and Φ_1 by operating the HEN as indicated above. The primary manipulated variable Φ_1 is used as the reference point for 100 samples with each sampling point considered as a neighborhood point; cf. Eq. (6). CVs as combinations of measurements were obtained using Eq. (8) through linear and polynomial regressions. A Monte Carlo experiment was carried out with 100 sets of uniformly distributed, randomly generated disturbances d to evaluate the CVs with no consideration for implementation errors.

4.2. Results & Discussion

The CVs using linear and second-order polynomial regressions are respectively given in Eqs. (13)- (14) as follows

$$CV_1 = -30.58 - 29.331\Phi_1 - 30.5T_1 - 0.0881T_2 - 1.0890T_3 \tag{13}$$

$$\begin{aligned} CV_2 = &-20.1311 - 40.3810\Phi_1 - 0.1311T_1 + 0.0460T_2 + 1.0565T_3 \\ &+ 0.0778\Phi_1T_1 + 0.0182\Phi_1T_2 + 0.2108\Phi_1T_3 + 0.0015T_1T_2 \\ &- 0.0172T_1T_3 - 0.0016T_2T_3 - 11.5729\Phi_1{}^2 + 0.0075T_1{}^2 \\ &- 4.240 \times 10^{-11}T_2{}^2 + 0.0091T_3{}^2 \end{aligned} \tag{14}$$

The R^2 indices for the two CVs are 0.9746 and 0.9999 which denote the acceptability of both the first and second-order regressions. Furthermore, the R^2 index for latter CV indicates that higher order polynomial regression is not required.

Table 2 shows different losses obtained from Monte Carlo experiments. The results indicate that measurement combinations can be used as self-optimizing CV of HEN with acceptable losses. The second-order CV gives less deviation with about 1.68 % average loss compared to the first-order polynomials which has an average loss of 4.12 % and a maximum loss and standard deviation of 11.1077 and 3.8.

Table 2. Average economic loss with measurement as CV

CV	Average loss	Maximum loss	Standard deviation
CV_1	6.2174	11.1077	3.8000
CV_2	2.5261	8.6073	3.0916

5. Conclusions

This paper presented a novel data-driven SOC procedure for CV selection without evaluation of derivatives from process model. The method uses finite difference method to evaluate the CV from measurement data in a single regression step. The method was tested on a HEN for first and second-order CVs obtained through regression with the second-order CV giving the best economic loss. The advantage of the new approach over all existing SOC methods is that the CV can be achieved without evaluating the derivative function. With the new approach, for complex industrial processes, CVs can be selected directly through simulation using commercial simulators such as HYSYS and UniSim.

Acknowledgment

Financial support from Petroleum Technology Development Fund (PTDF), Nigeria is gratefully acknowledged.

References

B. Glemmestad, S. Skogestad, T. Gundersen, 1999, Optimal operation of heat exchanger networks, Comput. Chem. Eng., 23, 509-522.

B. Srinivasan, D. Bonvin, E. Visser, S. Palanki, 2003, Dynamic optimization of batch processes: II. Role of measurement in handling uncertaitity, Comput. Chem. Eng., 27, 27-44.

I. J. Halvorsen, S. Skogestad, J. C. Morud, V. Alstad, 2003, Optimal operation of controlled variables, Ind. Eng. Chem Res., 42, 14, 3273-3284.

L. M. Umar, W. Hu, Y. Cao, V. Kariwala, 2012, Selection of controlled variables using self-optimization control method, Plantwide control: Recent developments and applications, John Wiley and Sons, West Sussex, UK.

L. Ye, Y. Cao, Y. Li, Z. Song, 2012, A Data-driven approach for selecting controlled variables, Proc. 8th International Symposium on ADCHEM, Singapore.

L. Ye, Y. Cao, Y. Li, Z. Song, 2013, Approximating necessary condition of optimality as controlled variables, Ind. Eng. Chem. Res., 52 , 2, 798–808.

S. Skogestad, 2000, Plantwide control: the search for the self-optimizing control structure, J. Process Control, 10, 5, 487-507.

S. Skogestad, 2004, Near-optimal operation by self-optimizing control: From process control to marathon running and business systems, Comput. Chem Eng., 29, 1, 127-137.

V. Alstad, S. Skogestad, 2007, Null space method for selecting optimal measurement combinations as controlled variables, Ind. Eng. Chem. Res., 46,3, 846-853.

V. Kariwala, 2007, Optimal measurment combination for local self-optimizing control, Ind. Eng. Chem Res., 46, 11, 3629-3634.

V. Kariwala, Y. Cao, S. Janardhanan, 2008, Local self-optimizing control with average loss minimization, Ind. Eng. Chem. Res., 47, 4, 1150-1158.

V. Lersbamrungsuk, T. Sarinophankun, S. Narasimhan, S. Skogestad, 2008, Control structure design for optimal operation of heat exchanger networks, AIChE J., 54, 1, 150-162.

Y. Cao, 2005, Direct and indirect gradient control for static optimization, Int. J. Autom. Comput., 2, 1, 60-66.

Jiří Jaromír Klemeš, Petar Sabev Varbanov and Peng Yen Liew (Editors)
Proceedings of the 24th European Symposium on Computer Aided Process Engineering – ESCAPE 24
June 15-18, 2014, Budapest, Hungary.

Optimal Management of Sewer Networks during Wet Weather Event by Stochastic Dynamic Programming

Sofiene Kachroudi[*], Damien Chenu, Nicolas David

Veolia Environnement Research and Innovation, Chemin de la digue, Maisons-Laffite 78600, France
sofiene.kachroudi@veolia.com

Abstract

The paper addresses the problem of how to manage real time operations of a sewer network pumping station under rainy episodes. Whereas rules-based control laws are already implemented, the paper proposes a new optimal control model based on stochastic dynamic programming with two approaches depending on how to represent the stochastic process of the model which is the water inflow of the pumping station. The first approach models the inflow at each time step as a stochastic variable with a known probability density while the second represents the inflow as a markovian process with a known transition matrix. Simulations performed with a typical rainy episode show the benefits of stochastic dynamic programming in reducing water overflowing in cities and water rejection in natural environment.

Keywords: pumping station management, stochastic control, dynamic programming, markovian process.

1. Introduction

Sewer networks operations managers face the problem of how to manage and optimize various operations in the whole sewer networks in order to meet operational goals such as minimizing overflowing in cities and rejections in natural environment. When a network is not complex and the operation choices are not too numerous, experience and good-sense can be sufficient to choose the best solution given some observed parameters. However when considering complex sewer networks with too many possible configurations, modeling and aid decision tools become required to meet aforementioned operation goals such as in (Schroeder et al., 2004) for global control of all sewage pump stations, (Leitão et al., 2009) for advanced sewer networks modeling and (Nielsen et al., 2009) for real time control of sewage system. Rules-based control laws are a simple and efficient way to automatically manage sewer networks operations. These strategies are based on simple "if…then…else" rules: if measured variables are in a given range, the algorithm recommends applying some actions with given computed parameters. For example, a rule can be as follows: if the measured inflow at a pumping station is beyond a threshold, the rotation speed of the pump that switches the water to the waste water treatment station has to be of a specified value. For these strategies the problem of how to specify the values of the parameters (for example thresholds) has to be addressed. Optimization techniques can be applied for such matters. In (Béraud et al., 2010) the computation of some parameters of rules-based strategies was performed using genetic algorithms coupled with an InfoWorks CS model of a given sewer network. Although the optimized strategy has enhanced the performance of the rules-based control law, it still has two shortcomings: (i) the optimization is performed offline with a given scenario of precipitation assumed to represent a typical rainy event; (ii) the rules-based control does not anticipate future since it does not consider a moving horizon. This study presents a stochastic dynamic programming (Bertsekas, 2005; Ross, 1983; Ruszcynski and Shapiro, 2003) algorithm which handles the problem of managing sewer operations by considering rainy episodes as stochastic processes over a future horizon. The case study of Berlin sewer network used in (Béraud et al., 2010) is considered as the main example. The paper is organized as follows. This case study is depicted in section 2: we present the simplified model of the pumping station based on simple conservation equations and discuss the issue of modeling the waste water inflow as a stochastic process. Section 3 deals with the stochastic dynamic programming where we present two approaches depending on how we model the inflow as a Markovian process or as a time series with a given probability density. Sections 4 is dedicated to the simulation results after which a general conclusion is given in section 5.

2. Case Study of Berlin and Modeling issues

2.1. Case Study and Existing Control Law

The catchment used for this case study is known locally as the Berlin VIII catchment. The combined flows produced by the catchment are directed to a main pumping station (Béraud et al., 2010). The pumping station has to direct the waste water to three treatment stations represented as a single one via a variable speed pump. When the water inflow is too high and the pumping tank water level is also high the pumping station can direct the surplus of water to a storage tank via a fixed speed pump. The stored water can be redirected to the pumping station via a controlled sluice (Figure 1). Under wet weather conditions, managing the pumping station consists of deciding at each time step which actions have to be made in order to avoid water overflowing and to minimize water rejection (Figure 1). The actions concerns three variables:

- Pumping speed from the pumping station to the treatment station.
- Pumping or not water to the storage tank.
- Opening or not the sluice.

The notations used in this paper are listed in Table 1.

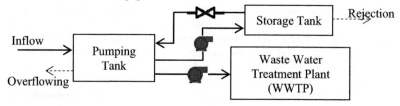

Figure 1. Pumping Station in Berlin Sewer Network

Table 1. Notations

t	Current time step	vt	State of the controlled sluice
ΔT	Length of time step	wt	Pump speed of the variable speed pump
at	Inflow at t	Vpt	Pumping tank maximum water level
ct	Overflowing flow at t	Vst	Storage tank maximum water level
bt	Rejection flow at t	xt	Water level in the pumping station at t
ut	State of the fixed speed pump	yt	Water level in the storage tank at t

The existing control strategy is rules-based. At each time step t, the following rules are applied:

- The speed of the pump toward the treatment station depends upon the water level in the pumping tank. There are five possible pumping speeds.
- When the inflow exceeds the maximum pumping capacity toward the treatment station and the water level within the tank reaches a defined threshold, pumping toward the storage tank is activated with a fixed pump speed. The pump stops when the water reaches back a defined lower level in the pumping tank.
- When the water level within the pumping tank reaches a defined low threshold the sluice is opened to empty the storage tank.

2.2. Sewer Network Modeling and Stochastic Modeling Issue

The objective of any control strategy for the pumping station is to avoid overflowing and minimize rejection. Thus the water overflowing c and water rejection b are the two key variables to regulate. At time step "t", c and b can be given respectively by Eq.1 and Eq.(2).

$$c_t = \max(0, x_{t+1} - V_{PT}) \tag{1}$$

$$b_t = \max(0, y_{t+1} - V_{ST}) \tag{2}$$

The state variables of the system are x and y. The conservation equations for the pumping and storage tanks give the following state equations of the system:

$$x_{t+1} = x_t + \Delta T.(a_t - u_t - w_t + v_t) \tag{3}$$

$$y_{t+1} = x_t + \Delta T.(u_t - v_t) \tag{4}$$

The compact state equation of the system can be written as follows:

$$Z_{t+1} = Z_t + B.U_t + C.a_t \tag{5}$$

Where $Z_t = \begin{bmatrix} x_t \\ y_t \end{bmatrix}, U_t = \begin{bmatrix} u_t \\ v_t \\ w_t \end{bmatrix}, B = \begin{bmatrix} -\Delta T & \Delta T & -\Delta T \\ \Delta T & -\Delta T & 0 \end{bmatrix}$ and $C = \begin{bmatrix} -\Delta T \\ 0 \end{bmatrix}$

If the values of the inflow "a" were known exactly the model would have been deterministic and a simple control law could have been easy to build. However the values of the inflow "a" cannot be known exactly and we can see "a" as a stochastic process. In this case, the model is called stochastic. In this study, two ways to represent the inflow as a stochastic process were investigated:

- Firstly, for each time step "t", "a_t" is considered as a stochastic variable with a given probability density.
- Secondly the inflow is considered as a markovian process (Sørup et al., 2011).

The dynamic programming model will be different between the two representations.

3. Stochastic Dynamic Programming Algorithm

3.1. The inflow as stochastic variables with known probability densities

The idea is to model the inflow at each time step as a stochastic variable with a given probability density. For that we assume having an estimator which can predict the inflow from initial time step "$t0$" for a future horizon of length "H". In this case, the model presented on Eq.(5) becomes as follows:

$$\begin{cases} Z_{t_0} = Z_0 \\ Z_{t+1} = Z_t + B.U_t + C.a_t \; \forall \, t_0 \le t < t_0 + H \end{cases} \tag{6}$$

The objective of the control strategy is to avoid water overflowing and to minimize water rejection. Therefore the criteria to minimize can be written as in Eq.7.

$$J = E\{\textstyle\sum_{t=t_0}^{t_0+H-1} b_t + \alpha.c_t + g_{t_0+H}(Z_{t_0+H})\} = E\{\textstyle\sum_{t=t_0}^{t_0+H-1} \max(0,[0\;1].Z_{t+1} - V_{ST}) + \alpha.\max(0,[1\;0].Z_{t+1} - V_{PT}) + g_{t_0+H}(Z_{t_0+H})\} \tag{7}$$

Where $\alpha > 1$ is a weighting coefficient, g_{t_0+H} is a final criteria and $E\{.\}$ is the mathematical expectation operator.

The additive structure of the optimization criteria, the fact that control variables are discrete and the structure of the system model fit very well using dynamic programming to build the optimal control law. The Bellman equation associated to the control problem is given as follows:

$$\begin{cases} J_{t_0+H}(Z_{t_0+H}) = g_{t_0+H}(Z_{t_0+H}) \\ J_t(Z_t) = \min_{U_t} E\{b_t + \alpha.c_t + J_{t+1}(Z_t + B.U_t + C.a_t)\} \; \forall \, t_0 \le t < t_0 + H \end{cases} \tag{8}$$

In order to calculate the Bellman function values $J_t(Z_t)$ the state space is discretized and linear interpolation is used when Z_t does not match a grid point. The computation of the expectation is performed with classic Monte Carlo sampling.

3.2. The inflow as markovian process

When we model the inflow as a markovian process the state space becomes of dimension3 as the inflow becomes a state variable. The discretization is hence applied to a three dimensional space. The computation of the expectation is performed with the transition matrix of the markovian process "a" and is given by the following equation:

$$E\{b_t + \alpha.c_t + J_{t+1}(Z_t + B.U_t + C.a_t)\} = \sum_{j=1}^{N_a^{max}} P_{ij}.\left(b_t + \alpha.c_t + J_{t+1}\left(Z_t + B.U_t + C.a_t^j\right)\right) \tag{9}$$

Where N_a^{max} is the number of possible discrete values of the inflow "a", a_t^j is the jth possible value of the inflow (j^{th} point of the grid) and P_{ij} is the (i,j) term of the transition matrix. P_{ij} is hence the transition probability from the state "i" at time step "t-1" to the state "j" at time step "t" and can be written as follows:

$$P_{ij} = P\left(a_t = a_t^j | a_{t-1} = a_{t-1}^i\right) \tag{10}$$

4. Results

Table 2 resumes the pumping station parameters values used to perform simulations. We perform simulations over 2 h with an inflow matching a typical rainy episode observed in Berlin City. The inflow shape function of time is illustrated in Figure 2.

Table 2. Parameters values for simulation

Vpt(m3)	766.35	Variable pump speed (m3/s)	{0, 0.13, 0.18, 0.35, 0.69}
Vst (m3)	1838.28	Sluice speed (m3/s)	{0, 1.15}
ΔT (s)	30	Fixed pump speed (m3/s)	{0, 1.05}

For the stochastic dynamic programming representing the inflow as a stochastic process with known probability density, we suppose that for each time step, the inflow has a uniform density with an expectation taken equal to the value of the inflow at the same time step presented on Figure 2 and with the variation range of ±40 % of the expectation value. The state space was discretized into 51 x 51 cells. For the markovian dynamic programming a transition matrix was considered and the state space was discretized into 51x51x41 cells. The two approaches considered in the paper are compared to the rules-based control law and the results are given in Figure 3.

Table 3 summarizes the total amount of water overflowing and rejected for the three strategies: rules-based, stochastic dynamic programming and markovian stochastic dynamic programming. Figure 3 and Table 3 demonstrate that stochastic dynamic programming is more efficient than rules-based control strategy. Moreover considering the inflow as a markovian process seems to give better results than when assuming the inflow at each time step as a stochastic variable with a known probability density.

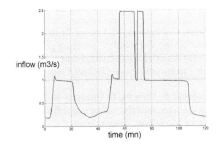

Figure 2. Inflow shape for simulation

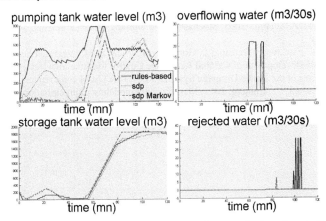

Figure 3. Simulation results - stochastic dynamic programing vs. rules-based control law

Table 3. Simulation results summarized

	Rules-based	Sdp	Sdp Markov
Total overflowing water (m3)	388.3	33.4	0
Total rejected water (m3)	137.2	0	7.2

5. Conclusion

The paper focused on the real time management of a Berlin city pumping station in a sewer network under uncertain rainy episodes. Two approaches based on stochastic dynamic programming were proposed. The first considers the inflow of the station at each time step as a stochastic variable with a known probability density. The second considers the inflow as a markovian process with a known transition matrix. The markovian stochastic dynamic programming requires more computational capacities as calculus are heavier than for classic stochastic dynamic programming. However for the markovian approach, we have to launch calculus once in off-line while for the other approach calculus have to be updated each time a new prediction on inflow is given. For the markovian approach a single Bellman matrix is computed once while for the other approach a new Bellman matrix has to be built each time a new prediction is achieved. Simulation results performed on a typical rainy episode show that stochastic dynamic programming is more efficient than rules-based control laws in minimizing water overflowing and rejection especially for the markovian approach.

References

B. Béraud, M. Mourad, E. Soyeux, C. Lemoine, M. Lovera, 2010, Optimisation of sewer networks hydraulic behaviour during wet weather: coupling genetic algorithms with two sewer networks modelling tools, NOVATECH 2010, Lyon, France.

D. P. Bertsekas, 2005, Dynamic Programming and Optimal Control, Athena Scientific, Nashua, USA..

J. Leitão, N. Simões, Č. Maksimović, F. Ferreira, D. Prodanović, J. Matos, A. Sá Marques, 2009, Real-time forecasting urban drainage models: full or simplified networks?, 8th International Conference on Urban Drainage Modelling, Tokyo, Japan.

N. Nielsen, J. Linde, C. Ravn, 2009, RTC optimisation of the sewage system in Kolding, 11th Nordic/NORDIWA Wastewater Conference, Odense, Denmark.

S. M. Ross, 1983, Introduction to Stochastic Dynamic Programming, Academic Press, Waltham, USA.

A. P. Ruszcynski, A. Shapiro, 2003, Stochastic Programming, Elsevier Science, Amsterdam, Netherlands.

K. Schroeder, E. Pawlowsky-Reusing, L. Gommery, L. Phan, 2004, Integrated Sewage Management-Development of a global Real Time Control for three interconnected Subcatchments of the Berlin Drainage System, 5th NOVATECH conference, Lyon, France.

H. Sørup, H.Madsen, K. Arnbjerg, 2011, Markov chain modeling of precipitation times series: Modeling waiting times between tipping bucket rain gauge tips, 12th International Conference on Urban Drainage, Porto Alegre, Brazil.

Jiří Jaromír Klemeš, Petar Sabev Varbanov and Peng Yen Liew (Editors)
Proceedings of the 24th European Symposium on Computer Aided Process Engineering – ESCAPE 24
June 15-18, 2014, Budapest, Hungary. Copyright © 2014 Alstom Technologie AG. Published by Elsevier B.V. All rights reserved.

A Data-Driven Approach for Analysing the Operational Behaviour and Performance of an Industrial Flue Gas Desulphurisation Process

Martin Gassner[a,]*, John Nilsson[b], Emma Nilsson[b], Thomas Palmé[a], Heiko Züfle[a], Stefano Bernero[a]

[a]*Alstom (Switzerland) Ltd., Brown Boveri Strasse 7, 5401 Baden, Switzerland*
[b]*Alstom Power Sweden AB, Kvarnvägen, 35241 Växjö, Sweden*
martin.gassner@power.alstom.com

Abstract

This paper investigates the use of data-driven modelling techniques, in particular artificial neural networks, to analyse the operational behaviour and performance of environmental control systems at the example of a flue gas desulphurisation (FGD) process. Using real data from a long-term campaign at an industrial plant, different stationary and dynamic models are developed and assessed, and issues related to sensor accuracy, non-stationary process phenomena and the effect of signal processing techniques are discussed. The work illustrates that flexible data-driven methods can represent the state and performance of such a process with good accuracy and provide useful indications about the relation between the process operation and its efficiency.

Keywords: Data-driven modelling, performance assessment, flue gas desulphurisation.

1. Introduction

1.1. Context
Increasing environmental awareness and corresponding legislation in the areas of pollutant emissions, energy and waste management are driving the use of a wide spectrum of fossil, waste and biogenic fuels for heat and power generation under strict emission limits. This requires flue gas cleaning processes to operate both more efficient and robust to the increasingly large fluctuations of the inlet flue gas contamination caused by inhomogeneous and diversely composed feedstock, which challenges well-established design, control and tendering procedures for conventional feedstock. In industrial practice, raw data from commercial plant operation is routinely recorded and screened for monitoring purposes. Further processing and detailed investigations are yet often limited by the availability of effective analysis procedures for field data. With respect to the challenges outlined above, such data has the potential to provide detailed insight into the behaviour of a specific plant or the characteristics of a process design, which can be exploited to further improve the process design and operation.

1.2. Objective
The objective of this paper is to investigate the use of data-driven modelling techniques for a systematic exploitation of industrial field data to assess, and ultimately improve, the operational behaviour and performance of an industrial flue gas cleaning process. In particular, it summarises the approach and results as applied to Alstom's NID[TM] process for semi-dry FGD with hydrated lime, which is used in a large fleet of coal- and waste-fired power plants and the iron & steel industry (Alstom Power, 2012).

2. Semi-dry flue gas deacidification with hydrated lime

Alstom's NID^{TM} system removes acidic pollutants from flue gases by injecting hydrated lime $Ca(OH)_2$, which is entrained in the flow to convert sulphur dioxide SO_2 and hydrochloric acid HCl to hydrated calcium sulphite $CaSO_3$ and calcium chloride $CaCl_2$:

$$SO_2 + Ca(OH)_2 \rightarrow CaSO_3 \cdot 0.5H_2O + 0.5H_2O \tag{1}$$

$$2HCl + Ca(OH)_2 \rightarrow CaCl_2 \cdot 2H_2O \tag{2}$$

These reactions are adsorption-controlled on the lime particles' wetted surface, and thus depend on a multitude of parameters like surface properties, humidity, particle size, local concentration etc. In literature, these influences have been repeatedly investigated and different physical, empirical and data-driven models have been developed. For semi-dry FGD focussing on SO_2, Irabien et al. (1992), Krammer et al. (1997) and Hill and Zank (2000) have analysed governing phenomena and proposed different reaction mechanisms and kinetics for particle drying, gas adsorption and surface reaction based on laboratory data. Applying a purely empirical approach, Zhang and Wang (2012) have investigated the effect of water injection in an upscaled plant. Garea et al. (2005) compared the performance of physical and neural network models on bench-scale test of a semi-dry FGD reactor and concluded better accuracy for the empirical approach, by using six input variables and less than 300 datapoints, the risk of overfitting is yet large. Plausibly due to the dependence of the rates on the solid reactant's surface properties and the usually very limited amount of available experimental data, models based on laboratory experiments have been found not to match the performance of upscaled plants, and Gutiérrez Ortiz and Ollero (2008) have combined such purely kinetic approaches based on laboratory data with empirical pilot plants. In an industrial application, a precise prediction of the conversion is indeed hindered by the complexity of the particle entrainment in the reactor, the large variations of the flow rates and pollutant loading especially in waste-to-energy applications, and the recirculation of unreacted lime after separation from the deacidated gas. For this reason, this contribution explores the performance of a purely empirical approach in capturing the behaviour of a full-scale industrial plant based on a large amount of operating data.

3. Approach

Data-driven modelling with artificial neural networks (ANN) is a popular semi-parametric technique to empirically represent complex non-linear, multidimensional relations by a flexible functional mapping (Bishop, 1996). Requiring no physical description of the system, they are typically used for monitoring purposes or within model-based control applications. For performance assessment, such techniques have received limited attention (e.g. by Sainlez et al. (2010; 2011) for steam production in a Kraft boiler) since they do not provide explicit knowledge on the underlying physical phenomena of the mapped relationship. To overcome this limitation, this paper compares the characteristics and accuracy of the empirical model for different formulations of the modelling problem. Several sets of variables are defined to assess their information content with respect to the performance indicator(s). As a basis for this comparison, the ANN models are benchmarked with a conventional parametric model.

3.1. Data characteristics and pre-processing

The operating data originates from a 2-month test campaign at a coal-fired power plant covering 13 main variables, i.e. four inlet boundary conditions (inlet flue gas flow, temperature and concentration of H_2O and SO_2), three control variables (flow of make-

up lime, water, and recirculated dust), five
system state variables (outlet flue gas flow
and temperature, reactor temperature and
humidity, and the corresponding wet bulb
temperature) and SO_2 removal efficiency.
Continuous recordings of 1-min averaged
data provide 42,000 observations. During
the campaign, the instrumentation has been
regularly checked and calibrated to ensure
data reliability. However, these procedures
cannot avoid stochastic uncertainty in the
signals, which are propagated and amplified

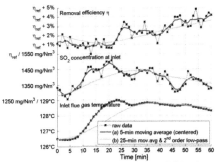

Figure 1. Exemplary raw signals and filtering.

in variables calculated by combining several signals (e.g. pollutant removal efficiency).
In order to quantify the influence of the measurement uncertainty on the model
accuracy, two different filters have been tested on the data. The filters target to (a)
remove stochastic signal noise while preserving the process dynamics, and (b) attenuate
transients to assess the influence of non-stationary operation. Figure 1 illustrates the
filter design, i.e. (a) a soft moving average filter to attenuate the amplitude of the signal
oscillations, and (b) a more aggressive filter to also attenuate amplitude and frequency
of these transients, and thus addresses instrument delay and the response of the control
system. A major drawback of individually applying such filters to each signal is that it
is impossible to distinguish stochastic measurement errors from real variations of the
process state, which may become physically incoherent. This issue can be overcome by
the use of data reconciliation techniques based on a process model, which inherently
assures physical coherence and can improve the overall accuracy of the data. Although
not yet applied in this work, such a strategy is envisaged for the future development.

3.2. Process model architectures

The operational behaviour and performance of the process is analysed by applying
several different model architectures shown in Figure 2. First, the process is considered
stationary (Section 4.1), which is a simplification since the variations of the inlet flow
and pollutant loading require continuous action by the control system. In Section 4.1.1,
the system state and performance are predicted from the inlet boundary conditions and
the control variables. In perfect steady-state, these should contain all physical
information for an exact prediction of the process conditions. As this is not the case due
to the process inertia and lime recirculation, some state variables are then included in
the set of input variables to identify conditions that are key for performance (Section
4.1.2). Since real process operation is not stationary due to variations of the flue gas
flow and quality, dynamic ANN architectures that also include information on previous
time periods are later investigated in Section 4.2. Although sometimes applied to simple
problems with a few variables (Norgaard et al., 2000), such architectures seem to be
rarely used in process engineering due to the drastic increase of model complexity and
related difficulties in model conditioning and training. Nevertheless, its use seems to
make sense in monitoring and control applications with on-line learning (Narendra and
Parthasarathy, 1990). More recently, dynamic model architectures have also been
applied for emission prediction of an industrial boiler (Sainlez et al., 2011).

3.3. Neural network architecture and training

All stationary models are configured as feedforward networks with linear in- and output
layers and one hidden layer with hyperbolic tangent sigmoid transfer functions. These
are able to represent any continuous functional mapping to arbitrary accuracy (Bishop,

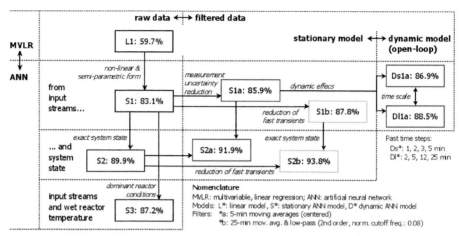

Figure 2. Selection of model architectures and accuracy of the mapping. R^2 is the coefficient of determination that quantifies the share of the data's variance that is explained by the model.

1996). In our context of performance assessment, this is a key property to detect if the input variables miss physically relevant information since a well-trained network should exactly predict the output variable(s) if all relevant information were provided. The property is thereby complementary, not contradictory to training robustness with respect to noise, which is ensured by cross-validation and applying early stopping. For the dynamic cases, both open-loop and recursive architectures are investigated. Compared to the stationary cases, the former also include past values of the input variables, while the latter considers past values of the output variable(s) as input. Network training follows good practices, i.e. data normalisation, preliminary sensitivity analyses to detect the minimum number of required nodes, and random split into training (25 %), cross-validation (25 %) and test (50 %) data sets. The weights are optimised with the scaled-conjugate gradient algorithm considering the mean squared error. A maximum number of 20,000 iterations has been verified to assure convergence. Overfitting is prevented by early stopping of the training when the error in the cross-validation set increases during 600 iterations. Training is repeated once to ensure that the optimum is not a local one.

4. Results and discussion

4.1. Stationary system

4.1.1. Modelling the system state from independent variables (inlet flows)
In an ideal stationary process, the system state and performance is only dependent on all its inlet streams, i.e. the flue gas, make-up lime and water. This relation is investigated by modelling process state and performance based on the state and flow of these streams. The resulting coefficient of determination R^2 varies between 80 % and 99.8 % for different variables (figures not shown). Outlet flow and dust recirculation, that are directly dependent on the inlet streams flow rates, are determined to over 99 %. Process temperatures and humidity are less well determined and reach 91 to 96 %, indicating the thermal inertia of the system. In the model with multiple outputs, the removal efficiency is only determined to 80 %. As the efficiency is known to be dependent on temperature and humidity, a better determination than the latter is indeed not to be expected. Besides its critical exposure to measurement uncertainty (Section 3.1), the lower R^2 shows that not all relevant information on the complex reaction mechanisms is provided by the inlet streams. The different effects are isolated in the remainder of this section.

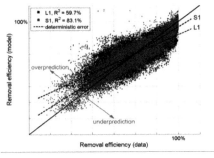
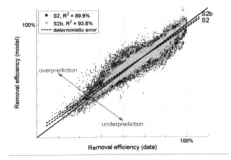

Figure 3. Error distribution for MVLR and ANN models (cases L1 and S1).

Figure 4. Filtering effect on error distribution (cases S2 and S2b).

4.1.2. Modelling the process performance

In order to provide a consistent reference, the ANN of Section 4.1.1 is retrained with the removal efficiency as single output variable. With $R^2 = 83$ % (Figure 2, case S1), this mapping is slightly more precise than before since no other output is targeted in the weight optimisation. With the same input, a multivariate linear regression (L1) only captures 60 % of the efficiency variation. The skewed distribution of its residuals (Figure 3, L1) shows that the ANN significantly reduces the deterministic error of the linear model, which is too stiff to represent the reaction and process characteristics. The influence of the process state on performance is quantified by using all variables as input for the model (S2). Figure 4 shows that this nearly eliminates the deterministic error and significantly reduces the stochastic one (R^2). The inlet streams of case S1 thus indeed miss relevant physical information on the system. Case S3 shows that the wet reactor outlet temperature alone is responsible for a major improvement. Cases S1a-S2b investigate the contribution of the measurement uncertainty by applying a mild (a) and more aggressive (b) filter on the signals (cf. Section 3.1). Both filters improve the accuracy of the mapping by up to 3.9-4.7 %, reaching $R^2 = 93.8$ % in the best case. This contribution can yet not be unambiguously attributed to uncertainty reduction since filtering spreads information among adjacent time periods. In particular, it distributes information on previous process states, and therefore part of the dynamic phenomena. This dispersion of information gets evident when comparing the residuals' distribution of Figure 4. Aggressive filtering (b) produces continuous lines of outliers in a few periods that do not match the behaviour observed in the bulk data. These patterns might indicate that the filter reduces the physical coherence of the data. This effect can be excluded by data reconciliation techniques, which is planned in future development.

4.2. Dynamic system

The influence of non-stationary operation has been assessed by several dynamic model architectures, of which only the open-loop models (cf. Section 2) are reported here. In real-scale problems, this critically increases the model size and the selection of some predominant variables is advisable. Cross-correlations between the performance indicator and the input variables have identified past data of the SO_2 concentration and lime flow to correlate most pronounced with the removal efficiency. Based on the shape of the cross-correlation, several values of these variables are included from shorter (case Ds1a) and longer (Dl1a) periods back in time. The increase of R^2 by 3.8 and 5.4 % with respect to the stationary model, respectively, demonstrates that non-stationary phenomena influence the performance during 30 to 45 mins. Considering that the number of input parameters with respect to case S1 is more than doubled, open-loop models are yet cumbersome and do not reach the significance and accuracy of a stationary model that uses information on the system state instead (cases S2-S2b). Indeed, the process temperatures and humidity already provide part of the dynamic information through their inertia with respect to changing boundary conditions and process control variables. Supplementary tests have further shown that the selection of the past data points is somewhat arbitrary. Although this selection can be optimised in an iterative procedure (Norgaard et al., 2000), a physically more coherent and computationally more efficient approach could be to aggregate the relevant information on past time steps based on a specific indicator.

5. Conclusions

This work has investigated the use of neural network models to analyse the operational behaviour and performance of a semi-dry FGD process. Several network architectures are benchmarked with a linear regression and demonstrate that the flexible functional form can accurately represent the system, reaching in our case a coefficient of determination of up to 93.8 % for the efficiency, which corresponds to an improvement by 20 to 30 % depending on the model. Contrary to physical models that provide direct information on underlying thermodynamics and chemistry, data-driven models yet only allow for indirectly extracting knowledge by observing the behaviour of the model. This paper has adopted an exploratory approach to identify valuable information on the relation between process operation, its pollutant removal efficiency, the influence of transient operation and data quality. Providing detailed insight into the characteristics of a specific process design and capturing the behaviour and performance of a plant, well-conditioned models based on these findings can be applied in several ways, including monitoring of individual units or across the fleet, or performance improvements by fine-tuning the operating strategy and ultimately model-based control.

References

Alstom Power, 2012, NID^{TM} Flue gas desulphurisation, Product brochure, <www.alstom.com/power/resources> accessed on 01/11/2012.

C. M. Bishop, 1996, Neural networks for pattern recognition, Oxford University Press, New York, USA.

A. Garea, J.A. Marques, A. Irabien, 2005, Mechanistical and non-linear modelling approaches to in-duct desulfurization, Chem. Eng. Proc., 44, 709-715.

F.J. Gutiérrez Ortiz, P. Ollero, 2008, A realistic approach to modeling an in-duct desulfurization process based on an experimental pilot plant study, Chem. Eng. J., 141,141-150.

F.F. Hill, J. Zank, 2000, Flue gas desulphurization by spray dry absorption, Chem. Eng. Proc., 39, 45-52.

A. Irabien, F. Cortabitarte, M.I. Ortiz, 1992, Kinetics of flue gas desulfurization at low temperatures: Nonideal surface adsorption model, Chem. Eng. Sci., 47, 1533-1543.

G. Krammer, C. Brunner, J. Khinast, G. Staudinger, 1997, Reaction of Ca(OH)2 with SO2 at low temperature, Ind. Eng. Chem. Res., 36, 1410-1418.

K. S. Narendra, K. Parthasarathy, 1990, Identification and control of dynamical systems using neural networks, IEEE Transactions on Neural Networks, 1, 4-27.

M. Norgaard, O. Ravn, N. K. Poulsen, L. K. Hansen, 2000, Neural networks for modelling and control of dynamic systems, Springer, London, UK.

M. Sainlez, G. Heyen, S. Lafourcade, 2010, Supervised learning for a Kraft recovery boiler: A data mining approach with Random Forests, 23rd ECOS Conference, Lausanne, Switzerland.

M. Sainlez, G. Heyen, S. Lafourcade, 2011, Recurrent neural network prediction of steam production in a Kraft recovery boiler, Computer Aided Chemical Engieneering, 29, 1784-8.

X. Zhang, N. Wang, 2012, Effect of humidification water on semi-dry flue gas desulfurization, Energy Procedia, 14, 1659-1664.

Jiří Jaromír Klemeš, Petar Sabev Varbanov and Peng Yen Liew (Editors)
Proceedings of the 24th European Symposium on Computer Aided Process Engineering – ESCAPE 24
June 15-18, 2014, Budapest, Hungary.

Algorithms and Methods for Identification of Multivariable Plants

Claudio Garcia,* Alain Segundo Potts, Rodrigo Juliani Correa de Godoy, Vitor Alex Oliveira Alves, Tiago Sanches da Silva

Politechnic School of the University of São Paulo, São Paulo/SP, 05508-900, Brazil
claudio.garcia@poli.usp.br

Abstract

In this work, techniques of multivariable identification that can be applied to the plant operating in open or closed loop are used. The idea is to improve the quality of the obtained models and to reduce the cost and time spent on identifying them. These models are essential for the deployment of advanced controllers like MPC (Model-based Predictive Controllers). It is known that multivariable MPC controllers reduce the variability of the process, allowing to operate closer to the constraints of quality of the various products, thereby maximizing the profit of the plants. The validation of the models obtained with the proposed tool reveals that they present a satisfactory behavior.

Keywords: System Identification, Multivariable Plants, Model Validation, Algorithms and Methods of Identification.

1. Introduction

Getting the model of the process is the most time-consuming task in the implementation of a MPC controller, so the application of a software that facilitates this activity would be very useful. Model identification is a critical step in the successful implementation of MPC controllers. In a recent work, Zhu et al. (2013) emphasize the importance of system identification in the implementation of a MPC system. Typically, the model is developed from a series of experimental tests in open loop, using the conventional approach of applying steps in individual variables. In the petrochemical industry, these tests can be very time consuming, ranging from several days to a few weeks. Thus, the identification process is the part of the design of an MPC controller that consumes more time and that directly affects the plant, because it is necessary to excite it with external signals. An identification procedure, in open or closed loop, that reduces the number of man-hours to obtain the model becomes a priority choice.

Žáčeková et al. (2013) state that "a model with good prediction properties is an ultimate condition for good performance of the predictive controller". They use MPC relevant identification – MRI to construct models to be used in the energy management of buildings. The technique MRI is one of the tools that we apply to obtain the models. The use of the multivariable identification instead of step tests in individual variables, brings the following benefits (Zhu, 1998):

a. The model quality is better and the validation is facilitated by the use of maximum error limits;

b. The disturbance in the quality of the manufactured products is minimized, due to the relatively small amplitude of the applied signals. An even better test condition can be achieved when the tests are conducted in closed loop, and

c. Identification costs are much reduced, reaching time reductions greater than 60 %.

The changes in the manipulated variables or in the setpoints are made by the computer and therefore there is no need of a control engineer running the tests. It requires of the user less experience in identification. Thus, an effective identification tool may warrant more processing units to apply the MPC. As reported in the literature, the economy typically achieved by making the multivariable identification is 50 % to 80 %, when compared with the traditional step tests, because all inputs are excited simultaneously.

This paper describes a set of algorithms for the identification of linear models with multiple inputs and multiple outputs - MIMO, with the plant operating in open or closed loop, wherein all manipulated variables or set points are excited simultaneously. The idea is to automate the identification, with a tool that systematizes this task, through the next steps: pre-test, experiment, data processing, selection of model structure and order, dead time and parameter estimation and model validation. The proposal is to implement and test in Matlab® several ways to obtain the models and to validate them.

This work includes the development of a library of algorithms for pre-processing the signals acquired from the process, the implementation of algorithms for generation of MIMO linear models using PEM (Prediction Error Methods) identification techniques such as ARX, ARMAX, OE, BJ and other techniques, such as the asymptotic method or techniques MRI that optimize the predictions k steps-ahead. The studies also aim to assist in the selection of the order of the models created by different structures, the detection of no-model IO pairs in the transfer matrix, the order reduction of linear multivariable models and techniques for the estimation of the dead time. We also intend to develop integrated tools for self-validation and cross-validation based on the step response and on pseudo-random binary signals. The evaluation of the identification algorithms will be held on simulated and real plants.

The novelty of this work is to concentrate in just one program all the resources cited in the two previous paragraphs. In addition, many of these algorithms are not present in the majority of the similar commercial programs. This way, one can obtain models employing a software that automatizes the main procedures normally employed in system identification. So, if it is necessary to generate dynamic models of a MIMO process, for instance a distillation column or a fluid catalytic cracking unit, typical in petrochemical industries, the proposed software could be used to generate the excitation signals of the input variables, to use the input/output collected signals to create different model structures, to select the best order and dead time for each model created and to choose the best model for each output variable, applying different validation techniques.

2. Minimizing the time spent in an identification

One of the main objectives of the proposed computational tool is to make the identification more productive, avoiding hours of work spent to obtain individual models for each output and improving the quality of the models found, by allowing a wide combination of structures and orders without supervision.

In an identification there are some decisions that the user must make, such as: the structure that will be used (e.g. FIR, ARX, ARMAX, BJ, MRI etc.), the order of each polynomial of the chosen structure and the dead time, aiming at obtaining a model that is as closest to reality as possible. The time spent on trying to find these parameters is usually high, due to the large amount of possibilities for structures and orders for each dataset. To facilitate this work of manual search for the best structure and order for the model to be identified, the proposed system was created to automatically test various structures, orders and dead times for any dataset. Thus, it is not necessary to spend time configuring and monitoring each of the identifications that must be performed, which normally consumes many hours or even days of work. In the proposed computational program, the user can leave the system identifying all possible combinations without intervention and the result of each combination of structure/order/dead time is stored in a model tree, so it can be later analysed by the user. This feature provides a large time gain and also better models, due to the fact that the system tests combinations that possibly should not be tried if the user had to test all of them, one by one.

A block diagram of the proposed program is shown in Figure 1. Three of the prominent features of the proposed computational program are detailed in the next sections.

3. Model Order Selection

The appropriate selection of a model for a chosen (parametric) model structure is a very important and time consuming task in system identification. It deals with the selection of the number of free parameters in the model to be estimated.

The influence of the model order in the model performance is very significant, especially when the available dataset is not very informative, which can occur due to a poor experiment, low signal-to-noise ratio (SNR) scenario, short experiment duration or some other conditions. Thus, selecting an appropriate model order is a critical feature in the identification process. Furthermore, a manual selection of model orders can be very time consuming, once it includes the choice of a family of order candidates, the identification of models using each one of such orders and the performance evaluation of the resulting models. Another key issue is the selection of a good performance criterion for the intended use of the model.

The presented computational package includes an automated methodology that selects, for a given dataset and a pre-selected model structure, the best order to be used in the model identification. The selection criterion can also be chosen from a group of available objective functions. By doing so, such methodology provides, not only better models, but also relieves the user from a manual procedure to do such choice.

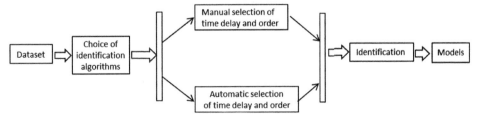

Figure 1. Block diagram of the proposed computational program.

4. Time Delay Estimation

Together with the model order selection problem, time delay estimation is another critical task in system identification. It deals with the estimation of the appropriate time delay to be used in the model. There are various methods to solve this problem, but most of them seek to estimate the true process time delay, which may be appropriate for some applications, but it is not always a good procedure in system identification. As is shown by Juliani et al. (2013), the time delay affects the model performance as much as its orders and needs to be estimated considering the available dataset, model structure and order, i.e., the true process time delay does not guarantee a good model, which must be obtained by an appropriate adjustment of the time delay.

This computational package solves the time delay estimation altogether with the model order selection, finding the best order and time delay for any dataset and selected model structure. Finding the best order and time delay in such an automatic manner, improves the identification results and reduces the time spent to obtain such results.

5. Model Predictive Controller Relevant Identification methods

In the majority of the commercial identification programs, the algorithms for identifying dynamic models use prediction error methods (PEM). These techniques are useful when one-step ahead predictions are needed, but in processes where it is used a MPC, they may be insufficient. The conventional multivariable system identification approach, which minimizes single-step ahead prediction errors, can result in models with poor prediction capacity. In this sense, the long-range prediction is important for MPC.

The MRI methods provide models suitable to generate multistep ahead predictions, more appropriate to MPC applications. It is important to say that the advantages of the MRI methods arise only when a certain model structure mismatch is expected, which is natural in practical situations. Hence, the MRI problem may be thought of as a way of distributing the modelling error in a frequency range that is less important for control purposes (Gopaluni, 2004). The predictor used in MRI algorithms is shown in Eq. (1).

$$\hat{y}(t|t-k) = W_k^{-1}(q)G(q)u(t) + [1 - W_k^{-1}(q)]y(t) \qquad (1)$$

In this equation, $y(t)$ and $u(t)$ represent the output and input signals, $G(q)$ is the process model and $\hat{y}$ is the predicted output. The method used to obtain the filter W_k defines the characteristic of the different MRI methods. In this sense, our program provides access to three MRI approaches: the method proposed by Gopaluni et al. (2004), based on the direct optimization of the disturbance model and filter W_k; the algorithm proposed by Huang and Wang (1999), based on the prefiltering of the input/output signals; and the method proposed by Potts et al. (2014) that gathers the advantages of the two previous methods and ensures the stability of the predictor.

Data from simulated and from real multivariable plants were used to evaluate the MRI methods available in the proposed program. They were compared with other multi and single-step ahead prediction algorithms and they showed to be more robust, when there is uncertainty in the time delay. In the absence of this uncertainty, their performance is similar to other PEM algorithms. Other important feature is their robustness, which is estimated from the numbers of local minima detected in the tests performed. The ability to estimate good models over a long prediction horizon was also shown in all the cases.

6. An example of application of the computational tool proposed

The first step is to configure the pre-test, by choosing the amplitude of the steps to be applied to the plant, in order to obtain a pre-model. Next, the system asks the user about previous knowledge concerning the time delays and the zeros in the transfer matrix that represents the plant. If it is not available, the software runs routines to estimate the time delays and the zeros in the transfer matrix.

The next step is to configure the experiment to obtain the input/output data of the plant. The excitation signals are selected, considering their features for each input and also the conditions of the experiment (open or closed loop, duration of the experiment). When a single dataset is available, it is necessary to divide it into two parts: identification and validation. It is also necessary to choose which identification methods will be used: direct identification (ARX, ARMAX, OE, BJ), asymptotic method or MRI methods. Another point is the order selection for each model.

After the identification, the obtained models can be validated. One of the options is to perform a cross-validation and to compare the output of the models with the output of the real plant. It is also possible to apply a step to each model and to compare its output to that of the plant obtained in the pre-test. The program allows analyzing the controlled and manipulated variables, the setpoints and the measured disturbances acquired in the pre-test and in the test, as shown in Figures 2 and 3, that represent a 7x6 plant.

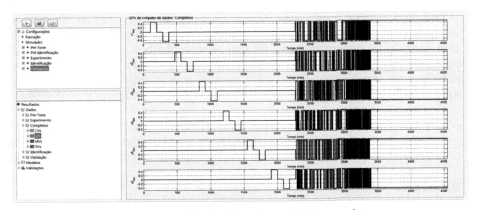

Figure 2. Complete dataset related to the signals used to excite the set points.

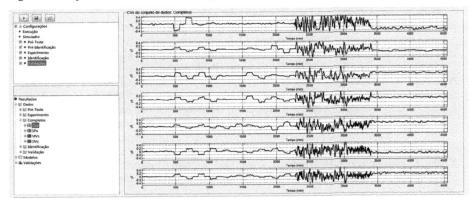

Figure 3. Complete dataset related to the controlled variables.

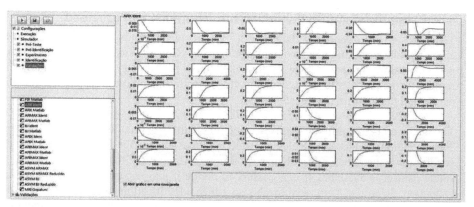

Figure 4. Models obtained with the test data using the structure ARX.

In Figure 4 are shown the step responses of the models identified according to one of the available structures (ARX).

7. Conclusions

This work presented the main concepts involved in a computational tool developed to automatically obtain models of a process. Its mains novelties were emphasized as well as the advantages it offers. Special attention was given to automation of the identification process. In this sense, the software provides two scenarios, the first one totally automatic and the other manual, where the user has the control step-by-step of each stage. In the automatic mode, the tool suggests the best model according to the algorithms used to detect the best order, structure and time delay of the process identified, based on various evaluation criteria. This is an important point of our tool, which usually is not present in the majority of the commercial identification programs.

All the algorithms used by our software were tested and validated with simulated and real plants. They were presented in congresses and in indexed journals. At this moment, our algorithms are being used to identify plants of the Brazilian refineries of Petrobras.

References

R. J. C. Godoy, V. A. O. Alves, C. Garcia, 2013, Time delay: an alternative definition for optimal system identification, 52nd IEEE Conference on Decision and Control, Florence, Italy, 3894-3899.

R. B. Gopaluni, R. S. Patwardhan, S. L. Shah, 2004, MPC relevant identification – tuning the noise model, Journal of Process Control, 14, 6, 699–714.

B. Huang, Z. Wang, 1999, The role of data prefiltering for integrated identification and model predictive control, 14th IFAC World Congress, Beijing, China, 151–156.

A. S. Potts, R. A. Romano, C. Garcia, 2014, Improving performance and stability of MPC relevant identification methods, Control Engineering Practice, 22, 1, 20-33.

E. Žáčeková, S. Prívara, Z. Váňa, J. Cigler, 2013, Building modeling: on selection of the model complexity for predictive control, Computer Aided Chemical Engineering, 32, 205-210.

Y. Zhu, 1998, Multivariable process identification for MPC: the asymptotic method and its applications, Journal of Process Control, 8, 2, 101-115.

Y. Zhu, R. Patwardhan, S. B. Wagner, J. Zhao, 2013, Toward a low cost and high performance MPC: The role of system identification, Computers and Chemical Engineering, 51, 124-135.

Jiří Jaromír Klemeš, Petar Sabev Varbanov and Peng Yen Liew (Editors)
Proceedings of the 24th European Symposium on Computer Aided Process Engineering – ESCAPE 24
June 15-18, 2014, Budapest, Hungary. Copyright © 2014 Elsevier B.V. All rights reserved.

Optimal Operation and Control of Divided Wall Column

Ambari Khanam[a], Mohammad Shamsuzzoha[b], Sigurd Skogestad[a,*]

[a]*Department of Chemical Engineering, Norwegian University of Science and Technology, N-7491 Trondheim, Norway*
[b]*Department of Chemical Engineering, King Fahd University of Petroleum and Minerals, 31261 Dhahran, Saudi Arabia*
skoge@ntnu.no

Abstract

In this paper, possible modes of optimal operations of the three-product divided wall column have been discussed. These modes differ in terms of the given energy price (expensive/cheap) and given product purity constraints. In addition, the control structure scheme for one of these modes has been proposed. In this mode energy is assumed to be cheap and product purity specifications are not fixed. Since, product purity specifications are not fixed, there are three unconstrained degrees of freedom in the column for which the self-optimizing control structure has been proposed.

Keywords: DWC, Petlyuk column, Optimal operation, Minimum energy

1. Introduction

Divided wall columns have gained increasing applications due to their lower energy consumption and investment costs compared with conventional distillation column sequences. A divided wall column (DWC) has a vertical partition that divides the column shell into a pre-fractionator and side draw section. Figure 1 shows the divided wall column with a single reboiler and a single condenser.

Various modes of operation based on operational objective and constraints have been studied by several investigators. Strandberg (2011) considered four different cases of optimal operation of the Kaibel column with feed rate as a degree of freedom. Ghadrdan et al. (2011) extended the investigation of two cases, namely minimizing energy usage for fixed product specifications (Mode-I_{ABC}) and maximizing product purities for fixed boilup (Mode-II_0), Table 1. Dwivedi et al. (2013) mainly focused on the control structure selection for fixed product specifications with minimum energy usage (Mode-I_{ABC}). Further, Khanam et al. (2013) have studied the optimal operation of divided wall (Petlyuk) column for fixed energy and non-optimal vapor split ratio R_v (Mode-II_0). Halvorsen and Skogestad (1999) studied steady-state optimal operation for minimum energy usage (Mode-I_{ABC}) and concluded that energy saving is difficult without a good control strategy. They also discussed candidate feedback variable for self-optimizing control scheme for minimizing the energy usage. In this paper we have investigated all possible modes of operation based on operational objective and constraints as given in Table 1. In addition, we have also studied the self-optimizing control scheme for minimizing the sum of impurities for fixed boilup (Mode-II_0).

2. Modes of Optimal Operation

The column for our study is modeled stage by stage. The column has 6 sections with 12 stages in each of these sections. The study has been conducted with the following assumptions: constant pressure, negligible vapor hold up, a total condenser, equilibrium on all stages, linearized flow dynamics constant relative volatilities and constant molar flows in column's sections.

The feed F is given and it contains three components A (lightest), B and C (heaviest). We have started with investigating all possible modes of optimal operation. The cost function for the three-product divided wall column for this study is:

$$J = p_F F + p_v V - p_D D - p_S S - p_R R \qquad (1)$$

where J is the scalar cost function (\$/kmol). F, V, D, S and R are the flow rates (kmol/min) of feed, boilup, distillate, side product and bottom product respectively. Since, B denotes one of the key components therefore R has been used to denote the bottom product flow rate. p_F, p_v, p_D, p_S and p_R are prices (\$/kmol) of respective flow streams. The feed is assumed to be a disturbance and thus there are five steady-state degrees of freedom. The steady-state degrees of freedom are V, S, R, R_l and R_v. R_l and R_v are liquid split ratio and vapor split ratio respectively. D and R are used to control levels and therefore have no steady-state effects. The plant's economics is mainly dependent on steady-state conditions therefore the effects of dynamics have been neglected in this study, Skogestad (2000). As mentioned earlier, we consider four constraints:

$$x_{D,A} \geq x_{D,A(min)} \; ; \quad x_{S,B} \geq x_{S,B(min)} \; ; \quad x_{R,C} \geq x_{R,C(min)} \; ; \quad V \leq V_{max} \qquad (2)$$

where A, B and C are key components in distillate D, side stream S and bottom product R respectively. With four possible constraints given in Eq. (2), there are $2^4 = 16$ different possible combinations of active constraints ("modes of operation") as given in Table 1. We assume that R_l and R_v are used to control the compositions in the prefractionator for stable operation of the main column. Then, there are three degrees of freedom for the main column, and it is therefore infeasible with four active constraints (Mode-II$_{ABC}$ is infeasible). This leaves 15 modes of operation, the two main modes of operations are:

(i) Mode-I (V < V$_{max}$): Minimize energy
(ii) Mode-II (V=V$_{max}$): Maximize the value of products

From economic perspective, Mode-I and Mode-II differ in terms of given energy price. Mode-I is suitable when energy is expensive and therefore the objective function turns out to be minimizing the energy. However, Mode-II is suitable when energy is cheap and consequently the objective function turns out to be maximizing the product recovery by using the maximum available energy. Further, these two modes can be subcategorized into various modes for optimal operations based on the objective function and active constraints as given in Table 1.

Different sub-modes of operation with a defined objective function are based on the fact that for a given column design, the active constraints region may change depending on the product, feed and energy price as well as the disturbances (feed rate and feed compositions). For example, in Mode-I$_{ABC}$, all three constraints on product compositions are active.

Table1. Possible modes of operation for the three-product DWC based on active constraints

Mode	No. of active composition constraints, $x_{D,A}$ in distillate D, $x_{S,B}$ in side stream S and $x_{R,C}$ in bottom product R			
	0	1	2	3
Mode-I Expensive Energy $V \leq V_{max}$	Mode-I$_0$ (1 case)	Mode-I$_A$/Mode-I$_B$/ Mode-I$_C$, (3 cases)	Mode-I$_{AB}$/Mode-I$_{BC}$ /Mode-I$_{CA,}$ (3 cases)	Mode-I$_{ABC}$ (1 case)
Mode-II Cheap Energy $V = V_{max}$	Mode-II$_0$ (1 case)	Mode-II$_A$/Mode-II$_B$/ Mode-II$_C$, (3 cases)	Mode-II$_{AB}$/Mode-II$_{BC/}$ Mode-II$_{CA}$ (3 cases)	Infeasible

In Mode-I, we minimize the energy for different sets of constraints on the main component fraction in the product. This mode of operation is optimal when energy is expensive and constraints on all three product purity compositions are active to avoid product give away (e.g., Mode-I$_{ABC}$). However when constraints on all three products are not active and the energy is expensive then optimal operation is a trade-off between minimizing impurities and minimizing energy. This is because the profit is dependent on both energy saving and the purity of the product (e.g., Mode-I$_0$).

Mode-II is generally optimal when the energy is cheap and thus we set the column to operate at maximum V=V$_{max}$. This mode of operation is also suitable when the price of product is dependent on its purity. In this case column can be operated for maximizing the sum of product purities or maximizing the profit for even and uneven pricing respectively. However when none of the constraints are active on the products (Mode-II$_0$) then the optimal operation is only justified for even pricing. While in case of uneven pricing for subcategories of Mode-II, we can minimize the sum of impurities or maximize the profit. According to Skogestad (2000) plantwide control procedure active constraints are controlled first followed by self-optimizing controlled variables for the remaining unconstrained degrees of freedom. As the number of active constraints and unconstrained degree of freedom vary in various modes of operation therefore the control strategy will also vary for various modes given in Table 1.

3. Self-Optimizing Control Structure for Mode-II$_0$

In Mode-II$_0$, the constraints on product purity specifications are not active and the boilup is only an active constraint. Also if we assume that the price of each of the three products distillate (D), side stream (S) and bottom product (R) is dependent on the key component present in it.

$$p_D = p_A^0 x_{D,A} ; \ p_S = p_B^0 x_{S,B} ; \ p_R = p_C^0 x_{R,C} \tag{3}$$

It is also assumed that the unit price of each component is same as given below:

$$p_A^0 = p_B^0 = p_C^0 = 1 \tag{4}$$

The cost function given by Eq. (1) can be rewritten as:

$$J = x_{D,B}D + \left(x_{S,A} + x_{S,C}\right)S + x_{R,B}R \tag{5}$$

The cost function as given above is the total sum of impurities in product streams coming out of the main column. The unconstrained degrees of freedom for self-optimizing control are reflux flow rate, side stream flow rate and the liquid split ratio as given below:

$$u^T = [L \quad S \quad R_l] \tag{6}$$

There are five disturbances and they are feed flow rate, composition of A and B in the feed, the boilup which is fixed and set at the maximum and the vapor split ratio:

$$d^T = [F \quad z_A \quad z_B \quad V \quad R_v] \tag{7}$$

Self-optimizing control scheme is the most suitable for Mode-II_0 because the product purity specifications are not fixed and there are three unconstrained degrees of freedom, Eq. (6). These unconstrained degrees of freedom can be used to control three controlled variables to run the column at optimal or near optimal conditions. The column data with feed conditions and other process parameters for this study are given in Table 2.

Table 2. Process data for the three-product divided wall column

Physical data	
Component A, B and C	Ethanol, Propanol and n-Butanol
Boiling points of A, B and C	[78.37 97 117.4]
Relative volatilities [A (lightest), B , C (heaviest)]	[4.2 2.1 1]
Number of stages	12 in each section
Nominal feed flow rate, F^*	1 [kmol/min]
Nominal feed composition, $[z_A^* \ z_B^* \ z_C^*]$	[0.333 0.333 0.333]
Nominal liquid feed, q_F^*	1
Disturbances (Deviations)	
Feed, F	$F^* \pm 10\%$
$[z_A \ z_B]$	$[z_A^* \pm 10\% \quad z_B^* \pm 10\%]$
V_{max}	$V_{max}^* \pm 10\%$
R_v	$R_v^* \pm 10\%$
Implementation errors	
Control error (integral action)	0.0000
Measurement error (temperatures)	$\pm 0.5 \,^{\circ}C$

Table 3. The steady state RGA (relative gain array) for the selected controlled variables

Temperature	L	S	R_l
T_{10}	-0.00026	1.05×10^{-5}	1.000252
T_{38}	0.989655	0.010629	-0.00028
T_{60}	0.010608	0.98936	3.17×10^{-5}

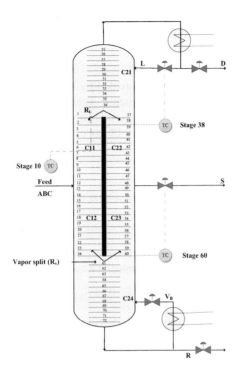

Figure 1. Self-optimizing control configuration (keeping three temperatures at their nominal setpoints using unconstrained degrees of freedom)

Bi-directional branch and bound method for average loss criterion (Kariwala et al. 2008) was used to find three best sets of temperatures. For these sets of measurements, the average loss was calculated by using H and norm of M(H) matrix as given in recent literature by (Yelchuru and Skogstad, 2012). The average loss calculated for first 10 sets of measurements were nearly same in magnitude. For example the loss corresponding to the best temperature sets (T_9, T_{38} and T_{58}) was 9.31e-4 and the losses corresponding to other next best sets of temperatures were 9.32×10^{-4}, 9.39×10^{-4}, 9.41×10^{-4}, 9.43×10^{-4}, and 9.63×10^{-4}. Also the average loss corresponding to the combination of all 72 measurements was 7.5166×10^{-4} which was nearly same as the loss corresponding to three temperatures used as measurements. The sets of temperatures with different combinations were tested on the non-linear model for larger disturbance in the feed flow rate. The temperatures to be kept constant for self-optimizing control which gives acceptable loss are: T_{10}, T_{38}, T_{60} (Figure 1). Based on the value of stead-state RGA as given in Table 3, it is found that these temperatures are also good for stabilizing control as suggested by Khanam (2014).

4. Conclusions

In this paper, it is found that there are 15 possible modes of optimal operation of the three-product divided wall column for given constraints on energy and product purity specifications. The control structure selection for one of these modes with fixed energy and unconstrained product purity specifications shows that the economic self-optimizing control layer is same as the regulatory control layer of the column.

Acknowledgements

The second author would like to acknowledge the support provided by King Abdulaziz City for Science and Technology (KACST) through the Science & Technology Unit at King Fahd University of Petroleum & Minerals (KFUPM) for funding this work through project number 11-ENE1643-04 as part of the National Science Technology and Innovation Plan.

References

A. Khanam, 2014, Control strategies for divided wall (Petlyuk) columns, MSc. Dissertation, Trondheim, Norway.

A. Khanam, M. Shamsuzzoha, S. Skogestad, 2013, Operation of energy efficient divided wall column, Computer Aided Process Engineering, 32, 235-240.

D. Dwivedi, I.J. Halvorsen, S. Skogestad, 2012, Control structure slection for three-product Petlyuk (dividing-wall) column, Chemical Engineering and Procesing : Process intensification, 64, 57-67.

I.J. Halvorsen, S. Skogestad, 1999, Optimal operation of Petlyuk distillation: steady-state behaviour, Journal of Process Control, 9, 407-424.

J.P. Strandberg, 2011, Optimal operation of dividing wall columns, Ph.D Thesis, Trondheim: Norwegian University of Science and Technology (NTNU), Norway.

M. Ghadradan, I.J. Halvorsen, S. Skogestad, 2011, Optimal operations of Kaible distillation columns, Chemical Engineering Research and Design, 89, 1382-1391.

R. Yelchuru, S. Skogestad, 2012, Convex formulations for optimal selection of controlled variables and measurements using mixed integer quadratic programming, Journal of Process Control, 22, 995-1007.

S. Skogestad, 2000, Plantwide control: The search for self-optimizing control structure, Journal of Process Control, 10, 487-507.

V. Kariwala, Y. Cao, S. Janandharan, 2008, Local self-optimizing control with average loss minimization, Ind. Eng. Chem. T.Res., 47, 1150-1158.

Jiří Jaromír Klemeš, Petar Sabev Varbanov and Peng Yen Liew (Editors)
Proceedings of the 24th European Symposium on Computer Aided Process Engineering – ESCAPE 24
June 15-18, 2014, Budapest, Hungary. Copyright © 2014 Elsevier B.V. All rights reserved.

On-line Fault Diagnosis by Combining Functional and Dynamic Modelling of Chemical Plants

Ismael Díaz*, Manuel Rodríguez

Autonomous Systems Laboratory, Technical University of Madrid, C/ José Gutiérrez Abascal, 2, Madrid 28006, Spain
ismael.diaz@upm.es

Abstract

In this paper we present a methodology that integrates the functional modelling (qualitative models) approach with the dynamic simulation (quantitative models) to perform on-line fault diagnosis. It uses D-higraph functional modelling methodology to capture and deal with the complexity of the plant. Our methodology presented herein produces dynamic responses based on the results of the analysis done by the functional model, and retrieves information about the possible causes determining abnormal situations.

Keywords: D-higraphs, functional modelling, dynamic simulation, fault diagnosis

1. Introduction

Process plants are becoming more and more complex, not only because of the process itself but the control system. Simultaneously, they are operated at extreme conditions of pressure and temperature to reduce costs and maximize profits, i.e., due to process optimization. The conjunction of these two aspects makes faults and failures more likely and, moreover, their consequences are more severe or even catastrophic. Abnormal situation management is of great importance in the operation of chemical and petrochemical plants. It is important to have an early detection of abnormal events or not desired disturbances. Abnormal situations can be defined as events that drive the process out of its normal operation state and can produce out spec products, equipment failures or even a complete plant shutdown. Some of these can have catastrophic consequences. Early event detection when the process is in a controllable region, in order to avoid any failure (event chain) propagation, can reduce significantly the loss. Abnormal situation management is estimated to cost $ 20,000,000,000 dollar yearly (in the U.S. alone) to the chemical and petrochemical industry, so efforts can be made in order to improve this situation. Thus, a way to deal with the problem could be trying to develop a functional modelling methodology (section 2) in order to qualitatively study the situation, and couple it with dynamic simulations (quantitative results).

Dynamic simulation is widely used to design the control system that can handle process disturbances and keep the process operating around the desired steady state. However, dynamic simulation can be also used to analyse process safety, to predict how different variables change in the event of operating emergencies or abnormal events. It is important to establish the critical response time, the time a variable takes to reach a high limit value that determines the needed corrective action to guarantee safety (actions that go from alarms to interlock activation or relief valves opened). This time determines how fast the safety system (sensors, valves, etc.) must react under different disturbances. Some previous work has been done on this subject, like W. Luyben's work (Luyben, 2007) on reactors and distillation columns safety using dynamic simulation

2. D-higraphs

D-higraphs is a functional methodology to represent the behaviour of complex process systems (Rodríguez and Sanz, 2009). They have been employed before in important applications such as HAZOP automatization (Rodriguez, 2012) or control system reconfiguration (Rodriguez, 2013). Based on Harel's work (Harel, 1987) it uses two main elements, blobs and edges, to represent transitions and states respectively. Every blob (pictured as a rounded box) indicates a function, the actor that performs the function and any needed condition for it to happen. Blobs can be included inside other blobs, meaning that the inner blob/s are necessary for the function of the outer blob. Edges (arrows) represent mass, energy and informational states. A blob (function) receives an edge (state) and produces another edge (new state).

Besides the functional representation, D-higraphs describe the process structurally (through the process variables) and behaviourally (using variable dependencies relationships).   Variable dependency is indicated as Z $(X^{++}, Y^{+-}, ...)$ where Z is the variable affected by deviations of X and Y. The symbol "++" indicates that deviations in X below or over the expected value increase the value of Z, the symbol "+-" indicates that deviations in Y above the expected value increase Z but deviations below it decrease the value of Z (the same logic applies for the other cases "-+" and "--").

These descriptions allow conducting causal and qualitative reasoning using this methodology. Figure 1 shows the main elements of the D-higraphs methodology.

3. Methodology

In this section, the steps taken to connect dynamic simulation results with functional modelling tools are described. To do this, it is necessary to develop the models (both dynamic and functional) of the system. The dynamic model is done using a commercial dynamic simulator for chemical processes such as Aspen Dynamics, following the conventional procedure of firstly developing the steady state model and then converting it to dynamic. The functional model is developed identifying actors, functions and state variables of the system. Details can be found in previous works (De la Mata and Rodriguez, 2010a; de la Mata and Rodriguez, 2010b).

To execute the functional model it is necessary to obtain variable (input or output variables in the dynamic model) values from the dynamic simulation model. These values are then used to exploit the functional model according to the D-higraphs methodology by executing the expert system software. Specifically, Aspen Dynamics output variables have to be measured and when an interlock is activated (that means the

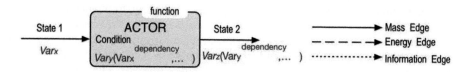

Figure 1. Software integration and information fluxes

variable has reached an operation limit), the functional analysis is executed to identify input variables that may have failed. This is done integrating different software tools as blocks in Simulink, as schemed in Figure 2.

The first point of the integration is to implement variable disturbances in Aspen Dynamics from Simulink software, which can be done by using source signal blocks in Simulink. The connection between Aspen Dynamics and Simulink is done through the commercial Aspen Modeler Simulink block provided by AspenTech. Output variables of the dynamic model being run, are recorded and sent as parameters to Matlab functions, comparing their value with the operational levels allowed. When these operational levels are reached, it means that a variable is failing, and fault diagnosis is executed. Executions are carried out by CLIPS (an expert system software). CLIPS has a representation of the D-higraph functional models of the system. This CLIPS/D-higraph execution is launched from the Matlab environment.

4. Case Study

To illustrate the application of the above methodology, the dynamic behavior of a jacketed continuous stirred tank reactor (JCSTR) is presented herein. The considered system is a piece of a whole process (ethylbenzene process) described in depth in literature (Luyben, 2007). It is a liquid phase reactor, where benzene (B), ethylbenzene (EB), ethylene (E) and diethylbenzene (DEB) react according to:

$$B + E \rightarrow EB$$

$$EB + E \rightarrow DEB$$

$$B + DEB \rightarrow 2EB$$

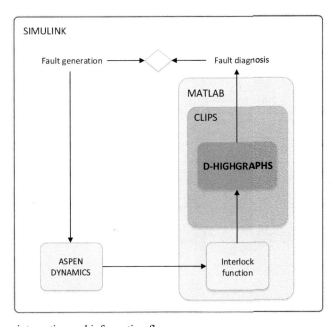

Figure 2. Software integration and information fluxes

The expected product is mainly EB. The reactor is cooled by a jacket, controlling reactor temperature by changing coolant flowrate. An extra control loop is also implemented to better illustrate this example, liquid level is controlled by varying the product flowrate. The flowsheet of the process as implemented in the dynamic simulator is shown in Figure 3.

According to the methodology described in section 3, the next step is to develop the functional model of the system. The resulting D-higraph is depicted in Figure 4. It can be easily identified the actors (name of the equipment involved), the functions (by the upper tag of the blobs) and the state variables. The functional model, as well as the causal and qualitative rules, is coded in CLIPS. The expert system execution allows tracking the evolution and propagation of the faults of the system. In this way, from a fault detected in the dynamic model, the functional model can predict what could cause such deviation and its consequences.

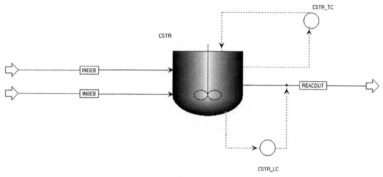

Figure 3. Aspen Dynamic flowsheet of the process

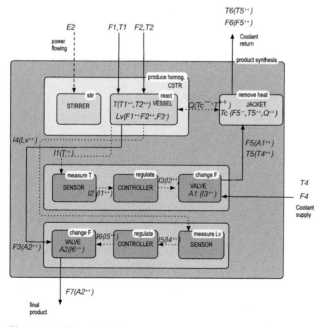

Figure 4. D-higraph of the process

Both dynamic and functional models were embedded in Simulink, resulting in the final model represented by blocks in Figure 5. The "*T INBEB*" and "*F INBEB*" blocks are variable disturbances created in Simulink and fed to Aspen Dynamics (*AMSimulation*). Matlab functions blocks are used to implement interlock actions as well as for calling the expert system CLIPS. The rest of blocks are for monitoring.

As an example, the result of a deviation on temperature of stream *INBEB* (*F1* in the functional model) was simulated. In this case, it was considered a fault for the system when the flowrate of the product stream *REACOUT* (*F7*) exceeds 2000 kmol/h. When this value is reached, the functional model predicts that it could be due to either an increasing in *F1* or *F2*, and the model also suggests that the level of the reactor could increase too. Figure 6 right shows the continuous evolution of the variables in a Simulink window with the data sent by Aspen Dynamics and the output of the production system (left) indicating the chain of events to the feasible root cause/s of the fault. In real plants, this methodology is very promising because it can be applied directly linking real-time process variables to the functional models, and then use dynamic simulation to discern what, of all the possible faults predicted by the functional model (in our case *F1* or *F2*), could quantitatively verify what really happened.

The same simulation was carried out varying the jacket heat duty due to a change in the stream temperature (*T1*). It can be observed (Figure 7 left) that the functional model also predicts that this could be the cause of the deviation in heat duty.

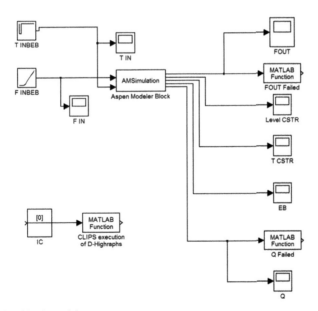

Figure 5. Simulink block model

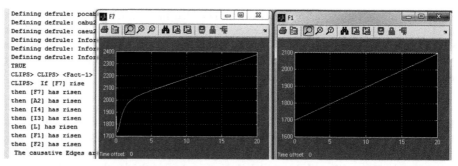

Figure 6. Results of the model for a deviation in feed flowrate (*F1*)

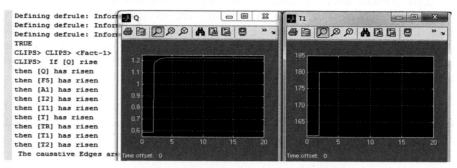

Figure 7. Results of the model for a deviation in inlet temperature (*T1*)

5. Conclusions

In this paper we have presented the integration of qualitative and quantitative models and used it to conduct fault diagnosis analysis. Simulink is the environment in which continuous dynamic models (Aspen dynamics) communicate with qualitative functional models (D-higraphs coded in the production system CLIPS) and these models send back the results of the causal/consequence reasoning performed. This methodology can be extended to other safety analyses such as HAZOP studies where the results of the qualitative models can be sent to the dynamic models in order to evaluate and quantify the magnitude of the fault and the time response needed.

References

D. Harel, 1987, Statecharts: A visual formalism for complex systems, Science of Computer Programming, 8, 231-274.

J. L. de la Mata, M. Rodriguez, 2010a, Abnormal Situation Diagnosis Using D-higraphs, Computer Aided Chemical Engineering, 28, 1477–1482.

J. L. de la Mata, M. Rodriguez, 2010b, D-higraphs report, <www.aslab.org> accessed on 31/01/2014.

W. L. Luyben, 2007, Chemical Reactor Design and Control., Wiley-VCH, New Jersey, USA.

M. Rodríguez, R. Sanz, 2009, Development of Integrated Functional-Structural Models, Computer Aided Process Engineering, 27, 573-578

M. Rodriguez, J. L. de la Mata, 2012, Automating HAZOP studies using D-higraphs, Comput. Chem. Eng., 45, 102-112.

M. Rodriguez, J. L. de la Mata, I. Diaz, 2013, Fault-Tolerant Self-Reconfigurable Control System, Computer Aided Chemical Engineering, 32, 901-906.

Jiří Jaromír Klemeš, Petar Sabev Varbanov and Peng Yen Liew (Editors)
Proceedings of the 24th European Symposium on Computer Aided Process Engineering – ESCAPE 24
June 15-18, 2014, Budapest, Hungary.

Developing a Soft Sensor for an Air Separation Process Based on Variable Selection in Dynamic Partial Least Squares

Jialin Liu,[a]* Ding-Sou Chen[b]

[a]*Center for Energy and Environmental Research, National Tsing Hua University, No. 101, Section 2, Kuang-Fu Road, Hsinchu, Taiwan, Republic of China*
[b]*New Materials Research & Development Department, China Steel Corporation, No. 1, Chung Kang Rd., Hsiao Kang, Kaohsiung, Taiwan, Republic of China*
jialin@che.nthu.edu.tw

Abstract

Soft sensors are used to predict response variables, which are difficult to measure, using the data of predictors that can be obtained relatively easier. Arranging time-lagged data of predictors and applying partial least squares (PLS) to the dataset is a popular approach for extracting the correlation between data of the responses and predictors of the process dynamic. However, the model input dimension dramatically soars once multiple time delays are incorporated. In the presented work, the variable importance in projection (VIP) method was used to shrink the insignificant inputs from the results of the sparse PLS (SPLS). An industrial soft sensor was developed based on the proposed approach. The prediction performance and the model interpretability could be further improved from the SPLS method using the proposed approach.

Keywords: Soft sensors; Process dynamic modeling; Variable selection; Partial least squares.

1. Introduction

Dynamic PLS (DPLS) has been widely applied in the design of soft sensors (Zamprogna et al., 2004). For a continuous process, the input variables of DPLS are formed using the presented data and some time-lagged data of the predictor variables. However, it is often unclear if the response variables are affected by the length of the predictors' delay, and how to determine the predictor time lags for the DPLS model remains an open question. Kano et al. (2000) evaluated the model performances of the predictors using different sampling intervals, and then collected the data with better modeling performances to form the training dataset to build the inferential model. Since the dimension of the input variables dramatically increases with the order of the modeling time lags, a high-dimensional dataset can easily be formed once several time delays are incorporated. The high-dimensional dataset often contains variables that are irrelevant for predicting the response variables. Even if the contribution to the model is small, the prediction performance can be deteriorated by these irrelevant variables.

If the modeling data contain a massive number of irrelevant predictors, the latent variables (LVs) of PLS will tend to capture the variances of that predictors rather than those of the responses. Chun and Keleş (2010) reformulated the object function of PLS to find the weight vector ($\mathbf{w}$) maximizing the covariance between predictors and responses by introducing penalty terms in order to shrink the elements in $\mathbf{w}$. This procedure was named sparse PLS (SPLS). They pointed out that the optimization problem could be converted to soft-thresholding PLS for a single response variable. Since the single cut-off value for $\mathbf{w}$ in SPLS was determined using the cross-validation procedure, the value may be a compromise for all LV directions. In this paper, the variable importance in projection (VIP) method was applied to the regression result of SPLS and called SPLS-VIP, in order to enhance the model prediction performance and model interpretability using less predictors. The remainder of this paper is organized as follows. Section 2 gives a preliminary of PLS and the VIP method for variable selection. The SPLS algorithm is briefed in section 3. In section 4, an inferential model is built using the SPLS-VIP method for predicting the oxygen concentration in the air separation process and the model interpretability is addressed. Finally, conclusions are given in section 5.

2. Partial Least Squares (PLS)

PLS regression is a popular statistical tool for modeling the predictor and response datasets (Indahl, 2014). The predictor ($\mathbf{X}$) and response ($\mathbf{Y}$) data matrices can be written according to a set of LVs: $\mathbf{X} = \mathbf{T}\mathbf{P}^T + \mathbf{E}$ and $\mathbf{Y} = \mathbf{T}\mathbf{Q}^T + \mathbf{F}$ where $\mathbf{T}$ is the first k terms of the LVs or the score vectors, $\mathbf{P}$ and $\mathbf{Q}$ respectively are the loading vectors of the data matrices $\mathbf{X}$ and $\mathbf{Y}$, and $\mathbf{E}$ and $\mathbf{F}$ are the residual terms of PLS. In general, each score is extracted through deflating $\mathbf{X}$ and $\mathbf{Y}$ by the algorithm of the non-linear iterative partial least squares (NIPALS) until all variance in the data structure is explained. The PLS-VIP method uses the VIP scores, which are evaluated according to the output variables influenced by the predictors on the latent space, to identify the important predictors. The jth predictor's VIP score to the ith response variable can be written as:

$$v_{j,i} = \sqrt{N \sum_{l=1}^{k} w_{j,l}^2 \left(q_{i,l}^2 \mathbf{t}_l^T \mathbf{t}_l \right) \bigg/ \sum_{l=1}^{k} q_{i,l}^2 \mathbf{t}_l^T \mathbf{t}_l}$$ where N is the dimension of input variables. For VIP

scores that are larger than a threshold, i.e., $v_{j,i} \geq s_{vip}$, the predictors should be selected as input variables. In general, the greater-than-one rule is used as a criterion for variable selection. Chong and Jun (2005) suggested that a proper threshold should be between 0.83 and 1.21, and that when the proportion of irrelevant predictors is higher, a higher threshold is preferred.

3. Spare Partial Least Squares (SPLS)

The PLS algorithm successively finds the direction vectors $\mathbf{w}$ that maximize the covariance between the predictor variables and the responses. The object function and the constrain respectively are: $\max_{\mathbf{w}} \left(\mathbf{w}^T \mathbf{M} \mathbf{w} \right)$ and $\mathbf{w}^T \mathbf{w} = 1$ where $\mathbf{M} = \mathbf{X}^T \mathbf{Y} \mathbf{Y}^T \mathbf{X}$. Chun and Keleş (2010) modified the object function of PLS by imposing a surrogate of vector $\mathbf{c}$ for iterations: $\min_{\mathbf{w},\mathbf{c}} \left(-\kappa \mathbf{w}^T \mathbf{M} \mathbf{w} + (1-\kappa)(\mathbf{c}-\mathbf{w})^T \mathbf{M}(\mathbf{c}-\mathbf{w}) + \lambda_1 \|\mathbf{c}\|_1 + \lambda_2 \|\mathbf{c}\|_2 \right)$. The first term of the equation is used to maximize the covariance between the predictors and the responses, and the second term keeps vectors $\mathbf{c}$ and $\mathbf{w}$ close to each other. Parameter κ is used to regulate the compromise of the two terms. The L_1-penalty encourages sparsity on $\mathbf{c}$ by imposing parameter λ_1, whereas the L_2-penalty is introduced by λ_2 to prevent all elements in $\mathbf{c}$ from shrinking to zero when λ_1 is large enough. For the case of a univariate response, Chun and Keleş (2010) pointed out that parameter κ is independent of the solution, whereas λ_2 can be set to infinity, leading to the formation of a soft-threshold estimator. The univariate SPLS algorithm is listed in Table 1, in which set A

represents the selected predictors and is initialized using a null set. The first eigenvector of covariance **M** is solved and denoted as vector **w**. In step 3, parameter η is an adjustable parameter between 0 and 1 and determines the sparsity of the SPLS solution. In that step, the elements in vector **w** that have magnitudes larger than the given proportion of the largest magnitude in **w** are selected as the important predictors. The NIPALS algorithm is then applied to solve the regression coefficients between the selected predictors and the response variable. The threshold and the number of latent variables are determined using cross validation.

4. Industrial Application

In this section, the SPLS-VIP algorithm was applied to predict the oxygen concentration for an air separation process. A schematic flow diagram of the air separation process is shown in Figure 1. There were five distillation columns that had been highly integrated to separate nitrogen, oxygen and argon from the compressed air. The compressed air

Table 1. SPLS algorithm for a univariate response

---

1. Set $a=1$, $\mathbf{y}_a = \mathbf{y}$, and the set of the selected variables is a null set, i.e., $A = \varnothing$.

2. Calculate $\mathbf{M} = \mathbf{X}\mathbf{y}_a^{\mathrm{T}}\mathbf{y}_a\mathbf{X}^{\mathrm{T}}$ and solve the first eigenvector of M, denoted as w.

3. Update the set of the selected variables according to the first eigenvector **w**, i.e.,

$$A = A \cup \left\{ i \,\middle|\, |w_i| > \eta \times \max_j \left[|w_j| \in \mathbf{w} \right] \right\}.$$

4. Apply the NIPALS algorithm to iterate the regression coefficient $\boldsymbol{\beta}$ for the retained inputs and the output.

5. Calculate $\mathbf{y}_a = \mathbf{y} - \boldsymbol{\beta}\mathbf{X}$ and set $a = a+1$; go back to step 2 if the stop criterion is not met.

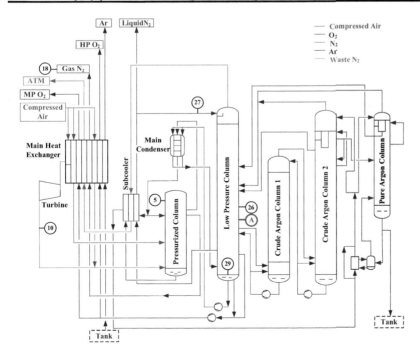

Figure 1. Brief flow diagram of the air separation process.

was fed into the main heat exchanger (MHE) and then fed into a pressurized column. The N_2 product streams were drawn from the top of the pressurized column. One stream was liquefied through the main condenser and the sub cooler as the liquid N_2 product, and the other stream went through the MHE as the gas N_2 product. The liquefied O_2 products were drawn from the bottom of the low pressure column and then pumped up to 32 kg/cm^2 and 12 kg/cm^2, which respectively were the high pressure (HP) and medium pressure (MP) products after the MHE. The argon was purified by crude argon columns 1 and 2, as well as the pure argon column. An online analyzer was installed to inspect the O_2 concentration, which is labeled as **A** in Figure 1. The O_2 concentration was monitored to assure the product qualities and prevent crude argon column 2 from dumping. However, online analyzers are usually not very reliable, and the sampling interval of the online analyzer was one hour; therefore, a soft-sensor counterpart was desired to confirm the results of the online analyzer measurements and to monitor the output values between two sampling points of the online analyzer. In the process, there were five products separated from the compressed air, which were gas and liquid nitrogen, HP and MP oxygen, and argon. The operators keyed in the demanded production rate for each product in the control panel, and then an empirical model controller manipulated 29 set points of the process variables to bring the process to the proper operating conditions. In this study, the inferential model of the air separation process was developed and tested using process data collected every five minutes from January 1, 2013 to July 31, 2013, and data of the oxygen concentration were collected once per one hour during the same period. In the data set, the input variables consisted of 29 manipulated variables with past one hour data, i.e., 348 (29×12) input variables, and one target output variable – the O_2 concentration. The part of manipulated variables is listed in Table 2. The January data were used to build the prediction model, and the data of the next six months were used to test the performance of the model. The PLS and SPLS algorithms were applied to the training dataset and the latent structures were determined by five-fold cross-validation. Figure 2 shows the regression coefficients of SPLS and PLS, in which the R^2 values were 0.62 and 0.64 for SPLS and PLS, respectively. It illustrates that the SPLS sacrificed the modeling capability using fewer predictor variables. As shown in Figure 2(b), most of the regression coefficients of PLS were between -0.1 and 0.1, i.e., indicating the model structure could not effectively capture the correlation between the input and output variables. The most significant predictors found by PLS were variable 26 with time lags 0, 1, and 2, and variable 18 with time lags 3 and 8, respectively; a similar situation was found using SPLS, as seen in Figure 2(a).

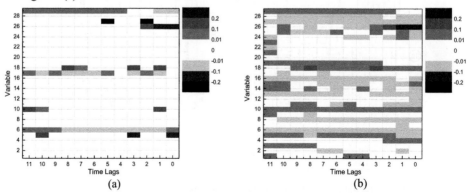

Figure 2. Regression coefficients for using (a) SPLS; (b) PLS.

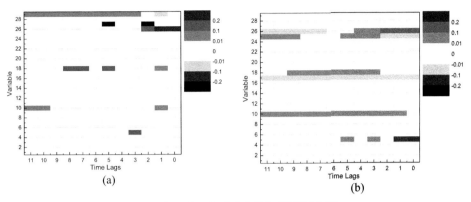

Figure 3. Regression coefficients for using (a) SPLS-VIP, (b) PLS-VIP.

Table 2. The manipulated variables for the process

ID	Description
5	Pressurized Column O_2 Concentration Control
10	Turbine Flow Control
17	Regeneration Gas Flow Control
18	Gas Nitrogen Product Flow Control
25	Pressure of Pure Argon Column
26	Side Draw Temperature of Low Pressure Column
27	Liquid Nitrogen Reflux to Low Pressure Column
29	Low Pressure Column Level Control

Variable 26 was identified as the side-drawn temperature, which was close to the sampling point of the online analyzer, as shown in Figure 1; therefore, this variable was highly correlated with the oxygen concentration. In addition, the composition of the process feed-in (the compressed air), was constant; once more nitrogen products were drawn from the system, the oxygen concentration left in the system would be higher. The ratio of designed specifications for the gas and liquid nitrogen products was 30. Therefore, the gas nitrogen production rate, variable 18, affected the output variable with some time delays. These variables were also identified as the important predictors using PLS and SPLS, as shown in Figure 2. Figure 2 shows that a more compact model could be found using SPLS than from using PLS; therefore, the thresholds of SPLS-VIP and PLS-VIP were set to 0.83 and 1.21, respectively (Chong and Jun, 2005). Figure 3 shows the regression coefficients using SPLS-VIP and PLS-VIP. After consulting with the field operators, some manipulated variables would be finely adjusted in order to maintain a stable oxygen concentration. For example, when the side-drawn temperature was too high there would be two possibilities: one was the whole system temperature was too high, and the other one was that only variable 26 was too high. For the former case, the turbine flow (variable 10) would increase to bring down the whole system temperature; for the latter, the liquid nitrogen reflux to the top of low pressure column (variable 27) would be increased. On the other hand, if the temperature was too low, the level of the low pressure column (variable 29) would be increased. As Figure 3(a) shows, these variables were identified as the significant variables using SPLS-VIP. Figure 3(a) also indicates that variable 5, which was the oxygen concentration of the pressurized column, was important. It was reasonable that the oxygen concentrations in the system would be correlated with each other. Comparing with the results of PLS-VIP

Table 3. Comparison of the prediction performances

	RMSE	Average	Standard Deviation
SPLS-VIP	0.1852	-0.0101	0.1850
SPLS	0.2026	0.0175	0.2018
PLS-VIP	0.2508	0.0619	0.2431
PLS	0.2175	0.0212	0.2156

in Figure 3(b), too many irrelative inputs were identified as significant predictors (such as variables 17 and 25), whereas some important variables were missed (such as variables 27 and 29). This demonstrated that since the latent structure of PLS was deteriorated by the irrelevant variables, the PLS-VIP, which was based on the improper model structure, would fail to select the correct variables.

The root-mean-square error (RMSE), and the average and standard deviation of the prediction errors are listed in Table 3. Since the SPLS provided a more compact model than that from the PLS, the SPLS-VIP model further improved the model prediction performance. It could be observed that the RMSE was reduced from 0.2026 to 0.1852, and that the average and the standard deviation of the errors were also reduced. On the contrary, the increase of the averages and the standard deviations for the prediction errors of PLS-VIP and the increasing RMSE for PLS-VIP indicated that the prediction performance was deteriorated after selecting the variables from the PLS model. Table 3 illustrates that the model prediction performance would be worse if the variable selection was conducted on an improper model structure.

5. Conclusions

Once the number of modeling time delays is increasing in DPLS, the number of irrelevant inputs will be dramatically increasing. The PLS modeling capability will be destroyed, since the latent variables tend to capture the variations of these irrelevant inputs. Therefore, the modeling capability of PLS-VIP may be worse than that of PLS, since the selected variables are based on an improper latent structure. In the presented work, the VIP scores were used to filter out the unimportant predictors in the SPLS model. An industrial soft sensor was built based on the proposed approach. The results showed that the prediction performance was improved in comparison to the SPLS model. Meanwhile, it was also demonstrated that the prediction performance of PLS-VIP was even worse than that of the PLS model, due to the destroyed latent structure of PLS.

References

I. Chong, C. Jun., 2005, Performance of some variable selection methods when multicollinearity is present, Chem. Intell. Lab. Syst., 78, 103-112.

H. Chun, S. Keleş, 2010, Sparse partial least squares regression for simultaneous dimension reduction and variable selection, J. R. Stat. Soc. Series B, 72, 3-25.

U.G. Indahl, 2014, The geometry of PLS1 explained properly: 10 key notes on mathematical properties of and some alternative algorithmic approaches to PLS1 modelling, J. Chemom., DOI: 10.1002/cem.2589.

M. Kano, K. Miyazaki, S. Hasebe, I. Hashimoto, 2000, Inferential control system of distillation compositions using dynamic partial least squares regression, J. Proc. Cont., 10, 157-166.

E. Zamprogna, M. Barolo, D.E. Seborg, 2004, Estimating product composition profiles in batch distillation via partial least squares regression, Cont. Eng. Prac., 12, 917-929.

Jiří Jaromír Klemeš, Petar Sabev Varbanov and Peng Yen Liew (Editors)
Proceedings of the 24th European Symposium on Computer Aided Process Engineering – ESCAPE 24
June 15-18, 2014, Budapest, Hungary.

Model Based Fault Diagnosis for Performance Control of a Decentralized Wastewater Treatment Plant

Rita Ribeiro[a], Carla I.C. Pinheiro[b,*], Tatiana Arriaga[b], Helena M. Pinheiro[b], Maria do Céu Almeida[a]

[a]*Laboratório Nacional de Engenharia Civil, Departamento Hidráulica e Ambiente, Avenida do Brasil, 101, 1700-066 - Lisboa, Portugal*
[b]*IBB - Institute for Biotechnology and Bioengineering, Instituto Superior Técnico/Universidade de Lisboa, Avenida Rovisco Pais, 1, 1049-001 - Lisboa, Portugal*
carla.pinheiro@ist.utl.pt

Abstract

The quality requirements for effluents from wastewater treatment plants (WWTP) have become stricter along the years, a trend likely to continue. Improved supervision and control provides conditions to increase the resilience of treatment processes. The lack of an appropriate tool applicable to small, decentralized WWTP is presently a limiting factor for improving the robustness of plant operation for pollution prevention. This paper presents a simulation study regarding the response to a sensor fault applied to a model based framework for performance supervision and control specifically adapted to small-scale, decentralized WWTP. This framework makes use of on-line data acquisition (flow and organic pollutant concentration) integrated in a developed dynamic model structure, further used for model-based predictive control. The results of this case study simulation show the potential of the proposed strategies for response to a fault in the affluent flow sensor, allowing continual operation in an energy conservation mode with respect to bioreactor aeration.

Keywords: control, decentralized WWTP, faults modelling, modelling, process diagnosis

1. Introduction

In rural areas, the use of decentralized systems for wastewater collection and treatment is an accepted practice. The small dimension and the dispersion across the territory have led to a largely unattended operation of many of these decentralized WWTP, with periodic visits of operators for treatment process control. The main issues that derive from this unmanned operation are a deficiency of sustained knowledge about wastewater inflow characteristics and the dynamic behaviour of the treatment system, and, also, the need for more intensive control actions to correct treatment system unbalance resulting from delayed detection of operational problems. The quality requirements for WWTP effluents have become stricter along the years, a trend likely to continue. To meet these standards, improved supervision and control is needed to increase the resilience of WWTP, despite disturbances and possible faults affecting the process (Olsson, 2012). In parallel, the drive towards better control is often associated with increased expectations of minimizing operational costs. The control strategies usually defined for the activated sludge process have to fulfil several operational goals and can be divided into three main fields (Chachuat et al., 2009): control of organic removal; control of nitrogen removal; and control of phosphorus removal. In all, the oxygen transfer rate is a crucial factor. Effective process control is dependent on a reliable stream of data. Even though significant improvements have been made in wastewater treatment sensor technology, sensor signals are still subject to many possible errors including noise, drift, catastrophic failure, power outages and transmission problems (Corominas et al., 2011).

Dynamic simulation of treatment performance can provide comprehensive process information, serving as a basis for optimized operation. The use of a calibrated model can help in the identification of process inefficiencies such as the impact of over-aeration, sub-optimal pumping rates and the impact of specific control loops on the process behaviour (Schraa et al., 2006).

The present paper presents a simulation study regarding the options for response to a flow sensor fault applied to a model based framework for performance supervision and control specifically adapted to small-scale, decentralized WWTP. This framework makes use of online data acquisition integrated in a developed dynamic model structure, which is used for model-based predictive control (MPC) for the ultimate goal of fault tolerant control of the WWTP. The model-based fault mitigation technique developed depends on a sufficiently accurate model of the WWTP.

2. Wastewater treatment plant modelling

2.1. Plant and process description
An intensive study was carried out in a full-scale decentralized WWTP treating wastewater from an 850-inhabitant rural community located in the north of Portugal. The wastewater is mainly of domestic origin, with episodic infiltration contribution. The treatment system is a prolonged aeration activated sludge process, following an initial preliminary stage for the removal of coarse solids. The biological treatment stage comprehends a completed mixed aeration tank and a secondary sedimentation tank. The aeration is performed by a surface aerator operated on a timer (intermittent aeration).

In the activated sludge process, the inflow wastewater is agitated and aerated in a bioreactor, in which microorganisms metabolize the wastewater's organic matter. The flocculent activated sludge is removed by sedimentation in the clarifier, and returned to the process or wasted as needed. The clarified overflow is the treated effluent. Figure 1 shows the diagram of the case study WWTP, where Q_{in} represents the wastewater input flow, Q_{ml} the output flow from the bioreactor, Q_{ef} the treated effluent flow, Q_a the air flow, Q_{sr} and Q_{sw} are respectively the sludge recycled and rejected flows.

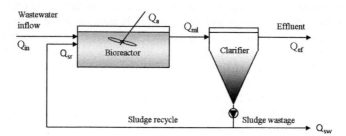

Figure 1. The wastewater treatment plant.

An extensive monitoring study was carried out in the case study WWTP. An online instrumentation system was installed in the plant for the period of one year, including continuous flow measurement (Q_{in} and Q_{ef}), pH and dissolved oxygen monitoring and spectroscopy in the ultraviolet-visible wavelength range for feed organic load quantification. Six campaigns were carried out, with online instrumentation coordinated with sampling and chemical analysis at different locations in the plant. The gathered data allowed the functional characterization of the treatment system, and provided information for the calibration and validation of the mathematical dynamic model used for process control analysis.

2.2. Process model

The nonlinear dynamic model developed in MATLAB®/Simulink comprises three modules, representing the main attributes of the treatment plant: hydrodynamic behaviour, biological treatment and suspended solids separation (Ribeiro, 2011). The hydrodynamic model is based on the continuity principle and considers the flow characteristics of the dischargers, integrating simulation of internal flows with impact on the flow of treated effluent.

The biological treatment module consists in a simplified description of the activated sludge process based on the ASM1, a mechanistic, nonlinear model developed by the International Water Association (Henze et al., 2000). In this case study, only the processes associated to the removal of carbonaceous material (i.e., heterotrophic grow, heterotrophic decay, hydrolysis) were considered. In addition, three modifications were made in the formulation. The first concerns the integration of inert particulate products resulting from the biomass decay in the inert particulate organic material, which becomes non-conservative unlike originally established in ASM1. The second change is the division of the variable Xs in particulate and solubilised fractions, attempting to reproduce the inflow of slowly biodegradable material with different characteristics to the treatment system. Finally, the effect of temperature on the kinetics was considered in the model implementation through the Arrhenius equation.

The suspended solids separation model comprises a function which reflects the efficiency of particulate material removal in the secondary settler, assumed equivalent to the organic particulate material separation efficiency. The application of this kind of model (point settler model) is admissible only in systems with high separation efficiency with mixture effect in the clarified liquid (Vanrolleghem et al., 2003), as it is the case.

3. Aeration profile simulation

Simulations of the process without any monitoring or operation faults were performed for a sample, 24-hour inflow dataset in order to define a set of aeration conditions that would determine the limits for alternating between three aeration profiles according to the inlet chemical oxygen demand (COD) load, calculated using real measurements of Q_{in} and the inlet COD concentration (COD_{in}). In this WWTP the surface aerator is normally operated on a fixed, 15 minutes on and 35 minutes off cycle, and the Q_{in} and COD_{in} measurements were collected every 5 minutes. This aeration profile will be referred as the reference aeration profile (RAP).

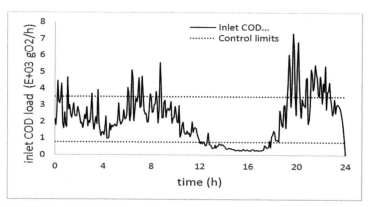

Figure 2. Inlet COD load profile during the sample, 24-hour operation period, and limits used for switching between aeration cycles in the model based simulation.

Figure 2 represents the sample, measured inlet COD load profile, and the control limits for the three aeration profiles included in the chosen control strategy are shown, namely:
- Inlet COD load < 750 gO_2/h, aeration profile 1 (AP1)
- Inlet COD load ≥ 750 and < 3500 gO_2/h, aeration profile 2 (AP2)
- Inlet COD load ≥ 3500 gO_2/h, aeration profile 3 (AP3)

As the WWTP is oversized, the RAP was set as the profile of maximum aeration (AP3) used when aeration control is simulated. The medium and minimum aeration profiles were obtained by decreasing the aeration on period to 10 minutes and increasing the off time to 45 mins (AP2) and 50 mins (AP1), respectively.

4. Results and discussion

The performance of the process under the aeration profiles described above was simulated using real Q_{in} and COD_{in} data (scenario B). As Figure 3 indicates, the predicted dissolved oxygen levels decrease substantially when compared to the uncontrolled scenario (scenario A, fixed aeration cycle). This indicates the onset of oxygen limitation which results in higher values of effluent COD (COD_{out}, Figure 3). In scenario A, the RAP delivers an excess of oxygen to the bioreactor promoting COD removal, and leading to COD_{out} levels much lower than the regulated discharge limit (150 gO_2/m^3). When the control conditions are applied, COD removal performance deteriorates (Figure 4 and Table 1) but the residual COD_{out} level is still kept well below the limit. The reduction in energy consumption is significant (Table 1) and may represent a cost saving of more than 900 €/y.

The aeration control strategy is however dependent on continuous flow and COD_{in} data. The same sample 24-h dataset was thus used to simulate the effect of a catastrophic flow measurement failure on the control strategy performance. In addition, different options for the response to the detection of this fault were also simulated. The aeration profile resulting from null Q_{in} value input in the 24-h period is AP1. Its erroneous application during the whole sample period still keeps COD_{out} under the discharge limit (Figure 4), but the increasing trend suggests accumulation of organic matter and a likely violation if no action was taken. These results confirm the importance of the Q_{in} data availability for the success of the aeration control strategy.

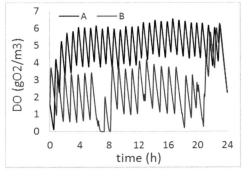

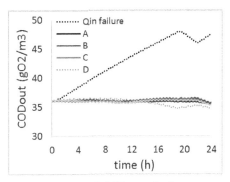

Figure 3. Simulation of dissolved oxygen (DO) profiles with aeration scenarios A (RAP) and B (aeration control mechanism).

Figure 4. Simulated COD_{ef} results from different aeration scenarios including flow measurement device failure responses.

To avoid the deterioration of the WWTP performance, the control strategy must then be able to respond in case of Q_{in} real time measurements being unavailable. The tested hypotheses were to replace the measured data with an average profile based on historical trend data (scenario C, the trend being derived from the six measurement campaigns), a constant profile (scenario D, a fixed average value) or a step profile (scenario E), all represented in Figure 5.

The model based simulation of the response of the aeration control strategy to the Q_{in} replacement profiles (strategies C-E in Table 1) show that the resulting COD load discharged and energy consumption levels are comparable to those resulting from scenario B with no COD_{out} increase trend (Figure 4). Thus any of the replacement Q_{in} profiles could be used in case of measurement failure, namely the simple, step profile.

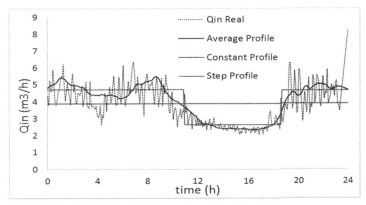

Figure 5 – Sample, 24-hour Q_{in} dataset and the tested replacement Q_{in} profile options in case of catastrophic failure of the inlet flow measurement device.

Table 1. Total discharged COD load and aeration time during 24-h simulated period and estimated energy consumption obtained for each replacement inlet flow profile.

Scenario	Total effluent COD load kgO$_2$/day	Total aeration time h/day	Total power consumption kWh/day
A	3.335	7.1	53.23
B	4.387	4.3	32.34
C	4.423	4.4	32.76
D	4.180	4.5	34.12
E	4.295	4.5	33.90

5. Conclusions

The present work demonstrates the usefulness of a model based approach to the operation of small, decentralized WWTP, for the simple case of energy saving through aeration control. Moreover, the sample simulation showed that the availability of the base model allows controlled operation of the WWTP even in case of catastrophic failure of inlet flow measurement, if the control strategy includes replacement of the inlet flow profile with a simple step profile once the fault is detected. In this case, the COD$_{in}$ measurement instrument (inline spectrophotometer) would provide a redundant detection of minimal inflow, providing the fault detection signal.

Acknowledgements

The authors gratefully acknowledge the contractor company (Águas da Serra) of the case study WWTP for the data and information provided. This work was financed by Portuguese national funds through FCT - Fundação para a Ciência e a Tecnologia in the framework of project PTDC/AAG-TEC/4124/2012.

References

B. Chachuat, B. Srinivasanb, D. Bonvinc, 2009, Adaptation strategies for real-time optimization, Computers and Chemical Engineering, 33, 1557–1567.

L. Corominas, K. Villez, D. Aguado, L. Rieger, C. Rosén, P.A. Vanrolleghem, 2011, Performance Evaluation of Fault Detection Methods for Wastewater Treatment Processes, Biotechnology and Bioengineering, 108, 2, 333–344.

M. Henze, W. Gujer, T. Mino, M.C.M. van Loosdrecht, 2000, Activated sludge models ASM1, ASM2, ASM2d and ASM3, Scientific and Technical Report No. 9, IWA Publishing, London, UK.

G. Olsson, 2012, ICA and me – A subjective review, Water Research, 46, 1585–1624.

O. Schraa, B. Tole, J.B. Copp, 2006, Fault detection for control of wastewater treatment plants. Wat. Sci. Tech., 53, 4-5, 375–382.

R. Ribeiro, 2011, Assessment and control of the efficiency of wastewater treatment – Application to small scale systems, PhD Thesis, Instituto Superior Técnico, Lisbon, Portugal.

P. Vanrolleghem, G. Insel, B. Petersen, G. Sin, D. De Pauw, I. Nopens, S. Weijers, K. Gernaey, 2003, A comprehensive model calibration procedure for activated sludge models. WEFTEC'03, Alexandria, USA.

Jiří Jaromír Klemeš, Petar Sabev Varbanov and Peng Yen Liew (Editors)
Proceedings of the 24th European Symposium on Computer Aided Process Engineering – ESCAPE 24
June 15-18, 2014, Budapest, Hungary.

CFD-Study for the Design of Injector / Conductivity Sensor Manifold

Heinz A Preisig

Department of Chemical Engineering; NTNU; Trondheim, Norway
Heinz.Preisig@chemeng.ntnu.no

Abstract

The experimental evaluation of the residence time distribution is a common method to characterise the hydraulic behaviour of a plant. It can be used to provide input/output models for reactive systems when overlapping the experimental hydraulics with a reaction kinetics through numerical convolution. A CFD study of different geometries both injection module and sensor module enable us to visualise the expected flow patterns in the manifold. Injection is critical. The standard T-piece approach exhibits a rather unfavourable behaviour, whilst injecting against the stream provides a rather effective plume of tracer that then is passing through sensor and plant.

Keywords: Residence time distribution, equipment characterisation, CFD

1. Motivation

Tracer experiments are used to characterise the hydraulic of a plant unit. The objective of the experiment is to characterise the hydraulic behaviour of a plant in terms of a residence time distribution. This distribution provides the information on how long material takes from the inflow to the outflow. Ideally one injects an impulse of tracer and measures the resulting output directly providing the impulse response. The impulse would be the ideal excitation signal, but it is not possible to physically realise an impulse. So one often uses steps or pulses instead. Also those two are strictly speaking physically not realisable as tracer concentrations cannot be changed instantaneously. Danckwerts was seminal in the definition and analysis of residence time distribution (see Danckwerts (1995) and Danckwerts (1953)). He states in his paper: *The F-diagram of a system is easy to obtain (for instance, by injecting tracer materials into the entering stream) ...*, where the F-diagram is the step response.

Today, residence-time distribution experiments are part of the standard laboratory techniques for characterising the hydraulic behaviour of equipment. Currently it is micro equipment that is of particular interest (see Wörner (2010), Cantu-Perez et al. (2011), and Georget et al. (2013)) but also in generic equipment (Georget et al. (2013)) and particulate systems (Harris et al. (2002))

The objective of this paper is to show that the injection of tracer to form a pulse or step is not a trivial matter. In fact this study induced the suspicion that many, if not most experimentalist deal with rather non-ideal input signals.

The study has its origin in committing to perform residence time distribution experiments on a tubular mili-reactor equipped with FluiTec's static mixing elements.

2. Experimental set-up

To enable the experiments we designed and constructed a work bench consisting of a water tank as source, a pump to drive the flow, an injection piece after the pump for the injection

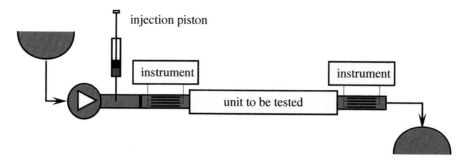

Figure 1: Concept of test bench

of tracer (NaCl) dissolved in water, the equipment to be analysed and a sensor again right at the end of the equipment (Figure 1). In a first design we used commercial sensors from Honeywell, though we found that they are much too large and clumsy for this application. In fact most of the mixing went on in the sensor and its build-in cavity rather than in the test equipment.

This then lead to the design of a new assembly consisting of injection and sensor. In order to minimise the contribution of the assembly to the residence time distribution, we aimed at realising it in the dimensions of the feeding pipe, which has an inner hydraulic diameter of 3.6 mm. The sensor is a conductivity sensor and must be designed to exhibit a sufficiently large sensitivity range for the tracer experiments to be effective. With the small dimensions, things get tight and it was decided to use a stack of paired electrodes. Each package consists of two metal sheets that withstand corrosion. The two essential parameter are surface of the electrodes and the distance between them. They must be aligned with the flow so as to not create any dead volume elements distorting the measurements. Also since one is interested in a measurement capturing the concentration in a cross section of the flow, the surfaces, being along the flow, should not be too long. It is physically not possible to construct a sensor that only takes a measurement on a cross section, thus a surface orthogonal to the flow, but the sensor will take an integral measure over the length, thus a corresponding volume element. Also, the measurement will be an integral aver the volume element that is captured between the electrodes and will simply not "see" the part that is flowing on the side around the sensor plates. Thus any physical arrangement is the result of a compromise.

3. CFD analysis of injection - sensor manifold

3.1. Geometry

3.1.1. Sensor

We tried several designs. In order to check feasibility the first prototype used simply two pieces of pipe being of different diameter.

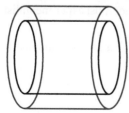

Figure 2: Ring sensor to be built into pipe

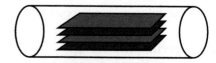

Figure 3: Plate sensor built into pipe

Apparently the ring sensor (Figure 2) must be of larger diameter in order to get the same surface without getting it too long. If doing so, the cross section of the flow enlarges and the pipe is not of constant with any more causing additional mixing effects, which are not desirable. The ring sensor also exhibits a large flow through the centre of the sensor which implies that the tracer is not detected. Whilst simple, this design is not giving the desired results and was dropped quickly.

3.1.2. Injection manifold

The first injection piece was standard starting from a T-piece though considering carefully the possible dead volumes. The T-arrangement allows the use of a simple syringe pushed through the attached membrane.

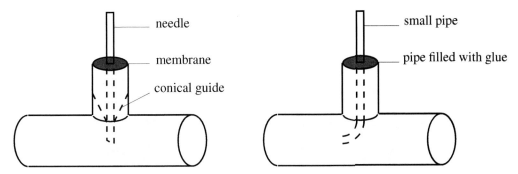

Figure 4: T-injector with membrane   Figure 5: Counter-stream injector

3.2. Simulations

Computational Fluid Dynamic (CFD) software requires the geometry in the form of a mesh as an input. The mesh is generated based on an electronic technical drawing. In our case we used Salome for both tasks, namely for drawing the geometrical objects as well as the isolation of the fluid body and the meshing of it.

The simulations were done with OpenFoam. Two solvers are used as shown in Figure 7. SimpleFoam computes the velocity fields for the two modes of operations, namely when no injection is taking place and when injection is taking place. The two resulting velocity and pressure profiles are used with ScalarFoam to compute the concentration distribution assuming thereby that the tracer fluid has the same density as the flowing fluid in this case being water.

Whilst this three-stage procedure appears cumbersome, it can readily be automised using a script language such as Python.

3.3. Results

Figure 6 shows the simulation results of the standard arrangement in detail. It is apparent that the arrangement does not result the desired plug of tracer fluid passing through the sensor into the equipment. It results in a U-shaped cloud that stretches out as long as the injection last hanging on to the injection point. Once the injection stops, the U is passing through the sensor and equipment.

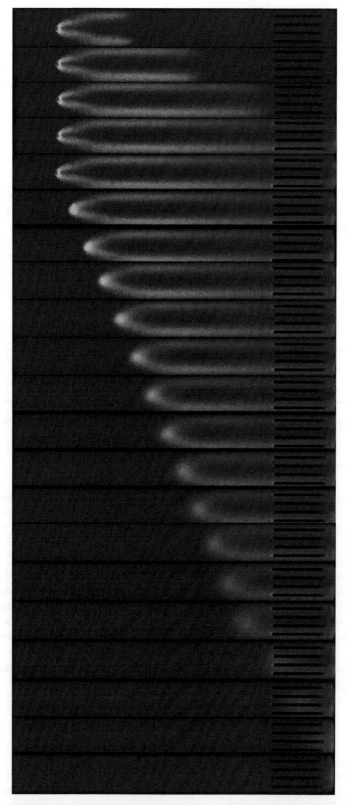

Figure 6: Evolution orthogonal injection. The injection is in the same plane as the sensor plates.

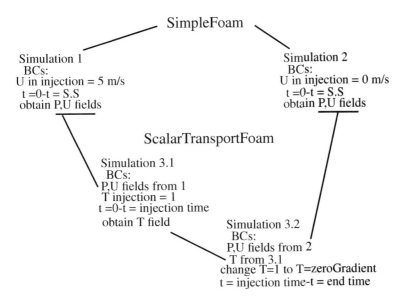

SimpleFoam

Simulation 1
BCs:
U in injection = 5 m/s
t =0-t = S.S
obtain P,U fields

Simulation 2
BCs:
U in injection = 0 m/s
t =0-t = S.S
obtain P,U fields

ScalarTransportFoam

Simulation 3.1
BCs:
P,U fields from 1
T injection = 1
t =0-t = injection time
obtain T field

Simulation 3.2
BCs:
P,U fields from 2
T from 3.1
change T=1 to T=zeroGradient
t = injection time-t = end time

Figure 7: Use of OpenFoam solvers

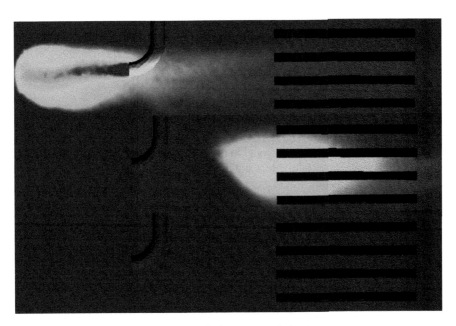

Figure 8: Evolution reverse injection

Figure 8 shows the most successful geometry for the injection, namely the reverse injection. Here the tracer fluid is injected against the flow stream. As we can see, this generates a plume of tracer fluid in front of the injection point. Whilst some of the tracer fluid is bleeding out forming two streams, the majority of the tracer stays in the plume until the injection ends and is then carried as a cloud through the sensor into the equipment.

Figure 9 shows a three snapshots of another arrangement in which three injection pipes were introduced through an elbow. The injection is done in the flow direction. The main issue here is the long tailing generating essentially a snake of tracer winding along the stream.

Figure 9: Evolution 3 injection points in flow direction

4. Conclusions

What have we learnt: First of all, that Danckwert's statement of *residence time distribution experiments are easy to set up by "just" injecting tracer before the equipment into the flow stream* is not so simply "just". The standard arrangement for the injector, namely a T-piece which is used to inject the tracer orthogonal to the flow, was one of the worst once we tried & simulated the behaviour. It certainly does not have the desired effect of mixing the tracer into the laminar fluid stream as one would expect when injecting at relatively high rate.

Injecting in the stream direction leads to even worse results independent of using one point or several.

Injecting against the stream is apparently the most effective in terms of forming a plume of tracer fluid that enters the sensing and thereafter the equipment.

References

A. Cantu-Perez, S. B, S. Barrass, M. Wood, A. Gavriilidis, 2011. Residence time distribution studies in microstructured plate reactors. Applied Thermal Eng 31, 634--639.

P. V. Danckwerts, 1953. Continuous flow systems. distribution of residence times. Chem Eng Sci 2 (1), 1--13.

P. V. Danckwerts, 1995. Continuous flow systems. distribution of residence times. Chem Eng Sci 50 (24), 3857--3866.

E. Georget, J. L. Sauvageat, A. Brubidge, A. Mathys, 2013. Residence time distributions in a modular micro reaction system. J Food Eng 116, 910--919.

A. T. Harris, J. F. Davidson, R. B. Thorpe, 2002. A novel method for measuring the residence time distribution in short time scale particulate systems. Chem Eng J 89, 127--142.

M. Wörner, 2010. Approximate residence time distribution of fully develop laminar flow in a straight rectangular channel. chem eng sci 65, 3499–3507.

Acknowledgements

The paper is derived from the master thesis of Oscar Farreró Pujol.

Jiří Jaromír Klemeš, Petar Sabev Varbanov and Peng Yen Liew (Editors)
Proceedings of the 24th European Symposium on Computer Aided Process Engineering – ESCAPE 24
June 15-18, 2014, Budapest, Hungary.

A New Functional Systems Theory based Methodology for Process Hazards Analysis

Manuel Rodríguez[*], Ismael Díaz

Autonomous Systems Laboratory, Technical University of Madrid, C/ José Gutierrez Abascal 2, Madrid 28006, Spain
manuel.rodriguezh@upm.es

Abstract

This paper presents a new methodology to cope with complex systems hazards analysis. Process safety is an important problem and has traditionally been tackled as a failure problem. Existing methodologies use a chain of events approach to analyse the system's safety. Today, with more complex and interacting systems, this approach has serious limitations because it does not consider, among others, systemic failures. To overcome these limitations, system based approach called STPA (Systems Theoretic Process Analysis) has been developed at MIT (Massachusetts Institute of Technology). In this work we present this methodology, apply it to a process system and integrate it with the use of functional models, a technique that allows to have a more direct, automatic and comprehensive analysis.

Keywords: Process safety, hazards analysis, functional modelling

1. Introduction

Process plants (refineries, chemical plants, petrochemical, pharmaceutical, etc.) deal with a large amount of potentially dangerous materials (toxic, inflammable, explosive, etc.) and many times in extreme conditions (such as high temperatures and pressures). This can lead to equipment failures, plant shutdowns or even worse accidents with catastrophic consequences. In spite of the safety layers of protection (basic process control system, alarms, safety instrumented systems, protective systems, etc.) there are accidents every day with losses up to 1,000 million $ each year only in the US refineries. The existence of accidents is due mainly to the increasing complexity of the process plants. This complexity appears because of two factors. The first one is a more complex process structure (energy integration, minimum waste, higher demands on yield and production, environmental constraints), the second one is a more complex control system (systems that performs many more tasks than before with a non-predictable software). This complexity problem is even worse because both factors are not independent but they are highly interrelated. In order to have safer and more robust plants Process Hazard Analyses (PHA) are carried out to identify the potential problems and also to propose possible solutions such as process changes. Traditional PHA techniques are HAZOP, What-If, FMEA, Checklists etc. This traditional approach is based on a chain of events (failures) analysis, being a loss the consequence of all these failures. The proposed solution is to protect the weakest or most dangerous elements in that chain. This approach has serious limitations: they do not consider systemic failures (due to the interaction between components), they simplify or even do not take into account some factors such as the human factor or the importance of software failures or the company's safety culture. Leveson (2012, 2014) has developed a methodology based on systems theory called STPA (Systems Theoretic Process Analysis) in order to consider interactions and to overcome the limitations of the traditional methods. This approach considers safety as an emergent property and treats it as a control problem. Thus, the methodology is oriented to enforce that the safety control constraints are met in the design and operation of the plant. The procedure has been applied to some domains (aeronautics, trains, etc.) but not to chemical processes. In this paper we present and apply STPA to a chemical process and then take its systems theory foundations into D-higraphs (De la Mata and Rodriguez, 2010), our functional modelling based hazards analysis methodology. The rest of the paper is organised as follows: section two presents the functional modelling methodology D-higraphs. Section three presents the STPA methodology. Section four applies STPA alone and integrated with D-higraphs to a case study. Finally, last section draws some conclusions and discusses the results.

2. Functional modelling methodology

2.1. From Higraphs to D-higraphs

D-higraphs are an adaptation (dualization) of Higraphs, a general kind of diagramming objects well suited to the behavioural specification of complex concurrent systems (Harel, 1987). They consist of blobs, representing transitions, and edges, representing states. They were first presented in Rodríguez and Sanz (2009) as a functional modelling technique that merges functional and structural information of the system modelled.

2.2. Blobs and Edges

Blobs and their basic constituents are depicted in Fig. 1 (above) along with the different types of edges. Blobs represent functions (transitions) that are performed by an ACTOR producing state/s 2 if the state/s 1 is enabled and if the *condition* is true. Edges represent flows of mass, energy, or information, which are responsible of all the interactions in a process system (Lind, 1994). Mass, energy and information edges are depicted differently, but the distinction is just a visual aid.

The main properties of blobs and edges are:

- Blob connection. An edge always links two blobs. Under certain conditions, one of the blobs is not represented (elliptic blob), but it exists.
- Blob inclusion. Blobs can be included inside other blobs (Venn diagram inclusion). This means that the inner blob performs a function that is necessary for the function of the outer blob (representation of functions hierarchy).
- Partitioning blobs. A blob can be partitioned into orthogonal components, establishing an OR condition between the partitions.

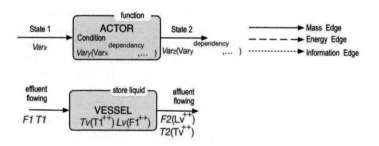

Figure 1. Basic blob and different types of edges.

2.3. Causal and qualitative reasoning

The main objective of D-higraphs is not only the representation of knowledge about process systems. There are a series of causation rules implemented that provides relating two events which allows us to track the evolution and propagation of failures across the system. These rules, combined with sensor data of the plant, enable the possibility of performing FDI analysis using D-higraph models. However, certain analyses require the use of deviations and not only failures, like HAZOP studies (Rodriguez and De la Mata, 2012). In a certain way, we need to simulate qualitatively the system in order to propagate these deviations. The description of a system is made using three different layers (Kuipers, 1984):

1. *Structural description*: variables that characterize the system, such as flow (F), pressure (P), temperature (T), composition (x), energy (E), information (I), level (L), valve opening (A), etc. The symbols in brackets will be used in D-higraphs.
2. *Behavioural description*: potential behaviour of the system as a network.

   $Z(X^{++}, Y^{+\square})$ indicates how the Z variable is affected by deviations of X and Y. The symbol "++" indicates that deviations in X below or over the expected value increase the value of Z, the symbol "+-" means that deviations in Y above the expected value increase Z but deviations below it decrease the value of Z.
3. *Functional description*: purpose of a structural component provided by the D-higraphs layout.

The three layers of this representation are shown in Fig. 1 (below), where there is a physical device (VESSEL) whose main purpose is to *store liquid*. The vessel has two characteristic variables: level (Lv) and temperature (Tv). Lv is affected by the inflow F1 with variations of the same sign (an increment of F1 always increases Lv, in this case the level is not affected by F2 considering the discharge by gravity). Flow F2 is affected by the level of the vessel in the same direction.

3. STPA methodology

3.1. STAMP (Systems-Theoretic Accident Model and Processes)

STAMP is a new type of accident model based on systems theory rather than the traditional analytic reduction using chains and reliability theory. In the STAMP model safety appears as an emergent property that arises when system components interact with each other. This property is enforced by a set of safety constraints that have to be guaranteed.

3.2. STPA

STPA is a hazard analysis technique that builds upon the STAMP accident causality model. As such, it is based on control and system theory rather than on the reliability theory used by most existing hazard analysis techniques. STPA, as any hazard analysis technique, tries to depict hazardous scenarios, the context that produces the hazard. Knowing the conditions for hazardous scenarios the information can then be used to eliminate, reduce, and control them in system design, development, manufacturing, and operations. One of the main differences between STPA and traditional techniques is that it does not generate a probability number related to the hazard. In contrast STPA is more powerful in terms of identifying more causal factors and hazardous scenarios, particularly those related to software, system design, and human behaviour due to its systems based nature.

3.3. The STPA Process

STPA supports and builds on top-down system engineering. STPA has 4 steps, these can be intertwined and in many cases an iterative process is necessary to complete the process. The steps are:

1. Identify Hazards and Accidents.
2. Identify potentially unsafe control actions. Fig. 2 shows potential control flaws to be considered.
3. Use the identified unsafe control actions to create safety requirements and constraints
4. Determine how each potentially hazardous control action could occur.

4. Integrating STPA in functional models: a case study

In this section we use the systemic approach introduced by the STPA methodology with the functional model developed. The information available in this model is enough to conduct the STPA steps identifying hazardous scenarios and proposing corrective alternatives to enforce safety constraints. In order to illustrate the procedure a simple process has been selected. The process is the polymerization reaction in a batch reactor. This reactor has two different feeds, one corresponds to the monomer and the other one corresponds to the initiator needed for the polymerization reaction to occur. The reactor is cooled with an internal coiling in which cooling water is circulated. There is a single control loop to keep the reactor temperature manipulating the cooling water supply as shown in Fig 3. According to the STPA methodology the first step is to identify hazards and accidents. In this case a High Temperature Hazard is identified, which can lead to an explosion with property damage and injuries or life losses. The second step is identifying unsafe control actions. The temperature controller is analysed in this stage, the consequences of the different types of control actions (provided, not provided, too short, etc.) have to be considered. Table 1 presents under different contexts (process variables) the incidence of not providing the control action (system states, directly related to the hazard, are also presented).

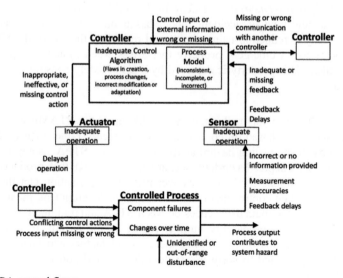

Figure 2. STPA control flaws

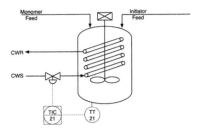

Figure 3. Polymerization Batch Reactor

Table 1. STPA Unsafe Control Actions Identification

Source Controller: Cooling Water Supply. Type: Not Provided				
Process Variables: Context		System (reactor) states		
Fmonomer	Finitiator	Reac Rate	Temperature	Hazard
Expected	Expected	Increase	Increase	Yes
Increase	Expected	Increase	Increase	Yes
Increase	No Flow	No reaction	Keep	No
No Flow	Increase	No reaction	Keep	No
Expected	Increase	Increase	Increase	Yes
...	...	...	...	...

There are different contexts that are hazardous provoking a runaway reaction that can lead to an explosion. This analysis can be used to deduce corrective actions. These actions consist in actively create contexts that are not hazardous (as cutting off the feed of monomer and/or initiator).

Figure 4 shows the functional model of the process, it includes variable dependencies between elements (streams and units). To carry out the second step of the STPA process the hazard is related to system states. The hazard is related to a temperature increase due to a reaction increase (runaway reaction). Once this relation is established it can be deduced using the functional relationships and variable dependencies what variables have to be enforced to guarantee that the hazardous state doesn't happen. It can be observed that a reaction increase depends on the monomer, the initiator and the reactor temperature, which depends on the heat removed. In order to preserve a safe state, at least one of the variables that affect the reaction rate has to be working properly and be accessible to manipulation. In the above selected scenario (not providing cooling water to the reactor) the conclusion obtained with this model is to act upon the monomer or initiator feed (as it was in the STPA standard procedure). Take into account that another possibility exists (and is indicated by the functional model), duplicating the cooling system or having a bypass line that can be open in the case of failure of the original one.

5. Conclusions

Traditional Hazard analysis techniques have shown limitations to deal with new existing complex systems. This work has presented a systems-based theory, STPA, that can deal with systemic failures when analysing a system. The methodology has been applied on a chemical process showing that it can provide the same safety recommendations as other techniques (like HAZOP) but also considering other factors out of the scope of those techniques. As a result STPA can be considered a valid alternative to HAZOP

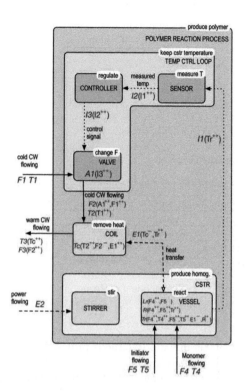

Figure 4. D-Higraph of the Batch Polymerization Process

studies although (as the former) it needs a team of experts to carry it out in a profound and exhaustive manner. STPA philosophy has also been integrated in D-higraphs, a functional modelling methodology. As D-higraphs includes variable dependencies it is easier to perform the systems-based analysis and to deduce the needed corrective actions to guarantee that the safety constraints (absence of hazardous states) are met. Future steps will focus on extending STPA-D-Higraphs to more complex systems (including not chemical ones), automating the analysis procedure and comparing it with existing techniques (HAZOP + SIS) on an industrial process.

References

J.L. De la Mata, M. Rodriguez, 2010, Abnormal Situation Diagnosis using D-higraphs, Computer Aided Chemical Engineering, 28,1679-1685.

D. Harel, 1987, Statecharts: A visual formalism for complex systems, Science of Computer Programming, 8, 231-274.

B.J. Kuipers, 1984, Commonsense reasoning about causality: Deriving behavior from structure. Artificial Intelligence, 24, 1-3, 169-203.

W. Young , N. Leveson, 2014, An Integrated Approach to Safety and Security Based on Systems Theory, Communications of the ACM, 57, 2, 31-35.

N. Leveson, 2012, Engineering a safer world, MIT Press, Massachusetts, USA.

M. Lind, 1994, Modeling Goals and Functions of Complex Plant. AAI, 8, 2, 259-283.

M. Rodriguez, J.L. De la Mata, 2012, Automating HAZOP studies using D-higraphs, Computers and Chemical Engineering, 45,102-113.

M. Rodríguez, R. Sanz, 2009, Development of Integrated Functional-Structural Models, Computer Aided Process Engineering, 27, 573-578.

Jiří Jaromír Klemeš, Petar Sabev Varbanov and Peng Yen Liew (Editors)
Proceedings of the 24th European Symposium on Computer Aided Process Engineering – ESCAPE 24
June 15-18, 2014, Budapest, Hungary. Copyright © 2014 Elsevier B.V. All rights reserved.

Global Sensitivity Analysis for Control of Biological Wastewater Treatment

Alicia Román-Martínez[a,*], Pastor Lanuza-Pérez[a], Margarito Cepeda-Rodríguez[b]

[a]*Facultad de Ciencias QuímicasUASLP,Manuel Nava 6, San Luis Potosí 78210, México*
[b]*Papelera Industrial Potosina S.A. de C.V., Eje 114 230, San Luis Potosí 78900, México*
alicia.romanm@uaslp.mx

Abstract

A mathematical dynamic model for a biological wastewater treatment plant (WWTP) which is located in a paper production facility of PIPSA (Papelera Industrial Potosina, S.A. de C.V.), was recently developed for the main purpose of the development of a control system to improve the water quality of its effluent (Román-Martínez et al., 2013). In this work, an uncertainty and sensitivity analysis of the model outputs is done in order to validate this model and make certain necessary simplifications for the reduction of its complexity. The framework used for the uncertainty management consists mainly in 1.-the model solution verification; 2.-the definition of the objective of the analysis; 3.-the framing containing: identification of the sources of uncertainty and a Monte-Carlo procedure followed by the sensitivity analysis; 4.-a sanity check; and 5.-a decision making process (Sin and Gernaey, 2009). The model of the WWTP bioreactor studied consists of seven ordinary differential and five reaction rates constitutive equations; which include seven output variables (state variables), nineteen input variables and twenty one parameters, from which only seven really affect the model outputs for the bioreactor.

Keywords: Biological WWTP, modelling and control, sensitivity analysis, bioreactor.

1. Introduction

Biological treatments for industrial wastewater treatment (WWT) are complexes systems to control; where a considerable number of variables and parameters are continuously changing. Mathematical models representing this kind of systems are necessary to analyze operational problems, implement control strategies, identify the most important variables, analyze costs, and/or improve a scenario. Different authors like Ostace et al. (2013) have employed assessment of control strategies for biological WWT reactors using the models ASM1 and ASM2 previously developed for systems of several bioreactors (aerobic and anoxic). In this work, an adapted model from the ASM2 is developed for our particular system, which only has one bioreactor instead of several bioreactors (Figure 1) and subjected to a global sensitivity analysis for purposes of validation and reduction of its complexity, to be implemented in a control system for the WWTP to achieve the water quality according to the federal laws in Mexico.

2. WWTP system and model description

The system is schematized in Figure 1. The composition of the wastewater stream coming from the paper plant and entering the WWTP is soluble fiber, insoluble fiber, small pieces of plastic, and sand. Unit 1 is a rotator filter where the small pieces of plastic and the sand are removed. Unit 2 is a stirred tank to homogenize the wastewater. In the unit 3 the soluble fiber is precipitated by addition of a cuagulant (cationic biopolymer) to neutralize the electric charges of the fiber, then, a flocculant (polyaluminum chloride) is added to do the bonding of coagulant-fiber with other bondings. The precipitated fiber is sent back to the paper plant for re-use, while a part of the clarified water by unit 3 is sent directly to the paper plant, and the other part is sent to an aerobic bioreactor (unit 4) where the reactions describe by Eq. (1) to (6) are taking place. The oxygen is added by a positive displacement compressor (unit 8). Amonium phosphate is added because nitrogen and phosphorous concentrations in the bioreactor are very low. Unit 5, a secondary settler, is fed by the output stream of the unit 4, and the rest is sent to the unit 7, a digester to decrease the biomass concentration. Then, it is sent to final disposal (drying beds). The clarified water from unit 5 is sent to a chlorination tank (unit 6) where the pathogen microorganisms die by sodium hypochlorite addition. The dynamic model for the bioreactor of this process is given by Eq. (1) to (7).

$$\frac{dV_b}{dt} = F_i + F_r + F_n + F_{ai} - F_{ob} - F_{ao} \tag{1}$$

$$\frac{dS_b}{dt} = \frac{F_i}{V_b} * S_i + \frac{F_r}{V_b} * S_s - \frac{F_{ob}}{V_b} * S_b - r_S \tag{2}$$

$$\frac{dNT_b}{dt} = \frac{F_i}{V_b} * NT_i + \frac{F_n}{V_b} * NT_n + \frac{F_r}{V_b} * NT_s - \frac{F_{ob}}{V_b} * NT_b - r_{NT} \tag{3}$$

$$\frac{dPO_4^{2-}{}_b}{dt} = \frac{F_i}{V_b} * PO_4^{2-}{}_i + \frac{F_n}{V_b} * PO_4^{2-}{}_n + \frac{F_r}{V_b} * PO_4^{2-}{}_s - \frac{F_{ob}}{V_b} * PO_4^{2-}{}_b - r_{PO_4^{2-}} \tag{4}$$

$$\frac{dX_b}{dt} = \frac{F_r}{V_b} * X_s - \frac{F_{ob}}{V_b} * X_b + r_X \tag{5}$$

$$\frac{dO_{2b}}{dt} = k_{La} * \left(O_2^* - O_{2b}\right) - VCO - \left(\frac{F_{ob}}{V_b} * O_{2b}\right) \tag{6}$$

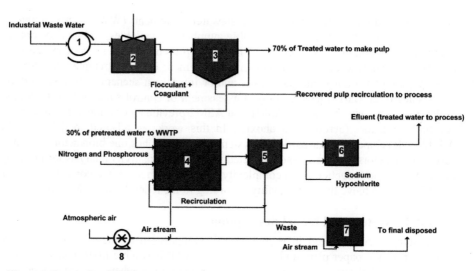

Figure 1. Paper plant WWT system

$$\frac{dSST_b}{dt} = \frac{F_i}{V_b} * SST_i + \frac{F_r}{V_b} * SST_s - \frac{F_{ob}}{V_b} * SST_b \tag{7}$$

where, V_b is the bioreactor volume, m^3; t is the time, day; F_i is input volumetric flowrate, m$^3 \cdot$d^{-1}; F_r is the recycled flowrate, m$^3 \cdot$d^{-1}; F_{ob} is the output flowrate, m$^3 \cdot$d^{-1}; S_b is the substrate concentration, kg$\cdot$m^{-3}; S_{floe} is the output clarified water of primary settler substrate concentration, kg$\cdot$m^{-3}; S_r is the recycled stream substrate concentration, kg$\cdot$m^{-3}; r_s is the substrate reaction rate, kg$\cdot$d^{-1}; NT_b is the total nitrogen concentration, kg$\cdot$m^{-3}; NT_{floe} is the output clarified water of primary settler total nitrogen concentration, kg$\cdot$m^{-3}; F_n is the amonium phosphate external dosage volumetric flowrate, m$^3 \cdot$day^{-1}; NT_n is the external dosage total nitrogen concentration, kg$\cdot$m^{-3}; NT_r is the recycled total nitrogen concentration, kg$\cdot$m^{-3}; r_{NT} is the total nitrogen reaction rate, kg$\cdot$d^{-1}; PO_{4b} is the phosphorous concentration, kg$\cdot$m^{-3}; PO_{4i} is the output clarified water of primary settler phosphorous concentration, kg$\cdot$m^{-3}; PO_{4n} is the external dosage phosphorous concentration, kg$\cdot$m^{-3}; PO_{4r} is the recycled phosphorous concentration, kg$\cdot$m^{-3}; r_{PO4} is the phosphorous reaction rate, kg$\cdot$d^{-1}; X_b is the biomass concentration, kg$\cdot$m^{-3}; X_r is the recycled biomass concentration, kg$\cdot$m^{-3}; r_x is the biomass growth rate, kg$\cdot$d^{-1}; O_2 the oxygen concentration, kg$\cdot$m^{-3}; O_2^* is the equilibrium oxygen concentration, kg$\cdot$m^{-3}; k_{La} is the mass transfer coefficient, d^{-1}; r_{O2} is the oxygen reaction rate, kg$\cdot$d^{-1}; SST_b is the total suspended solids concentration, kg$\cdot$m^{-3}; SST_i is the output clarified water of primary settler total suspended solids concentration, kg$\cdot$m^{-3}; and SST_r is the recycled total suspended solids concentration, kg$\cdot$m^{-3}. The kinetic expressions, taken and modified by adding the temperature and pH dependency, were taken from Mannina et al. (2012), and are given by the constitutive Eq. (8) to (12). Table 1 shows the corresponding meaning and values of the kinetic parameters.

$$r_s = \left[K_H \frac{X_S/X_H}{K_X + X_S/X_H} X * \left(\frac{O2_b}{K_{OH} + O2_b} + \eta_{NO3H} \frac{K_{OH}}{K_{OH} + S_{O2}} \right) \right]$$
$$- \left[\frac{1}{Y_H} * \mu_H \frac{S_b}{K_F + S_b} \frac{O2_b}{K_{OH} + O2_b} \frac{PO4_b}{K_{PO4} + PO4_b} \frac{NT_b}{K_{NH4} + NT_b} X \right. \tag{8}$$
$$\left. * \left(1 + \eta_{NO3H} \frac{K_{OH}}{K_{OH} + O2_b} \right) \right]$$

$$r_{NT} = \left(i_{NBM} - \frac{1}{Y_A} \right) * \mu_{AUT} \frac{O2_b}{K_{OH} + O2_b} \frac{PO4_b}{K_{PO4} + PO4_b} \frac{NT_b}{K_{NH4} + NT_b} X_{AUT}$$
$$- \left[i_{NBM} * \mu_H \frac{S_b}{K_F + S_b} \frac{O2_b}{K_{OH} + O2_b} \frac{PO4_b}{K_{PO4} + PO4_b} \frac{NT_b}{K_{NH4} + NT_b} X_H \right. \tag{9}$$
$$\left. * \left(1 + \eta_{NO3H} \frac{K_{OH}}{K_{OH} + O2_b} \right) \right]$$

$$r_{PO4} = -q_{PP} \frac{O2_b}{K_{OH} + O2_b} \frac{PO4_b}{K_{PO4} + PO4_b} X_{PAO}$$
$$- \left[i_{PBM} * \mu_{PAO} \frac{O2_b}{K_{OH} + O2_b} \frac{PO4_b}{K_{PO4} + PO4_b} \frac{NT_b}{K_{NH4} + NT_b} X_{PAO} \right. \tag{10}$$
$$\left. * (1 + \eta_{NO3PAO}) \right] - i_{PBM} * b_{AUT} X_{AUT}$$

$$r_x = \left[\mu_H \frac{S_b}{K_F + S_b} \frac{O2_b}{K_{OH} + O2_b} \frac{PO4_b}{K_{PO4} + PO4_b} \frac{NT_b}{K_{NH4} + NT_b} X * 0.33 \right.$$
$$* \left(1 + \eta_{NO2H} \frac{K_{OH}}{K_{OH} + O2_b} \right) \right] - 0.33 \, b_H X$$
$$+ \left[\frac{O2_b}{K_{OH} + O2_b} \frac{PO4_b}{K_{PO4} + PO4_b} X * 0.33 \right.$$
$$\left. * \left(\mu_{PAO} * \frac{NT_b}{K_{NH4} + NT_b} * (1 + \eta_{NO2PAO}) + q_{PP} \right) \right] - 0.33 \, b_{PAO} X$$
$$+ \mu_{AUT} \frac{O2_b}{K_{OH} + O2_b} \frac{PO4_b}{K_{PO4} + PO4_b} \frac{NT_b}{K_{NH4} + NT_b} X * 0.33 - 0.33 \, b_{AUT} X \tag{11}$$

$$r_{O2} = \left[\left(1 - \frac{1}{Y_H} \right) \left(\left(\frac{PO4_b}{K_{PO4} + PO4_b} \frac{NT_b}{K_{NH4} + NT_b} \right) \right.\right.$$
$$\left. * \left(\mu_H \frac{S_b}{K_F + S_b} \frac{O2_b}{K_{OH} + O2_b} X_H + \mu_{PAO} \frac{O2_b}{K_{OH} + O2_b} X_{PAO} \right) \right) \right]$$
$$- \left(Y_{PHA} * q_{PP} \frac{O2_b}{K_{OH} + O2_b} \frac{PO4_b}{K_{PO4} + S_{PO4}} X_{PAO} \right)$$
$$- \left[\left(\frac{4.75 - Y_A}{Y_A} \right) * \mu_{AUT} \frac{O2_b}{K_{OH} + O2_b} \frac{PO4_b}{K_{PO4} + S_{POPO4,4}} \frac{NT_b}{K_{NH4} + NT_b} X_{AUT} \right] \tag{12}$$

3. Model simulation and experimental data

Simulations of the model were carried out for 28 days of operation and changing initial conditions each day. The model simulations and the experimental data for the biomass, total nitrogen, phosphate, substrate and total suspended solids concentrations are shown together with the real plant data in Figure 2, there, the last plot shows the consumption of external water reduction during May-July 2013, due operational modifications identified by the model analysis. The model simulations were done, first, with parameters reported from the literature (Åmand and Carlsson, 2012), to subsequently perform the parameter estimation.

4. Parameter estimation, uncertainty and sensitivity analysis.

The values of the new estimated parameters by a Maximun Likelihood non-linear least squared method approach are μ_H 3.17; μ_{AUT} 1.20; K_H 2.96; K_X 0.15; K_{OH} 0.17; η_{NO3H} 0.899; K_F 7.964; K_{PO4} 1.5e^{-5}; K_{NH4} 0.762; q_{PP} 1.5; μ_{PAO} 0.67; η_{NO3PAO} 0.457; b_H 0.20; b_{AUT} 0.05; b_{PAO} 0.1; i_{NBM} 0.86e^{-3}; Y_{PHA} 0.1; i_{PBM} 0.05; Y_A 0.3; Y_H 0.181; K_{La} 8.0. As a result of the Monte-Carlo uncertainty analysis and Morris screening sensitivity analysis, parameters 3 to 9 of Table 1 affect significantly the biomass concentration in the bioreactor, while the rest do not. The parameters presented do not affect significantly the total suspended solid concentration. For this, analysis of the settlers in the system, which is not presented here, was performed.

Table 1. Parameters numerical values

Number	Symbol	Meaning	Value
1.	μ_H	Maximum growth rate of substrate[*]	1.8 d^{-1}
2.	μ_{AUT}	Maximum growth rate of nitrifyiers[+]	1.09 d^{-1}
3.	K_H	Hydrolysis rate constant[*]	2.76 d^{-1}
4.	K_X	Hydrolysis saturation constant[*]	0.036 kgX_S/kgX_H
5.	K_{OH}	Oxygen saturation coefficient for heterotrophic biomass[*]	0.29 $kgO2/m^{-3}$
6.	η_{NO3H}	Reduction factor for anoxic hydrolysis.[+]	0.72
7.	K_F	Saturation coefficient for $S_f(COD)$[+]	7.55 $kgCOD/m^{-3}$
8.	K_{PO4}	Saturation coefficient for PO4[*]	$1.13e^{-5}$ $kgPO4/m^{-3}$
9.	K_{NH4}	Saturation coefficient for total nitrogen[*]	1.41 $kgNH4/m^{-3}$
10.	q_{PP}	Storage rate constant of PO4[+]	1.34 d^{-1}
11.	μ_{PAO}	Maximum growth rate of biomass accumulating PO4	0.912 d^{-1}
12.	η_{NO3PAO}	Reduction factor accumulating biomass anoxic PO4[*]	0.5
13.	b_H	Decay rate constant of heterotrophic biomass[+]	0.264 d^{-1}
14.	b_{AUT}	Decay rate constant of autotrophic biomass[+]	0.05 d^{-1}
15.	b_{PAO}	Decay constant of biomass accumulating PO4[*]	0.1 d^{-1}
16.	i_{NBM}	Total nitrogen content in biomass[*]	$1.0e^{-3}$ $kgNT/kgX$
17.	Y_{PHA}	Storage Efficiency of PO4[+]	0.15 kgDQO/kgPO4
18.	i_{PBM}	Total phosphorus content in the biomass[*]	0.086 $kgPO_4/kgX$
19.	Y_A	Efficiency of autotrophic microorganisms[+]	0.23
20.	Y_H	Efficiency of heterotrophic microorganisms.[*]	0.45
21.	k_{La}	Volumetric coefficient of mass transfer[*]	6.0 d^{-1}

5. Conclusions

The identification of the most significant parameters by global sensitivity analysis can be oriented to monitoring only these significant parameters more accurately, reduction of the model complexity and leading us to more reliability of the model predictions for control purposes. The novelties of this work are the model adaptation, the specific parameters values determination for the system presented and the real application for economical water savings (102,147.66 MXN in July 2013) and environmental management in the paper industry.

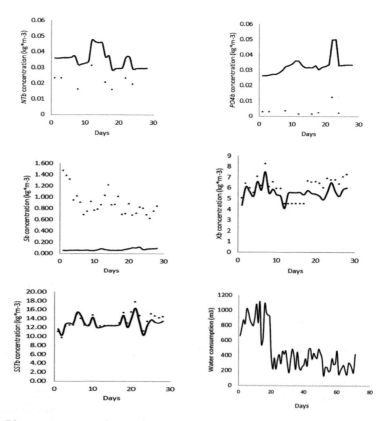

Figure 2. Bioreactor concentrations and external water consumption

Acknowledgements

The researh of this work was financed by the funding PROMEP/103.5/12/7965 of the Ministry of Public Education (SEP) in Mexico.

References

A. Román-Martínez, P. Lanuza-Pérez, E.M. Mata-Padrón, M. Cepeda-Rodríguez, 2013, Control system development for integrated Biological Waste Water Treatment Plant of a Paper Production plant, Computer Aiden Chemical Engineering, 32, 925-930.

G. Sin, K.V. Gernaey, 2009, Course: Uncertainty and Sensitivity Analysis of Numerical Models, Technical University of Denmark.

G.S. Ostace, J.A. Baeza, J. Guerrero, A. Guisasola, V.M. Cristea, P.S. Agachi, J. Lafuente, 2013 Development and economic assessment of different WWTP control strategies for optimal simultaneous removal of carbon, nitrogen and phosphorous, Computers and Chemical Engineering, 53, 164-177.

G. Mannina, A. Cosenza, G. Viviani, 2012, Uncertainty assessment of a model for biological nitrogen and phosphorus removal: Application to a large wastewater treatment plant, Physics and Chemistry of the Earth, 42-44, 61-69.

Jiří Jaromír Klemeš, Petar Sabev Varbanov and Peng Yen Liew (Editors)
Proceedings of the 24th European Symposium on Computer Aided Process Engineering – ESCAPE 24
June 15-18, 2014, Budapest, Hungary. Copyright © 2014 Elsevier B.V. All rights reserved.

Fast Nonlinear Predictive Control and State Estimation of Distillation Columns Using First-Principles Reduced-order Model

Guilherme A. A. Gonçalves, Argimiro R. Secchi*, Evaristo C. Biscaia Jr.

Chemical Engineering Program - COPPE - Universidade Federal do Rio de Janeiro, CT – G116 CP. 68502 – Ilha do Fundão, Rio de Janeiro – 21941-972 , Brazil
arge@peq.coppe.ufrj.br

Abstract

In this work, the performance of two first-principles reduced-order models of distillation columns are evaluated for using in nonlinear model predictive control and state estimation. The results reveal that the reduced-order model based on moment technique have a superior performance in comparison with the classic orthogonal collocation method. The analysis of the linearized models in each sampling time shows that the reduced models have a full rank observability matrix while the full model is rank deficient. In addition, the moments technique does not present the oscillatory behaviour of the classical orthogonal collocation, producing a jacobian matrix without complex eigenvalues, similarly to the full model. The control action with the reduced-order model can be obtained in less than 50 % of the CPU time spent by the full model.

Keywords: Reduced-order models, State estimation, Nonlinear predictive control.

1. Introduction

The online use of first-principles models for distributed systems is not an easy task, since the rigorous models of distillation columns may have a large number of differential equations and algebraic constraints that should be solved simultaneously. The system dimension can preclude the application of those models in nonlinear predictive control strategies or state estimation, since these techniques demand several evaluations of the model equations. In order to use models of staged systems in real-time applications, many efforts for reducing the model order have been made in recent years, such as nonlinear wave propagation (Marquardt, 1986), aggregated modelling (Linhart and Skogestad, 2012),linearization (Georgakis and Stoever, 1982), and orthogonal collocation (Levien et al., 1985). Gueddar and Dua (2012) proposed the use of artificial neural networks for model reduction and energy optimization in a refinery process, instead of using linear models. Recently, Biegler et al. (2014) show a good review about model order reduction applied to real-time optimization. In a nonlinear model predictive control strategy with state feedback, the number of states of the model is crucial. In general, these models are evaluated repeatedly by the optimization algorithm, since the objective function depends on the model response over a prediction horizon. Once the control action is computed, the actual state of the plant must be estimated by another optimization problem, in which all model states over a moving past horizon are optimization variables. In real-time applications, all those calculations must be done in a time limit lower than the sampling time. Additionally to the computing time constraint, Singhand Hahn (2005) have pointed out that high-dimensional models may result in a poor observability that can be improved by a proper model reduction. The purpose of this work is to apply an adaptive technique of model order reduction in nonlinear predictive control and state estimation algorithms, showing that such reduced model has attractive properties to be used with these strategies. The reduction method is based on the work of Ribeiro et al. (2010), which uses discrete Gauss-Lobatto quadrature to evaluate the moment-weighted sums of heat and mass balance residuals. The resulting high-accurate reduced model, especially at the top and bottom stages of the distillation column, and its adaptive characteristic of moving mesh of null-residuals location can be exploited in a control or estimation strategy, where the model is evaluated at different operating conditions.

2. Reduction, control and estimation methodology

The technique of model reduction is based on the cancellation of the weighted moments residuals. Given a general section of a staged process that can be written as:

$$\frac{dx_i}{dt} = f[x_{i-1}(t)] + g[x_i(t)] + h[x_{i+1}(t)] \tag{1}$$

Using a scaled variable s, for improved precision of computations (Ribeiro et al., 2010), we can write an interpolation polynomial for the approximate solution. Using the Lagrange polynomials $l_j(s)$:

$$\hat{x}(x,t) = \sum_{j=0}^{n} l_j(s)x_j(t) \tag{2}$$

The residual function is then ($\hat{x}_i(t) \equiv \hat{x}(s^{(i)}, t)$):

$$R^{n+1}\left(s^{(i)}, t\right) = \frac{d\hat{x}_i}{dt} - f\left[\hat{x}\left(s^{(i)} - 1, t\right)\right] - g[\hat{x}_i(t)] - h\left[\hat{x}\left(s^{(i)} + 1, t\right)\right] \tag{3}$$

In the orthogonal collocation method, the residual functions are cancelled in the collocation points, chosen using a discrete orthogonal polynomial. However, in the moments technique, the residuals are weighted by the moments, and the sum of those weighted-residuals are cancelled (Ribeiro et al., 2010):

$$R_K^{n+1}(t) = \sum_{j=1}^{N} \left(\frac{j-1}{N}\right)^{K-1} R^{n+1}\left(\frac{j-1}{N}, t\right) = 0 \tag{4}$$

This summation can be evaluated using a discrete Gauss-Lobatto quadrature:

$$R_K^{n+1}(t) = \sum_{i=0}^{n+1} M_{K,i} R^{n+1}\left(s^{(i)}, t\right) = 0 \tag{5}$$

where $M_{K,i} = \omega_i \left(s^{(i)}\right)^{K-1}$ and ω_i are the weights of the Gauss-Lobatto quadrature. These techniques retain all the physical parameters of the full model. In other words, it is not necessary to carry out any additional experiment to obtain the reduced model, and the same thermodynamics relations for vapour-liquid equilibrium of the full model can be used. More details about this technique can be found in Ribeiro et al. (2010).

The state estimation strategy used here is the Constrained Extended Kalman Filter (CEKF), with a linear measurement equation. This problem can be formulated as quadratic programming and, hence, can be solved efficiently. Details are provided by Gesthuisen et al. (2001). The measurement equation is given by $\boldsymbol{y}_k = \boldsymbol{h}(\boldsymbol{x}_k) + \boldsymbol{v}_k$, and the prediction step is:

$$\hat{\boldsymbol{x}}_{(k|k-1)} = f\big(\hat{\boldsymbol{x}}_{(k-1|k-1)}, \boldsymbol{u}_{k-1}\big) \tag{6}$$

Using a linearized model in each sampling time, the correction step can be written as:

$$\min_{\Theta_{(k|k)}} \hat{\Theta}^T_{(k|k)} S^{-1}_{(k|k)} \hat{\Theta}_{(k|k)} \tag{7}$$

$$\text{s.t.:} [H\ I]\Theta_{(k|k)} = y_k - h\big(\hat{\boldsymbol{x}}_{(k|k-1)}\big),$$
$$\hat{\boldsymbol{x}}_{min} \leq \hat{\boldsymbol{x}}_{(j|k)} \leq \hat{\boldsymbol{x}}_{max}, \quad \hat{\boldsymbol{w}}_{min} \leq \hat{\boldsymbol{w}}_{(j-1|k)} \leq \hat{\boldsymbol{w}}_{max}, \quad \hat{\boldsymbol{v}}_{min} \leq \hat{\boldsymbol{v}}_{(j|k)} \leq \hat{\boldsymbol{v}}_{max} \tag{8}$$

$$\Theta_{(k|k)} = \begin{bmatrix} \hat{\boldsymbol{W}}_{(k-1|k)} \\ \hat{\boldsymbol{v}}_{(k|k)} \end{bmatrix}, \quad S = \begin{bmatrix} P_{k-1|k-1} & 0 \\ 0 & R_k \end{bmatrix}, \quad H = \frac{\partial h}{\partial x}\bigg|_{\hat{x}_{(k-1|k-1)}} \tag{9}$$

Then the states and outputs are updated using the optimal values $\hat{\boldsymbol{w}}^*_{(k-1|k)}$ and $\hat{\boldsymbol{v}}^*_{(k|k)}$:

$$\hat{\boldsymbol{x}}_{(k|k)} = \hat{\boldsymbol{x}}_{(k|k-1)} + \hat{\boldsymbol{w}}^*_{(k-1|k)}, \hat{\boldsymbol{y}}_k = \boldsymbol{h}\big(\hat{\boldsymbol{x}}_{(k|k)}\big) + \hat{\boldsymbol{v}}^*_{(k|k)} \tag{10}$$

where $\hat{\boldsymbol{x}}_{(k|k)}$ are the estimated states of the system and $\hat{\boldsymbol{y}}_k$ are the filtered outputs. $\boldsymbol{P}$ and $\boldsymbol{R}$ are the covariance matrices of the linearized system and the measurements, $\boldsymbol{w}_k$ and $\boldsymbol{v}_k$ are the noise vectors of the model and measurements, respectively.

The nonlinear model predictive control problem can be formulated in the classical form as a nonlinear programming (NLP):

$$\min_{\Delta u} V(k) = \sum_{i=1}^{Hp} \big(\boldsymbol{y}_{sp}(k + i|k) - \boldsymbol{y}(k + i|k)\big)^T \boldsymbol{Q}\big(\boldsymbol{y}_{sp}(k + i|k) - \boldsymbol{y}(k + i|k)\big) + \sum_{i=1}^{Hc} \Delta \boldsymbol{u}(k + i - 1|k)^T \boldsymbol{G} \Delta \boldsymbol{u}(k + i - 1|k) \tag{11}$$

$$s.t.:\ \boldsymbol{x}_{k+1} = f(\boldsymbol{x}_k, \boldsymbol{u}_k), \quad \boldsymbol{y}_{k+1} = h(\boldsymbol{x}_{k+1}, \boldsymbol{u}_{k+1}),$$
$$\boldsymbol{u}_k \in U, \ \boldsymbol{x}_k \in X, \ \Delta \boldsymbol{u}_{min} \leq \Delta \boldsymbol{u} \leq \Delta \boldsymbol{u}_{max} \tag{12}$$

This NLP was solved using the sequential approach, where the simulation of the model and the optimization problem are done in separated routines; a good explanation about the methods for solving this problem is given in Manenti (2011).

3. Results

For sake of simplicity, the model used as the plant was a binary distillation column with 40 trays. In Ribeiro et al. (2010), the model reduction technique was also successfully applied to multicomponent systems. The mass balance was applied in each tray, and a constant relative volatility ($\alpha = 1.55$), resulting in a simple nonlinear vapour-liquid equilibrium equation, was used for the mixture. The equations and operating conditions used in the distillation model can be viewed in Smith and Corripio (2006). The number of stages in each section of the full and reduced models is displayed in Table 1. As we can see in Figure 1, the moments model responseof the top and bottom composition, for a perturbation in the initial condition, is closer to the full model, having the collocation model a worse prediction of the final steady state.

3.1. State Estimation

For the state estimation simulation, the full model was used as the plant, having a single measurement of the top composition corrupted by a Gaussian noise with a standard deviation of 2.5 % of the true value. The state estimators were designed using the same tuning matrices and the same initial estimate for the covariance matrix. In Figure 2, a significant noise reduction can be seen for all models. However, the collocation model remains with offset and is more oscillatory, while the moments model approaches the true value and the full nominal model estimation. One way to reduce the offset of the collocation model is to design a filter with larger elements in the model covariance matrix, nevertheless this cause a poor filtering of the measurements. For linear systems, all states are observable if the rank of observability matrix is the same as the number of system states. The third part of Figure 2 shows the rank of the observability matrix in each iteration of the Kalman filter estimation. This result reveals that the reduced models are, at least, locally observable while the full model is poorly observable. This can be justified by the reduced model structure, where one state depends directly on all states in its section instead of depending directly only on the above and below stages, like in the full model. A similar result was obtained by Singh and Hahn (2005), where a state estimator was designed for linear systems and, with some modifications, it was applied in nonlinear systems. Here, a nonlinear estimator with better observability properties can be directly obtained, which is essential for process control purposes. As mentioned by Soroush (1998), it is important to have guidelines for improving the observability of a process when it is low, since poor observability may lead to inconsistent results. The presented methodology can increase the "degree" of observability without additional measurements. It should be said that further investigations about global observability of the system must be carried out in order to obtain a less restrictive result. The average time reduction obtained by the use of the reduced-order models was expressive: 67 % for the collocation model and 65 % for moments model in the CEKF estimation.

Table 1. Number of stages in each section of the models

Model	Rectifying Section	Stripping Section	Total Stages
Full	14	23	40
Reduced	2	3	8

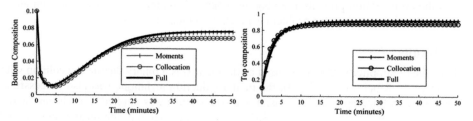

Figure 1. Initial response of the bottom and top composition.

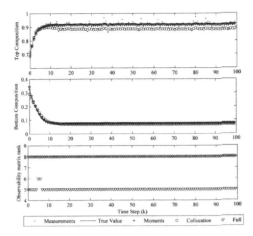

Figure 2. State estimation using the full and reduced models.

3.2. Nonlinear Model Predictive Control

The controller was designed using the same models used in previous section, but it was inserted an uncertainty between the controllers models and the full model used as the plant, which was made for a real condition simulation, where the plant model mismatch is present. The control objective is to maintain the top and bottom composition in the desired setpoints using the top reflux and the reboiler steam flow rates as manipulated variables. The results indicate that the average time to obtain a control action can be reduced in 42 % by the use of moments model and 75 % using the collocation model. The maximum time spent for a setpoint change was reduced in 53 % for the moments model and 70 % for the collocation.Despite the lower time for computations obtained by the use of collocation model, the performance achieved by the controller using the moments model is considerably better, as can be seen in Figure 3.In this simulation, a setpoint change was performed first in the bottom composition (k=10), and then in the top composition (k=40), to verify the performance of the controllers for a setpoint change and a disturbance rejection, caused by the column interactions.

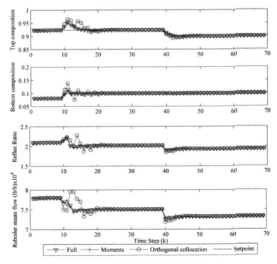

Figure 3. Nonlinear model predictive control results.

The collocation predictive controller is more oscillatory and has a larger overshoot. The computation of the performance index IAE shows that the moments achieved a value of 0.02 while the collocation method had 0.12, which represents a result six times worse for the bottom composition. The full model performed equally the moments under mismatch conditions achieving an IAE of 0.02 for the bottom composition. For the top composition, using the same index, the moments model performs two times better than collocation model (IAE = 0.26) and with the same index of the full model (IAE = 0.12). A local analysis of the models eigenvalues, at the desired setpoint, indicates that the plant model does not have any complex eigenvalue. Nevertheless, the collocation model presents two complex eigenvalues, in contrast to the moments that retains the full model properties. This result of the moments, combined with the high-quality of the top and bottom composition prediction, are very attractive for control purposes and the results showed that it has similar performance to the full model with less computing time.

4. Conclusions

The techniques presented in this work can perform the NMPC controller and the state estimation tasks with a great quality and a reduction of CPU time around 60 % for state estimation and 40 % for the NMPC optimization in comparison with the full model. The results show that the use of weighted-moments technique has superior performance to the classic orthogonal collocation method, eliminating the undesired oscillations of the latter. Finally, the reduced-order models have better observability properties than the direct application of the full model in the observer design, allowing the use of fewer measurements.

References

L. T. Biegler, Y. Lang, W. Lin, 2014, Multi-scale optimization for process systems engineering, Computers and Chemical Engineering, 60, 17 – 30.

C. Georgakis, M. A. Stoever, 1982, Time domain order reduction of tridiagonal dynamics of stagedprocesses—i: Uniform lumping, Chemical Engineering Science, 37, 5, 687 – 697.

R. Gesthuisen, K. Klatt, S. Engell, 2001, Optimization-based State Estimation: a Comparative study for the batch Polycondensation of PET, In: ECC, No. 2, Porto, 1062–1067.

T. Gueddar, V. Dua, 2012, Novel model reduction techniques for refinery-wide energy optimisation, Applied Energy, 89, 1, 117 – 126.

A. Linhart, S. Skogestad, 2012, An Aggregation Model Reduction Method for One-Dimensional Distributed Systems, AIChE Journal, 58, 5, 1524–1537.

F. Manenti, 2011, Considerations on nonlinear model predictive control techniques, Computers and Chemical Engineering, 35, 2491–2509.

W. Marquardt, 1986, Nonlinear Model Reduction for Binary Distillation, In: IFAC Symp., Bournemout, 123–128.

L. D. Ribeiro, A. R. Secchi, E. C. Biscaia Jr., 2010, A New Technique of Model Order Reduction Based on Weighted Residuals in Discrete Domain, In: ESCAPE20, Naples, 1639–1644.

A. K. Singh, J. Hahn, 2005, State estimation for high-dimensional chemical processes, Computers and Chemical Engineering, 29, 2326–2334.

C. A. Smith, A. B. Corripio, 2006, Principles and Practice of Automatic Process Control, John Wiley & Sons, New Jersey, USA.

M. Soroush, 1998, State and parameter estimations and their applications in process control, Computers and Chemical Engineering, 23, 229–245.

W. E. Stewart, K. L. Levien, M. Morari, 1985, Simulation of fractionation by orthogonal collocation, Chemical Engineering Science, 40, 3, 409-421.

Jiří Jaromír Klemeš, Petar Sabev Varbanov and Peng Yen Liew (Editors)
Proceedings of the 24th European Symposium on Computer Aided Process Engineering – ESCAPE 24
June 15-18, 2014, Budapest, Hungary.

Auto-Tuning of Multivariable PI/PID Controllers Using Iterative Feedback Tuning: Design Examples

Steffen Sommer[a]*, Hoang N. Nguyen[a], Achim Kienle[a,b]

[a]*Institute for Automation Engineering, Faculty of Electrical Engineering and Information Technology, Otto von Guericke University Magdeburg, Universitätsplatz 2, 39106 Magdeburg, Germany*
[b]*Max Planck Institute for Dynamics of Complex Technical Systems, Sandtorstraße 1, 39106 Magdeburg, Germany*
steffen.sommer@ovgu.de

Abstract

A new auto-tuning method for the design of multivariable PID controllers and unknown process models based on iterative feedback tuning (IFT) is demonstrated and validated by means of two design examples. A real process and a complex simulation example are discussed.

Keywords: auto-tuning; MIMO; PID; iterative feedback tuning (IFT).

1. Introduction

Most chemical processes are multivariable. Normally, decentralized strategies are used to control such systems. An attractive alternative is to apply centralized control concepts. Centralized (fully cross coupled) multivariable controllers are needed for processes with significant interactions where the control objective cannot be achieved by decentralized control. However, it is essential to have a method available that allows a reliable determination of the controller parameters.

It is shown in Sommer and Kienle (2012) that iterative feedback tuning (IFT) can be successfully used to design multivariable PI/PID controllers. The result is a new model-free auto-tuning method for centralized PI/PID controllers based on IFT (Hjalmarsson, 1999). Auto-tuning methods are extremely popular in industry. Most published work on PI/PID auto-tuning is restricted to SISO systems. The advantage of the IFT technique is that it is an optimization based approach, where no empirical rules are needed. The controller parameters are computed by minimizing an input and error based quadratic cost function. A special control structure is introduced to reduce the number of free parameters from $3 \cdot r^2$ to 3, where r is the number of controlled variables. That is, only three parameters have to be tuned, independently from the number of process inputs/outputs. Thus, the tuning effort is decreased. Another tuning approach for MIMO PID controllers is a relay feedback based strategy by Wang et al. (1997). The PID tuning method using extremum seeking (Killingsworth and Krstć, 2006) can also be extended to the multivariable case.

The main focus of this contribution is to examine the feasibility of the new approach, especially in combination with a real plant. Therefore, two application examples are discussed in this work, an air mass and temperature system and a reactive distillation process.

The proposed tuning method is summarized in Section 2. The design examples are presented in Section 3. Finally, a conclusion is given.

2. Auto-tuning of MIMO PID controllers using IFT

A multivariable PID controller can be represented by the transfer function matrix

$$C(s) = \beta \widetilde{K}_P + \alpha \widetilde{K}_I \frac{1}{s} + \delta \widetilde{K}_D s, \tag{1}$$

where α, β, and δ are scalar fine tuning parameters and $\widetilde{K}_P$, $\widetilde{K}_I$, and $\widetilde{K}_D$ are rough tuning matrices. Different approaches for the computation of these matrices are summarized in Sommer and Kienle (2012). For example, the inverse of the static gain matrix of the process can be taken: $\widetilde{K}_P = \widetilde{K}_I = \widetilde{K}_D = G^{-1}(0)$. The fine tuning parameters are found through parameter optimization. Therefore, they are collected in a parameter vector:

$$p = \begin{pmatrix} p_1 & p_2 & p_3 \end{pmatrix}^T = \begin{pmatrix} \alpha & \beta & \delta \end{pmatrix}^T \in \mathfrak{R}^3. \tag{2}$$

Thus, a parameter dependent controller $C(s,p)$ is obtained. p is determined by solving the optimization problem Eq.(3) subject to $C(s,p)$ stabilizing the closed loop.

$$\min_{w.r.t.\ p \in \mathfrak{R}^3} J(p) \tag{3}$$

The deterministic cost $J(p)$ is a quadratic criterion of the control error vector $e(t,p)$ and the manipulated variable vector $u(t,p)$:

$$J(p) = \frac{1}{2T_f} \int_0^{T_f} \left\{ e^T(t,p) Q e(t,p) + u^T(t,p) Q u(t,p) \right\} dt. \tag{4}$$

T_f is the duration of each tuning experiment. Q and R are diagonal weighting matrices. The optimal controller parameters are found by solving the following set of equations:

$$0 = \frac{\partial J(p)}{\partial p} = \frac{1}{T_f} \int_0^{T_f} \left\{ \left[\frac{\partial e(t,p)}{\partial p} \right]^T Q e(t,p) + \left[\frac{\partial u(t,p)}{\partial p} \right]^T R u(t,p) \right\} dt. \tag{5}$$

Eq.(5) represents the necessary condition for optimality of the unconstrained problem Eq.(3). The solution of Eq.(5) can be found iteratively by:

$$p_{k+1} = p_k - \gamma_k H_k^{-1} \frac{\partial J(p)}{\partial p}. \tag{6}$$

k denotes the current iteration. γ_k represents the step size and H_k is a positive definite matrix. In this contribution, H_k is chosen as the Gauss-Newton approximation of the Hessian of $J(p)$. The gradient $\partial J(p)/\partial p$ Eq.(5) can be determined by means of closed loop experiments. $e(t,p)$ and $u(t,p)$ are measured directly (see Figure 1, a). $\partial e(t,p)/\partial p_i$ and $\partial u(t,p)/\partial p_i$, $i=1,...,3$, are recorded by doing three additional experiments (see Figure 1, b), where the error $e(t,p)$ of the first experiment is the input signal of the

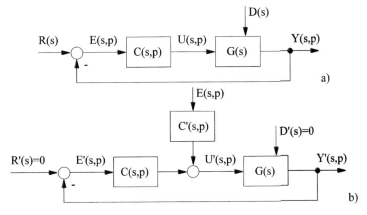

Figure 1. Experimental setup

feedback loop. $'$ denotes $\partial / \partial p$. The number of additional gradient experiments can be reduced when moving the block $C'(s,p)$ of Figure 1, b to the outputs. Hence, only one additional gradient experiment has to be performed per iteration. The disadvantage of the resulting approximated gradient is that a commutation error occurs.

3. Examples

3.1. Air mass and temperature system

First, a real process, the laboratory experiment LTR 701 by LD DIDACTIC GmbH (Figure 2) is taken into account. The LTR 701 experiment, an air mass and temperature system, is a MIMO process. Air flowrate and air temperature are controlled by a ventilator and a heater. A throttle acts as a disturbance. It is investigated if the proposed method is applicable for a real world process or not. Because of the sensitivity of the D-term to measurement noise, only a PI controller is designed. The manipulated variables are the voltages supplied to the ventilator and the heater in V. The controlled variables are the output voltages of the temperature and the air mass sensor in V. The nearest temperature sensor to the heater is used for all experiments. The process is not fully coupled. The temperature is affected by both the ventilator speed and the heater while the air flow rate only depends on the ventilator speed. A tracking scenario is considered to examine the auto-tuning approach.

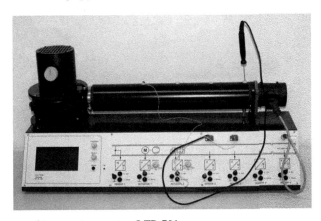

Figure 2. Air mass and temperature system LTR 701

The rough tuning matrices are chosen as the inverse of the measured static gain matrix:

$$\widetilde{K}_P = \widetilde{K}_I = G^{-1}(0) = \begin{pmatrix} 1.38 & 0 \\ -0.8 & 2.25 \end{pmatrix}^{-1} = \begin{pmatrix} 0.7246 & 0 \\ 0.2576 & 0.444 \end{pmatrix}, \tag{7}$$

and the initial fine tuning parameters are set to $\alpha_0=\beta_0=1$. All Experiments start from the same operating point which is $y_{OP}=(4\ 4.3)V$. The set-points are always increased by $1V$ in the first experiment (see Figure 1, a). The recorded error $e(t,p)$ is taken as the input signal of two additional gradient experiments (see Figure 1, b). The following design parameters are defined: $Q=diag(10,\ 2)$, $R=10^{-4}\cdot diag(1,\ 1)$, $\gamma_k=2$, and $T_f=15$ s. The initial controller parameters result in the cost function value of $J_0=0.764$ and the minimum value of $J=0.1238$ was found after eight iterations, where the three above mentioned experiments had to be performed per iteration for the complete PI auto-tuning approach. The optimization was aborted when the gradients $\partial J(p)/\partial p_1$ and $\partial J(p)/\partial p_2$ reached 5 % of their initial values. The optimal controller parameters are $\alpha=7.4717$ and $\beta=6.3884$. The step responses are presented in Figure 3. The controller provides steady-state accuracy. The speed of the responses is improved iteratively. Only slightly changes are observed after the fifth iteration. Regarding the manipulated inputs, no saturation occurs during the experiments. The results show that the suggested strategy is absolutely practical in the real world.

3.2. Reactive distillation process

The second example, a reactive distillation process (Figure 4) , is a complex simulation example. The column consists of $n_{RX}=10$ reactive trays, $n_S=5$ stripping trays, $n_R=5$ rectifying trays, a reboiler, and a condenser. The reaction A+B↔C+D takes place on every reactive tray.

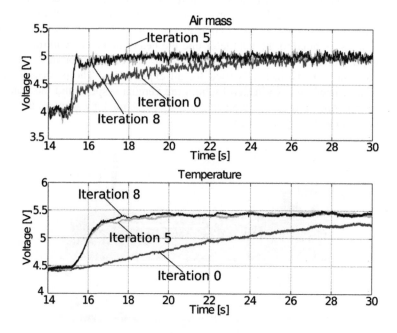

Figure 3. Closed loop step responses

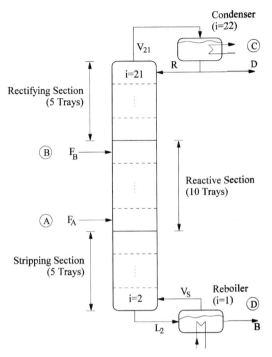

Figure 4. Reactive distillation column

The control task is to minimize perturbations of the product compositions during the chemical production process, particularly in the case of unforeseen disturbances. This problem is solved using a two-temperature control strategy. An optimal multivariable PID controller has to be found by means of the introduced auto-tuning method that solves the control problem. The feed flow rates F_A and F_B [kmol/s] are the manipulated variables. At steady-state, all valves are regarded to be half open. The tray temperature T_3 [K] in the stripping section and the tray temperature T_{12} [K] in the reactive section are the controlled variables. Furthermore, the molar holdups in the condenser and in the reboiler are controlled using P controllers via distillate flowrate D and bottom flowrate B. The ratio of reflux flowrate R to distillate flowrate D is kept constant. The remaining input reboiler vapor flowrate V_S [kmol/s] is the disturbance input. Additionally, an anti-reset windup strategy is combined with the PID controller. The rough tuning matrices are given by:

$$\widetilde{K}_P = \widetilde{K}_I = \widetilde{K}_D = G^{-1}(0) = \begin{pmatrix} -14{,}959 & 6{,}483 \\ 345 & -4{,}403 \end{pmatrix}^{-1} = 10^{-3} \cdot \begin{pmatrix} -0.0692 & -0.1019 \\ -0.0054 & -0.2351 \end{pmatrix}. \tag{8}$$

The initial controller parameters are chosen arbitrarily: $\alpha_0=0.3$, $\beta_0=55$, $\delta_0=750$. In contrast to the original cost function Eq.(4), the function $J(p)$ is multiplied by the time to improve the response behavior at large time values. The first experiment (see Figure 1, a) is always performed with a $+20$ % change in the reboiler vapor flowrate. With $Q=diag(1, 50)$, $R=diag(10{,}000, 10{,}000)$, and $T_f=1{,}500$ s, the initial value of the cost function is $J_0=159.7$. In order to reduce the design effort, the approximated gradient is determined. As already mentioned in Section 1, only one additional gradient experiment has to be performed per iteration. The step size γ_k was adapted after each iteration.

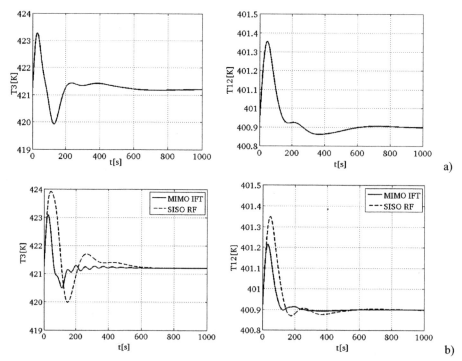

Figure 5. Closed loop temperature responses, *+20 % change in* V_S, a) initial controller, b) final result

The minimum value of the cost function seems to be approximately equal to *J=144.5*. The value was reached after 5 iterations where the gradients were reduced to *10 %* of the initial values. The corresponding final controller parameters are *α=0.54*, *β=105.9*, and *δ=1,690.4*. The optimization results are shown in Figure 5. The MMO PID controller compensates for the disturbance with steady-state accuracy in the temperatures, and therefore it solves the control problem. The results are compared with those of a standard decentralized control scheme. Two SISO PID controllers were designed sequentially by means of relay feedback and Tyreus/Luyben tuning rules.

4. Conclusions

All in all, the results of the design examples demonstrate that the considered auto-tuning method is very positive and applicable to tune centralized multivariable PI/PID controllers for real processes and complex simulation examples by means of IFT.

References

Q. Wang, B. Zou, T.-H. Lee, Q. Bi, 1997, Auto-tuning of Multivariable PID Controllers from Decentralized Relay Feedback, Automatica, 33, 3, 319-330.
H. Hjalmarsson, 1999, Efficient tuning of linear multivariable controllers using iterative feedback tuning, Int. J. Adapt. Control Signal Process., 13, 553-572.
N. Killingsworth, M. Krstć, 2006, PID Tuning Using Extremum Seeking, IEEE Control Systems Magazine, February, 70–79.
S. Sommer, A. Kienle, 2012, Auto-Tuning of Multivariable PID Controllers Using Iterative Feedback Tuning, at Automatisierungstechnik, 60, 1, 20-27.

Jiří Jaromír Klemeš, Petar Sabev Varbanov and Peng Yen Liew (Editors)
Proceedings of the 24th European Symposium on Computer Aided Process Engineering – ESCAPE 24
June 15-18, 2014, Budapest, Hungary.

MIMO Control during Oil Well Drilling

Márcia Peixoto Vega[a*], Marcela Galdino de Freitas[a], André Leibsohn Martins[b]

[a]*DEQ - UFRRJ, BR 465, km7, CEP: 23890-000, Seropédica, RJ, Brazil*
[b] *PETROBRAS S.A./CENPES, Av. Hum Quadra 07, Ilha do Fundão, Rio de Janeiro, 21494-900, Rio de Janeiro, RJ, Brazil*
vega@ufrrj.br

Abstract

A drilling system consists of a rotating drill string, which is placed into the well. The drill fluid is pumped through the drill string and exits through the choke valve. An important scope of the drill fluid is to maintain a certain pressure gradient along the length of the well. Well construction is a complex job in which annular pressures must be kept inside the operational window (limited by fracture and pore pressure). Monitoring bottom hole pressure to avoid fluctuations out of operational window limits is an extremely important job, in order to guarantee safe conditions during drilling. Under a conventional oil well drilling task, the pore pressure (minimum limit) and the fracture pressure (maximum limit) define mud density range and pressure operational window. During oil well drilling, several disturbances affect bottom hole pressure; for example, as the length of the well increases, the bottom hole pressure varies for growing hydrostatic pressure levels. In addition, the pipe connection procedure, performed at equal time intervals, stopping the drill rotation and mud injection, mounting a new pipe segment, restarting the drill fluid pump and rotation, causes severe fluctuations in well fluids flow, changing well pressure. Permeability and porous reservoir pressure governs native reservoir fluid well influx, affecting flow patterns inside the well and well pressure. In this work, a non linear mathematical model (gas-liquid-solid), representing an oil well drilling system, was developed, based on mass and momentum balances. Besides, for implementing classic control (PI), alternative control schemes were analyzed using mud pump flow rate, choke opening index and weight on bit as manipulated variables in order to control annulus bottomhole pressure and rate of penetration. Classic controller tuning was performed for servo and regulatory control studies, under MIMO frameworks.

Keywords: PI, feedback, RGA.

1. Introduction

Usually at normal drilling operations the choke valve is adjusted manually. The fluid composition and pressures are evaluated based on steady state values, and the choke is adjusted accordingly. Recently, new procedures for adjusting the flow rates and choke opening, based on a dynamic two-phase flow model, during pipe connections, using under-balanced drilling operations, are suggested (Perez-Tellez et al., 2004). A different approach for solving pipe connection pressure fluctuations is described by Suter (1999), adjusting the opening of the choke automatically, according to the choke differential pressure. Jenner et al. (2004) presented another mechanical system developed to be able to continue to pump the drill fluids even during the pipe connections. Another approach, utilizing classic PI and a nonlinear model predictive control scheme combined with first-principles model (gas-liquid phase), is suggested by Nygaard et al (2013), where an automatic control system is proposed for operating the choke on-line during the pipe connection.

Concerning the oil well drilling process, its intrinsic nature is distributed and dynamic, because of the increase of the well length, as the well is drilled, and the periodic stopping and starting of the mud pump; in addition, the process can be classified as ranging from open-closed system as the choke opening index reaches its limits. Finally, cuttings (rocks with varying densities and salt) from the drilling process; barite sag, improperly thought to occur under static conditions, but in fact occurring more readily under dynamic, low-shear-rate conditions, resulting in problems such as lost circulation, well control and stuck pipe and reservoir permeability, influencing on the influx of the native fluids to the well, change well density, viscosity and flow characteristics. As a result, modelling, optimization and control techniques are important research areas for oil well drilling, under narrow operational windows, commonly observed, nowadays, at deepwater and pre-salt layer environments. This job presents the results of the implementation of a phenomenological liquid-gas-solid phase flow model aiming the development of a classic PI (proportional - Integral) controller for regulating annulus bottomhole pressure and the rate of penetration, during oil well drilling. MIMO simulation strategies were investigated by handling flow rate, choke opening index and weight on bit as the manipulated variables under servo and regulatory control tests (typical disturbances of the well drilling process were analyzed, for example, pipe connection procedure, drilling rate changes, kick and mud invasion). This fundamental study represents an important step in the understanding the requirements for the implementation of the drilling automation process.

2. Process modelling

A nonlinear mathematical model (gas-liquid-solid), representing the drilling system, was developed based on mass and momentum balances (Martins et al., 2013). The annulus bottomhole pressure was defined as the summation of annulus compression and hydrostatic pressures, frictional losses, pressure loss over the choke and atmospheric pressure. The state vector for the drilling problem includes liquid, gas and solid masses inside the drill string; liquid, gas and solid masses inside the annulus; well length; mass flow of the mixture at the bit and mass flow of the mixture at the choke, Eq. (1). The set of time varying control inputs (manipulated variables: choke opening index and weight on bit, WOB) to the process are shown in Eq. (2).

$$x(t) = \left[m_{gd}, m_{ld}, m_{sd}, m_{ga}, m_{la}, m_{sa}, L, W_{mix,bit}, W_{mix,choke} \right] \tag{1}$$

$$u(t) = [zchoke, WOB] \tag{2}$$

The mass balance comprised two systems: the drill string and the annulus between the wall of the well and the drill string. The momentum balance was evaluated at the drill bit and at the choke valve, taking into account frictional losses and compression and hydrostatic pressures. The flow from the reservoir into the well was modelled using a simple relation named productivity index, which is a constant scalar defining the mass flow rate based on the pressure difference between the reservoir and the well. The dynamic simulation of the drilling system phenomenological model for varying choke opening index and flow rates is shown in Figure 1.

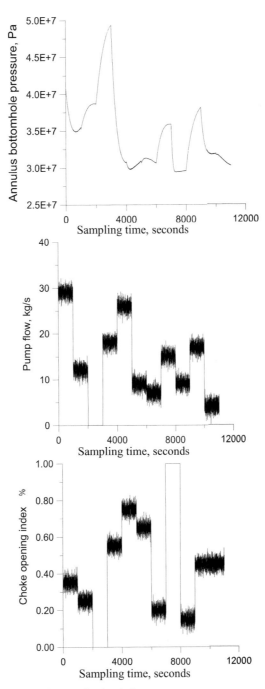

Figure 1. The drilling system model dynamic simulation.

3. Process control

Ray (1983) and Luyben (1990) pointed out that the implementation of advanced control techniques in industrial scenarios has been growing slowly due to the lack of robust algorithms; in addition, proportional–integral–derivative (PID) controllers have been successfully employed under the majority of process conditions.

Several operational parameters have a direct impact on annulus bottomhole pressure such as flow rate, rate of penetration, drilling fluid properties, etc. This way, due to the several parameters to be handled, bottomhole pressure control is a complex task and is (nowadays) a manual and very subjective job. Deepwater environments are directly linked with narrow operational window scenarios which require a stable value of bottomhole pressure inside the operational window. Thus, control and automation of drilling operations is important for future challenges of drilling engineering.

The rate of penetration is the speed at which the drill bit can break the rock under it and thereby producing an increase in depth in the desired direction. Variables that affect the rate of penetration are bit type, formation characteristics, drilling fluid properties (circulation rate and density) and bit operating conditions (bit weight and rotary speed). The rate of penetration can be expressed as a function of a number of parameters and has been defined by various equations. The first of such equations is the Maurer equation (1962), developed for rolling cutter bits rate of penetration with respect to bit weight, rotary size, bit size and rock strength. The assumptions made in this equation are the crater volume is proportional to the square of the depth of cutter penetration and the depth of cutter penetration is inversely proportional to the rock strength. Maurer (1962) relationship assumes perfect hole cleaning and incomplete bit tooth penetration. With respect to well control issues, the rate of drilled gas to volume of mud can also be calculated or correlated from the rate of penetration and other parameters.

As a result, the present study presents MIMO classic process control theory to a major concern in drilling operations: annulus bottom hole pressure and rate of penetration (ROP) control. In order to represent the process of ROP evolution as a function of mechanical parameters (weight on bit – WOB and drillstring rotation – RPM), the well known Maurer model was considered (Figure 2).

Systems with more than one control loop are known as multi-input multi-output (MIMO) or multivariable systems. The problem associated with control loop interactions, Shinskey (1979), can be alleviated by a proper choice of input-output pairings, such that interactions will be minimised. The relative gain technique has become a valuable tool for the selection of manipulative-controlled variable pairings (Seborg et al., 2011). Following the methodology stating that control loops should have input-output pairs which give positive relative-gains that have values which are as close to unity as possible, the best paring for the drilling process was controlling annulus bottomhole pressure using choke opening index and controlling rate of penetration using weight on bit manipulation (Figure 3).

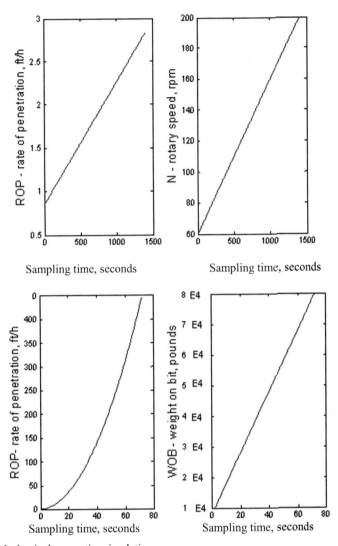

Figure 2. Mechanical properties simulation

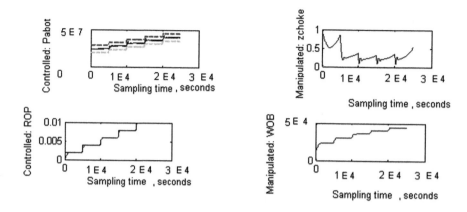

Figure 3. MIMO control fracture pressure pore pressure.

4. Conclusions

A phenomenological liquid-gas-solid phase flow model was developed aiming the development of a classic PI (proportional - Integral) MIMO controller for regulating annulus bottomhole pressure and the rate of penetration, during oil well drilling. MIMO simulation strategies were investigated by handling flow rate, choke opening index and weight on bit and rotation speed as the manipulated variables under servo and regulatory control tests.

References

A. L. Martins, R. A. Gandelman, M. Folsta, E. L. Resende, M.P. Vega, R.A. Dimitrios, Pirovolou, R. March, D. Gullo, 2013, On the Path for Offshore Drilling Automation, SPE/IADC Drilling Conference and Exhibition, Amsterdam, The Netherlands.

C. Perez-Téllez, J.R. Smith, J.K., Edwards, Improved bottomhole pressure control for underbalanced drilling operations, Proceedings for the IADC/SPE Drilling Conference, no. SPE 87225, 2004, Dallas,TX, USA.

D. E.,Seborg, T. F. Edgar, D. A. Mellichamp, 2011, Process Dynamics and Control, 3rd Edition., John Wiley and Sons, New York, USA.

G.H. Nygaard, E. Hauge,O.M. Aamo, J.-M. Godhavnc, G. Naevdal, 2013, A novel model-based scheme for kick and loss mitigation during drilling, Journal of Process Control, 23, 4, 463-472.

F.G. Shinskey, 1979, Process Control Systems, 2nd Ed., McGraw Hill, New York, US.

J.W. Jenner, H.L. Elkins, F.Springett, P.G. Lurie, J.S. Wellings, 2004, The continuous circulations systems: an advance in constante pressure drilling, in SPE anual technical Conferenca and Exhibition, no. SPE 90702, Houston, TX, USA.

W.C. Maurer, 1962, The "Perfect - Cleaning" Theory of Rotary Drilling, Journal of Petroleum technology, 14, 11, 1270-1274.

W.H. Ray, 1983, Multivariable Process Control - A Survey, Comput. Chem. Engng., 7, 4, 367-394.

W.L. Luyben, 1990, Process Modeling, Simulation and Control for Chemical Engineers, McGraw-Hill, Singapore.

Jiří Jaromír Klemeš, Petar Sabev Varbanov and Peng Yen Liew (Editors)
Proceedings of the 24th European Symposium on Computer Aided Process Engineering – ESCAPE 24
June 15-18, 2014, Budapest, Hungary.

Optimisation of a Sequencing Batch Reactor for Production of Polyhydroxybutyrate Using Process Characterisation Method and Neural Network Modelling

Amin Ganjian [a], Jie Zhang [a,*], Rui Oliveira[b]

[a]*School of Chemical Engineering and Advanced Materials, Newcastle University, Newcastle upon Tyne, NE1 7RU, UK*
[b]*Department of Chemistry, CQFB/REQUIMTE, FCT/Universidade Nova de Lisboa, Caparica 2829-516, Portugal*
jie.zhang@newcastle.ac.uk

Abstract

This paper presents neural network based modelling and optimisation of a sequencing batch reactor (SBR) for the production of polygydroxybutyrate (PHB), a bio-graded plastic with similar physical properties to polyethylene. A process characterisation method is developed for PHB production under mixed microbial culture. Based on the results obtained from the method, two major biological phases are identified and characterised. SBR recipes are designed to impose occurrence of both phases within each cycle of the SBR for sustainable productions. In order to overcome the difficulties of developing complicated mechanistic models and using such models in optimisation, bootstrap aggregated neural network models are developed and used to maximise PHB production. Simulation results show that the proposed method can improve PHB production.

Keywords: Polyhydroxybutyrate, sequencing batch reactor, neural networks, process characterisation, optimisation

1. Introduction

Producing PHB with mixed microbial culture (MMC) in SBR is economically more attractive than under single strain cultures. A detailed mechanistic model for PHB production under MMC in SBR is developed in (Dias et al., 2005) and is used in simulating the process. A characterisation method based on the simulation results is developed to classify batch operation trajectories (Ganjian et al., 2013) where the key element of process analysis is the total PHB concentration produced by the mixed microbial culture monitored over batch operation time. Additionally, it is proven that the amounts of carbon and nitrogen source in the form of acetate and ammonia respectively play dominant roles on the overall batch conditions (Ganjian et al., 2013).

In this paper, a process recipe is introduced to assure occurrence of the two operational phases in each sequence of the SBR. The bootstrap aggregated neural network (BANN) modeling is used to relate operational variables to total PHB concentration exploited from a SBR run. In this case, neural network is a proper modeling technique to fit severely nonlinear data for the optimization purpose and application of BANN further improves the model accuracy and reliability (Woźniak et al., 2014).

In this work, BANN models are successfully developed for PHB production in SBR process approved by regime type analysis of the characterisation method and are applied in optimisation of SBR recipes to maximise PHB production.

2. Process characterisation and SBR recipe

2.1. Process characterisation

Considering a single batch of the process, the initial concentration of the two feeding substrates plays a major role in directing the operational pathways. For a batch process initiated with a certain biomass concentration and medium conditions, regime type alterations can be predicted based on studies carried out in Ganjian et al. (2013).

In summary, three process pathways were identified with two performing in "famine" phase and one performing in "feast" phase at the end of the process maturity point. In general terms, a batch operation encountering nutrition shortage is operating under a "famine" phase; and on the other side, a nutrient rich batch with steady augmentation of product is operating under a "feast" phase. Regime Type 1 (RT1) is the initial regime with both acetate and ammonia available in the process. From RT1, process pathway ramifies into two directions with detection of either of the two acetate or ammonia stability points. RT2 is the regime type that appears with initial acetate stability detection. RT3 appears after RT2 when ammonia depletion follows the acetate stability point. Therefore, the first pathway is identified as RT1-RT2-RT3 with PHB decline at the end for a mature process. Detection of the ammonia depletion point at the initial stage presents occurrence of RT4 which later ramifies into RT5 and RT6. In RT5 ammonia depletion point is followed by complete exhaustion of acetate; whereas in RT6, acetate reaches to a stable positive value after ammonia depletion point. The second pathway ends in RT5 with total PHB decline at the end of a mature process. The third pathway consists of RT1-RT4-RT6 leading to two other regime types when batch reaches to optimal exploitation point (RT7) and process maturity (RT8). RT9 appears at the end of the third pathway when acetate is completely exhausted in the medium and cells start to consume their PHB content for their metabolic activities; hence, its occurrence is undesirable in production operations.

In each successful SBR cycle, both "famine" phase and "feast" phase operations are required to take place. This is to assure sustainable production, i.e. to maintain the operational cells in their productive state. The "feast" phase is the main operation to form the PHB product; however, the "famine" phase plays a significant role in bacterial activity change required for cells wellbeing (Dias et al., 2005). Ganjian et al. (2013) developed regime type identification method to differentiate between the phase operations based on initial process condition. Application of the method in this study is to provide a window of operational interval to perform successful SBR operations, i.e. occurrence of the two phases in the majority of the SBR sequences.

2.2. SBR recipe

Occurrence of both "feast" phase and "famine" phase operations in a SBR sequence is crucial. Apart from the method reported in Ganjian et al. (2013), no other means is reported to differentiate a "feast" phase from a "famine" phase operation. In practice, SBR productions aimed for PHB under MMC are operated based on process recipes developed from a series of tests carried out on trial and error basis. A model based optimisation approach for calculating SBR recipe is desirable.

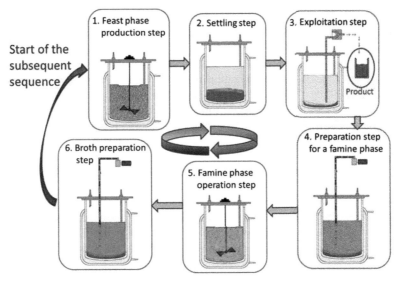

Figure 1. SBR general recipe structure

In Figure 1, six steps are defined within each sequence of a SBR process run. The main production step is considered to be the initial step for each sequence in a SBR process. For a given initial biomass concentration, a pair of feeding concentrations is considered on the basis of the regime type classification to ensure occurrence of the "feast" phase. At the end, batch reactor undergoes a period of quiescence for biomass to precipitate. In the third step, the majority of the biomass containing high percentage of PHB is exploited and the remained biomass is prepared to undergo a "famine" phase operation. Acetate and ammonia concentrations are monitored and feeding substances are added to the reactor such that conditions for "famine" phase operation in the subsequent step is satisfied. In the fifth step, biomass initially grows and eventually starts to consume PHB content of cells due to nutrition shortage in the medium. At the end of the "famine" phase operation, a great deal of PHB content is consumed and biomass is prepared for a productive operation in the subsequent sequence of the SBR. In the last step of the sequence, medium condition is monitored and manipulated in accordance with the "feast" phase requirements. The subsequent sequence of the SBR starts with the "feast" phase operation described for the first step aforementioned. Simulation program is developed to replicate process condition of the SBR recipe and generate data for model development.

3. Neural network modelling and optimisation

3.1. Neural network modelling
In order to overcome the difficulties associated with mechanistic model development and its application in optimisation, BANN empirical models predicting accumulated PHB product exploited over a course of SBR run are developed. The following representation illustrates the BANN input-output structure.

$$y = f(u_1, u_2, u_3, u_4, u_5) \tag{1}$$

The model input variables are initial acetate (u_1) and ammonia (u_2) concentrations at the initial point of SBR runs, the amount of biomass remained inside the reactor in the third step of each sequence (u_3), the amount of ammonia added to the reactor in the fourth step of each sequence (u_4), and the amount of acetate added to the reactor in the sixth step of each sequence (u_5) in the SBR operation.

In the sixth step of each sequence, ammonia concentration is specified such that occurrence of a "feast" phase operation is potent for the subsequent batch operation. Duration of the "feast" phase, "famine" phase and quiescence steps is 30, 15 and 5 hours respectively to allow sufficient time for each stage to reach to process maturity point. In simulations, SBR runs of 30 sequences with initial biomass concentration of 45 C-mmol/L and 50 % PHB content of the cells maximum storage capacity for a MMC of 32 populations were considered.

A series of simulation runs were carried out to obtain a window of SBR operability region in which successful SBR runs i.e. operations with occurrence of both phases in each sequence of process is potent to take place. For the aforementioned SBR operation, permissible variable alterations are in the range of 120 to 160 C-mmol/L for u_1, 0.1 to 1.4 N-mmol/L for u_2, 2 to 18 C-mmol/L for u_3, 1.8 to 3 N-mmol/L for u_4, and 100 to 190 C-mmol/L for u_5.

For modelling purposes, 200 simulation runs were executed with u_1 to u_5 taking random values within their respective ranges. Of the 200 samples of data, 80 % are randomly selected for model development and the remaining is used for model validation. Data is scaled to the range between -1 and 1 prior to model development. The BANN model contains 20 feed forward single hidden layer networks developed from 20 bootstrap replications of the original modelling data. The modelling data for each network is randomly partitioned into training (65 %) and testing (35 %) data. The optimal number of hidden neurons is determined using cross validation for each neural networks. The individual neural network models are aggregated to form a robust BANN model.

Figure 2 shows the number of hidden neurons for the 20 individual models (left) and their sum of squared errors (SSE) values (right). The SSE value for the BANN model is also depicted to demonstrate capability of the BANN model in providing accurate and robust prediction of the accumulated PHB.

Figure 3 shows the actual and BANN model predicted final PHB concentration on the unseen validation data. It can be seen that the model predictions are very accurate for majority of the data.

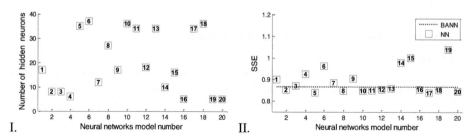

Figure 2. Numbers of hidden neurons and SSE of individual networks

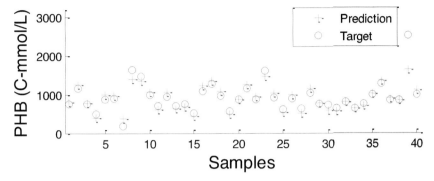

Figure 3. Model prediction performance on unseen validation data

3.2. Optimisation of SBR recipe

With a reliable model in hand, sequential quadratic programming (SQP) optimization method is applied to find the optimum condition to execute a successful SBR run which includes both operational phases for maximum PHB production. Reliable optimisation through incorporating model prediction confidence bound in the optimisation objective function is carried out (Zhang, 2004). These optimal values are 158 C-mmol/L, 0.1 N-mmol/L, 2.1 C-mmol/L, 2.8 N-mmol/L and 188 C-mmol/L for u_1, u_2, u_3, u_4 and u_5 respectively.

Applying the BANN model in the optimisation problem demonstrates that optimum condition is obtained when decision variables are at a boundary of their permissible intervals. SBR operations exceeding the boundary conditions result in unsuccessful recipe release with improper phase alterations in addition to undesired accumulation of materials inside the reactor.

For the optimal variable operation, maximum PHB accumulation is predicted to be about 1,800 C-mmol/L by the BANN model which is close to the maximum value generated for model development data. However, simulation of the SBR process with the optimal variable selection results into a much higher value for PHB accumulations (about 2,700 C-mmol/L). This difference is due to data absence in model development data set reflecting the optimal operational conditions. Although the BANN model was unable to provide an accurate prediction for optimal result, it was capable of drawing robust relationships between the process variables and the total PHB accumulated in the SBR. This technique provided successful release of an optimised recipe for the SBR.

3.3. Results

Figure 4 shows simulation results for the SBR operation under optimised conditions. Based on the SBR recipe depicted in Figure 1, initial and final concentrations of biomass, PHB, acetate and ammonia are shown in addition to the RT numbers for each sequence of the SBR. As depicted, the recommended recipe is approved since "feast" (RT7, RT8) and "famine" (RT3, RT5) phases occur in the first and the fifth steps respectively as defined in the recipe. Description of the two biomass divisions defined in the third step of the recipe is also shown in Figure 4. The PHB obtained from biomass exploitation in the first sequence is about 120 C-mmol/L with subsequent decrease to about 90 C-mmol/L in later sequences. This results in accumulation of more than 2,700 C-mmol/L PHB in 30 sequences of the overall operation.

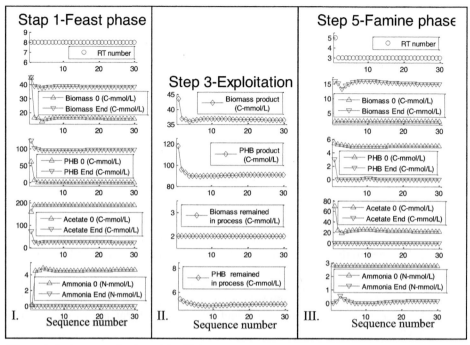

Figure 4. Optimum production of the SBR

4. Conclusions

A reliable neural network based modelling and optimisation method is developed for enhancing PHB production in SBR. A process characterisation method is used to assure the occurrence of both "feast" and "famine" phases within each sequence. Additionally, regime type identification technique is applied to provide a window of operability region for acceptable SBR runs. The acceptable ranges of process variables are identified for SBR runs to generate model development data. Bootstrap aggregated neural network model is able to build reliable and accurate model between the process variables and overall accumulated PHB in a SBR. Optimisation of the SBR recipe through incorporating model prediction confidence bounds successfully provided optimal values for process variables to maximise PHB production. Simulation results show that the proposed method can significantly enhance PHB production.

References

J. M. L. Dias, L. S. Serafim, P. C. Lemos, M. A. M. Reis, R. Oliveira, 2005, Mathematical modelling of a mixed culture cultivation process for the production of polyhydroxybutyrate, Biotechnology and bioengineering, 92, 209-222.

A. Ganjian, J. Zhang, J. M. L. Dias, R. Oliveira, 2013, Modelling of a sequencing batch reactor for producing polyhydroxybutyrate with mixed microbial culture cultivation process using neural networks and operation regime classification, Chemical Engineering Transactions, 32, 1261-1266.

M. Woźniak, M. Graña, E. Corchado, 2014, A survey of multiple classifier systems as hybrid systems, Information Fusion, 16, 1, 3-17.

J. Zhang, 2004, A reliable neural network model based optimal control strategy for a batch polymerization reactor, Industrial & Engineering Chemistry Research, 43, 4, 1030-1038.

Jiří Jaromír Klemeš, Petar Sabev Varbanov and Peng Yen Liew (Editors)
Proceedings of the 24th European Symposium on Computer Aided Process Engineering – ESCAPE 24
June 15-18, 2014, Budapest, Hungary.

Active Disturbance Rejection Control of a Neutralisation Process

Alison Brown, Jie Zhang[*]

*School of Chemical Engineering and Advanced Material, Newcastle University,
Newcastle upon Tyne, NE1 7RU, UK,
jie.zhang@newcastle.ac.uk*

Abstract

This paper presents active disturbance rejection control (ADRC) of pH in a neutralisation process. As pH dynamics is highly nonlinear and not control-affine, direct application of ADRC using pH as the controlled variable is not effective. To overcome this problem, an artificial variable, which has one-to-one mapping with pH and is control affine, is defined as the controlled variable for ADRC. A method for tuning ADRC using step response data is proposed. Application results show that ADRC can give excellent control performance for pH control.

Keywords: active disturbance rejection control, nonlinear processes, pH control.

1. Introduction

ADRC is a recently developed control technique that intends to bridge the gap between control theory and practice (Han, 2009). It has the simplicity as the widely use PID control but incorporates more advanced features such as smoothing setpoint jump through a transient profile generator and nonlinear feedback combination. ADRC considers all the unknowns in the controlled process such as unknown process model and disturbances as a "generalized disturbance" and the controller is designed to reject this generalized disturbance. Like PID control, ADRC does not require a model of the controlled process and, thus, has strong practical appeal (Gao, 2013). ADRC has been shown to give better control performance than PID control (Tian and Gao, 2009). However, most of the reported applications of ADRC are in the area of motion control (Tian and Gao, 2009). Applications of ADRC to the control of nonlinear chemical processes have not been commonly reported.

pH control is a well-known nonlinear chemical process control problem. Many control schemes have been developed for pH control, such as nonlinear control (Wright, 1991) and neuro-fuzzy network based control (Zhang and Morris, 1999). This paper presents a study on applying ADRC to pH control in a neutralisation process. The purpose is to demonstrate the potential of applying ADRC in nonlinear chemical process control. The dynamics of pH is highly nonlinear and not control affine. This paper uses a transformed control variable, which is control affine and has a one-to-one mapping with pH, in the ADRC framework. A method for estimating the ADRC tuning parameter based on step response data is presented.

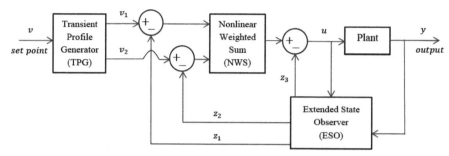

Figure 1. Basic structure of ADRC

The paper is organised as follows. Section 2 briefly introduces the ADRC method. A method of estimating the ADRC tuning parameter is given. Section 3 presents pH control using ADRC. A transformed control variable is introduced to convert a non-control affine problem into a control affine problem. The last section concludes the paper.

2. Active Disturbance Rejection Control

2.1. ADRC structure

Figure 1 shows the basic structure of ADRC. An ADRC scheme is based around an Extended State Observer (ESO) which takes the measured process input and output, and estimates the underlying noise-free trend in real time (z_1). In addition, the ESO estimates the total disturbance acting on the system (z_2) which is then fed back into the control scheme and cancelled via the ADRC law. By cancelling the total disturbance, the plant is reduced to its simplest form and as such is easily controllable via proportional means. A transient profile generator is used to smooth out sudden setpoint jumps. The nonlinear weighted sum gives the opportunities of have nonlinear gains depending on the magnitude of control errors.

Many chemical processes can be represented by a first order differential equation in the following form:

$$\frac{dy}{dt} = f(t, y, d) + bu \tag{1}$$

where y is the controlled variable, u is the manipulated variable, d is an external disturbance, t is time, and b is a parameter indicating the effect of the manipulated variable. In ADRC design, the model $f()$ is unknown and is considered as a "generalized disturbance". The effect of this "generalized disturbance" can be estimated by using an ESO. Control action is then calculated to eliminate the effect of disturbance so that the controlled variable can track its desired setpoint trajectory.

$$u = \frac{g - \bar{f}(t, y, d)}{b} \tag{2}$$

where g is the desired closed loop dynamics and $\bar{f}(t, y, d)$ is an estimation of $f(t, y, d)$.

2.2. Tuning of ADRC

One tuning parameter for ADRC is the approximation of the parameter *b*. Previous publications on ADRC did not give rules on how to determine this tuning parameter. This paper presents a method for estimating the tuning parameter using open loop step response data. The gradient of the response characteristic, *dy/dt*, was taken at the steepest point of the open loop step response. As the generalized disturbance *f*() is to be rejected, dropping *f*() in Eq(1) indicates that a reasonable estimate of the parameter *b* is the estimated gradient, *dy/dt*, divided by the step size, Δu.

For a control problem of relative order 1, *b* represents the relationship between rate of output change, *dy/dt*, and a step change in the manipulated variable (MV), Δu. In a non-linear process, *b* will vary throughout operation. However, a constant estimate of *b* (b_0) is sufficient to use within an ADRC scheme due to its robust nature (Chen et al., 2007). The value of b_0 can be determined from the open loop response to a known step change in the manipulated variable. Thus Eq(1) can be transformed as follows:

$$\frac{dy}{dt} = \hat{d} + b_0(\Delta u) \tag{3}$$

The gradient of the response characteristic (*dy/dt*) should be found at the steepest point and the applied Δu is known. The estimated disturbance $\hat{d}$ can be ignored as it will be cancelled via the ADRC law. Through rearranging the remaining terms of Eq(3), b_0 can be estimated as follows:

$$b_0 = \frac{dy/dt}{\Delta u} \tag{4}$$

This method can be used to estimate b_0 when applying ADRC to relative order 1 control problems. For relative order 2 systems, the second order derivative, d^2y/dt^2, needs to be estimated from open loop step response data. Results in this paper show that the ADRC tuning parameter estimated in such a way gives good control performance.

3. Active Disturbance Rejection Control of pH

3.1. A neutralisation process

The neutralisation process considered in this paper is taken from McAvoy et al. (1972). The neutralisation process takes place in a continuous stirred tank reactor (CSTR). Two streams are fed into the CSTR of constant volume: acetic acid at a flow rate of F_1 and a concentration of C_1, and sodium hydroxide at a flow rate of F_2 and a concentration of C_1. The control objective is to maintain a specified pH in the outlet stream. The flow rate of acetic acid is used as the manipulated variable in pH control.

Assuming that tank contents are perfectly mixed and isothermal, the following dynamic process model is obtained (McAvoy et al., 1972):

$$g_1 = [HAC] + [AC^-] \tag{5}$$

$$g_2 = [Na^+] \tag{6}$$

Acetate balance: $V\dfrac{dg_1}{dt} = F_1C_1 - (F_1 + F_2)g_1$ (7)

Sodium balance: $V\dfrac{dg_2}{dt} = F_2C_2 - (F_1 + F_2)g_2$ (8)

$$[H^+]^3 + [H^+]^2(K_a + g_2) + [H^+]\{K_a(g_2 - g_1) - K_w\} - K_aK_w = 0$$ (9)

$$pH = -\log_{10}[H^+]$$ (10)

where $[H^+]$ is the concentration of hydrogen ions present, K_a is the acetic acid equilibrium constant and K_w is the water equilibrium constant. In this case, F_1 was chosen as the MV. Clearly there exists an extremely non-linear relationship between pH and the MV which would be extremely difficult to write down.

3.2. Active disturbance rejection control of the neutralisation process

In the reported applications of ADRC, the controlled process is generally in a kind of control affine form as in Eq.(1). However, pH in a neutralisation process is well known to be highly nonlinear and is not control affine. Direct application of ADRC to control pH is expected to be ineffective. To address this issue, a new control variable, γ, is defined as

$$\gamma = g_1 - g_2\left(1 + \frac{10^{-7}}{K_a}\right)$$ (11)

where g_1 is concentration of acetate, g_2 is concentration of sodium, and K_a is acetic acid equilibrium constant. This transformed variable was first suggested in (McAvoy, 1972). This new control variable has a one-to-one mapping with pH and has a control affine structure. ADRC is then applied to control the new control variable. The setpoint profile for pH is translated to the setpoint profile of the new control variable. Table 1 shows the relationship between some values of γ and pH.

Specifying γ as the controlled variable and F_1 as the MV, the following relationship holds:

$$V\frac{d\gamma}{dt} = F_1C_1 - \left(1 + \frac{10^{-7}}{K_a}\right)F_2C_2 - (F_1 + F_2)\gamma$$ (12)

Eq.(12) can be rearranged into control affine form as shown below:

$$\frac{d\gamma}{dt} = -\left\{\left(1 + \frac{10^{-7}}{K_a}\right)F_2C_2 - F_2\gamma\right\}/V + \left(\frac{C_1 - \gamma}{V}\right)F_1$$ (13)

Table 1. Corresponding values of γ to pH

pH	5.5	6	7	7.5	9.5	12
γ	0.0071900	0.0021471	0	-0.00016452	-0.00027113	-0.010248

The followings can then be obtained.

$$\hat{d} = -\frac{\left(1+\dfrac{10^{-7}}{K_a}\right)F_2C_2 - F_2\gamma}{V} \tag{14}$$

$$b_0 = \frac{C_1 - \gamma}{V} \tag{15}$$

By finding the values of γ which correspond to various pH values of interest, the pH of this process can be indirectly controlled; this is because controlling γ to a specified value impacts on the concentrations g_1 and g_2 which then impact on pH. By introducing a step change in F_1 and observing the response characteristic of γ, b could be estimated as 0.2 following the method shown in the previous section.

Figure 2 shows the setpoint tracking performance of ADRC across a wide range of setpoint changes. The setpoint was smoothed by a transient profile generator. It can be seen that pH tracks its setpoint closely. The controlled variable settles down to its sepoint quickly without overshoot. To test the external disturbance rejection ability of ADRC for this process, changes were made to the concentration of acetic acid feed and sodium hydroxide flow rate. The applied disturbances are summarised as follows: C_1 was increased by 0.02 mol/L at 300 s and then reduced by 0.02 mol/L at 400 s, F_2 was increased by 0.5 L/s at 600 s and then reduced by 0.5 L/s at 700 s. Figure 3 shows the disturbance rejection control performance. In Figure 3, the operating point is selected as pH = 7, which is in the high process gain and difficulty to control region. It can be seen from Figure 3 that ADRC can reject disturbances and settle down to the setpoint quickly.

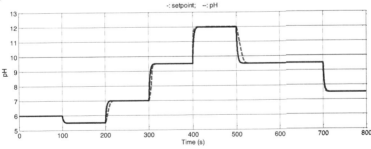

Figure 2. ADRC performance for setpoint tracking

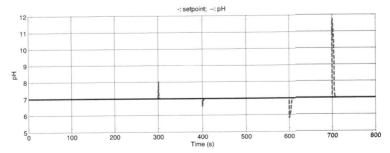

Figure 3. Disturbance rejection performance of ADRC

Table 2. SSE from ADRC and PI control

	Setpoint tracking	Disturbance rejection
ADRC	324.43	702.94
PI	335.41	11164

The performance of ADRC is compared with that of a PI controller. Table 2 gives the sum of squared control errors (SSE). It can be seen that ADRC gives better setpoint tracking and disturbance rejection performance. It should be noted that even though some other "advanced" control schemes, such as nonlinear model predictive control, can give excellent control performance, their practical implementation is complicated as they require an accurate model of the controlled process. On the other hand, ADRC does not need a model of the controlled process but can also give good control performance. ADRC bridges the gap between control theory and industrial practice and has strong appeal in the practical control of chemical processes.

4. Conclusions

Active disturbance rejection control of pH in a neutralisation process is studied in this paper. As the controlled variable pH is not control affine, a new control variable having a one-to-one mapping with pH is defined. ADRC is then applied to this new control variable. A method for finding the appropriate values of the tuning parameter in ADRC based on step response data is proposed in this paper. Simulation results show that ADRC can give excellent setpoint tracking and disturbance rejection performance.

References

Z. Chen, Q. Zheng, Z. Gao, 2007, Active Disturbance Rejection Control of Chemical Processes, Proceedings of the 2007 IEEE International Symposium on Intelligent Control, 1-3, 850-856.

Z. Gao, 2013, On the centrality of disturbance rejection in automatic control, ISA Transactions, in press, DOI:10.1016/j.isatra.2013.09.012.

J. Han, 2009, From PID to Active Disturbance Rejection Control, IEEE Transactions on Industrial Electronics, 56, 3, 900-906.

T. J. McAvoy, E. Hsu, S. Lowentha, 1972, Dynamics of pH in Controlled Stirred Tank Reactor, Industrial and Engineering Chemistry Process Design and Development, 11, 1, 68–70.

T. J. McAvoy, 1972, Time optimal and Ziegler-Nichols control, Industrial & Engineering Chemistry Process Design and Development, 11, 1, 71–78.

G. Tian, Z. Q. Gao, 2009, Benchmark Tests of Active Disturbance Rejection Control on an Industrial Motion Control Platform, 2009 American Control Conference, 1-9, 5552-5557.

R. A. Wright, 1991, Nonlinear control of pH processes using the strong acid equivalent, Industrial and Engineering Chemistry Research, 30, 7, 1561-1572.

J. Zhang, A. J. Morris, 1999, Recurrent neuro-fuzzy networks for nonlinear process modelling, IEEE Transactions on Neural Networks, 10, 2, 313-326.

Jiří Jaromír Klemeš, Petar Sabev Varbanov and Peng Yen Liew (Editors)
Proceedings of the 24th European Symposium on Computer Aided Process Engineering – ESCAPE 24
June 15-18, 2014, Budapest, Hungary.

A Novel Real-Time Methodology for the Simultaneous Dynamic Optimization and Optimal Control of Batch Processes

Francesco Rossi,[a] Flavio Manenti,[a,]* Iqbal M. Mujtaba,[b] Giulia Bozzano[a]

[a]*Politecnico di Milano, Dipartimento di Chimica, Materiali e Ingegneria Chimica "Giulio Natta", Piazza Leonardo da Vinci 32, 20133 Milano, Italy*
[b]*School of Engineering & Informatics, University of Bradford, Bradford BD7 1DP, UK*
flavio.manenti@polimi.it

Abstract

A novel threefold optimization algorithm is proposed to simultaneously solve the nonlinear model predictive control and dynamic real-time optimization for batch processes while optimizing the batch operation time. Object-oriented programming and parallel computing are exploited to make the algorithm effective to handle industrial cases. A well-known literature case is selected to validate the algorithm.

Keywords: dynamic optimization; batch process control; nonlinear model predictive control; optimal batch time operation.

1. Introduction

Discontinuous and multi-stage processes are often (and still) managed by means of traditional and heuristic recipes, conventional controls and/or manual operations. This is mainly due to their batch nature that requires frequent manual interventions, e.g., to switch from on (operating) to off conditions, to enable/disable cooling and heating operations or loading and unloading procedures. Moreover, the control methodology adopted is often only partially effective to handle the setpoint changes dictated by the recipes of batch productions and the uncertainties typical of semi-batch operations. For these reasons, many authors focused on batch processes to find efficient solutions to make them more automatic and better controlled with the aim of improving safety and optimizing discontinuous operations: Balasubramhanya and Doyle (1997) developed a MPC algorithm for the optimal control of distillation columns where the column model was based on the wave theory, Mahadevan et al. (2001) studied a MPC procedure using the differential flatness, Abel and Marquardt (2003) worked on a scenario integrated MPC for batch reactors with the aim of avoiding the loss of control even in failure circumstances, Vallerio et al. (2014) defined the tuning rules, Logist et al. (2012) proposed some dedicated tools, and, finally, Joly and Pinto (2004) made a comparison between the efficiency of sequential and simultaneous methodologies for the dynamic optimization of discontinuous processes. Several other authors have shown the potential for applying the dynamic optimization to batch systems using either neural networks (Greaves et al., 2003) or standard simultaneous procedures (Zavala et al., 2005) or novel adaptive shooting techniques (Vite-Martínez et al., 2014). Also, the importance of selecting the most appropriate control methodology to be used in dynamic optimization of discontinuous processes has been recently broached (Pahija et al., 2013b) to make it more appealing. The real problem is that the implementation of dynamic optimization has several similarities to the traditional recipe. Actually, although optimized, the setpoint changes are calculated a priori, they are usually applied offline to the batch process, and possible uncertainties or condition changes are not handled during the operations, reducing in practice the benefits of dynamic optimization. This problem is dramatically emphasized with long batch operations such as fermentations or chemical vapor depositions, e.g., the Siemens process for polysilicon production requires several days of batch operation (Viganò et al., 2010). The aim of this paper is to present a novel real-time methodology that is able to solve simultaneously the dynamic real-time optimization coupled with the nonlinear model predictive control, while the same batch time of operations is also continuously re-optimized to maximize the yield. Real-time effectiveness for industrial applications is ensured by means of a simple case-study from the literature.

2. The optimization and control algorithm

The simultaneous model-based dynamic optimization and control methodology (SMBO&C) proposed in this article derives from a coupling, a generalization and an extension of nonlinear model predictive control (NMPC) and dynamic real-time optimization (DRTO) algorithms. The aim of SMBO&C is to provide an on-line control for batch systems where the manipulated variable time-variant profiles and the batch operational time are simultaneously calculated by means of an optimization procedure in which the objective function is partially assigned as an input data (most of the times the user defined objective function is an economic indicator for the process, for instance the process net income). In order to introduce the formulation of SMBO&C algorithm, let $\mathbf{d}$, $\mathbf{m}$ and $\mathbf{w}$ be, respectively, the vectors of the perturbations, the manipulated variables and the dependent variables of a discontinuous process. Therefore the process model can be written as:

$$\mathbf{I}_M \frac{d\mathbf{w}}{dt} = \mathbf{f}(\mathbf{w}(t), \mathbf{m}(t), \mathbf{d}(t))$$
$$\mathbf{w}(t_0) = \mathbf{w}^0 \tag{1}$$

where $\mathbf{I}_M$ is a diagonal matrix that can be either nonsingular, i.e. the process model is an ODE system, or singular, i.e. the process model is a DAE system. The proposed SMBO&C scheme is based on the steps indicated in Figure 1. First of all, an initial number of control intervals (N_{CI}) and the standard length of each interval (Δt_{CI}^0) are assigned as input data, then, starting from a general time instant (t^*) where the process working point (i.e. $\mathbf{d}$, $\mathbf{m}$ and $\mathbf{w}$ values) is known, the optimal manipulated variable profiles ($\mathbf{m}_i^{opt}$) and the optimal residual operational time (Δt_{BC}^{opt}) are estimated through an optimization procedure, described in Eq.(2) and analysed in detail in the following pages. To perform this optimization the manipulated variable profiles are approximated via piecewise constant functions (Figure 1). The nearest optimal values of the manipulated variables ($\mathbf{m}_1^{opt}$) are implemented to the controlled system for Δt_{CI} units of time and the response to the control actions measured; at the same time, the initial time value for the calculation of the next control move (t_{new}^*) is evaluated and the number of control intervals is updated. The evaluation/update logics of t_{new}^* and N_{CI} can be found in the block diagram in Figure 1: in detail, N_{CI} can only be reduced or kept constant in the proposed scheme. If the updated number of control intervals is zero, then the optimal operational time has been reached and the procedure of simultaneous control and optimization is stopped, otherwise a new "iteration", which starts from the controlled system working point that relates to t_{new}^*, is executed. The overall algorithm is based on differential and differential-algebraic solvers and optimizers of BzzMath library (Buzzi-Ferraris and Manenti 2012) to exploit object-oriented programming features and parallel computing.

After describing the SMBO&C algorithm, it is important to focus the attention on the optimization sub-step; the objective function is constituted by two user-defined performance functions (f and g), an anti-ringing term (in the third line of Eq.(2)), and a third term (in the second line of Eq.(2)). This last term is quite important: its task is to avoid an excessive variation in the process variables due to a high sensitive response of the controlled system to the manipulated variables change.

$$
\underset{m_{ji};\Delta t_{BC}}{Min}
\left[
\begin{array}{l}
f\left(\Delta t_{BC},t^{*},\mathbf{w}\left(t^{*}+\Delta t_{BC}\right)\right) \; g\left(\Delta t_{BC},t^{*},\mathbf{w}\left(t^{*}+\Delta t_{BC}\right)\right) \; + \\[2mm]
+f\left(\Delta t_{BC},t^{*},\mathbf{w}\left(t^{*}+\Delta t_{BC}\right)\right) \displaystyle\sum_{k=1}^{N_v^w} Dc_k \left(\frac{w_k\left(t^{*}+\Delta t_{CI}\right)-w_k(t^{*})}{\Delta t_{CI}}\right)^2 \\[4mm]
+f\left(\Delta t_{BC},t^{*},\mathbf{w}\left(t^{*}+\Delta t_{BC}\right)\right) \displaystyle\sum_{j=1}^{N_v^m} ARc_j \sum_{i=1}^{N_{CI}+1}\left(m_{ji}-m_{j(i-1)}\right)^2
\end{array}
\right]
$$

s.t.

$$\mathbf{I}_M \frac{d\mathbf{w}}{dt} = \mathbf{f}(\mathbf{w}(t),m_{ji},\mathbf{d}(t)) \tag{2}$$

$$\mathbf{w}(t^{*}) = \mathbf{w}^{*}$$

$$m_{ji} \in \left[m_{ji}^{MIN};m_{ji}^{MAX}\right]; \Delta t_{BC} \in \left[\Delta t_{BC}^{MIN};\Delta t_{BC}^{MAX}\right]; w_k \in \left[w_k^{MIN};w_k^{MAX}\right]$$

In conclusion, it is apparent that SMBO&C algorithm is an optimization tool, which is able to drive a discontinuous process to profitable operating conditions, and at the same time a control tool, which can handle random perturbations entering into the controlled system, providing just-in-time optimal corrections; at last, it continuously re-optimize the optimal batch operation time according to the variations of trajectories, together with manipulated variables and process uncertainties.

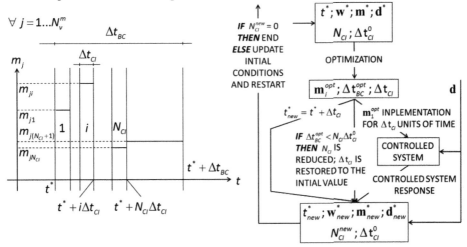

Figure 1. Manipulated variables discretization scheme and SMBO&C algorithm.

3. Case study

The case study where the SMBO&C procedure has been implemented and verified is the simultaneous optimization and control of a batch reactor using pseudo-scheduling performance functions. All the process data are summarized in Table 1. The reactor model is summarized in Eq.(3). A drawing of the reacting system is provided in Pahija et al. (2013).

Table 1. Process conditions, structural data and components economic values

Kinetic scheme	$A + B \rightarrow C$ (1) ; $2B \rightarrow D$ (2);	
Kinetic parameters	$R_1 = k_1^0 \exp\left(-\dfrac{E_1}{RT}\right) C_a C_b$ $R_2 = k_2^0 \exp\left(-\dfrac{E_2}{RT}\right) C_b^2$	$k_1^0 = 5.55\mathrm{E}{+}8\,\mathrm{m}^3/(\mathrm{kmol}{*}\mathrm{s})$ $k_2^0 = 3.55\mathrm{E}{+}11\ \mathrm{m}^3/(\mathrm{kmol}{*}\mathrm{s})$ $E_1 = 7.97\mathrm{E}{+}4\mathrm{kJ}/\mathrm{kmol}$ $E_2 = 1.02\mathrm{E}{+}5\mathrm{kJ}/\mathrm{kmol}$
Heats of reaction	$\Delta H_{R,1} = {-}1.835\mathrm{E}{+}5$ kJ/kmol; $\Delta H_{R,2} = {-}2.25\mathrm{E}{+}5$kJ/kmol	
Reacting mixture and cooling fluid thermodynamical properties	$Cp_a = 75.31$ kJ/(kmol*K); $Cp_b = 167.36$ kJ/(kmol*K) $Cp_c = 217.57$ kJ/(kmol*K); $Cp_d = 334.73$ kJ/(kmol*K) $Cp_j = 4.186$ kJ/(kg*K) $\rho_j = 1000$ kg/m³;	
Reacting mixture components molecular weights	$PM_a = 30$ kg/kmol; $PM_b = 100$ kg/kmol $PM_c = 130$ kg/kmol; $PM_d = 160$ kg/kmol	
Reactor and cooling jacket structural parameters	$D_R = 0.75$ m; $H_R = 3$ m $V_j = 0.08$ m³	
Reacting mixture volume	$V_R = 1$ m³	
Global heat transfer coefficient	$U = 9.842$ kJ/(m²*K*s)	
Reactor and cooling jacket operating conditions	$T_j^{IN} = 340$ K; $T_j^{MIN} = 315$ K; $T_j^{MAX} = 378$ K $T_R^{MIN} = 330$; $T_R^{MAX} = 378$ K	
Problem initial conditions	$C_a^0 = 1$ kmol/m³; $C_b^0 = 1$ kmol/m³ $C_c^0 = 0$ kmol/m³; $C_d^0 = 0$ kmol/m³	$T_R^0 = 340$ K $T_j^{OUT,0} = 340$ K
Economic weights	$EV_a = 0.15$ [-]; $EV_b = 0.25$ [-]; $EV_c = 1$ [-]; $EV_d = 0.05$ [-] $EV_{coolant} = 1\mathrm{E}{-}6$ kg/m³	

$$\frac{dC_i}{dt} = \sum_{j=1}^{N_R} \nu_{ij} R_j$$

$$\frac{dT_R}{dt} = \frac{4U}{D_R \sum_{i=1}^{N_C} C_i Cp_i} \left(T_j^{OUT} - T_R \right) - \frac{\sum_{j=1}^{N_R} \Delta H_{R,j} R_j}{\sum_{i=1}^{N_C} C_i Cp_i}$$

$$\frac{dT_j^{OUT}}{dt} = \frac{F_j}{V_j} \left(T_j^{IN} - T_j^{OUT} \right) + \frac{4U V_R}{D_R V_j \rho_j Cp_j} \left(T_R - T_j^{OUT} \right)$$

$$j = 1, 2; \quad i = a, b, c, d$$

(3)

The performance functions f and g are reported in Eq.(4); moreover, for the current case, $t_{pseudo-scheduling} = 36{,}000$ s, $t_{dead} = 900$ s, $\Delta t_{CI}^0 = 30$ s and $N_{CI} = 10$ (this is only the initial value).

$$f = floor \left(\frac{t_{pseudo-scheduling}}{t^* + t_{dead} + \Delta t_{BC}} \right)$$

$$g = V_R \left(\begin{array}{l} C_a^0 PM_a EV_a + C_b^0 PM_b EV_b + \dfrac{EV_{coolant}}{V_R} \displaystyle\int_{t^*}^{t^* + \Delta t_{BC}} F_j dt + \\[2mm] -C_c \left(t^* + \Delta t_{BC} \right) PM_c EV_c - C_d \left(t^* + \Delta t_{BC} \right) PM_d EV_d \end{array} \right) \tag{4}$$

Choosing F_j as the only manipulated variable and T_j^{IN} as the only perturbation, two simulations are carried out: in case I, T_j^{IN} is kept constant; in case II, T_j^{IN} is given a piecewise constant profile. Numerical results are summarized in Figure 2 and Table 2.

The results of the simulations clearly show that the SMBO&C procedure is able to efficiently optimize the batch reaction process: the yield of the most valuable product (c) is acceptable while the yield of the sub-product (d) is limited both in case I and II; moreover the reactant conversions are elevated in both cases. These results also prove that the SMBO&C method is able to efficiently handle the presence of perturbations without significant impact on the process profitability because it is able to dynamically

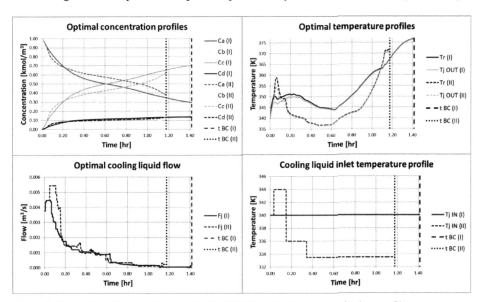

Figure 2. Optimal profiles achieved with SMBO&C method and perturbation profiles

Table 2. Optimal values of the products yields, the reactant conversions and the performance functions

	CASE I	CASE II		CASE I	CASE II
η_c	0.704	0.621	$-g$	92.564	81.802
η_d	0.168	0.160	f	6	7
χ_a	0.704	0.621	$-f*g$	555.384	572.617
χ_b	0.976	0.881			

change the operating conditions of the process in order to always get the maximum profitability, depending on the perturbations that are affecting the controlled system. A clear example of this can be found in Figure 2: when T_j^{IN} increases almost in t = 0, the SMBO&C algorithm decides to completely change the successive process operating conditions in order to aim for the best profitability.

4. Conclusions

A novel real-time methodology to handle the dynamic optimization, nonlinear model predictive control and optimization of batch time operations has been defined, implemented and validated on a well-known literature case. It is based on differential and differential-algebraic solvers of BzzMath library and it fully exploits object-oriented programming and parallel computations to be effective at the industrial scale too. Numerical results have demonstrated the economic benefits of such methodology. Indeed, as the results in Table 2 suggest, this new approach might lead, if applied to real industrial cases, to significant improvements in the capability of running batch processes in efficient, safe and convenient ways, especially when these processes are very responsive and\or strongly non-linear, thus difficult to control with standard systems.

References

O. Abel, W. Marquardt, 2003, Scenario-integrated on-line optimisation of batch reactors, Journal of Process Control, 13, 8, 703-715.

L.S. Balasubramhanya, F.J. Doyle, 1997, Nonlinear control of a high-purity distillation column using a traveling-wave model, AIChE Journal, 43, 3, 703-714.

G. Buzzi-Ferraris, F. Manenti, 2012, BzzMath: Library Overview and Recent Advances in Numerical Methods, Computer Aided Chemical Engineering, 30, 2, 1312-1316.

M. A. Greaves, I.M. Mujtaba, M. Barolo, A. Trotta,M. A. Hussain, 2003, Neural-network approach to dynamic optimization of batch distillation - Application to a middle-vessel column, Chemical Engineering Research and Design, 81, A3, 393-401.

M. Joly, J. M. Pinto, 2004, Optimal Control of Product Quality for Batch Nylon-6,6 Autoclaves, Chemical Engineering Journal, 97, 2-3, 87-101.

F. Logist, M. Vallerio, B. Houska, M. Diehl, J. Van Impe, 2012, Multi-objective optimal control of chemical processes using ACADO toolkit, Computers and Chemical Engineering, 37, 3, 191-199.

R. Mahadevan, S.K. Agrawal, F.J. Doyle, 2001, Differential flatness based nonlinear predictive control of fed-batch bioreactors, Control Engineering Practice, 9, 8, 889-899.

E. Pahija, F. Manenti, I.M. Mujtaba, 2013a, Optimization of batch and semi-batch reactors, Computer Aided Chemical Engineering, 32, 739-744.

E. Pahija, F. Manenti, I.M. Mujtaba, 2013b, Selecting the best control methodology to improve the efficiency of discontinuous reactors, Computer Aided Chemical Engineering, 32, 805-810.

M. Vallerio, J. Van Impe, F. Logist, 2014, Tuning of NMPC controllers via multi-objective optimisation, Computers and Chemical Engineering, 61, 1, 38-50.

L. Viganò, M. Vallerio, F. Manenti, N.M.N. Lima, L. Zuniga Linan,G. Manenti, 2010, Model Predictive Control of a CVD Reactor for Production of Polysilicon Rods, Chemical Engineering Transactions, 21, 523-528.

P. Vite-Martínez, C. Durán-Valencia, J. A. Cruz-Maya, A. Ramírez-López, S. López-Ramírez, 2014, Optimization of reagents injection in a stirred batch reactor by numerical simulation, Computers and Chemical Engineering, 60, 10, 307-314.

V.M.Zavala, A. Flores-Tlacuahuac, E. Vivaldo-Lima, 2005, Dynamic optimization of a semi-batch reactor for polyurethane production, Chemical Engineering Science, 60, 11, 3061-3079.

Jiří Jaromír Klemeš, Petar Sabev Varbanov and Peng Yen Liew (Editors)
Proceedings of the 24th European Symposium on Computer Aided Process Engineering – ESCAPE 24
June 15-18, 2014, Budapest, Hungary.

A Simple PID Tuning Rule with Robustness Analysis for the Time Delay Process

Ambari Khanam[a], Mohammad Shamsuzzoha[b,*]

[a]*Department of Chemical Engineering, Norwegian University of Science and Technology, N-7491 Trondheim, Norway*
[b]*Department of Chemical Engineering, King Fahd University of Petroleum and Minerals, 31261 Dhahran, Saudi Arabia*
mshams@kfupm.edu.sa

Abstract

A unified method has been proposed to obtain single PID tuning rule for different types of processes with enhanced disturbance rejection. It provides consistently better performance compared to several well-known methods for stable, integrating and unstable processes for the same degree of robustness. Based on the M_s-value τ_c guideline is provided over a wide range of θ/τ ratios. An analysis has been performed for the uncertainty margin in the different process parameters for the robust controller design. It gives the guidelines of the M_s-value settings for the PI controller design based on the process parameters uncertainty. Furthermore, a guideline has been developed for the uncertainty margin in the different process parameters (k, τ and θ).

Keywords: Parameters uncertainty, PI/PID controller, stable process, unstable process.

1. Introduction

Proportional integral and derivative (PID) controller has been the most popular and widely used controllers in the process industries because of their simplicity, robustness and wide ranges of applicability with near-optimal performance. The stable and integrating processes are very common in the process industries in flow, level and temperature loop. The open-loop unstable processes are also encountered in chemical processing units and are known to be difficult to control, especially when there exist a time delay, such as in the case of continuous stirred tank reactors, polymerization reactors and bioreactors which are inherently open-loop unstable by design.

Although the PID controller has only three adjustable parameters, they are difficult to be tuned properly in real process. There are variety of controller tuning approach reported in the literature and among these two types are widely used for the controller tuning, one may use open-loop or closed-loop plant tests. Most tuning approaches are based on open-loop plant information; typically the plant's gain (k), time constant (τ) and time delay (θ). The effectiveness of the internal model control (IMC) design principle has made it attractive in the process industries. Lee et al. (1998) proposed IMC-PID tuning method for single input single output systems based on the Maclaurin series expansion. A simple SIMC rule has been proposed by Skogestad (2003) for different types of processes which gives near about optimal settings. Shamsuzzoha and Lee (2007) have suggested an optimal IMC filter structure to design a PID controller that produces an improved disturbance rejection response. For the unstable process, Lee et al. (2000) and Yang et al. (2002) proposed IMC based PID tuning rule which gives consistently better performance for broad class of processes. Shamsuzzoha and Lee (2008) proposed generalized method for the PID controller with lead lag filter for both the stable and unstable second order processes. Recently, Shamsuzzoha (2013) has developed a new tuning method which eliminates the shortcoming of the well-known Ziegler-Nichols continuous cycling method. Alcantara et al. (2013) have addressed the model-based tuning of the PI/PID controller based on the robustness/performance and servo/regulator trade-offs. K-SIMC method which is modification of SIMC rule has been proposed by Lee et al. (2013). The IMC-PID tuning rule has the advantage of using only a single tuning parameter (τ_c) to achieve a clear trade-off between the closed-loop performance and robustness.

Therefore, in this paper, a simple analytical rule is proposed for the design of the PI/PID controller tuning. Single tuning rule is capable of handling different types of processes with improved performance. A τ_c guideline was recommended for a wide range of time-delay/time-constant ratios (θ/τ). A guideline of the M_s-value settings has also been proposed based on the process parameters uncertainty (k, τ and θ) margin.

2. IMC-PID controller design

Figure 1-(a) and (b) show the block diagrams of the IMC control and equivalent classical feedback control structures, respectively, where G_p is the process, $\tilde{G}_p$ the process model, q the IMC controller, f_r the set-point filter, and G_c the equivalent feedback controller. For the nominal case (i.e., $G_p = \tilde{G}_p$), the set-point and disturbance responses in the IMC control structure can be simplified as:

$$y = G_p q f_r r + (1 - \tilde{G}_p q) G_p d \tag{1}$$

According to the IMC parameterization used by Shamsuzzoha and Lee (2007), the process model $\tilde{G}_p$ is factored into two parts:

$$\tilde{G}_p = p_m p_A \tag{2}$$

where p_m is the portion of the model inverted by the controller, p_A is the portion of the model not inverted by the controller and $p_A(0)=1$. The noninvertible part usually includes the dead time and/or right half plane zeros and is chosen to be all-pass.

To get a superior response for unstable processes or stable processes with poles near zero, the IMC controller q should satisfy following conditions.

If the process G_p has unstable poles or poles near zero at $z_1, z_2, \cdots, z_m$, then

(i) q should have zeros at $z_1, z_2, \cdots, z_m$

(ii) $1 - G_p q$ should also have zeros at $z_1, z_2, \cdots, z_m$

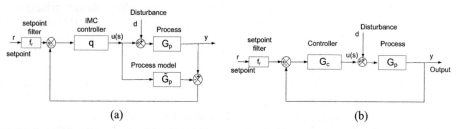

(a)   (b)

Figure 1. Block diagram of (a) the IMC control systems and (b) classical feedback

Since the IMC controller q is designed as $q = p_m^{-1} f$, the first condition is satisfied automatically. The second condition can be fulfilled by designing the IMC filter (f) as

$$f = \frac{\sum_{i=1}^{m} \alpha_i s^i + 1}{(\tau_c s + 1)^r} \tag{3}$$

where τ_c is an adjustable parameter which controls the tradeoff between the performance and robustness; r is selected to be large enough to make the IMC controller (semi-)proper; α_i are determined by Eq. (4) to cancel the poles near zero in G_p

$$1 - G_p q \Big|_{s=z_1, \cdots z_m} = \left| 1 - \frac{p_A \left(\sum_{i=1}^{m} \alpha_i s^i + 1 \right)}{(\tau_c s + 1)^r} \right|_{s=z_1, \cdots, z_m} = 0 \tag{4}$$

Then, the IMC controller comes to be

$$q = p_m^{-1} \frac{\left(\sum_{i=1}^{m} \alpha_i s^i + 1 \right)}{(\tau_c s + 1)^r} \tag{5}$$

The numerator expression $\left(\sum_{i=1}^{m} \alpha_i s^i + 1 \right)$ in resulting closed-loop causes an excessive overshoot in the servo response, which can be eliminated by introducing the set–point filter f_r to compensate for the overshoot in the servo response. From the above design procedure, a stable, closed–loop response can be achieved by using the IMC controller. The ideal feedback controller which is equivalent to the IMC controller can be expressed in terms of the internal model $\tilde{G}_p$ and the IMC controller q is $G_c = q / \left(1 - \tilde{G}_p q \right)$.

The desired form of the controller can be obtained by using the proper approximation of the dead time term of G_c for example Taylor series expansion.

First Order Plus Dead Time (FOPDT) process is representative model and commonly used in the chemical process industries.

$$G_p = \frac{K e^{-\theta s}}{\tau s + 1} \tag{6}$$

where K is the process gain, τ the time constant, and θ is the time delay, the IMC filter structure for the FOPDT is selected as $f = (\alpha s + 1) / (\tau_c s + 1)^2$.

After utilizing the above design principle the resulting PI controller can be obtained using Taylor series expansion ($e^{-\theta s} = 1 - \theta s$) and given as

$$K_c = \frac{\alpha}{K(2\tau_c - \alpha + \theta)}; \quad \tau_I = \alpha \tag{7}$$

The value of α is selected so that it cancels out the pole at s=-1/τ. From Eq. (4), this requires $\left[1 - (\alpha s + 1) e^{-\theta s} / (\tau_c s + 1)^2 \right]_{s=-1/\tau} = 0$ and the value of α is obtained as

$$\alpha = \tau \left[1 - \left(1 - \frac{\tau_c}{\tau} \right)^2 e^{-\theta/\tau} \right] \tag{8}$$

For the second order process, the resulting controller tuning should be PID in series form $\tau_D = \tau_2$.

Note: First order unstable process with time delay can be easily transformed to FOPDT by adjusting their sign for the PI/PID controller design e.g., for the FODUP $-K$ and $-\tau$.

3. Results and discussions

Although the simulation study is conducted on the different types of processes, only few of them are discussed below. The proposed tuning rule provides acceptable controller settings in all cases with respect to both performance and robustness. The closed-loop performance is evaluated by introducing a unit step change in both the set-point and load disturbance i.e., $y_s=1$ and $d=1$. To evaluate the robustness, we compute the maximum closed-loop sensitivity, defined as $M_s=\max_\omega |1/[1+g\ c(j\omega)]|$. A small M_s-value indicates that the control system has a large stability margin. To achieve the fair comparisons in the simulation study, all controllers have been tuned by adjusting τ_c for the same degree of robustness by fixing M_s. In the simulation of the second order process, series form, $G_c = K_c (1+1/\tau_I s)((\tau_D s+1)/(\tau_D/Ns+1))$ of the PID structure has been used with N=100 and no differentiation of the setpoint (Skogestad, 2003).

The results of two different processes are given in Figures 2&3. The comparison of the proposed with other methods like SIMC (Skogestad, 2003), DCLR (Lee et al., 1998), and Yang et al. (2002) have been shown in the figures. In case of stable and integrating process, the proposed method gives faster disturbance rejection and has a clear advantage over the DCLR and SIMC method. The proposed method also works well in first and second order unstable processes with dead time. The result of second example clearly shows that the proposed method gives both smaller overshoot and faster disturbance rejection while maintaining setpoint performance for unstable process. From the above analysis it seems that the proposed method constantly gives better closed-loop response for several types of processes at same M_s-value compared with other methods.

τ_c guideline for the proposed tuning rule: Based on our analysis it is observed that a good tradeoff between robustness and performance can be achieved for $\tau_c =2\theta$ for the proposed method. In stable process, It gives $M_s=2.0$ for lag dominant process and $M_s=1.26$ for delay dominant process.

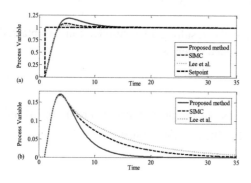

Figure 2. Responses of PI-control of first-order process $e^{-s}/(10s+1)$. For both setpoint and load disturbance of magnitude 1 at t=0

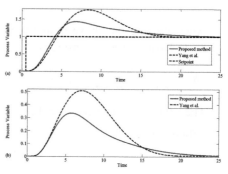

Figure 3. Responses of PID control for high order unstable process $G_p = e^{-0.5s}/((5s-1)(2s+1)(0.5s+1))$. For both setpoint and load disturbance of magnitude 1 at t=0

4. Robustness study

This section presents the analysis of the control system design for system affected by parametric uncertainty. It indicates the maximum uncertainty margin in different process parameter for the fixed M_s-value. It is important to obtain the relationship between M_s-value and parametric uncertainty in the control system design. It is because these uncertainties play important role in control system and cause poor performance and sometimes instability of closed-loop control systems. A typical first order delay process ($e^{-\theta s}/(10s+1)$) is considered for the analysis of various dead time to lag time ratios by changing θ while fixing $\tau=10$. The Kharitonov's theorem is used to obtain the uncertainty margin in the process parameter and further it is verified by using simulation for each case of different θ/τ ratio. The percentages of the uncertainty margin in different parameters have been analyzed for different M_s-value. Figure 4 shows the variation in dead time margin for different M_s-value. The figure clearly indicates that for a fixed M_s-value, as the θ/τ ratio increases the dead time margin also increases. The variation in the process gain uncertainty for the different M_s-value is shown in Figure 5. The trend in Figure 5 shows different patterns, and for the fixed M_s-value, as θ/τ ratio increases the percentage of the gain margin decreases. The uncertainty in the process time constant τ has been shown in Figure 6. The uncertainty margin in the τ is lower than the original value whereas in the k and θ are higher than original values. These combinations have deteriorating impact on the control system response. The maximum tolerance limit for wide range of θ/τ ratio of the uncertainty in different process parameters (k, θ and τ) is given in Table 1. Based on this information one can select the proper M_s-value for safe PI controller design for the uncertain process. The other PI tuning rules have almost same uncertainly margin for fixed M_s-value.

5. Conclusions

A simple analytical design method for the PI/PID controller was proposed based on the IMC principle in order to improve disturbance rejection performance. It can be used for the stable, integrating and unstable process in a unified way. The proposed tuning rule gives better performance and robustness compared with other well-known method for

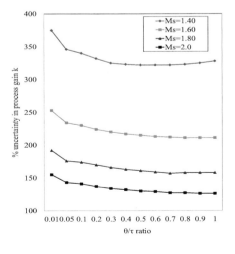

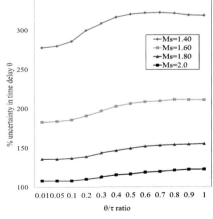

Figure 4. Variation of the uncertainty margin in k with θ/τ ratio for different M_s-value

Figure 5. Variation of the uncertainty margin in θ with θ/τ ratio for different M_s-value

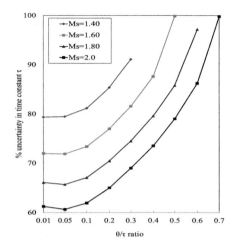

Table 1. Maximum uncertainty margin in θ, k and τ for the different M_s-value

M_s	% uncertainty margin		
	θ	k	τ
1.40	278	322	79.4
1.60	183	211	72.0
1.80	136	157	66.1
2.0	108	126	61.2

Figure 6. Variation of the uncertainty margin in τ with θ/τ ratio for different M_s-value.

different types of processes. The recommended choice of the closed-loop time constant is $\tau_c = 2\theta$, which gives $M_s = 2.0$ for lag dominant process and $M_s = 1.26$ for delay dominant process. The guideline of the M_s-value is also given for the PI controller design for the uncertain process. The proposed investigation of the M_s verses uncertainty margin in the process parameter can be very useful for the robust controller design.

Acknowledgement

The authors would like to acknowledge the support provided by King Abdulaziz City for Science and Technology (KACST) through the "KACST Annual Program" at King Fahd University of Petroleum & Minerals (KFUPM) for funding this work through project number 613-11.

References

S. Alcantara, R. Vilanova, C. Pedret, 2013, PID control in terms of robustness/performance and servo/regulator trade-offs: A unifying approach to balanced autotuning, Journal of Process Control, 23, 527-542.

J. Lee, W. Cho, T. F. Edgar, 2013, Simple analytic PID controller tuning rules revisited, Industrial and Engineering Chemistry Research, 52, 12973-12992.

Y. Lee, J. Lee, S. Park, 2000, PID controller tuning for integrating and unstable processes with time delay, Chemical Engineering Science, 55, 3481-3493.

Y. Lee, S. Park, M. Lee, C. Brosilow, 1998, PID controller tuning for desired closed–loop responses for SI/SO systems, AIChE Journal, 44, 106–115.

M. Shamsuzzoha, 2013, Closed-loop PI/PID controller tuning for stable and integrating process with time delay, Industrial and Engineering Chemistry Research, 52, 12973-12992.

M. Shamsuzzoha, M. Lee, 2007, IMC–PID controller design for improved disturbance rejection of time–delayed processes, Industrial and Engineering Chemistry Research, 46, 2077–2091.

M. Shamsuzzoha, M. Lee, 2008, Design of advanced PID controller for enhanced disturbance rejection of second order process with time delay, AIChE Journal, 54, 1526-1536.

S. Skogestad, 2003, Simple analytic rules for model reduction and PID controller tuning, Journal of Process Control, 13, 291–309.

X. Yang, Q. Wang, C. Hang, C. Lin, 2002, IMC-based control system design for unstable processes, Industrial and Engineering Chemistry Research, 41, 4288–4294.

Jiří Jaromír Klemeš, Petar Sabev Varbanov and Peng Yen Liew (Editors)
Proceedings of the 24th European Symposium on Computer Aided Process Engineering – ESCAPE 24
June 15-18, 2014, Budapest, Hungary.

Process Design and Control of a Xylitol Production Reactor

Hector Hernandez-Escoto,[a] Divanery Rodriguez-Gomez,[b] Ricardo Morales-Rodriguez[c,*]

[a]Departamento de Ingeniería Química, Universidad de Guanajuato, Noria Alta s/n, 36050, Guanajuato, Gto., México.
[b]Departamento de Biotecnología, Universidad Autónoma Metropolitana-Iztapalapa, Av. San Rafael Atlixco 186, C.P. 09340, México, D.F., México.
[c]Departamento de Ingeniería de Procesos e Hidráulica, Universidad Autónoma Metropolitana-Iztapalapa, Av. San Rafael Atlixco 186, C.P. 09340, México, D.F., México.
rmro@xanum.uam.mx

Abstract

This study visualizes the production of xylitol by a fermentation process in a continuous stirred tank bioreactor. In the first step, a validated dynamic kinetics model was recalled and extended for describing a continuous process. Next, through a likewise sensitivity analysis the uniqueness of steady states was established, and the process conditions for maximum xylitol production were settled down. Dynamical simulations around several steady states along trajectories drawn by sensitivity analysis showed that the process was stable, and a regulatory control system was designed on the basis of a conventional PI controller and considering two possible control pairs: it was shown how the process was not controllable at the state of maximum xylitol production, but with a little displacement from that state, the reactor became controllable.

Keywords: Xylitol production, control structures, fermentation, process design.

1. Introduction

Annually, large quantities of biomass in the form of agroindustrial residues rich in carbohydrates are produced worldwide. The bioconversion of these materials to fuels and high value-added chemicals has been considered for the following years. Therefore, continued research on developing production processes for conversion of biomass into bioproducts (e.g., xylitol), has been conducted via experimental approaches. As far as industrial production of xylitol is concerned, this is produced by reducing pure xylose in the presence of a metallic catalyst (Granström et al., 2005). However, recent research has focused on the biotechnological production through fermentation process by yeast, including genera *Saccharomyces*, *Candida* and *Pichia*.

Moreover, recent studies have been conducted on the xylitol production process on the model-based simulation area, where some mathematical models describing xylitol production through a biological pathway have been developed (Tochampa et al, 2005). Complementary to the current experimental work in the bioprocess framework, the use of mathematical models offers an alternative to explore several matters in production processes, which have not been explored and analyzed yet. As far as this work is concerned, the design and control analysis of a xylitol production process carried out in a stirred tank reactor in continuous operation (CSTR) can give a good picture about its practical implementation. Thus, the objective of this work was to analyze the operation feasibility of a CSTR for xylitol production using a validated mathematical model.

2. A systematic methodology for process and control system design of a continuous production of xylitol.

Fermentation of xylose to produce xylitol has been explored in a batch reactor implying a production rate bounded by the time of the batch; however, fermentations in CSTRs could be an alternative in order to obtain higher yields or faster productions. Before developing the experimental design and providing a kinetics model for the CSTR operation, a feasibility evaluation in a simulation framework might be worthwhile. Hence, a systemic methodology involving 4 steps for xylitol production in a CSTR was proposed and followed in order to perform both statics and dynamics analysis, and the design of a control system, as well. The four steps are: 1) Model selection and development: A mathematical model for a xylitol production reactor was previously developed and validated with experimental data by Tochampa et al. (2005); 2) Analysis of the reactive system productivity by a sensitivity analysis related to the process conditions and settlement down of the process conditions for maximum xylitol production; 3) Evaluation of the stability and sensitivity of the xylitol CSTR on the basis of dynamical simulation around several steady states, including one at the maximum production of xylitol; 4) Evaluation of the operability of the reactor through the design of control systems with conventional PI controllers, taking into account the alternative for control inputs and process conditions related to maximum productivity of xylitol. The solution of the mathematical model and the implementation of the control structure were carried out in MatLab (The MathWorks, Inc., 2008).

3. The process of continuous xylitol production from xylose.

The study considered a CSTR for xylitol production from xylose via an aerobic fermentation process by the yeast *Candida mogii* (Figure 1).

Recalling Tochampa et al. (2005), glucose was also considered as substrate since it complements the yeast nourishment and is consumed more rapidly than xylose, therefore improving xylitol production. However, higher glucose concentration can inhibit xylose transport into the cell, repressing the enzymatic activity involved in the xylitol production pathway. Thus, the stream entering the reactor at certain flowrate, Q_{in}, contains glucose, xylose and cells at watered concentrations (G_{in}, X_{in}, and C_{in},

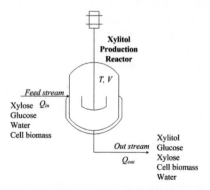

Figure 1. Continuous stirred tank reactor for xylitol production.

respectively). The output stream of flowrate (Q_{out}) equal to feed flowrate (Q_{in}), contains xylitol and remaining reactants, which correspond to the concentrations in the reactor of xylitol (P), glucose (G), xylose (X) and yeast (C). Without the eagerness of downplaying importance of other process factors as pH, temperature and composition of the fermentation medium, which are assumed as constant, the process can be regarded as a system of 4 state variables (P, G, X and C) affected by 5 factors (Q_{in}, G_{in}, X_{in}, C_{in} and Q_{out}).

For this study, firstly the reactor model in batch operation of Tochampa et al. (2005) was extended to the case of continuous operation by assuming, in the mass balance, that the density is constant and equal in the reactor, as well as in the input and output streams. The reactor is described by the same set of ordinary differential equations of Tochampa et al. (2005), plus a term where the difference between input and output concentrations of corresponding components is pondered by the dilution rate (D = Q_{in}/V). On this basis, a first engineering process problem lies on defining values for the inputs in such a way that the xylitol production is maximized. Next, a second problem corresponds to settle the feasibility of operating the process at those process conditions.

4. Process design

Since this process is nonlinear and its dynamics characteristics have not been analysed (up to the knowledge of the authors of this work), firstly the possibility of finding multiplicity of steady states was determined. This was done by evaluating the steady states reached along the space of values available for each possible control input, considering as basic condition an input stream of similar composition as the initial condition settled down by Tochampa et al. (2005): (G_{in}, X_{in}, C_{in}) = (5, 30, 5) (g/L). In addition, from a process design point of view, a sensitivity analysis was performed in order to identify possible improvements of the base case, such as, higher xylitol concentration in the output stream.

The results were as follows: (i) In the homotopic evaluation, by evaluating different values for Q_{in}, a curve without bifurcation was obtained for every state variable, (ii) for the curve of P, there is a maximum point: Q_{in} = 0.33 L/h and P = 7.81 g/L, (iii) in the homotopic evaluation, by varying G_{in} (at Q_{in} = 0.33 g/L), it was also obtained a curve without bifurcation for every state variable, and (iv) for the curve of P, it existed a maximum point: G_{in} = 5.9 g/L and P = 7.85 g/L. For the sake of space, this bifurcation analysis is not illustrated in this manuscript.

Afterwards, dynamic simulations were performed around several steady states with the initial conditions deviated from them. As a result, every state trajectory converges to the steady state.

The analysis described above allowed arguing that the process does not have steady state multiplicity and that it is stable. Moreover, the process presents points of maximum xylitol concentration for the considered input.

5. Control system design

One of the main characteristics of the xylitol production process is its level of sensitivity to some operating factors and also its nonlinear feature, which can generate a complex behaviour in the system. For instance, since it is assumed that xylose could be obtained from agroindustrial residues, a lessening of the xylan composition (as a result of the environmental conditions) can result in a lower xylose concentration (after pretreatment) in the feeding stream of the reactor, which can directly affect the productivity of xylitol. Another example could be the presence of certain toxic compounds in the feed stream, which can modify the kinetics characteristics of the process, and potentially resulting in a lower xylitol production, etc. The list of challenges can be extensive due to the fact that there are more possible troubles that could be found during the operation of the reactor. Therefore, in order to guarantee a production rate provided by the design task, it is necessary to introduce a control system in the xylitol reactor. Diverse approaches can be implemented to control the processes, for instance, from a conventional one up to nonlinear-advance schemes; thus, a very important question can be posed: why not to begin with a conventional PI controller?; because, it is the most economic among any controller type and it can be used as a reference for further studies about implementing advanced (model-based) techniques.

A key point to highlight is that in this class of processes, not all the variables can be directly measured on-line; however, the concentration of xylitol is a variable that can be easily measured, and in addition, it is directly related to the obtained yield from the production process. On the other hand, a typical control input is the feed flowrate of the total mixture or the individual components, among them, the most used is the substrate feeding, that in terms of instrumentation, it only requires one valve or pump to be manipulated. Other variables can be used as control inputs, but require more sophisticated or not existing instrumentation to determine the lack or excess of certain compound in the reacting system. Then, in order to construct the control system, two options of control configurations are considered: (i) (Q_{in}, P), or (ii) (G_{in}, P), where Q_{in} and G_{in} are the manipulated variables according to the measured xylitol concentration (P). Then, the conventional PI controller to implement is illustrated in Eq. (1):

$$u = \bar{u} + K_c \left(\bar{P} - P \right) + \int_0^t \frac{K_c}{\tau_i} \left(\bar{P} - P \right) \cdot d\tau \qquad u = G_{in} \text{ or } Q_{in} \qquad (1)$$

Once the control configuration and controller are settled down, the remaining problem is to tune the controller gains (K_c, τ_i) as illustrated in Eq. (2) and Eq. (3). Tuning relationships are recalled from Zavala-Guzmán et al. (2012), and applied in a straightforward manner:

$$K_c = \frac{(2n-1)}{K_p} \qquad (2)$$

$$\tau_i = \frac{\tau_p f_a^2 (2n-1)}{n^2} \qquad (3)$$

Therefore, it was only identified the static gain (K_p) and the time constant (τ_p) of the process, on the basis of the output trajectory generated by a step change on the corresponding control input. Then, the tuning parameters were n and f_a. n is the number of times that the control system performs faster than the process response in an open-loop and f_a is the damping factor that determines the type of response of the control system (damped if $f_a < 1$, or overdamped if $f_a > 1$).

6. Control system implementation

6.1. Scenario 1: maximum xylitol production
To test and discuss the feasibility of controlling the process, firstly, it was considered the following conditions as the nominal ones:

$(V, C_{in}, X_{in}, G_{in}, Q_{in}) = (5 \text{ L}, 5 \text{ g/L}, 30 \text{ g/L}, 5 \text{ g/L}, 0.33 \text{ L/h})$,
$(P, G, X, C) = (7.8135, 0.1825, 13.9760, 10.4115) \text{ (g/L)}$

In this case, P achieves a maximum point. To evaluate the control system performance, the system was perturbed through certain important parameters of the mathematical model (such as, maximum growth rates from glucose and from xylose) to simulate a change in the quality of the raw material and kinetics properties of the process; which in turn causes an undesirable decrease in P. The perturbed scenarios are such of an approximate diminishing in P of 4 %, 6 %, 8 % and 10 % with respect to its nominal condition.

For the first nominal condition, Q_{in} could not be a control input for the reason that the rate of change of P with respect to Q_{in} is equal to zero. Using G_{in} as control input seemed to be the correct choice; however, the static gain of P with respect to G_{in} was excessively small in such a way that large and unpractical movements on G_{in} were required to reject any of the scenarios of perturbation.

6.2. Scenario 2: reduced xylitol production
The following conditions were set down for the second scenario, in which the static gains of P with respect to either Q_{in} or G_{in} are away from zero:
$(V, C_{in}, X_{in}, G_{in}, Q_{in}) = (5 \text{ L}, 5 \text{ g/L}, 30 \text{ g/L}, 5 \text{ g/L}, 0.30 \text{ L/h})$
$(P, G, X, C) = (7.4144, 0.12960, 10.6888, 11.9470) \text{ (g/L)}$

In this case, productivity was sacrificed for the sake of the operability of the process. The performance of the Q_{in}-controller for the above-mentioned scenarios of perturbation is shown in Figure 2. The controller could not reject a perturbation scenario of 10 % of P-decrease (not shown). For the scenario of 8 % of P-decrease, it can be noticed that the control input is close to the value of flow in which P achieves its maximum. On the other hand, it means that it reaches a region where the rate of change of P with respect to Q_{in} becomes zero. Therefore, the ability of the process to be regulated with Q_{in} deteriorates during large perturbed scenarios.

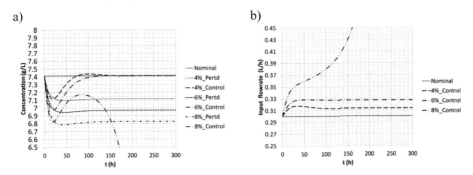

Figure 2. Q_{in}-controller performance under different perturbed scenarios: a) trajectories of xylitol concentration; b) trajectories of input flowrate. Pertd: open loop perturbed trajectory; Control: closed-loop trajectory.

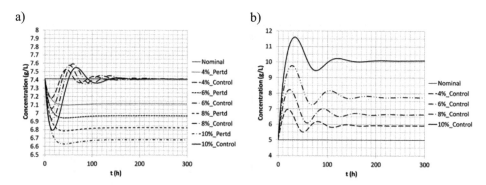

Figure 3. G_{in}-controller performance under different perturbed scenarios: a) trajectories of xylitol concentration; b) trajectories of glucose concentration in the input stream. Pertd: open loop perturbed trajectory; Control: closed-loop trajectory.

The performance of the G_{in}-controller is shown in Figure 3. It can be noticed that this controller was able to face and control the system even though the scenario had great perturbation. This is because the control input trajectory was quite away from the G_{in} value (12 g/L) in which P achieves a maximum, on the basis of $Q_{in} = 0.33$ L/h.

7. Conclusions

This work showed the operating scheme of a xylitol production process carried out in a CSTR. The study also proposed a systematic methodology where one of the key steps was the appropriate identification of possible critical scenarios during the operation of the xylitol production reactor. Although this class of processes is complex due to the nature of its components and its kinetics, it exhibited uniqueness of steady state for its respective control inputs, and stability. Moreover, conventional PI controllers were capable of rejecting disturbances and maintaining the production rate of xylitol in a smoother and faster way than the natural response of the process. It is also important to highlight the relevance of this type of analysis, due to the increasing research interest and urgent need of implementation of xylitol production process at industrial scale.

Acknowledgments

The authors acknowledge Dr. Sarote Sirisansaneeyakul for facilitating the code of the mathematical model for a batch reactor to produce xylitol. Ricardo Morales-Rodriguez acknowledges PROMEP-Mexico (project number: UAM-PTC-454) for the financial support on the development of this work.

References

T.B. Granström, K. Izumori, M. Leisola, 2007, A rare sugar xylitol. Part II: Biotechnological production and future applications of xylitol, Applied Microbiology and Biotechnology, 74, 273–276.

W. Tochampa, S. Sirisansaneeyakul, W. Vanichsriratana, P. Srinophakun, H.H.C. Bakker, Y. Chisti, 2005, A model of xylitol production by the yeast *Candida mogii*, Bioprocess and Biosystems Engineering, 28, 175-183.

A.M. Zavala-Guzmán, H. Hernández-Escoto, S. Hernández, J.G. Segovia-Hernández, 2012, Conventional proportional–integral (PI) control of dividing wall distillation columns: Systematic tuning, Industrial and Engineering Chemistry Research, 51, 10869-10880.

Jiří Jaromír Klemeš, Petar Sabev Varbanov and Peng Yen Liew (Editors)
Proceedings of the 24th European Symposium on Computer Aided Process Engineering – ESCAPE 24
June 15-18, 2014, Budapest, Hungary. Copyright © 2014 Elsevier B.V. All rights reserved.

ANN-based Virtual Sensor for On-line Prediction of In-cylinder Pressure in a Diesel Engine

Katarzyna Bizon[a],*, Gaetano Continillo[a,b], Simone Lombardi[a], Ezio Mancaruso[b], Bianca M. Vaglieco[b]

[a]*Dipartimento di Ingegneria, Università del Sannio, Piazza Roma 21, 82100 Benevento, Italy*
[b]*Istituto Motori CNR, Via Marconi 8, 80125 Naples,Italy*
katarzyna.bizon@unisannio.it

Abstract

This study presents the process design and tune-up of robust artificial neural networks (ANN) to be used as virtual sensors for the diagnosis of a three-cylinder Diesel engine operating at various conditions. Particularly, a feed-forward neural network based on radial basis functions (RBF) is employed. The use of different radial basis functions, and their relevant parameters, is investigated in detail, with their effect on the network accuracy. The RBF network is validated using data not included in training, showing good correspondence between measured and reconstructed pressure signal. The accuracy of the predicted pressure signals is analyzed in terms of mean square error and in terms of a number of pressure-derived parameters. Results are promising in terms of performance and accuracy, both for the predicted pressure signals and for the pressure-derived engine parameters that can be used in a closed loop engine control system.

Keywords: Internal combustion engine, neural networks, radial basis functions in-cylinder pressure, accelerometer.

1. Introduction

In-cylinder pressure is perhaps the most important parameter for engine diagnosis and control as it contains useful information on the phenomena taking place in the combustion chamber. Direct measurement of in-cylinder pressure requires expensive pressure probes (Docquier and Candel, 2002) which are able to resist severe conditions and also represent a substantial intrusion. A better solution would certainly be the application of non-intrusive sensors placed outside of the combustion chamber, that could indirectly give information on the quality of the combustion process. Good candidates should be able to measure quantities which strongly correlate with the in-cylinder pressure. Particularly, combustion pressure signal and engine block vibrations have been found as being well related to each other, both for single (Bizon et al., 2011) and multi-cylinder (Chiavola et al., 2010, 2 cylinders, and Taglialatela et al., 2011, 4 cylinders) engine applications It is thus logical to try and correlate combustion-related quantities with the vibration signal coming from accelerometers placed externally on the engine block. However, the transformation of the vibration signal into in-cylinder pressure is not straightforward. This is not only due to the strongly nonlinear character of this relation but also, apparently, to the fact that the vibration signal contains some noise introduced, among the others, by piston slaps and valve impacts. In this view, artificial neural networks (ANN) are recognized as a tool having a great flexibility in the approximation of non-linear mappings and capable to learn both the associations and patterns in the measured data, even in presence of noise and uncertainty. Earlier studies have shown the potential of neural networks in engine diagnostics. Different types of ANN models have been used to model, for example, the relationship between crankshaft speed and parameters derived from in-cylinder pressure. Particularly, Saraswati and Chand (2010) proposed a recurrent ANN for reconstruction of in-cylinder pressure of a spark ignition engine; Gu et al., 1996, used a non-parametric RBF ANN to predict pressure in the cylinders from the instantaneous angular velocity of the crankshaft, whereas in (Taglialatela et al., 2013) the same issue was approached by a multilayer perceptron ANN. Other applications include prediction of diesel/biodiesel fuel mixture properties (Kologeras et al., 2010) and exhaust NO_x emission prediction based on engine operating variables (Krijnsen et al., 2000). Recently, Wai and Vishy (2013) investigated the use of ANN as virtual sensors for emissions prediction and control.

The present study aims at building an efficient and robust radial basis functions (RBF) – ANN model able to reconstruct real-time the in-cylinder pressure signal starting from the vibration signal.

2. Experimental setup and procedure

In-cylinder pressure and engine block vibrations signals used in this work were collected during experiments conducted on a three-cylinder real Diesel engine. The engine has 1 liter of displacement and is equipped with a common-rail (CR), electronically-controlled direct injection system. Details can be found in (Bizon et al., 2013). The in-cylinder pressure was recorded by means of a piezoelectric pressure transducer placed in the glow plug seat of the engine head (Cylinder 1, Figure 1) with measuring range 0-250 bar and nominal sensitivity of 16 pC/bar, whereas the vibrations of the engine were monitored by means of a low-cost (near to Cylinder 3), low power linear capacitive accelerometer, manufactured by STMicroelectronics®, capable of measuring accelerations over a bandwidth of 1.5 kHz for all axes. To build a robust network, which guarantee flexibility in terms of operation parameters, measurements were made at four engine operating points (OP) which differ in engine speed (Table 1). Both the in-cylinder pressure and the acceleration signal were recorded at 0.5° crank angle (CA) increments for a large number of motored and fired engine cycles.

Figure 1. Photograph of experimental setup showing the location of probes: accelerometer (to the left) and pressure transducer (to the right).

Table 1. Engine operating conditions.

OP	Speed [rpm]	P_{rail} [bar]	Fuel	Injection strategy
1	1,800	870	Diesel	Pilot+Main
2	1,800	780	Diesel	Pilot+Main
3	3,000	1,160	Diesel	Pilot+Main
4	3,400	430	Diesel	Pilot+Main

3. RBF neural network

A radial basis function (RBF) artificial neural network (ANN) is characterized by a feed-forward architecture and basically consists of an input layer, a single hidden layer and an output layer (Broomhead and Lowe, 1988). Formally, for a given input x, the network output y can be written as:

$$y = \sum_{i=1}^{N} \omega_i R_i(x) + \omega_0 \tag{1}$$

where ω_i are weights, ω_0 is a bias term, N denotes the number of the neurons in the hidden layer, whereas R_i are the activation functions, given by:

$$R_i(x) = \varphi\left(\|x - c_i\|\right) \tag{2}$$

In Eq. (2), φ is the radial function providing the non-linear feature of the model, and c_i are the so-called RBF centers. The most popular RBF is given by the Gauss function:

$$\varphi(r) = \exp\left(-r^2 / \sigma^2\right) \tag{3}$$

with r indicating the Euclidian distance between the input vector x and center c_i, and σ being the so-called spread parameter, to be determined. In this work, the influence of other types of RBF on the network accuracy is analyzed, particularly inverse multiquadratic and cubic, given respectively by:

$$\varphi(r) = \left(r^2 + \sigma^2\right)^{-1/2} \quad \text{and} \quad \varphi(r) = r^3 \tag{4}$$

4. Results and discussion

4.1. Influence of axis and RBF type

The ANN was first trained using a set of data collected as a single operating conditions, that is accelerometer and pressure signals collected at engine speed of 1800 rpm and P_{rail} equal to 780 bar (OP2 in Table 1). This allows for a detailed investigation of the influence of individual network parameters, i.e. spread and number of centers (neurons) on the network performance. Moreover, the mean square error (MSE) using different inputs (single or combined axes of acceleration signal) and RBFs is evaluated. The set of signals measured at OP2 over 350 fired cycles were divided into two subsets: a training set (50 % of the data) and a validation set (the remainder). Figure 2 reports typical signals collected during experiments: in-cylinder pressure curve (target/output of the network) and accelerometer signal (input). Here the acceleration along the x-axis is pressure is measured. The change is even stronger, at around +240° and -240° CA –

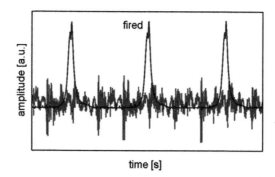

Figure 2. Typical in-cylinder pressure curve and accelerometer signal (*x*-axis), fired condition.

angular position at which combustion occurs in Cylinder 3, on which the accelerometer is placed, and Cylinder 2, respectively. This confirms the expected strong correlation between the in-cylinder pressure and the accelerometer signal. Figure 3 reports the MSE for the network with different settings: the first question to be answered is the choice of the acceleration axis to be used as an input to the network. It can be observed in Fig. 3a that the accuracy, expressed in terms of overall MSE, is of the same order when a single axis (x, y or z) or their combination (concatenated signal) is used. It appears that, when a single axis is considered, the choice of x – corresponding to the direction of the piston movement – is preferable. Figures 3b-c report the MSE for the network employing the Gaussian RBF, calculated for varying number of neurons and spread parameter,

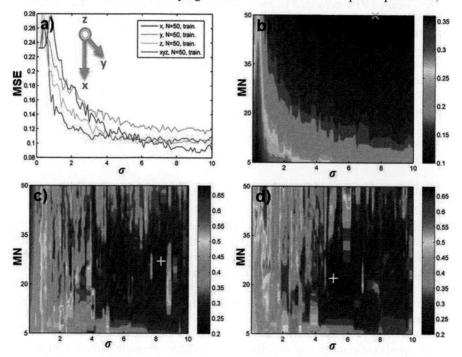

Figure 3. Training MSE error as a-function of σ for different inputs to the network (a); training (b) and validation MSE error (c) of the ANN employing Gaussian RBF; validation MSE error of the ANN employing inverse multiquadratic RBF (d). White crosses denote minima for the MSE.

Table 2. Validation error for networks employing different RBF.

RBF	σ	N	MSE
Gaussian	8.3	27	0.24
Inv. multiquad.	5.1	22	0.23
Cubic	-	15	0.32

respectively for the training (Figure 3b) and validation phase (Figure 3c). Increasing the number of neurons leads to a decrease of the MSE, nevertheless this does not reflect in a lower validation error. In fact, the latter has to be taken into account when determining optimal network parameters. Figure 3d shows validation MSE for the ANN employing inverse multiquadratic RBF: it is of the same order as the error calculated for the Gaussian RFB (Figure 3c). Table 2 summarizes the optimal pairs of the parameters, giving the lowest validation MSE. It can be observed that Gaussian and inverse multiquadratic RBF perform slightly better as compared to the cubic function. The Gaussian RBF is to be preferred, also due to the facility of application.

4.2. Robust RBF-ANN

To build a robust RBF ANN which provides accurate predictions of in-cylinder pressure for varying engine parameters, the network is tuned by using a training set created from input-target pairs of accelerometer and pressure signals acquired at four different engine operating points (OP1-OP4), described in Table 1. Exactly 100 cycles from each OP are selected by picking events that are uniformly spaced in the set of the available data. The detailed analysis of the influence of the number of neurons N employed and the value of σ on the network performance, both in terms of training and validation error, led to the choice of N=25 and σ=3.1 respectively, with an overall MSE equal to 0.768 bar^2. Fig. 4 illustrates a comparison of measured and simulated in-cylinder pressure signals for a

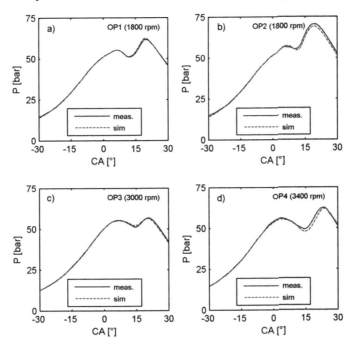

Figure 4. Measured and simulated in-cylinder pressure at different engine conditions (OP1-OP4).

selection of cycles from the validation set, one for each operating point. Very good agreement between the simulated and measured signals can be observed, especially for OP 1 (Fig. 4a) and OP3 (Fig. 4c), during the entire combustion process. The accuracy of the model is also characterized in terms of root mean square error (RMSE), both in the prediction of the peak pressure value and of its angular location. The RMSE in the prediction of the peak value was recorded as ranging between 1.153 bar (OP1) and 3.236 (OP2), whereas the RMSE on the predicted angular location, ranging between 0.269°CA (OP1) and 0.957°CA (OP4), is consistently low.

5. Conclusions

In this paper, a RBF neural network for the prediction of the in-cylinder pressure is built and tested. It uses as an input the vibration signal coming from a single accelerometer - a perfect non-intrusive replacement for expensive probes, prospectively suitable for production vehicles - mounted on the engine block of a three-cylinder real engine operating at various conditions. The work sought optimal parameters, i.e. number of neurons and value of the spread parameter, as well as the choice of the input signal and type or RBF of the network, by performing training runs with different combinations. Despite of the distance between the cylinders in which the pressure and the corresponding acceleration signal are measured, the results of the reconstruction obtained using the RBF network are promising in terms of accuracy and performance.

References

K. Bizon, G. Continillo, E. Mancaruso, B.M. Vaglieco B.M, 2011, Reconstruction of in-cylinder pressure in a Diesel engine from vibration signal using a RBF neural network model, SAE Technical Paper 2011-24-0161.

K. Bizon, G. Continillo, E. Mancaruso, B.M. Vaglieco B.M, 2013, Towards on-line prediction of the in-cylinder pressure in Diesel engines from engine vibration using artificial neural networks, SAE Technical Paper 2013-24-0137.

D.S. Broomhead, D. Lowe, 1988, Multivariable functional interpolation and adaptive networks, Complex Systems, 2, 321-355.

O. Chiavola, G. Chiatti, L. Arnone, S. Manelli, 2010, Combustion characterization in diesel engine via block vibration analysis, SAE Technical Paper 2010-01-0168.

N. Docquier, S. Candel, 2002, Combustion control and sensors: a review, Progress in Energy and Combustion Science, 28, 107-150.

F. Gu, P.J. Jacob, A.D. Ball, 1996, A RBF neural network model for cylinder pressure reconstruction in internal combustion engines, IEE Colloquium on Modelling and Signal Processing for Fault Diagnosis, 4/1 – 411.

K. Kalogeras, S. Bezergianni, V. Kazantzi, P.A. Pilavachi, 2010, On the prediction of properties for diesel/biodiesel mixtures featuring new environmental considerations, Computer Aided Chemical Engineering, 28, 973-978.

H.C. Krijnsen, J.C.M. van Leeuwen, R. Bakker, H.P.A. Calis, C.M. van den Bleek, 2000, Optimum deNOx performance using inferential feedforward reductant flow control, Computer Aided Chemical Engineering, 8, 883-888.

S. Saraswati, S. Chand, 2010, Reconstruction of cylinder pressure for SI engine using recurrent neural networks, Neural Computing and Applications 19, 935-944.

F. Taglialatela-Scafati, M. Lavorgna, E. Mancaruso, 2011, Use of Vibration Signal for Diagnosis and Control of a Four-Cylinder Diesel Engine, SAE Technical Paper 2011-24-0169.

F. Taglialatela Scafati, M. Lavorgna, E. Mancaruso, B.M. Vaglieco, 2013, Determination of combustion parameters using engine crankshaft speed, Mechanical Systems and Signal Processing, 38, 628-633.

K.Y. Wai, K. Vishy, 2013, Comparative analysis of artificial neural network and dynamic modles as virtual sensors, Applied Soft Computing, 13, 181-188.

Jiří Jaromír Klemeš, Petar Sabev Varbanov and Peng Yen Liew (Editors)
Proceedings of the 24th European Symposium on Computer Aided Process Engineering – ESCAPE 24
June 15-18, 2014, Budapest, Hungary.

Temperature Control of Enzymatic Batch Esterification Reactor Using Nonlinear Model Predictive Control (NMPC): A Real-Time Implementation

Siti Asyura Zulkeflee, Suhari Abd Sata, Norashid Aziz[*]

School of Chemical Engineering, Engineering Campus, Universiti Sains Malaysia, Seri Ampangan, 14300 Nibong Tebal, Seberang Perai Selatan, Malaysia
chnaziz@eng.usm.my

Abstract

This paper presents the real-time implementation of the Nonlinear Model Predictive Control (NMPC) controller in controlling the temperature in batch esterification process. In the real time application, the MATLAB Simulink external mode and Real-Time Windows target software (MATLAB-Simulink-Real-Time-Windows Target) is integrated. The Simulink model is used as a Graphical User Interface (GUI) for signal visualization and parameter tuning in the real-time implementations. From the results achieved, it can be concluded that the proposed embedded design architecture is able to deliver the real-time desired outcome.

Keywords: Nonlinear model predictive control, NARX model, esterification, batch process, real-time implementation.

1. Introduction

Nonlinear control systems such as Nonlinear Model Predictive Control (NMPC) have been the subject of an interest in process control design (Camacho and Bordons, 2007) and have been applied in numerous industrial scale process (Lopez-Negrete et al., 2013). The advantages of NMPC such as the ability to handle constraints, the applicability to nonlinear processes and to multivariable problems, make this control strategy a feasible and attractive choice especially in batch processes (Lauri et al., 2014). However, when applying NMPC into such systems in the real-time environment, the controller capability can be questionable. In the last decade, many realistic approaches have been proposed to ensure the control is reliable for the real implementation (Alamir, 2009). Nowadays, the computational and graphical power of modern computers have led to more flexible control systems including higher-level functions and advanced algorithms where it can be implemented successfully in the real time implementation (Enikov and Campa, 2012).

In this work, NMPC has been designed to control the temperature in enzymatic batch esterification reactor and then tested in the real-time implementation. In esterification process, temperature has a strong influence on the product yield and it should preferably be above the melting points of the substrates and the product, but not too high, as the enzyme's activity and stability decreases at elevated temperature. Therefore, temperature control is important in the esterification process ensure the maximum ester production can be obtained.

In the NMPC framework proposed, a reliable Nonlinear Auto-Regressive with eXogenous inputs (NARX) model and nonlinear optimization programming (NLP) were used. The entire framework was built in the Simulink model and was used as a Graphical User Interface (GUI) for signal visualization and parameter tuning in the real-time implementations. This is attained by integrating between MATLAB Simulink external mode and Real-Time Windows target software (MATLAB-Simulink-Real-Time-Windows *Target)*.The rest of this paper is organized as follows. Section 2 introduces the batch esterification reactor system and problem motivation. In Section 3, the proposed NMPC controller strategy is derived based on NARX model. In Section 4, performance results of NMPC in controlling the batch esterification reactor system are presented to demonstrate the effectiveness of the proposed controller. Finally, some concluding remarks are given in Section 5.

2. Real-time batch esterification reactor system

In this work, the reactor's temperature is controlled by manipulating the flowrate of cooling water into the reactor jacket. The esterification processes were conducted in 1.5 L jacketed batch reactor. The reaction mixture in iso-octane of Citronellol, Lauric acid and immobilized lipase was stirred at 200 rpm. Computer control and the instrumentations for the experimental apparatus are shown in Figure 1. The current signal, after appropriate signal conditioning, is converted to a digital signal by a 12-bit A/D converter (Advantech PCI-1710). The I/O card is getting the signal from all sensors such as thermocouples, flow sensors, pressure sensor, humidity sensor, conductivity sensor, and pH sensor. The computer used in the experiment is an IBM PC/XT with an Intel 80286 16-bit CPU with a 20 Mhz clock speed. The real time control and interface routines are written using Real-Time Windows Target in MATLAB software. The digital outputs are given to Advantech PCI-1710 to control solenoid valves and converted into an analog electrical signal by a 12-bit D/A converter (National Instruments, PCI-6704) which controls the proportional valve, stirrer and dosing pump. The developed controller computations are carried out in the PC whereas the actual control is implemented through the hardware controller with sampling time of 10s.

In the temperature control loops, one pneumatic control valves, one flow meter, two solenoid valves are installed. At the inlets and outlets of the jacket, two thermocouples are located (-18-538 $^{\circ}$C Platinum + 10 % rhodium + platinum); accuracy ±0.1 to 0.3 $^{\circ}$C).

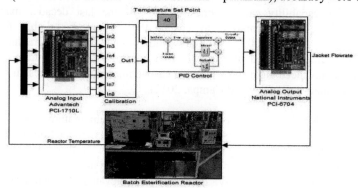

Figure 1. Schematic Diagram of the Batch Esterification Reactor with RTWT Interface for Temperature Control Systems

The reactor temperature is measured by the thermocouple of the same type (accuracy ±0.1 °C). The volumetric flow rates inside the jacket are measured by flow transmitter which output a 4-20mA signal proportional to the flow rate. The measured temperature of the reactor was compared with the set-point and the cooling water flow into the jacket was manipulated via a proportional valve.

The experiment also illustrates the use of the MATLAB-Simulink RTWT environment. The RTWT module performs classical control experiments using hardware-in-loop simulations. Using RTWT, the sampling time was reduced by an order of magnitude to 5ms. The corresponding Simulink model was developed in order to send and receive signals to/from the real batch esterification system, as depicted in Fig. 2. Some configuration of the simulation parameters need to be done.

where:
A: Integration to input/output card Advantech PCI-1710L
B: Filter and rate limiter to stabilize the input signal from sensor instruments.
C: Calibration equation to convert analog input into the actual readings
D: PID controller to control proportional valve of jacket flow rate
E: Output signal to input/output card National Instruments PCI-6704

3. Nonlinear model predictive control based on NARX model

The NARX model is characterized by the non-linear relations between the past inputs, past outputs and the predicted process output and it is approximated by the regression model of the form:

$$y(t) = \sum_{i=0}^{n_u} a(i).u(t-i) + \sum_{j=1}^{n_y} b(j).y(t-j) + \sum_{i=0}^{n_u}\sum_{j=i}^{n_u} a(i,j).u(t-i).u(t-j)$$

$$+ \sum_{i=1}^{n_y}\sum_{j=i}^{n_y} b(i,j).y(t-i).y(t-j) + \sum_{i=0}^{n_u}\sum_{j=1}^{n_y} c(i,j).u(t-i).y(t-j) \quad (1)$$

$$+ e(t)$$

where $u(t)$ and $y(t)$ represent input and output of the model at time t in which the current output $y(t) \in \Re$ depends merely on the current input $u(t) \in \Re$. Here n_u and n_y

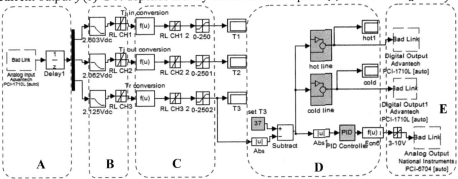

Figure 2.Simulink model for the RTWT application for batch esterification reactor

are the maximum lags of past input and output entering the dynamical model. The function f is a nonlinear function. $\bar{X} = [y(t-1)...y(t-n_y)\,u(t-1)...u(t-n_u)]^T$ denotes the system input vector with a known dimension $n = n_y + n_u$. Terms $a(i)$ and $a(i,j)$ are the coefficients of linear and nonlinear for originating exogenous terms; $b(i)$ and $b(i,j)$ are the coefficients of the linear and nonlinear autoregressive terms; $c(i,j)$ are the coefficients of the nonlinear cross terms. $e(t)$ is assumed to be a white noise sequence. The constants a, b, A, B, C in (1) are the coefficients of the term cluster contains the form $u^{n_u}(t-i)y^{n_y}(t-j)$ for $n_u + n_y \leq n_l$, where i and j are any time lags. Such coefficients are called cluster coefficients and are represented as $\theta_{n_u n_y}$. The model parameters are approximated by convergence in mean square sense. The model $y_m(t,u,y,n_u,n_y)$ converges in mean square sense to a system $y(t,u,y)$, if for all column vector of the model residuals, $\varepsilon > 0$, $\exists M_\varepsilon$ independent of $\theta_{n_u n_y}$.

$$\exists \theta_M \Rightarrow \forall u \in \mathbb{U}: \xi\left\{\left|y(t,u,y) - y_m\left(t,u,y,n_u,n_y,\theta_{n_u n_y}\right)\right|^2\right\} < \varepsilon \qquad (2)$$

A formulation of the MPC on-line optimization can be as follows:

$$\min_{u[t|t],...u[m+p|t]} \sum_{k=0}^{P} w_k(y[t+k|t] - y_{sp})^2 + \sum_{k=1}^{M} r_k \Delta u[t+k|t]^2 \qquad (3)$$

Where P and M is the length of the process output prediction and manipulated process input horizons respectively with $P \leq M$. $u[t+k|t]_{k=0,...P}$ is the set of future process input values. The vector w_k and r_k are the weight vector.

Remark 3.1: The above on-line optimization problem could also include certain constraints. There can be bounds on the input and output variables: $u_{max} \geq u[t+k|t] \geq u_{min}$, $\Delta u_{max} \geq \Delta u[t+k|t] \geq -\Delta u_{min}$ and $y_{max} \geq y[t+k|t] \geq y_{min}$.

It is clear that the above problem formulation necessitates the prediction of future outputs. The full derivation for k step ahead prediction in NARX model can represent as (Zulkeflee et al., 2011);

$$\min_{u[t|t],...u[m+p|t]} \sum_{k=1}^{P} w_k \left(\left(\sum_{i=0}^{n_u} a(i).u(t-i+k) + \sum_{j=1}^{n_y} b(j).y(t-j+k) + \right.\right.$$
$$\sum_{i=0}^{n_u}\sum_{j=i}^{n_u} a(i,j).u(t-i+k).u(t-j+k) + \sum_{i=1}^{n_y}\sum_{j=i}^{n_y} b(i,j).y(t-i+k).y(t-j+k) +$$
$$\sum_{i=0}^{n_u}\sum_{j=1}^{n_y} c(i,j).u(t-i+k).y(t-j+k) + y(t) - \sum_{i=0}^{n_u} a(i).u(t-i) -$$
$$\sum_{j=1}^{n_y} b(j).y(t-j) - \sum_{i=0}^{n_u}\sum_{j=i}^{n_u} a(i,j).u(t-i).u(t-j) - \sum_{i=1}^{n_y}\sum_{j=i}^{n_y} b(i,j).y(t-i).y(t-$$
$$j) - \sum_{i=0}^{n_u}\sum_{j=1}^{n_y} c(i,j).u(t-i).y(t-j)) - y_{sp})^2 + \sum_{k=1}^{M} r_k \Delta u[t+i|t]^2 \qquad (4)$$

where, $y_{sp}(t) = [y_{sp}(t+1)y_{sp}(t+2)....y_{sp}(t+P)]^T$ and $\Delta u(t) = [\Delta u[t|t]\ \Delta u[t+1|t]\ ...\ \Delta u[t+M-1|t]]^T$

The above optimization problem is a nonlinear programming which can be solved at each time t. Even though the input trajectory is calculated until M-1 sampling times into the future, only the first computed move is implemented for one sampling interval and the above optimization is repeated at the next sampling time.

4. Results and discussion

In the NARX model identification, the convergence and consistency of the proposed models are proved that the model order $n_u=1$ and $n_y= 2$ is chosen as the best model order to represent the real process data. Then, the identified NARX model of the process has been implemented in the NMPC algorithm where some criteria to select the significant tuning parameters (prediction horizon, P; control horizon, M; penalty weight matrices w_k and r_k) for the NMPC controller are determined. The optimization problem is solved using constrained nonlinear optimization programming (*fmincon*) function in the MATLAB (in simulation basis), the best tuning parameters for the developed NMPC controller found is P = 11; M = 2; w_k = 0.1 and r_k = 1. Based on the final tuning, the performances of the NMPC controller are evaluated for set-point tracking and load change in a real-time environment.

The responses obtained from the NMPC controllers during the set-point tracking and load change with their corresponding input responses are shown in Fig. 3. The results show that the NMPC controller has driven the process output to the desired set-point with a response time of 16 minutes and no overshoot or oscillatory response. For load change, the initial jacket temperature is considered as the process disturbance. A step change of the initial jacket temperature from 25 ‑ 27 ºC was implemented into the system after 25 minutes. For both tests, the real-time reactor temperature profile show slower response compared to the simulation result, this is due to delayed deviation responses from real-time jacket flowrate profile as can be seen in lower plot of Fig. 3. However, it is still proves the feasibility of MATLAB-Simulink Real-Time-Windows Target algorithm implementation in controlling the batch esterification reactor. Based on the previous works on implementation of IMC based PID controller which have been reported by Zulkeflee et al. (2013), it shows that the PID controller drives the process output to the desired set-point with slow response time (35 min) and there are some

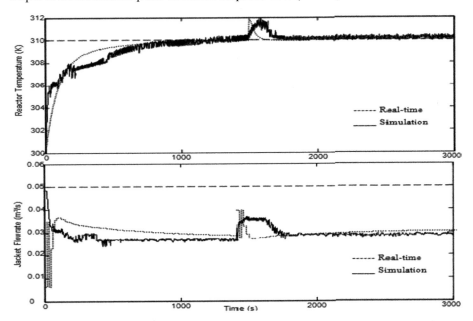

Figure 3. Control response of NMPC controller in real-time (solid-line) and simulation (dotted-line) for set-point tracking and load change with their respective manipulated variable action.

oscillatory responses in tracking the set-point. It proves that the performance of NMPC controller was better than IMC based PID controller in controlling the reactor temperature of batch esterification reactor.

5. Conclusions

In this work an interactive and effective tool to design control loops in real-time for batch esterification reactor using MATLAB-Simulink Real-Time-Windows Target has been presented. The relevance of real-time implementation has been exposed by implementing the NMPC based on NARX model controller in controlling the temperature of batch esterification reactor. The results from this work show that the proposed NMPC based on the NARX model are effective to control the reactor temperature in batch esterification reactor.

Acknowledgments

The authors wish to acknowledge the financial support by Universiti Sains Malaysia through the RU-Grant (Project No.:814077) and PRGS-Grant (Project No.: 8046007) and also to Ministry of Science, Technology & Innovation, Malaysia through the NSF scholarship for the first author.

References

E.F. Camacho, C. Bordons, 2007, Nonlinear model predictive control: An introductory review, Assessment and future directions of nonlinear model predictive control, Springer Berlin Heidelberg, 1-16.

R. Lopez-Negrete, F.J. D'Amato, L.T. Biegler, A. Kumar, 2013, Fast nonlinear model predictive control: Formulation and industrial process applications, Computers and Chemical Engineering, 51, 55-64.

D. Laurí, B. Lennox, J. Camacho, 2014, Model predictive control for batch processes: Ensuring validity of predictions, Journal of Process Control, 24, 1, 239-49.

M. Alamir, 2009, A framework for monitoring control updating period in real-time NMPC schemes. Nonlinear Model Predictive Control, Springer Berlin Heidelberg, 433-445.

E.T. Enikov, G. Campa, 2012, Mechatronic Aeropendulum: Demonstration of Linear and Nonlinear Feedback Control Principles With MATLAB/Simulink Real-Time Windows Target, IEEE Transactions on Education, 55, 4, 538-45.

S.A. Zulkeflee, S.A. Sata, N. Aziz, 2011, Nonlinear Autoregressive with Exogenous Inputs Based Model Predictive Control for Batch Citronellyl Laurate Esterification Reactor, Advanced Model Predictive Control, InTech, DOI: 10.5772/16963.

S.A. Zulkeflee, S.A. Sata, N. Aziz, 2013, PID Controller for Batch Process using MATLAB-Simulink-Real-Time-Windows Target, in Proceedings of the National Colloquium on Process Control, Oct 1, Penang, Malaysia, ISBN: 978-967-394-157-5.

Jiří Jaromír Klemeš, Petar Sabev Varbanov and Peng Yen Liew (Editors)
Proceedings of the 24th European Symposium on Computer Aided Process Engineering – ESCAPE 24
June 15-18, 2014, Budapest, Hungary. Copyright © 2014 Elsevier B.V. All rights reserved.

Multiple Input Multiple Output Nonlinear Autoregressive with Exogenous Input Model for Enzymatic Batch Esterification Reactor

Siti Asyura Zulkeflee, Suhari Abd Sata, Norashid Aziz*

School of Chemical Engineering, Engineering Campus, Universiti Sains Malaysia, Seri Ampangan, 14300 Nibong Tebal, Seberang Perai Selatan, Malaysia
chnaziz@eng.usm.my

Abstract

In this paper, a multiple inputs multiple outputs (MIMO) Nonlinear AutoRegressive with eXogenous input (NARX) model for enzymatic batch esterification process is developed. The model developed is aimed to be used to control the temperature and water content of enzymatic batch esterification reactor. The MIMO model developed is then evaluated and analyzed in order to ensure its feasibility to be implemented in the NMPC algorithm. The results demonstrate that the proposed model developed showed good predictive capability for the batch esterification reactor system.

Keywords: NARX model, esterification, batch process, model identification

1. Introduction

Ester has been continuously developed and gained an important role in our daily life. They can become as a good alternative to organic flavor and fragrances in the food and pharmaceuticals industry. Most of esterification processesuse enzyme as a catalytic agent that can accelerate the reaction process. In order to control this esterification process, the understanding of factors that influencing the process are crucial and important to be determined.Temperature is one of the factors that has a strong influence on the production rate. The temperature should preferably be above the melting points of the substrates and the product, but cannot too high, as the enzyme's activity and stability decreases at elevated temperature. It is also reported that any addition of water beyond the critical amount probably would increase the thickness of the water layer around the enzyme particle to a point where it could present external mass transfer problem which lead to enzyme denaturation (Yadav and Lathi, 2004). Further, for esterification reactions which water is one of the products, it is not only affects the intrinsic activity of lipases but also acts as a competitive nucleophile. Therefore, the temperature and water content controlare important in order to achieve optimum ester production. However, the enzymatic esterification process characteristics such as enzyme stability, complex subreaction and operating variable interactions which contribute to nonlinearity behaviour of the process cansignificantly affect the control performance. Due to these difficulties, nonlinear control systems, including strategies using explicitly a nonlinear model of the process such as Nonlinear Model Predictive Control (NMPC) have been the subject of an increasing interest (Jr and Richards, 2013).

One of the major issues concerned in NMPC application is the development of feasible model (Zhu et al., 2013). There are a lot of dynamic model developments for the enzymatic batch esterification process reported in the literature but most of them are wisely complex (Zou et al., 2010). The characteristic of the state vector of these complex models is generally very large andthe time required for simulation is often in the same order as the simulated interval. Due to these reasons, the use of these complex models for state estimation and other online applications which lead tohigh computational burden to solve the models have been prevented (Singh Amit et al., 2013). As a result, a different modelling approach such as black-box model to represent the process behaviour has become more attractive (Pantelides and Renfro, 2013). This black-box model has much simpler model structure and the computational burden to solve the models is low enough, so that they can be used for online state estimation and other process applications. Furthermore, the realization of NMPC requires the application of a fast nonlinear programming (NLP) solver for time-critical and on-line optimization make the black model as a better choice (Xi et al., 2013).

In recent years, a wide stream of research focused on black-box nonlinear model identification can be described by Nonlinear AutoRegressive with eXogenous input (NARX) models. This type of model has received great attention because it has shown great potential in its ability to approximate nonlinear input-output relationship (Baldacchino et al., 2012). Motivated by the above considerations, in this work, a NARX model for a batch esterification reactor is developed which, later, will be embedded in a nonlinear controller to control the temperature and water content of batch esterification reactor. The rest of this paper is organized as follows. Section 2 introduces the batch esterification system and problem formulation for input output data generation. Next, the proposed identification method is derived in Section 3. In Section 4, simulations results of batch esterification reactor system are presented to demonstrate the effectiveness of the proposed modeling. Finally, some concluding remarks is highlighted in Section 5.

2. Batch esterification process and problem formulation

In this work, the production of Citronellyllaurate using a immobilized lipase as a catalyst is chosen as a case study (Zulkeflee et al., 2013). Consider a batch reactor system shown in Figure 1. In the temperature control loops, the reactor temperature is controlled by manipulating the cooling water flowrate within the jacket. The reactor's temperature control can be achieved by treating the limitation of the jacket's flowrate, Fj_{in}, which can be viewed as a state of the process and as the constraint control problem. In the water content control loops system, the water content is measured in the gaseous phase and the inflow of dry air Fa_{in} is varied to maintain the water content at the set point value.Based on the control objectives, the water content, Cw (v/v%) and temperature, Tr (K) in the reactor are the two measured outputs of the system. The inlet air flowrate, Fa_{in} (m³/s) and inlet jacket flowrate, Fj_{in} (m³/s) are used as manipulated variables and jacket temperature, Tj (K) is treated as unmeasured disturbance.

Based on Pearson (2006), a good strategy in designing the input sequences is by choosing the range, distribution, and switching probability to yield sequences that are as similar as possible to those seen in practice during process operations when the control inputs are "active". The state vector is comprised of the water content and reactor temperature: $y(t) = [C_w \ T]^T$ and the manipulated inputs are $u(t) = [Fa_{in} Fj_{in} \ Tj]^T$, with constraints $u_{min}(t) = [0 \ 0 \ 291]^T$ and $u_{max}(t) = [0.025 \ 0.05 \ 300]^T$. The 1,000 training data is set for time span (0:2:2000) and the 500 validation data is set for time span (0:3:1500). The fundamental equations of the mass and energy balances of the

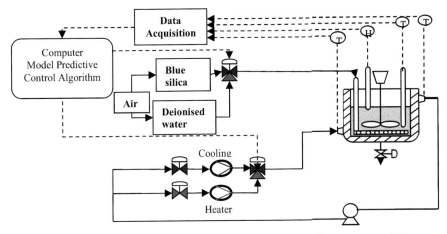

Figure 1. Schematic Diagram of the Batch Esterification Reactor with Temperature and Water Activity Control System

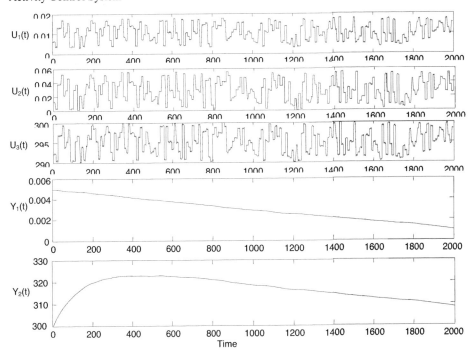

Figure 2. Input Output Data for NARX model identification

process in Zulkeflee and Aziz (2009) are used to generate data for NARX model identification. The input and output data used for nonlinear identification are shown in Figure 2.

3. NARX model identification

Consider the NARX model which is characterized by the nonlinear relations between the past inputs, past outputs and the predicted process output and can be delineated by high order difference equation as follows:

$$y(t) = f\{y(t-1), \dots y(t-n_y), u(t-1) \dots u(t-n_u)\} + e(t) \tag{1}$$

where $u(t)$ and $y(t)$ represent input and output of the model at time t in which the current output $y(t) \in \Re$ depends merely on the current input $u(t) \in \Re$. Here n_u and n_y are the maximum lags of past input and output entering the dynamical model. The function f is a nonlinear function. $\bar{X} = [y(t-1) \dots y(t-n_y) \, u(t-1) \dots u(t-n_u)]^T$ denotes the system input vector with a known dimension $n = n_y + n_u$. Since the function f is unknown, it is approximated by the regression model of the form:

$$y(t) = \sum_{i=0}^{n_u} a(i).u(t-i) + \sum_{j=1}^{n_y} b(j).y(t-j) + \sum_{i=0}^{n_u}\sum_{j=i}^{n_u} a(i,j).u(t-i).u(t-j) +$$
$$\sum_{i=1}^{n_y}\sum_{j=i}^{n_y} b(i,j).y(t-i).y(t-j) + \sum_{i=0}^{n_u}\sum_{j=1}^{n_y} c(i,j).u(t-i).y(t-j) + e(t) \tag{2}$$

where $a(i)$ and $a(i,j)$ are the coefficients of linear and nonlinear for originating exogenous terms; $b(i)$ and $b(i,j)$ are the coefficients of the linear and nonlinear autoregressive terms; $c(i,j)$ are the coefficients of the nonlinear cross terms. $e(t)$ is assumed to be a white noise sequence. Eq. 2 can be written in matrix form:

$$\begin{bmatrix} y(t) \\ y(t+1) \\ \vdots \\ y(t+n_y) \end{bmatrix} = a.u^T + b.y^T + A.[U]^T + B.[Y]^T + C.[X]^T \tag{3}$$

<u>Definition 3.1:</u> The constants a, b, A, B, C in (3) are the coefficients of the term cluster contains the form $u^{n_u}(t-i)y^{n_y}(t-j)$ for $n_u + n_y \leq n_l$, where i and j are any time lags. Such coefficients are called cluster coefficients and are represented as $\theta_{n_u n_y}$.

<u>Remark 3.1:</u> With full state measurements, choosing the number of input and output lags is crucial and the process conditions can be initially described by the current states and inputs which $n_u \geq 0$, $n_y \geq 1$. Accordingly, the state and input transition matrices are estimated by regressing a matrix of concatenated states and inputs on a matrix of forward shifted states.

<u>Remark 3.2:</u> The method can be implemented more easily by decomposing the MIMO system model (2) into x-MISO sub-system models and treating each sub-system separately. The process is decomposed into two MISO sub-systems of the water content $y_1(t)$ and the reactor temperature $y_2(t)$, which can be represented in the following form; $NARX: y_1(t) = f_1[u_1(t), u_2(t), u_3(t), y_2(t), t]$ and $NARX: y_2(t) = f_2[u_1(t), u_2(t), u_3(t), y_1(t), t]$.

In model identification, the model matrices function is written in *mfile* MATLAB software and the degree of NARX models accuracy is evaluated by changing the model order. The model parameters are approximated by evaluated the performance of convergence in mean square sense. Finally, the model was validated with set of validation data. The model $y_m(t, u, y, n_u, n_y)$ converges in mean square sense to a system $y(t, u, y)$, if for all column vector of the model residuals, $\varepsilon > 0$, $\exists M_\varepsilon$ independent of $\theta_{n_u n_y}$.

$$\exists \theta_M \Rightarrow \forall u \in \mathbb{U}: \xi \left\{ \left| y(t,u,y) - y_m\left(t, u, y, n_u, n_y, \theta_{n_u n_y}\right) \right|^2 \right\} < \tag{4}$$

4. Results and discussion

Different orders of NARX models, $NARX: y_1(t)$ and $NARX: y_2(t)$ which was a mapping of past inputs (n_u) and output (n_y) terms to future outputs were tested and the best one was selected according to the error convergence $\exists \theta_M$ value. The results obtained have been summarized in Table 1. From Table 1, the $\exists \theta_M$ and $\exists \theta_U$ value decreased by increasing the model order until the value of $n_u=2$ and $n_y = 2$ for $NARX: y_1(t)$ and $n_u=1$ and $n_y= 2$ for $NARX: y_2(t)$. Higher NARX model order (more complex model) shows a larger value of error and gives unsatisfactory results. The $NARX: y_1(t)$ and $NARX: y_2(t)$ model output plot with the best model order are plotted in Figure 3. Here, the NARX modelling approach has been proved to provide good representations for nonlinear system dynamics of the batch esterification process.

5. Conclusions

In this work, the MIMO-NARX model has been developed for batch esterification process by decomposing the NARX model into two MISO sub-system models. In NARX model identification, the model performance is studied based on the selected number of input and output lags. The model order $n_u = 2$ and $n_y = 2$ for $NARX: y_1(t)$ and $n_u=1$ and $n_y= 2$ for $NARX: y_2(t)$ has been chosen as the best

Table 1. Convergence values of NARX model for different number of n_u and n_y

| (n_u, n_y) | $NARX: y_1(t)$ | | $NARX: y_2(t)$ | |
| | Training | Validation | Training | Validation |
	Error: $\exists \theta_M (10^{-2})$	Error: $\exists \theta_M (10^{-2})$	Error: $\exists \theta_M$	Error: $\exists \theta_M$
0,1	16.900	25.839	0.143	3.689
1,1	12.743	17.783	0.099	1.433
1,2	7.072	9.735	**0.024**	**0.548**
2,1	1.084	5.835	0.138	1.062
2,2	**0.713**	**2.116**		
3,2	8.527	13.644		

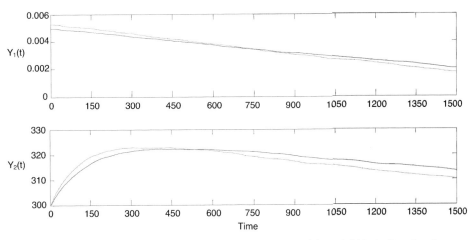

Figure 3. Model output plot for the $NARX: y_1(t)$ and $NARX: y_2(t)$ model (dashed) and real process (solid)

model order to represent the real process data. Finally, it can be concluded that, the developed NARX models are effective to represent the process system in batch esterification reactor.

Acknowledgments

The authors wish to acknowledge the financial support by Universiti Sains Malaysia through the RU-Grant (Project No.:814077) and PRGS-Grant (Project No.: 8046007) and also to MOSTI, Malaysia through the NSF scholarship for the first author.

References

T. Baldacchino, S. R. Anderson, V. Kadirkamanathan, 2012, Structure detection and parameter estimation for NARX models in a unified EM framework, Automatica, 48, 5, 857-865.

C. C. Pantelides, J. G. Renfro, 2013, The online use of first-principles models in process operations: Review, current status and future needs, Comput Chem Eng, 51, 136-148.

R. K. Pearson, 2006, Nonlinear empirical modeling techniques, Comput Chem Eng, 30, 10–12, 1514-1528.

K. Singh Amit, B. Tyagi, V. Kumar, 2013, First Principle Modeling and Neural Network–Based Empirical Modeling with Experimental Validation of Binary Distillation Column, Chemical Product and Process Modeling, 8, 53.

Y.-G. Xi, D.-W. Li, S. Lin, 2013, Model Predictive Control — Status and Challenges, Acta Automatica Sinica, 39, 3, 222-236.

G. D. Yadav, P. S. Lathi, 2004, Synthesis of citronellol laurate in organic media catalyzed by immobilized lipases: kinetic studies, J Mol Catal B-Enzym, 27, 2-3, 113-119.

Y. C. Zhu, R. Patwardhan, S. B. Wagner, J. Zhao, 2013, Toward a low cost and high performance MPC: The role of system identification, Comput Chem Eng, 51, 124-135.

Y. Zou, Z. Tong, K. Liu, X. Feng, 2010, Modeling of Esterification in a Batch Reactor Coupled with Pervaporation for Production of n-Butyl Acetate, Chinese Journal of Catalysis, 31, 8, 999-1005.

S. A. Zulkeflee, S. Abd Sata, N. Aziz, 2013, Kinetic Model with Effect of Water Content for Enzyme-Catalyzed Citronellyl Laurate Esterification Process, Applied Mechanics and Materials, 284 - 287, 423-428.

S. A. Zulkeflee, N. Aziz, 2009, NARX-Model-Based Control (NARX-MBC) for Citronellyl Laurate Esterification Reactor, Computer Aided Chemical Engineering, 27, 1569-1574.

Jiří Jaromír Klemeš, Petar Sabev Varbanov and Peng Yen Liew (Editors)
Proceedings of the 24th European Symposium on Computer Aided Process Engineering – ESCAPE 24
June 15-18, 2014, Budapest, Hungary.

Model Development and Experimental Validation for Crystal Shape Control by Using Tailored Mixtures of Crystal Growth Modifiers

Ákos Borsos,[a] Aniruddha Majumder,[a] Zoltán K. Nagy[a,b],*

[a]Loughborough University, Loughborough LE11 3TU, United Kingdom
[b]Purdue University, West Lafayette IN 47907-2100, USA
zknagy@purdue.edu

Abstract

The quality of crystalline products is often determined by the shape distribution, because its significant effect on downstream processes as well as on biological activity. Thus, controlling the crystal shape is important, especially in the pharmaceutical industry. In this work, we describe a new methodology of investigation, simulation and control of the crystal shape by using tailored mixtures of crystal growth modifiers (CGM). Particle Vision Measurement (PVM) and image analysis were applied to track the shape in real time. The effect of CGMs on the morphology is investigated by combining the growth kinetic model with competitive adsorption mechanism of the CGMs on the crystal face and their incorporation in the population balance model (PBM). The model parameters are identified using experimental data. The process simulator is proven to be an effective tool for investigating the process and calculation of the required CGM concentrations to achieve desired crystal shape.

Keywords: Crystal shape, impurity, population balance, real-time monitoring, image analysis.

1. Introduction

The size and shape of crystals play crucial roles in industrial crystallization. Investigation, design and control of crystal size and shape distribution are well-studied areas, including the analysis of their effect on the efficiency of downstream processes and the biological activity of products (Nagy and Braatz, 2012). Impurities often have impact on the crystal shape, which is investigated experimentally in many studies (Ding et al., 2010). A mathematical model of the impurity effect was developed by Kubota and Mullin (1995). The morphological population balance modeling technique is capable of describing the evolutions of crystal shape. Majumder and Nagy (2013) developed a multidimensional population balance equation (PBE) based model for investigation of the effect of impurities in crystal shape distribution and proposed a control approach for the aspect ratio (AR) by feedback control-based CGM dosing. Measurement of the shape is often performed by using off-line techniques, while Zhou et al. (2009) overviewed the literature and developed methodology of on-line particle size and shape monitoring and measurement. In this work, we applied PVM and image analysis for real-time investigation of crystal AR. The effect of impurity on the growth was investigated as an effective tool of shape control. Morphological PBM is developed and calibrated by physical experiments. The experimental results confirm the simulation based investigations and indicate the potential of the method as a shape control tool.

2. Experimental procedure

In all experiments, 150 g potassium dihydrogen phosphate (KDP), aluminium sulphate (CGM1) and sodium hexametaphosphate (CGM2) were used in 400 g water. In situ images were captured by using a PVM probe and were analysed based on blob analysis in the PVM Image Acquisition and Lasentec PVM Stat Acquisition software in order to extract information of crystal shape distribution (Figure 1). Initially, the system was heated up until solid particles dissolved, then linear cooling rate was applied between 45 °C and 20 °C in 180 min. Table 1 shows the used amounts of CGMs in all experiments. The effect of CGMs on the shape is linked to the internal structure of the KDP crystal. The different facets of the crystal exhibit different charges because of the internal structure (Ding et al., 2010) as it can be seen on Figure 2. Numerous researchers investigated the effect of different CGMs on the shape (Fu et al., 1999; Kubota and Mullin, 1995). Generally, divalent and trivalent metal ions preferably adsorb on the {100} facet resulting decreased growth rate on the site, while anionic impurities preferred to adsorb and inhibit growth rate of the positive charged facet {101}. Hence, the aluminium sulphate results increased AR of the crystal and the effect of sodium hexametaphosphate on the crystal shape has opposing effect.

3. Mathematical model

The crystallization of KDP from solution is a well-studied system in terms of simulation and experiments and multidimensional PBMs are often used to describe the particle size and shape distribution (Borsos and Lakatos, 2012; Majumder and Nagy, 2013; Ma et al., 2008). The shape of KDP crystal is presented on the Fig. 2. As it is shown, two characteristic sizes (x_1, x_2) are necessary to describe the shape properly. In the presence of a CGM, Kubota and Mullin (1995) developed a growth kinetic model based on the Langmuir adsorption isotherms, considering only single CGM in the system. For investigation of the effect of mixed CGMs on the crystal shape the Kubota-Mullin model requires extension. According to the different adsorption mechanisms (i.e. competitive adsorption) in terms of different CGMs, the developed growth rate can be expressed as

$$G_i = k_{gi} \left(\frac{C - C_{sat}}{C_{sat}} \right)^{g_i} \left[1 - \sum \left(\alpha_i \theta_{i,j} \right) \right] \tag{1}$$

where G_i is the growth rate of the ith characteristic crystal facets, α_i is the effectiveness factor for the CGM on the crystal face i, $\theta_{i,j}$ is the adsorption coverage due to CGM on the crystal face i. Parameter k_{gi} is the growth kinetic coefficient which depends on the temperature. The variables C and C_{sat} denote the concentration and the saturation concentration respectively; g_i is growth exponent.

Table 1. Amount of CGMs

	Exp1	Exp2	Exp3	Exp4	Exp5
CGM1 [g]	-	-	0.007	0.005	0.005
CGM2 [g]	0.002	-	-	0.003	-

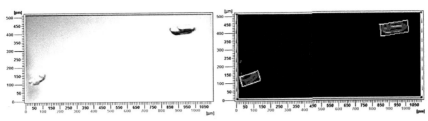

Figure 1. Crystals captured by PVM and detected particles by using image analysis software

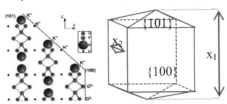

Figure 2. Molecular arrangement and morphology of KDP crystal (Ding et al., 2010)

The effectiveness factor of the adsorption on the ith characteristic crystal size described by Kubota's model as follows:

$$\alpha_i = \frac{\gamma_i a}{kT\sigma L_i} = \frac{\alpha_i'}{T\sigma} \tag{2}$$

where γ is the edge free energy on the crystal facet per unit length, a denotes the area of the crystal per unit, k is the Boltzmann constant, T is temperature, σ denotes to the relative supersaturation while L is average distance between same type of active sites. The coverage function according to the Langmuir competitive adsorption model for multiple CGMs takes the form:

$$\theta_{i,j} = \frac{K_{i,j}C_{CGM,j}}{1 + \sum_j K_{i,j}C_{CGM,j}}\left[1 - \exp\left(-\frac{\eta}{\tau_j}\right)\right] \tag{3}$$

where K is the Langmuir constant, C_{CGM} is the concentration of CGM and η denotes the contact time of the crystals. The adsorption time constant, τ is defined as $\tau_j = \left(k_{ads,j}C_{CGM_j} + k_{des,j}\right)^{-1}$ by Kubota and Mullin (1995). The parameters k_{ads} and k_{des} denote the rate of adsorption and desorption, respectively. Langmuir constant can be expressed as

$$K = \frac{k_{ads}}{k_{des}} = k_{ads,0}\exp\left(-\frac{\Delta G_{ads}}{RT}\right)\left[k_{des,0}\exp\left(-\frac{\Delta G_{des}}{RT}\right)\right]^{-1} \tag{4}$$

where ΔG_{ads} and ΔG_{des} are free energies of the CGM adsorption and desorption on the crystal surface. It is necessary to track the contact time of the crystals in the presence of the CGMs. Majumder and Nagy (2013) introduced a new distribution function to incorporate the new property:

$$n(t,\underline{x}) = \int_0^t \phi(t,\underline{x},\eta)d\eta \tag{5}$$

Then the PBE considering two characteristic lengths $\{x_1, x_2\}$ to describe the evolution of the crystal shape distribution can be written as

$$\frac{\partial}{\partial t}\phi(t,\underline{x},\eta)+\frac{\partial}{\partial x_1}[G_1\phi(t,\underline{x},\eta)]+\frac{\partial}{\partial x_2}[G_2\phi(t,\underline{x},\eta)]+\frac{\partial}{\partial \eta}\phi(t,\underline{x},\eta)=B \qquad (6)$$

where B means the primary nucleation rate defined as

$$B_p = k_p \exp\left[-k_e \ln^{-2}\left(\frac{C}{C_{sat}}\right)\right] \qquad (7)$$

The k_p is the coefficient of primary nucleation and k_e is a kinetic constant. The initial and boundary conditions of the PBE takes the form of $\phi(0,\underline{x},0)=\phi(\underline{x})$ and $G_i\phi(t,\underline{x},\eta)=0$, $\underline{x}\in\partial\Omega_x$, $\eta=0$. Here $\partial\Omega_x$ is the boundary of the size space. The mass balance is also required for the solution of PBE. Concentration of KDP expressed as the follow (Majumder and Nagy, 2013)

$$\frac{dc(t)}{dt}=-\rho_c\int_0^\infty\int_0^\infty\left(2G_1 x_1 x_2 - G_2 x_1^2 - 2G_1 x_1^2 \tan\theta\right)dx_1 dx_2 \qquad (8)$$

where ρ is the density of KDP crystals and x_1, x_2 are the characteristic crystal sizes respectively. The mass balance for the impurity concentration in the solution is

$$\frac{dc_{CGMj}}{dt}=\frac{\chi_{c,j}}{1-\sum_j\chi_{c,j}}\frac{M_{CGMj}}{M_c}\frac{dc}{dt} \qquad (9)$$

where M_{CGM} and M_C are the molecular weights of the CGM and KDP. The $\chi_{c,j}$ is the mole fraction of the jth CGM in the crystal phase (Majumder and Nagy, 2013). The solution of multidimensional PBE is a computationally expensive, time consuming procedure. It can be solved however by using numerical methods or developing set of moment equations. Standard method of moments is able to calculate the mean particle size and also the mean AR in two dimensional cases.

$$\frac{d\mu_{0,0}}{dt}=B \qquad (10)$$

$$\frac{d\mu_{k,m}}{dt}=kG_1\mu_{k-1,m}+mG_2\mu_{k,m-1} \qquad (11)$$

The closed system of the ordinary differential equations of moments and mass balances provide information about particle number, mean crystal sizes and $AR=\mu_{0,1}/\mu_{1,0}$.

4. Simulation and experimental results

The moment model was solved in Matlab environment. In order to achieve reliable investigation by simulation, the kinetic parameters are necessary to be estimated and validated using physical experiments. The nucleation kinetic parameters were fitted by using data from Exp2, while the growth kinetic parameters were estimated by using the results of Exp1 and Exp3. The parameter estimation problem is defined as

$$\min_{P} \sum_{k} \left(y_k - \tilde{y}_k \right)^2 , \tag{12}$$

where y_k and $\tilde{y}_k$ are the measured and calculated values of the AR in the kth point in time and P is the model parameter vector. The results of the parameter estimation are presented in Table 2. Physical experiments Exp4 and Exp5 are used for validation of the model. As it can be seen on Fig. 3, the AR trends from simulation are in good correlation with the physical experiments. The proposed model can be used to develop an AR surface that describes the effect of two different CGMs on the crystal AR (see Fig. 4). One of the CGMs is considered as the impurity with variable concentration in the raw material, which can lead to large variations in the product AR. The model and/or surface can be used to calculate the required amount of compensating CGM to decrease the variations in the final AR. This open loop AR-corrective control can be implemented based on the model or the experimentally determined AR surface.

Table 2. Estimated kinetic parameters

Primary nucleation:						
$k_{p0} = 5.80$	$E_p = 65,710.5$		$k_e = 93,674.6$			
Growth-1:						
$k_{ads,0} = 26.35$	$k_{des,0} = 0.49$	$\alpha' = 7.66$	$k_{m,o} = 2.40$	$K_e = 6.86$	$\Delta G_{ads} = 735$	$\Delta G_{des} = 23,233$
Growth-2:						
$k_{ads,0} = 22.42$	$k_{des,0} = 0.46$	$\alpha' = 5.37$	$k_{m,o} = 2.15$	$K_e = 7.50$	$\Delta G_{ads} = 2,156$	$\Delta G_{des} = 23,863$

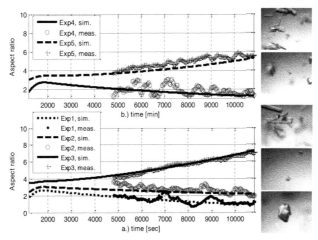

Figure 3. Trends of crystal AR obtained from experiments and simulations: (a.) Parameter estimation; (b.) Validation

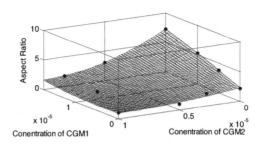

Figure 4. Dependence of the AR on mixtures of CGMs

5. Conclusions

Model-based and experimental investigations of the effect of mixtures of CGMs on the crystal shape were presented. The crystallization process was investigated and monitored quantitatively in real-time using particle vision measurement (Lasentec PVM) tool. The aspect ratio (AR) distribution of the crystals was obtained by using image analysis technique. In the modelling framework the proposed competitive adsorption model of CGMs with a two-dimensional PBE were combined to calculate the evolution of crystal size and shape distributions in time. The model was fitted to the physical experiments. The developed simulator is suitable to calculate optimal amount of CGMs in order to control the crystal AR.

Acknowledgements

Financial support provided by the European Research Council grant no. [280106 - CrySys] is acknowledged.

References

A. Borsos, B.G. Lakatos, 2012, Simulation and analysis of crystallization of high aspect ratio crystals with fragmentation, Computer Aided Chemical Engineering, 30, 1028-1032

J. Ding, Y. Lu, S. Wang, X. Mu, Q. Gu, Z. Wang, Y. Sun, X. Liang, X. Xu, X. Sun. W. Liu, G. Liu, S. Zhu, 2010, Influence of SiO3-2 impurity on growth habit of potassium dihydrogen phosphate crystal, Crystal Research and Technology, 45, 8, 800-804

Y-J. Fu, Z-S. Gao, J-M. Liu, Y-P. Li, H. Zheng, M-H. Jiang, 1999, The effect of anionic impurities on the growth habit and optical properties of KDP, Journal of Crystal Growth, 198/199, 682-686

N. Kubota, J.W. Mullin, 1995, A kinetic model for crystal growth from aqueous solution in the presence of impurity, Journal of Crystal Growth, 152, 3, 203-208

C.Y. Ma, X.Z. Wang, K.J. Roberts, 2008, Morphological population balance for modeling crystal growth in face directions, 54, 1, 209-222

A. Majumder, Z.K. Nagy, 2013, Prediction and control of crystal shape distribution in the presence of crystal growth modifiers, Chemical Engineering Science, 101, 593-602

Z.K. Nagy, R.D. Braatz, 2012, Advances and new directions in crystallization control, Chemical and Biomolecular Engineering, 3, 55-75

Y. Zhou, R. Sirinivasan, S. Lakshminarayanan, 2009, Critical evaluation of image processing approaches for real-time crystal size measurements, Computers and Chemical Engineering, 33, 1022-1035

Jiří Jaromír Klemeš, Petar Sabev Varbanov and Peng Yen Liew (Editors)
Proceedings of the 24th European Symposium on Computer Aided Process Engineering – ESCAPE 24
June 15-18, 2014, Budapest, Hungary.

Batch-to-batch Steady State Identification via Online Ensemble Empirical Mode Decomposition and Statistical Test

Bi-Ling Huang, Yuan Yao*

Department of Chemical Engineering, National Tsing Hua University, Hsinchu, Taiwan, R.O.C
yyao@mx.nthu.edu.tw

Abstract

In batch processes, online steady state identification (SSID) is important for ensuring the quality consistence of final products. This paperpresents a robust method for batch process SSID by the use of ensemble empirical mode decomposition (EEMD) and statistical test. First, EEMD and moving-window technique areadoptedto decompose batch process signalsinto multiple intrinsic mode function (IMF) components in real time. Then, by computingthe instantaneous frequencies of each IMFthroughthe generalized zero-crossing (GZC) method, the IMFs are divided into three levels corresponding to high-frequency noise, intra-batch variation, and inter-batch trend, respectively. By utilizing the inter-batch trend instead of the original signal in SSID, the identification results are robustto measurement noise and process disturbance. Injection molding, a typical batch process, is usedto demonstratethe proposed method.

Keywords: batch process, steady state identification, ensemble empirical mode decomposition, variance ratio test

1. Introduction

Batch processes play an important role in the production of low volume and high value-added products. In general, batch processes can be divided into two stages: batch-to-batch start-up and steady-state operation. Following the definition of Aguado et al. (2008), a batch process is considered at batch-to-batch steady state when the trajectory of each process variable follows a stable pattern with random noise. Until the start of steady-state operation, the incoming materials usually have not mixed well, while the material properties and the machine conditions have not been stabilized. Therefore, batch operations in start-up are unsteady, which cannot guarantee the reliable products with consistent quality. Since the durations of the start-up periods are usually unknown and varied from one process to another, the defective products cannot be rejected until conducting a series of laboratory analyses. Such analyses may cost quite a lot of labor, material, and financial resources. Therefore, efficient online steady state identification (SSID) is critical for batch processes.

In the research field of SSID, several different types of approaches have been proposed (Rhinehart, 2013). Nevertheless, in most of these approaches, a signal is defined as in steady state when it is constant with noise, which is obviously different from the definition in batch process applications. Therefore, these methods cannot be applied to batch process SSID directly. To the best of our knowledge, Aguado et al. (2008) first discussed the SSID problem for batch processes. In their method, a multiway principal component analysis (MPCA) model is used to summarize the variable trajectory information. Then, the conventional SSID algorithm is performed on the extracted principal components and model residuals. However, in order to build an MPCA model, historical data from dozens of batches are required, which limits the online application of this method. Yao et al (2009) attempted to solve such problem by calculating the similarities between batch trajectories. Such method is more suited to online SSID, but is tend to be affected by measurement noise and process disturbance.

To overcome the deficiencies of the existing methods, this paper proposes to utilize ensemble empirical mode decomposition (EEMD) (Wu and Huang, 2005) andvariance ratio test for batch process SSID. In the first step of the proposed method, EEMD and moving-window technique are combined to achieve online decomposition of batch process signals, i.e. trajectories of process variables, resulting in a series of intrinsic mode function (IMF) components. Then, according to the instantaneous frequencies of each IMF calculated using the generalized zero-crossing (GZC) method, these IMFs are divided into three levels corresponding to high-frequency noise, intra-batch variation, and inter-batch trend, respectively. For each variable, the IMFs in the third level are then combined into a sub-signal. The information for SSID is only contained in such sub-signal, while the measurement noise and most process disturbance information are extracted by the other two levels. Therefore, robust identification results can be achieved by conducting variance ratio test on the inter-batch trend sub-signal. The effectiveness of the proposed method will be verified using an injection molding process.

2. EEMD of batch process signals

Batch process signals are characterized by a variety of nonlinear and nonstationary characteristics that should be taken into consideration during decomposition. In 1998, Huang et al. (1998) proposed empirical mode decomposition (EMD) as an adaptive time-frequency data analysis method which can separate a time series into a finite number of components, called intrinsic mode functions (IMFs), corresponding to different frequencies and a residue. Formally, an IMF is a function whose upper and lower envelopes are symmetric, and the number of zero-crossings and the number of extremes are equal or differ at most by one. In comparison to Fourier transform and wavelet analysis, EMD makes no assumption about the composition of the signal and does not depend on any given wavelet basis. Instead, it successively traces out IMFs by interpolating between maxima and minima. As a result, EMD is better suited to the decomposition of nonlinear and non-stationary signals, e.g. the trajectory signals of batch process variables, than the other two approaches.

The algorithm for the extraction of IMFs from a given signal, $x(t)$, is called sifting, which consists of the following steps.
1. Initialize $r_0(t) = x(t)$. Set the index of IMF $k = 1$.
2. Set $i = 1$ and $d_0(t) = r_{k-1}(t)$.
3. Identify all extrema of $d_{i-1}(t)$ and interpolate between minima (resp. maxima) by the cubic spline method, ending up with some "envelope" $e_{min,i-1}(t)$ (resp. $e_{max,i-1}(t)$).
4. Computethe mean values by averaging the upper envelope and the lower envelope:$m_{i-1}(t) = (e_{min,i-1}(t)+e_{max,i-1}(t))/2$;
5. Extract the detail $d_i(t) = d_{i-1}(t)-m_{i-1}(t)$ and set $i = i + 1$.
6. Repeat steps 3-5 until $d_i(t)$being an IMF. If so, $IMF_k(t) = d_i(t)$. Update the

residue$r_k(t)=r_{k-1}(t)-IMF_k(t)$.Set $k = k + 1$.
7. Repeat steps 2-6 until the final residual component $r(t)$ becomes monotone.
At the end of this process, the initial time series is decomposed into KIMF components
and afinal residue:

$$x(t) = \sum_{k=1}^{K} IMF_k + r \tag{1}$$

In batch process data, $x(t)$ can be the trajectory signal of each process variable, where t
is the sample index. For a measurement value collected at the ath sampling interval in
the bth batch, $t = (b-1) \times A + a$, where A is the total number of sampling intervals
in each batch.

One of the major drawbacks of EMD is mode mixing caused by signal intermittency,
which is defined as a single IMF either consisting of signals of widely disparate scales,
or a signal of a similar scale decomposed into different IMF components. Such signal
intermittency is commonly observed in batch process signals, especially in the variable
trajectories of multiphase batch processes (Yao and Gao, 2009). Such problem can be
solved by EEMD (Wu and Huang, 2009), a noise-assisted EMD method, which defines
a "true" IMF component as the average of the corresponding IMFs obtained via EMD
over an ensemble of trials, each consisting of the original signal plus a white noise of
finite amplitude.

The original EEMD algorithm is based on the complete signals and for offline
applications.Yet, in batch process SSID, the variable trajectory signals are collected
online, which requires enabling EEMD to handle real-time analysis. At the same time,
end effect is often observed in EEMD, which is a distortion of the upper and lower
envelopes at the endpoints of the signal. Enlightened by the overlapping block
approach(Yip, 2010), both problems are solved simultaneously using moving window
as follows.
1. Define the window length as L batches, i.e. $A \times L$ time intervals, and the step size as
one batch, i.e. Atime intervals. Set the initial window index $j = 1$. Therefore, the first
window contains the signals from batch 1 to batch L.
2. For the signals in window j, perform EEMD. Denote the kth IMF in the jth window
as $IMF_k^j(t)$, where t is the index of time intervals in the window. If $j = 1$, IMF_k^{all} is
constructed from IMF_k^j by discarding the first f and the last h batches, where f and h are
parameters to be specified for eliminating end effect. Otherwise, IMF_k^{all} is updated by
adding $IMF_k^j(f \times L + 1)$ to $IMF_k^j((A-h) \times L)$ to the end of the IMF_k^{all} calculated in the last
iteration. Set $j = j + 1$.
3. Repeat the last step when the all measurements from a new batch are collected.

3. Identification of inter-batch trend

After online EEMD, the inter-batch trend involves useful information for batch-to-batch
SSID should be identified. Note that such information may be contained in not only the
residue but also the low-frequency IMFs. Here, the generalized zero-crossing (GZC)
approach (Huang, 2006) is adopted to calculate the instantaneous frequencies for the
nonlinear and nonstationary IMF components, based on which the IMFs can be divided
into three levels.In the GZC approach, all zero-crossingsand local extremaare defined as

critical points. The period between two consecutive up (or down) zero-crossings or twoconsecutive maxima (or minima) can be counted as oneperiod, denoted as T_{11}, T_{12}, T_{13} and T_{14}; the period between consecutive zero-crossings or consecutive extrema can be counted as a half period, denoted as T_{21} and T_{22} ; and the period betweenone kind of extremum to the next zero-crossing point, or fromone kind of zero-crossing point to the next extremum can becounted as a quarter period, denoted as T_4. In total, there are seven different period values at each point along the timeaxis.Accordingly, the local frequency at each point can be computed as:

$$\omega = \frac{1}{7}\left\{\frac{1}{4T_4} + \left(\frac{1}{2T_{21}} + \frac{1}{2T_{22}}\right) + \left(\frac{1}{T_{11}} + \frac{1}{T_{12}} + \frac{1}{T_{13}} + \frac{1}{T_{14}}\right)\right\} \tag{2}$$

The IMFs with mean frequency higher than a threshold are classified into the level of high-frequency noise. Otherwise,if the mean frequency of an IMF is higher than the multiplicative inverse of the process cycle length, such IMF mainly contains intra-batch variation or disturbance information.The remaining IMFs (supposing from IMF_H to IMF_K) and the residue describe inter-batch trend, which can then be added together as

$$y = \sum_{k=H}^{K} IMF_k + r$$

to reconstruct a sub-signal for the following SSID steps.

4. Batch-to-batch SSID via variance ratio test

For batch-to-batch SSID, the inter-batch trend sub-signal of each batch is summarized to a single value by taking the average. Let $y_1, ..., y_n$ represent n successive observations in a window of the transformed signal, corresponding to n batches. There are two ways to estimate the variance in the window. The ordinary formula for variance estimation is:

$$s^2 = \frac{\sum_{i=1}^{n}(y_i - \bar{y})^2}{n-1} \tag{3}$$

where $\bar{y}$ is the mean of the n observations. Such estimate is easily affected by the trend contained in the window. Another estimate of variance can be derived from the mean square successive difference:

$$\delta^2 = \frac{\sum_{i=1}^{n-1}(y_{i+1} - y_i)^2}{n-1} \tag{4}$$

$\delta^2/2$ is an estimation of variance which minimizes the trend effect.Von Neumann (1941) suggested that the ratio $\eta = \delta/s^2$ can be utilized to judge whether there isa trend in the investigated window. In the situation that there is no trend in the data, the value of $R = 2/\eta$ is expected to be near 1; otherwise, R is statistically greater than 1. The confidence bound for such variance ration test can be found in the book (Crow, 1960).

5. Application results

Injection molding, a typical batch process, is an important polymer processing technology, which transforms polymer materials into various shapes and types of products. The filtered trajectories of nozzle temperature show that such variable has distinctive start-up features, as plotted in Figure 1. Therefore, SSID for the injection molding process is conducted using this variable in the following paragraphs. In this study,the data from totally 82 batches are collected online, with uneven cycle durations. The window length is selected as 5 batches for online EEMD, and only retains the IMFs corresponding to the 3rd batch in window to avoid the end effect.As an example, the raw trajectories of the nozzle temperature in batch 33-37 are plotted in Figure 2, while the corresponding decomposition results are shown in Figure 3. Next, the instantaneous

frequencies of the IMFs are computed by theGZC method. By comparing them to the
multiplicative inverse of the process cycle length, it is found that the IMF10 and IMF11
consist of the inter-batch trend. Therefore, the sub-signal for batch-to-batch SSID is
formed as the sum of these two IMFs and the residue. Figure 4 plots both the raw signal
of the nozzle temperature and the extracted inter-batch trend. In order to proceed to
SSID, the extracted sub-signal is then transformed by taking the average value of the
entire batch data to represent the overall batch performance, as shown in Figure 5. The
window length for conducting the variance ratio test is selected to be 10. The SSID
results based on the R valuesare shown in Figure 6 together with the 95 % control limit,
where the batch-to-batch steady state is identified at the 71st batch. According to the
laboratory analysis of the products, the process starts steady operationat batch 69. The
identification results are very close to the true value, verifying the effectiveness of the
proposed method.

6. Conclusions

In this paper,the techniques of EEMD and variance ratio test are combined to achieve
efficient batch process SSID. EEMD separates high-frequency measurement noise and
intra-batchvariation/ disturbance information from inter-batch trend, which increases the
degree of confidence on steady state identification. In the meantime, the utilization of
moving window technique eliminates the end effect andmakes it possible to conduct
EEMD online. Using variance ratio test, the batch-to-batch steady state can be identified
in a statistical way.Note that, in this paper, only SSID results based on a single variable
signal is provided. Indeed, the proposed method is also applicable on multiple signals
by using a statistical test on covariance matrices instead of variances. Related results
will be provided in our future work.

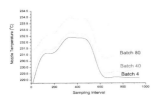

Figure 1. Trajectories of
nozzletemperature batches 33-37

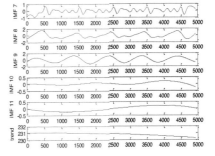

Figure 2. Trajectory signal of nozzle temperature of

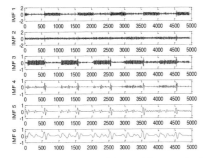

Figure 3. The IMFs and the residue trend of the nozzle temperature signal

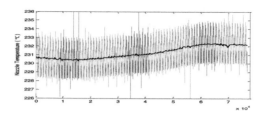

Figure 4. Trajectories of nozzle temperature and the extracted sub-signal of inter-batchtrend

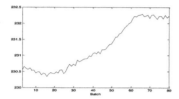

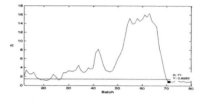

Figure5. Transformed inter-batch trend   Figure 6. Results of batch-to-batch SSID

Acknowledgements

This work was supported in part by the National Science Council of R.O.C. under Grant No. NSC 102-2221-E-007-130-.

References

D. Aguado, A. Ferrer, A. Seco,J. Ferrer, 2008, Using Unfold-PCA for batch-to-batch start-up process understanding and steady-state identification in a sequencing batch reactor, Journal of Chemometrics, 22, 81-90.

E. Crow, F. Davis, 1960, Statistics Manual, Dover Publications, Mineola, NY.

N. E. Huang, 2006, Computing frequency by using generalized zero-crossing applied to intrinsic mode functions, United States patent.

N. E. Huang, Z. Shen, S. R. Long, M. C. Wu, H. H. Shih, Q. Zheng, N.-C. Yen, C. C. Tung,H. H. Liu, 1998, The empirical mode decomposition and the Hilbert spectrum for nonlinear and non-stationary time series analysis, Proceedings of the Royal Society of London. Series A: Mathematical, Physical and Engineering Sciences, 454, 903-995.

R. R. Rhinehart,2013, Automated steady and transient state identification in noisy processes, Proceedings of the 2013 American Control Conference (ACC), Washington DC,United States, 4477-4493.

Z. Wu, N. E. Huang, 2005, Ensemble empirical mode decomposition: a noise-assisted data analysis method, Advances in Adaptive Data Analysis, 16, 3, 177-188.

Y. Yao, F. Gao, 2009, A survey on multistage/multiphase statistical modeling methods for batch processes, Annual Reviews in Control, 33, 172–183.

Y. Yao, C. Zhao,F. Gao, 2009, Batch-to-batch steady state identification based on variable correlation and Mahalanobis distance, Industrial and Engineering Chemistry Research, 48, 11060-11070.

L. Yip, 2010, Realtime Empirical Mode Decomposition for Intravascular Bubble Detection, Ph.D. Thesis, School of Engineering and Physical Sciences, James Cook University, Queensland, Australia.

J. Von Neumann, 1941, Distribution of the ratio of the mean square successive difference to the variance, Ann. Math. Stat., 367–395.

Jiří Jaromír Klemeš, Petar Sabev Varbanov and Peng Yen Liew (Editors)
Proceedings of the 24th European Symposium on Computer Aided Process Engineering – ESCAPE 24
June 15-18, 2014, Budapest, Hungary.

Robust NMPC of a Hydrodesulfuration Unit Using Multi-stage Stochastic Programing

Rubén Martí[a,*], Daniel Navia,[b] Daniel Sarabia,[c] César de Prada[a]

[a]Dpt. Systems Engineering and Automatic Control, University of Valladolid, Spain
[b]Dpt. Ingeniería Química y Ambiental, Universidad Técnica Federico Santa María, Santiago, Chile
[c]Dpt. Electromechanical Engineering, University of Burgos, Spain
ruben@autom.uva.es

Abstract

This paper deals with the uncertainty present in the raw materials used in the operation of a hydrodesulphurization unit (HDS), when a change in the hydrocarbon feed is produced. To overcome the changing concentrations of the hydrogen and the sulphur in the feed and achieve an optimal transition of the unit, an economic-based control is implemented using the concept of two-stage programing, discretizing the uncertain values in different scenarios. The stochastic optimization problem with the scenario approach has been applied in close loop, testing two ways to solve the stochastic optimization: a) solving the entire problem for all the scenarios, and b) splitting the centralized scheme using price-driven coordination.

Keywords: Two-Stage Optimization, Robust NMPC, Price-Driven Coordination

1. Introduction

Uncertainty is always present in the operation of processes. Therefore, when optimal decisions have to be made, differences between the model and the reality must be considered in order to propose feasible actions. In the classical approach of optimization, equations and parameters are considered totally known. However, when the computed solution is applied to the reality, frequently the value of the objective function is worse than expected and/or the constraints are violated (Birge and Louveaux, 1997). These problems can be attributed to the uncertainty that affects the system that usually can be described using random variables (ξ) that belong to a probability space Ξ with a given probability distribution function (PDF).

One of the methods to solve an optimization problem is the multistage programming (Dantzig, 1955), where the decision variables can be classified according to the degree of knowledge of ξ. Recently, it has been proposed the multistage optimization problem as an alternative to manage the uncertainty in model predictive control, with the so called Non Conservative Robust (N)MPC (Navia et al., 2011).

In this approach, the concept of several stages of knowledge of the stochastic optimization is applied in the predictive control, splitting the time horizon in the corresponding stages, each of them with different degrees of knowledge of the uncertain variables. To solve the infinite-dimensional problem in the space of ξ, a discretization using the scenario approach is suggested (Birge and Louveaux, 1997).

The difficulty associated with the multistage approach solved with scenarios is the exponential growth in the size of the problem. To manage this issue, only two-stages (0 and 1) can be considered in the stochastic-based control problem, as Eq.(1) shows.

$$\min_{u_0^j, u_1^j} E_j \left[f_0^j \left(u_0^j, x_0^j, \xi^j \right) + f_1^j \left(u_1^j, x_1^j, \xi^j \right) \right]$$

s.t.:

$$
\left.
\begin{aligned}
&h_k \left(\dot{x}^j, x^j, u_k^j, \xi^j, t \right) = 0, \quad x_0^j(t_0) = x_{0,i} \\
&g_k \left(u_k^j, x^j, \xi^j \right) \leq 0 \\
&x^j \in X, \quad u_k^j \in U_k \\
&\xi^j \in \Xi,
\end{aligned}
\right\}
\begin{aligned}
&j = 1 \ldots n_{Sc} \\
&k = \{0,1\}
\end{aligned}
$$

$$u_0^i = u_0^j, \qquad \{i, j\} = 1 \ldots n_{Sc}, i \neq j$$

(1)

In (1), the superscript j denotes the scenario and n_{Sc} is the number of scenarios considered. ξ^j is the value of the uncertain variable. u_k^j represents the decision variable applied in stage k. Notice that these variables can take values according to a certain time-parameterization in each stage, but the notation has been shortened for simplicity. The states are represented as x^j with initial value $x_{0,i}$. The functions that must be minimized are denoted as f_0^j and f_1^j for each decision stage. Due to the fact that these functions depend on the value of the random variables, their expected value over the scenarios (E_j) must be used to group them in a single objective function. The model of the process and the inequality constraints are represented by $\{h_0^j, h_1^j\}$ and $\{g_0^j, g_1^j\}$ for both stages respectively.

The last constraint in Eq.(1) is the so called, nonanticipativity constraint and represents the idea of different degrees of knowledge in the process. Basically the constraint forces that during the stage 0 (from t_0 to t_1), the trajectory of the decision variables for all the scenarios must be the same, due to the fact that a decision has to be made without the exact value of the uncertain variable. After a certain period of time (from t_1 to t_f), the uncertainty is assumed be known and the optimization considers as many optimal trajectories as scenarios are. The only constraint that relates the scenarios is the non-anticipativity one, noting that if it is managed in an upper layer, in charge to force this equality (Price-driven Coordination), a set of deterministic optimizations, using the value of the stochastic variable in each scenario, can be solved independently.

In this paper, the two-stage optimization has been implemented in an economic-driven NMPC, to overcome the incertitude associated with the raw materials in a HDS when a change in the load of the hydrocarbon is produced. The optimization has been solved in two ways: (a) centralized, which means that Eq.(1) is solved for all the scenarios in a single dynamic problem, and (b) coordinated, where the nonanticipativity constraint is managed in an upper layer that forces the accomplishment of the constraint using the idea of price-driven coordination (Jose and Ungar, 1998) with the sensitivity information given by the solution of a QP problem (Ganesh and Biegler, 1987).

2. Stochastic NMPC in a HDS unit

In petroleum refineries, the HDS process is used to remove sulphur from the hydrocarbons to fulfil environmental regulations. To do this, hydrogen is put in contact with the corresponding hydrocarbon in a fixed bed reactor with a specific catalyst

(Bellos and Papayannakos, 2003). The optimal management of the hydrogen provided is very important in order to operate efficiently: If the quantity of hydrogen supplied is less than the minimum required, then the catalysts can suffer important damage, while if the supply is in excess, economic losses will be experienced.

Figure 1 shows a simplified structure of a HDS plant. Several problems are related to the hydrogen management that are worth to mention; among them, the lack of reliable information about many streams and compositions, and the uncertainty of the demands. Regarding the first one, the uncertainty comes fundamentally in the hydrogen composition of the LP stream since it depends on the operation of other units. The other significant source of uncertainty comes from the changes in the composition of the hydrocarbon stream being treated in the HDS plants.

A typical pattern in the operation of a HDS plant is a transient lasting some hours followed by a stable demand. This happens approximately every two days when new products are processed and the plant takes some hours to stabilize in the new operating point, which is desired to be optimum. Therefore, it is necessary to implement a supervisory layer in the HDS, capable to estimate the optimal trajectories of the manipulated variables, to perform the transition and the optimal operating point at the end of the time horizon, taking into account the main sources of uncertainty previously mentioned. If both sources of uncertainty are denoted as ξ_1 and ξ_2 respectively, the optimal stochastic optimization using a two-stage approach is summarized in Eq.(2), where the objective function is the production cost of the hydrogen during the transient. The model implemented in Eq.(2) is based in mass balances applied in: a) the mixing point (h_1 and h_2) and b) the control volume composed by R-1, R-2 and T-1 (h_1 and h_4). h_5 represents an approximated first-order dynamics of the hydrogen consumption inside the reactor. Inequality constraint g_1 ensures a correct operation of the compressor and avoids damages in the catalyst inside the reactor. On the other hand, g_2 is the capacity constraint of the collectors. In both inequalities, superscript LO and UP denote the lower and the upper bounds of the variables respectively. At last, h_6 is the nonanticipativity constraint to force that all the trajectories implemented in the first stage must be the same for all the scenarios.

3. Decomposition of Stochastic NMPC

In this section, the generic formulation of the NMPC problem for large-scale systems with shared resources is shown. The optimization problem Eq.(3) can be summarized as

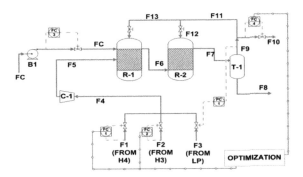

Figure 1. PFD of the HDS plant.

$$\min_{\{F_{1,k}^j, F_{2,k}^j, F_{10,k}^j\}} \sum_{k=\{0,1\}} \sum_{j=1}^{N_{Sc}} Pr^j \left\{ \int_{t_k}^{t_{k+1}} C_{H4} x_1 F_{1,k}^j + C_{H3} x_2 F_{2,k}^j dt \right\}$$

s.t. :

$$h_1 := F_{1,k}^j x_1 + F_{2,k}^j x_2 + F_3^j \xi_2^j = F_5^j x_5^j$$

$$h_2 := F_{1,k}^j + F_{2,k}^j + F_3^j = F_5^j$$

$$h_3 := F_5^j - F_{10,k}^j - F_X^{H_2,j} = 0$$

$$h_4 := \frac{VP}{ZRT}\left[\dot{x}_{H2}^j\right] = F_5^j x_5^j - F_{10,k}^j x_{10}^j - F_X^{H_2,j} x_{H2}^j,$$

$$x_{H2}^j(t_0) = x_{H2,0}$$

$$h_5 := \tau \dot{F}_X^j + F_X^j = F_{HC} \xi_1^j, \quad F_X^j(t_0) = F_{X0}$$

$$g_1 := x_5^j \geq x_5^{LO}, \qquad x_{H2}^j \geq x_{H2}^{LO}$$

$$g_2 := F_m^{LO} \leq F_{m,k}^j \leq F_m^{UP}, \quad m = \{1,2,10\}$$

$$\xi_1^j, \xi_2^j \in \Xi$$

$$t \in [t_k, t_{k+1}], \quad t_f = t_2$$

$$\left. \begin{array}{l} \\ \\ \\ \\ \\ \\ \\ \\ \\ \\ \\ \end{array} \right\} \begin{array}{l} j = 1 \ldots N_{Sc} \\ k = \{0,1\} \end{array} \qquad (2)$$

$$h_6 := F_{m,0}^j = F_{m,0}^i, \quad j = 1..N_{Sc}, \quad i = 1..N_{Sc}, j \neq i, \quad m = \{1,2,10\}$$

an economic-control objective function subject to nonlinear models *hi(.)* and *gi(.)*, corresponding to the dynamics of each subsystem and local constraints and a set of shared resource constraints or global constraints linking all subsystems. In Eq.(3), *n* corresponds to the total number of subsystems, *N* represents the number of shared resources, RT_j is the availability of the shared resource *j*, and $R_{ji}(u_{ji})$ represents the consumption of the shared resource *j* in each subsystem *i*, which is a function of the corresponding manipulated variable u_{ji}. In addition, each subsystem can have its own, independent, manipulated variables v_i.

The solution of the problem using a centralized architecture can be complex if the number of manipulated variables or subsystems is large, which sometimes implies that the solution cannot be applied in real time due to the excess of computational time.

$$\min_{\{u,v\}} J = \sum_{i=1}^n J_{local,i}$$

st :

$$h_i(\dot{x}_i, x_i, v_i, u_{1i}, \ldots, u_{Ni}, t) = 0 \quad \forall i = 1,..,n$$

$$g_i(\dot{x}_i, x_i, v_i, u_{1i}, \ldots, u_{Ni}, t) \leq 0 \quad \forall i = 1,..,n \qquad (3)$$

$$\sum_{i=1}^n R_{ji}(u_{ji}) \leq RT_j \quad \forall j = 1,\ldots,N$$

Therefore, a compromise between centralized and decentralized architecture is desired in order to improve the system performance. One scheme solution can be a hierarchical architecture based on price coordination which provides a good compromise between performance and ease of implementation.

Supposing an optimization problem of the form Eq.(3) where a price coordination method is used, each subsystem *i* can be decomposed into *n* subproblems (4).

$$\min_{\{u_{1i},\dots u_{Ni},v_i\}} J_i = J_{local,i} + \sum_{j=1}^{N} p_j R_{ji}(u_{ji}) \tag{4}$$

$st:$

$$h_i(\dot{x}_i, x_i, v_i, u_{1i},\dots u_{Ni}, t) = 0$$

$$g_i(\dot{x}_i, x_i, v_i, u_{1i},\dots u_{Ni}, t) \le 0$$

where p_j represents the price or Lagrangean multipliers related to each share resource j. Provided the Eq.(5) are fulfilled, the outcomes of the decomposed problem (4) are equivalent to the ones from the initial global problem (3) (Jose and Ungar, 1998).

$$\sum_{i=1}^{n} R_{ji}(u_{ji}) - RT_j \le 0 \quad \forall\, j = 1,\dots,N$$

$$p_j\left(\sum_{i=1}^{n} R_{ji}(u_{ji}) - RT_j\right) = 0 \quad \forall\, j = 1,\dots,N \tag{5}$$

$$p_j \ge 0 \quad \forall\, j = 1,\dots,N$$

The role of the coordinator consists in updating the prices p_j until Eq.(5) is satisfied. In order to use this decomposition in problem (2) is necessary to transform inequality constraints to equality constraints (nonanticipativity constraint). Supposing that the centralized problem has two different scenarios, therefore in stage 0 the non anticipativity constraint is:

$$u_1 = u_2 \Leftrightarrow (u_1 - u_2) = 0 \Leftrightarrow (u_1 - u_2)^2 = 0 \tag{6}$$

$$\underbrace{\frac{1}{2}(u_1 - u_2)^2}_{R_{Subsystem1}} + \underbrace{\frac{1}{2}(u_2 - u_1)^2}_{R_{Subsystem2}} \le \underbrace{0}_{R_{T\,Supply}} \tag{7}$$

In this work, authors present an updating technique based on Newton's method (8). This technique is an iterative method, where the index k denotes the iteration step, α is the step size in Newton's method and Q (9) is the sensibility matrix with $N \times N$ dimension which can be calculated as:

$$P_{[k+1]} = P_{[k]} - \alpha Q^{-1} T_{[k]} \quad p^T = [p1, p2,\dots, p_N] \tag{8}$$

$$T = \left[\sum_{i=1}^{n} R_{1i}(u_{1i}) - RT_1,\dots,\sum_{i=1}^{n} R_{Ni}(u_{Ni}) - RT_{Ni}\right]^T$$

$$Q = \frac{d\sum_{i=1}^{n} R_{ji}(u)}{dp}\bigg|_{[k]} = \sum_{i=1}^{n} \frac{dR_{ji}}{du_{ji}} \frac{du_{ji}}{dp}\bigg|_{[k]} \tag{9}$$

In (9), information of sensitivity du/dp is needed to calculate Q. In this paper, it is used a QP problem (Ganesh and Biegler, 1987) in order to obtain the sensitivity analysis for the nonlinear system.

4. Results and conclusions

In this section, multi-stage NMPC is applied to the example (HDS) in presence of uncertainties in ξ_1 and ξ_2. The first step for applying multi-stage NMPC is to design a

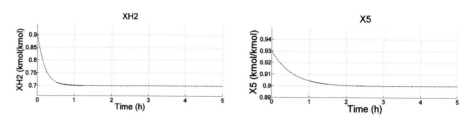

Figure 2. Simulation of multi-stage NMPC using centralized and coordination scheme.

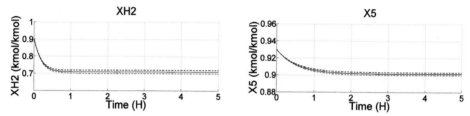

Figure 3. Simulation of multi-stage NMPC for different values of uncertain parameters using coordination scheme.

suitable tree. In this case 3 scenarios are chosen. In addition, the scenario tree is branched only in the first stage, that is, the robust horizon is chosen to be 1. In Figure 2 it is shown that centralized and coordinated scheme obtain the same behavior when they are applied on the process (worst scenario), both achieve robust constraint satisfaction. In addition, using coordinated scheme the computational time is reduced because each NMPC controller, implemented in parallel way, solves a different scenario.

On the other hand, in Figure 3 multi-stage NMPC is applied solving the problem (2) using Price-Driven Coordination with 3 scenarios each sampling time, where the controller automatically implements a back-off. The behavior of the system is as it can be expected, due to the fact that at t_0 both hydrogen purities are above their lower bound, the N(MPC) looks for optimality modifying the decision variables driving the system into a region where the inequality constraints are active. Because of the Multi-stage approach guarantees feasibility for all the scenarios and the simulation is considering the worst case, once that the purities have reached their limits, the system remains stable and feasible in this point.

References

G. D. Bellos, N. G. Papayannakos, 2003, The use of a three phase microreactor to investigate HDS kinetics, Catalysis Today, 79-80, 349-355.

J. R. Birge, F. Louveaux, 1997, Introduction to stochastic programming, New York, Springer.

R. Cheng, J. F. Forbes, W. S. Yip, 2007, Price-driven coordination method for solving plant-wide MPC problems, Journal of Process control, 17, 429-438

G. B. Dantzig, 1955, Linear programming under uncertainty, Management Science, 1, 197-206.

A. V. Fiacco, 1983, Introduction to Sensitivity and Stability Analysis in Nonlinear Programing, Academic Press, New York, US.

N. Ganesh, L. T. Biegler, 1987, A reduced hessian strategy for sensitivity analysis of optimal flowsheets, AIChE Journal, 33, 282-296.

R. Jose, L. Ungar, 1998, Auction-driven coordination for plantwide control, Foundations of computer-aided process operation FOCAPO.

D. Navia, D. Sarabia, R. Martí, E. Gómez, C. De Prada, S. Lucia, C. Sonntag, 2011, Preliminary report on the state of the art and research needs in hierarchical coordination in energy systems and processes, Technical report of HYCON2 European Project (http://www.hycon2.eu/).

Jiří Jaromír Klemeš, Petar Sabev Varbanov and Peng Yen Liew (Editors)
Proceedings of the 24th European Symposium on Computer Aided Process Engineering – ESCAPE 24
June 15-18, 2014, Budapest, Hungary. Copyright © 2014 Elsevier B.V. All rights reserved.

Optimal Fuzzy Control of Batch Polymerization Reactors: Application to PMMA Production for Biomedical Purposes

Nádson M. N. Lima,[a]* Lamia Zuniga Linan,[a] Felix S. Farias Júnior,[b] Flavio Manenti,[c] Rubens Maciel Filho,[a] Marcelo Embiruçu,[d] Maria R. Wolf Maciel[a]

[a]*University of Campinas (UNICAMP), Department of Processes and Products Development (DDPP), 13083-852, Campinas/SP, Brazil*
[b]*LLTECH Research, Avenida Caxangá 2474, SL103, Recife/PE, Brazil*
[c]*Politecnico di Milano, CMIC Dept. "Giulio Natta", Piazza Leonardo da Vinci 32, 20133, Milano, Italy*
[d]*Federal University of Bahia (UFBA), Polytechnic Institute, 40210-630, Salvador/BA, Brazil*
nadson@feq.unicamp.br

Abstract

The use of polymers in the biomedical field requires that such materials have a high degree of purity and specific properties, so that their production processes must be continuously monitored and manipulated. However, the control of polymerization reactors is considered a challenging task since such systems present non-linear and transient behaviour. In this study, in order to produce poly(methyl methacrylate) scaffolds for bone tissue engineering applications, an advanced control methodology based on fuzzy models and genetic algorithms (GA) was developed to control the temperature of a pilot-scale jacketed batch reactor in which methyl methacrylate polymerization takes place. Firstly, an optimal temperature trajectory was estimated using GA. Then, a fuzzy controller was designed and applied to adjust the reactor temperature to the instantaneous profile previously calculated. The proposed control algorithm was compared to conventional PID controller, proving to be robust and more suitable and reliable for such process type.

Keywords: optimal fuzzy control; temperature trajectory; batch reactor; poly(methyl methacrylate); biomaterials.

1. Introduction

Polymeric biomaterials have experienced widespread use in several applications, such as for tissue and organ regeneration, drug delivery, degradable sutures, bone screws, and contact lenses to name a few. Among the polymers used in medicine, the Poly(Methyl MethAcrylate) [PMMA] is a Food Drug Administration (FDA) approved synthetic biomaterial widely used to fabricate reconstructive structures, including dental implant, implants for craniofacial defects or as bone cement to remodel lost bone and affix implants (Atala et al., 2011). The use of PMMA on scaffolds for bone tissue engineering applications comprises a promising field in the biomedical area; however, your specifications have not been yet defined. It is only understood that high mechanical properties are necessary, which strongly depend on the weight and number average molecular weights (Mw and Mn). Therefore, the characteristics of PMMA used for fabrication of bone cement could be considered as a reference. The properties ranges are: Mw from $(3.00 \times 10^5$ to $6.02 \times 10^5)$ Daltons and Mn from $(1.48 \times 10^5$ to $3.30 \times 10^5)$ Daltons. More specifically, optimal features are obtained from approximately Mw = 3.00×10^5 Daltons PMMA (Lima et al., 2013).

It is well-known the fact that batch systems are gaining wider ground in chemical processes. Batch reactor is an essential operation unit of scale laboratory pilot-plants, since it is convenient for small-scale operation, for testing new processes that have not been fully developed, for the manufacture of expensive products and for processes that are difficult to convert to continuous operations. According to Aziz and Mujtaba (2002), batch processes are particularly suitable for products such as pharmaceuticals, polymers, biotechnological or other fine chemicals products for which total requirement can be manufactured in a few days or a few batches in an existing plant. Nevertheless, the control of batch reactors is a laborious task because the system oscillates from one steady state to another or never reaches a steady state at all. Thus, the physical and chemical properties of the contents, such as viscosity, heat transfer coefficient, heat capacity, and reaction rate vary with time. Further, polymerization dynamic is usually complex mainly due to the nonlinearity and multivariable nature of the process, the existence of interactions and constraints, and the challenge to measure controlled variables in real time (such as molecular weights). Therefore, the control of batch polymerization reactors has been a hard-going task.

This paper presents the development of an optimal control methodology, based on two artificial intelligence techniques [i.e., fuzzy models and genetic algorithms (GA)], to regulate the operation of a pilot-scale jacketed batch reactor during the solution free-radical polymerization of Methyl MethAcrylate (MMA) with ethyl acetate and AzobIsisoButyroNitrile (AIBN) as initiator. The objective of the control problem is to achieve the desired Mw and Mn at the maximum final monomer conversion (X) in a fixed time by adjusting the reactor temperature. For this, initially an optimal temperature profile for defined initial operating conditions, which are required to produce the desired PMMA, was obtained using GA. The GA is a parameter search procedure, based on the mechanics of natural genetics, widely and successfully utilized in problems where the traditional optimization methods are difficult and/or inaccurate to be implemented, as batch polymerizations. Next, a fuzzy controller was designed and applied on computer and experimentally tested to adjust the reactor temperature to the estimated temperature trajectory. The use of fuzzy systems is interesting in this case study because it is quite effective to handle modeling and control issues that are characteristics of processes with nonlinear and time-varying behaviors and complex dynamics. Moreover, it simplifies numerical procedures as well as reduces computational time (Lima et al., 2010). The proposed control algorithm was compared to conventional PID controller, proving to be robust and more suitable and reliable for the analyzed process. Furthermore, it is rather flexible and can be adapted to different polymerization systems.

2. Experimental apparatus

Figure 1 provides the schematic diagram of the batch MMA polymerization system used in this work. The jacketed stainless-steel reactor has a capacity of 15 L and it is equipped with a pitched-turbine stirrer for mixing the reactants. An inverter is adopted to maintain the stirring speed at 360 rpm. The reactor temperature may be controlled by manipulating the electrical power of the thermal oil heater (serpentine) and/or by manipulating the electrical power supplied to the six resistances that act on the water stream in the jacket. The collar type resistances connected in parallel to the tube of the jacket inflow can vary in the range of 0.0 – 581.0 W. A HP (s5520br) personal computer and a PLC (P7C, HI Tecnologia) are employed for data acquisition and polymer process control. The MMA is treated by using the Sigma-Aldrich prepacked column (306312) to remove the inhibitor. The ethyl acetate (99.5%, Labsynth) and the AIBN® 64 (Du Pont) are used as they are supplied. A flow rate of 0.04 l/min of gaseous nitrogen (grade 5.0 White Martins) is bubbled through the reacting medium to keep oxygen out of the reactor. Samples of polymeric mixture were taken each 40 min to determine the density, viscosity and the conversion by the gravimetric method. These samples were quenched with methanol to precipitate the produced PMMA, and, next, were dissolved into tetrahydrofurane for molecular weight analysis by gel permeation chromatography (GPC). A Viscotek GPCmax VE2001 GPC solvent/sample module equipped with RI detector and two ViscoGel I-Series columns (I-MBLMW-3078 and I-MBLMW-3078) were used.

3. Working equations and process simulation

The free-radical polymerization mechanism that represents the reaction kinetics is given in Liu et al. (2011). Each kinetic rate constant is computed by Arrhenius expression and the kinetic parameters are obtained from Lima et al. (2013). Based on this kinetic mechanism, the peculiar design of the scale laboratory pilot-plant, the real-time volume shrinkage of the reaction contents and the gel effect, a rigorous mathematical model was developed. The equations of mass and energy balance, volume change, gel effect, physicochemical properties and molecular weight are described in Zuniga et al. (2012). The phenomenological model was solved by a Runge-Kutta type algorithm implemented in Fortran 90 programming language. The initial operating conditions for the desired objectives (i.e., $Mw = 300 \times 10^3$ Daltons and $Mn = 180 \times 10^3$ Daltons, based on the information previously described), keeping the reactor temperature constant in open-loop, were estimated using the GA subroutine 'Fortran Genetic Algorithm Driver' by David Carroll, version 1.7a (Carroll, 2001). Table 1 shows this information. A volume of 10 L is considered for the reaction mixture.

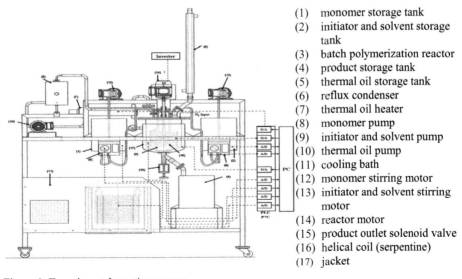

(1) monomer storage tank
(2) initiator and solvent storage tank
(3) batch polymerization reactor
(4) product storage tank
(5) thermal oil storage tank
(6) reflux condenser
(7) thermal oil heater
(8) monomer pump
(9) initiator and solvent pump
(10) thermal oil pump
(11) cooling bath
(12) monomer stirring motor
(13) initiator and solvent stirring motor
(14) reactor motor
(15) product outlet solenoid valve
(16) helical coil (serpentine)
(17) jacket

Figure 1. Experimental reaction system.

Table 1. Experimental reaction data.

Reactor temperature (K)	317.15 K
Temperature of the jacket water (K)	309.65 K
Temperature of the thermal oil heater (K)	327.65 K
Volume fraction of MMA (-)	0.45
Volume fraction of AIBN (-)	7.50×10^{-3}

4. Advanced fuzzy control

At the beginning, the GA method (Carroll, 2001) was adopted to calculate the optimal trajectory of the reactor temperature. A total simulation time equal to 28,800 seconds was considered and divided into eight intervals. In the next step, a Takagi-Sugeno fuzzy model was formulated for the real-time identification of the reactor temperature (Tr). For this, an algorithm for functional dynamic fuzzy modeling was developed in Fortran 90 by using subtractive clustering and least-squares methods (Lima et al., 2010). A sampling rate equal to 5 seconds was adopted. The temperature of the thermal oil heater (Th) is used as manipulated variable. Three inputs are considered for the model: Th at the kth sampling times, Th at the $(k - 1)$th sampling time, and Tr at the $(k - 1)$th sampling time. Two rules were generated for the fuzzy model. Thus, the obtained model was inserted in the control law defined by Equation 1, which must be instantly minimized:

$$\min_{\Delta Th} \left\langle J = w_1 \left(Trset[i] - Trf \right)^2 + w_2 \left(\Delta Th \right)^2 \right\rangle \tag{1}$$

where set = setpoint, $[i]$ = instantaneous value, f = fuzzy model prediction and w_j = weighting factor. NCONF subroutine of the IMSL Fortran library, which solves the constrained optimization problem based on the successive quadratic programming algorithm and a finite difference gradient, was used to solve the optimization problem. The adjustment of the fuzzy model for control purposes was performed by simulation using the IAE, ISE and ITAE indexes. The results of validation are illustrated in Figure 2, which shows a very good prediction for the output variable, since fuzzy and phenomenological models are practically overlapped. In addition, the long-range predictions are quite accurate leading to a reliable optimal control policy.

5. Results and discussions

The developed fuzzy control algorithm was evaluated computationally and then inserted in the control system of the pilot plant to observe the efficiency of the proposed methodology. Figures 3 and 4 present the experimental results for the controlled and manipulated variables, respectively. A comparison between fuzzy control and PID is showed for the batch polymerization reactor. It be observed that the temperature trajectory is tracked nearly for both the controllers. However, the fuzzy control has quicker time response and a smaller overshoot. Also, it can be seen that the PID controller provides some small oscillations.

Table 2 registers the experimental and simulated data for Mw, Mn and X on the end-of-batch, where the control objective is focused. As can be observed, the simulated control results are in good agreement with experiments. From Table 3, which reports the control errors it could be concluded that the proposed controller performs better than PID, with lower IAE and ITAE values. ISE index values are almost the same.

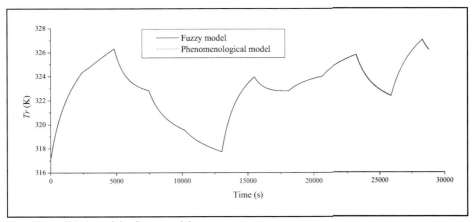

Figure 2. Validation of the fuzzy model.

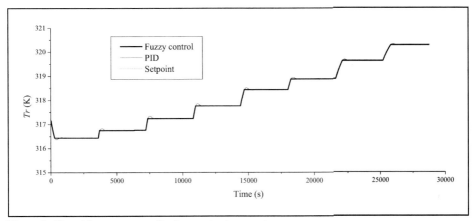

Figure 3. Closed-loop response for the reactor temperature.

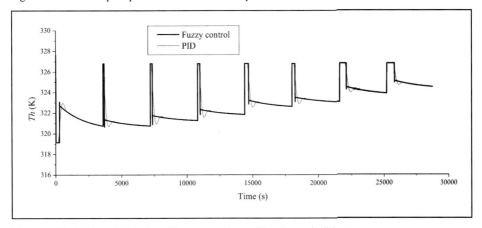

Figure 4. Closed-loop behavior of the temperature of the thermal oil heater.

Table 2. Control policy for the batch polymerization reactor.

Reaction time (tr)= 28,800 s	Mw (tr)	Mn (tr)	X (tr)
Control target	300×10^3	180×10^3	Max
Calculated by simulation	297×10^3	184×10^3	0.29
Experimental measurement	259×10^3	176×10^3	0.32

Table 3. Control errors for the polymerization plant.

IAE (K)		ISE (K²)		ITAE (Ks)	
Fuzzy control	PID	Fuzzy control	PID	Fuzzy control	PID
165	188	313	312	2,397,710	2,675,237

6. Conclusions

A fuzzy control methodology was developed to control the temperature of a jacketed batch polymerization reactor to produce PMMA scaffolds for bone tissue engineering applications. Volume variation and gel effect are considered. GA technique was used off-line to obtain the initial operating conditions and the optimal temperature profile required to produce the desired polymer. The fuzzy control law was calculated by NCONF subroutine. Experimental and simulated results demonstrated effectiveness and performance of the proposed control strategy, that is, the fuzzy controller has successfully tracked the temperature trajectory with reduced fluctuations observed around temperature setpoints and achieving the desired values of molecular weights. A comparison with conventional PID controller presents better action for fuzzy control, showing this controller to be robust, more suitable and reliable for such process type.

Acknowledgements

Authors acknowledge FAPESP and CNPq for the financial support given to this work.

References

A. Atala, R. Lanza, J. Thomson, R. Nerem, 2011, Principles of Regenerative Medicine, 2nd Edition, Academic Press, Elsevier, Oxford, UK.

N. Aziz, I. Mujtaba, 2002, Optimal Operation Policies in Batch Reactors, Chemical Engineering Journal, 85, 313-325.

D. Carroll, 2001, Fortran Genetic Algorithm (GA) Driver, <www.cuaerospace.com/carroll/ga.html> Accessed on 20.07.2011.

N. Lima, L. Zuniga, F. Manenti, R. Maciel Filho, M. Embiruçu, M. Wolf Maciel, 2013, Novel Two-Steps Optimal Control of a Batch Polymerization Reactors and Application to PMMA Production for the Fabrication of Artificial Bone Tissue, Computer Aided Chemical Engineering, 32, 163-168.

N. Lima, L. Zuniga, R. Maciel Filho, M. Wolf Maciel, M. Embiruçu, F. Grácio, 2010, Modeling and Predictive Control using Fuzzy Logic: Application for a Polymerization System, AIChE Journal, 56, 965-978.

Z. Liu, R. Kádár, M. Kind, 2011, Hydrodynamic Activation of the Batch-Polymerization of Mehtyl Methacrylate in a Taylor-Couette Reactor, Macromolecular Symposia, Weinheim, Germany, 302, 169-178.

L. Zuniga, N. Lima, L. Tovar, F. Manenti, R. Maciel Filho, M. Wolf Maciel, M. Embiruçu, 2012, Pilot-plant Simulation, Experimental Campaign and Rigorous Modeling of a Batch MMA Polymerization Reactor for the Fabrication of Bone Tissue, Computer Aided Chemical Engineering, 30, 1352-1356.

Jiří Jaromír Klemeš, Petar Sabev Varbanov and Peng Yen Liew (Editors)
Proceedings of the 24th European Symposium on Computer Aided Process Engineering – ESCAPE 24
June 15-18, 2014, Budapest, Hungary. Copyright © 2014 Elsevier B.V. All rights reserved.

Modelling and Design a Controller for Improving the Plating Performance of a Hard Chromium Electroplating Process

Surasit Tanthadiloke[a], Paisan Kittisupakorn[a,*], Iqbal M. Mujtaba[b]

[a]*Department of Chemical Engineering, Faculty of Engineering, Chulalongkorn University, Bangkok 10330, Thailand.*
[b]*School of Engineering Design & Technology, University of Bradford, West Yorkshire BD7 1DP, UK.*
paisan.k@chula.ac.th

Abstract

A hard chromium electroplating process is normally used for preventing mechanical and electrical parts such as roller, piston and mold from the harmful environments and giving the good physical properties on the surface such as increased wear resistance, increased hardness, low frictional coefficient as well as good aesthetic look on the surface of workpieces. The problem that often found in this process is the deflected workpieces after plating process due to the low plating performance during a plating period. These deflected workpieces are needed to replating it again. However, the replating method causes a large amount of resource consumptions and increases the production time. To handle this problem, the plating solution temperature is needed to maintain the plating solution temperature at a set point about 50 °C in order to improve the plating performance during the plating period and decrease the occurrence of the deflected workpieces. In this work, the mathematical models are developed to explain the dynamic behavior of the plating solution temperature during the plating time and validated with the real data from a plant. The conventional (PID) controller is applied to this process for the purpose of keeping the plating solution temperature at the set point throughout the plating time. The result demonstrates that the developed mathematical models can be used to explain the dynamic behavior of the plating solution temperature because it gives the good simulation of the plating solution temperature with a slightly different from the real data. Furthermore, the PID controller shows the high control performance for maintaining the plating solution temperature at the set point throughout the plating period with small overshoot at the beginning of every batch.

Keywords: Hard chromium electroplating, Mathematical model, PID controller.

1. Introduction

In the surface finishing technology, a hard chromium electroplating is one technique that uses a chromium metal deposited on the material surface such as roller, piston and mold (Lausmann, 1996). The thickness of chromium is greater than 0.80 μm to provide the hardness on the material surface (Mandich et al., 2010). The advantage of the hard chromium electroplating is giving the good physical properties on the surface such as increased wear resistance, low frictional coefficient, increased corrosion resistance and extended the maintenance time for the components (Svenson, 2006). The hard chromium electroplating process has five main steps as shown in Fig. 1.

Most problems found in the hard chromium electroplating plants in Thailand are the undesired thickness of chromium deposition and the appearance of deflect such as a burn or dull coating on the surface of workpiece, because these are caused by the low plating performance throughout the plating period (Boriboonsri and Kongthep, 2008). Practically, this problem can be solved by replating the workpieces again. This replating method causes longer production time, the large consumption of electricity, water and chemicals as well as it increases the operating cost to the manufacturers. Generally, the plating performance of the hard chromium electroplating depends on plating conditions during the plating time such as the plating solution temperature and the electric current density. Many literatures have reported techniques for improving plating performances such as the use of optimization techniques to get the maximum thickness (Bayramoglu et al., 2008) and to reduce operating cost per batch (Tanthadiloke et al., 2013), the use of neural network technique and a support vector machine to develop a new methodology for predicting the thickness of chromium deposit (Lasheras et al., 2010 and 2014), etc. In this case study, the plating solution temperature is needed to control to its optimal value throughout the plating period for preventing undesired problems occur on the surface of workpieces. An optimal temperature range of the plating solution during the plating time should be around 47 – 53 °C in order to give an aesthetic look and a hardness on the surface of workpieces (Zitko et al., 2010)

Consequently, the objectives of this work are study the mathematical models to represent the plating solution temperature profile and use the proportional-integral-derivative (PID) control approach to the models for improving the plating performance by maintaining the plating solution temperature at the optimal value during the plating period.

2. Mathematical models

In the hard chromium electroplating process, the main units in this process including with a plating bath, a cooling system and a power supply are shown in Figure 2.

The mass and energy balance principle around the main units is used to formulate the mathematical models of the hard chromium electroplating process for representing the dynamic behavior of the process. The dynamic models of the hard chromium electroplating process are expressed as follow,

$$\frac{dT_p}{dt} = \frac{IV - U_0 A_{ht}(\Delta T_{lm}) - Q_{loss}}{\rho_p C_{pp} V_p} \tag{1}$$

$$\frac{dT_{wo}}{dt} = \frac{U_0 A_{ht}(\Delta T_{lm}) + F_w(T_{wi} - T_{wo})}{\rho_w C_{pw} L_{tube} A_o} \tag{2}$$

Where, T_p is the plating solution temperature and T_{wo} is the outlet cooling water temperature. The equations of the logarithmic mean temperature difference (ΔT_{lm}) and the overall heat transfer coefficient (U_0) are shown in Eqs.(3) and (4).

$$\Delta T_{lm} = \frac{(T_p - T_{wi}) - (T_p - T_{wo})}{ln\dfrac{(T_p - T_{wi})}{(T_p - T_{wo})}} \tag{3}$$

Table 1. List of initial parameters

Parameters	Units	Values
Electric current (I)	A	3,500
Voltage (V)	V	5.5
Outer diameter of heat exchanger tube (d_o)	m	0.0254
Inner diameter of heat exchanger tube (d_i)	m	0.0224
Outside surface area for heat transfer (A_o)	m^2	5.067 x 10^{-4}
Inside surface area for heat transfer (A_i)	m^2	3.942 x 10^{-4}
Heat transfer area of heat exchanger (A_{ht})	m^2	1.489
Heat exchanger length (L_{tube})	m	18.66
Overall heat transfer coefficient (U_0)	kW/m^2 °C	0.58484
Density of plating solution (ρ_p)	kg/m^3	1,174.4
Density of water (ρ_w)	kg/m^3	992.25
Specific heat capacity of plating solution (C_{pp})	kJ/kg °C	4.9172
Specific heat capacity of water (C_{pw})	kJ/kg °C	4.181
Plating bath volume (V_p)	m^3	11.35

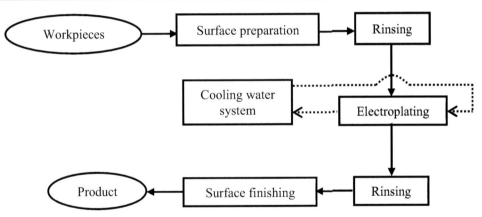

Figure 1. Process flow diagram of the hard chrome plating process.

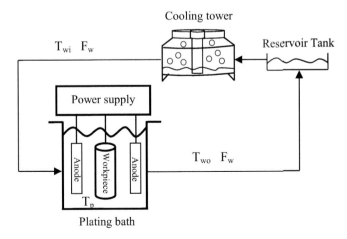

Figure 2. The schematic of the electroplating section.

$$U_0 = \cfrac{1}{\cfrac{A_o}{A_i h} + \cfrac{A_o \ln(d_o/d_i)}{2\pi K L_{tube}} + \cfrac{1}{h}} \tag{4}$$

To perform the correction of the developed mathematical models, the real data with conventional operating condition that collected from Siam Hard Chrome Co., Ltd., a hard chrome plating plant, Thailand, are used to validate the models. The parameters which used in the simulation are listed in Table 1.

3. Control Strategy

The proportional-integral-derivative (PID) controller is a popular approach that use for controlling in many chemical processes since it is not complicate and easy to apply to the real industries. In this work, the PID controller is proposed to keep the plating solution temperature (T_p) to the desired set point at 50 °C by using the cooling water flow rate (F_w) as a manipulated variable. This set point is obtained from a previous work (Kittisupakorn et al., 2012). The control study is performed in set point tracking case and this controller is normally expressed in Eq.(5).

$$u(t) = K_c \left[e'(t) + \frac{1}{\tau_I} \int_0^t e'(t)dt + \tau_D \frac{de'}{dt} \right] \tag{5}$$

Where, e'(t) is an error of a control variable value and a set point value. For PID parameters tuning, the trial and error tuning method is chosen to use in this work. The value of PID tuning parameters such as a controller gain (K_c), an integral time constant (τ_I) and a derivative time constant (τ_D) are 0.0025, 100 and 200, respectively.

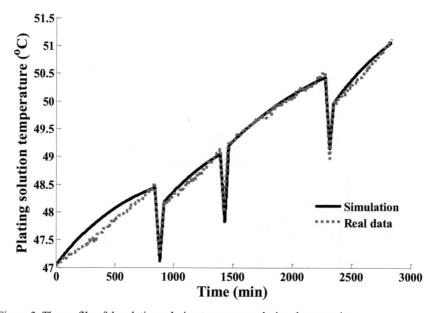

Figure 3. The profile of the plating solution temperature during the operation.

4. Results & Discussions

In the simulation, the dynamic models of the hard chromium electroplating process are solved by using an Euler's numerical method. The simulation result of the hard chromium electroplating process validated with the real data is demonstrated in Figure 3. This result shows that these developed mathematical models can be used to explain the dynamic behavior of the hard chromium electroplating process because the simulation trend has a slightly different from the real data even if the process is in the cooling down or the heating up period between every batch. Furthermore, the results from using the PID controller to control the plating solution temperature during the plating time and the cooling water flow rate profile are shown in Figure 4 and Figure 5. In Figure 4, the PID controller shows a good control performance to keeping the plating solution temperature at the set point during the plating period with some oscillate at the start of every batch. This result also demonstrates a control action to raise the plating solution temperature to the set point and it has some overshoot before the temperature is tracked to the set point.

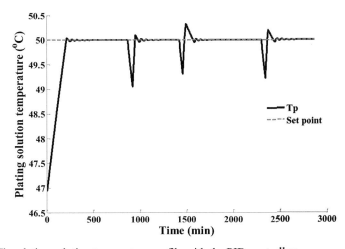

Figure 4. The plating solution temperature profile with the PID controller.

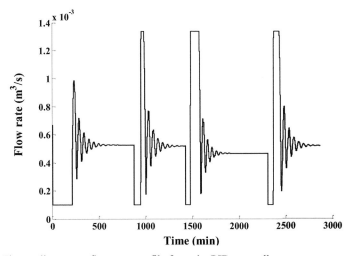

Figure 5. The cooling water flow rate profile from the PID controller.

Figure 5 shows the changing of the cooling water flow rate that use as a manipulated variable in order to keep the plating solution temperature at the set point value.

5. Conclusion

The developed mathematical models that are obtained from the mass and energy balance principle around the operating units in the hard chromium electroplating process give the best result for simulating the plating solution temperature profile with a slightly different from the real data even if the process is in the cooling down or the heating up period between every batch. These models are applicable for using to explain the dynamic behavior of the plating solution temperature during the plating period. Furthermore, the conventional controller (PID) is sufficient to use for improving the plating performance of the hard chromium electroplating process by controlling the plating solution temperature at the set point value. This controller shows the high control performance for maintaining the plating solution temperature at the set point throughout the plating time with some overshoot at the beginning of every batch.

Acknowledgement

The authors would like to thank Thailand Research Fund (TRF) under The Royal Golden Jubilee Ph.D. Program (PHD/0158/2550) for financial support and Siam Hard Chrome Co., Ltd. for information support during the research.

References

G. A. Lausmann, 1996, Electrolytically deposited hard chrome, Surface and Coating Technology, 86-87, 814-820.

N. V. Mandich, D. L. Snyder, 2010, Electrodeposition of chromium, In M. Schlesinger, M. Paunovic (Eds.), Modern electroplating (5th edition, 205-248), John Wiley & Sons, Inc., New Jersy, USA.

E. Svenson, 2006, Plating resources, Inc., <www.plating.com> accessed on 14/09/2013.

P. Boriboonsri, 2008, Study of dynamic behavior of heat exchanger system in hard chrome electroplating (Master's Thesis), Chulalongkorn University, Bangkok, Thailand.

A. Kongthep, 2008, Modeling and optimization of a flow-induced vibrating tube heat exchanger for a hard chrome plating process (Master's Thesis), Chulalongkorn University, Bangkok, Thailand.

M. Bayramoglu, B. Onat, N. Geren, 2008, Statistical optimization of process parameters to obtain maximum thickness and brightness in chromium plating, Journal of Materials Processing Technology, 203, 277-286.

S. Tanthadiloke, P. Kittisupakorn, I. M. Mujtaba, 2013, Improvement of production performance of a hard chromium electroplating via operational optimization, Proceeding of the 5th Regional Conference on Chemical Engineering, Thailand.

F. S. Lasheras, J. A. Vilán Vilán, P. J. G. Nieto, J. J. del Coz Díaz, 2010, The use of experiments to improve a neural network model in order to predict the thickness of the chromium layer in a hard chromium plating process, Mathematical and Computer Modelling, 52, 1169-1176.

F. S. Lasheras, P. J. G. Nieto, F. J. de Cos Juez, J. A. Vilán Vilán, 2014, Evolutionary support vector regression algorithm appied to the prediction of the thickness of the chromium layer in a hard chromium plating process, Applied Mathematics and Computation, 227, 164-170.

L. Zitko , G. Cushnie, P. Chalmer, R. Taylor, 2010, Hard chrome plating traing course, The National Center for Manufacturing Sciences, Michigan, USA.

P. Kittisupakorn, A. Thaikua , S. Tanthadiloke , 2012, Temperature control by heat exchanger incorporating with vibration type coiled-tube, Proceedings of the International MultiConference of Engineers and Computer Scientists 2012, Vol II, Hong Kong.

Jiří Jaromír Klemeš, Petar Sabev Varbanov and Peng Yen Liew (Editors)
Proceedings of the 24th European Symposium on Computer Aided Process Engineering – ESCAPE 24
June 15-18, 2014, Budapest, Hungary.

Investigations on Information-rich Visualizations to Explore Process Connectivity and Causality

David D. Romero[a,b,*], Nina F. Thornhill[b], Tone-Grete Graven[a]

[a]*ABB OGP Technology and Innovation, Ole Deviks vei 10, Oslo, Norway*
[b]*Department of Chemical Engineering, Imperial College London, London SW7 2AZ*
david.romero@no.abb.com

Abstract

Complexity in large-scale chemical processes poses a challenge to engineers who need to understand causality and interconnectivity. Previous work has already taken advantage of the use of visualization for alarm correlation and plant-wide oscillation detection for small scale example processes, but the resulting correlation maps are limited in the number of variables that can be easily managed. This paper proposes a new approach to the visualization of connectivity information, which is capable of representing a large number of connections between process variables and units, as well as process-specific information and alarm history. The novel visualization is based on the Circos© framework which is widely used for analysis of connectivity and causality in the field of genomics. The benefit of adapting information-rich visualizations for the field of process systems engineering will be discussed based on an academic use-case.

Keywords: process connectivity, information visualization, XML

1. Introduction

Tight coupling and complexity in modern process plants make it difficult to obtain a clear and accurate assessment of the state of the process, especially during disturbance situations. Advanced automated control systems and the use of recycle flows often create complex dynamic interactions between plant components and subsystems. The biggest problem when analysing connectivity is that the information needed originates from disparate sources, often in different data formats and structures, and it is the engineer's task to make an assessment of the situation based on experience and the data he or she is able to access. This problem becomes more critical for plants with a high number of systems and processes, or when analysing causality between variables.

Process connectivity and causality has been studied in the literature by following two approaches. One is based on a priori knowledge from the system such as first principles and mathematical models which lead to structural equations, causal graphs and rule-based models. A second approach infers causality from process data based on the fact that cause-and-effect relationships can be observed from non-linearity indexes, propagation time (delays) and signal analysis methods such as transfer entropy from information theory. Hybrid approaches combining more than one approach also exist. However, the use of human labor to pin-point the source of a disturbance which could have many origins becomes time-consuming, difficult and expensive.

With such methods starting to be developed commercially, it is timely to investigate the best way to present the results of such analyses. What is needed are information-rich displays to help the user and shorten the time spent on accessing and linking data from different sources. Previous work has involved ethnographic research and user analysis to discover the needs and challenges for visualization of connectivity (Romero and Graven, 2013). That research contributed to the definition of functional requirements and identification of industrial use-cases, by including the human factors in the design of tools to be applied in chemical processes.

The main focus of investigation in this paper and, consequently, the novel contribution towards the CAPE community, is methods to merge structural representations, first principles models and process-specific information inside a common visualization, considering the human factor in the process. The hypothesis is that when it comes to making sense of the overall situation, interactive visualizations and richer displays can better support the analysis rather than static representations of the process. Specifically, this paper proposes a methodology to create visual representations from data extracted from signed directed graphs and process schematics.

The paper is laid out as follows. The next section gives the motivation for the work and highlights relevant background to place the work in context. Section 3 presents the methods needed to create information-rich displays concerning process connectivity and causality. Section 4 demonstrates the results in a case study originating with Maurya et al. (2003, 2004), and the paper ends with concluding remarks in Section 5.

2. Motivation, background and context

Methods for graphic representation of process knowledge include signed directed graphs, also referred as SDGs (Maurya et al., 2003), adjacency matrices (Di Geronimo Gil et al., 2011), and query systems based on electronic versions of process schematics (Thambirajah et al., 2009). A recent way to obtain connectivity information is by parsing 'smart P&IDs' (Piping and Instrumentation Diagrams), which are available in XML format, and then applying search algorithms and logic rules to extract the connectivity. This method has been followed before in Di Geronimo Gil et al. (2011) for the generation of connectivity and reachability matrices, and in Schleburg et al, (2013) for the reduction of alarms based on topology. Other work (Kondaveeti et al., 2010) had explored visualization for alarm correlation and plant-wide oscillation detection. A challenge for the resulting correlation maps is that they rapidly become unwieldy as the number of variables grows, although the technique of zoomable tree maps has been used to deal with this limitation (e.g. Matrikon, 2004).

A semantic network is a graphical representation of knowledge, where related facts are elements inside, and chemical processes can be modeled in this fashion. In contrast to rule-based systems, which are ideal for problems that are regulated by an "if-then" knowledge representation, semantic networks have some unique properties for use in the visualization of interconnected data. The reason is that they provide a hierarchical method for organizing data, a means of inheritance from upper levels to lower level in the hierarchy, and a means of organizing spatial relationships and control structures. This approach seems promising for the task of visualization. Figure 1 presents some widely used visualization methods for semantic networks from the literature. As will be shown below, the circular layout outlined by Holten et al. (2006) known as 'balloon tree' gives a display that is well adapted to discerning patterns such as close or distant interactions and the strength of the topological link.

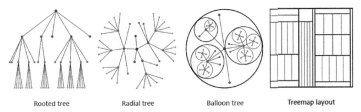

Figure 1.Visualization metaphors for hierarchical networks (Adapted from Holten, 2006)

The visualization should be able to represent inclusion (parent-child) and adjacency (non-hierarchical) relationships. A comprehensive study on the visualization of such relationships has been carried out by Holten et al. (2006), generating algorithms to present information-rich displays for hierarchical source code and citation networks.

3. Methods

The sequence of methods required to create the information-rich displays is shown in Figure 2. The method started by gathering the different datasets and by extracting the relevant information from each of them. This is then consolidated into a standard XML model that is imported in Circos© (see Section 3.2) to render the graphics according to a series of dynamic rules and algorithms defined during this investigation. The process to integrate first principles models with information about topology and the methodology to obtain SDGs have been documented elsewhere (Maurya et al., 2003). The steps of building the topology model and designing the connectogram are the authors' contribution, and will be explained in this section.

3.1. Topology model

One important requirement specification from the user survey was that the information had to be stored in non-proprietary XML format. This might be achieved by modeling the data in AutomationML (AML), which is a neutral data format based on XML for the storage and exchange of plant engineering information. The flexibility of this format allows incorporating the topology, or physical dependencies, as well as the functional structure, geometry and logic; information that is generally defined in other technical documentation. In this work, the AML was constructed by hand because the automatic generation of AML files from differential equations and "smart P&IDs" is still an open question (Barth and Fay, 2010).

3.2. Connectogram design

Structure and connectivity information are graphically rendered in a circular diagram using the open source tool Circos©, which has been described in detail in Krzywinski et al. (2009). The term 'connectogram' has been adopted from the genomics community, and it denotes the information-rich visualization. In brief, Circos© is a Perl application that employs circular layouts to facilitate the visualization of relationships between elements by the use of graphical elements, including links and scatter plots. The details of how this is applied to process connectivity are explained in Section 4.3.

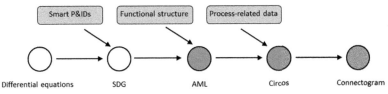

Figure 2. Data processing methodology used in this investigation (authors' contribution on gray)

4. Case-study

4.1. Process description

The concept is demonstrated by using the process flowsheet obtained from Maurya et al. (2004), which also been used widely in other research studies. The model is composed of two settling tanks, level controllers for the tanks, flow controller for the inlet flowrate to tank 2 (to maintain molar flowrates of A and B in their stoichiometric ratio), a mixer, a counter-current heat exchanger, a CSTR (Continuous Stirred Tank Reactor), temperature controller for the CSTR, a product separator, a recycle stream around the CSTR, a preheater and a flash vaporizer, and pressure, temperature and lever controllers for the flash vaporizer. The flowsheet for this process is shown in Fig 3.

4.2. AML description

Figure 4(a) presents the XML model which was created by using the AML model description version 2.15. The model shows the normal syntax specified under the international standard IEC 62424. Information about the different units is mapped to the XML classes as attributes. The connectivity representation, Figure 4(b), contains the connections of the process equipment as shown in the schematic. The AML file is object oriented; this means that every element is defined with a corresponding role and class, which aids in the task of recognizing parent-child relations and a series of internal links that define the non-hierarchical relations.

4.3. Connectogram

Figure 4(c) shows the different layers of information presented in the connectogram. This section explains the different parts of the information-rich display:

Unit level: The outermost label represents the tag or equipment, denoting the top level of the hierarchy. The tags are organized clockwise following the process flow.

Variable level: This circle maps the internal variables from each unit extracted from the first principle models in Di Geronimo Gil et al. (2011). The names of the variables are indicated with radial labels, and the difference in width is proportional to the number of connections (inputs and outputs). The incoming links to this circle represent the connectivity (continuous line for process connection, and dashed line for a logical one).

Contextual data: Additional data can be plotted into a circular graph as shown in the figure, performance indicators are shown here, in a circular axis with positive and negative regions, like in any other two-dimensional graph.

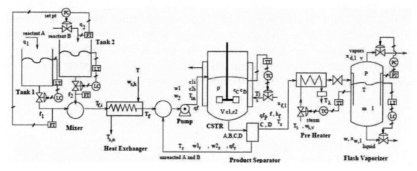

Figure 3. Case study from Maurya (From Maurya, 2003)

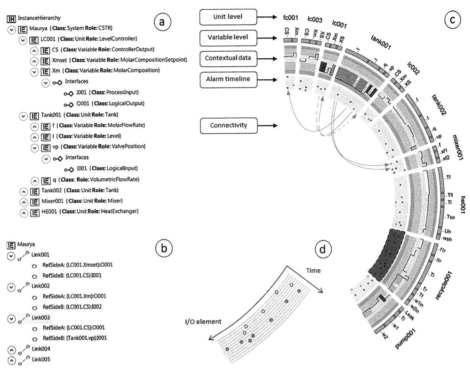

Figure 4. Description of the elements inside the connectogram

Alarm timeline: Alarm logs are represented as a circular scatterplot. The distance to the center of the circle indicates the time that it occurred, and each of the twelve divisions of the graph, Figure 4(d), represent a certain period of time. Color codes are used.

Connectivity: This inner part represents the actual links of the connectivity. Strength and direction are easily plotted in Circos© as well as the type of connection.

The information-rich display presented in Figure 4(c) is a part (roughly one third) of the complete 360 degree connectogram. The region shaded on recycle001 (c) is zoomed in and shown in (d). The way the information is taken from the AML to the connectogram is straightfoward; for example, the dashed link on (c) represents a logical connection between the level controller 'lc001' and the 'tank001'. More specifically, the display shows that the causality of this link is between the variable 'Xm' (molar composition) inside lc001 and 'vp' (valve position) inside tank001, which is also highlighted in (b) as 'Link003'. In contrast to previous algorithms which produced connectivity matrices where only information about the physical topology is available, the use of Circos© allows the user to visualize performance indicators and alarm information in the same place, so he/she can make a better assessment of the connectivity. Moreover, by using dynamic rules and queries it is feasible to draw focus to data positions or values, and to apply algorithms for filtering and bundling of the links in order to reduce visual clutter. Adding interactivity to the displays would potentially improve the usability of these displays and their usage for decision support or troubleshooting activities.

Some of the challenges foreseen are some aesthetic aspects and the reduction of clutter as the aggregation of data scales to larger examples. Additionally, as the design of several elements involves the use of specific colour coding, colour misinterpretation or even colour blindness are other challenges to overcome.

5. Conclusions and future work

A novel information-rich visualization capable of integrating and showing connectivity information in chemical processes was presented. This approach of applying tools from the field of biomolecular engineering to the field of process systems engineering is proposed as an alternative for users to access connectivity information. This concept can potentially improve the way domain experts are presented with specific information about relationships between the different systems, units, and variables in any chemical process. The results have been demonstrated by a simple example available from the literature, but the benefits of information-rich displays are expected to be more substantial when applied to larger processes. Furthermore, the integration in AML shows potential for the addition of other contextual data, such as graphical attributes and interlocks or internal behavior of objects and I/O connections. The concept is being tested with other academic and industrial use-cases and future work contemplates evaluations by experts in the field.

Acknowledgements

The financial support from the Marie Curie FP7-ITN project 'Energy savings from smart operation of electrical, process and mechanical equipment– ENERGY-SMARTOPS', Contract No: PITN-GA-2010-264940 is gratefully acknowledged.

References

M. Barth, A. Fay, 2010, Efficient use of data exchange formats in engineering projects by means of language integrated queries, Proceedings of the 36th Annual Conference on IEEE Industrial Electronics Society, 1335–1340.

G.J. Di Geronimo Gil, D.B. Alabi, O.E. Iyun, N.F. Thornhill, 2011, Merging Process Models and Plant Topology, Proceedings of the 4th International Symposium on Advanced Control of Industrial Processes, 15-21.

D. Holten, 2006, Hierarchical Edge Bundles: Visualization of Adjacency Relations in Hierarchical Data, IEEE Trans Vis Comput Graph, 12, 5, 741-748.

S.R. Kondaveeti, I. Izadi, S.L. Shah, T. Black, 2010, Graphical Representation of Industrial Alarm Data, Proceedings of the 11th IFAC/IFORS/IEA Symposium on Analysis, Design and Evaluation of Human-Machine Systems, 11, 181-186.

Krzywinski, M.I., Schein, J.E., Birol, I., 2009, Circos: An information aesthetic for comparative genomics. Genome Res, 19, 9, 639-1645.

Matrikon, 2004, Matrikon sets revenue and earnings records, <www.matrikon.com/corporate/downloads/documents/q404_full.pdf > accessed on 11/13/13.

M.R. Maurya, R. Rengaswamy, V. Venkatasubramanian, 2003, A Systematic Famework for the Development and Analysis of Signed Digraphs for Chemical Processes 2: Control Loops and Flowsheet Analysis, Ind. Eng. Chem. Res., 42, 4811–4827.

M.R. Maurya, R. Rengaswamy, V. Venkatasubramanian, 2004, Application of signed digraphs-based analysis for fault diagnosis of chemical process flowsheets, Eng. Appl. Artif. Intell., 17, 501–518.

D.D. Romero, T.G. Graven, 2013, Visual representation of connectivity information for efficient system understanding, Proceedings of the Human Factors and Ergonomics Society Annual Meeting, 17, 1, 2012-2016.

J. Thambirajah, L. Benabbas, M. Bauer, N.F. Thornhill, 2009, Cause-and-effect analysis in chemical processes utilizing XML plant connectivity and quantitative process history, Comput. Chem. Eng., 33, 503–512.

Jiří Jaromír Klemeš, Petar Sabev Varbanov and Peng Yen Liew (Editors)
Proceedings of the 24th European Symposium on Computer Aided Process Engineering – ESCAPE 24
June 15-18, 2014, Budapest, Hungary. Copyright © 2014 Elsevier B.V. All rights reserved.

Computer-Aided Template for Model Reuse, Development and Maintenance

Marina Fedorova, Gürkan Sin, Rafiqul Gani*

Computer Aided Process Engineering Center, Department of Chemical and Biochemical Engineering, Technical University of Denmark, DK-2800 Lyngby, Denmark
rag@kt.dtu.dk

Abstract

A template-based approach for model development is presented in this work. Based on a model decomposition technique, the computer-aided template concept has been developed. This concept is implemented as a software tool, which provides a user-friendly interface for following the workflow steps, as well as the guidance through the steps providing additional information and comments. The application of the tool is highlighted with a multiscale modelling case study involving a catalytic membrane fixed bed reactor. The modelling templates for reactor as well as particle scales have been developed. For the particle scale, two alternative mechanisms to describe the diffusion inside catalyst pellets are available: a Fickian diffusion model and a dusty gas model. Moreover, the effects of isothermal and non-isothermal catalyst are also considered during the model development process. Thereby, any number of problem-specific models can be generated through the template and maintained for the future reuse.

Keywords: modelling framework, computer-aided template, catalytic fixed bed reactor.

1. Introduction

Models are playing important roles in design and analysis of chemical processes and products. They help to reduce the number of expensive and time consuming experiments and to give better understanding of the process domain. However, when the required models are complex, and involve multiple time and/or length scales, their development and application for product-process design is not trivial. Also, once a model (or a template) is developed, it should be possible to adapt it for various similar modelling objectives with a minimum of effort. Therefore, a modelling framework with the associated tools can contribute by reducing the time and resources needed for model development and application. Moreover, better application of the developed models can be achieved by reusing them through a specially developed modelling framework. This will allow one to make a proper documentation of the created models, will increase reuse of the models and also will allow different users to exchange and work with a variety of models. The main objectives of this computer-aided modelling framework are to provide structure, guidance and support during model development and application; increase the efficiency of the modelling process; and, improve the quality and reliability of the models. This is in agreement with the study of Foss et al. (1998), which emphasizes that a solid understanding of the model development process is required for the development of modelling tools, which in turn aims to improve the efficiency of the modelling process and the quality of the models. However these study notes also the lack of implementation of modelling techniques in existing computer-aided modelling tools. Moreover, Klatt and Marquardt (2009) identify prospective improvements for the present modelling tools, such as multi-scale modelling features together with documentation, maintenance and reuse of models in an efficient and economical way. The benefits of the integration of modelling tools are highlighted in the study of Zhao et al. (2011), which shows the potential for generic, non-case-specific tools, while Kraus et al. (2012) emphasizes the need for unification of modelling documentation.

In this contribution, the concept of novel template-based modelling approach together with its software implementation is presented. The template approach refers to the part of the modelling framework that allows already developed models to be manipulated, adopted and/or reused for various purposes (Fedorova et al., 2013).

2. Computer-aided template-based modelling

The purpose of the template-based modelling approach is to enable modeller to create a general model (with all known phenomena and assumptions) for a given system, which will be used later to generate problem-specific models. To achieve this, the modeller is systematically guided through the steps of the different workflows and, at each step, the framework for template-based modelling identifies and integrates the required guidance, tools, database and library connections. Depending on the modeling needs and goals, the modeller has the possibility to create a new model when the needed problem-specific model is not available in the library. The modeller has also the possibility to identify, validate and solve the new models or use existing models from the templates library. The model templates are a part of the model generation feature of the modelling framework. Furthermore, model templates enable the idea of model reuse as the user can employ the template as a base to generate various problem-specific models for different applications. The templates aim to provide structured domain-specific knowledge, speed-up of the model development/derivation process and improve model quality. Modeller has a possibility to choose a model template from the database, according to the phenomena found in the system volume. This model template includes model equations, model description and solution strategy among others. Modeller can use the template for a new modelling problem or can update it in order to extend its application range. A template tool is connected to the tool for solving and identification of model - ICAS-Mot (Heitzig et al., 2011) and the tool for model equation generation from scratch - ICAS-ModDev (Jensen and Gani, 1999), forming the modelling framework (Fedorova et al., 2013).As the template library includes validated models, the creation of a new template-based model will reduce the modelling time and increase efficiency in the subsequent steps of model analysis, solving and identification. In the template, a model is decomposed into three sets of equations: balances, constitutive relations and connection and/or conditional equations. This decomposition is based on the hierarchy given by Cameron and Gani (2011).

The work flow for the template use consists of 6 general steps (as shown in Fig. 1):

1. Select a template from a library of templates, e.g. catalytic membrane fixed bed reactor.

2. Define process system. What is the system volume, number of phases, presence or not of reactions, accumulation, number of components, number of scales etc.? Information from this step is used in the subsequent steps.

3. Define balance volumes, the model type (steady state, dynamic state), etc. This step includes generation of mass, energy and momentum balance equations. Every template has default option for model type, but user can apply his/her preference and the equations will be changed accordingly.

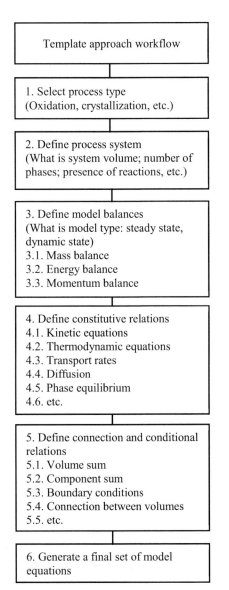

Figure1. Workflow for the template use.

4. Define constitutive equations. In this step user identifies the models needed to describe the system volume behaviour, such as thermodynamic relations, transport and reaction rates, diffusion, phase equilibrium, etc.

5. Define connection and conditional relations. These are equations describing surroundings and system connections, such as summation of mole fraction, etc. Equations given in this step are mostly generated by default. User can define additional boundary and/or initial conditions if necessary and also the connection between different system volumes.

6. Generation of the final set of model equations by aggregating all the model specifications done in previous steps. In this step a model is ready to be sent to the solver or for further identification and analysis.

3. Software implementation

Software implementation of the framework for the template-based modelling includes several libraries, which provide building blocks for the templates. A schematic flow-diagram of the implementation is shown in Figure 2.

In the process of following the workflow for the template step by step, model equations, which in this case are building blocks for the future model, are taken from the certain libraries of balance, constitutive or connection equations. Regarding the user changes (for example, dynamic state instead of steady state), the program engine modifies chosen equations and includes them in the final model. In the end all equations from the previous stages are collected together and combined in a final model, which is translated to an MoT object and can be solved and identified in the ICAS-MoT

Equations libraries

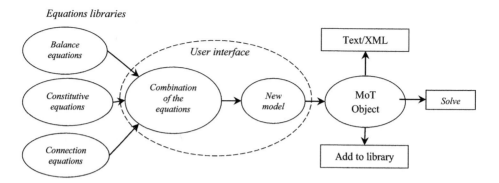

Figure 2. Schematic flow-diagram of the software implementation of the template as a tool.

modelling platform or can be transferred to a text or xml file in order to use it in external programs. Moreover, the newly created model can be added to the model library and can be as well used for template creation and/or updates.

The creation of template building blocks is based on the models, which are related to the certain phenomena and have already been verified. This makes possible for the program engine to connect different equations after modifying them. However, it is always required for a new model to be checked in order to prevent potential mistakes in equations linking, e.g. use of different names for the same variable.

4. Case study application

The application of the template tool is highlighted with a case study related to the modelling of a catalytic membrane fixed bed reactor coupling dehydrogenation of ethylbenzene with hydrogenation of nitrobenzene (model is taken from Abo-Ghander et. al, 2012). In the previous work (Fedorova et al, 2013) the mathematical equations of the model have been implemented in ICAS-MoT, have been numerically analysed, solved and identified. Now this model is stored as a template and different problem specific versions of it are generated.

The schematic view of the reactor is shown at the Figure 3. The reactor is composed of two compartments within a shell containing a bundle of hydrogenation tubes. On the shell side, dehydrogenation of ethylbenzene takes place producing styrene and hydrogen. Five side reactions also occur, producing benzene, toluene, and non-

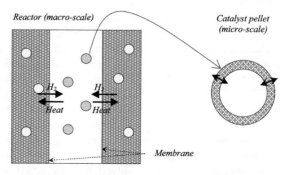

Figure 3. Schematic sketch of the reactor and catalyst pellets in it.

condensable gases like ethylene, methane, carbon monoxide, and carbon dioxide. Inside the membrane tubes, cocurrently flowing nitrobenzene reacts with hydrogen to produce aniline as a second major useful product from the integrated membrane reactor (Abo-Ghander et al., 2012).

The workflow for the template to be employed in this case study is the following.
1. Template for the catalytic membrane fixed bed reactor is chosen.
2. System has two volumes, separated by membrane; one vapour phase; 6 reactions on the dehydrogenation side and one reaction on the hydrogenation side. Every volume is considered as 2-scale system with catalyst particles as micro-scale and reactor as macro-scale.
   Other options in template are to have one volume, e.g. catalytic fixed bed reactor without membrane, and to use one-scale model only for reactor.
3. For both volumes models are in steady state, distributed in angular direction, for mass, energy and momentum balances (the independent variable is the reactor length). No external mass or heat loss. Catalyst pellets are isobaric.
4. Reaction rates are chosen based on the original model of Abo-Ghander et al. (2012). Catalyst pellets are isothermal. Diffusion inside catalyst pellets is represented by Fick's law. Ideal gas behaviour in both volumes.
5. Two volumes are connected by hydrogen transfer across membrane from volume 1 to volume 2 and by heat transfer from volume 2 to volume 1.
6. Final model is constructed based on answers from steps 1-5. It contains 46 ODE and 582 AE, including all constitutive and connection equations of both volumes and both macro and micro scales. After generating the final model, it has been translated into a model object and solved by using ICAS-MoT.

Screenshot showing the workflow of the template in the user interface of the template tool is highlighted in Figure 4. It presents an example of how the template approach workflow (Figure 1) actually looks in program implementation.

5. Conclusions

Template-based modelling approach has been presented and implemented as a computer-aided software tool, which guides user through workflow steps in order to generate a problem-specific model based on the available template. The application of the tool was highlighted with catalytic membrane fixed bed reactor template, which shows various aspects of model decomposition in template, for example, different system volumes, connection between volumes, modification of constitutive equations etc. The possibility of combination and modification of the model templates is making the model development process easier and more efficient.

Current and future work is extending the application range for the template-based modelling including unsaturated fatty acid oxidation, as well as improving the different aspects of workflow and its software implementation.

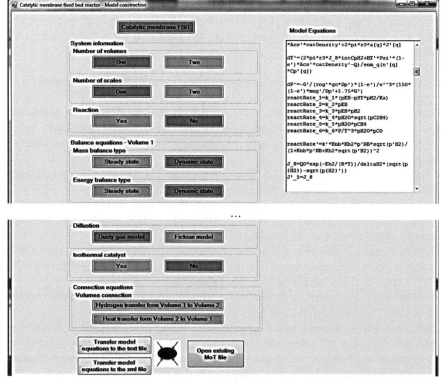

Figure 4. Program screen of the template tool (upper and lower parts) highlighting the selected options; lighter colour of rectangles indicate selected options.

References

N.S. Abo-Ghander, F. Logist, J.R. Grace, J.F.M. Van Impe, S.S.E.H. Elnashaie, C.J. Lim, 2012, Comparison of diffusion models in the modeling of a catalytic membrane fixed bed reactor coupling dehydrogenation of ethylbenzene with hydrogenation of nitrobenzene, Computers and Chemical Engineering, 38, 11-23.

I. Cameron, R. Gani, 2011, Product and Process Modelling. A Case Study Approach, Elsevier, Oxford, UK.

M. Fedorova, G. Sin, R. Gani, 2013, Computer-aided modeling framework – a generic modeling template for catalytic membrane fixed bed reactors, Computer Aided Chemical Engineering, 32, 775-780.

B. Foss, B. Lohmann, W. Marquardt, 1998, A field study of the industrial modeling process, Journal ofProcess Control, 8, 5-6, 325-338.

A.K. Jensen, R. Gani, 1999, A Computer Aided Modeling System, Computers and Chemical Engineering, 23, 673-678.

M. Heitzig, G. Sin, M. Sales-Cruz, P. Glarborg, R. Gani, 2011, Computer-Aided Modeling Framework for Efficient Model Development, Analysis, and Identification: Combustion and Reactor Modeling, Industrial and Engineering Chemistry Research, 50, 9, 5253-5265.

K.-U. Klatt, W. Marquardt, 2009, Perspectives for process systems engineering - Personal views from academia and industry, Computers and Chemical Engineering, 33, 536-550.

R. Kraus, V.A. Merchan, H. Arellano-Garcia, G. Wozny, 2012, Hierarchical simulation of integrated chemical processes with a web based modeling tool, Computer Aided Chemical Engineering, 31, 15-19.

Y. Zhao, C. Jiang, A.Yang, 2011, Towards a Generic Simulation Environment for Multiscale Modelling based on Tool Integration, Computer Aided Chemical Engineering, 29, 76-80.

Jiří Jaromír Klemeš, Petar Sabev Varbanov and Peng Yen Liew (Editors)
Proceedings of the 24th European Symposium on Computer Aided Process Engineering – ESCAPE 24
June 15-18, 2014, Budapest, Hungary.

Public Protection Integrated Program Development for Chemical and Radiological Disasters

Seungnam Kim, Kwanghee Lee, Il Moon*

Department of Chemical and Biomolecular Engineering, Yonsei University, 50 Yonsei-ro, Seodaemun-gu, Seoul 120-749, Korea
ilmoon@yonsei.ac.kr

Abstract

Recently in Gumi, Korea, toxic hydrofluoric acid gas leak led to five deaths, while 18 others were hospitalized after exposure to the gas. Usually, due to the complex causes of Chemical and Radiological accidents, forecasting the damage is not a simple work. And these unexpected disasters have occurred and will go on. In this research, a public evacuation and protection information program is developed for helping government officers to make quick and effective decisions. The major users of this program are the officers who can control public evacuation in the initial phase of disasters; especially related to civil defence department. The prototype Chemical and Radiological civil defence management program helps them for efficient control over public evacuation. It supplies logical information, shelter locations, available emergency resources and so on. This research consists of below 4 steps; 1. Scenario development, 2. Chemical/ Radiological dispersion model development, 3. Resource DB collecting, analysis and converting, 4. Dispersion models and DBs installed prototype public protection program development. This research is belongs to a short-term R&D project for assessment of the practicality. Main project for establishing this system over the country is planned to start in 2014.

Keywords: Integrated program, Public protection, Safety, Contingency

1. Introduction

On September, 2012, in Gumi, Korea, toxic hydrofluoric acid gas leak led to five deaths, while 18 others were hospitalized after exposure to the gas. Economic loss was up to 17.7 M USD and 323.8 ha crops, 67.6 ha forest and 3,209 domestic animals were damaged by the accident. In addition 43 companies had operation failure. Usually, due to the complex causes of Chemical and Radiological accidents, various type of damages are occurred and the forecasting the damage is not a simple work.

Rapid and efficient public evacuation is absolutely needed when a natural or man-made disaster occurs (Sayyady and Eksioglu, 2010). Guanquan et al. (2012) introduced their research about the occupant evacuation in terms of time-dependent risk and Manley and Kim (2012) reported their model for emergency evacuation. In this research, prototype public evacuation program is developed which supports government officers to make decisions.

2. General Contingency Plan

According to the general contingency plan, when a chemical accident occurs, two track reactions proceed simultaneously. Those are 'Public evacuation' focused on protecting public and 'On-field contingency' focused on decontamination and rescue.

2.1. Public evacuation

Public evacuation procedure starts with recognition of an accident. Public who are nearby the accident move to outside of the preliminary restricted zone. At the same time, related departments forecast dispersion of the accident material using computational method. With those results, first modification on restricted zone takes place. After the first modification, precise detection starts. Precise detection and measurement need specific instruments. Second modification proceeds with detected real contaminated region.

2.2. On-field contingency

In the track of On-field contingency, the procedure starts with evacuation, too. After that, establishment of control system is followed with continuous emergency rescue. In second initial reactions phase, monitoring and sampling to find out decontamination methods. Full-out hazardous caring is performed in the Hazardous control phase. The decontamination proceeds by professionals using all available equipment and resources.

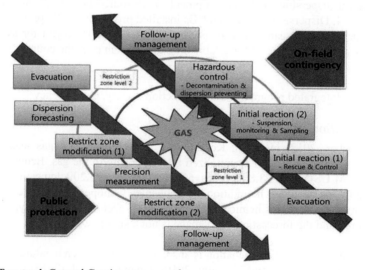

Figure 1. Two-track General Contingency procedure

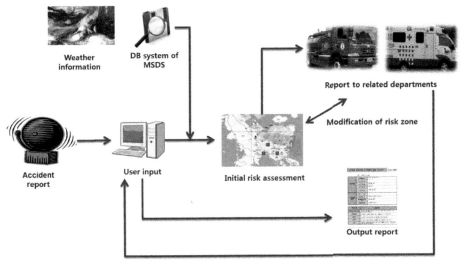

Figure 2. Scheme of the prototype public evacuation program

2.3. Research purpose in general contingency procedure

Prototype Chemical and Radiological civil defense management program is developed focused on the initial phase in both tracks. The initial reaction steps are the most important to reduce damages. So, the effective and fast responses are needed. In this research, a public evacuation and protection information program is developed for helping government officers to make quick and effective decisions. Using rapid accessible accident data, this program suggests available evacuation plan to officers.

3. Prototype public evacuation program

The major users of this program are the officers who can control public evacuation in the initial phase of disasters; especially related to civil defense department. Usually, even civil defense department, most related department have similar program. However, in this research the purpose of development is focused on the initial reaction and evacuations. So, the most important value of this program is the immediacy. This program has a simple input procedure, rapid dispersion calculation models, damage forecasting models and a function of automatic reporting to related organizations.

Some programs and database systems are used for forecasting Hazardous dispersion already. However, those programs supply only dispersion results. When those disasters occur, the officers cannot get information about public evacuation. In this research, the Prototype public protection program helps them for efficient controlling public evacuation. It supplies logical information, shelter locations, available emergency resources and so on.

This research consists of below 4 steps; 1. Scenario development, 2. Chemical /Radiological dispersion model development, 3. Resource DB collecting, analysis and converting, 4. Dispersion models and DBs installed prototype public protection program development.

3.1. Scenario development

For development of public evacuation program, proper accident and contingency scenarios were essential. In this research, five types of major threat are selected and a scenarios is developed at each threaten. These scenarios include detail accident sequence, damages, reactions of each organizations and public evacuation plan. These are the basis of the program.

3.2. Chemical/Radiological dispersion model

The Public protection integrated program in this research was developed focused on emergency evacuation. The swift calculation is absolutely essential in emergent situation. For that reason, we choose simple models for forecasting chemical and radiological dispersion rather than robust models which have computational burden.

For the chemical release, ALOHA (Areal Locations of Hazardous Atmospheres) is used which is already qualified and commercialized. For the radiological dispersion, CAL-PUFF model is used for forecasting.

Table 1. Five types of major threat

Typical Threat	Chemical weapons attacks on metropolitan area
Accident	Leak accidents in chemical industry
Accident	Emergency accidents in nuclear power plant
Terror	Spraying toxic chemicals
Terror	Dirty bomb terror

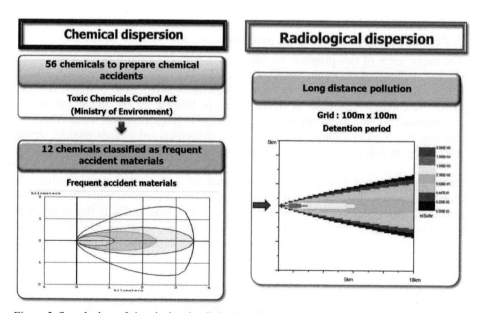

Figure 3. Sample data of chemical and radiological dispersion model

3.3. Resource DB collecting, analysis and converting

Two preparedness regions were selected according to the scenarios. Those are Yeong-gwang and Yeosu. Yeong-gwang has nuclear power plants and Yeosu has national complex. Collecting, analyzing and converting Chemical and radiological preparedness resources data are needed for applying the data to the program. A purpose of this program is helping officers to make efficient and rapid decisions. For that reasons, DB treatment was needed.

3.4. The prototype Chemical and Radiological Civil defence management program

Input data includes accident region information, specific address, accident time, material type, storage type, accident type and weather conditions. Direction velocity of the wind, atmospheric stability and precipitation belong to weather condition.Using these input data, damage region is forecasted. The program supplies forecasted damage region with installed DB.

Figure 4 is a screen of suggesting available and efficient evacuation phase in the program. The red and cyan circles are preliminary restricted zones. The red region describes forecasted dispersion area. Out of the dispersion area, the program shows available shelters, hospitals and other departments related to contingency procedure. In addition, more specific information of police station, hospital, fire station and shelter are described in the left frame.

4. Differences

The most advanced function of this program is supplying accurate real-time contingency information. With real time resources and circumstance data, dynamic dispersion data is calculated. Continuously, more detailed evacuation plan is described

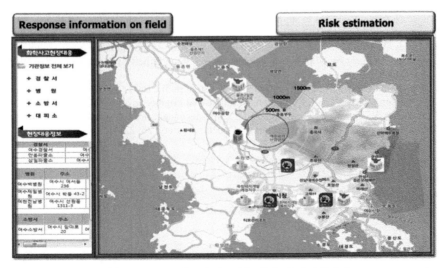

Figure 4. Report page of the prototype Chemical and Radiological civil defense management program

on the map; risk rate of zones, evacuation order with priority, assigned shelter of each zone and so on. Another a valuable function of this program is an addition of the 'Sensitive Zone' which classified by levels of dispersions of hazardous materials.

5. Conclusions

The prototype Chemical and Radiological Civil defense management program is developed in this research. This program can enhance regional public protection plan for chemical and radiological disaster, including establishment detail contingency plan. In addition, this program can contribute to damage minimization as supplying personal-customized information to officers. With this information, officers can lead rapid and efficient public evacuation. When an accident occurs, more detail information about evacuation and contingency status will be reported to the control tower. This smooth information network can improve the ability of on-field reaction. Government, Conglomerates and research associates in Korea are trying to improve safety, continuously. This program in one of those trials and can lead noticeable improvement of the public protection.

Acknowledgement

This work was supported by Man-Made Disaster Prevention Research Center under the program of NEMA (National Emergency Management Agency). This paper is a result of "Development of Chemical and Radiological Civil defence management system".

References

M. Dorasamy, M. Raman, M.Kaliannan, 2013, Knowledge management systems in support of disasters management: A two decade review, Technological Forecasting and Social Change, 80, 9, 1834-1853.
M.H. Han, E.H. Kim, W.T. Suh, W.T. Hwang, H.J. Jeong, 2012, Development of radiological dose assessment systems to support a radiological emergency preparedness in Korea, Annals of Nuclear Energy, 43, 187-191.
M. Manley, Y. Kim, 2012, Modeling emergency evacuation of individuals with disabilities (exitus): An agent-based public decision support system, Expert Systems with Applications, 39, 8300-8311.
F. Sayyady, S.D. Eksioglu, 2010, Optimizing the use of public transit system during no-notice evacuation of urban areas, Computers and Industrial Engineering, 59, 488-495.
C. Cuanquan, W. Jinhui, W. Qingsong, 2012, Time-dependent fire risk assessment for occupant evacuation in public assembly buildings, Structural Safety, 38, 22-31.

Jiří Jaromír Klemeš, Petar Sabev Varbanov and Peng Yen Liew (Editors)
Proceedings of the 24th European Symposium on Computer Aided Process Engineering – ESCAPE 24
June 15-18, 2014, Budapest, Hungary.

Forecasting of Naphtha Demand and Supply using Time Serial Data Causal Analysis

Byeonggil Lyu[a], Hweeung Kwon[a], Jinsuk Lee[b], Haesub Yoon[b], Jaehyung Jin[b], Il Moon[a*]

[a]*Department of Chemical and Biomolecular Engineering, Yonsei University, 50 Yonsei-ro, Seodaemun-gu, Seoul, 120-749, Korea*
[b]*Samsung Total Petrochemicals co., Ltd, 411-1, Dokgod Ri, Daesan Up, Seosan Si, Chung Nam, 356-711, Korea*
longs25@yonsei.ac.kr

Abstract

Naphtha is an important resource used to produce petrochemical products. Historically, petrochemical companies have been keen to the variations of naphtha prices as it has had great effects on their profits. Naphtha price is closely aligned with crude oil price. In particular, more directly, supply and demand of naphtha affect its price fluctuations. This research is focused to propose an approach for forecasting supply and demand of naphtha, with an emphasis on key affecting factors such as the margin of petrochemical companies and the use of alternative raw material. The demand of naphtha is estimated on the basis of the margin and operation rate of a petrochemical plant, while its supply is affected by operation rate of refinery. Modeling of forecasting naphtha supply/demand, based on time series method, is developed along with absolute errors derived from a statistical analysis; the model at present time is used to forecast future supply/demand over historical time series data from March 2010 to September 2012. Key set of affecting factors are identified by combined heuristic and statistical analysis and a set of equations correlating between those factors are set up. The proposed model was validated by actual data for the underlying period, which should be useful to forecast the price of naphtha

Keywords: naphtha, forecasting, demand, supply

1. Introduction

Naphtha, raw material of petrochemical plants, is an important product of crude oil distillation. Price variability of naphtha affected various aspects such as supply and demand, prices, margin of naphtha and petrochemical products, global economy and the operational rate of Oil Companies.

Several studies for forecasting naphtha have been reported. Artificial neural networks (ANN) have been employed to forecasting price. Szkuta et al. (1999) developed the System Marginal Price short-term forecasting using artificial neural networks. Pai (2005) presented a hybrid model that combines the autoregressive integrated moving average (ARIMA) and the support vector machines (SVMs). This model is evaluated that its prediction performance is better than those of the single ARIMA model and single SVMs model. Zhang (2010) conducted a research on forecasting agricultural and livestock products price using statistical approach.

Visetsripong (2008) built up a model using the Adaptive Neuro-fuzzy Inference System (ANFIS). The proposed model was claimed to be more powerful than the statistical and exponential smoothing method, particularly when the formulated model is nonlinear. Sung (2012) applied a multiple regression model to forecast naphtha crack, taking into account more than 20 factors. Yan (2013) proposed hybrid model of least squares support vector machine (LSSVM) and auto-regressive moving average with external input (ARMAX). Salehnia (2013) forecast natural gas spot price using gamma test analysis and nonlinear models; local linear regression (LLR), dynamic local linear regression (DLLR), artificial neural networks (ANN). The set of models mentioned above were reliable in forecasting future prices of products of interest. Proposed models are based on statistic methods. This study aims to forecast demand and supply of naphtha as are main factors on its price, using causal model. Operation rate and T/A (Turn Around) are mainly used as a key factor in forecasting demand and supply of naphtha. Equations used between factors in models are based on regression method. The model is based on real data ranging from March 2010 to September 2012. Predicted value of demand and supply of naphtha using this causal model is validated with its actual values.

2. Data preparation

Among a variety of factors affecting supply and demand of naphtha, the key set was identified to build a causal model: margin, capacity of a plant, T/A of plant and a naphtha substitute. Major factors for monthly data were collected from March 2010 to September 2012. Collected data is shown briefly on Table 1 and 2.

Table 1. Data for demand of naphtha

Date	Margin of naphtha ($/t)	Capacity (kt/month)	Turn Around (kt/month)	LPG usage (kt/month)
Mar-2010	296.653	5,460	723.333	0
Apr-2010	323.239	5,310	486.667	0
May-2010	302.653	5,486.667	343.333	0
		•		
		•		
		•		
Jul-2012	261.059	5,576.667	546.667	233
Aug-2012	223.173	5,576.667	350	313
Sep-2012	238.57	5,396.667	413.333	146.5

Table 2. Data for supply of naphtha

Date	Capacity (kt/month)	Turn Around (kt/month)	PX production (kt/month)
Mar-2010	3,645.036	245	763.538
Apr-2010	3,527.454	375	716.632
May-2010	3,645.036	415	643.276
		.	
		.	
		.	
Jul-2012	3,675.155	296	801.415
Aug-2012	3,675.155	337	850.524
Sep-2012	3,556.602	416	764.379

3. Demand and supply of naphtha

3.1. Demand of naphtha

The demand of naphtha is almost same as demand of petrochemical company's raw material demand. Thus, the capacity of a petrochemical plant and its rate of operation were considered as a key set of factors on its demand. Capacity of a petrochemical plant was based on Asian petrochemical plant and the rate of operation is affected by economic situation and T/A (Turn Around) again. The larger capacity petrochemical plants have, the more naphtha can be cracked at a time. Therefore, a petrochemical plant having bigger capacity has higher demand of naphtha. However, the operation rate of a plant is not always 100 %. Thus, the operation rate of a plant is the most important. The factors affecting the operation rate can be classified into economic factors (the margin of product) and non-economic factors (T/A of a plant). Petrochemical companies perform repair of their plants according to their plans of T/A. During T/A, the cracking unit needs to stop operation. Thus, the operation rate is reduced by T/A. Except the effect of T/A, the operation rate of a plant depends on market conditions as an economical factor. If the margin of petrochemical industry gets high, the inventory will be reduced, which leads to an increase of the operation rate and vice versa. Thereby, the naphtha demand can be calculated using its margin and operation rate of a plant. The margin is defined as a difference of prices of main products of petrochemical plants and naphtha. Using equation between margin and operation rate developed by linear regression method, predicted operation rate was calculated.

Additionally, the use of LPG, which is known as alternative of naphtha, affects the demand of naphtha. The product of naphtha cracking such as ethylene and propylene can be obtained through the cracking of LPG. Therefore, LPG can be used as an alternative of naphtha and the use of LPG causes to reduce demand of naphtha. The price of LPG gets to rise in winter as its demand on a heating fuel increase. However, vice versa in summer. In fact, petrochemical companies use LPG when the price of LPG gets lower than that of naphtha. Therefore, the demand of naphtha can be determined by the operation rate of a plant and usage of LPG. Based on Figure 1, calculation of Petrochem Naphtha Demand has conducted.

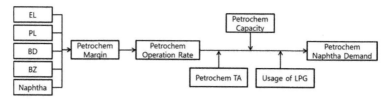

Figure 1. Causal loop of naphtha demand

3.2. Supply of naphtha

The supply of naphtha can be calculated through the production of oil company. Produced naphtha is used to produce petrochemicals, for example, para-Xylene (PX), which is also an important factor on the supply of naphtha. T/A affects oil plant's rate of operation as a non-economic factor. The rate of operation and T/A enable to calculate the supply of naphtha. However, it is hard to calculate the operation rate using its margin only as it is affected by several factors. Therefore, an average operation rate was used to forecast its supply. Production of PX is taken into account as it yields high margin than naphtha. Because of this, oil companies are unlikely to supply naphtha to petrochemical companies, instead, more inclined to produce it for themselves. Therefore, the amount of naphtha used to produce PX should be excluded from the supply of naphtha, which can thus be calculated using the relationship between operation rate of oil plants and production of PX. Based on Figure 2, calculation of Refinery Naphtha Supply has conducted.

4. Forecast result

4.1. Demand of naphtha

The demand of naphtha is predicted with a focus on margin, operation rate, T/A of petrochemical companies and usage of alternative raw material. The prediction period is taken March 2010 to September 2012 and the predicted and actual demands of naphtha are shown in Figure 3, with the prediction accuracy of 97.32 % with real value and the accuracy of directionality of 90 %. This result presents a high potential that the demand of naphtha could be predicted by an operation rate dependent on margin, T/A and usage of alternative raw material.

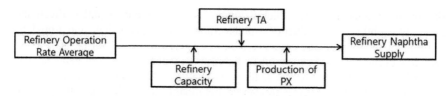

Figure 2. Causal loop of naphtha supply

4.2. Supply of naphtha

The supply of naphtha is predicted with a focus on operation rate average of an oil plant, T/A and production of alternative raw material. The prediction period is taken March 2010 to September 2012 and the predicted and actual supply of naphtha is shown in Figure 4 with the prediction accuracy of 95.35 % with real value (although prediction accuracy for the supply is slightly lower than that of its demand) and the accuracy of directionality of 63.3 %, which represents poor prediction performance than that of demand because average value of operation rates are used in case of supply prediction as too many factors involved to apply its margin.

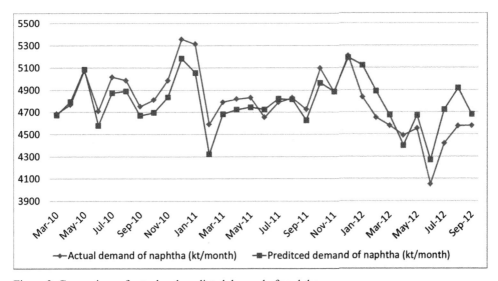

Figure 3. Comparison of actual and predicted demand of naphtha

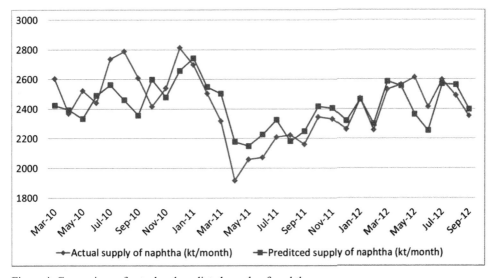

Figure 4. Comparison of actual and predicted supply of naphtha

5. Conclusion

Naphtha is a basic feedstock for petrochemical plants and the price fluctuation is most likely to have a great impact on the company profit. Thus, the predictability of the demand and supply of naphtha has been the most interest of petrochemical companies. In this study, demand and supply of naphtha was taken as a key set of a target for forecast. Applying causal model approach, the prediction accuracies of demand and supply were 97.32 % and 95.35 %, which indicates a good fit with actual trend. This study can be extended to forecast naphtha price and crack with an emphasis on global economic representative factors (e.g. unexpected economic crisis, disasters) and crude oil price and its trend.

Acknowledgement

Financial support from Samsung total co., Ltd is gratefully acknowledged.

References

A. Ghaffari, S. Zare, 2009, A novel algorithm for prediction of crude oil price variation based onsoft computing, Energy Economics, 31, 4, 531-536.

B.R. Szkuta, L.A. Sanabria, T.S. Dillon, 1999, Electricity Price Short-Term Forecasting UsingArtificial Neural Networks, IEEE Transactions on Power Systems, 14, 854-857.

C. Sung, H. Kwon, J. Lee, H. Yoon, I. Moon, 2012, Forecasting Naphtha Price Crack Using Multiple Regression Analysis, Computer Aided Chemical Engineering, 31, 145-149.

F. Gori, D. Ludovisi, P.F. Cerritelli, 2007, Forecast of oil price and consumption in the short term under three scenarios: Parabolic, linear and chaotic behavior. Energy, 32, 1291-1296.

J. Deng, P. Jirutitijaroen, 2010, Short-Term Load Forecasting Using Time Series Analysis: A Case Study for Singapore, 2010 IEEE Conference. 231-236.

N. Salehnia, M. A. Falahi, A. Seifi, M. H. M. Adeli, 2013, Forecasting natural gas spot prices with nonlinear modeling using Gamma test analysis, Journal of Natural Gas Science and Engineering, 14, 238-249.

P. Pai, C. Lin, 2005, A hybrid ARIMA and support vector mahines model in stock priceforecasting, The International Journal of Management Science, 33, 497-505.

P. Visetsripong, P. Sooraksa, P. Luenam, 2008, Naphtha's Price Forecasting using Neuro-fuzzySystem, Society of Instrument and Control Engineers Annual Conference, 659-663.

W. Zhang, H. Chen, M. Wang, 2010, A forecast model of agricultural and livestock productsprice, Mechanics and materials, 20-23, 1109-1114.

Y. Fan, Q. Liang, Y.M. Wei, 2006, A generalized pattern matching approach for multistep prediction of crude oil price. Energy Econ., 30, 889-904.

Y. Wei, Y. Wang, D. Huang, 2010, Forecasting crude oil market volatility: Further evidence using GARCH-class models, Energy Econ., 32, 1477-1484.

X.Yan, N.A. Chowdhury, 2013, Mid-term electricity market clearing price forecasting: A hybrid LSSVM and ARMAX approach, Electrical Power and Energy Systems, 53, 20-26

Jiří Jaromír Klemeš, Petar Sabev Varbanov and Peng Yen Liew (Editors)
Proceedings of the 24th European Symposium on Computer Aided Process Engineering – ESCAPE 24
June 15-18, 2014, Budapest, Hungary.

Eigenvector Analysis for the Ranking of Control Loop Importance

Simon J. Streicher, St. Elmo Wilken, Carl Sandrock*

University of Pretoria, Lynnwood Rd, Pretoria, 0002, South Africa
carl.sandrock@up.ac.za

Abstract

A method for optimizing the prioritization of base layer control loop maintenance by identifying control loops that have the greatest impact on overall plant-wide profitability is presented. The method is based on a modified form of the LoopRank algorithm originally proposed by Farenzena and Trierweiler (2009) and takes into account connectivity metric, performance measures and economical attributes. Various methods of obtaining a connectivity metric are discussed. The well-known Tennessee Eastman Plant problem is used to demonstrate the effectiveness of the method.

Keywords: prioritization, maintenance, fault detection, connectivity, causal mapping

1. Introduction

The large number of loops present on a typical industrial chemical processing plant necessitates the prioritization of control loop maintenance and optimization. Base layer control engineers and technicians often follow a "fighting today's fire" approach as no definite measure is available to identify the faulty control loops that have the highest effect on overall performance. In the proposed method connectivity, control loop performance measures and economical attributes are combined to identify control loops with the greatest influence on profitability and/or stability. This will allow more efficient use of control engineer and instrumentation specialist man hours, in turn leading to safer and more economical plant operation.

The main contribution of this paper is the integration of various known ranking, causal mapping and control loop assessment methods and algorithms into a tool that can prioritize control loop maintenance on a plant-wide or even site-wide scale.

2. General approach

In order to prioritize control loops for maintenance it is necessary to identify control loops with the largest influence which are performing the worst while having the greatest impact on profitability. A metric for the influence of a control loop on a plant-wide scale can be determined by modeling the plant as a directed graph where the nodes represent the variables and the edge connectivity is inferred from the physical and logical structure of the plant. This directed graph may be then used to prioritise control loop maintenance by ranking the relative importance of the nodes in the system using eigenvector analysis (see Section 3). If the actual connectivity is not available, it may be possible to infer it from routine plant data or through direct testing. Methods of determining causality between variables on a plant-wide scale have been an active research topic with various papers being published in literature over the past few years (see Section 4).

Performance and profitability triage metrics are associated with each control loop. As many industrial operations already employ performance monitoring software the aim is to integrate the connectivity with predetermined performance scores. Depending on the amount of information available the profitability metric can be either categorical or numerical.

Alternative methods for calculating an interaction index by employing canonical correlation and IAE or ISE have been presented by Rahman and Choudhury (2011).

A good ranking algorithm will identify under-performing control loops and rank them in such an order that the control loop which is affecting the most important variables in the system will be given higher priority than a control loop which may be under-performing to a greater extent but affecting less important variables.

3. Ranking algorithm

3.1. Original LoopRank algorithm
A modified form of the Google PageRank algorithm (Bryan and Leise, 2008) is used to rank control loops based on their connectivity, interaction and importance scores (weights). This concept has been introduced by Farenzena and Trierweiler (2009) who dubbed the algorithm LoopRank when applied to the ranking of control loops.

In order to apply the method a directed graph defining the interactions between process variables is needed. For a review of directed graphs, see Narsingh (1974). A convenient method for representing a binary directed graph is an adjacency matrix as defined in Eq.(1).

$$\mathbf{A}_{ij} = \begin{cases} 1 & \text{If } v_j \text{ has an edge directed towards } v_i \\ 0 & \text{Otherwise} \end{cases} \tag{1}$$

The importance of a node x_k depends on the importance of the nodes pointing towards x_k as displayed in Eq.(2).

$$x_k = \sum_{j \in \mathbf{L}_k} e_j x_j \tag{2}$$

In Eq.(2) $\mathbf{L}_k$ is the set of nodes which have an incident edge to node x_k and the edge weight e_j ensures that node x_j contributes importance to node x_k in proportion to the extent to which it affects node x_k. If this system is expressed in matrix form the ranking problem reduces to the standard eigenvector problem of Eq.(3).

$$\mathbf{Ax} = \mathbf{x} \tag{3}$$

The **A** matrix is a normalized adjacency matrix such that each column sums to unity. The importance scores of the nodes are the elements of the normalized eigenvector corresponding to the eigenvalue of one in Eq.(3).

3.2. Shortcomings addressed by modifications previously published
If the graph is disconnected non-unique rankings may occur as the eigenvector for a disconnected graph is k-dimensional (where k is the number of components) leading to

ambiguity as to which basis eigenvector should be used to interpret importance. A remedy for this situation is to modify the normalized adjacency matrix **A** by adding a **S** matrix which is a normalized adjacency matrix for a fully connected system of the same size as the system being ranked. The modification is expressed in Eq.(4). The resulting **M** matrix is used in the eigenvector calculations (Bryan and Leise, 2008).

$$\mathbf{M} = (1-m)\mathbf{A} + m\mathbf{S} \text{ where } m \in (0,1] \tag{4}$$

If dangling nodes (nodes that do not point to any other nodes) are present, an adjacency matrix which is column-substochastic is generated. The maximum eigenvalue will then be less than or equal to unity. In this case an appropriate ranking can still be achieved by using the largest positive (Perron) eigenvalue and accompanying eigenvector to calculate the importance scores (Bryan and Leise, 2008).

3.3. Shortcomings addressed by new proposed modifications
Some shortcomings remain when the above mentioned ranking algorithm is applied to a chemical plant structure.

3.3.1. Input importance
Some process inputs may be more important to downstream processes than others. However, inputs to the plant serve as importance sources and hence their importance cannot be boosted by incident nodes. The importance of nodes can be modified to incorporate a contribution of the importance score of each variable generated when the connectivity of the plant is reversed as indicated in Eq.(5) – this effectively increases the importance of inputs which have a greater effect on downstream processes.

$$x_i = (1-q)x_i^{\text{forward}} + (q)x_i^{\text{backward}} \text{ where } q \in [0,1] \tag{5}$$

3.3.2. Nodes with one outward edge only
The normalization of the **M** matrix will cause a loss of scale if any node with only one outward edge is present in the directed graph. This problem is not present if the node in question has more than one outwards directed edge as the edge weightings are automatically scaled in the normalization routine. An additional modification is therefore proposed whereby all nodes with a single outward directed edge are scaled by adding a dummy node and edge. The weight of the dummy edge constitutes a constant which brings the value of the other edge into perspective. The edge weight should typically be selected to be some small value. The dummy variables should be ignored when interpreting the results.

Adding dummy variables will result in the sum of all non-dummy variable nodes' importance scores not summing to unity. However, as the interest is not in the absolute importance of each node – which is in any event not what the eigenvector analysis calculates – but only in the relative importance which is preserved this is not an issue.

3.4. Edge weightings
In the Google PageRank algorithm the value of an edge between nodes on a directed graph is considered to be a binary state. In order to refine the sensitivity by which control loops with the greatest sphere of influence can be isolated it is desired to assign some weight instead. These weights can be derived from the causality measures discussed in Section 4.

4. Methods for determining causality

As discussed in Section 3 the ranking algorithm requires a suitable connectivity matrix to be identified. Setting up this matrix involves 1) determining the causal connections between process variables and 2) assigning weights and importance scores to the connections between process variables as well as the variables themselves.

The connectivity between process variables can be determined in at least two different ways: 1) defining connections by making use of known physical and logical connectivity information and 2) determining causality using data-driven methods. Knowledge-based methods for determining causality are generally limited to generating a binary adjacency matrix and are commonly used in combination with data-driven techniques. If knowledge-based methods are combined with data driven methods the main contribution of the knowledge-based methods will be to ensure that the network structure is correct while the data driven methods can be used to calculate appropriate weights for the connections.

Knowledge-based methods seek to determine causal connections by employing information on physical and logical connections coupled with reasoning algorithms. Yim et al. (2006) reported on the development of a software package combining plant topology information captured using packages compatible with the Computer Aided Engineering Exchange (CAEX) format and a reasoning engine written in Prolog to generate a signed directed graph (SDG) of the network of tags involved. The SDG is then augmented by the use of a plant disturbance analyser to produce an effective hybrid approach for generating the required connectivity matrix.

In data-driven methods historical data is analysed using various statistical methods in order to identify probable causal relationships. Methods reported in literature include partial correlation (Farenzena and Trierweiler, 2009), cross correlation time delay estimation (Bauer and Thornhill, 2008), nearest neighbours (Bauer, 2005) as well as the relatively new concept of transfer entropy first introduced by Schreiber (2000) and applied by Bauer et al. (2007). The significance levels are compared to threshold values obtained by analysing surrogate random time series data and selecting a required minimum deviation, usually six sigma (Bauer, 2005).

The transfer entropy method has been shown to be the most robust compared to the cross-correlation and nearest neighbour methods and is also useful in the absence of noticeable time delays between variables (Bauer, 2005). Bauer (2005) proposed a modified transfer entropy calculation that allows for estimating the dead time. Shu and Zhao (2013) proposed an additional modification to this method that has been shown to be more accurate and also reported how the obtained time delays can be used to eliminate redundant connections.

5. Example

The proposed method for the ranking of base layer control loop importance is demonstrated using the well-known Tennessee Eastman (TE) plant challenge problem (Downs and Vogel, 1993). A model incorporating a decentralised control scheme proposed by Ricker (1996) and available in the TEMEX archive (Ricker, 2005) was used to generate results. The TE plant was operated in Mode 1 (base case) as defined by Downs and Vogel (1993). Process knowledge was used to generate a binary adjacency matrix and edge weights were determined using partial correlation. The values of m and q in Eqs.(4) and (5) were set at 0.15 and 0.35.

Importance scores were calculated using time series data recorded during the occurrence of disturbances and set point step changes. The results for a random variation disturbance in the reactor cooling water (CW) inlet temperature as well as a 10 % downwards step change in the reactor pressure set point are presented in Table 1.

In both cases, the correlations between pressure nodes were very strong compared to other process measurements, concealing smaller connections. During the analysis of the reactor CW temperature variation, the strong correlations that exist in the gas pressure system were supressed by eliminating two edges from the process digraph. In practice this could be justified if it was known that these edges did not contribute to the disturbance being investigated.

Due to the fact that certain variables will typically always have large importance scores it may be more useful to look at deviations of importance scores over time to identify the effects of new faults on control loop performance. Comparison of current importance scores to benchmark values or long time averages will allow the extent of deviation to be quantified. This remains to be investigated.

Table 1. Variable importance ranking for different scenarios

Rank	Reactor CW inlet temperature variation		Reactor pressure setpoint step change	
1	Reactor temperature	0.0899	Reactor pressure	0.3099
2	Reactor CW flow (MV)	0.0839	Stripper pressure	0.2377
3	Stripper temperature	0.0757	Product separator pressure	0.2002
4	Product separator temperature	0.0560	B mol% in reactor feed	0.0163
5	E feed flow (MV)	0.0465	B mol% in purge	0.0116
6	G mol% in product stream	0.0369	Stripper temperature	0.0095
7	D feed flow (MV)	0.0365	E feed flow (MV)	0.0093
8	Purge rate	0.0286	A mol% in reactor	0.0090
9	Condenser CW flow (MV)	0.0284	A feed flow	0.0086
10	A feed flow	0.0284	Stripper underflow (MV)	0.0081

6. Future work

The application of other eigenvector ranking methods, mostly originating from the field of computer science, to the ranking of control loops in a chemical plant will be investigated. Two promising methods include semi-supervised ranking of graphs with rich metadata (Gao et al., 2010) and the use of weighted inter-cluster edge rankings for clustered graphs (Padmanabhan et al., 2010).

To the end of developing a tool that is practically useful in industry, various case studies on industrial data are planned. Minimizing the effort required to implement and maintain the system will be key for its practical usage by already overburdened control personnel.

7. Conclusions

A method for ranking base layer control loop maintenance on a plant-wide scale is presented. The method makes use of a modified LoopRank algorithm and requires a connectivity metric to be calculated. The plant-wide effects of selected disturbances in the Tennessee Eastman challenge problem were successfully identified.

References

M. Bauer, 2005, Data-driven methods for process analysis, PhD Thesis, Imperial College London, London, UK.

M. Bauer, J.W. Cox, M.H. Caveness, J.J. Downs, N.F. Thornhill, 2007, Finding the direction of disturbance propagation in a chemical process using transfer entropy, IEEE Transactions on Control Systems Technology, 15, 1, 12-21.

M. Bauer, N.F. Thornhill, 2008, A practical method for identifying the propagation path of plant-wide disturbances, Journal of Process Control, 18, 707-719.

K. Bryan, T. Leise, 2008, The $25,000,000,000 eigenvector: The linear algebra behind Google, Rose-Hulman Institute of Technology, Terre Haute, Indiana, United States of America.

J.J. Downs, E.F. Vogel, 1993, A plant-wide industrial process control problem, Computers and Chemical Engineering, 17, 3, 245-255.

M. Farenzena, J.O. Trierweiler, 2009, LoopRank: A novel tool to evaluate loop connectivity, Proceedings of ADCHEM-2009, 1023-1028.

B. Gao, T. Liu, W. Wei, T. Wang, H. Li, 2010, Semi-supervised ranking on a very large graph with rich metadata, Microsoft Research Asia, Beijing, China.

D. Narsingh, 1974, Graph theory with applications to engineering and computer science, Prentice-Hall, New Jersey, United States of America.

D. Padmanabhan, P. Desikan, J. Strivastava, K. Riaz, 2010, WICER: A weighted inter-cluster edge ranking for clustered graphs, University of Minnesota, Minneapolis, United States of America.

A. Rahman, M.A.A.S Choudhury, 2011, Detection of control loop interactions and prioritization of control loop maintenance, Control Engineering Practice, 19, 7, 723-731.

N.L. Ricker, 1996, Decentralized control of the Tennessee Eastman challenge process, Journal or Process Control, 6, 4, 205-221.

N.L. Ricker, 2005, Tennessee Eastman Challenge Archive, <depts.washington.edu/control/LARRY/TE/download.html> accessed on 15/11/2013.

T. Schreiber, 2000, Measuring information tranfer, Physical Review Letters, 85, 2, 461-464.

Y. Shy, J. Zhao, 2012, Data-driven causal interference based on a modified transfer entropy, Computer Aided Chemical Engineering, 31, 156-1260.

S.Y. Yim, H.G. Ananthakumar, L. Benabbas, A. Horch, R. Drath, N.F. Thornhill, 2006, Using process topology in plant-wide control loop performance assessment, Computers and Chemical Engineering, 31, 86-99.

Jiří Jaromír Klemeš, Petar Sabev Varbanov and Peng Yen Liew (Editors)
Proceedings of the 24th European Symposium on Computer Aided Process Engineering – ESCAPE 24
June 15-18, 2014, Budapest, Hungary.

Towards a Re-Usable Ontology for Waste Processing

Nikolaos Trokanas*, Franjo Cecelja, Tara Raafat

PRISE Group, Chemical & Process Systems Engineering, University of Surrey, Guildofrd, UK
n.trokanas@surrey.ac.uk

Abstract

The potential of ontologies and knowledge modeling in process systems engineering has been realised and researched, efforts were directed to create semantic models representing the process industry domain. In this paper we present a re-usable ontology that consists of two main classification modules: i) Waste and ii) Processing Technology. The ontology has been developed, validated and used for processing of waste within the framework of Industrial Symbiosis. It supports a web platform that enables Industrial Symbiosis practice. The ontology is used for collecting information, user registration and semantic input output matching.

Keywords: Waste Processing, Ontology, Knowledge Modelling, Semantics.

1. Introduction

The potential of ontologies and knowledge modeling in process systems engineering has been realized and researched, efforts were directed to create semantic models representing the process industry domain (Muñoz et al., 2013). Also, ontologies have been developed to represent the domain of process engineering (Morbach et al., 2007), industrial standards (Batres et al., 2007) and processes in general (Hai et al. 2009). Nonetheless, no ontology has been proposed so far to support the re-use of waste and hence to support waste processing.

In this paper we present a re-usable ontology that has been developed, validated and used for processing of waste within the framework of Industrial Symbiosis. It consists of two main representation modules: i) resource (waste and other materials) and ii) processing technology. The process relevant associations between the two classifications are established by respective object properties which define the inputs and outputs of the processing technologies.

2. Ontologies and Knowledge Modelling

Many definitions exist for ontologies. Originating from philosophy, meaning the explanation of being, today it is used in knowledge engineering. The most common and cited definition, coming from Gruber (1993), defines ontology as an explicit specification of a shared conceptualisation. In practical terms, ontology is a group of terms that describe a domain, organised in a hierarchical structure in sets sharing common properties. Sets are defined by links to data values (data type properties) and properties between sets (object properties). The representation of the domain is complete with the instantiation of the ontology with specific elements of the domain. In terms of ontological engineering, the ontology consists of i) classes, ii) relations, iii) restrictions and iv) instances.

3. The Ontology

3.1. Ontology Engineering Methodology

No specific single methodology was followed for the development of the ontology. Instead, a combination of steps of existing methodologies was employed in a middle-out approach. Firstly, the domain and scope are defined. The proposed ontology aims in representing the domain of waste processing and Industrial Symbiosis (IS). Therefore, in its design it accurately represents different types of waste, processing technologies and industries. In addition it facilitates the capture of information about all of these concepts.

Secondly, important terms are identified and classified. Several existing classifications have been used for term identification. These include the European Waste Catalogue (EWC) and Central Product Classification (CPC). The greater part of the ontology has been custom developed from other sources such as literature, industry information extracted from industries and existing databases and expert knowledge. All identified, extracted and created terms were then organised in a hierarchy consisting of four main levels of abstraction.

Finally, properties and restrictions are defined. All concepts are characterised in terms of their chemical, physical, economic, environmental and operational properties. Properties are also organised in a hierarchy. Restrictions are a core element of the ontology as they enable practical use of the ontology in specific applications.

3.2. Metrics

The ontology consists of more than 2,000 concepts, 80 properties and 600 restrictions. Instances are formed from user registrations.

3.3. Structure

The ontology consists of four levels of abstraction (Figure 1): i) meta-level, ii) top-level, iii) domain level and iv) application specific level.

The domain level is re-usable while other levels are defined for the application. The meta-level is used to allow sharing and it defines very generally the entities of the ontology. The top-level generally defines the domain of application, therefore providing a better understanding of the use of the ontology and its contents. The domain level represents the waste processing domain based on the principle of Industrial Symbiosis. This includes knowledge about different types of waste, materials, processing technologies and their properties. Finally, the application specific level is the instantiation level where the specific entities of the domain are created.

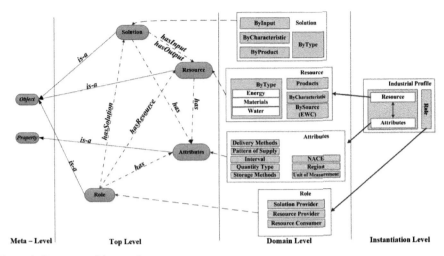

Figure 1. Structure of the ontology

3.4. Classes

There are four main ontology modules in the domain level.

3.4.1. Resources

It represents knowledge about waste, materials and products. It is divided into four sub-modules (Waste, Products, By-Characteristic, and By-Type – representing materials) which are interlinked using object properties. All sub-modules have links to the By-Type sub-module (Figure 2) which represents materials classified by their type (Metals, Plastics etc.) and serves as a reference for comparison. Waste sub-module was developed following the structure of EWC and EWC STAT, two European catalogues for waste. The main link between waste and material is the hasComposite property. It is used to define composition of waste enabling the identification of waste processing opportunities based on substitute or similar materials. Products sub-module is based on a simplified version of CPC. The main link between products and materials is the hasComposite property. The characteristics sub-module contains concepts that are reclassified based on their characteristics e.g. biodegradability. By-Type (materials) sub-module has been designed to intrinsically invoke similarity for classes that are close to each other in the ontology structure unless otherwise stated e.g. corn stover and straw are both modelled under lignocelluloses, in the case where one of them is requested the other is considered similar and used as a suggestion. By Type sub-module is used as the common reference for all other sub-modules.

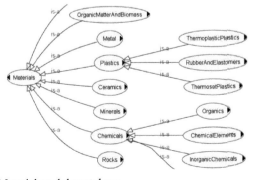

Figure 2. Excerpt of Material module ontology.

3.4.2. Solutions

The solution module represents the processing and enabling technologies (Raafat et al. 2013). Modeling of solutions follows the structure of resources. They are modeled in four sub-modules based on their Inputs, Characteristics, Industry and Type (Mechanical, Thermochemical etc.). All solutions are linked to the materials sub-module through properties that define their inputs and outputs (canProcess, hasProduct).

3.4.3. Attributes

This module contains all the peripheral information that describes and defines the concepts of the ontology. This includes information imported from existing ontologies such as geographic locations ontology (geo:lat, geo:lon) and units of measurement. It also includes custom made information such as the physical form of materials (Quantity Type).

3.4.4. Role

This module represents the industries that participate in industrial symbiosis and the role they assume in potential synergies. Participants can assume one of three roles – ResourceProducer – when they have a resource to offer, ResourceConsumer – when they need a resource and SolutionProvider – when the have a solution (processing or enabling technology).

3.5. Properties

Object properties (Table 1) are used to provide links between concepts of the ontology. They are used to model mainly qualitative information such as the composition of waste and possible uses for it. This enhances the process of comparison between concepts, therefore ameliorate decision making process and also increase the potential opportunities that can be identified. E.g. Modelled information about known uses of waste (hasApplicationIn) is used to provide more suggestions for valorisation when a participant has this type of waste available.

Data type properties are used to model mainly quantitative information such as the quantity of waste and the level of hazardousness.

3.6. Restrictions

In ontology engineering, restrictions are used to add high level of detail. In practical terms, restrictions are used to define links between lower level concepts (Figure 3), restrict the possible values of properties for different concepts and to model specific values on properties for different concepts.

3.7. Annotations

Annotations of concepts and properties have several uses in the ontology. Label annotations are used to provide explicit descriptions of concepts and properties. Other custom annotations are used to specify other application related information such as the importance of properties in the decision making process and synonyms. Annotations also allow the modelling of information in more than one natural language. Currently the ontology is modelled in English and Greek.

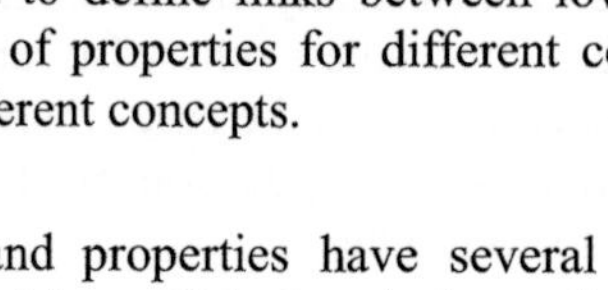

⊜ hasDisposalCost **has** 43
⊜ hasEmbodiedCarbon **has** 1350
⊜ hasFeedstockPrice **has** 1000
⊜ hasResourcePrice **has** 845

Figure 3. Example restrictions

Table 1. Key Properties

Relationship	Description
geo:location	Provides a namespace for representing **lat**(itude), **long**(itude), using WGS84 as a reference datum.
hasResource	Link between a resource provider and the type of resource they have available.
hasTechnology	Link between a solution provider and the type of solution they have available.
hasPatternOfSupply	Links resources to the PatternOfSupply attribute concept. The concept is about the pattern of the demand or availability (Continuous, Batch).
hasApplicationIn	Link between resources and industry sectors for the integration of tacit knowledge about the use of resources in different industries.
hasQuantityType	Links resources to the QuantityType attribute concept. The concept is about the physical form of the resource (Solid, Liquid etc.).
hasUnitOfMeasurement	Links resources and solutions to the UnitOfMeasurement attribute concept.
hasComposite	Relation used to provide information about the composition of products and waste types.
hasInput	Relation used to link solutions to their inputs.
canProcess	Relation used to link solutions to their main inputs.
needsWater	Relation used to link solutions to their water inputs.
needsEnergy	Relation used to link solutions to their energy inputs.
hasOutput	Relation used to link solutions to their outputs.
hasProduct	Relation used to link solutions to their products.

4. Implementation

The ontology has been implemented in the eSymbiosis web service that facilitates and automates the process of Industrial Symbiosis. The purpose of the ontology in this application is threefold.

4.1. Data Acquisition

During the data acquisition process, the ontology is used to navigate the user while collecting information using data type properties. Custom labels are used to address the user with specific information about concepts and properties.

Figure 4. Collecting Information

4.2. Common Vocabulary

The ontology provides a standardised vocabulary for waste and processing technologies, two concepts characterised by heterogeneity. It also facilitates the use of synonyms.

4.3. Support Identification of Opportunities

The materials module of the ontology is used as the reference during the process that identifies potential symbiotic relations. The structure of the ontology is used to identify relations and similarities between concepts and calculate a relevance score that represents the level of agreement between what a participant is looking for and what is available

4.4. Indication of Use

In brief, when a user enters the web service, the ontology is used to provide the navigation path while acquiring data that is used for the creation of a unique user profile. The profile comprises a separate ontology. After all available information has been collected; the user profile is compared (matched) against existing user profiles in an effort to identify opportunities for waste processing through the establishment of symbiotic synergies.

5. Conclusions

The presented ontology represents the domain of waste processing with a focus on Industrial Symbiosis practice. It has been implemented, tested and verified through a web platform that enables IS practice in Viotia, Greece. The ontology has been successfully used to support the web platform. It supports the registration process by collecting information form the user and also navigating the user through its structure. It provides a common vocabulary for a field that is defined by heterogeneity and it also supports the process of identifying potential options for symbiotic synergies.

Acknowledgment

This work has been partly funded by the LIFE+ initiative (LIFE 09 ENV/GR/000300) which authors acknowledge.

References

R. Batres, M. West, D. Leal, D. Price, Y. Naka, 2005, An upper ontology based on ISO 15926, Computer Aided Chemical Engineering, 20, 1543-1548.

T.R. Gruber, 1995, Toward principles for the design of ontologies used for knowledge sharing?, International Journal of Human-computer Studies,43, 5, 907-928.

R. Hai, M. Theißen, W. Marquardt, 2009, An Integrated Ontology for Operational Processes, Computer Aided Chemical Engineering, 26, 1087-1091.

J. Morbach, A. Yang, W. Marquardt, 2007, Onto CAPE—A large-scale ontology for chemical process engineering, Engineering Applications of Artificial Intelligence, 20, 2, 147-161.

E. Muñoz, E. Capón-García, J. Miguel Laínez, A. Espuña, L. Puigjaner, 2013, Integration of enterprise levels based on an ontological framework, Chemical Engineering Research and Design, 91, 8, 1542-1556.

T. Raafat, N. Trokanas, F. Cecelja, X. Bimi, 2013, An ontological approach towards enabling processing technologies participation in industrial symbiosis, Computers and Chemical Engineering, 59, 33-46.

N. Trokanas, T. Raafat, F. Cecelja, A. Kokossis, A. Yang, 2012, Semantic Formalism for Waste and Processing Technology Classifications Using Ontology Models, Computer Aided Chemical Engineering, 30, 167-171.

N. Trokanas, T. Raafat, F. Cecelja, A. Kokossis, 2013, OFIS – Ontological Framework for Industrial Symbiosis, Computer Aided Chemical Engineering, 32, 523-528.

Jiří Jaromír Klemeš, Petar Sabev Varbanov and Peng Yen Liew (Editors)
Proceedings of the 24th European Symposium on Computer Aided Process Engineering – ESCAPE 24
June 15-18, 2014, Budapest, Hungary.

Optimising Environmental Performance of Symbiotic Networks Using Semantics

Nikolaos Trokanas*, Franjo Cecelja, Mingyen Yu, Tara Raafat

PRISE Group, Chemical & Process Engineering, University of Surrey, Guildford, UK
n.trokanas@surrey.ac.uk

Abstract

Industrial Symbiosis (IS) is an ecological approach aiming to promote waste valorization opportunities. To date, efforts related to IS process rely on data generated in the aftermath of IS network formation. We propose the integration of the process of screening of IS network options and optimisation of respective environmental performance with the use of semantics.

Keywords: Industrial Symbiosis, Optimisation, Environmental, Metrics.

1. Introduction

Industrial Symbiosis (IS) is an innovative approach that brings together companies from different sectors in an effort to promote the valorisation of waste, improvement of resource efficiency and reduction of environmental impact. IS also aims in delivering benefits to all participating parties. Several efforts (Martin et al., 2012; Mattila et al., 2010) have been made to identify and quantify these benefits but mostly based on data generated in the aftermath of the formation of symbiotic networks. Since, the process of identifying of symbiotic networks has been automated and enhanced with the use of semantics (Raafat et al., 2013). Hence in this paper we propose the integration of IS network identification and optimisation of its environmental performance which will allow not only for the pre-assessment of the impact of the symbiotic network but also for providing optimised solutions given the custom user requirements.

2. Industrial Symbiosis

Industrial Symbiosis (IS) was developed from the concept of Industrial Ecology. It aims in creating symbiotic networks to process waste by sharing of facilities, water and energy. Ultimately, the establishment of symbiotic synergies produces environmental, social and economic benefits for all parties involved as well as local communities. Current practice of identifying synergies takes place in the form of manual workshops that require mediation by trained practitioners, hence making the process time consuming and expensive. Also, the benefits of symbiotic synergies are assessed from user feedback and after synergies have been established. Predicting benefits beforehand is still a challenge.

3. IS Metrics

The metrics currently in use for the evaluation of the performance of IS synergies fall into three categories (Trokanas et al., 2013a): i) environmental, ii) economic and iii) social. Focus of this work is on environmental benefits of IS.More specifically they include: i) Landfill Diversion Savings, ii) Embodied Carbon Impact, iii) Transportation Impact and iv) Virgin Materials Saved.

Numerous research efforts have been made to quantify environmental impact and benefits, which include techniques such as life cycle analysis (LCA) (Mattila et al., 2010) and flow analysis (Martin et al., 2013).Still, a gap in proposed frameworks and methods has been identified (van Berkel, 2010). More precisely, the proposed techniques focus on the comparison of benefits before and after a symbiotic synergy has been established which inevitably requires intensive monitoring by practitioners and reporting from participants. In this paper, we propose a method that employs semantic technologies and enables the pre-assessment and optimisation of the environmental output of screened symbiotic synergies. To achieve that, five different environmental indicators are calculated and hence converted into monetary metrics for comparison and aggregation.

3.1. Landfill Diversion Savings

This metric quantifies re-use of waste instead of landfilling it. It uses the quantity of resource exchanged between participants i and j,$Q_{i,j}$, the disposal cost for the resource $DC_{i,j}$ and the landfill tax LT.

$$LDS = \sum_{i,j}^{Resource} Q_{i,j} * (DC_{i,j} + LT) \tag{1}$$

3.2. Embodied Carbon Impact

This metric accounts for the embodied carbon of the resource exchanged between participants i and j. Re-used and recycled materials have lower embodied carbon, hence lower impact. It uses quantities $Q_{i,j}$ of exchanged resources, embodied carbon value of the resources $EC_{i,j}$ and the credit price of carbon dioxide CO_2^P as formed by the carbon trading scheme:

$$ECI = \sum_{i,j}^{Resource} (Q_{i,j} * EC_{i,j} * CO_2^P) \tag{2}$$

3.3. Transportation Impact

Transportation of resources between participants also affects the environmental performance of a synergy. This metric is calculated from the quantities $Q_{i,j}$ of the exchanged resources, the factor $TF_{i,j}$ characterizing the emission of particular mode of transportation, the distance between IS participants$i$ and j and the credit price of carbon dioxide CO_2^P.

$$TI = \sum_{i,j}^{Synergy} (Q_{i,j} * TF_{i,j} * distance_{i,j} * CO_2^P) \tag{3}$$

3.4. Virgin Materials Savings

This metric quantifies replacement of virgin materials by waste. For that, it uses capacities $C_{i,j}$ between participants i and j, price of the resource as a raw material $FP_{i,j}$ and price as a recyclate $RP_{i,j}$.

$$VMS = \sum_{i,j}^{Synergy} C_{i,j} * (FP_{i,j} - RP_{i,j}) \tag{4}$$

4. Identifying and Optimising Synergies

4.1. Identifying Synergies

Synergies are identified by semantic matching of user profiles, the process supported by the domain ontology and otherwise performed by practitioners (Raafat et al., 2012a). The domain ontology (Figure 1) represents the domain of IS (Trokanas et al., 2012), which includes the resources (waste, material, and energy), processing technologies, participants and other necessary peripheral information, such as geographic location, physical form and unit of measurement. The domain ontology is used for acquisition of user profile data, i.e. type of resource/solution available, location, availability period, pattern of supply, quantity, for calculation of similarity between user profiles and also for modelling of information used for performance evaluation and optimisation.

More precisely, each participant is represented as the instance of the domain ontology and then described by a separate ontology, the Semantic Web Service Ontology modelled in OWL-S (Martin et al., 2004) for more elaborated matching, as demonstrated in Figure 2 (Raafat et al., 2012b).

As such, the process of semantic matching benefits from currently available tacit knowledge embedded in the domain ontology and captured explicit knowledge on participants and enables evaluation of semantic relevance scores ($Similarity_{i,j}$) between participants i and j (Trokanas et al., 2013b). For this, the matching process uses

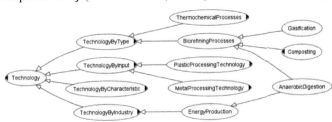

Figure 1. Excerpt of the domain ontology

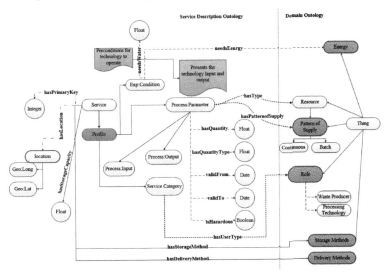

Figure 2. Semantic Web Service Ontology

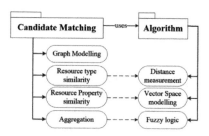

Figure 3. Structure of the Semantic Matching Algorithm

a combination of vector similarity and distance measurement techniques, the scores of which are normalised for informed comparison (Figure 3). After semantic relevance scores have been calculated the network is being optimised in terms of its environmental performance.

4.2. Optimising Synergies

The objective function, representing the environmental benefits of the symbiotic networks, of the optimisation model is derived from the aggregation of the metrics given by Eqs. (1) – (4) as:

$$ENVI = LDS - ECI - TI + VMS \tag{5}$$

Linear programming is employed to maximise the environmental benefits of the synergy. The constraints of the optimisation problem stem in availability and demand of resources. It is worth noting that the demand or availability of the participant that initiates a request must be satisfied. Other participants of the network act as facilitators.

4.3. Final Aggregation

After the optimisation of the environmental performance, ENVI is normalised by observing Eq. (6) and the optimised results are aggregated with the semantic results and presented to the user as a single score.

$$ENVI_{i,j}^{normalised} = \frac{ENVI_{i,j} - ENVI_{min}}{ENVI_{max} - ENVI_{min}} \tag{6}$$

The normalised ENVI score is aggregated with similarity scores between participants, using weighting factors that have been established through practice:

$$Final\ Aggregated\ Score_{i,j} = (70\% * Similarity_{i,j} + 30\% * ENVI_{i,j}^{normalised}) \tag{7}$$

The similarity score required for this calculation is calculated as a percentage of the available quantities:

$$Similarity_{optimised\ network} = \sum_{i,j}^{synergy} Similarity_{i,j} * \frac{Q_{i,j}^{optimised}}{Q_{i,j}} * 100\% \tag{8}$$

5. Case Study

A number of users registered with the system have provided information as in Table 1. The request to form symbiotic network is initiated by User 9 who needs 810 kg of Polypropylene. There are two other sources of Polypropylene, User 2 and User 5. Following the backward chaining method (Raafat et al, 2013) User 2, a solution provider, matches against User 6 and User 1 who have available Propylene. Based on this information, the semantic relevance scores are shown in Table 2. After all the

Table 1. Registration Details

ID	User Type	Resource Output	Resource Input	Output Quantity	Lat	Lon	Valid from	Valid to	Pattern of Supply
6	RP	Propylene	-	550	22.8286	38.5188	01/01/2013	01/01/2015	b
1	RP	Propylene	-	850	22.8923	38.4459	01/03/2013	01/03/2014	b
9	RC	-	Poly-propylene	810	22.9165	38.6466	01/06/2013	01/06/2015	c
2	SP	Polypropy-lene	Propylene	830	22.8563	38.5251	01/06/2013	01/01/2015	b
5	RP	PP Scrap Bags	-	600	22.9380	38.4323	10/09/2013	01/07/2014	c

potential synergies have been identified the respective environmental performances are calculated (Table 2) and used as a benchmark.

In the following step the optimisation process is employed to maximise the environmental performance of the symbiotic network. One more advantage of the employment of optimisation is that it enables decomposition of the quantities. The objective function (Eq. 5), representing environmental benefits, is maximised, given Eqs. (1–4). The optimised results are presented in the map presented in Figure 4. The optimised quantities are given in Table 3, these quantities result in optimised $ENVI =$ 873,662.

Observing Eq.(6), the optimised ENVI and the results in Table 3, all results are normalised as shown in Table 4. After normalisation, the similarity and normalised ENVI scores are aggregated into a single metric observing Eq.(7). Finally, the similarity score for the optimised network is calculated from Eq.(8).

The optimised network which has the best environmental performance is the most relevant. Other potential synergies follow with lower aggregated scores.

Table 2. Semantic Matching Results

Synergy	Score	ENVI
5-9	0.9017	782,172
1-2-9	0.8351	294,393
6-2-9	0.8297	129,908

Table 3. Optimised Quantities

Synergy	Quantity
5-9	600
1-2	0
6-2	280
2-9	210

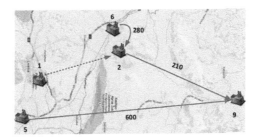

Figure 4. Optimised network results

Table 4. Normalised Results and Aggregated Results

Synergy	ENVI	Similarity	Norm ENVI	Aggregated Scores
5-9	782,172	0.9017	0.8770	0.8844
1-2-9	294,393	0.8351	0.2212	0.4053
6-2-9	129,908	0.8297	0.0000	0.2489
Optimised Network	873,662	0.88298	1.0000	0.9648

6. Conclusions

The presented approach enables the pre-assessment of IS network. It also allows the optimisation of environmental output of IS networks. For that, it employs semantic technologies that also automate IS practice. Currently, the presented method takes into account only environmental benefits. This work can serve as a framework for further development that will include other aspects of industrial symbiosis such as economic and social benefits.

References

D. Martin, 2004, OWL-S: Semantic Markup for Web Services. <www.w3.org/Submission/OWL-S>, accessed on 12/11/2013.

M. Martin, N. Svensson, M. Eklund,2012, Who gets the benefits? An approach for assessing the environmental performance of industrial symbiosis. In Greening of Industry Network: Support your future today! Turning environmental challenges into business opportunities.

T.J. Mattila, S. Pakarinen, L. Sokka, 2010, Quantifying the Total Environmental Impacts of an Industrial Symbiosis-a Comparison of Process-, Hybrid and Input– Output Life Cycle Assessment, Environmental Science and Technology, 44, 11, 4309-4314.

T. Raafat, N. Trokanas, F. Cecelja, X. Bimi, 2013, An ontological approach towards enabling processing technologies participation in industrial symbiosis, Computers & Chemical Engineering, 59, 33-46

T. Raafat, F. Cecelja, A. Yang, N.Trokanas, 2012a, Semantic Support for Industrial Symbiosis Process, Computer Aided Chemical Engineering, 30, 452-456

T. Raafat, N. Trokanas, F. Cecelja, A. Kokossis, A. Yang, 2012b, Semantically-enabled Formalisation to Support and Automate the Application of Industrial Symbiosis, Computer Aided Chemical Engineering, 31, 1055-1059

N. Trokanas, T. Raafat, F. Cecelja, A. Kokossis, A. Yang,2012, Semantic Formalism for Waste and Processing Technology Classifications Using Ontology Models, Computer Aided Chemical Engineering, 30, 167-171

N. Trokanas, F. Cecelja, T. Raafat, 2013a, Semantic Approach for Pre-assessment of environmental indicators in Industrial Symbiosis, Journal of Cleaner Production, DOI: 10.1016/j.jclepro.2013.12.046.

N. Trokanas, T. Raafat, F. Cecelja, A. Kokossis, 2013b, OFIS – Ontological Framework for Industrial Symbiosis, Computer Aided Chemical Engineering, 32, 523-528

R.Van Berkel, 2010, Quantifying sustainability benefits of industrial symbioses, Journal of Industrial Ecology, 14, 3, 371-373.

Jiří Jaromír Klemeš, Petar Sabev Varbanov and Peng Yen Liew (Editors)
Proceedings of the 24th European Symposium on Computer Aided Process Engineering – ESCAPE 24
June 15-18, 2014, Budapest, Hungary.

A Novel Knowledge Management System Based on Workflows

Girish Joglekar, Arun Giridhar, Gintaras V. Reklaitis[*]

School of Chemical Engineering, Purdue University, West Lafayette, IN 47907, USA
reklaiti@purdue.edu

Abstract

A large quantity of data, information, and knowledge are generated and accessed over the life cycle of a chemical product, from molecule discovery to process development to scale-up and production. Organizing this knowledge and making it available to support decisions has been a challenge due to its quantity, complexity, and the hierarchical data usage structure. This paper presents the functionality and technical details of a workflow-based knowledge management system and demonstrates its use in supporting the operation of a pilot plant for manufacturing liquid-based drug products.

Keywords: Workflow, Knowledge Management, Product Life-cycle Management.

1. Introduction

The technical knowledge generated over the product life cycle spans that generated in research studies (by experimentalists and mathematical modelers), during development as well as in manufacturing The groups responsible for various stages in a product's life-cycle tend to be highly compartmentalized, and often follow a formal 'hand-over' and reinterpretation of information as a product transitions through those stages. These transitions can be both time-consuming as well as inefficient. Often, multiple copies of the same information are created, which become reinterpreted thereby increasing the chances of errors as well as inconsistencies. The quantity of knowledge requires solutions that scale well from lab experiments to production; its high complexity precludes traditional database implementations. Moreover, the knowledge management (KM) system should accommodate the hierarchical nature of the data and its usage.

Knowledge can be broadly divided into explicit and tacit. Explicit knowledge is generated from experimentation, modeling or manufacturing, and is typically recorded and made available as quantitative information or models stored in a repository. In addition, there is a tremendous amount of know-how that exists as tacit knowledge, which is often experiential and resides with individuals. The decisions made in running all aspects of an organization are made by individuals who draw upon their tacit knowledge and combine it with the explicit knowledge as they see fit. Indeed, manufacturing is the manifestation of concrete decisions made based on the cumulative knowledge base, tacit or explicit, that is available to an organization.

In order to use knowledge effectively as many details about the process and circumstances under which that knowledge was created must be available. This is referred to as the context or provenance of knowledge. Additionally, the context should be machine accessible and structured it such a manner that it is easy to understand. The context of knowledge is crucial in determining its quality, provides a blueprint for reproducing it and provides the information necessary for validating it and learning from it. We propose a workflow-based framework to fully capture the provenance of knowledge. We posit that for creating every item of information, a well-defined procedure, or workflow, is followed which captures its context. A workflow can be modeled as a network of tasks that are performed in a specific order with interactions between various tasks that represent exchange of information and/or entities.

There are four main categories of workflows: business workflows, scientific workflows, experimental procedures and manufacturing recipes. A business workflow is concerned with the modeling of business rules, policies, and project management, and therefore are often control-and activity-oriented. A scientific workflow describes the execution of computational or data manipulation steps in a scientific application. An experimental workflow models the steps executed while running an experiment and serves as a framework for recording the conditions defining a given run and the values of the observed variables. A manufacturing recipe models the steps executed during the manufacture of a finished product in a plant. The recipe typically defines the values of operating variables and the operating sequence in order to manufacture a given product.

Most of the procedures related to creating knowledge or utilizing the knowledge for making decisions are hierarchical in nature. For example, to make a certain amount of finished product within a specified time, the team responsible for scheduling may use a scientific workflow that computes the schedule for a production facility. The schedule is then implemented in a manufacturing facility following the recipe for each operation. In general, such hierarchies are several levels deep spanning multiple business units within an organization, and utilizing at times all four types of workflows mentioned above.

Several workflow management systems have been developed for scientific workflows, such as, Taverna (Olin et al., 2006). Typically, a scientific workflow is modeled as a directed acyclic graph, with nodes representing executable programs connected to nodes representing data. The use of ontologies to provide a common information model in supporting specific applications such as mathematical modeling has been demonstrated (Hailemariam et al., 2010). The KM system described here is an integrated system that can provide a complete provenance for the hierarchical relationships between the various workflow types described. It is intended not only for knowledge creation but also for knowledge access by all involved in its life cycle.

2. Workflow Model

The proposed workflow modeling framework consists of the following building blocks: workflow, task, subtask, raw material, sink, subtask material input and output ports, information input and output ports, material flow line, information flow line and data node. A list of parameters can be specified with the building blocks to fully describe associated details.

A workflow is the sum total of all the building blocks that fully describes the details of a procedure. Also, it defines the scope of the activities encompassed. A task represents a series of steps performed on or by assigned resources. In the case of experimental or manufacturing workflows, a task is performed on an assigned equipment or instrument. In the case of scientific workflows, it may be the hardware on which a computation task is performed. Whenever a resource is shared by multiple tasks, its allocation to perform a given task is dictated by its availability, suitability and the priority of the task to be

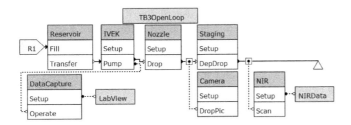

Figure 1. Workflow for the drop-on-demand pilot plant

performed. A task is similar to the concept of unit process defined in the ANSI/ISA-88 standards. A <u>subtask</u> is an elementary step that is used in constructing a task. When a task is initiated, it begins the execution of its first subtask and continues until the last subtask in its series is completed.

For example, the workflow for the manufacturing for a drop-on-demand pilot plant is shown in Figure 1. The workflow/recipe consists of 4 operational tasks (Reservoir, IVEK, Nozzle and Staging) and 3 instrumentation and data acquisition tasks (DataCapture, Camera and NIR) shown as green rectangles. Each task is modeled as a series of subtasks (white boxes) corresponding to the individual steps performed when a task is executed. The R1 icon represents input material, which is a mixture of the active pharmaceutical and excipients. The recipe proceds as follows. First, the reservoir is filled with the required amount of raw material and heated to the desired temperature. Next, the other three operations as well as the instrumentation and data acquisition tasks go through an initialization setup. Once all tasks are ready, the Pump subtask takes the material from the reservoir and passes it through the nozzle and drops are deposited on a substrate on a staging system.. A camera records an image of each drop gnerated by the nozzle and an NIR probe scans the deposit on the substrate. A Peltier controls the substrate temperature. A LabVIEW based system sets the operating parameters for all units and records the time series data associated with the key variables

As shown in Fig 1, material transfers are represented by solid lines, originating either from a raw material or subtask output and terminating either in a sink or a subtask. A dotted line represents information flow between the associated building blocks. For example, the information flow between the subtask Setup of task DataCapture and data node LabView is shown in Figure 1. Also, an information flow may be connected to a material flow signifying either an outgoing flow of information to an instrument or an incoming flow of information from a controller to a final control element.

A <u>data node</u> is a workflow component that can either be a <u>data creation</u> node or a <u>data specification</u> node. It is connected to a subtask by an information flow. A <u>data creation node</u> defines completely the structure, or the metadata, of the data created during the execution of the associated subtask. A data structure may comprise a set of values, a table, or a combination thereof. The metadata of a set of values is simply a set of terms from a predefined vocabulary. A vocabulary in turn may be defined as an ontology or simply via a table. A <u>data specification node</u> identifies the specific data item(s) that is to be retrieved from a data repository. A data item in a data specification node is the reference to a specific metadata item from any of the data creation nodes defined in the library of workflows in a repository.

A workflow plays the following roles during the use of the KM system: consensus builder, guide during knowledge creation, reference to all information stored in the repository, and starting point for developing new workflows. At the top level, the subtasks of a task can represent graphically the underlying steps in that task to a desired level of detail. Additionally, the material and information flows not only represent temporally the interactions between the various building blocks, but they also show the execution controls as necessary conditions and the precedence order when material flows take place. It can explicitly model the push and pull mechanisms as they occur when a workflow is executed (Joglekar et al. (2013)). Thus, a workflow provides a convenient mechanism for collaboration among all stakeholders and explicitly expresses all of the experiential knowledge. This social aspect of the workflow creation process facilitates adoption of procedures that have the approval of all collaborators.

New information is created by executing a workflow. The execution could be manual, by an operator in a plant or an experimenter in a laboratory, or automated, for example, as a scientific workflow being implemented on a computer. We have developed an engine, a finite state machine, which interprets a workflow as represented by the graphical network and determines the order in which the tasks and subtasks are to be executed. During execution it shows via color codes the status of currently 'active' tasks and subtasks, thereby ensuring that the procedure is followed as intended. Since most of workflows are executed manually and have hierarchical relationships, the engine provides the up to date status of all workflow that are being implemented at any given time. Since each completed workflow is an instance of the associated template, the set of all templates provides the entry point for accessing any specific piece of information.

3. Architecture of the Knowledge Management System

The key components of the KM system are shown in Figure 2.The KM system has been developed for use on HUBzero (McLennan et al., 2010), a middleware based on Joomla. Both Joomla and HUBzero are available under the LGPL 3.0 license. HUBzero provides the MySQL server for the relational database and the Apache web server. The server side scripting was done using PHP and the graphics are rendered using SVG. HUBzero also provides the functionality for managing user accounts, item tagging, the ability to post information such as educational material, forums and so on.

3.1. Workflow Editor

One of the key components of the KM system is a workflow editor/builder. It has a menu of icons for all the workflow building blocks. Thus, the user can create the graphical workflow representation via the editor. With each icon the user can specify any number of parameters, which are the attributes associated with that icon. With each data creation node in a workflow, the metadata and the extension of the file generated must be defined. When an instance of a workflow is created, the user is expected to supply the values of the parameters. Typically, the creation of a workflow goes through

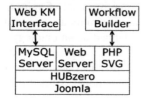

Figure 2. Components of the KMS

several stages as team members verify the accuracy of the activity model as well as the set of parameters with various icons. Therefore, the workflow editor is structured so that members of the group can access and post comments about any workflow that is being developed. Once the details of a workflow are approved, a template is created and incorporated in the HUBzero database. The workflow editor uses the Tcl/Tk scripting language and is available as a 'Tool' on HUBzero.

3.2. Web Interface for the Knowledge Management System

The web interface for the KMS consists of three main components: the web page along with the Javascript (the GUI) that initiate the AJAX protocol to communicate with the server, a MySQL database, the finite state machine and server side scripts that define the contents to be displayed on the web page and implement the user actions in the browser. The main web page of the system is shown in Fig 3. The functions available to the user are listed in the top left area on the page. The contents of the other non-overlapping work areas are dynamic and are used for displaying either workflow networks, presentation graphics or dialog boxes for entering or viewing information. An example of a workflow displayed in a work area and the form for specifying raw material information is shown in Fig 3. The other two work areas on the left display a legend for the color code associated with various icons and any messages to the user. The area in the upper left corner gives the menu of main functions of the KMS. The tables in the database are of two types. The basic tables define information that changes rarely, such as table of equipment items, table of species and phases, parameter value types and measuring units, and so on. These tables are defined as typical relational tables. However, in order to manage the workflow related information the Entity-Attribute-Value (EAV) model was used. A workflow is rife with one to many relationships, which are in turn hierarchical. For example, a workflow may have a number of tasks, which may have a number of subtasks, and which may have a number of material inputs and outputs. The EAV data model is the best way for accommodating these relationships because it keeps the number of tables required low.

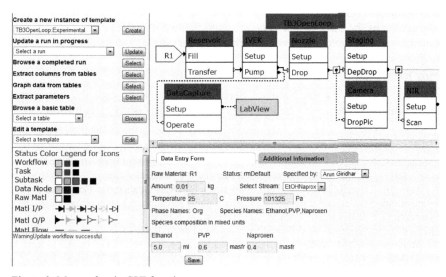

Figure 3. Menu of main GUI functions.

A finite state machine was developed to execute a workflow. The logic was implemented in Javascript and the updating of status was implemented using PHP. The execution controls as defined by the network are implemented by means of the engine.

4. Drop-on-Demand Pilot Plant

The drop-on-demand pilot plant shown in Fig 1 is used for demonstrating some of the functionalities of the KMS.. In a sample study, 8 runs were made depositing drops of ethanol (solvent) containing the Naproxen (API) and PVP (excipient) on a polymer film with the objective of understanding the effect of two operating parameters on drop formation. A total of 23 parameters were recorded in each run, Also, an image was recorded of each drop after it was released from the nozzle. During each run, LabView provides the set points to the reservoir, IVEK pump and the Stager, and for each drop creates a record of the time stamp, drop size calculated by an image analyzer program and current values of various process parameters. The metadata of the .csv file generated by LabView is defined in the data node. Also, the metadata for the raw NIR spectra and crystallinity data are defined in the NIRData data node.

The GUI provides the functionality to search access any parameter associated with any run. A parameter can be uniquely identified by the associated material, task or subtask name and the name of the parameter. Similarly, since the metadata of the data generated during a run are defined with each data node, a specific column can be extracted by identifying the data node, the file name and the column name. The data can be extracted for a single or multiple runs, and can be presented as a table or displayed on an x-y plot. The information recorded in the KMS is fully machine accessible with all relationships defined by the graphical model of the associated workflow.

5. Conclusions

The KM system readily models workflows and their hierarchical relationship. It allows efficient sharing of information between diverse groups and a structured way to capture the provenance of the information generated and thus its knowledge content. Although illustrated using a pharma case study, it is designed for general application.

Acknowledgement

The funding provided by the National Science Foundation through the Engineering Research Center for Structured Organic Particulate Synthesis is very much appreciated.

References

G. Joglekar, A. Giridhar, G. V. Reklaitis, 2013, Knowledge management in pharmaceutical manufacturing, AIChE Annual Meeting, San Francisco, CA, Paper 710e.

M. McLennan, R. Kennell, 2010, HUBzero: A Platform for Dissemination and Collaboration in Computational Science and Engineering, Computing in Science and Engineering, 12, 2, 48-52.

G. A. Howlett, G. S Joglekar, A. Giridhar, 2013, Workflow Editor, <pharmahub.org/resources/workfloweditor>, accessed on 16/01/2014.

T. Olin, M. Greenwood, M. Addis, M.N. Alpdemir, J. Ferris, K. Glover, C. Goble, A. Goderis, D. Hull, D. Marvin, P. Li, P. Lord, M.R. Pocock, M. Senger, R. Stevens, A. Wipat, C. Wroe, 2006, Taverna: Lessons in creating a workflow environment for the life sciences: Research articles, Concurr. Compt. Pract. Exp., 18,10, 1067-1100.

L. Hailemariam, V. Venkatasubramanian, 2010, Purdue ontology for pharmaceutical engineering: Part I. Conceptual framework, J. Pharm Innov, 5, 88-99.

Jiří Jaromír Klemeš, Petar Sabev Varbanov and Peng Yen Liew (Editors)
Proceedings of the 24th European Symposium on Computer Aided Process Engineering – ESCAPE 24
June 15-18, 2014, Budapest, Hungary.

Integration of Methods for Optimization in a Knowledge Management Framework

Edrisi Muñoz[a], Elisabet Capón-García[b], Jose Miguel Laínez-Aguirre[c], Antonio Espuña[d], Luis Puigjaner[d*]

[a] Centro de Investigación en Matemáticas A.C., Jalisco S/N, Mineral y Valenciana 36240, Guanajuato, Mexico
[b] Department of Chemistry and Applied Biosciences, ETH Zürich, Wolfgang-Pauli-Str. 10, 8093 Zürich, Switzerland
[c] School of Chemical Engineering, Purdue University, West Lafayette, IN, USA
[d] Department of Chemical Engineering, Universitat Politècnica de Catalunya, Av. Diagonal, 647, E08028 Barcelona, Spain
luis.puigjaner@upc.edu

Abstract

The solution of process systems engineering problems involves their formal representation and application of algorithms and strategies related to several scientific disciplines, such as computer science or operations research. In this work, the domain of operations research is modelled within a semantic representation in order to systematize the application of the available methods and tools to the decision-making processes within organizations. As a result, an operation research ontology is created. Such ontology is embedded in a wider framework that contains two additional ontologies, namely, the enterprise ontology project and a mathematical representation, and additionally it communicates with optimization algorithms. The new ontology provides a means for automating the creation of mathematical models based on operations research principles.

Keywords: Operations Research, Enterprise Wide Optimization, Decision Support Systems, Knowledge Management.

1. Introduction

Process industries are highly complex systems consisting of multiple business and process units, which interact with each other, ranging from molecule to enterprise level. Therefore, in order to solve real world problems, it is necessary to develop algorithms and computational architectures so that large-scale optimization models can be posed and solved effectively and reliably. Hence, the collaboration among different scientific disciplines, namely process systems engineering, operations research and computer science, is highly important (Grossmann, 2005). In this sense, enterprise-wide optimization (EWO) is a discipline related to the optimization of supply operations, manufacturing and distribution in a company (Grossmann, 2005). A challenge in EWO consists in developing flexible modeling environments for the problem representation, which is the ultimate basis for reaching efficient decision-making. A key feature in EWO is the integration of information and decision-making along the various functions and hierarchical levels of the company's supply chain. Current information technology tools, such as data mining, allow a high degree of information flow in the form of transactional systems (e.g. ERP's). Efforts have been recently devoted to integrate them with analytical models (e.g. optimization and simulation). However, further development is still necessary to easily develop, build and integrate different enterprise models. Such integration should reflect the complex trade-offs and interactions across the components of the enterprise. In this sense, the use of Operations Research (OR) techniques results in an attractive approach from a semantic perspective, which has not been identified in the literature so far.

This work proposes the creation of an OR semantic model as a step forward in capturing the nature of problem conception for decision-making. Specifically, the whole process of decision-making and the creation and classification of equations according to their structure are qualitatively represented in terms of OR principles. This OR ontology (ORO) is integrated with other two semantic models previously developed, namely the Enterprise Ontology Project (EOP) (Muñoz et al., 2013) and the Ontological Math Representation (OMR) (Muñoz et al., 2012), thus enhancing the functionalities of the original ontological framework. The scope of these models comprises the representation of the real system for EOP, the mathematical representation domain for OMR, and finally the problem design representation for ORO.

2. Operations research ontology

The operations research ontology has been developed according to a continuous improvement cycle as proposed by Muñoz (2011), which provides systematic methodology for ontology development. The first step consists in establishing the scope and domain, as well as the sources of knowledge for the domain definition. In this case, the ontology considers the domain of operations research, as a scientific discipline, which applies theory, methods, and special techniques in order to search the solution to decision making problems related to the conduction and coordination of operations and activities. Therefore, all the different steps within operation research process are formalized (Figure 1), giving special importance to the model construction, structuring and solution steps. Several sources of knowledge, including handbooks (Ravindran, 2007; Gass and Fu, 2013) and reference books (Taha, 1995), have been consulted and the result of the formalization has been validated with engineers currently involved in operations research and its application to the area of process systems engineering.

From the sources of knowledge, main concepts and their formal definitions have been extracted and documented. Those concepts define the classes of the ontology, such as, algorithm, decision-making, feasible solution, model construction, model, model validation, optimal solution, optimization, problem definition, problem recognition, system, among others, which describe the operations research domain and are taxonomically organized as shown in Figure 2.

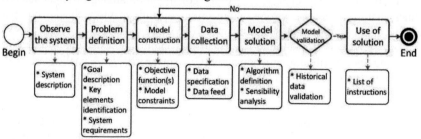

Figure 1. Flow diagram of the operations research process.

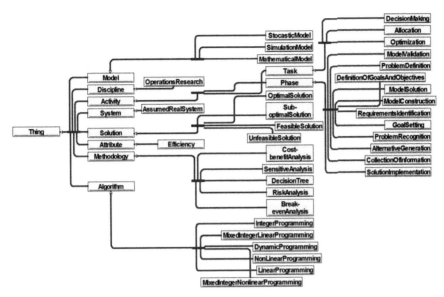

Figure 2. Extract of the taxonomy of the ORO in unified modeling language (UML).

Even more the properties of the model have also been extracted establishing relations between all the classes. Some examples of properties are "appliesAlgorithm", "testsModel", "HasPhase", "derivesInOptimalSolution", "examinesSystem", "establishesGoals", "hasMathematicalContraint". Finally, axioms structure the classes within the domain and rules are also implemented in order to set relationships within the model. Quantitatively speaking, the ontological model contains 72 main classes, 52 properties and 9 axioms.

3. Proposed framework

In this section, the procedure of the whole framework is presented. As a first step, the actual state of the process is captured by the instantiation of the Enterprise Ontology Project which contains an integrated representation of the enterprise structure, ranging from the supply chain planning to the scheduling function, thus comprising activities related to the operational, tactical and strategic functions. As a next step, by means of the instantiation of the Ontological Math Representation, the various mathematical models (mathematical elements) already established or the design of new ones are translated into a semantic representation as mathematical expressions in order to capture the mathematical meaning of enterprise domain elements. This model relates existing classes belonging to the enterprise domain ontology to mathematical elements to understand and translate the system abstraction in equations. Finally, this work proposes the Operations Research Ontology in order to, on the one hand, formalize and support the processes of: i) problem abstraction, ii) analytical model building, iii) problem solution, iv) verification and v) deployment of the best solution; and on the other hand, allow automated representation of the results of this whole process in standardized formats (e.g., the so-called mathematical programming formats MPS and nl).

In the workflow diagram (Figure 3), the first phase aims at reaching a formal conceptualization of the real system of the process industry under study. This step encompasses the standardized semantic description of the system using the enterprise ontology project (EOP), and the definition and acquisition of the required dynamic and static data. The second phase pursues the future formalization of the mathematical equations describing the system abstraction using the ontological mathematical representation (OMR), this phase results in a potential mathematical description of the entire system. The OMR can capture both mathematical expressions already in use and new developments for the system conceptualization. Thirdly, the structure of optimization model system along with the mathematical semantic model are the basis for instantiating the operations research ontology (ORO) and obtain a semantic decision model for optimization purposes. ORO has the task of designing the structure and the equation system in order to define a certain problem following the operations research guidelines. Finally, the mathematical programming standards are applied to the semantic decision model and the problem is solved to reach the optimal integrated solution, supporting decision making task in the real system. The combination of ORO with the EOP represents a new approach towards the systematization of automatic model creation and solution of OR based problems in the area of enterprise decision-making.

4. Case study

To demonstrate the functionalities of this integrated ontological framework, a case study presented by Muñoz et al. (2013) is considered. It consists of an integrated supply chain network planning and scheduling problem. In this work, the processes encompassing the problem definition, the problem formulations, as well as the solution procedure are represented within the "Operations Research Ontology". Therefore, the whole process of operations research has been applied to the problem solving supported by the knowledge management framework.

As a result of the "Observe the system" phase, the case study has been captured using of the Enterprise Ontology Project, which allows to instantiate all the features of the system, from the production process level to the whole supply chain network. The following phase concerning "Problem definition" aims to capture four key issues: i) goal description, ii) key elements identification, iii) system limitations, and iv) system requirements (Table 1).

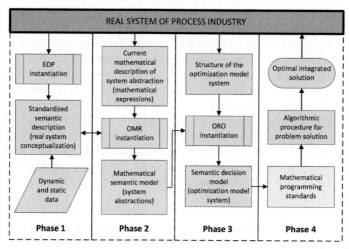

Figure 3. Flow diagram of the design of problem system construction framework.

Table 1. Extract of "Problem definition" in the case study.

Goal definition	Key elements identification
Maximize the economic performance of the whole supply chain structure.	Direct cost parameters, such as production, handling, transportation, storage, and raw materials.
Determine the assignment of manufacturing and distribution tasks to the network node.	Indirect expenses, associate with the capacity utilization.
Determine the amount of final products to be sold.	Prices of the final products in the markets.
Determine the amount of transported material among facilities.	Set of suppliers with limited capacity provide raw materials to the different production plants.
Determine the detailed batching, sequencing and timing of tasks in each production plant.	Set of production plants and the distribution centers are located in specific geographical sites and provide final products to the markets.

System limitations	System requirements
Mass balances have to be respected.	Each production plant produces certain amounts of final products using equipment technologies which have defined installed capacity and minimum utilization rate.
The final products are stored in one of the distribution centers before being sent to the markets.	Maximum capacity limitations have to be considered for each treatment technology.
Each market has a nominal demand of final products along a fixed time horizon.	Available transportation links.
A certain supply chain network structure.	Production routes are defined in the product recipes, which contain mass balance coefficients and the consumption of production resources.
	Unfulfilled demand cannot derive in back orders.

The "Model construction" has been derived from the "Problem definition", which provides the elements for the model creation. Specifically, links among the four different issues identified in the "Problem definition" are established by means of a relation matrix, and the sets, parameters, variables and groups of equations are accordingly derived. For example, the goal "Determine the amount of final products to be sold" is related to the continuous variable $SL_{sff't}$, which represents the sales of product s at time period t produced in facility f to market f'. Thus, the semantic modeling of the model is supported by the "Ontological Mathematical Representation", which is also related to the "Enterprise Ontology Project".

The "Data collection" stage concerns the relation of the different sets and parameters of the specific problem instantiation to their current value, which are usually stored in organized databases. Thus, the "Model solution" considers the algorithm selection according to the specific features of the mathematical model, and proceeds to the problem solution. Finally, the steps "Model validation" and "Implementation" consider the validation of the model according to historical data and decision-maker expertise, and the acceptance and application of the resulting solution for the real system.

5. Conclusions

The ontological framework provides a tool to build computational optimization models for the enterprise decision-making and to allow the comprehensive application of enterprise wide optimization throughout the process industry. This framework encompasses the steps of OR, and communicates with two previously existing semantic models related to enterprise wide and mathematical representation. This extended framework also allows the building of more accurate models for the chemical process industry and the full integration and solution of large-scale optimization models. The main contribution of this work is the systematic and rigorous representation of the whole decision-making process from the problem conception to implementation. As a result, creation and re-use of analytical models in the industry can be semantically supported, providing a higher flexibility and integration for model building of enterprise operations.

Acknowledgements

Authors would like to acknowledge the Spanish Ministerio de Economía y Competitividad and the European Regional Development Fund for supporting the present research by projects EHMAN (DPI2009-09386) and SIGERA (DPI2012-37154-C02-01). Finally the financial support received from CIMAT México is also fully acknowledged.

References

S.I. Gass, M.C. Fu, 2013, Encyclopedia of operations research and management science, Springer, New York, USA.

I.E. Grossmann, 2005, Enterprise-wide optimization: A new frontier in process systems engineering, AIChE Journal, 51, 1846- 1857.

E. Muñoz, 2011, Knowledge management tool for integrated decision-makingin industries, PhD Thesis, Universitat Politècnica de Catalunya, Barcelona, Spain.

E. Muñoz, E. Capón García, J.M. Laínez, A. Espuña, L. Puigjaner, 2012, Mathematical knowledge management for enterprise decision making, Computer Aided Chemical Engineering, 32, 637-642.

E. Muñoz, E. Capón García, J.M. Laínez, A. Espuña, L. Puigjaner, 2013, Integration of enterprise levels based on an ontological framework, Chemical Engineering Research and Design, 91, 1542-1556.

A.R. Ravindran, 2007, Operations research and management science handbook. CRC Press Taylor and Francis Group, NW, USA.

H.A. Taha, 1995, Operations research. Prentice Hall, New Delhi, India.

Jiří Jaromír Klemeš, Petar Sabev Varbanov and Peng Yen Liew (Editors)
Proceedings of the 24th European Symposium on Computer Aided Process Engineering – ESCAPE 24
June 15-18, 2014, Budapest, Hungary.

A Graph Approach to Representing the Pressure Distribution in Complex Plants

Heinz A Preisig

Department of Chemical Engineering; NTNU; Trondheim, Norway
Heinz.Preisig@chemeng.ntnu.no

Abstract

Based on a network description of the plant we argue analytically to split the model into two sections: an event-dynamic one for the description of the momentum dissipation and a capacity-driven one capturing the dynamics of the mass and energy distribution. The network representation is generic and may include any type of multi-phase fluid transport systems, multi-phase fluid storage, jets of one phase in another and multiple inflow/outflow systems. Thus we cover the whole range of equipment configurations. The transposed of the incidence matrix of the network model multiplied with the effort variables provides the expressions for the driving forces of the flows due to the affecting fields. An example is used to illustrate the systematic approach.

Keywords: process modelling, hazop, safety

1. Motivation

Mechanistic process models describe the distribution of mass, energy and momentum in the modelled process. The core of the description is the conservation of these quantities for each part of the plant. Each part is seen as a separate dynamic entity, a control volume. For distributed systems the conservation principle are partial differential equations, whilst for lumped systems they are ordinary differential equations. In both cases they are linear. The conserved quantities of all these control volumes span the state space of the modelled process. This initial splitting into dynamic control volumes is the main time-scale and length-scale assumption being made in the modelling process (Preisig (2010)).

Next an additional time-scale assumption is commonly made, namely that the pressure wave propagates with the speed of sound throughout the plant, which in most applications is much faster then the rest of the process. Consequently it is assumed that the pressure distribution adjusts instantaneously compared to the dynamics associated with the distribution of mass and energy in the whole plant. The plant description for the momentum distribution defining the pressures in the various parts is thus event-dynamic and consists of algebraic equations only. These equations are though coupled with the mass and energy balances.

The description of the pressure distribution is most often based on the static mechanical energy balance instead of the momentum balance. This assumes a separation of the thermal / thermodynamic behaviour of the involved materials, from the mechanical work and the kinetic and potential energy. This event-dynamic part of the plant model is usually established independently and then added as a appendix to what is considered the central description, namely the behaviour of the plant in terms of mass and energy dissipation.

This paper provides a systematic approach, starting with a process model that, through the making of explicit time-scale assumptions, is mapped into two coupled models: one which describes the pressure distribution in the plant and one that describes the behaviour of the plant in terms of mass and energy. The advantage of the approach is that we start with a common model and end up with a complete description in a systematic way. Also the assumptions are made explicit and thus visible and whilst the splitting is algorithmic and thus can be proven correct.

Not at least, a systematic approach to the representation of the pressure distribution has a direct impact on safety and hazard analysis, as well as any warning and alarm handling in processes operating systems.

The paper discusses time-scale assumptions in generic terms, proceeds to introducing a simple, but representative system for which a graphical models is taken as a starting point. Since it describes the assumed granularity of the physical containment of the plant we often refer to this representation as the physical topology of the process. It shows the control volumes and the dynamic assumptions made about each of the volumes in terms of event, lumped, distributed or constant. It thus clearly depicts the process model and the made dynamic assumptions.

2. Time-scales

When establishing a process model, the first step is to decide on what is the plant and what is its environment. This first decision is a time-scale assumption in that the environment is considered constant whilst the plant is what is changing with time. The environment is on the outside limited by assuming no interactions, thus defining a local universe.

In a next step, the plant is split into control volumes based on physical considerations, dynamic considerations and effective interactions. The physical considerations are often based on mechanical consideration, such as units, phases or the like. These dynamic considerations are ultimately linked to the time-scale assumptions.

Any mathematical process representations splits the description into three time scales: a dynamic one, which is embedded into a constant one on one side and an event-dynamic one on the other side. In other words, the process description includes parts that are assumed to not change, represented by reservoirs that form the environment or larger embedding of the process, the process itself being dynamic and a part that "just happens", thus is of event dynamic.

3. The example

For the analysis, we take a very simple but illustrative system, namely a tank with a liquid feed through the top, a bottom outlet, an overflow and a breathing pipe fixed on the lid. No reactions is considered as it does not add any complication to what is being derived. For the same reason, we consider the normal operation mode only.

The Figure 1 shows the system in normal operation mode as a graph, with the capacities as reservoirs, distributed, lumped and event-dynamic systems. The mass flows are indicated by black arrows and volume work with blue, dashed arrows. Each of the capacities is separated from its neighbours by a boundary. The mass streams in and out of the systems are all connected to lumped system either event dynamic (liquid) or of finite dynamic (gas). If two transport systems are in series, then an intermediate event-dynamic lump is added because these locations are essential for the description of the pressure distribution. Again for simplicity reasons we do only consider mass and not energy, thus there is no reaction, no heat exchange, no thermal effects. Again this is not essential for the splitting of the topologies.

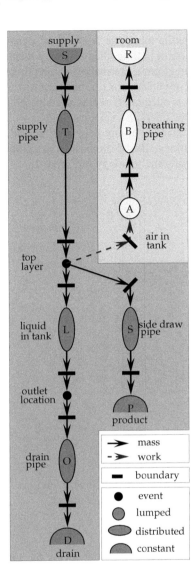

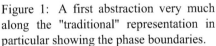

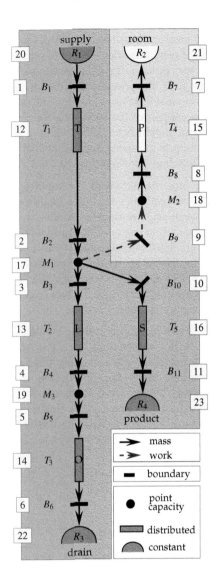

Figure 1: A first abstraction very much along the "traditional" representation in particular showing the phase boundaries.

Figure 2: The topology for the event dynamics of the momentum dissipation. The yellow boxed numbers are the numerical identifiers used in the incidence lists in algorithms.

The graph can be interpreted as a **bipartite graph** in that every transfer between two adjacent systems is going through a boundary. If we define two types of nodes, one for the boundaries and one for the capacities (event, lumped, distributed and reservoir) then we have a bipartite graph.

4. The topology split

The split into two topologies - a fast one for the pressure distribution and a slow one for the mass/energy dynamics - is the next goal. The slow topology will take the form as shown in Figure 3. We start with the topology in Figure 1 and add time-scale assumptions to the individual parts. We also indicate which of the capacities is subject to a significant velocity field and gravity field.

The pressure distribution includes a set of assumptions, the main one being event-dynamic thus if conditions that affect the pressure change at any point in time, the pressure will adjust at every point in the plant instantaneously. Assuming negligible thermal effects on this fast time scale, the pressure distribution the mechanical energy behaviour can be separated from the thermal behaviour and thus the pressure distribution is adequately represented by the mechanical part of the energy balance. This description considers the velocity field as well as the gravitation field. Thus both the information about the flow at any point in time and the location in the space must be available for the computations. Based on these considerations the topology shown in Figure 2 is established by modifying the topology of Figure 1.

The bipartite nature of the topology is retained. Also we have added another condition, namely that between any two transfer systems a capacity must be present, so that one could also talk about a tripartite graph with the classes: (i) transport systems (T), (ii) lumped event dynamic capacities (M) and reservoirs (R) and (iii) boundaries (B). The incidence lists are constructed for the two graphs, namely the momentum topology and the mass topology.

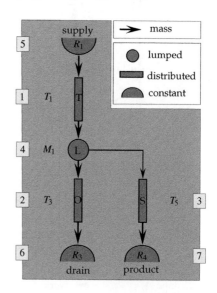

The transfer systems and the boundaries have only one inflow and one outflow. They will in general be exposed to both a velocity field and a gravitation field, whilst the mixing points, being event-dynamic lumps, serve as stream splitters and are not exposed to either of the fields. They are seen as points in space. They introduce formally internal streams from all the inflows to all the outflows.

Figure 3: A very simple topology for the mass dissipation

4.1. Reduction algorithm

We now turn to reducing the base graph as shown in Figure 1. In order to get the graph in Figure 3 one needs to remove the corresponding nodes. We define "output nodes" as the adjacent nodes to the one being removed in the arcs direction and correspondingly as the "input nodes" as the ones that have arcs pointing to the node to be removed.

First we construct the adjacency matrix from the incidence list. Based on the adjacency matrix we compute first the reconnection of the "input nodes" to the "output" nodes for a given node to be removed. Next the original adjacency matrix is overlaid with the resulting reconnection matrix and finally the row and column associated with the node to be removed are deleted. The algorithm *remove-node* is readily constructed.

Constructing the adjacency matrix for the full model the *remove-node algorithm* is utilised to remove all the boundary nodes, the mixing node M_1 is combined with the transport system T_2 by removing the latter and the mixing node M_3. The gas phase is also removed, thus M_2, T_4 and R_2. The nodes being removed are the boundaries, the non-flow transport systems and in this case the gas-phase is completely removed.

5. Constructing the core model equations

In the last stage, the equations for the two topologies are being constructed.

The state space is spanned by the mass and energy of all control volumes used to represent the plant. We have already mentioned that we model the fast topologies using the mechanical energy balance, whilst the slow part is described by the mass balances and in cases where thermal effects are of significance also the energy balance.

5.1. Dynamics: conservation principles

The balance equation for an arbitrary conserved extensive quantity ϕ have the generic form: $\dot{\phi} = \mathbf{F}\hat{\phi}$. The dot and the hat indicate time derivative and flow, respectively. The matrix $\mathbf{F}$ is the incidence matrix of the directed graph and thus contains the information of the reference co-ordinates as each arc introduces a local reference co-ordinate system relative to which the flow is measured. For simplicity reasons we assume for the fluid phase: (i) incompressible (ii) constant density (iii) iso-entropic, iso-termal process, thus no energy conversion such as friction into internal energy.

5.2. Flows

The **flows** occur over event-dynamic transport systems, so the balance equations reduce to transport equations that describe the flow of extensive quantity as a function of the difference in the conditions at the opposite boundaries. By choosing the conductivity as the perturbation parameter, singular perturbation leads to eliminating the accumulation term (Kokotovic et al. (1999), Vasileva Adelaida B (1995)). Figure 3 shows the transport term for what they are, namely physical entities. This is not the usual way one commonly thinks about these parts. One usually considers them of having no capacity, an assumption which also leads to a zero accumulation term. Reality is though different: The event-dynamic assumption, whilst yielding the same zero accumulation term, does though not indicate that there is no capacity. It merrily indicates that it exhibits an instantaneous behaviour. This may be seen as a detail, but has many practical consequences as for example energy is stored in these parts without being kept in the balances and thus are out of considerations, which contributed to accidents like Seveso in Italy 1976.

Though, if we do consider the transport to show no capacity effect, then we can reduce the graph further by removing the transport system nodes thereby representing the transport systems as arcs.

Flows of extensive quantities is due to a difference in the corresponding potential across the transport system. It is the effort variables, here being defined as the conjugates to the potentials, that drive the flows. For conductive heat it is the temperature and for the volumetric flow pressure, to mention just two. With the event assumption, the state of the transport system adjusts instantaneously to the changes at the boundaries.

The flow is thus also changing instantaneously and inflow and outflow are same. The flow is driven by the discrete gradient of the effort variables. The discrete gradients are then given by multiplying the transposed of this matrix with the effort variables associated with the system S, L, M, and P. Defining a the vector of effort variables $\underline{\pi} := [\pi_S, \pi_L, \pi_M, \pi_P]$ the flows take the form: $\hat{\underline{\phi}} := \mathbf{f}\left(\mathbf{F}^T \underline{\pi}\right)$

For the mass transfer in pipes and containers it is the gravitation field, the velocity field and the pressure field that must be taken into consideration. $\underline{\mathbf{0}} := \underline{\underline{\mathbf{F}}}_k \, \hat{\mathbf{K}} \left(\underline{\underline{\mathbf{F}}}_k^T \, \mathbf{v}_k^2 \right) + \underline{\underline{\mathbf{F}}}_p \, \hat{\mathbf{P}} \left(\underline{\underline{\mathbf{F}}}_p^T \, \mathbf{h}_p \right) + \underline{\underline{\mathbf{F}}}_k \, \hat{\mathbf{W}}_f \left(\underline{\underline{\mathbf{F}}}_k^T \, \mathbf{v}_k^2 \right) + \underline{\underline{\mathbf{F}}}_k \, \hat{\mathbf{W}}_v \left(\underline{\underline{\mathbf{F}}}_k^T \, \mathbf{p}_k \right)$ It is always the reservoirs that drive the system. So in our example the pressures in the reservoirs are known, whilst the pressure in the central tank is the unknown having ignored the gas phase. The dimension of the set of the above equations is 3 one for each transport system. The heights are all known and 3 pressures in the reservoirs are known. Three velocities and one pressure remaining, namely the velocities in each of the pipes and the pressure in lump L. Thus one equation is missing, which is the event-dynamic mass balance for the liquid body.

	$S\vert L$	$L\vert D$	$L\vert P$
S	-1		
L	1	-1	-1
D		1	
P			1

Table 1: The incidence matrix for the simplistic model, Figure 3

6. Application

The target application is in the hazard analysis of a gas supply station consisting of a liquid-gas storage tank, a compressor to move the gas, an turbine to extract the energy from expanding the liquid gas to a gas, a very long transport line to a filling station where customers fill their gas tanks (Preisig and Manenti (2012); Preisig (2013).

7. Conclusion

The **Topology** of both the event-dynamic momentum dissipation and the dynamic mass / energy balance can be derived from a first basic topology that captures the dynamics of the physical containments. It is the differences in the state of the reservoirs in terms of the intensive quantities that drive the plant's dynamics. The fact that the pressure wave moves at speed of sound is taken as the argument to model the momentum dissipation as event-dynamic network. Also the slower behaviour of mass and energy is generated from the same base model. The discussed approach derives the two topologies from a common source thus provides models that are consistent within the made assumptions. The algorithms are all based on the incidence and the adjacency matrices of the plant representation in the form of a graph in which the capacities are the nodes and the flows between adjacent systems are the arcs.

Model equations are the conservation of mass, energy and momentum in their basic form, namely the sum of the inflows an the outflows as well as the conversion from one conserved quantity into another. This is supplemented with transport equations and in this case transport equations. The transport is given as a function of the driving force, the difference of the effort variables on the boundary of the capacities. The discrete gradients are the transposed of the graph's incidence matrix times the vector of effort variables associated with the individual capacities. This leads to a very compact description of the overall model.

References

P. Kokotovic, H. K. Khalil, J. O'Reilly, 1999. Singular perturbation methods in control : analysis and design. SIAM.

H. A. Preisig, 2010. Constructing and maintaining proper process models. Comp & Chem Eng 34(9), 1543--1555.

H. A. Preisig, 2013. Systematic modelling of flow and pressure distribution. Chem Eng Trans 32, 1267 -- 1272.

H. A. Preisig, F. Manenti, 2012. Hazop - an automaton-inspired approach. Computer Aided Chemical Engineering 30, 1242--1246.

K. L. V. Vasileva Adelaida B, Butzov Valentin F, 1995. The Boundary Function Method for Singular Perturbation Problems. SIAM Studies in Applied Mathematics.

Jiří Jaromír Klemeš, Petar Sabev Varbanov and Peng Yen Liew (Editors)
Proceedings of the 24th European Symposium on Computer Aided Process Engineering – ESCAPE 24
June 15-18, 2014, Budapest, Hungary. Copyright © 2014 Elsevier B.V. All rights reserved.

Towards Automatic Construction of Domain Ontologies: Application to ISA88

Javier Farreres[a], Moisès Graells[b], Horacio Rodríguez[a], Antonio Espuña[b],*

[a] Software Department,
[b] Chemical Engineering Department,
Escola Universitària d'Enginyeria Tècnica Industrial de Barcelona, Consorci Escola Industrial de Barcelona, Universitat Politècnica de Catalunya, BARCELONATECH.
antonio.espuna@upc.edu

Abstract

Process Systems Engineering has shown a growing interest on ontologies to develop knowledge models, organize information, and produce software accordingly. Although software tools supporting the structure of ontologies exist, developing a PSE ontology is a creative procedure to be performed by human experts from each specific domain.

This work explores the opportunities for automatic construction of domain ontologies. Specialised documentation can be selected and automatically parsed; next pattern recognition methods can be used to extract concepts and relations; finally, supervision is required to validate the automatic outcome, as well as to complete the task. The bulk of the development of an ontology is expected to result from the application of systematic procedures, thus the development time will be significantly reduced.

Automatic methods were prepared and applied to the development of an ontology for batch processing based on the ISA88 standard. Methods are described and commented, and results are discussed from the comparison with a previous ontology for the same domain manually developed.

Keywords: Standards, ISA88, Knowledge Management, Ontology, Pattern recognition.

1. Introduction

Informatics and knowledge management is increasingly recognized as a keystone for Chemical Engineering (Venkatasubramanian, 2009). Ontologies play a central role in modeling knowledge and allow users and software modules to share a consistent view of the structure of information, which enhances the reusability and scalability of software developments. Still, the creation of ontologies, particularly domain ontologies for specialized fields, requires experts to produce the ontology on the basis of their knowledge and specific language. This is a task demanding time and training: experts need to understand ontologies since knowledge cannot be systematically transferred from brains to computers. However, this may be attempted from specialized texts.

Although methods for automatic ontology construction have been reported (Hearst, 1992), the differences between domains and the corresponding specialized language indicates that a general approach is very unlikely to be produced in the near future. However, first experiences for the extraction of terminology in the biomedical domain have been reported by Vivaldi and Rodríguez (2010). Also, Küçük and Arslan (2014) have very recently presented an approach for the wind energy domain.

Hence, this paper contributes an approach to automatic / supervised ontology construction in Process Systems Engineering, based on the parsing of specialized texts, subsequent information extraction by means of a mix of textual pattern matching, linguistic analysis and grammatical parsing, and final review by human experts.

This study addresses the case of modelling batch processes according to the ISA88 standard, which is selected, in addition to its significance to Process Systems Engineering, because ISA88 provides a consistent terminology unambiguously defining a domain by means of a common model for batch control (including physical and logical models for equipment, procedures, and recipes) that has proved efficient for batch automation professionals to easily share concepts and communicate.

Process engineering has a general and growing interest in integrating information across the enterprise decision-making hierarchy. Specifically, an ontology was proposed based on ISA88 to coordinate information flows among scheduling and control decision levels (Muñoz et al. 2011). The semantic framework provided proved to allow consistent coordination of models at different time and space scales (Muñoz et al. 2012).

However, the manual development of such an ontology demanded an important effort during a long period within the development of a Ph.D. thesis (Muñoz, 2011), which also included the necessary training in ontologies and the ISA88. The ontology, limited to the Part I of the ISA88 standard, consisted of 181 concepts and 157 relations.

2. Methodology

The methodology employed is next described. The ISA88 text (Parts I to IV) was taken as a PDF document and the first task was to extract the clean text. As formatting in PDF breaks lines according to page width, line breaks had to be removed from the text, thus obtaining a text without line breaks. Next, line breaks were generated for each dot (full stop or period) in the text. In cases such as sentences containing dots ("i.e." or "etc."), line breaks were wrongly inserted, dividing sentences inadequately. Since these errors have no significant effect in the final result, they were given no further consideration.

2.1. First pattern matching stage: taxonomic relations

After all phrases were separated, the first effort was to extract the backbone relations all ontologies must have: the taxonomical relation "is a" which relates a child with its parent. Following the work by Hearst (1992) the idea is to detect the occurrence of some patterns within each phrase. Usually, this can be carried out by simply applying plain pattern matching, but sometimes it may require some extra linguistic analysis.

This work uses a linguistic analyser, Freeling (Carreras et al., 2004), a pattern matching tool, Python (van Rossum, 1993), and a grammar parser, pyparsing (Mc Guire, 2007). In order to extract taxonomical relations, the patterns proposed by Hearst (1992) had to be adapted to the text under study. The patterns were reduced to three productive ones.

2.1.1. Pattern 1: is a

The pattern proposed by Hearst (1992) is NP is a NP, that is, two noun phrases separated by the "is a" construct. Whenever the construct "is a" or some variant such as "is an" or "is the" was found in a text, this sentence was processed in order to extract some taxonomic relation. For example, the phrase "The general recipe is an enterprise level recipe that serves as the basis for lower-level recipes." reveals, after a linguistic analysis, that SN("The general recipe") V("is") SN("an enterprise level recipe") that serves as the basis for lower-level recipes. Thus, the pattern SN1 V(is) SN2 allows deriving that SN2 is the parent of SN1, which in the example reflects that the concept "Enterprise level recipe" is the parent of the concept "General recipe". In order to extract this pattern and properly detect the noun phrases, a full syntactic analysis had to be performed. Pattern 1.1 resulted in 104 candidate relations.

2.1.2. Pattern 2: definitions

One variant of the previous case, and a common particular one of the ISA88 standard, is the definition of concepts. Within the ISA88 standard, some sections are dedicated to specify the definition of terms that are the keystone of the standard. These definitions take the form "id concept: definition", where "id" is the definition number identifier; the colon takes the place of the "is a" construct in previous pattern.

In this case, no linguistic analysis could be performed because the sentence was not fully constructed. Thus a shallow parsing was performed and the task was to detect the first noun after the colon. Pattern 1.2 resulted in 71 candidate relations. For example, "11 control recipe: A type of recipe which, through its execution, defines the manufacture of a single batch of a specific product." indicates that a control module is a kind of recipe, thus recipe concept is the parent of recipe control concept.

2.1.3. Pattern 3: such as

This pattern is proposed by Hearst (1992) as "such NP as NP", but in the text of the ISA88 standard no occurrence of this pattern can be observed. Alternatively, a lot of "NP such as NP" are found. Thus, the pattern was adapted to this second case.

No linguistic analysis could be performed for this case because the analyser didn't properly detect the "such as" construct to subsequently detect the two noun phrases surrounding it. A tagging process (Carreras et al., 2004) was performed in order to know the grammar category of each word and then nouns were detected before and after the "such as" construct. For example, in the phrase "Example 8: Process Management events such as allocation of equipment to a batch, creation of a control recipe, etc.", allocation of equipment to a batch and creation of a control recipe are given as examples of Process Management events, thus the "Process Management event" concept is the parent of former concepts. Pattern 1.3 resulted in 305 candidate relations.

2.1.4. Evaluation

After applying the three patterns, 480 candidate relations between 633 candidate concepts have been extracted. The 480 candidate relations have then been manually validated. 219 were found correct, 71 were found partially correct and needed manual edition, 187 were found incorrect and 3 remained undecidable. After this task, adding up the correct and partially correct results, a number of 290 different taxonomic relations were extracted relating 334 concepts.

2.2. Second pattern matching stage: meronymy relations

As the taxonomic relations are the backbone of an ontology, it was expected that all or almost all of the concepts would have been discovered at this point of the task. However, as the text of the standard is written for humans, a lot of information is implicit. So there may be non-explicit relations that wouldn't be automatically detected by the program. In this second stage, although designed for detecting new relations between existing concepts, new concepts can be discovered.

In this second stage, "part of" relations are extracted from the text. Extraction of this kind of relations has also been studied by Girju (2006). Accordingly, four patterns have been investigated and sought in the text of the ISA88 standard. For all these patterns the results of the previous stage were used. All meaningful words extracted from the first stage were used as candidate concepts for this second stage. Only those words from the previous stage are considered to detect "part of" relations, as is next described.

2.2.1. Pattern 1: part of

This pattern finds concepts in a phrase that are related by the construct "part of" within the text. For example, in the definition "Equipment unit procedure: A unit procedure that is part of equipment control." the equipment unit procedure concept is defined as a part of the equipment control concept. Pattern 2.1 resulted in 79 candidate relations.

2.2.2. Pattern 2: includ*

This pattern tries to find concepts within a phrase that are being related by the construct "includ" within the text. Words such as "included", "includes", "including" fall in this pattern. For example, this definition "2 Formula The formula is a category of recipe information that includes process inputs, process parameters, and process outputs." explains that the formula concept includes (or is composed by) three other concepts: process inputs, process parameters, and process outputs. That is, these three concepts are parts of a formula. Pattern 2.2 resulted in 169 candidate relations.

2.2.3. Pattern 3: contain*

This pattern finds concepts in a phrase related by the construct "contain". Words such as "contain", "contains", "contained" fall in this pattern. For example, "NOTE: An area may contain process cells, units, equipment modules, and control modules." explains that cells, units, etc. can be parts of an area. Thus, these concepts are related by a meronymy. Pattern 2.3 resulted in 193 candidate relations.

2.2.4. Pattern 4: consist*

This pattern finds concepts within a phrase that are being related by the construct "consist" within the text. Words such as "consist of", "consists", etc. of fall in this pattern. For example, in the definition "2 Process operations: Each process stage consists of an ordered set of one or more process operations." process operation is defined as part of a process stage. Pattern 2.4 resulted in 26 candidate relations.

2.2.5. Evaluation

The three patterns generated 346 candidate relations coming from 458 different phrases relating 177 candidate concepts. Their evaluation required a harder manual job, because if the same phrase codified more than one instance of meronymy relation, only one of them were detected and the rest had to be added manually. In addition, the phrasing is much more variable than in the case of taxonomic relations, and no automatic process can expect good precision rates if no knowledge is applied to the process. After the evaluation, 254 relations were obtained (92 manually added) between 205 concepts.

Table 1. Comparison of the sizes of the ontologies obtained from ISA88 standard

	Manual (Muñoz, 2011)	Automatic / Supervised (this work)
Concepts / Classes	181	465
Relationships / Properties	157	544

3. Results

As given in Table 1, once the execution of these two stages was completed, a total of 465 concepts and 544 relationships had been extracted (290 taxonomic and 254 meronymic). The execution cost has been approximately quantified in one man-month; two weeks were dedicated to program the new pattern matching algorithms, one week was required for validation. Indeed, progression was not sequential but underwent continuous improvement, and decisions were revised in regard of outcomes. Thus, engineering was the key issue and computational time was not the limiting stage.

Table 1 also gives the figures of the ontology by Muñoz (2011). Regarding the 181 concepts manually incorporated, 54 of them were detected by the automatic process after the first stage, and 38 (3 new) after the second. Therefore, 57 of 181 concepts were correctly detected, which is about 31 %. It is worth noting, though, that among the 181 concepts manually incorporated there are some that do not exist in the standard (usually common sense concepts that don't need to be included in a text for humans but need to be represented in an ontology). Additionally, some concepts not existing in the standard were added for other purposes (environmental concepts, etc.). Thus, the intersection between manual and automatic outcome is much higher than this 31 %.

Comparison between manual and automatic methods is difficult in quantitative terms. Suitable metrics should be proposed and used, including the effort and the quality of the ontology obtained. Table 1 provides an estimation of the completeness of the ontologies in terms of size. It's clear that the automatic approach is producing a larger ontology with a lesser development effort (it covers all parts, I to IV, instead of only Part I).

The exhaustive, non-selective identification and extraction of concepts should be considered an advantage that reduces the chances of omitting significant concepts (false negatives) at the expense of increasing the extraction of irrelevant ones (false positives). However, the manual method is clearly prevented from including irrelevant concepts, but may fail to be wide enough. In any case, further work is required in order to carefully analyse the intersection of both ontologies (which is a manual procedure) and determine to which extent they overlap or cover different parts of the domain.

4. Conclusions

The ontology produced shows that a promising methodology has been applied that may significantly reduce the time to develop a reliable domain ontology. Tools are available that allow to be adapted and tuned efficiently in order to parse texts, perform pattern recognition from text strings, and extract concepts and relations between them. Specialized texts are also available that provide a source of knowledge in natural language and can be used to build domain ontologies.

In particular, technical standards have shown to be easier to undergo automatic knowledge extraction (purpose of clarity, definitions, glossary of terms, etc.), however, pattern recognition tools need to be adjusted since the occurrence of patterns is different from usual patterns in most texts (i.e. literature). This has been shown when using the ISA88 standard to automatically build an ontology for batch processing.

Automatic process is fast, extensive and highly productive but tends to produce the extraction of irrelevant concepts and misleading relations. Thus, a supervised procedure is required in order to manually complete the ontology. However, increasing efficiency in the development of domain ontologies may be expected from the availability and use of systematic procedures and tools for producing the core of the ontology from reliable and acknowledged technical documents.

Future work can be envisaged towards expanding this preliminary work to other standards (i.e. ANSI/ISA-95), as well as to the detection of other kinds of relations between concepts (causes).

Acknowledgements

Financial support received from the Spanish "Ministerio de Economía y Competitividad" and the European Regional Development Fund, both funding the research Projects EHMAN (DPI2009-09386), SIGERA (DPI2012-37154-C02-01), and SKATER (TIN2012-38584-C06-01), is fully appreciated.

References

X. Carreras, I. Chao, Ll. Padró, M. Padró, 2004, FreeLing: An Open-Source Suite of Language Analyzers, Proc. of the 4th International Conference on Language Resources and Evaluation.

R., Girju, A. Badulescu, D. Moldovan, 2006. Automatic discovery of part-whole relations. Computational Linguistics, 32, 1, 83-135.

M. Hearst, 1992, Automatic Acquisition of Hyponyms From Large Text Corpora, Proc. of Coling-92.

P. McGuire, 2007, Getting started with pyparsing, O'Reilly, California, US.

E. Muñoz, 2011, Knowledge management technology for integrated decision support systems in process industries, Ph.D. Thesis, Univesitat Politècnica de Catalunya, Spain.

E. Muñoz; E. Capón-García, A. Espuña, L. Puigjaner, 2012, Ontological framework for enterprise-wide integrated decision-making at operational level, Comput. Chem. Engng., 42, 11, 217-234.

E. Muñoz, E. Capón-García, M. Moreno-Benito, A. Espuña, L. Puigjaner, 2011, Scheduling and control decision-making under an integrated information environment. Comput. Chem. Engng, 355, 774-786, 2011.

G. van Rossum, 1993, An Introduction to Python for Unix/C Programmers, Proc. of the NLUUG najaarsconferentie, Dutch UNIX users group.

V. Venkatasubramanian, 2009, DROWNING IN DATA: Informatics and modeling challenges in a data-rich networked world, AIChE Journal, 55, 1, 2–8.

D. Küçük, Y. Arslan, 2014,Semi-automatic construction of a domain ontology for wind energy using Wikipedia articles, Renewable Energy, 62, 2, 484-489.

J. Vivaldi, H. Rodríguez, 2010, Using Wikipedia for term extraction in the biomedical domain: first experiences, Procesamiento del Lenguaje Natural, 45, 251-254.

Jiří Jaromír Klemeš, Petar Sabev Varbanov and Peng Yen Liew (Editors)
Proceedings of the 24th European Symposium on Computer Aided Process Engineering – ESCAPE 24
June 15-18, 2014, Budapest, Hungary. Copyright © 2014 Elsevier B.V. All rights reserved.

Natural Language Modelling in Process Synthesis and Optimization

Vassilis Magioglou, Marinella Tsakalova, Antonis Kokossis*

School of Chemical Engineering, National Technical University of Athens, Greece
akokossis@mail.ntua.gr

Abstract

The paper addresses the development of synthesis and optimization models by adopting a natural language approach that assumes less context knowledge and is more amenable to the formulation of multi-disciplinary applications. The approach deploys ontologies and enables the integration of data from different resources, the re-use of generic mathematical formulations, and the deployment of object-oriented models. The approach is illustrated for screening of biochemical paths, a task that involves domains in engineering, agricultural sciences, biochemistry and economics. Concerning bioenergy and biomass, there is a large list of available knowledge, data and models from heterogeneous sources. The paper explains the use of ontologies to integrate and automate decisions, also to automate the synthesis of superstructrures. Illustrations include 82 different chemistries that lead to the production of more than 80 intermediate and final products based on biomass. The use of ontologies explains means to systematize the development of the superstructure, to customize features, also to invoke and optimize for the preferred paths and technologies. The work is extended to include scheduling and planning problems.

Keywords: Biorefineries, Management, Ontologies, Process Synthesis

1. Introduction

The conventional description of an optimization problem typically assumes (e.g. 'is given') the problem domain (e.g. units, properties, economics, chemistries, mass and energy balances) further seeking the optimal combinations of options that satisfy selected criteria. Such a problem description, assumes the familiarity of the expert with her/his contextual knowledge (e.g. the domain, its components and the properties/data of the domain), especially as subsequent tasks require the configuration of synthesis schemes (e.g. superstructures, task networks) and the development of optimization models. In conventional problem descriptions, rather than processing information and knowledge, the optimization experts share their own version of knowledge about the problem and access data appropriate for the problem.

Although the natural translation of the context is always desired when efficiently performed by the expert, the translation constitutes a challenging task in multi-disciplinary and/or in large-scale applications. In such problems, people hardly communicate queries as *given-to-optimize* statements but instead as less formal statements of the form: "what is the potential to build a biogas plant in Texas?", "what is the best waste treatment to use?". In the majority of real-life problems, the context has to be conceptualized and reviewed whereas the data need be extracted from different scattered and heterogeneous resources located at various places. In the case of multi-disciplinary applications the conceptualization relates to expertise shared among several people who could only analyze context in their own narrow domain.

The need to translate context, knowledge and data into problem statements outlines the challenge addressed by this paper. The paper uses ontology engineering as an enabling technology. The idea supports a vocabulary-based approach where vocabulary terms are linked to problem concepts (ontology concepts) that trigger background and tacit knowledge (ontology concepts already conceptualized) further identifying sets of model clusters available for analysis. The case is illustrated with a biorefinery application that combines optimization, synthesis, biochemistry, process design, engineering, economics and agricultural sciences. The work presented, enables users to address their queries using a natural language environment, also useful to analyze and review results.

2. Proposed Approach

2.1. Concepts Classification

The field examined is analysed into concepts and all the available relevant data, resources, knowledge are collected. The approach establishes concepts that provide a natural communication with end-users who pose questions using fixed vocabularies (the word-concepts play a key role enabling methods, models or being matched with data or knowledge). Each concept might have multiple translations, assigning methods, data, models and knowledge. Concepts are concentrated in four categories:

- Problem description concepts: include all statements that are used to define a problem. Specifications of the problem (specific feedstock, final products, co-products) and selection criteria (cost, profit, energy, environmental, uncertainties) are such concepts. Problem concepts are defined by the end-user and trigger the other types of concepts. They can either be integrated in the ontologies (specifications) or the framework (selection criteria).
- Background knowledge & tacit knowledge concepts: Background knowledge includes all the available knowledge in the form of data stored in excel files (Life Cycle Analysis data, geospatial data, costing data, mass energy balances etc.). Tacit knowledge includes the knowledge that integrates vital but not apparent information relevant with the frame of the problem (enabling technologies, intermediate chemicals, co-products, uncertainties in supplies and technology, upstream and downstream processes). Tacit knowledge is integrated in the ontologies and is extracted using queries depending on problem concepts.
- Model concepts: these concepts determine single or multiple models that need to be invoked in order to provide the desired outcome, depending on problem description concepts (input). The output is analysis or results concepts. The models are stored in libraries in the system and are invoked and processed selectively by the established framework. The context of the models is updated according to the available background and tacit knowledge.
- Analysis/Results concepts: once the model concepts provide their optimal solutions the results and the analysis are subsequently translated, via the vocabulary established, to concepts that can be easily interpreted by the user exempting him/her to relate his/her expertise with all the domains that have been used. The analysis or results display can either be data-type (excel files) or visual in the framework.

2.2. Concepts Interaction

The concepts categories presented in the approach interact establishing links and eventually resulting to complete progressive handling of the problem. The problem

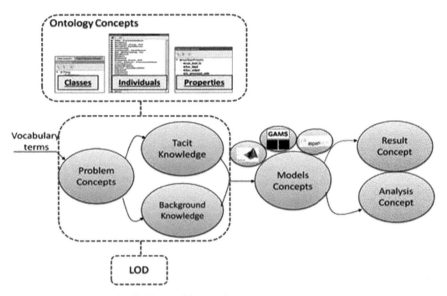

Figure 1. Concepts categories linking and interaction

concepts are interrelated with the vocabulary terms, which describe the problems composition. These terms (e.g. potential, cost, wood, Teeside) are defined directly by the user through the framework (user queries) and enable the required problem description concepts. Once problem concepts are determined, background and tacit knowledge are triggered accordingly. Subsequently, the required models are imported through the framework to serve the problems purpose. The context of the models is automatically filled with the necessary data, depending on the tacit and background knowledge. The models output is results or analysis concepts, which provide the desired outcome to the user in the appropriate format. The succession of the concepts categories is presented in Figure 1.

2.3. Ontology Engineering

The approach enables ontology engineering to convert the problem concepts and tacit knowledge in usable form, establishing a natural vocabulary to filter the alternative interpretations of a described given problem. The terms are organized in classes where particular properties are assigned, giving the capability of reuse and grow. Following seizing upon biorefineries domain, where in optimization problems the superstructures developed have as building elements raw materials, technologies, intermediate chemicals and final products, four different classes were used to determine the ontology. Further information functionalizing a higher level of representation can be achieved by assigning properties which characterize classes and their individuals. Using the necessary properties (has input, has output) simple relationships among particular individuals (feedstock, technology, intermediates product) are described. More complicated relationships describing larger, multiple or inverse paths, are also employed using extra properties (can lead to, is processed with, produces, is produced by, produced through the process) and inferred ones. The classes, along with the properties assigned to describe the superstructure are presented in Figure 2 (Class 1: Feedstocks, Class 2: Technologies, Class 3: Intermediates, Class 4: Products). Additionally the ontology includes secondary classes such as Applications.

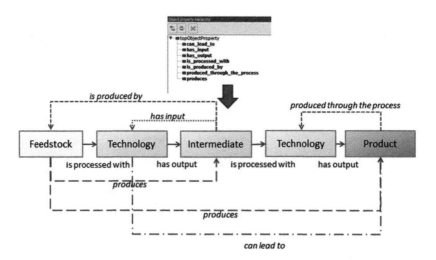

Figure 2. Classes range and domain for properties

Practically those properties are enabling the semantic aspect of ontology. This aspect makes the use of ontologies in optimization domain a highly valuable tool, since the final users will be able to extract chemical paths, networks and integrated superstructures by stating a single question.

2.4. Model Selection

One of the goals of the approach is to achieve user-friendly access to optimization tools through ontology engineering. On this purpose, the translation of information and knowledge to ontology classes, individuals, properties is conceptualized to feed the mathematical models. Models can have different type of backgrounds or even an integration of them. Some examples of frequently used models are GAMS, Aspen, MATLAB etc. The models used have a steady core, consisting of equations, solvers etc. The second part of the models is changeable and requires input from the user according to the problems nature and characteristics. The vocabulary established translating the problem posed by the user, provides via ontology, key input data (sets, subsets, constraints) to the appropriate model. The selection of the model is also based on the conceptualized statement of the user, translated into proper terms.

2.5. Framework

The approach established a central framework to incorporate natural language modeling. A Java-based application was designed to allow the user declare the problem description, to trigger the connection of ontologies with the models and to automate the development of models. The dynamic framework provides to the user the option of declaring the problem to examine (problem concepts). Accordingly, the necessary data (tacit knowledge) are extracted by the ontology through successive queries (using Jena API). The data are then transferred to the models in the appropriate format and update the changeable part. Simultaneously, the models are filled with the code of the steady core by the framework. Furthermore, the background knowledge is invoked by the models. Once the models development is completed, the execution is launched. A summary of the results/analysis of the models is visualized in the framework, according to the user preferences. Beyond these features, the user interface integrates heterogeneous resources such as word documents, excel databases, pdf files, flowsheeting models etc that are originated from various and scattered sources.

3. Illustration

In this section the implementation takes the form of two biorefinery problems (8 types of feedstock, 25 intermediate chemicals, 25 final products, 59 technologies) integrated in the same framework where the optimization models are basically used to support decisions and conduct uncertainty analysis (BIOCORE project). In this case the ontology is consisted of four classes and their respective individuals: (i) feedstock: including corn stover, wood chips, plant oil, municipal solid waste, rice straw, wheat straw, birch hardwood, poplar hardwood (ii) technologies: including biochemical, thermochemical and conventional processes (e.g. fermentations, gasifications, transesterifications, reforming, dehydration) (iii) intermediate and final chemicals such as syngas, biogas, glycerol, propylene, biodiesel, ethylene, ammonia, butanol, acetone, propylene glycol, polyamides, polyester, ethanol, methanol, hydrogel, carbon black, pyrolysis oil, resins, pvc. Additional properties of the data are product and feedstock properties: components, temperature, pressure, purity, and other data as geospatial, economic, green gas emissions, energy consumption and production (23 variables and 104 parameters). Figure 3 shows the main interface of the developed application for the specific biorefinery case, along with the actions integrated and the results produced. The illustration of modeling this biorefinery field begins with the identification and analysis of the terms into concepts for a user query such as "What is the potential to cost from agricultural residues and municipal solid waste in Teeside?".

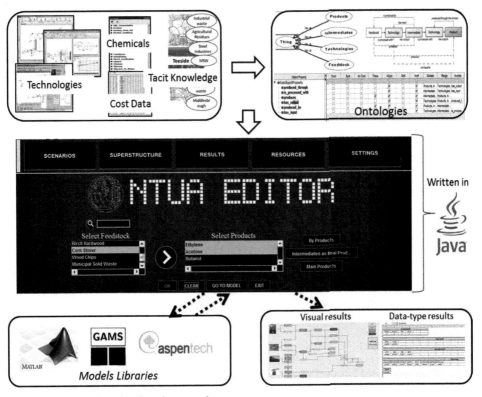

Figure 3. Framework and actions integrated

This query is declared in the interface by providing to the user the options to select feedstock (agricultural residues, municipal solid waste), scenario (cost). The information about Teeside is integrated in the ontology. The terms "potential" and "cost" indicate that an optimization tool should be selected (here GAMS). Subsequently the ontologies are triggered resulting to a semantic network constituted by chemicals, technologies and products that are related to the concepts agricultural residues, municipal solid waste, Teesside. The appropriate GAMS model is automatically invoked to satisfy the selection criteria of the user (based on cost). Following, the relevant data extracted from the ontology are transferred through the interface to the model, along with the necessary coding for the steady core of the model. This model identifies the raw materials, the technologies and the final products that are worth to produce in Teesside. Other variations of the same problem could be the observation of profit or cost, imposing sustainability factors in terms of environment (e.g. CO_2 emissions).

4. Conclusions

The paper introduces a new approach of natural language modeling, which is enhanced by ontology engineering. The approach explains how optimization models can be conceptualized and incorporated by ontology engineering. The methodology seems to be promising since there is vital need of a common established language between experts of modeling and final users. The paper explains how scattered and multidisciplinary knowledge can be captured and represented using real life paradigms from the field of biorefining. The automation of translating common words to complex mathematical optimization models seems to be notably promising serving sharing and reuse of knowledge, incorporating capabilities of development and extension in further growing areas.

Acknowledgements

Integrated Collaborative Project BIOCORE supported by the 7th Framework Programme (FP7) and Project consortium are acknowledged for the input data.

References

F. Cecelja, T. Raafat, N. Trokanas, S. Innes, A. Yang, M. Smith, Y. Zorgios, X. Bymi, Z. Palaskas, N. Markatos, A. Kokossis, 2012, e-Symbiosis: a technology-enabled industrial symbiosis targeting SMEs and innovation, Proceedings of Conference on the Greening of Industry Network, Linkoping, Sweden.
A.C. Kokossis, A. Yang, M. Tsakalova, T.-C. Lin, 2012, Systematic Screening of Multiple Processing Paths in Biorefineries: The ABC (Accessing Biomass to Chemicals) Project and Its Potential to Build Process Synthesis Capabilities, Integrated Biorefineries: Design, Analysis, and Optimization, Taylor and Francis.
E. Munoz, A. Espuna, L. Puigjaner, 2011, Integration of a multilevel control system in an ontological information environment, Comput. Chem. Eng. 29, 648–657.
A. H. Preisig, T. Haug-Warberg, 2012, Ontology approach to model construction, Comput. Chem. Eng. 30, 992–996.
A. Yang, J. Morbach, W. Marquardt, 2004, From conceptualization to model generation: the roles of ontologies in process modeling, Sixth International Conference on Foundations of Computer Aided Process Design, 591-594.
S.C. Brandt, J. Morbach, M. Miatidis, M. Theißen, M. Jarke, W. Marquardt, 2006, Ontology-based information management in design processes, Computer Aided Chemical Engineering, 21, 2021-2026.

Jiří Jaromír Klemeš, Petar Sabev Varbanov and Peng Yen Liew (Editors)
Proceedings of the 24th European Symposium on Computer Aided Process Engineering – ESCAPE 24
June 15-18, 2014, Budapest, Hungary.

Soft Sensor Development with Nonlinear Variable Selection Using Nonnegative Garrote and Artificial Neural Network

Kai Sun[a], JiaLin Liu[b], Jia-Lin Kang[c], Shi-Shang Jang[c], David Shan-Hill Wong[c,*], Ding-Sou Chen[d]

[a]Department of Automation, Qilu University of Technology, Jinan, Shandong, 250353, China
[b]Center for Energy and Enviromental Research, National Tsing-Hua University,Hsin-Chu, 30013, Taiwan
[c]Department of Chemical Engineering, National Tsing-Hua University,Hsin-Chu, 30013, Taiwan
[d]New Materials Research & Development Department, China Steel Corporation, Kaohsiung, 81233，Taiwan,
dshwong@gmail.com

Abstract

This paper developed a new variable selection method for soft sensor applications using the nonnegative garrote (NNG) and artificial neural network (ANN). The proposed method employs the ANN to generate a well-trained network, and then uses the NNG to conduct the accurate shrinkage of input weights of the ANN. This paper took Bayesian information criterion as the model evaluation criterion, and the optimal garrote parameter s was determined by v-fold cross-validation. The performance of the proposed algorithm was compared to existing state-of-art variable selection methods. A real industrial application for air separation process were applied to demonstrate the performance of the methods. The experimental results showed that the proposed method presented better model accuracy with fewer variables selected, compared to other state-of-art methods.

Keywords: Variable selection; Soft sensor; Nonnegative garrote; Artificial neural network

1. Introduction

Soft sensors are inferential models that use easily measured variables to estimate process variables that are hard to measure due to technological limitations, large measurement delays, or high investment costs(Kadlec et al., 2009) . In addition, soft sensors can give useful information in terms of fault detection by working with hardware sensors in parallel (Kaneko et al., 2009). It is possible to eliminate redundant variables, reduce the complexity of the model, and improve the accuracy of the model through the use of appropriate variable selection techniques. A variety of variable selection techniques for soft sensor applications and modeling methods have been studied in recent years. Ma et al. (2008) proposed an adaptive soft sensor based on statistical identification of key variables, in which the key variables are captured using the statistical approach of stepwise linear regression. Lin and Jørgensen(2011) deleveped a soft sensors based on a multivariable data fusion where a dynamic partial least squares is implemented to build the regression model. Xiang et al. (2012) presented a framework of discriminative least squares regression (LSR) for multiclass classification and feature selection.

However, these linear regression methods may not have adequate accuracy in describing highly nonlinear industrial processes. Artificial neural networks (ANN) are powerful tools for nonlinear statistical data modeling or decision making and have been widely used for variable selection in recent years. Castellano and Fanelli (2000) proposed a backward selection, called IANN, by successively removing the input nodes of a satisfactorily trained neural network with the complete set of variables as inputs. Enrique and Sopena (2008) proposed a feature selection method using sequential backward multi-player perceptron (SBS-MLP) , which retrained the network with every feature temporarily removed before computing its saliency. Souza et al. (2013) developed a method for variable selection applications by using a multi-layer perceptron (MLP) and applied the method to monitor the fluoride concentration in the effluent of an urban water treatment plant. Recently, Breiman (1995) proposed a new shrinkage method called the nonnegative garrote (NNG). The mechanism of this shrinkage method conducts variable selection by shrinking or setting some coefficients of a "greedy" model to zero. Yuan (2007) proposed a non-parametric extension of NNG and applied it to solve the problem of component selection in a functional analysis of variance (ANOVA) model. Pan et al. (2012) revised the original NNG by combining enumerative PLS with NNG, and the results showed better performance than original NNG and LASSO.

The motivation of this paper was to develop a robust variable selection method for the application of soft sensors that could describe complex nonlinear industrial processes. This paper is organized as follows. Section 2 presents the development of the methodology. In Section 3, the proposed method is applied to predict the oxygen concentration for the air separation process. Finally, some concluding remarks are given in Section 4.

2. Proposed methodology

This paper proposes an input variable selection methodology by introducing NNG into ANN to solve the nonlinear problem. Similar to the original NNG, the new methodology can be divided into two stages. At the first stage, it obtains a well-trained MLP network, in which the activation functions f, g, the bias b_j^h, b^o, the input weight w_{ij} and the output weight w_j^o are known and fixed. At the second stage, ANN can be reformulated by adding the new magnitude coefficients $c = \{c_1, c_2, ..., c_p\}$ in front of the input variables:

$$y = g\left(\left(\sum_{j=1}^q w_j^o f\left(\left(\sum_{i=1}^p c_i w_{ij} x_i\right) + b_j^h\right)\right) + b^o\right) \tag{1}$$

where $x = \{x_1, x_2, ..., x_p\}$ and y are input and output variables separately. Suppose $\widehat{w_{ij}}(i = 1,2 ... p; j = 1,2 ... q)$ is the initial input weight of the well trained neural network; the NNG-ANN is formulated as:

$$c^*(s)=\text{argmin}\{ \sum_{k=1}^n (y_k\text{-}g\left(\left(\sum_{j=1}^q w_j^o f\left(\left(\sum_{i=1}^p c_i w_{ij} x_i\right) + b_j^h\right)\right) + b^o\right))^2 \} \tag{2}$$

subject to: $c_i \geq 0, \sum_{i=1}^{p} c_i \leq s$

Obviously, Eq. (2) is a non-linear constrained quadratic problem. This paper used the trust-region-reflective optimization algorithm, which is a subspace trust-region method based on the interior-reflective Newton method proposed by Coleman and Li (1996). There is no stability problem and computation time increases only moderately as the number of input variables increases. A new set of input weights $\widetilde{w}_{ij}$ can be obtained by:

$$\widetilde{w}_{ij} = c_i \widehat{w}_{ij}, i = 1,2 \ldots p; j = 1,2 \ldots q \tag{3}$$

The input variable i is eliminated in the new neural network if $c_i = 0$. Consequently, the prediction model of y is obtained by:

$$\tilde{y} = g\left(\left(\sum_{j=1}^{q} w_j^o f\left(\left(\sum_{i=1}^{p} \widetilde{w}_{ij} x_j\right) + b_j^h\right)\right) + b^o\right) \tag{4}$$

This paper used the Bayesian information criterion (BIC) which was proposed by Schwarz and Gideon (1978) as the evaluation criterion for model selection among a finite set of models. For a given garrote parameter s, a model can be obtained by solving the non-linear constrained quadratic problem of Eq. (2). Consequently, the accuracy and model size of the NNG-ANN estimate depends highly on the choice of the garrote parameter s . The optimal s can be determined using v-fold cross-validation (Zhang, 1993). An overall NNG-ANN procedure for input variable selection using BIC as the evaluation criterion is presented in Figure 1.

3. Application to an air separation process

In this section, the proposed algorithm was applied to predict the oxygen concentration for an air separation process. A schematic flow diagram of the air separation process is shown in Figure 2. There were five distillation columns that had been highly integrated to separate nitrogen, oxygen and argon from the compressed air. The compressed air was fed into the main heat exchanger (MHE) and then fed into a pressurized column. The N_2 product streams were drawn from the top of the pressurized column. One stream was liquefied through the main condenser and the sub cooler as the liquid N_2 product, and the other stream went through the MHE as the gas N_2 product. The bottom stream

Step 1: Initialization. Train a new neural network using the training dataset, and get initial input weights of the network, $\widehat{w}_{ij}, \forall i, j$.
Step 2: Choice of garrote parameter s.
Step 2-1: Initialize s, ie $s \leftarrow s_{lb}$ and $v \leftarrow 1$.
Step 2-2: For current s and v obtain dataset $\overline{\mathcal{L}}_v$, and solve the optimization problem (2) to get $c(s) = \{c_1, c_2, \ldots, c_p\}$.
Step 2-3: Update the input weights by equation (3) and obtain a new network
Step 2-4: $v \leftarrow v + 1$ and if $v < V$ go to step 2-2.
Step 2-5: $s \leftarrow s + \Delta s$, if $s < s_{ub}$, set $v \leftarrow 1$ and goto step 2-2
Step 2-6: Find the optimal s with v-fold cross-validation and denote as s^*.
Step 3: Solve the optimization problem by equation (2) with s^*, obtain the
$$c^*(s) = \{c^*_1, c^*_2, \ldots, c^*_p\}.$$
Step 4: Update the input weight by equation $\widetilde{w}_{ij} = c_i \widehat{w}_{ij}$ and obtain new network by equation (4).

Figure 1. The over-all procedure of NNG-ANN algorith

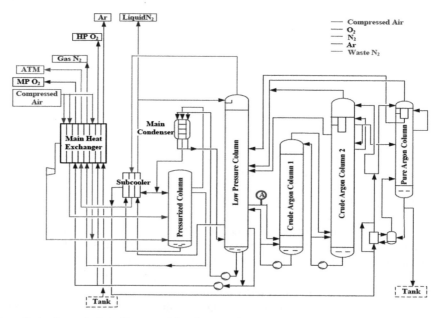

Figure 2. A schematic flow diagram of the air separation process

of the pressurized column went through the sub cooler and was used as a coolant of the condensers of crude argon column 2 and the pure argon column. After that, it was fed into the low pressure column in order to withdraw the rest of the N_2 from the top of the column. The liquefied O_2 products were drawn from the bottom of the low pressure column and then pumped up to 32 kg/cm^2 and 12 kg/cm^2, which respectively were the high pressure (HP) and medium pressure (MP) products after the MHE. The argon was purified by crude argon columns 1 and 2, as well as the pure argon column. The liquefied Ar was stored in the tanks and the Ar product was then vaporized through the MHE from the tanks in order to reduce the compressed air temperature.

The data set consists of 18 candidate input variables and one target output variable – the O_2 concentration. The inferential model of the air separation process was developed and tested using process data collected every five minutes from January 1, 2011 to June 30, 2011. The January data were used to build the prediction model, and the data of the next five months were used to test the performance of the model.

Table 1 presents the average prediction performance of ANN models with different variable selection methods when the January data was used as the training data and the February data was used as the test data. The proposed NNG-ANN method presented better prediction accuracy with a smaller number of input variables selected than SBS-MLP and IANN.

Table 1. Statistical results for the air separation process of the February

	NNG -ANN	SBS-MLP	IANN
PMSE	0.035	0.051	0.072
M.S	6.1	7.5	9.3

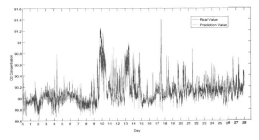

Figure 3. Measured and the predicted O2 concentrations during the month of February

Figure 3 gives the measured and the predicted O_2 concentration with NNG-ANN during the month of February. The result showed that the NNG-ANN could track the dynamics of the O_2 concentration successfully. Figure 4 gave the variable selection frequency over 100 runs by the three methos. It showed that the proposed approach identified that variables 17, 4, 7 and 3 were selected over 70%, and other variables were selected below 45%. Comparing with the results of the other approaches, which are shown in Figures 4.b and 4.c, there are 7 and 10 variables were selected over 50% respectively. A more compact model structure could be obtained using the proposed approach than from the results of SBS-MLP and IANN. In order to illustrate the robustness of the model obtained by proposed algorithm, this study used the model built by the January data to predict the O_2 concentration for the next five months. Figure 5 shows the average PMSE over five months by the three methods. It can be seen that as the process drifted from the original modeling condition, the PMSE would increase. However, the rate of increase in PMSE of NNG-ANN was slower than that for SBS-MLP and IANN, indicating better robustness.

4. Conclusions

This paper developed a new variable selection method for soft senor applications using the nonnegative garrote and artificial neural network. In the first stage, the proposed method trained an artificial neural network and obtained the initial input weights of the network. In the second stage, it performed magnitude coefficient shrinkage on the input weights to construct the prediction model. The proposed method was applied to predict the oxygen concentration for the air separation process, and it presented a better model error with fewer variables selected than SBS-MLP and IANN.

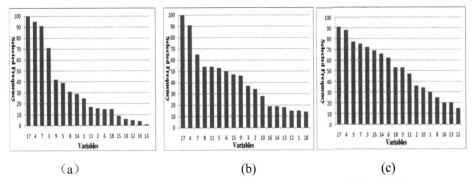

(a)   (b)   (c)

Figure 4. Variable selection frequency over 100 runs by NNG-ANN(a), SBS-MLP(b) and IANN(c)

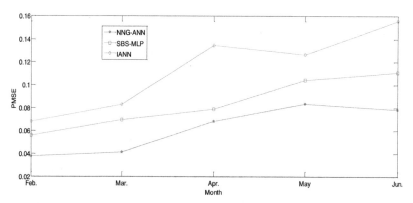

Figure 5. Increase in prediction error over a period of five months

Acknowledgement

The work is partially supported by Ministry of Economic Affairs through the grant 102-EC-17-A-09-S1-198, and National Science Council through the grant NSC 100-2221-E-007-058-MY2, Advanced Manufacturing and Service Management Research Center, National Tsing-Hua University (Grant 101N2072E1) and the Shandong Provincial Natural Science Foundation of China (Grant No.ZR2010FQ009).

References

L. Breiman, 1995, Better Subset Regression Using the Nonnegative Garrote, Technometrics, 37, 373-384.

G. Castellano, A. M. Fanelli, 2000, Variable selection using neural-network models, Neurocomputing, 31, 1-13.

T. F. Coleman, Y. Li, 1996, An interior trust region approach for nonlinear minimization subject to bounds, SIAM Journal on optimization, 6, 418-445.

R. Enrique, M. Sopena, 2008, Performance Feature Selection With Multilayer Perceptrons, IEEE Transcations On Neural Networks, 19, 431-441.

P. Kadlec, B. Gabrys, S. Strandt, 2009, Data-driven soft sensors in the process industry, Computers and Chemical Engineering, 33, 795-814.

H. Kaneko, M. Arakawa, K. Funatsu, 2009, Development of a new soft sensor method using independent component analysis and partial least squares, AIChE Journal, 55, 87-98.

B. Lin, S. B. Jørgensen, 2011, Soft sensor design by multivariate fusion of image features and process measurements, Journal of Process Control, 21, 547-553.

M. D. Ma, J. W. Ko, S. J. Wang, M. F. Wu, S. S. Jang, S. S. Shieh, D. S. H. Wong, 2008, Development of Adaptive Soft Sensor Based on Statistical Identification of Key Variables. Control Engineering Practice, 17, 9, 1026 – 1034.

C. C. Pan, J. Bai, G. K. Yang, D. S. H. Wong, S. S. Jang, 2012, An inferential modeling method using enumerative PLS based nonnegative garrote regression, Journal of Process Control, 22, 1637-1646.

G. Schwarz, 1978, Estimating the dimension of a model, The annals of statistics, 6, 461-464.

F. A. Souza, R. Araújo, T. Matias, J. Mendes, 2013, A multilayer-perceptron based method for variable selection in soft sensor design, Journal of Process Control, 23, 1371-1378.

S. Xiang, F. Nie, G. Meng, C. Pan, C. Zhang, 2012, Discriminative least squares regression for multiclass classification and feature selection, IEEE Transactions on Neural Networks and Learning Systems, 23, 11, 1738-1754.

M. Yuan, 2007, Nonnegative garrote component selection in functional anova models, International Conference on Artificial Intelligence and Statistics, 660-666.

P. Zhang, 1993, Model selection via multifold cross validation. The Annals of Statistics, 299-313.

Jiří Jaromír Klemeš, Petar Sabev Varbanov and Peng Yen Liew (Editors)
Proceedings of the 24th European Symposium on Computer Aided Process Engineering – ESCAPE 24
June 15-18, 2014, Budapest, Hungary. Copyright © 2014 Elsevier B.V. All rights reserved.

Automation in Process Industry: Cure or Curse? How can Training Improve Operator's Performance

Salman Nazir[a], Annette Kluge[b], Davide Manca [a,*]

[a]*PSE-Laboratory – Dipartimento di Chimica, Materiali e Ingegneria Chimica. Politecnico di Milano – Piazza Leonardo da Vinci 32, 20133 Milano, Italy*
[b]*Cognitive Science, Business and Organizational Psychology, University of Duisburg-Essen – Lotharstr. 65, 47057 Duisburg, Germany*
davide.manca@polimi.it

Abstract

Automation in the process industry has seen its implication and implementation since 1960's. However, during last decades the "trend" of integrating advanced and sophisticated process control techniques like process optimization, soft sensors, MPC, RTO has significantly increased. The reasons that can be attributed to the increase in automation are mainly the implementation cost respect to expected revenues and the wide range of alternatives and suppliers. Unfortunately, the inclusion of automation coupled to either new plants/processes or process retrofitting and revamping neglected often the operator's characteristics that can be summarized with the human factor term. This paper provides an insight to the extensive use of automation and the associated challenges that an industrial operator faces because of information overload, human machine interface, and automation complexity. The forgotten part, *i.e.* the human (operator) element, is emphasized with respect to the operations in control room and in the field. The impact of complexity of automation on the nature of operator error is discussed for both normal operating conditions and abnormal situations. A case study reflecting automation failure combined with human error(s) is presented. Finally, a Hierarchal Training Syllabus (HTS) is proposed by using a so called Plant Simulator. The features and relevant benefits of HTS are also outlined.

Keywords: Operator training; Automation; Process safety; Industrial Accidents; Information management.

1. Introduction

Nowadays, automated systems are integrated into several industries including aviation, transportation, medical and chemical sectors. The main purpose behind introducing automation in these industries has been to improve system performance, system resiliency, optimize energy utilization, improve yields and selectivity, and facilitate operator's tasks (Wickens et al., 2008). However, the reliability and consistency of automated systems have been questioned with time (Woods et al., 2010). The trend of deploying significantly automated solutions for industrial processes is rather recent. The apparent benefits of using such tools in increasing the production, energy efficiency, and safety of operations, encouraged the practitioners to invest in sophisticated and modern tools. Indeed, the assumption of reducing the operator's workload with automation and the probability of process errors was soundly grounded. However, automation induced unwanted and unintended human behaviors and importantly the occasional failure of automated systems brought catastrophic consequences, which were not anticipated before (Wickens et al., 2010). Additionally, it is generally granted that automated plants worldwide are either underperforming or partially inefficient because their complexity is not extensively understood and subsequently handled/exploited by operators.

This study emphasizes the challenges associated with automated systems and proposes solutions to cope with them. The concept of Plant Simulator, PS, is introduced as a training tool to improve operator's performance in modern chemical plants saturated with advanced control systems. A unique training syllabus is also presented as a solution to new challenges that emerged in the training sector of chemical plants.

2. Complexity and automation in the process industry

Chemical processes inherently contain multilevel control loops and interconnections, which need to be monitored and supervised for normal operations. Once the system becomes unstable, the conditions are referred to as abnormal situation, which can lead to near misses and possible accidents with both economic and human losses.

The number of inter-connected hardware components, by means of software procedures and tools, assembled to optimize processes has increased dramatically in last decades. High-level algorithms having the capability of integrating measured data and numerical models to generate low-level control signals have been implemented progressively to reach some optimal operating conditions that comprise costs, production, safety, environment, and production continuity and flexibility. These multidimensional automated optimization tools go beyond the capability of human beings (and therefore of industrial operators). The automated solutions may also underperform and essentially lack the ability to intervene or tackle abnormal and unforeseen situations since as a rule they are designed for optimal operating conditions. In addition, automation may also fail in terms of design features for instance failure to encounter deviations from normal operating conditions or triggering false alarms.

Automation and complexity go side by side. In chemical plants, the combination is more sensitive, if not risk-prone, as the operations are continuous unlike in aviation or medical operations (Manca et al., 2012). Actually, several activities and operations occur simultaneously in chemical plants. In addition, the dynamics of normal operating conditions vary according to the state of the process. Operating conditions may not be *normal* in case of startup and shutdown. Similarly, abnormal situations and accident scenarios call for completely different algorithms and actions, which may have been neglected during the design phase.

The aforementioned dynamics of processes and involved automation presents an insight into the job of current operators. In the control room, operators are supposed to manage large amounts of data, and deal with process details, control systems, set points and the delicate balance between safety and production. During the failure of automated systems and under abnormal situations, the urgency and sensitivity of decisions increase manifold. The modification of plant dynamics as a function of optimal operating conditions, startup, shutdown, and abnormal conditions calls for an adaptive behavior and expert skill of operators. These features entail also a comprehensive and precise understanding of the process in terms of dynamic response of the plant and of the degrees of freedom of the process to be managed according to specific situations and operations.

3. A case study of failure in automation

On August 19th, 2004, an explosion at the Sterigenics International, Inc., California, Ethylene Oxide (EO) sterilization process and its associated air pollution control system, injured four workers and caused extensive damage to the 6,200 m^2 facility. The plant and neighboring facilities were evacuated, and plant operations were disrupted for nine months. The sterilization of pallets of boxed medical products was performed by a series of batch reactors as shown in Figure 1 (CSB, 2004).

EO possesses exposure hazard in addition to its high flammability. The exhaust gasses, which are rich in EO were sent to the chemical scrubber (see Figure 1). After the purging of EO the chamber door was raised to allow the exhaust venting into the catalytic oxidizer. In the catalytic oxidizer, the system was designed to ensure the concentration of EO to be less than 25 % of the lower explosion limit (LEL). A higher concentration would favor a possible ignition. This operation was automated through a computerized control system (CSB, 2004). The operators could switch the automated system to manual operation by providing the correct password. The control system was designed to monitor only the pressure of the chamber and not the concentration of EO, thereby, leaving the possibility of EO accumulating in the chamber. Following the signal from the automated system, the operators took the necessary actions (*e.g.,* abortion of sterilization cycle, maintenance, calibration). In the final stage of maintenance, the operators jointly decided to skip last step and start venting by opening the chamber.

Soon after that, the LEL alarm in the chamber was triggered, indicating the release of EO. The ignition of EO-air mixture took place before the oxidizer could be shut down.

A deeper look into the events (CSB, 2004) reveals that the operators had difficulties to understand the behavior and limitations of the automated system, which thus induced in correct assumptions and led to wrong actions. The automation failure combined with operator's incorrect understanding resulted in the accident.

A further drawback of improperly designed automated systems is the progressive reduction of process understanding by the operators as they spend more time in passive vigilance instead of taking active decisions/actions. Consequently, they are unable to

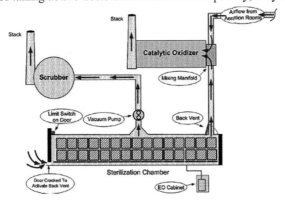

Figure 1. Control devices for facility emission.

perform correctly when the system calls for unconventional and even manual actions under abnormal situations. The study by Antonovsky et al., 2013, amplifies the relevance of incorrect assumptions. It surveys 45 petroleum industries and shows that the most common reason among all failures is the incorrect interpretation of events by the operator(s). As existing chemical plants, with their control systems and high mental demands on operators, can be neither re-designed nor extensively retrofitted, the authors propose a specific training method to overcome the risk of inaccurate understanding and subsequent incorrect actions.

4. Operator training

At our knowledge, the proposal of reducing operator errors by introducing novel training methodologies is not extensively discussed in the scientific literature. Training and development activities allow organizations to improve adaptability, competence, profits, production, and safety (Salas, 2001). As reported by Patel, 2010 for the USA, the amount of money spent in industrial training is about US$ 135 billion (*i.e.* US$ 135,000,000,000).

The authors emphasize the need for and the significance of advancements in training methods for process industry coupled to a cross-disciplinary approach, which can facilitate the operators performing their tasks better *i.e.* ensuring smoother, safer, and optimal operations within the available domain of degrees of freedom. Manca et al. (2013) introduced the concept of training based on a PS, which comprises a 3D immersive virtual environment that couples both dynamic process and accident simulators. Figure 2 summarizes the conceptual structure of the PS.

In order to improve the skills of operators in handling the automation of control/supervisory systems and their possible malfunction/failure, a training syllabus is proposed within the PS, which is coined Hierarchical Training Syllabus (HTS). As shown in Figure 3, the syllabus is divided into three stages, each featuring unique and specific characteristics with the aim of addressing the aforementioned issues for a comprehensive understanding of automated systems.

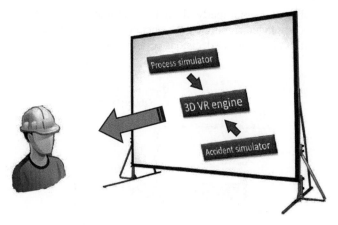

Figure 2. Conceptual representation of the PS structure where the operator faces a 3D immersive virtual environment during the training session.

The most important technical features of the three-stage HTS are:

1. An immersive 3D environment with a stereoscopic reproduction of the chemical plant for realistic experience of the operator.
2. Spatial sounds to reproduce similar sound effects as those in the real plant.
3. Augmented Virtual Reality (AVR) feature to allow the operators increasing their understanding and mental mapping with superimposed information.
4. Automated systems and their two-way interconnections with the 3D environment (*i.e.* the PS).
5. Possibility of simulating various malfunctions, automation failure, near misses, and abnormal situations during the training and assessment session of operators.

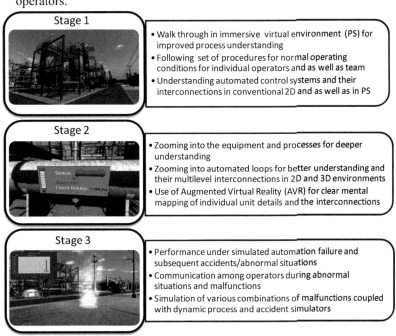

Stage 1
- Walk through in immersive virtual environment (PS) for improved process understanding
- Following set of procedures for normal operating conditions for individual operators and as well as team
- Understanding automated control systems and their interconnections in conventional 2D and as well as in PS

Stage 2
- Zooming into the equipment and processes for deeper understanding
- Zooming into automated loops for better understanding and their multilevel interconnections in 2D and 3D environments
- Use of Augmented Virtual Reality (AVR) for clear mental mapping of individual unit details and the interconnections

Stage 3
- Performance under simulated automation failure and subsequent accidents/abnormal situations
- Communication among operators during abnormal situations and malfunctions
- Simulation of various combinations of malfunctions coupled with dynamic process and accident simulators

Figure 3. The Hierarchical Training Syllabus.

These technical features allow training operators with high physical and cognitive fidelity in a way that is appropriate for adult education and that fosters skill and knowledge acquisition based on experiential learning principles (Kluge et al., 2009). Previous studies showed that training sessions with a PS improve the performance of operators during a simulated accident scenario (Nazir et al., 2012). This evidence encourages extending the training method to deal with automation and its possible malfunction/failure. The PS training (Nazir et al., 2013) not only supports mental mapping and retention abilities of the participants, but also sets up an effective communication among operators working at different plant sections. The concept deployed by third stage of training (Figure 3) is referred to as stress exposure training and its theoretical background and implementation is extensively discussed in Driskell et al. (1998). The HTS allows the operator to learn, understand, and practice the process details, control loops, interconnections, and constraints in a 3D immersive environment. In addition, simulated automation failures (which cannot be tested in a real plant) instill the skills of handling malfunctions, abnormal situations, coordination, skill acquisition, and adaptability. This unique training syllabus integrates the details of process plants, interconnections, and control loops and allows the operators to live real situations (in a virtual environment) by practicing the tasks and experiencing the imperfect features of automated systems and their possible consequences. We believe that adequately trained operators can properly interact with automated systems so to transform automation from curse to cure.

5. Conclusions

The paper explored the question: if automation is cure or curse for the process industry and raised the question on how training can improve operator's skill to handle automation and its possible malfunction/failure. The complexity of chemical processes was presented and discussed to demonstrate the increased mental workload of the operator. A case study, demonstrating the automation failure and related incorrect operator behavior, was also presented. In the light of previous experiments conducted on training in the Plant Simulator, PS, (Nazir et al., 2013), it is reasonable to maintain that the proposed Hierarchal Training Syllabus (HTS) can be a solution to support operators in handling automation, its imperfection and relevant complexity of the real tasks both under normal operating conditions and abnormal situations. Nevertheless, there is the need for investigating the improvements achievable with the PS when training real industrial operators so to understand the PS impact in detail and to determine the possible compromises among levels of automation, operator technology interaction, operator mental work load, financial goals, environmental constraints, and optimization of large sets of process parameters. This paper paves the way to further studies aiming at revealing additional practical benefits of HTS with relevance to automation of industrial processes.

References

Chemical Safety and Hazard Investigation Board (CSB), 2004, Investigation Report: Sterigenics, Washington, DC, U.S.

J.E. Driskell, J.H. Johnston, 1998, Stress Exposure Training, making decisions under stress. Implications for Individual and Team Training, APA, Washington, DC, 191–217.

A. Kluge, J. Sauer, K. Schüler, D. Burkolter, 2009, Designing training for process control simulators: a review of empirical findings and common practice, Theoretical Issues in Ergonomic Science, 10, 489–509.

D. Manca, S. Brambilla, S. Colombo, 2013, Bridging between virtual reality and accident simulation for training of process-industry operators, Advances in Engineering Software, 55, 1-9.

D. Manca, S. Nazir, F. Lucernoni, S. Colombo, 2012, Performance indicators for the assessment of industrial operators, Computer Aided Chemical Engineering, 30, 1422–1426.

S. Nazir, R. Totaro, S. Brambilla, S. Colombo, D. Manca, 2012, Virtual Reality and Augmented-Virtual Reality as Tools to Train Industrial Operators, Computer Aided Chemical Engineering, 30, 1397–1401.

S. Nazir, S. Colombo, D. Manca, 2013, Testing and analyzing different training methods for industrial operators: an experimental approach, Computer Aided Chemical Engineering, 32, 667–672.

E. Salas, J. A. Canoon-Bowers, 2001, The science of training: A decade of progress, Annual Review of Psychology, 52, 471–499.

C.D. Wickens, H. Li, A. Santamaria, A. Sebok, N.B. Sarter, 2010, Stages and Levels of Automation: An Integrated Meta-Analysis, Proceedings of the Human Factors and Ergonomics Society 54th Annual Meeting, 54, 4, 389–393.

D.D. Woods, S. Dekker, R. Cook, L. Johannesen, N. Sarter, 2010, Behind Human Error, 2nd ed, Burlington, VT, Ashgate.

Jiří Jaromír Klemeš, Petar Sabev Varbanov and Peng Yen Liew (Editors)
Proceedings of the 24th European Symposium on Computer Aided Process Engineering – ESCAPE 24
June 15-18, 2014, Budapest, Hungary.

Decision Support Tool for Strategic Planning in Supply Chains

Pedro Costa[a], Maria Isabel Gomes[b], Ana Carvalho[a*], Ana Barbosa-Póvoa[a]

[a]CEG-IST, Instituto Superior Técnico, Universidade de Lisboa, Av. Rovisco Pais, 1049-001, Lisboa, Portugal
[b]CMA, Universidade Nova de Lisboa, Monte da Caparica, 2829-526 Caparica, Portugal
anacarvalho@tecnico.ulisboa.pt

Abstract

This paper proposes a systematic methodology for supply chain planning optimization and assessment of different scenarios. This methodology will help companies throughout the difficult process of strategic decision-making in what concerns the design of an efficient supply chain structure. The proposed methodology allows the analysis of complex systems as it integrates a decision support tool developed to agile the process of scenario comparison, when designing network structures. This tool allows practitioners to take advantage of the optimization models without the need of learning modelling languages. An example based on a real case study is presented, showing the methodology/tool applicability.

Keywords: Decision Support Tool, Supply Chains, Network Design

1. Introduction

The globalization growth has caused industry and organizations to function and compete on a supply chain basis. Improving supply chain performance has become a critical goal for companies to gain competitive advantages in the markets (Cai et.al, 2009). Alongside with the increased requirements in terms of supply chains strong economic performance, organizations are now held responsible for the environmental and social performance of their suppliers and partners. Achieving a sustainable supply chain has now become one of the major goals (Seuring, 2013). In order to attain such sustainability, organizations have to look at the whole products/services life-cycle. Therefore it is crucial that the complete supply chain, including the forward and reverse flows, is planned in an integrated manner in order to ensure that the entire system is sustainable (Guide and Van Wassenhove, 2009). In the above context, closed-loop supply chains have become a cornerstone in companies' performance (Barbosa-Póvoa 2012). However, such supply chains are complex systems, which are difficult to optimise since they involve several interdependent decision variables. Companies thus require generic and systematic methodologies to help their decision processes when managing such systems, allowing them to plan effective and efficiently their supply chains. In order to achieve this goal those methodologies need to be incorporated in decision-support tools (DST), which will link the academic work to companies' problems, allowing a fast and precise analysis of supply chain structures. Within this context, the present work aims to present a systematic methodology enabling the analysis of different scenarios of supply chains structures, through the application of mathematical models, which are incorporated in a DST called *VisualSC*. The models are developed within mathematical language software (such as GAMS) and solved by commercial solver (as for instance, CPLEX).

2. Methodology

The proposed methodology, presented in Figure 1, follows a systems approach that intends to create and assess different optimized supply chain structures in a fast an efficient way. The methodology is able to deal with direct supply chains (such as forward or reverse flows) to complex structures (such as closed-loop supply chains), which simultaneously account for forward and reverse flows). Evaluating different scenarios of complex structures is a real time consuming problem involving complex models and therefore companies are usually reluctant to spend time learning and performing such type of analysis, ending up rejecting these methodologies. In order to overcome this problem a DST called *VisualSC* (in detail below) has been integrated within the methodological approach described, in order to agile the scenario comparison, turning complex optimization models more easily available for practitioners' analysis. The steps of the methodology are going to be explained in a step-by-step procedure.

2.1. Step 1: Problem Definition
In this step the type of problem in study is specified. The supply chain is characterized determining the type of flows that should be considered in the analysis (forward, reverse, closed-loop). Supply chain details, such as entities (suppliers, manufacturers, warehouses, customers, etc) and their connections are also specified within this step.

2.2. Step 2: Data Collection
In step 2 data regarding the supply chain is collected. Since this is a framework for supply chain network design, the possible locations of the facilities should be defined and distances between entities should be determined. Capacities ranges are to be established for each entity. This step usually is the first bottleneck for the analysis of different scenarios in network design problems. In complex structures this task is very time consuming, since a huge amount of data is required for the analysis. In that sense this methodology takes advantage of a DST (*VisualSC*) where the possible entities are inserted directly through the interface and the distances between them automatically calculated by *VisualSC*. All data of this step is entered directly through *VisualSC*. The tool automatically creates a file with all the required data for the optimization model. The user does not need to understand how to work with software such as GAMS/CPLEX.

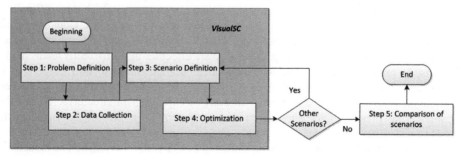

Figure 1. Methodology

2.3. Step 3: Scenario Definition

In this step a scenario with its particular characteristics is specified. As example, different facility capacities might be analysed, different demand scenarios studied, different transportation modes considered or even a scenario where the network may face disruptions could be analysed. This step should be performed whenever a new scenario is required for comparison. New specifications for the supply chain are inserted in *VisualSC* and a new input file for GAMS is generated.

2.4. Step 4: Optimization

In step 4 the optimization model representing the supply chain should be selected. This step includes a model library where several models taking into consideration different strategic and tactical aspects of the supply chain are available. At present *VisualSC* incorporates a generic model that allows the modelling of different supply chains networks (forward, reverse or both forward and reverse) (Salema et al., 2010). As above mentioned, *VisualSC* generates a data file in step 3, which is at this step exported to GAMS enabling the model optimization. It is important to mention that this model library can easily be updated with new models. The models just need to be implemented in GAMS, since the input files generated by *VisualSC* are designed for GAMS software. Any strategic/tactical model, which includes supply chains networks can be added and used to assess different supply chains. Moreover, the optimization model might be a single- or a multi-objective formulation modelling, for instance, the three pillars of sustainability: economic, environmental and social aspects.

2.5. Step 5: Comparison of scenarios

In this step the different scenarios are compared. After solving the problem, the GAMS output file is read by *VisualSC* and the optimal network structure and related data are displayed by the *VisualSC* interface. The file with the optimized problem can be saved and used at different times to allow the scenarios comparison. In this step the solution computed with the different objectives functions or different network characteristics are compared which eases the selection of the best alternatives.

2.6. Decision Support Tool- VisualSC

VisualSC is an online decision support tool supported by Google maps (geographic information), which allows the creation of optimized supply chain networks (forward, reverse and closed-loop). This DST is a strategic and tactical decision level tool, since the model now available determines the optimal supply chain network (strategic decisions) and defines facilities capacities, production levels, acquisition and distribution plans, collection amounts, among others, for the different supply chain entities (tactical decisions). To use this DST, the user inserts in the *VisualSC* all possible locations for the different supply chain entities and defines the echelons (links between entities) and associated data such as capacities, demands, costs, etc. *VisualSC* collects the required data through a GIS server (as the distances), creating an input file that will be uploaded into optimization software (GAMS/CPLEX). Specific network characteristics of the network might manually introduced/altered by the user. GAMS reads the input file and optimizes the proposed supply chain network. The output generated by GAMS is translated into nodes, which are displayed over the map of *VisualSC* interface, graphically showing the optimal supply chain structure. *VisualSC* software serves three main objectives: 1) facilitates the development of the network superstructure, 2) builds GAMS inputs files and connects with the optimizer, reducing significantly the required time involved in data collection and 3) visually presents the optimal solution provided by the optimizer. Figure 2 illustrates the architecture of DST *VisualSC*.

Figure 2 shows the main modules of the decision-support tool. *VisualSC* is connected with Arcgis Online, which provides services such as geometry, locator, routing and maps. These are opened access internet services avoiding the complex process of licence acquisition. An intermediate level between the user interface and GAMS/CPLEX provides all the files that connect both levels. These files are available is if a more knowledgeable user wants to access them.

3. Example

This case study is related to the strategic planning decisions, in a closed-loop supply chain, for a Portuguese glass company. In order to design its forward and reverse supply chain, the glass company has preselected five locations to build factories, warehouses and sorting centres so that its customers, clustered into 11 Portuguese districts, have their demand and returns fulfilled. When disposed by customers, glass is collected and sent to sorting centres. After quality evaluation and selection process, products are sent back to the factories to be incorporated in the production process or sent to proper disposal. Together with the location decisions, several tactical plans are determined. Namely, the plans for acquisition, production, distribution, and collection amounts are established for two-month periods within a five-year time horizon. Facilities and flows in between are limited in terms of capacities. The number of opened facilities is also limited, since the company wants to have at most two factories in operation and at most three warehouses and sorting centres. The company aims at defining the best network structure and operation plan so that the global supply chain cost is minimized.

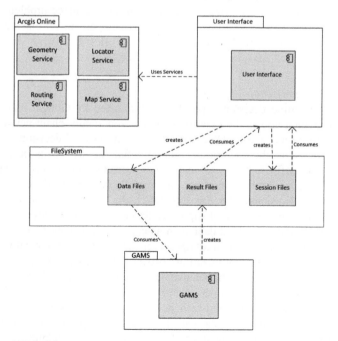

Figure 2. *VisualSC* Architecture

Due to lack of space only two scenarios will be analysed. The first one (case 1) sets all factories costs and capacities as initially estimated by the company. After analysing case 1 solution, the company wanted to investigate if it's preferable to invest in a factory in Lisboa with a larger production capacity and consequently higher opening costs (Case 2).

Using the *VisualSC* tool, all possible facility and customer locations were introduced, setting for each node its characteristics. The superstructure was then defined as shown in Figure 3. Notice that colours distinguish the supply chain echelons (e.g, flows from factory to warehouses, from warehouses to customer). All input files were then generated and fed to GAMS. After solving the problem, the output was uploaded to *VisualSC* and plotted over the map of Portugal (see Figure 4).

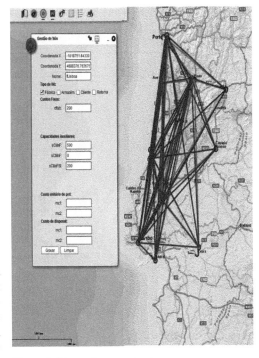

Figure 3. Network superstructure

The optimal supply chain has two factories, one located in Lisboa (southern Portugal) and the other in Porto (northern Portugal). Warehouses and sorting centres are opened at the same locations. All customers are served but not fully served. A penalty cost of 2,802 monetary units (u.m.) representing about 61% of the total supply chain cost is incurred. This low quality of service is due to under capacitated factories, therefore the company decided to investigate the consequences of investing in a larger and more expensive factory in Lisboa.

Concerning the structure, case 2 optimal network is the same as case 1, as the same locations are chosen. As it is possible to verify from Table 1, changes appear at the planning decision level since now it´s possible to satisfy almost all customers demand and return (not shown due to lack of space).

The penalty cost represents now less than 10% of the total cost. Since more products are flowing in the network, therefore the transportation costs increased, more than doubling the initial value.

Figure 4. Network optimal structure

Table 1. Optimal cost structure for cases 1 and 2 (in monetary units)

	Optimal cost	Fixed cost	Transportation cost	Penalty cost
Case 1	4,578	700	1,075	2,802
Case 2	3,608	900	2,379	329

Figure 5. Detail of case 1 optimal supply chain

However, the trade-off between transportation costs increased and penalty costs decrease leading to a better supply chain total cost. It decreased from 4,578 m.u. to 3,608 m.u. which is about 21 % reduction.

Figure 5 zooms the network in Porto region (northern Portugal). It shows with more detail the different facility locations and its connections. Although represented by straight lines, the distance between each node was calculated using Google Maps services, which bring more accuracy to transportation cost calculation. Both cases were solved in GAMS/CPLEX (bluit 23.9.1).

4. Conclusions

In this work we proposed a systematic methodology to help companies throughout the difficult process of strategic decision-making. A *VisualSC* decision-support tool is also developed and presented in this work. The main advantage of this tool is that it allows users (usually companies), which are not familiar with the mathematical models, to optimize their supply chain network, in an easier and user-friendly way. It is important to mention that the proposed methodology integrated with the tool *VisualSC* is generic and it can be easily extended to include any model. Moreover and as mentioned, some parameters required for the model are calculated automatically by *VisualSC*, reducing significantly the planning process, and allowing the creation and study of different scenarios. Currently a second model is being developed to expand *VisualSC* library. Several improvements have to be made in order to rend it even user-friendlier.

References

J. Cai, X. Liu, Z. Xiao, J. Liu, 2009, Improving supply chain performance management: A systematic approach to analysing iterative KPI accomplishment, Decision Support Systems, 46, 512–521.

V.D.R. Guide, L.N. Van Wassenhove, 2009, OR FORUM-The Evolution of Closed-Loop Supply Chain Research, Operations Research, 57, 10–18

A.P. Barbosa-Póvoa, 2012, Progresses and challenges in process industry supply chains optimization, Curren. Opinion in Chemical Engineering, 1, 446–452.

M.I.G. Salema, A.P. Barbosa-Povoa, A.Q. Novais, 2010, Simultaneous design and planning of supply chains with reverse flows: A generic modelling framework, European Journal of Operional Research, 203, 336–349.

S. Seuring, 2013, A review of modeling approaches for sustainable supply chain management, Decision Support Systems, 54, 4, 1513-1520

Jiří Jaromír Klemeš, Petar Sabev Varbanov and Peng Yen Liew (Editors)
Proceedings of the 24th European Symposium on Computer Aided Process Engineering – ESCAPE 24
June 15-18, 2014, Budapest, Hungary.

A Novel MaxEnt Method for the Solution of Two-Dimensional Population Balance Equation with Particle Growth

Menwer Attarakih,[a] Hans-Jörg Bart[b]

[a]*The University of Jordan, Faculty of Engineering & Technology, Department of Chemical Engineering, 11942 Amman, Jordan*
[b]*Chair of Separation Science and Technology, TU Kaiserslautern, 67653 Kaiserslautern, Germany*
m.attarakih@ju.edu.jo

Abstract

The population balance equation for particle growth finds many applications in chemical process industries and physical sciences. It is a hyperbolic partial differential with few known analytical solutions. We propose in this paper a novel converging sequence of continuous approximations to this equationfor the case of one- and two-dimensional particle growth. The uniqueness and convergence of such a sequence are assured by maximizing the Shannon entropy function, which is associated witha set of Lagrange multipliers. In contrast to the classical Maximum Entropy Method (MaxEntM), the Lagrange multipliers are estimated using a meshless method by point wise sampling of the continuous distribution. The proposed method provides local information about this distribution and is consistent with its low-order moments.

Keywords: PBE, Differential Maximum Entropy, Particle growth.

1. Introduction

The population balance equation is applied in many scientific and engineering applications. Such applications include multiphase flows and turbulence modelling, aerosol science and kinetic theory and biological and biomedical engineering (Ramkrishna, 2000). Fluid phases which are discrete either at the molecular or particle levels are described by the Boltzmann-type equation, which is called the population balance equation (PBE). One of the accepted efficient methods for solving of the PBE is the Quadrature Method of Moments (QMOM) due to its accuracy with no enormous number of transport equations. In this regard, Attarakih (2013) introduced the Cumulative QMOM, where the full size particle distribution is recovered using the a continuous version of the QMOM, while, Favero et al. (2014) highlighted problems associated with extending the QMOM to bivariate population problems.The QMOM solves the PBE, where a finite set of population moments is conserved. However, the QMOM cannot reproduce entire particle size distribution, where in many industrial particulate system applications, the full particle size distribution plays a decisive role in determining the physicochemical and mechanical product properties. Moreover, recent advances and development in online measurements and control provide real-time access to system parameters, which are estimated based on the whole size distribution (Mickler et al., 2013). Motivated by solving the PBE moment problem with distribution reconstruction, the mathematical problem at hand lends itself to the maximum entropy method (MaxEntM). The method proceeds by finding the least biased probability density subject to priori moment or general integral information. Solution consistency is preserved by maximizing the Shannon entropy function under the condition that the first $N+1$ moments of the lost solution are reproduced. In this work, we introduce a novel idea to extract the optimal Lagrange multipliers (which are a solution of the a variational problem) based on arbitrary pointwise sampling of the MaxEnt solution, instead of solving a convex nonlinear optimization problem (NLP) in the space-time domain. Since mesh points are arbitrary, and the approximate solution is continuous, the convection terms in the hyperbolic partial differential equation for particle growth are exactly evaluated independent of mesh structure. This leads to a few number of transport equations, where mesh points have its own convection velocities with a true meshless structure.

2. The DmaxEntM for the Solution of the Particle growth equation

The two-dimensional PBE which describes particle growth in two particle property spaces (e.g. size) with an average number concentration function $f(t,x,y)$ is given by:

$$\frac{\partial f(x,y,t)}{\partial t} + \sum_{u=x,y} \frac{\partial G_u f(x,y,t)}{\partial u} = 0 \tag{1}$$

Where G_u is the particle growth rate or convection velocity along the particle property space, which may depend on the two particle properties (x & y). A popular approach for solving the monovariate form of Eq.(1) is by using the Method Of Moments (MOM), where the particle size distribution is destroyed. Due to the general form of theparticle growth rate, the integral form of Eq.(1) presents a closure problem. An efficient solution to this problem is by using the Quadrature MOM (QMOM); however, with a limited success for multivariate problems (Favero et al., 2014). Recovering of f during the evolution of these low-order moments in space and time is a nontrivial problem.This problem is known in theoretical physics as the classical moment problem (CMP) and in particular the Stieltjes or Hausdorff moment problem (Gzyl and Tagliani, 2010). The CMP tries to recover the associated non-negative number concentration function from its low order moments with limited success (Falola et al., 2013).On the other hand, methods that uses direct discretization of Eq.(1) using finite difference schemes are well known to suffer from numerical diffusion. Therefore, hundreds of grid points are required to get reasonable resolution of the number density function. A novel idea that preserves the efficiency of method of moments and provides at the same time continuous approximation to f(x,t) is introduced by Attarakih and Bart (2012) to solve the one dimensional particle aggregation equation. Here, the Maximum Entropy was used for the construction of a sequence of approximations to the one-dimensional number concentration function by maximizing its entropy function under the consistency constraint to the first $N+1$ moments. This recovered number concentration, which maximizes the Shannon entropy (information) function, is statistically most likely to occur (Baker-Jarvisa, 1989). The solution of this is a constrained NLP problem results in the following optimal functional (Attarakih and Bart, 2012):

$$f_N(x,t) = \exp\left(-\sum_{r=0}^{N} \lambda_r(t)x^r\right) \tag{2}$$

In this equation λ_r are the Lagrangian multipliers, which are found by solving a convex NLP problem such that a given set of a priori moments is reproduced (Attarakih and Bart, 2012). This solution for Lagrange multipliers by optimization is by no means a straight forward problem especially in complex computational domains (like coupling the PBE with CFD). Therefore, we introduce an alternative approach to calculate the Lagrange multipliers appearing in Eq.(2) by arbitrary pointwise sampling of the number concentration function. This is accomplished by utilizing distributed nodal points, where the coefficients of the exponential polynomial in Eq.(2) can be estimated. Now, if $f(x,t)$ is supported on $[a,b]$, then let the distinct nodal points x_i, $i = 0, 1, ..N \in [a,b]$ can be defined in such a way that the error of interpolation of $p_N(x) = \sum \lambda_k x^k$ is minimized. With $p_N(x,t) = \ln(f(x,t))$ one can use the orthogonal collocation method to derive transport equations for $f(x_i,t)$. Therefore, the discrete counterpart of Eq.(1) in one-dimensional space (x) is given by:

$$\frac{\partial f(x_i,t)}{\partial t} + G_x(x_i)\frac{\partial f(x_i,t)}{\partial x} + f(x_i,t)\frac{\partial G_x(x_i)}{\partial x} = 0 \tag{3}$$

Where the initial condition is $f^0(x_i) = f(x_i,0)$, $i = 0, 1, ... N$. The Lagrange multipliers, which are the coefficients of the exponential polynomial are found by solving the following linear system of algebraic equations: $\mathbf{M}\lambda = \mathbf{R}$. The elements of the matrix $\mathbf{M}$ and the vector $\mathbf{R}$ are given by: $m_{i,j} = x_i^j$, $r_i(t) = \ln(f(x_i,t))$, $i, j = 0,1,...N$

Accordingly, Eq.(1) can be written in terms of the sampled $f(x)$ as follows:

$$f_N(x,t) = \exp\ m(\mathbf{x})^T \mathbf{M}^{-1}\mathbf{R}(\mathbf{x},t) \tag{4}$$

Where $m(\mathbf{x}) = [1\ xx^2x^3\ ...\ x^N]^T$. The derivative of $f_N(x)$ (w.r.t. x) can now be determined explicitly from Eq.(4):

$$\frac{\partial f_N(x,t)}{\partial x} = f_N(x,t)[c(\mathbf{x})^T \mathbf{M}^{-1}\mathbf{R}(\mathbf{x},t)] \tag{5}$$

Where $c(\mathbf{x}) = [0\ 1\ 2x\ 3x^2\ 4x^3\ ...\ Nx^{N-1}]^T$. The substitution of Eqs.(5 - 4) into (3) results in the one-dimensional PBE for particle growth which can be written as

$$\frac{df_N(x_i,t)}{\partial t} + \left(G_x(x_i)[c(\mathbf{x})^T \mathbf{M}^{-1}\mathbf{R}(\mathbf{x},t)] + \frac{dG_x(x_i)}{\partial x} \right) f_N(x_i,t) = 0 \tag{6}$$

By specifying the functional form of the growth law G(x), Eq.(6) represents a set of ODEs, which can be readily solved using any general purpose integrator. The only assumptions required to derive Eq.(6) are that $f(x,t)$ and $G(x)$ should be smooth enough to allow at least the existence of the first derivative. Since $f_N(x,t)$ is a continuous approximation of $f(x,t)$, then the solution of Eq.(6) is a true meshless solution and is consistent with respect to the low-order moments of $f(x,t)$. This is because the determined exponential polynomial coefficients (λ) are guaranteed to satisfy the constraints imposed during the maximization of the Shannon entropy function. The advantage of finding the Lagrange multipliers using the present DmaxEntM is twofold: First, the need for solving a NLP is replaced by a solution of linear system of equations. Second, the sampling of the continuous distribution function provides rich information about the behaviour of the function and hence improves its reconstruction.

3. Numerical Results and Discussion

The meshless DMaxEntM is first tested using the one-dimensional from of particle growth using Eq.(6). Two growth laws are used with size dependent and size independent particle growth; namely $G_x(x) = ax^n$. The growth rate constant is taken as $a = 0.5$ and the initial condition is $f(x,0) = 3x^2\exp(-x^3)$. The analytical solutions for these cases are given by Attarakih (2013). Jacobi nodes are used to sample the continuous solution, where they are scaled to map the real particle size domain $x = [a, b]$.

Figure(1) shows the reconstruction of the initial condition using 15 Jacobi nodes, which are available for $x \in [0, 2]$. Due to the constant particle growth, the initial condition is propagated along the particle property space with constant velocity. This preserves the number concentration function at any instant of time thanks to the exact derivative of the convection term in Eq.(6), which eliminated the numerical diffusion.

The interpolation power of the continuous approximation of $f(x,t)$ is clear ,where the reconstructed solution is indistinguishable from the analytical one. The consistency of the DMaxEntM solution with continuous one is shown by reproducing the first $N+1$ low-order moments with a high accuracy as shown in Figure (2).Note that the growth in the magnitude of the low-order moments for the case of linear particle growth law (Figure(2) right panel) as compared to the case of constant particle growth (Figure(2) left panel).

The second case for testing the meshless DMaxEntM is applied to the two dimensional particle growth with a convective velocity vector $\mathbf{G} = [0.15x, 1]^T$. The maximum entropy functional for the this case is given by $f(x,y,t) = \exp[g(\mathbf{x})^T \mathbf{M}^{-1}\mathbf{R}(\mathbf{x},t)]$,

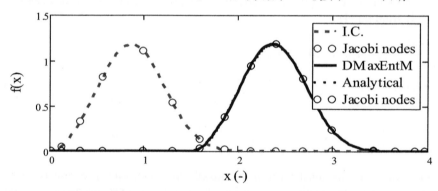

Figure 1. Comparison between analytical and DMaxEntM solutions using size independent growth rate law at final simulation time of 2.5 s with 15 Jacobi nodal points.

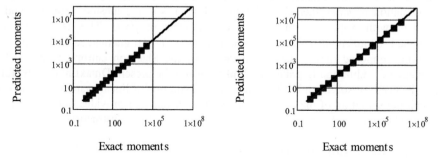

Figure 2. Comparison between the predicted and exact first 16 low-order moments for particle size independent growth rate (left) and linear particle growth rate (right).

where $g(\mathbf{x}) = [1 \quad x x^2 y y^2 x y]^T$. Note that the interaction term (xy) is introduced to take into account the correlation between the variables x and y. The coefficients of the bivariate second order polynomial are determined using Jacobi nodes along the x-and y-particle property spaces.

A minimum norm solution is obtained due the presence of nine Jacobi nodes with only six independent Lagrangian multipliers for a second order bivariate exponential polynomial. The elements of the matrix M are found by evaluating this second order polynomial using the nodal points of the two-dimensional grid.

As a numerical example, the initial conditions is a strongly correlated two-dimensional normal distribution with ($\sigma_1 = 0.65$, $\mu_1 = 3$, $\sigma_2 = 0.85$, $\mu_2 = 3$, $\rho_{12} = 0.5$). The particle phase space $\{x,y\}$ is sampled using Jacobi nodes along the lines $x = [0,10]$ and $y =[0,10]$. Transport equations for these sampled values are then solved using an adaptive Runge-Kutta method (orders 4 and 5) as an ODE solver. The values of the two-dimensional function at these nodal points are then used to evaluate the Lagrange multipliers appearing in the MaxEnt solution. Since, this MaxEnt solution is a continuous

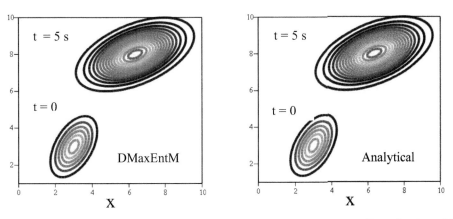

Figure3. Contours of the initial condition and the final solutions for two-dimensional particle growth using the meshless DMaxEntM and the analytical solution.

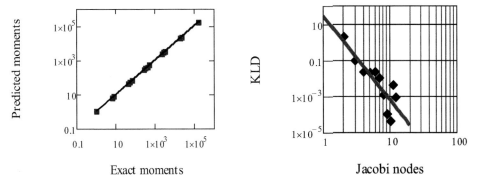

Figure 4. (Left): Comparison between the exact and predicted moments using all possible combinations of $m = 0,1, 3$ and $n = 0, 1, 3$. (Right): Convergence of the DMaxEntM for the case of linear particle growth as measured by the Kullback-Leibler Divergence (KLD).

distribution, the convection derivatives are evaluated exactly. This provides an extremely accurate solver of the convective term, which is essentially free of artificial numerical diffusion and oscillation. The initial condition and the final solutions are shown in Figure 3, where the particle growth along both dimensions are compared to the analytical solution. Note that the linear growth rate in the x-direction results in fast expansion of the initial condition in this direction. Figure (4-Left) shows the bivariate distribution moments with all possible combinations of orders $m = 0,1, 3$ and $n = 0, 1, 3$ at the final simulation time of 5 s. Again, the remarkable ability of the meshless MaxEntM to reproduce all of these low-order moments is obvious. The rapid rate of convergence for the meshless DMaxEntMis shown in Figure (4-Right) as measured by the Kullback-Leibler Divergence (KLD) (Gzyl and Tagliani, 2010). The rate of convergence is proportional to $(1/N^{4.67})$, where N is the number of Jacobi nodes. The computational time is found to be proportional to N and requires few seconds using a state art laptop with 2.5 GHz speed.

4. Conclusions

The concept of the meshless DMaxEntM was derived and applied to one-and two-dimensional particle growth. The messhless property allowed us to evaluate exactly the convective derivatives, which completely eliminated numerical diffusion and dispersion. The pointwise sampling technique was found efficient to calculate the Lagrange multipliers, which are coefficients of the exponential solution. By being an unbiased estimator to the sought number density function, the optimal sequence of functional was found to converge rapidly to the exact solutions of the PBE using the Kullback-Leibler divergence (strong convergence) as a convergence measure.

Acknowledgements

The authors would like to thank DFG for the financial support.

References

M. Attarakih, 2013, Integral formulation of the population balance equation: Application to particulate systems with particle growth, Comp. Chem. Eng., 48, 1-13.

M.M. Attarakih, H.-J. Bart, 2012,On the Constrained Maximum Entropy Solution of thePopulation Balance Equation. Proceedings of the 22nd European Symposium on Computer-Aided Chemical Engineering, 17 – 20, June 2012, London.

J. Baker-Jarvisa, M. Racine, J. Alameddine, 1989, Solving differential equations by a maximum entropy-minimum norm method with applications to Fokker-Planck equations, J. Math. Phys., 30, 1459-1463.

A. Falola, A. Borissova, X.Z. Wang, 2013, Extended method of moment for general population balance models including size dependent growth rate, aggregation and breakage kernels, Comp. Chem. Eng., 56, 1–11.

J.L. Favero, L.F.L.R Silvab, P.L.C. Lage, 2014, Comparison of methods for multivariate moment inversion-introducing the independent component analysis, Comp. Chem. Eng., 60, 41–56.

H. Gzyl, A. Tagliani, 2010, Stieltjes moment problem and fractional moments, App. Math. Comp., 216, 3307–3318.

M. Mickler, H.B. Jildeh, M. Attarakih, H.-J. Bart, 2013, Online monitoring, simulation and prediction of multiphase flows. Can. J. Chem. Eng., DOI: 10.1002/cjce.21893.

D. Ramkrishna, 2000, Population balances: Theory and applications to particulate systems in engineering, Academic Press, San Diego, USA.

Jiří Jaromír Klemeš, Petar Sabev Varbanov and Peng Yen Liew (Editors)
Proceedings of the 24th European Symposium on Computer Aided Process Engineering – ESCAPE 24
June 15-18, 2014, Budapest, Hungary.

Large Eddy Simulation of Non-spherical Particle Deposition in a Vertical Turbulent Channel Flow

Derrick O. Njobuenwu*, Michael Fairweather

Institute of Particle Science & Engineering, School of Process, Environmental & Materials Engineering, University of Leeds, Leeds LS2 9JT, UK
d.o.njobuenwu@leeds.ac.uk

Abstract

Non-spherical particle deposition in a vertical turbulent channel flow is studied using large eddy simulation and a stochastic Markov model that represent the effect of unresolved sub-grid scale fluctuations on particle dispersion. A Lagrangian particle tracking algorithm, accounting for drag, lift, gravity and Brownian forces, as well as particle shape, orientation and rotation, is developed and used to predict particle deposition. Results show good agreement with measurements, demonstrating that the characteristics of the flow and particle force balance are well captured, and the effects of particle shape and orientation are demonstrated.

Keywords: Large eddy simulation, spheroid, orientation, deposition, channel flow

1. Introduction

Deposition of solid suspension on the surface of a wall is of importance in many applications such as the deposition of corrosion oxides in nuclear reactors, heat exchangers and turbine blades, as well as in the respiratory tract (Alexopoulos et al., 2010). In nuclear reactor applications, for example, in-circuit dusts from metal surfaces exposed to gaseous coolant are small but these corrosion products generally evolve into larger particles due to agglomeration and deposition. Such interactions result in particle sizes ranging from 0.1 μm - 1 mm and a shape spectrum that varies from needle-like, through near-spherical to platelets or flakes. Understanding the dynamics of particle dispersion and developing methods to predict and control particle deposition rates in different levels of turbulence as a function of particle shape, size and orientation is of value in aiding the design and optimisation of such systems. Particle deposition is defined here as the process by which suspended particles from a fluid in motion become attached to the surface of a wall. For deposition to occur, the particle is assumed to have contact with the wall surface and to adhere to the wall at the point of contact. In most industrial applications of interest, the flow involved is turbulent and the rotational dynamics, alignment trends and correlation of anisotropic particles (such as needles, flakes or more general ellipsoidal shapes) with the flow field become of considerable interest. It is expected that accounting for particle shape and orientation in the linear and angular momentum equations in a particle simulation will give more accurate predictions of particle dispersion and deposition in a turbulent flow, with the accurate prediction of turbulent flow fields a prerequisite for the reliable calculation of such phenomena. Large eddy simulation (LES) is considered the appropriate computational fluid dynamic (CFD) tool to capture the complicated near-wall phenomena present in these industrially relevant multiphase flows, when compared to Reynolds-averaged Navier-Stokes (RANS) techniques and direct numerical simulation (DNS), in terms of the balance required between accuracy and computational cost.

Experimental studies of spherical particle deposition present a classical "S-shaped" curve that illustrates the basic characteristics of deposition rate in terms of the non-dimensional particle deposition velocity and the non-dimensional particle relaxation time. There exists a great deal of scatter in the deposition rate curve due to variability in the data, with predictions using differing methods also showing wide variability. This degree of disparity in predictions in some cases depends on the CFD modelling approach, the forces and deposition mechanisms, and the deposition model applied. Most RANS models under-predict the flow field turbulence, which affects the accuracy of the deposition rate. Another debateable issue in the literature is the use of the maximum computing time t_{max} in computing deposition rate, which has been proven to be misleading (Gao and He, 2012). Therefore, LES and the correct deposition model (Gao and He, 2012) which is similar to experimental results (Liu and Agarwal, 1974) is adopted in this paper.

2. Numerical Methods

In this study, the fluid flow in a turbulent channel flow is solved by the LES. The sub-grid scale (SGS) stress arising from the top-hat filtering operation on the Navier-Stokes equations was modelled using the Germano dynamic model. The resulting large eddy simulation transport equations were solved with the computer program BOFFIN (Njobuenwu and Fairweather, 2014) to obtain flow and turbulence characteristics. The channel flow with shear Reynolds number $Re_\tau = hu_\tau/v = 300$ has inertial coordinates $x = [x.y.z]$, computational domain size $(2h \times 2h\pi \times 4h\pi)$ and grid nodes (129 x 128 x 128) in the wall-normal, spanwise and streamwise directions; where $u_\tau = (\tau_w/\rho)^{1/2}$ is the shear velocity, h is the channel half height, v is the air kinematic viscosity, τ_w is the wall shear stress and ρ is the air density. The initial and boundary conditions are the same as in (Njobuenwu and Fairweather, 2013).

The simulation of particle motion was based on the assumption that the particles do not affect the flow field. The particle inertia, shape and orientation, with low density ratio $\rho/\rho_p << 1$, are considered to affect the particle motion. Here, the motion of a stochastic particle in a turbulent flow field can be viewed as a random process with its position determined by two parts. A deterministic part, obtained from known filtered velocities that contains the resolved scales of turbulence, and a stochastic component arising from the SGS turbulent motions of the fluid phase and Brownian motion. The deterministic part is taken from the Maxey and Riley formulation for the force per unit mass, such as drag, F_D, and lift, F_L, forces. We adopt a stochastic Markov model to represent the influence of the unresolved fluid velocity fluctuations experienced by a stochastic particle p over a time, dt (Bini and Jones, 2008). Adding the deterministic part, buoyancy-gravity term, F_{BG}, and the stochastic part (Brownian force term, F_{BM} and SGS dispersion) together gives:

$$\mathbf{du}_p = (\mathbf{F}_D + \mathbf{F}_{BG} + \mathbf{F}_L + \mathbf{F}_{BM})dt + \sqrt{(C_0 k_{sgs}/\tau_t)}d\mathbf{W}_t. \tag{1}$$

Note that in Eq. (1), for a spherical particle ($\lambda = 1$), the Mie variant of the Saffman lift force is applied, whereas the profile lift force is used for non-spherical particles ($\lambda \neq 1$). The drag coefficient is calculated using the Ganser drag coefficient correlation with a dynamic projected area normal to the direction of the drag force. The Cunningham slip correction for sub-micron particles was also accounted for in Eq.(1). The last term in Eq. (1) models the SGS particle dispersion (Bini and Jones, 2008); k_{sgs} is the unresolved kinetic energy of the gas, C_0 is a model constant, dW_t represents the increment of the

Wiener process and τ_t is a sub-grid timescale which affects the rate of interaction between the particle and turbulence dynamics. The rotation of the particle is given by the Euler rotational equation as:

$$\mathbf{I} \cdot \frac{d\boldsymbol{\omega}(t)}{dt} + \boldsymbol{\omega}(t) \times [\mathbf{I} \cdot \boldsymbol{\omega}(t)] = \mathbf{T}(t), \tag{2}$$

where $\mathbf{I}$ is the inertia tensor, $\omega = [\omega_{x'}, \omega_{y'}, \omega_{z'}]$ is the angular velocity, and $T = [T_1 + T_2]$ is the net torque exerted on the particle caused by the non-coincident centres of mass and of pressure, T_1, and the torque due to the resistance on a relatively rotating body, T_2, which always acts to attenuate the relative rotation. Note that in Eq. (2), I, T and ω are given in the particle frame of reference x' = $[x', y', z']$ whereas the parameters in Eq. (1) are expressed in the inertial frame, x = $[x, y, z]$. The transformation between both frames is expressed as x'=A·x, where A = $[a_{ij}]$ is the transformation matrix, whose elements a_{ij} represent the direction cosines of the particle axes x' relative to the inertial frame x. Due to the singularities inherent in the use of Euler angles (ϕ, θ, ψ), the four Euler quaternions, q=$[q_0, q_1, q_2, q_3]$, are used to represent the transformation matrix, which then becomes a rotational matrix subject to the constraint $q_0^2 + q_1^2 + q_2^2 + q_3^2 = 1$. The rate of change of orientation $\dot{\mathbf{q}}$ due to the rotational velocity is given as $\dot{\mathbf{q}} = \frac{1}{2}\mathbf{q} \cdot (0, \boldsymbol{\omega})$. Note that bold-faced variables represent a matrix-vector and expressions for the forces and torques in Eqs. (1) and (2) were taken from the literature (Yin et al., 2004, Bini and Jones, 2008; Njobuenwu et al., 2013).

The particle equations of linear and angular momentum were both integrated using a fourth-order Runge-Kutta method. Particle trajectories $x_p = [x_p, y_p, z_p]$ are calculated by integrating Eq. (1) twice using this approach. The particle integration time for both the translational and rotational motion is equal or less than to the LES time step depending on the particle size, and it is chosen to be smaller than the particle response time, τ_p. During each time step, the fluid flow field is first updated and then interpolated to the particle position using a trilinear interpolation scheme and then subsequently passed to the Lagrangian particle tracker.

3. Particle Deposition on Smooth Surface

On reaching the wall, the particles are considered to stick to it with zero probability of re-bound or resuspension. This is a reasonable assumption for the olive oil droplets used in the experiment of Liu and Agarwal (1974). The wall boundary condition is straightforward for spherical and complex for non-spherical particles. In the latter case, therefore, it is important to find the precise location of the touch point of the particle surface on the wall. Spherical particles are assumed to touch the wall when the distance from their centre of mass to the wall is less than the particle radius. However, for the ellipsoidal particles, three deposition scenarios could occur (Fan and Ahmadi, 1995). First, if the distance of the particle centroid from the boundary surface is less than the semi-minor axis, *a*, it will be deposited. Second, if this relative position is greater than the semi-major axis, *c*, the ellipsoid is in suspension. Third, when the distance between the particle centroid and the wall is within the range of the *a* and *c* axes, whether the ellipsoid is deposited or not depends on its orientation relative to the wall.

The particle to fluid density ratio was set to $\rho/\rho_p = 770$, which represents the density ratio used in the olive oil in air experiments of Liu and Agarwal (1974). Several thousand particles $O(10^5)$ with a diameter range 0.1–300 μm where uniformly distributed at the inlet of the channel with their initial linear and rotational velocity equal to those of the fluid at the particle position. The particle initial streamwise velocity was set equal the bulk air velocity, $w_{p0} = U_b$, and zero in the other directions, $u_{p0} = v_{p0} = 0$, while the orientation was specified randomly by Euler angles. The number of particles used was found to be sufficiently large to provide stationary statistics. Of particular interest is the number of particles deposited and the particle deposition rate monitored as a fractional penetration, as reported in Liu and Agarwal (1974). Using these data the deposition rate was calculated for each particle size and shape by:

$$u_d = \ln\left(\frac{N_0}{N_{out}}\right)\frac{U_b L_x}{L_z} = \ln\left(\frac{N_0}{N_0 - N_d}\right)\frac{U_b L_x}{L_z} \tag{3}$$

where N_d is the number of particles deposited onto the walls, U_b the bulk air velocity, L_z is the length of the channel section where deposition is studied, L_x is the height of the channel. Therefore, the time required to flush particles through the channel should be L_z/U_b and not the maximum computing time t_{max}. At the inlet, $N = N_0$; at the outlet, $N = N_{out}$, $N_{out} = N_0 - N_d$. The results of the deposition rate calculations are presented as curves of the non-dimensional deposition velocity, $u_d^+ = u_d/u_\tau$, plotted against the non-dimensional particle relaxation time, $\tau_p^+ = \tau_p u_\tau^2/v$.

4. Results and Discussion

Results obtained in this work indicate that LES is a viable approach for predicting particle deposition in turbulent boundary layers, with predictions found to be in reasonable agreement with DNS results (Njobuenwu and Fairweather, 2014). Results for the deposition of particles with varying particle aspect ratios, such as disk ($\lambda = 10^{-1}$), spherical ($\lambda = 10^0$) and needle-like ($\lambda = 10^1$) particles, are reported below.

Variation in the predicted dimensionless deposition velocity with particle dimensionless relaxation time is given in Figure 1 for each of the three particle shapes. The experimental data of Liu and Agarwal (1974) and Sehmel (1968) for spherical particles are also shown in the figure. There is a striking difference in the results produced by the three particle shapes. First, for the spherical particle, which is the same shape as the experimental measurements, the model predicts the classic "S-shaped" curve with good agreement with the Liu and Agarwal (1974) data, and with reasonable qualitative agreement with the Sehmel data. Deposition rate has been shown to be less dependent on flow Reynolds number, and the good agreement with the Liu and Agarwal (1974) data is expected since the particle density ratio and methods of deriving the results are similar. The level of agreement obtained is also superior to other comparisons available in the literature. Wood (1981) and other authors distinguish three regimes for the deposition velocity over vertical smooth surfaces with respect to particle inertia, τ_p^+: the turbulent particle diffusion regime $(\tau_p^+ < 1)$, the eddy diffusion-impaction regime $(0.1 \leq \tau_p^+ < 10)$, and the particle-inertia-moderated regime $(\tau_p^+ > 10)$. In the first regime, which forms the left side of the "S-shaped" curve where v_d^+ decreases with τ_p^+, the combination of Brownian motion and eddy diffusion are the major mechanisms of particle transport to the wall, and they are well captured by the LES, Brownian motion induced force and the stochastic Markov model for the effect of SGS fluctuations on particle dispersion. The second regime, which is characterized by a sharp increase in v_d^+ with τ_p^+, and the third regime where v_d^+ does not increase with τ_p^+, rather it is saturated and eventually decreases with an increase in τ_p^+, are again well captured except for a slight under-prediction in the high inertia region, $\tau_p^+ \gg 1$. This region is dominated by turbophoresis and the results suggest that this particle transport mechanism may have been under predicted. Note that turbophoresis is particle acceleration caused by the negative gradient of the turbulence kinetic energy in the wall vicinity.

Although calculated over a narrower range of τ_p^+, the non-spherical particles generally show a lower deposition rate than the spherical particles of equal equivalent volume diameter. Among other mechanisms, this lower deposition rate is likely due to the profile lift caused by their dynamic orientation, attributable to their size anisotropy. More detailed analysis would, however, be useful in further elucidating this finding.

The position and orientation (in the non-spherical case) of particles on the wall surface, at $x^+ = 0$, is shown in Fig. 2 for spherical and needle-like particles, with both sets of results having an equal dimensionless particle relaxation time, $\tau_p^+ = 162$. These results clearly illustrate the importance of shape in terms of how particles deposit on a surface and, ultimately for many practical applications, how they will form particle beds that may, for example, block a flow or affect heat transfer rates.

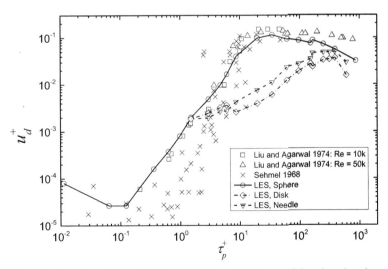

Figure 1. Dimensionless deposition velocity versus dimensionless particle relaxation time.

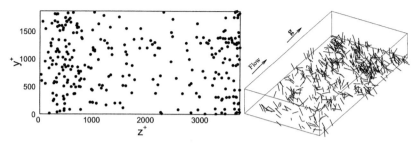

Figure 2. Deposition of spherical (left) and needle-like (right) particles on the wall.

5. Conclusions

Predictions of spherical particle deposition rate are in good agreement with experimental data, with improvements over previous results due to the use of the correct flushing time, as well as the predictions being based on the unresolved velocity scale and the correct force and torque balance for the particle linear and rotational dynamics. Preliminary results for non-spherical particles show significant differences that will be explored further in future work.

Acknowledgements

The authors wish to thank the Engineering and Physical Sciences Research Council for their financial support of the work reported under EPSRC Grant EP/I003010/1.

References

A.H. Alexopoulos, P. Karakosta, C. Kiparissides 2010. Particle transfer and deposition using an integrated CFD model of the respiratory system. Computer Aided Process Engineering, 28, Ischia Italy, 211-216.

M. Bini, W.P. Jones, 2008, Large-eddy simulation of particle-laden turbulent flows, Journal of Fluid Mechanics, 614, 207-252.

F.-G. Fan, G. Ahmadi, 1995, A sublayer model for wall deposition of ellipsoidal particles in turbulent streams, Journal of Aerosol Science, 26, 813-840.

N. Gao, Q. He, 2012, Calculation of particle deposition velocity in the Lagrangian frame, Indoor and Built Environment, 21, 348-350.

B.Y.H. Liu, J.K. Agarwal, 1974, Experimental observation of aerosol deposition in turbulent flow, Journal of Aerosol Science, 5, 145-155.

D.O. Njobuenwu, M. Fairweather, 2014, Effect of Shape on Inertial Particle Dynamics in a Channel Flow, Flow, Turbulence and Combustion, 92, 83-101.

D.O. Njobuenwu, M. Fairweather, J. Yao, 2013, Coupled RANS–LPT modelling of dilute, particle-laden flow in a duct with a 90° bend, International Journal of Multiphase Flow, 50, 71-88.

G.A. Sehmel, 1968, Aerosol deposition from turbulent airstreams in vertical conduits: Pacific Northwest Lab., Battelle-Northwest, Richland, Washington, USA.

N.B. Wood, 1981, A simple method for the calculation of turbulent deposition to smooth and rough surfaces, Journal of Aerosol Science, 12, 275-290.

C. Yin, L. Rosendahl, S. K. Kær, T. J. Condra, 2004, Use of numerical modeling in design for co-firing biomass in wall-fired burners, Chemical Engineering Science, 59, 3281-3292.

Jiří Jaromír Klemeš, Petar Sabev Varbanov and Peng Yen Liew (Editors)
Proceedings of the 24th European Symposium on Computer Aided Process Engineering – ESCAPE 24
June 15-18, 2014, Budapest, Hungary. Copyright © 2014 Elsevier B.V. All rights reserved.

An Integral Approach to Multi-physics Application for Packed Bed Reactors

Bernhard Peters*, Xavier Besseron, Alvaro Estupinan, Florian Hoffmann, Mark Michael, Amir Mouhmadi, Mohammad Mohseni

University of Luxembourg, 6, rue Coudenhove-Kalergi, L-1359 Luxembourg, Luxembourg
bernhard.peters@uni.lu

Abstract

A large number of engineering applications involve granular material or a particulate phase in combination with a gaseous or liquid phase. Predominant applications are as diverse as pharmaceutical industry e.g. drug production, agriculture food and processing industry, mining, construction and agricultural machinery, metals manufacturing, energy production and systems biology. Common to all these application is that they cover a large spectrum of length scales ranging from inner particle length scales to global dimensions of the reactor. In order to describe the processes and their interaction accurately, tailored algorithms are required for prediction and analysis. The current numerical approach of the Extended Discrete Element Method (XDEM) is based on an Eulerian-Lagrange coupling. For this purpose the solid phase consisting of individual particles is treated by the Lagrange method that describes both the dynamic state i.e. position and orientation of each particle in space and time and its thermodynamic state e.g. internal temperature and species distribution. The flow of gas in the void space between the particles is predicted by traditional and well-proven Computational Fluid Dynamics (CFD) taking into account heat and mass transfer between the particles and the surrounding gas phase. Hence, the entire process represented by the sum of all particle processes in conjunction with fluid dynamics. The afore-mentioned numerical concept was applied to predict pyrolysis of a packed bed of wood particles in a cylindrical reactor. A comparison of predicted results with experimental data show good agreement. Hence, the numerical concept is able to resolve a large range of length scales for solid reaction engineering. An analysis of detailed results helps to uncover the underlying physics of the process, and thus, allows for an improved design and operation conditions.

Keywords: Extended Discrete Element Method, numerical modelling, multi-physics

1. Introduction

Contrary to continuum models an alternative approach considers the solid phase as discrete, while the flow of liquids or gases is treated as a continuum phase in the void space between the particles, and therefore, is labelled the Combined Continuum and Discrete Model (CCDM) as employed by Tsuji et al. (1993), Hoomans et al. (1996), and Xu and Yu (1997; 1998). Due to a discrete description of the solid phase, constitutive relations are omitted, and therefore, leads to a better understanding of the fundamentals. This was also concluded by Zhu et al. (2007; 2008) during a review on particulate flows modelled with the CCDM approach. Based on this approach Sheng et al. (2013) investigated into the micro-scale heat transfer of packed beds and micro-fibrous entrapped catalysts and concluded that the thermal resistance of the contact points account for more than 90 % of the total resistance. Similarly, Kon et al. (2013) modelled the liquid flow in the lower part of a blast furnace by the MPS method. CCDM has seen a mayor development in last two decades and describes motion of the solid phase by the Discrete Element Method (DEM) on an individual particle scale and the remaining phases are treated by the Navier-Stokes equations.

However, current CCDM approaches should be extended to a truly multi-phase flow behaviour as opposed to the Volume-of-Fluid method and the multi-phase mixture model [7]. Furthermore, particle shapes other than spherical geometries have to be taken into account to meet engineering needs according to Zhu et al. (2007; 2008). This efforts should ideally be complemented by poly-disperse particle systems as employed by Peters and Dziugys (2011). All these efforts should contribute to a general link between continuum and discrete approaches so that results are quantified for process modelling.

2. Numerical Approach

A novel technique referred to as Extended Discrete Element Method (XDEM) (Wikipedia, 2012; Peters, 2013) has emerged only recently that offers a significant advancement for multi-physics applications. It is based on a coupled discrete and continuous i.e. Lagrange-Euler simulation concept. XDEM treats the solid phase representing the particles and the fluid phase or a structure as two distinguished entities that are coupled through heat, mass and momentum transfer. An outstanding feature of the numerical concept is that each particle in addition to its position and orientation in time and space is described by its thermodynamic state e.g. temperature and reaction progress. The thermodynamic state is described by one-dimensional and transient differential conservation equations for mass, energy and momentum for each individual particle and thus, characterizes the overall behaviour of the reactor as the sum of all particle processes. Predicted results for all individual particles allow a detailed analysis of the reaction process.

Through predicting position and orientation of all particles their arrangement in space is known that determines the 3-dimensional distribution of void space between the particles. This essentially represents a porous structure through which the fluid e.g. liquid or gas streams. The fluid is in contact with the surface of the particles and determines heat and mass exchange between the particle's surface and the fluid i.e. temperature and composition in the vicinity of the particle. In order to predict flow through the interstitial space a classical CFD approach is preferred for which the software framework of OpenFoam is employed. Its library offers a large selection of solves for different applications and allows as an open-source software a tailored development of solvers suiting the needs of the above-mentioned applications.

Hence, the proposed methodology provides a high degree of resolution ranging from scales within a particle to the continuum phase as global dimensions and offers superior features as compared to traditional and pure continuum mechanics approaches. The latter does not include detailed information on a particulate scale that has to be compensated for by empirical correlations such as distribution of void space in a packed or moving bed. For a more detailed description the reader is referred to Peters and Dziugys.

3. Results

This concept was applied to predict drying and pyrolysis of spruce wood particles in a packed bed of which the properties are given in the following table 1.

For an efficient validation process as described by Peters and Smula-Ostaszewska (2010), predicted results were first compared to measurements of a single particle for which Gronli (1996) carried out pyrolysis experiments of spruce cylinders. One of the circular side surfaces was exposed to a radiative flux of 80.0 kW and 130.0 kW, respectively. The temperatures were recorded at 5 different positions (L = 1, 4, 8, 12, 24 mm) along the cylinder axis during an experiment. Minimum and maximum temperatures at different positions were evaluated under identical conditions for several experiments so that experimental uncertainty related to the unavoidably difference in wood samples was obtained. Thus, an improvement of predictions within the experimental error is not necessary. For a more detailed description of the experimental set-up and pyrolysis model the reader is referred Gronli (1996).

Figues 1 and 2 depict a comparison between the measured temperature and the predictions at different locations within the sample.

In general, the temperature profiles attain the exponential characteristics of heat conducted within a solid material (Carslaw, M. S. and Jaeger, J. C., 1959). The measured maximum and minimum temperatures express differences of more than 100 K during its evolution for the temperatures measured closest to the sample surface. However, these differences reduce to app. 30 - 50 K for inner locations of temperature

Table 1. Properties of spruce wood

Property	Value
Density	450 kg/m^3
Specific heat	(1500.0+T) J/kgK
Conductivity spruce	0.35 W/mK
Conductivity char	0.1 W/mK
Porosity	0.68
Pore diameter	50 10^{-6} m

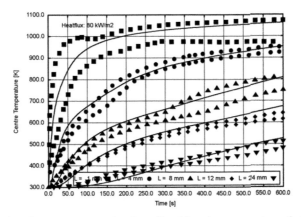

Figure 1. Comparison between measured and predicted interior temperatures during pyrolysis of a cylindrical spruce wood sample at a radiative heat flux of 80.0 kW/m^2

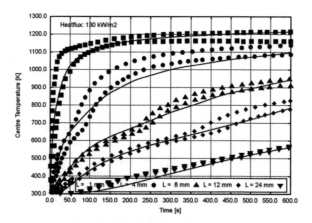

Figure 2. Comparison between measured and predicted interior temperatures during pyrolysis of a cylindrical spruce wood sample at a radiative heat flux of 130.0 kW/m^2

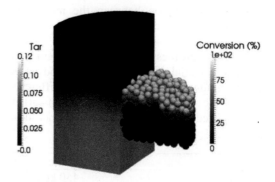

Figure 3. Predicted conversion rates of individual particles during pyrolysis in a packed bed in conjunction with the tar distribution in the gas phase

measurements. The predicted transient temperature profiles at the 5 locations fall mostly between the maximum and minimum measured temperature profiles, and thus, agree well with experiments.

After a successful validation of pyrolysis for a single particle, the model with its kinetic parameters was applied to each individual particle of a packed bed in a cylindrical reactor depicted in Figure 3. Hot inert gas streamed through the reactor to heat-up the particles and to provide sufficient heat for pyrolysis. A detailed description of the experimental set-up is found in Schröder (1999).

Figure 3 shows the rather inhomogeneous pyrolysis process taking place in the upper part of the reactor where the hot enters the void space of the packed bed. Rather advanced pyrolysis is observed for particles near the circumference of the reactor as compared to particles located at the centre which is due to higher temperatures around the inner reactor wall. The latter is due to increased porosity in conjunction with higher mass flow rates than in the centre of the reactor, and thus, augmented heat transfer and pyrolysis rate.

Furthermore, Figure 4 depicts the spatial and temporal distribution of temperature for two particles located at the top and bottom of the reactor. Although the particles do not experience a spatial gradient for temperature due to a slow convective heat transfer from the hot in-flow of gas, a spatial resolution is in general required for particles of larger size or high heating rates, for which significant temperature gradients within the particles develop. These temperature differences affect the reaction progress to a large extent and cannot be described with a space-averaged mean of the particle temperatures. Furthermore, the heat-up process for the bottom particle for the right sub-figure in Figure 4 is significantly delayed due to an earlier heat-up of the particles in the upper part of the reactor where the hot incoming air transfers its heat much earlier to these particles as to be seen in the left sub-figure of Figure 4. Once the hot incoming gas has transferred its heat to the upper particles, the gas temperature decreases and consequently, particles in the lower part of the reactor experience a reduced heating rate in conjunction with a delay of app. 1000 s. Hence, the Extended Discrete Element Method offers results with a high degree of resolution in both time and space of which the analysis contributes significantly to the understanding of the underlying physics. Additionally, many empirical correlations such as the distribution of void space in a reactor are omitted, and thus reduce experimental work to a large extent.

4. Conclusions

The current contribution describes the Extended Discrete Element Method (XDEM) that is applied to thermal conversion of packed beds as often encountered in process engineering. The methodology relies on a Lagrange-Eulerian approach that couples effectively the particulate phase with a gas streaming through the void space of a packed bed reactor. The particle processes of the packed bed are described by the solution of one-dimensional and transient differential conservation equations for mass and energy. This set of equation is solved individually for each particle of the packed bed by fast and efficient algorithms. Thus, the thermodynamic state of each particle is determined taking into account space and time-dependent boundary conditions prevailing within the reactor such as heat and mass transfer between the particle surface and the surrounding gas phase. The latter is described by solving the conservation equations of classical Computational Fluid Dynamics (CFD). Hence, the numerical concept provide results over a large range of length scales ranging from inner particles processes to the global dimensions of the reactor. The presented approach deals with poly-disperse particle shapes and takes heat and mass transfer between the particles' surface and the surrounding gas phase into account that distinguishes the presented concept from curre-

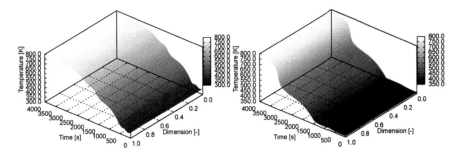

Figure 4. Predicted conversion rates of individual particles during pyrolysis in a packed bed in conjunction with the tar distribution in the gas phase

nt approaches. Thus, physics are described to a fine degree that allows an in-depth analysis of obtained results. It unveils the underlying physics of the processes involved and as a computer-aided tool contributes significantly to an improved design and operating conditions.

Acknowledgement

This work was funded by the Fond National de la Recherche Luxembourg.

References

Y. Tsuji, T. Kawaguchi, T. Tanaka, 1993, Discrete particle simulation of two- dimensional uidized bed, Powder Technol., 77, 1, 79-87.

B. P. B. Hoomans, J. A. M. Kuipers, W. J. Briels, W. P. M. Van Swaaij, 1996, Discrete particle simulation of bubble and slug formation in a two-dimensional gas-uidized bed: A hard-sphere approach. Chem. Eng. Sci., 51, 99-118.

B. H. Xu, A. B. Yu, 1997, Numerical simulation of the gas-solid ow in a fluidized bed by combining discrete particle method with computational fluid dynamics, Chemical Engineering Science, 52, 16, 2785-2809

B. H. Xu, A. B. Yu, 1998, Comments on the paper numerical simulation of the gas-solid flow in a fluidized bed by combining discrete particle method with computational fluid dynamics-reply, Chemical Engineering Science, 53, 2646-2647.

H. P. Zhu, Z. Y. Zhou, R. Y. Yang, A. B. Yu, 2007, Discrete particle simulation of particulate systems: Theoretical developments, Chemical Engineering Science, 62, 3378-3396.

H. P. Zhu, Z. Y. Zhou, R. Y. Yang, A. B. Yu, 2008, Discrete particle simulation of particulate systems: A review of major applications and findings, Chemical Engineering Science, 63, 5728-5770.

M. Sheng, C. Gonzalez, W. Yantz, D. Cahela, H. Yang, D. Harris, B. Tatarchuk, 2013, Microscale heat transfer comparison between packed beds and micro-fibrous entrained calalysts, Engineering Applications of Computational Fluid Mechanics, 7, 4, 471-485.

T. Kon, S. Natsui, K. Shin, S. Ueda, R. Inoue, T. Ariyama, 2013, Modelling of liquid flow in the lower part of blast furnace by mps method, In The 5th International Conference STEELSIM 2013, Ostrava, Czech Republic.

C. Y. Wang, 1998, Modelling Multi- phase Flow and Transport in Porous Media, Transport Phenomena in Porous Media, Oxford Pergamon, Oxford, UK.

B. Peters, A. Dzuigys, 2011, Prediction of Conversion of a Packed Bed of Fuel Particles on a Forward Acting Grate by the Discrete Particle Method (DPM), Computer Aided Chemical Engineering, 29, 1894-1898.

Wikipedia, 2012, Extended discrete element method, <en.wikipedia.org/wiki/Xdem>, accessed on 13/09/2012

B. Peters, 2013, The extended discrete element method (XDEM) for multi-physics applications, Scholarly Journal of Engineering Research, 2, 1, 1-20.

B. Peters, J. Smula-Ostaszewska, 2010, Evaluation of kinetic data and modelling of sulphur dioxide during combustin of switcgrass, 20th European Symposium on Computer Aided Process Engineering, Naples, Italy.

M. Gronli, 1996, A theoretical and experimental study of the thermal degradation of biomass, PhD thesis, NTNU Trondheim,

M. S. Carslaw, J. C. Jaeger, 1959, Conduction of Heat in Solids, Oxford University Press, Oxford, UK.

E. Schröder, 1999, Bestimmung des Druckverlustes und des Wärmeüberganges von gasdurchströmten Feststoffschüttungen in der PANTHA Anlage, Forschungszentrum Karlsruhe, FZKA 6373.

Jiří Jaromír Klemeš, Petar Sabev Varbanov and Peng Yen Liew (Editors)
Proceedings of the 24th European Symposium on Computer Aided Process Engineering – ESCAPE 24
June 15-18, 2014, Budapest, Hungary. Copyright © 2014 Elsevier B.V. All rights reserved.

Measurement and Modelling of the Near-field Structure of Large-scale Sonic CO_2 Releases from Pipelines

Robert M. Woolley,[a]* Michael Fairweather,[a] Christopher J. Wareing,[a] Samuel A.E.G. Falle,[b] Christophe Proust,[c] Jerome Hebrard,[c] Didier Jamois[c]

[a] School of Process, Environmental and Materials Engineering, University of Leeds, Leeds LS2 9JT, UK.
[b] School of Mathematics, University of Leeds, Leeds LS2 9JT, UK.
[c] INERIS, Dept. PHDS, Parc Technologique ALATA, BP 2, 60550 Verneuil-en-Halatte, France
r.m.woolley@leeds.ac.uk

Abstract

The work presented in this paper describes a novel multi-phase discharge and dispersion model capable of predicting the near-field fluid dynamics and phase-transition phenomena associated with accidental CO_2 releases. Also presented in this paper are previously unpublished data describing the near-field structure of a number of large-scale CO_2 experimental releases, obtained through the EU-FP7 CO2PipeHaz (2009) project. The calculations employed an adaptive finite-volume grid algorithm to solve the Favre-averaged fluid-flow equations. This equation set was closed with the inclusion of both a two-equation k-ε model and a second-moment Reynolds stress model to represent turbulent fluctuations. Results demonstrate the superior performance of the Reynolds stress transport model when compared to its compressibility-corrected counterpart.

Keywords: CO_2; high pressure pipeline; CFD modelling; second-moment closure

1. Introduction

Carbon capture and storage (CCS) refers to a set of technologies which is currently viewed as one of the most promising options for reducing carbon dioxide emissions during the transition period between the current fossil-fuel based economy and that of a new sustainable-energy era. The CCS chain is designed to reduce carbon dioxide emissions from large point-sources of production by extracting CO_2 from flue gases, and its subsequent transportation in dedicated pipelines to facilities such as depleted oil and gas fields or saline aquifers, for the purpose of permanent storage and exclusion from the planet's atmosphere. The transportation network will very likely also involve some means of intermediate storage, and for the design and risk assessment of these components, a quantitative understanding of the consequences of an accidental or operational high-pressure release is required.

The work presented in this paper describes a novel multi-phase discharge and dispersion model capable of predicting the near-field fluid dynamics and phase-transition phenomena associated with accidental CO_2 releases. This represents a significant step towards the development of models capable of accurately predicting the thermofluid behaviour at the interface with the pipe, typically in the vicinity of a crack. These predictions, including details of heat transfer, can subsequently be used in the formulation of crack propagation and in-pipe behaviour models, thus providing essential information required for pipeline design and regulation. Additionally, the accurate prediction of the correct thermodynamic phase during the discharge process in the near-field is of particular importance given the very different hazard profiles of CO_2 in the gas and solid states. The modelling of CO_2 fluid dynamics therefore poses a unique set of problems, and the theoretical developments presented in this paper go some way to elucidating the observed physics. To date, most modelling techniques have been limited by homogeneous equilibrium assumptions and CO_2 expansion described by one-dimensional calculations. These models can not accurately predict the near-field characteristics of these complex releases which is required in predicting the major hazards used in safety and risk assessments. Also, they cannot be used to assess the impact of such releases on surrounding plant. Previous works concerned with the near-field modelling of CO_2 releases are well covered in a review by Dixon et al. (2012), and Witlox et al. (2013) and Herzog and Egbers (2013) should be consulted for the most recent developments by other research groups. Additionally, the work presented here builds upon previous models, validated against less detailed experimental data sets as described in Woolley et al. (2013). Also presented in this paper are previously unpublished data describing the near-field structure of a number of large-scale CO_2 experimental releases, obtained through the EU-FP7 CO2PipeHaz project (CO2PipeHaz, 2009). These data are used in the validation of the near-field model.

2. Mathematical Modelling

2.1. Turbulent Flow Field
Predictions were based on the solutions of the Favre-averaged, density-weighted forms of the transport equations for mass, momentum, two conserved scalars (CO_2 mass fraction, and CO_2 dense phase fraction), and total energy per unit volume (internal energy plus kinetic energy). This model is capable of representing a fluid flow-field comprising a mixture of CO_2 (vapour/liquid/solid) and air. The equations employed in this study were cast in an axisymmetric form, and further details can be found in Woolley et al. (2013). The equation set is closed via the prescription of the turbulence stress tensor ($u_i'' u_j''$) as prescribed by the k-ε model (Jones and Launder, 1972) and also a second-moment transport model. Although the standard k-ε model has been extensively used for the prediction of incompressible flows, its performance is well known to be poor in the prediction of their compressible counterparts. The model consistently over-predicts turbulence levels and hence mixing due to compressible flows displaying an enhancement of turbulence dissipation. For flows typical of those observed here, a model proposed by Sarkar et al. (1991) has demonstrated the most reliable predictions (Fairweather and Ranson, 2006) when applied. Hence, calculations were undertaken using the modifications to the turbulent Mach number and the turbulence viscosity as prescribed therein. Figure 1 depicts predictions of axial velocity, plotted against the experimental data of a highly under-expanded air jet (Donaldson and Snedeker, 1971), obtained with and without the application of this modification. The intended effect of a notable reduction in the turbulence dissipation is clearly evident. The second-order Reynolds stress model used was that prescribed by Jones and Musonge (1988), modified only in-line with recommendations made by Dianat et al. (1996) for round jets. Eq. (1) represents the transport equation for the turbulence stress tensor in Cartesian tensor notation.

$$\frac{\partial}{\partial t}\left(\bar{\rho}u_i''u_j''\right)+\frac{\partial}{\partial x_k}\left(\bar{\rho}u_i''u_j''\tilde{u}_k\right)=C_s\frac{\partial}{\partial x_k}\left(\tau\bar{\rho}u_k''u_l''\frac{\partial}{\partial x_l}u_k''u_l''\right)+P_{ij}+A_{ij}-\frac{2}{3}\delta_{ij}\bar{\rho}\varepsilon \qquad (1)$$

Figure 1 also depicts predictions of axial velocity, plotted against the experimental data, but obtained using the second-moment turbulence closure. No modification has been made to account for compressibility, and yet its performance can be seen to be in line with that of the corrected k-ε model, and indeed slightly superior.

2.2. Equation of State

The Peng-Robinson equation of state (Peng and Robinson, 1976) is satisfactory for predicting the gas phase properties of CO_2, but when compared to that of Span and Wagner (1996), it is not so for the condensed phase. Furthermore, it is not accurate for gas pressures below the triple point and, in common with any single equation, it does not account for the discontinuity in properties at the triple point. In particular, there is no latent heat of fusion. Span and Wagner (1996) give a formula for the Helmholtz free energy that is valid for both the gas and liquid phases above the triple point, but it does not take account of experimental data below the triple point, nor does it give the properties of the solid. In addition, the formula is too complicated to be used efficiently in a computational fluid dynamics code. A composite equation of state has therefore been constructed to determine the phase equilibrium and transport properties for CO_2. The inviscid version of this model is presented in detail elsewhere (Wareing et al., 2013) and the method reviewed here is now extended for the turbulence closure of the fluid equations detailed in the previous section. In this, the gas phase is computed from the Peng-Robinson equation of state, and the liquid phase and saturation pressure are calculated from tabulated data generated with the Span and Wagner equation of state and the best available source of thermodynamic data for CO_2, the Design Institute for Physical Properties (DIPPR) 801 database, access to which can be gained through the Knovel library (DIPPR, 2013).

2.3. Homogeneous Relaxation Model

A homogeneous relaxation model was developed to represent the relaxation of the condensed phase to equilibrium. In this, the relaxation time was introduced with respect to the transport of the dense phase. A full model requires the inclusion of discrete drops or particles, but it is possible to derive a simple sub-model for the relaxation to equilibrium in which the temperature relaxation is ignored and it is simply assumed that the condensed phase mass fraction is given by its transport equation with an appropriate source term. Again, further details of this model can be found in a previous publication (Woolley et al., 2013)

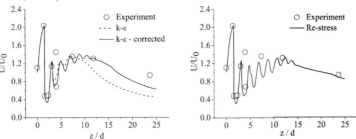

Figure 1. Non-dimensionalised axial velocity predictions in the Donaldson and Snedeker air jet (left – k-ε, right – Reynolds stress).

Figure 2. Experimental rig, including filling sphere and discharge pipe.

The relaxation time chosen to represent behaviour in the near-field of releases such as those considered herein was in the order of 10^{-3} s and obtained by the assessment of the rate that the calculated CO_2 saturation pressure relaxed to the local vapour pressure. In post-shock regions of the flow, a relaxation time of the order 2.5 s was chosen, representing the non-equilibrium state of the condensed phase.

3. Experimental Arrangement

Figure 2 depicts the 2 cubic metre spherical experimental pressure vessel, with the filling sphere in-situ in the foreground, and the discharge pipe exiting the building wall to the right. This spherical pressure vessel is thermally insulated, and can contain up to 1000 kg of CO_2 at a maximum operating pressure and temperature of 200 bar and 473 K, respectively. It is equipped internally with 6 thermocouples and 2 high-precision pressure gauges as well as sapphire observation windows. The vessel has a mass of approximately 5000 kg, and is supported by 4 'Mettler 0745 A' load cells, enabling a continuous measurement of the CO_2 content with an uncertainty of ±500 g. The response time of these devices is fast enough to consider the accurate measurement of mass flow during an experiment, which is obtained by derivation of the best trend-line passing through the points of mass versus time. It is estimated that the accuracy of this technique is ±0.2 $kg.s^{-1}$. The pressure within the sphere is measured using a Piezoresistive-type 'KISTLER 4045 A 200' sensor with a range of 0-200±0.1 bar, and the internal temperature is measured at 6 points on the vertical axis of the sphere using sheathed, 1 mm type-K class-A thermocouples with an accuracy of ± 0.3 °C. The orifices used at the exit plane of the discharge pipe are interchangeable, and are all drilled into a large screwed flange. The thickness of this flange is typically 15 mm and the diameter of the orifice is constant over a length of 10 mm and then expanded with an angle of 45° towards the exterior. Discharge nozzle diameters of 12 and 25 mm, and a full bore of 50 mm were used in these experiments, and further details of the releases are provided in Table 1.

4. Results and Discussion

Figure 3 presents calculated centerline temperatures of the three test cases, plotted against the experimental data, and obtained using the Reynolds stress and two-equation turbulence closures. It is evident from these plots that both models qualitatively reproduce the physics present within such releases, and features such as the stationary shock wave are prominent. The effect of the latent heat of fusion can be observed in

Table 1. Parameters of the experimental releases.

Test Number	Observed Mean Mass Flow Rates/ kg s^{-1}	Ambient Temperature/ K	Air Humidity/ %	Reservoir Pressure / bar	Nozzle Diameter / mm
11	7.7	276.15	>95	83	12
12	24.0	276.15	>95	77	25
13	40.0	276.65	>95	69	50

each of the sets of predictions as a small step-change prior to the shock region. This is indicative of the system passing through the triple point, and the subsequent formation of solids. It can be seen that in all the test cases, little difference is observed between the two closure approaches in the prediction of temperatures prior and post of the shock region. This may be expected due to the region being of low turbulence, and inviscid in nature. Temperatures are also comparable in magnitude at the stationary shock front, although the prediction of its location differs between the turbulence closures. The second-moment model predicts the Mach disk location to be slightly closer to the release plane, which conforms with a slightly reduced level of mixing when compared to the two-equation model. This conforms to the observations made of the predictions of the air jet described in Section 2.1.

5. Conclusions

Presented are predictions obtained from the application of both a compressibility-corrected k-ε and a Reynolds stress transport model, to the modelling of the near-field of three previously un-reported, CO_2 jet releases. Both models are seen to perform well both qualitatively and quantitatively in the representation of the observed physics and the measured temperature field. It can be said that the performance of the two models is

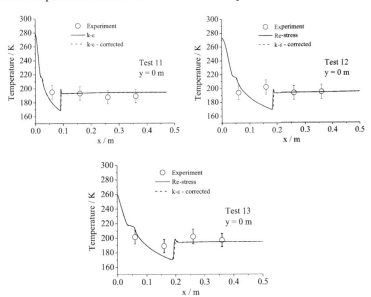

Figure 3. Centreline axial prediction of temperature in INERIS test cases, undertaken using the Re-stress and corrected k-ε models.

comparable, and discrepancy is only observed in the prediction of the location of the stationary shock front. Although it is difficult to locate the precise position of the Mach disc from the data, the second-moment model can be said to marginally conform more to these data due to its improved ability in predicting the effects of compressibility upon the turbulence dissipation. It is concluded that the nature of the second-moment closure is such that for the flows being investigated, it can be applied unmodified, with a similar level of success as a modified k-ε model within the near-field. Further investigation is currently being undertaken with respect to the models' performance in other jet regions.

6. Acknowledgements

The research leading to the results contained in this paper received funding from the European Union 7th Framework Programme FP7-ENERGY-2009-1 under grant agreement number 241346. The paper reflects only the authors' views and the European Union is not liable for any use that may be made of the information contained therein.

References

CO2PipeHaz, 2009, Quantitative Failure Consequence Hazard Assessment for Next Generation CO2 Pipelines: The Missing Link, CO2PipeHaz Project Website, <www.co2pipehaz.eu/> accessed on 03/12/13.

M. Dianat, M. Fairweather, W.P. Jones, 1996, Reynolds Stress Closure Applied to Axisymmetric Impinging Turbulent Jets, Theor. Comp. Fluid. Dyn., 8, 6, 435-447.

Imperial College London, 2013, DIPPR 801 Database, <www.aiche.org/dippr/> accessed on 12/09/13.

C.M. Dixon, S.E. Gant, C. Obiorah, M. Bilio, 2012, Validation of Dispersion Models for High Pressure Carbon Dioxide Releases, IChemE Hazards XXIII, IChemE, Southport, UK, 153-163.

C.D. Donaldson, R.S. Snedeker, 1971, A Study of Free Jet Impingement. Part 1. Mean Properties of Free and Impinging Jets, J. Fluid Mech., 45, 2, 281-319.

M. Fairweather, K.R. Ranson, 2006, Prediction of Underexpanded Jets Using Compressibility-Corrected, Two-Equation Turbulence Models, Prog. Comput. Fluid Dy., 6, 1-3, 122-128.

N. Herzog, C. Egbers, 2013, Atmospheric dispersion of CO2 released from pipeline leakages, Energy Procedia, 40, 232-239.

W.P. Jones, B.E. Launder, 1972, The Prediction of Laminarization with a Two-Equation Model of Turbulence, Int. J. Heat Mass Tran., 15, 2, 301-314.

W.P. Jones, P. Musonge, 1988, Closure of the Reynolds Stress and Scalar Flux Equations, Phys. Fluids, 31, 12, 3589-3604.

D.-Y. Peng, D.B. Robinson, 1976, A New Two-Constant Equation of State, Ind. Eng. Chem. Fun., 15, 1, 59-64.

S. Sarkar, G. Erlebacher, M.Y. Hussaini, H.O. Kreiss, 1991, The Analysis and Modelling of Dilatational Terms in Compressible Turbulence, J. Fluid Mech., 227, 1, 473-493.

R. Span, W. Wagner, 1996, A New Equation of State for Carbon Dioxide Covering the Fluid Region from the Triple-Point Temperature to 1100 K at Pressures up to 800 MPa, J. Phys. Chem. Ref. Data, 25, 6, 1509-1596.

C.J. Wareing, R.M. Woolley, M. Fairweather, S.A.E.G. Falle, 2013, A Composite Equation of State for the Modelling of Sonic Carbon Dioxide Jets, AIChE J., 59, 10, 3928-3942.

H.W.M. Witlox, M. Harper, A. Oke, J. Stene, 2013, Phast Validation of Discharge and Atmospheric Dispersion for Pressurised Carbon Dioxide Releases, J. Loss Prevent. Proc. 10.1016/j.jlp.2013.10.006.

R.M. Woolley, M. Fairweather, C.J. Wareing, S.A.E.G. Falle, C. Proust, J. Hebrard, D. Jamois, 2013, Experimental Measurement and Reynolds-Averaged Navier-Stokes Modelling of the Near-Field Structure of Multi-phase CO2 Jet Releases, Int. J. Greenh. Gas Con., 18, 1, 139-149.

Jiří Jaromír Klemeš, Petar Sabev Varbanov and Peng Yen Liew (Editors)
Proceedings of the 24th European Symposium on Computer Aided Process Engineering – ESCAPE 24
June 15-18, 2014, Budapest, Hungary.

Efficient Model Reduction of SMB Chromatography by Krylov-subspace Method with Application to Uncertainty Quantification

Yao Yue, Suzhou Li*, Lihong Feng, Andreas Seidel-Morgenstern, Peter Benner

Max Planck Institute for Dynamics of Complex Technical Systems, Sandtorstrasse 1, D-39106 Magdeburg, Germany
suzhou@mpi-magdeburg.mpg.de

Abstract

We address the model reduction of the high-dimensional model for the simulated moving bed process by a Krylov-subspace method. Full-update and partial-update schemes are proposed to derive the reduced-order models. The performance of each scheme for the calculation of the cyclic steady state solution is evaluated using a glucose-fructose separation example. The simulation and uncertainty quantification studies demonstrate that both schemes share the same advantage of high accuracy. The full-update scheme results in reduced models of a significantly lower order, while the partial-update scheme is computationally more efficient.

Keywords: simulated moving bed chromatography, model order reduction, Krylov-subspace method, uncertainty quantification

1. Introduction

Simulated moving bed (SMB) chromatography is a continuous multi-column process (Broughton and Gerhold, 1961) and has been recognized as a crucial separation technique (Rajendran et al., 2009). Usually, a detailed SMB model with high dimension is preferred for the purpose of design, optimization and control, since it captures more process dynamics and leads to higher accuracy and reliability. However, because of the nonlinear distributed property and periodic behavior of the process, such a model is often complex and computationally expensive. Thus, it is highly desirable to develop cost-efficient simplified models, which can serve as surrogates of the original system for various purposes. Model order reduction (MOR) techniques are powerful tools for generating cheap approximations and are used in many engineering areas (Antoulas, 2005). However, very limited research efforts have been devoted to the development of reduced-order models (ROMs) for SMB. Existing approaches include balanced model reduction (Erdem et al., 2004) and a proper orthogonal decomposition (POD) based strategy (Vilas and Vande Wouwer, 2011). In our previous work (Li et al., 2012), we also constructed POD-based ROMs aimed at accelerating SMB optimization. However, the reduction in computational costs achieved by all methods mentioned above is less satisfactory. For a better speedup, we develop a new Krylov-type MOR method for the SMB process with linear isotherms in this paper. Depending on how to update the projection bases, full-update and partial-update schemes are proposed, and their performance for predicting the cyclic steady state (CSS) solution is analyzed in terms of accuracy and efficiency. To evaluate the quality of the ROMs built by the schemes, the uncertainty quantification of a pilot-scale SMB unit for the glucose-fructose separation is examined with the Monte Carlo approach.

2. Mathematical modelling of SMB

The SMB process is often described by a partial differential algebraic equations (PDAEs) system. It consists of single column models and balance equations around the inlet and outlet nodes. We assume that each chromatographic column is governed by an axially dispersed plug-flow model with a limited mass-transfer rate characterized by a linear driving force (LDF) approximation. In this model, the differential mass balance of component α ($\alpha = a, b$) in the liquid phase of each column can be written as:

$$\frac{\partial c_\alpha}{\partial \tau} + \frac{1-\varepsilon}{\varepsilon} \frac{\partial q_\alpha}{\partial \tau} = \frac{t_s Q}{\varepsilon A_c L} \left(\frac{1}{Pe} \frac{\partial^2 c_\alpha}{\partial z^2} - \frac{\partial c_\alpha}{\partial z} \right), \qquad z \in (0, 1), \tag{1}$$

where c_α and q_α are the concentrations of solute α in the liquid and solid phases, Q is the volumetric flow-rate, ε is the column porosity, t_s is the switching period, A_c is the column cross-sectional area, L is the column length, Pe is the Péclet number, $\tau = t / t_s$ and $z = Z / L$ are the dimensionless temporal and spatial coordinates, respectively. The adsorption rate described by the LDF approximation reads as:

$$\frac{\partial q_\alpha}{\partial \tau} = t_s K_\alpha \left(q_\alpha^{Eq} - q_\alpha \right), \qquad z \in [0, 1], \tag{2}$$

where K_α is the mass-transfer coefficient of component α and q_α^{Eq} is the adsorption equilibrium concentration determined by the adsorption isotherm equation: $q_\alpha^{Eq} = H_\alpha c_\alpha$, with H_α being the Henry constant. It is assumed that $H_a > H_b$. The boundary conditions of Eq. (1) are: $\left. \frac{\partial c_\alpha}{\partial z} \right|_{z=0} = Pe \left(c_\alpha |_{z=0} - c_\alpha^{in} \right)$, $\left. \frac{\partial c_\alpha}{\partial z} \right|_{z=1} = 0$, where c_α^{in} is the concentration of component α at the column inlet. Depending on how to calculate the CSS, integration and full-discretization methods can be distinguished in the literature (Minceva et al., 2003). In this work, we follow the integration method. The orthogonal collocation on finite elements (OCFE) was used to discretize the spatial coordinate, resulting in a multi-stage system of differential algebraic equations (DAEs) of order n :

$$M\dot{x}_i(\tau) = A(p)x_i(\tau) + B(p), \quad i = 1, 2, \ldots, \tau \in [0, 1], \tag{3}$$

$$x_1(0) = x^0, \quad x_i(0) = P_s x_{i-1}(1), \qquad i = 2, 3, \ldots, \tag{4}$$

where $x_i(\tau) \in \mathbb{R}^n$ is the state vector representing the concentrations at the i-th period (or stage), $M \in \mathbb{R}^{n \times n}$, $A \in \mathbb{R}^{n \times n}$, $B \in \mathbb{R}^n$ are the coefficient matrices, $P \in \mathbb{R}^{n_p}$ is the vector consisting of n_p parameters of interest in uncertainty quantification, $P_s : \mathbb{R}^n \mapsto \mathbb{R}^n$ is the permutation operator and i is the period index. Here, the port switching triggers the stage transition with the mapping conditions given by Eq. (4). To evaluate the CSS solution, the multi-stage model is integrated consecutively with a given initial conditions x^0 until the convergence criterion $\| x_{i+1}(0) - x_i(0) \| \le \varepsilon_{css}$ is fulfilled, with ε_{css} being the specified CSS tolerance and $\| \cdot \|$ the Euclidean norm. A fine spatial discretization is often needed in the OCFE scheme to guarantee high approximation accuracy, rendering Eq. (3) to be of high dimension. The high dimension poses a significant computational challenge to the CSS evaluation. In the next section, we will detail a Krylov-based MOR method that tackles this computational challenge.

3. Krylov-type model order reduction for multi-stage linear systems

In this section, we study the usage of Krylov-type MOR for a general multi-stage linear system. We propose full-update and partial-update schemes. Both schemes aim at approximating the FOMs accurately for all stages by building a ROM for each stage. They divide this multi-stage system into a sequence of initial value problems (IVPs), where we can only compute the initial state of the i-th stage after we have computed the end state of the $(i-1)$-st stage. This is shown in Figure 1 (a–b). Then we can replace these FOMs with ROMs in all IVPs as is shown in Figure 1 (b–c). The conventional Krylov method (Feng et al., 2006) to reduce the i-th IVP

$$M_i \dot{x}_i(\tau) = A_i x_i(\tau) + B_i, \quad x_i(0) = x_i^0, \tag{5}$$

where $M_i, A_i \in \mathbb{R}^{n \times n}, B_i \in \mathbb{R}^n$ are coefficient matrices and A_i is nonsingular, first conducts the shift $\xi_i(\tau) = x_i(\tau) - x_i^0$ to obtain the shifted system

$$\Sigma_i : \quad M_i \dot{\xi}_i(\tau) = A_i \xi_i(\tau) + A_i x_i^0 + B_i, \quad \xi_i(0) = 0. \tag{6}$$

Then we build an order k Krylov subspace

$$K_k \left\{ A_i^{-1} M_i, A_i^{-1}(A_i x_i^0 + B_i) \right\}, \quad (k \le n \text{ and normally } k \ll n) \tag{7}$$

where we define $K_k \{A, b\} = \text{span}\{b, Ab, A^2 b, \dots, A^{k-1} b\}$. \tag{8}

As is well known, simply computing these vectors to build the Krylov subspace is numerically unstable. The standard method to deal with non-symmetric A is the Arnoldi process, which yields an orthonormal basis of the Krylov subspace (Antoulas, 2005). Assume that the resulting basis vectors of Eq. (7) are column vectors of the matrix $V_i \in \mathbb{R}^{n \times k}$. Define $M_{r,i} = V_i^T M_i V_i$, $A_{r,i} = V_i^T A_i V_i$ and $B_{r,i} = V_i^T \left(A_i x_i^0 + B_i \right)$.

$$\Sigma_{i,r} : \quad M_{r,i} \dot{\xi}_{r,i}(\tau) = A_{r,i} \xi_{r,i}(\tau) + B_{r,i}, \quad \xi_{r,i}(0) = 0, \tag{9}$$

serves as a ROM of order k. Note that although in the SMB system described in Section 2, $A_i = A$, $M_i = M$ and $B_i = B$ hold for all i's, we must build a new ROM for each i, because a Krylov-type ROM depends on x_i^0, which differs among stages.

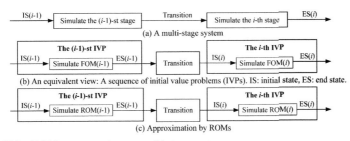

(a) A multi-stage system

(b) An equivalent view: A sequence of initial value problems (IVPs). IS: initial state, ES: end state.

(c) Approximation by ROMs

Figure 1. Using ROMs to approximate a multi-stage system.

3.1. The full-update scheme

The full-update scheme directly follows the procedure described above. Given an initial point $x_1^0 = x^0$, ROM $\Sigma_{1,r}$ can be built directly. For $i \geq 2$, using the transition condition

$$x_i^0 = P_s \left(V_{i-1} \xi_{r,i-1} + x_{i-1}^0 \right), \tag{10}$$

we can obtain a ROM for each stage in a sequential manner. In this scheme, the computationally dominant parts are: 1) one LU factorization of A for the whole algorithm; 2) large-scale linear system solves with A for k times at each stage. This is much cheaper than using the FOM, which requires solving large-scale system Eq. (3) at all interpolation points in the numerical integration for a single stage.

3.2. The partial-update scheme

Since $A_i = A$, $M_i = M$ and $B_i = B$ hold for the SMB system, we have

$$K_k \left\{ A^{-1}M, A^{-1}(Ax_i^0 + B) \right\} \subseteq K_k \left\{ A^{-1}M, A^{-1}B \right\} \oplus K_k \left\{ A^{-1}M, x_i^0 \right\} \tag{11}$$

for Eq. (7). Note that: 1) the Krylov subspace $K_k \left\{ A^{-1}M, A^{-1}B \right\}$ does not change with i; 2) the two Krylov subspaces in the right-hand side may converge at different rates as were pointed out by Heres and Schilders (2005). Thus, we define

$$K \left\{ k_1, k_2 \right\} \subseteq K_{k_1} \left\{ A^{-1}M, A^{-1}B \right\} \oplus K_{k_2} \left\{ A^{-1}M, x_i^0 \right\}. \tag{12}$$

The partial-update scheme computes $K_{k_1} \left\{ A^{-1}M, A^{-1}B \right\}$ only once at the beginning, and then updates $K_{k_2} \left\{ A^{-1}M, x_i^0 \right\}$ at each stage. If $k_2 \ll k$, where k is the order of ROMs in the full-update scheme, we expect that the partial-update scheme outperforms the full-update scheme, because for each stage, we only need to update $K_{k_2} \left\{ A^{-1}M, x_i^0 \right\}$, which requires linear solves with A for only k_2 times rather than k times.

4. Results and discussion

4.1. Evaluation of full- and partial-update schemes

In this section, we will evaluate the performance of the full- and partial-update schemes in terms of the CSS calculation. For this purpose, a glucose-fructose separation on a pilot-scale SMB unit (Azevedo and Rodrigues, 2001) was examined. The model parameters and operating conditions are summarized in Table 1. The FOM was constructed by combining five finite elements and three internal collocation points for the spatial discretization of the PDAE model. For all ROMs, we used a residual-based

Table 1. Model parameters and operating conditions

Column configuration [-]	3/3/3/3	Pe [-]	500	K_a [1/s]	0.0218	Q_I [ml/s]	0.567
Column diameter [cm]	2.6	H_a [-]	0.53	K_b [1/s]	0.0310	Q_{II} [ml/s]	0.465
Column length [cm]	30	H_b [-]	0.27	t_s [s]	198	Q_{III} [ml/s]	0.521
ε [-]		0.4	Feed concentrations [mol/l]		0.2222	Q_{IV} [ml/s]	0.400

a and b represent fructose and glucose, and $Q_I \sim Q_{IV}$ are the flow-rates in the four zones of SMB.

method to select their order. The DASPK3.1 package was chosen as the integrator. The dimensionless concentration profiles were used to check CSS numerically with the tolerance $\varepsilon_{css} = 1.0 \times 10^{-5}$. All calculations were performed on a Linux machine with an Intel 3.0 GHz Pentium D processor and 2 GB RAM. The results are listed in Table 2. For convenience, the ROM system built by the full-update scheme is referred to as ROM1, while ROM2, ROM3 and ROM4 are ROMs obtained by the partial-update scheme with different orders. For this case study, the CSS is achieved after integrating the FOM for 292 periods and 612 seconds are consumed in total. By contrast, ROM1 with an order of 50, which is only $1/20^{th}$ of that of the FOM, leads to a significant acceleration in computational time. Both product purities obtained are accurate up to 4 digits, which is perfectly acceptable for practical purposes. Furthermore, as expected, ROM2 allows to further reduce the CPU time: it achieves 25 times speed-up. With the same order of 50, however, ROM2 is less accurate and only achieves 2 significant digits for purity prediction. Since the computational cost of the partial-update scheme is less sensitive to k_1 in Eq. (12), we can increase k_1 to improve the accuracy at a low cost. This is clearly validated by the results with ROM3 and ROM4. We observe that to achieve the similar accuracy, the total order ($k_1 + k_2$) should be nearly twice as high as that of ROM1.

4.2. Uncertainty quantification

For the example examined in Section 4.1, Kurup et al. (2008) are the first to use a Monte Carlo-based method to quantify the effect of the isotherm uncertainty on the separation performance. This method often requires a large number of simulations to yield accurate results, rendering the analysis procedure expensive. In this section, we will demonstrate the potential of our schemes for fast and accurate uncertainty analysis. We follow the same assumption as that in Kurup et al. (2008) that the isotherm parameters are the random input variables with uniform distribution. They are subject to a ±10% deviation from the nominal values in Table 1. The product purities are chosen as the output variables. The Latin hypercube sampling was used to generate the sample set. The probabilistic metrics of the output parameters are summarized in Table 3. It is observed that both schemes can achieve almost the same mean value and standard deviation as the FOM. The uncertainty analysis is sped up by a factor of nearly 4 and 17 for ROM1 and ROM2, respectively. The effect of variations in the isotherm parameters on the purities is shown in Figure 2 in the form of a scatter plot. Clearly, the ROM

Table 2. Comparison of the FOM and ROM systems for the CSS calculation

Model	Construction method	Order	CPU time [s]	Periods	Pu_a	Pu_b [%]
FOM	OCFE discretization	1008	612	292	95.276	86.068
ROM1	Full-update	50	192	277	95.271	86.066
ROM2	Partial-update	45+5	24	269	95.344	86.096
ROM3	Partial-update	65+5	28	269	95.249	86.054
ROM4	Partial-update	85+5	37	268	95.277	86.064

Table 3. Comparison of results of uncertainty analysis for the sugar separation

Model	Order	CPU time [min]	$E[Pu_a]$ [%]	$E[Pu_b]$ [%]	$\sigma[Pu_a]$ [%]	$\sigma[Pu_b]$ [%]
FOM	1008	363.8	94.48	85.64	3.25	1.64
ROM1	50	106.6	94.48	85.64	3.25	1.64
ROM2	85+5	21.5	94.49	85.64	3.25	1.64

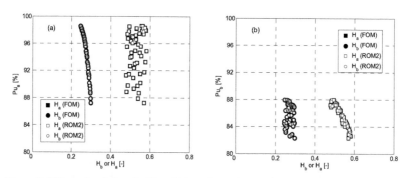

Figure 2. Effect of variations in H_a and H_b on the purity of fructose (a) and glucose (b).

system captures a trend nearly identical to that of the FOM. With an increase in H_b, Pu_a sharply decreases but does not follow an obvious trend with respect to the change in H_a. In contrast, Pu_a is more sensitive to the variation in H_a than H_b.

5. Conclusions

A Krylov-type MOR method was proposed to reduce the high-dimensional SMB model. The full- and partial-update schemes were developed and their performance in terms of CSS simulation was evaluated by a glucose-fructose separation. The partial-update scheme is computationally more efficient, and the full-update scheme allows for accurate ROMs of a significantly lower order. Both schemes were employed for the uncertainty quantification of the same sugar separation. The results proved that they reproduce the required probabilistic metrics at remarkably reduced computational expense. Our future research will extend to SMB systems with nonlinear isotherms.

References

D. B. Broughton, C. G. Gerhold, 1961, Continuous sorption process employing fixed bed of sorbent and moving inlets and outlets, U.S. Patent, 2,985,589.

A. Rajendran, G. Paredes, M. Mazzotti, 2009, Simulated moving bed chromatography for the separation of enantiomers, J. Chromatogr. A, 1216, 709-738.

A. C. Antoulas, 2005, Approximation of large-scale dynamical systems, SIAM, Philadelphia, US.

G. Erdem, S. Abel, M. Morari, M. Mazzotti, M. Morbidelli, J. H. Lee, 2004, Automatic control of simulated moving beds, Ind. Eng. Chem. Res., 43, 405-421.

C. Vilas, A. Vande Wouwer, 2011, Combination of multi-model predictive control and the wave theory for the control of simulated moving bed plants, Chem. Eng. Sci., 66, 632-641.

S. Li, L. Feng, P. Benner, A. Seidel-Morgenstern, 2012, Efficient optimization of simulated moving bed chromatographic processes using reduced order models, Computer Aided Chemical Engineering, 30, 1232-1236.

M. Minceva, L. S. Pais, A. E. Rodrigues, 2003, Cyclic steady state of simulated moving bed processes for enantiomers separation, Chem. Eng. Process., 42, 93-104.

D. C. S. Azevedo, A. E. Rodrigues, 2001, Fructose-glucose separation in a SMB pilot unit: modelling, simulation, design and operation, AIChE J., 47, 2042-2051.

A. S. Kurup, H. J. Subramani, M. T. Harris, 2008, A Monte Carlo-based error propagation analysis of simulated moving bed systems, Sep. Purif. Technol., 62, 582-589.

P. Heres, W. H. A. Schilders, 2004, Practical issues of model order reduction with Krylov-subspace methods, Progress in Electromagnetic Research Symposium: PIERS 2004.

L. Feng, D. Koziol, E. B. Rudnyi, J. G. Korvink, 2006, Parametric model reduction for fast simulation of cyclic voltammograms, Sensor Letters, 4, 165-173.

Jiří Jaromír Klemeš, Petar Sabev Varbanov and Peng Yen Liew (Editors)
Proceedings of the 24th European Symposium on Computer Aided Process Engineering – ESCAPE 24
June 15-18, 2014, Budapest, Hungary. Copyright © 2014 Elsevier B.V. All rights reserved.

Efficient Computational Methods for Microscopic Simulations in Multi-scale Systems

Ioannis S. Fragkopoulos, Constantinos Theodoropoulos[*]

School of Chemical Engineering and Analytical Science, University of Manchester, Sackville Street, Manchester M13 9PL, UK.
k.theodoropoulos@manchester.ac.uk

Abstract

In this work we exploit the capability of state-of-the-art multi-scale simulators of complex (electro)chemical processes for model-based design and scale-up. For this purpose we investigate intelligent coarse graining methodologies based on the "equation-free" framework. The paradigm of the gap-tooth methodology is analysed through sensitivity analysis studies using different interpolation schemes. The area of the microscopic lattice of interest, representing a catalytic surface where reaction-diffusion micro-processes take place, is split into a number of representative micro-lattices whose area is only a fraction of the original lattice. Diffusion effects are efficiently represented through lattice-to-lattice lateral interactions. Hence, the computationally intensive or even intractable microscopic and multi-scale simulations are handled with efficiency. We utilise the multi-scale simulator of the Electrochemically Promoted CO oxidation as an illustrative system to demonstrate the capabilities of our computational approach.

Keywords: multi-scale systems, lattice kMC, coarse graining, gap-tooth method, lateral interactions.

1. Introduction

Engineering systems are by nature multi-scale hence non-elementary system models are always multi-scale ones. However, multi-scale modelling and the corresponding meaningful bridging of different length- and time-scales, poses a number of challenges in model development (Gorban et al., 2006). The computational demand of such models in particular, is significant and becomes even more strenuous as the size of the system at hand increases, requiring the use of efficient coarse-graining and model reduction technologies. In this work we exploit such a computationally efficient coarse–graining methodology, the so-called gap-tooth method (Gear et al., 2002) where intelligent interpolation techniques are employed for accurate microscopic simulations of complex multi-scale systems (Armaou et al., 2005). In this scheme the (microscopic or multi-scale) system is efficiently represented by a small subset of the spatial domain (a tooth) separated by spaces -the gaps- (Fig. 1). While microscopic simulations within each individual tooth are used to predict the corresponding evolution of the micro-processes, the system's behaviour at the gaps is obtained through macroscopic interpolation of the averaged evolution profiles of the corresponding teeth (Gear et al., 2002). Although this method has been extensively employed in complex multi-scale frameworks for modelling transport in heterogeneous catalytic reactors (Schaefer and Jansen, 2013) and for simulations of catalytic micro-reactors (Hari and Theodoropoulos, 2009), a sensitivity analysis study through employing various lattice interpolation techiques has

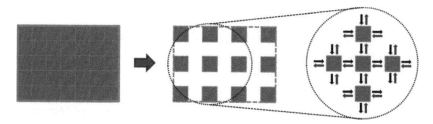

Figure 1. Schematic of the Gap-Tooth geometry.

not been performed yet in cases where lattice micro-kinetics are utilised. Here, we investigate the effect of interpolation rules on the accuracy of the multi-scale predictions, and we employ the one that works best to perform efficient multi-scale simulations of a complex electrochemically promoted catalytic system (Fragkopoulos et al., 2012).

2. Gap-tooth interpolation rules

A 1-D gap-tooth scheme is constructed (Fig.2) to investigate different lateral interaction options between the teeth, here related to species micro-diffusion in the domain. For this purpose, the exchange fluxes between two consecutive teeth (Fig. 2) are taken into account, which are based on 1st order interpolation rules (Gear et al., 2003):

$$I_{i,k,l} = \alpha_x \cdot O_{i-1,k,r} + (1-\alpha_x) \cdot O_{i,k,r} \qquad (1)$$

$$I_{i,k,r} = \alpha_x \cdot O_{i+1,k,l} + (1-\alpha_x) \cdot O_{i,k,l} \qquad (2)$$

where I and O are the ingoing and outgoing particles respectively, i the number of each tooth, k is the species type, r and l the right and left sides of each tooth respectively and a_x the interpolation coefficient in x-direction which depends on the gap-tooth geometry, expressed as:

$$\alpha_x = \frac{d_x}{D_x} = \frac{d_x}{d_x + gap_x} \qquad (3)$$

where d_x is the length of each tooth, D_x the distance between the centres of two teeth and gap_x the corresponding gap (as in Fig.2). This 1st order interpolation is equivalent to

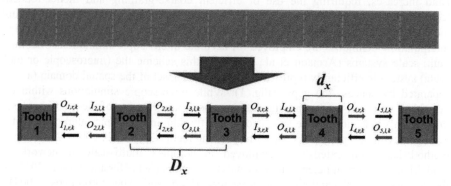

Figure 2. 1-D Gap-Tooth representation of a single lattice. Zones in each tooth are depicted in red.

directing a_x of the particles outgoing from tooth i as an influx to tooth $i+1$ (or to tooth $i-1$) and re-direct the remaining $(1-a_x)$ particles back to tooth i.

3. Gap-Tooth framework validation

We have first validated the performance of the gap-tooth scheme described above against a single lattice simulation using an in-house developed spatial version of the kinetic Monte Carlo (kMC) method (Reese et al., 2001) and taking into account only the diffusion micro-process (as in Eq. (4)) of a single species, which is simulated in 2 dimensions both in the single lattice and in each tooth.

$$X + * \xrightarrow{k_{diff}} * + X \tag{4}$$

Here, a single lattice of 1100x100 sites is represented by 5 teeth 100x100 sites each (d_x = 100 sites) and a gap of 150 sites (D_x = 250 sites) between neighbouring teeth (see Fig. 2). A flux of 100 species per 10^{-4} s is introduced at the left boundary of the single lattice and correspondingly at the left of the first (left) tooth in the gap-tooth framework. At time $t = 10^{-2}$ s the species provision (flux) is stopped in order to let species diffuse without the effect of external driving forces. Moreover, a (high) diffusion probability ($k_{diff} = 10^6$ s^{-1}) is utilised in order to illustrate the effects of lateral interactions between the teeth. The interpolation of particles between teeth was chosen to take place at a reporting horizon T of 10^{-6} s.

Two options are utilised for the distribution of incoming species in each tooth:
- Random distribution over the whole micro-lattice (tooth) area.
- Random distribution but within thin 'zones', i.e. a small number of lattice sites arranged in columns around the left and right boundaries of each tooth as depicted in Figure 2.

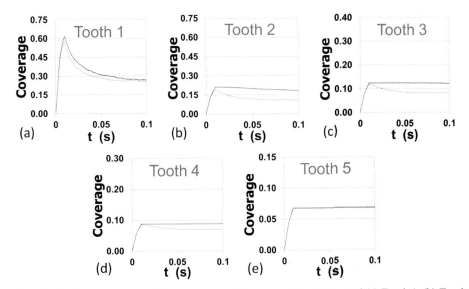

Figure 3. Species coverage profiles comparison between a single lattice and (a) Tooth 1, (b) Tooth 2, (c) Tooth 3, (d) Tooth 4, (e) Tooth 5, using random distribution. The solid lines represent the single lattice simulation and the dashed lines represent the gap-tooth simulation.

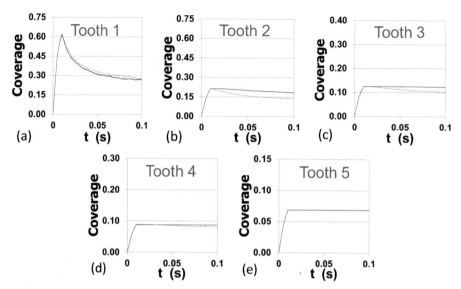

Figure 4. Species coverage profiles comparison between a single lattice and (a) Tooth 1, (b) Tooth 2, (c) Tooth 3, (d) Tooth 4, (e) Tooth 5, using 'zone' distribution. The solid lines represent the single lattice simulation and the dashed lines represent the gap-tooth simulation.

In Figure 3, a comparison of the coverage profiles of species X in each tooth computed by the single lattice microscopic simulator and that computed by the gap-tooth one is presented. As we can see, the former is well represented by the gap-tooth simulation albeit with differences in the middle teeth. Using the thin 'zone' distribution (here found through sensitivity analysis as 10 sites from the left and right boundaries respectively), we get better agreement with the single lattice simulation as can be seen in Figure 4.

4. Multi-scale simulations using the Gap-Tooth framework

We have employed the validated gap-tooth methodology, using the thin zone distribution option, in a multi-scale system of electrochemically promoted catalytic CO oxidation (Fragkopoulos et al., 2012) where the catalytic reactions are simulated through lattice kMC. In this multi-scale system we have taken into account all the chemical and electrochemical reactions presented in Fragkopoulos et al. (2013) along with their corresponding parameter values, augmented by reactions (5) and (6) which represent the diffusion of CO and of BackSpillover Species (BSS). The corresponding diffusion probabilities of CO and BSS are chosen to be equal to 1 s^{-1}.

$$CO + * \xrightarrow{k_{diff}^{CO}} * + CO \tag{5}$$

$$BSS + * \xrightarrow{k_{diff}^{BSS}} * + BSS \tag{6}$$

A comparison between the CO coverage computed by the multi-scale simulation, where the catalytic surface is represented by single lattice and that computed by the gap-tooth multi-scale scheme, where the catalytic surface is represented by 5 teeth with gaps as in section 2) is illustrated in Figure 5. CO is chosen as the main diffusing species due to its high relative coverage compared with the BSS one. As we can see in Figure 5, the gap-tooth framework can very accurately capture both the short- and long-term dynamics of

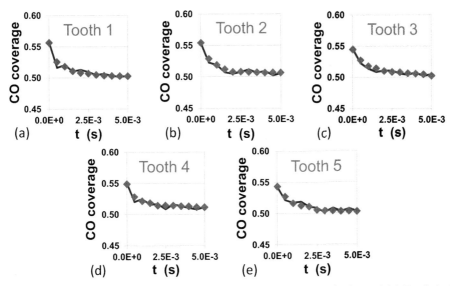

Figure 5. CO average coverage profiles comparison between a single lattice and (a) Tooth 1, (b) Tooth 2, (c) Tooth 3, (d) Tooth 4, (e) Tooth 5. The solid (blue) lines represent the single lattice simulation and the (red) diamonds represent the gap-tooth simulation.

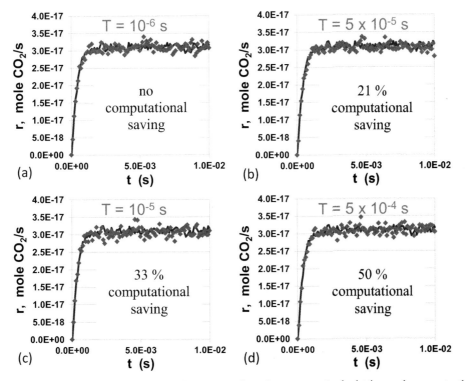

Figure 6. CO_2 production rate profiles comparison between a single lattice and a gap-tooth simulation for an updating time repoting horizon (a) $T = 10^{-6}$ s, (b) $T = 5 \times 10^{-5}$ s, (c) $T = 10^{-5}$ s, (d) $T = 5 \times 10^{-4}$ s. The solid (blue) lines represent the single lattice simulation and the (red) diamonds represent the gap-tooth simulation.

the main diffusing species. In Figure 6, a comparison between the CO_2 production rates computed by the single lattice multi-scale framework and by the gap-tooth one is depicted. As we can see the gap-tooth simulation produces very accurate results for all reporting horizon updates between 10^{-6} and 5×10^{-4} s. The corresponding computational gain ranges between 21 % and 50 % depending on the chosen reporting horizon update. The use of parallelisation techniques, which can be seamlessly introduced in the scheme, can lead to even greater computational savings.

5. Conclusions and future work

A lattice gap-tooth framework has been presented which can be used to increase the computational efficiency of microscopic and multiscale simulations. The microscopic domain is split into a number of representative micro-lattices whose area is only a fraction of the total lattice area. Efficient coarse-graining methodologies implemented through the gap-tooth technique are employed for the simulation of the lateral interactions between micro-lattices. The framework can accurately capture the system's dynamics with computational efficiency. We have found that an alternative interpolation rule where incoming fluxes are distributed within 'zones' around the micro-lattice boundaries (rather than randomly in the whole micro-lattice domain) gives more accurate results. Employing this methodology for an electrochemically promoted catalytic CO oxidation multi-scale system, produced accurate dynamic profiles of the resulting CO_2 production rates for a fraction of the computational cost. Employing this gap-tooth multi-scale framework to scaled-up electrochemically promoted systems in conjunction with high-fidelity experiments, will significantly enhance our understanding, and will help to quantify the promotion effect on these systems and significantly enhance their industrial potential.

Acknowledgements

The financial support of EPSRC (grant EP/G022933/1) is gratefully acknowledged.

References

A. Armaou, I.G. Kevrekidis, C. Theodoropoulos, 2005, Equation-free gaptooth-based controller design for distributed complex/multiscale processes, Comput. Chem. Eng., 29, 731-740.

I.S. Fragkopoulos, I. Bonis, C. Theodoropoulos, 2012, Multiscale modelling of spillover processes in heterogeneous catalytic systems, Comput. Aided Chem. Eng., 30, 1013-1017.

I.S. Fragkopoulos, I. Bonis, C. Theodoropoulos, 2013, Macroscopic multi-dimensional modelling of electrochemically promoted systems, Chem. Eng. Sci., 104, 647-661.

C.W. Gear, I.G. Kevrekidis, C. Theodoropoulos, 2002, 'Coarse' integration/bifurcation analysis via microscopic simulators: Micro-Galerkin methods, Comput. Chem. Eng., 26, 941-963.

C.W. Gear, J. Li, I.G. Kevrekidis, 2003, The gap-tooth method in particle simulations, Phys. Lett. A, 316, 190-195.

A.N. Gorban, N. Kazantzis, I.G. Kevrekidis, H.C. Ottinger, C. Thedoropoulos, 2006, Preface pp. V-VIII, in Model Reduction and Coarse-Graining Approaches for Multiscale Phenomena, Spinger: Complexity, Berlin-Heidelberg, Germany.

B. Hari, C. Theodoropoulos, 2009, Integrated multi-scale models for simulation and design of microreactor systems, Chem. Eng. Trans., 17, 1269-1274.

J.S. Reese, S. Raimondeau, D.G. Vlachos, 2001, Monte Carlo algorithms for complex surface reaction mechanisms: Efficiency and accuracy, J. Comput. Phys., 173, 302-321.

C. Schaefer, A.P.J. Jansen, 2013, Coupling of kinetic Monte Carlo simulations of surface reactions to transport in a fluid for heterogeneous catalytic reactor modeling, J. Chem. Phys., 138, 054102-1-9.

Jiří Jaromír Klemeš, Petar Sabev Varbanov and Peng Yen Liew (Editors)
Proceedings of the 24th European Symposium on Computer Aided Process Engineering – ESCAPE 24
June 15-18, 2014, Budapest, Hungary. Copyright © 2014 Elsevier B.V. All rights reserved.

Molecular Dynamics Simulations of Competitive Protein Adsorption onto Chromatographic Media

Juan Liang,[a,]* Georg Fieg,[a] Sven Jakobtorweihen[b]

[a]*Institute of Process and Plant Engineering, Hamburg University of Technology, Hamburg 21073, Germany*
[b]*Institute of Thermal Separation Processes, Hamburg University of Technolgy, Hamburg 21073, Germany*
juan.liang@tu-harburg.de

Abstract

To get a further understanding of protein adsorption onto ion-exchange chromatographic media, the binary adsorption of serum albumin and hemoglobin onto Q Sepharose FF was investigated with molecular dynamics (MD) simulations. Considering the adsorption sequence, both simultaneous and sequential adsorption has been simulated. The protein underwent a competing adsorption. The results show that serum albumin is preferentially adsorbed. A multi-layer adsorption was observed in the sequential binary simulations. Hence, this study provides a detailed description of protein adsorption on a molecular scale.

Keywords: serum albumin, hemoglobin, ion-exchange adsorption, MD simulation, binary components

1. Introduction

Ion-exchange chromatography (IEC) is the most extensively applied chromatographic technique for the separation and purification of proteins. For an efficient application of IEC, it is important to understand the adsorption of proteins onto ion-exchange media. Since the target proteins in feedstock with miscellaneous solutes are competitively adsorbed in IEC, the understanding of multi-component adsorption is essential. The multi-component adsorption of proteins has been studied by static adsorption (Liang et al., 2012a), dynamic adsorption (Shi et al., 2012) and chromatographic experiments (Traylor et al., 2011). However, due to the lack of experimental methods that can investigate adsorption processes in pores, the microscopic adsorption process is still not well understood. Molecular dynamics (MD) simulation, a research tool with sufficiently small scales in both time and space, has been used to gain molecular insights into adsorption phenomena (Zhang et al., 2010). Previously, we have applied MD simulations to investigate the ion-exchange adsorption processes a single protein on a microscopic scale (Liang et al., 2012b). Therefore, in this work, MD simulations with a coarse-grained (CG) model were applied to investigate the ion-exchange adsorption of multi-component proteins in detail. Two proteins, human serum albumin (HSA) and bovine hemoglobin (bHb), were introduced to investigate their binary adsorption onto a strong anion exchanger Q Sepharose FF. To study the influence of the adsorption sequence, both simultaneous and sequential binary adsorption was simulated. To obtain a reliable set of data, several different initial arrangements of proteins were investigated. Comprehensive analyses of the adsorption and competition process were carried out. Single (Liang et al., 2012b) and binary MD simulation results were compared to the experimental data (Liang et al., 2012a).

938   *J. Liang et al.*

2. Methods

2.1. Simulation models

Considering the large size of the ion-exchange systems, the MARTINI coarse-grained force field (Marrink et al., 2007; Monticelli et al., 2008) was used. As a general rule, a mapping of four heavy atoms (non-hydrogen atoms) onto one CG bead is followed in this CG force field. Hydrogen atoms are neglected due to their small size and mass. Four main types of CG particles are available: polar (P), nonpolar (N), apolar (C) and charged (Q). As shown in Figure 1(a), the 14 heavy atoms of the ligand of Q Sepharose FF (a quaternary amine group) were modelled with three MARTINI particles, whereas one particle is positively charged. This CG representation of the ligand has been tested by comparing results from CG and atomistic simulations (Liang et al., 2012b). CG models of the proteins were generated according to the protein mapping principle of the MARTINI force field, starting from the crystal structures from the Protein Data Bank (human serum albumin (HSA) PDB code 1AO6, in which chain B, which is identical to chain A, was deleted, bovine hemoglobin (bHb) PDB code 1G0A). At the condition simulated in this work (pH 7.0, C_s=230 mM) HSA has a charge of -15 and bHb has a charge of +2. In order to prevent the CG water from freezing, 10 % of the water particles (standard CG waters are modelled as P_4 particles) were modelled as BP_4 (Marrink et al., 2007). The ion particles are taken from the standard MARTINI force field. The simulated binary ion-exchange systems contained two proteins, the ion exchange ligands and the chromatographic base, as shown in Figure 1(b). The simulation box had a size of 19.604 nm ×20.404 nm × 20 nm. The matrix of the media was set as a rigid wall (defined as P_4, according to the polarity of sepharose) at the bottom of the simulations box (z=0nm). 1116 ligands were distributed as a uniform layer on top of the wall, with the roots restrained to mimic the immobilization. According to the total ionic capacity and the specific surface area of Q Sepharose FF (Chang et al., 1998), the surface density of the immobilized ligands is 2.67 /nm^2.

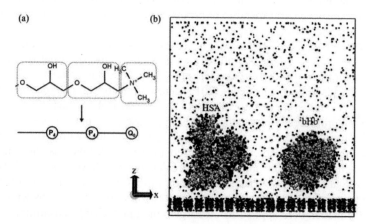

Figure 1. Model of the ligand and binary ion-exchange system: (a) sketch of atomistic to coarse grained mapping of a ligand, (b) snapshot of the binary ion-exchange system at the beginning of a simulation (protein-ligand minimum distance is set to 1.0 nm). For a better view water particles are not shown here, but the ions in the liquid phase are shown.

2.2. Simulation details

The simulations were carried out with GROMACS 4.5.5 (Pronk et al., 2013). Periodic boundary conditions were used in the x and y directions. In order to use pressure coupling, another wall without ligands was set at the other side of the box (opposite to the ligand surface), defined as P_4 particles. The basic parameters for the simulations were set as in previous simulations employing the MARTINI force field (Marrink et al., 2007). As the electrostatic interactions are the main driving forces for ion-exchange systems, the reaction field approach was used to take into account the long range electrostatic interactions, here we used a long-range dielectric constant of ε_{rf} =78 (Rzepiela et al., 2010), and a short-range dielectric constant of ε_r =15 (Marrink et al., 2007). More simulation details are given in our earlier publication (Liang et al., 2012b). All systems have been energy minimized before starting a MD simulation. MD simulations of ion-exchange adsorption of proteins were divided into two parts: 1) 100 ns equilibration of chromatographic media, where the positions of the protein particles were restrained; 2) simulation with unrestrained protein. Only the results of the second part were analyzed and will be discussed here. To study the influence of the adsorption sequence as well as the phenomena of displacement and multi-layer adsorption, two proteins (HSA and bHb) were initially placed into the liquid phase in two different configurations.

1) Simultaneous adsorption: initially, both protein molecules were placed into the liquid phase next to each other with a minimum distance to the ligands of 1.0 nm. The distance between the center-of-mass of these two proteins was set to be 10.0 nm. The systems were simulated for 600 ns. Due to the need of substantive computer resources for each simulation, it is only possible to investigate a small amount of initial conditions. For the simultaneous adsorption simulations, four different arrangements of the two protein molecules were investigated. They differ by the sides of the proteins which face each other. These four arrangements will be denoted as A1 to A4 (see Figure 2 (a-d)).

2) Sequential adsorption: one protein molecule was initially adsorbed, taken from the single component adsorption simulations (Liang et al., 2012b), and the other protein was put into the liquid phase on top of the pre-adsorbed protein (the center-of-mass was placed 12.5 nm away from the ligands), see Figure 2 (e-f). The systems were simulated for 2,000 ns.

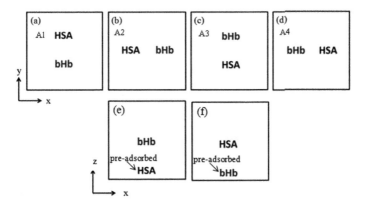

Figure 2. Different initial arrangements of proteins in simultaneous binary simulations (top-view) (a-d): A1-A4; and in sequential binary simulations (side-view) (e): bHb is added on top of the pre-adsorbed HSA; (f): HSA is added on top of the pre-adsorbed bHb. The ligand layer at the bottom of the simulation box is not shown here.

3. Results and Discussion

3.1. Simultaneous adsorption simulations

During the simultaneous binary adsorptions, the proteins interacted with the ligands due to the attractive protein-ligand interactions. Of course, the proteins also interacted with each other. For a better understanding of the competitive adsorption of the proteins, the HSA-ligand, bHb-ligand and HSA-bHb potential energy in simulations with different initial arrangements are shown in Figure 3. HSA was preferentially adsorbed. With the existence of the co-adsorbed protein bHb, a stable adsorption of HSA from all the arrangements was observed at the beginning of the simulations, indicated by the low values of the HSA-ligand potential energy (see Figure 3), which are similar to single adsorption simulations (Liang et al., 2012b). This was due to the relative high negative charge of HSA (isoelectric point = 4.9) at 7.0, which led to strong interactions between HSA and the ligands. bHb could reach a stable adsorption onto the ion-exchange adsorbent only in two of these four arrangements during binary adsorptions (see Figure 3 (a) and (b)). Indicated by the low bHb-ligand potential energy, bHb adsorbed stable after 380 and 250 ns in A1 and A2, respectively. For the A4 simulation an unstable bHb adsorption was observed. The bHb-ligand interaction energy is higher compared to the other simulations. In A3, the bHb stayed away from the ligands without adsorption. This is because bHb's isoelectric point equals 7.0. Its overall charge is relative low at pH 7.0, and hence there was no strong electrostatic interaction between bHb and the ion-exchange media. As can be seen in Figure 3, HSA and bHb interacted with each other in all simulations after 400 ns.

Of particular interest are the binding sites of one protein with the ligands. Here, since the minimum distance between the protein and the ligands stayed between 0.42 nm and 0.45 nm during adsorption (the protein could not get closer due to the van der Waals radii used in the MARTINI force field), the protein residues having a minimum ligand

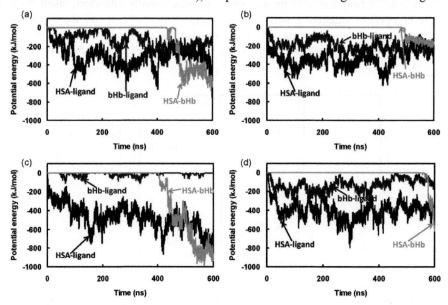

Figure 3. Potential energy plotted against simulation time for simultaneous binary adsorption simulations between HSA and ligands, bHb and ligands, HSA and bHb, for different initial positions: (a) A1, (b) A2, (c) A3 and (d) A4.

distance less than 0.45 nm were considered as binding sites. An average value of 2.5 binding sites of HSA was reached, which is similar to the 3 binding sites of HSA from single adsorption simulations (Liang et al., 2012b). Besides, HSA showed a diversity in possible binding sites. This is due to the large amount of negative charges loaded on its protein surface. For bHb, one binding site has been seen only in the binary adsorption from A1 and A2, similar to the results of single adsorption simulations (Liang et al., 2012b). The results suggest that the relative binding strength of HSA and bHb onto the media is the same as for single adsorption.

3.2. Sequential adsorption simulations

For a better understanding of the competitive adsorption processes, sequential binary adsorption simulations were carried out. The minimum distances (HSA-ligand, bHb-ligand and HSA-bHb) in the simulations of bHb on top of HSA and HSA on top of bHb, are shown in Figure 4 (a), and (b), respectively. As can be seen in Figure 4, the later added protein moved close to the pre-adsorbed protein (protein-protein interaction). It moved further to make contact with the ion-exchange adsorbent (protein-ligand interaction). Hence, first a protein made contact with the other protein, where this contact was relatively stable. Therefore, it can be concluded that if the ion-exchange adsorbent would be saturated with adsorbed proteins, proteins could adsorb onto the first layer of proteins. This is consistent with the phenomenon of multi-layer adsorption of bHb, which has been found and discussed in adsorption experiments (Liang et al., 2012a; Höök et al., 1998). However, the displacement of the pre-adsorbed serum albumin by hemoglobin, a speculation in former experiments (Liang et al., 2012a), was not seen in these simulations. This is because the ion-exchange adsorbent did not reach saturation in the simulations. There were free ligands for the other protein. Another reason is the limited simulation time. When a stable adsorption was reached, similar numbers of binding sites for HSA and bHb as in the single and simultaneous binary adsorption studies have been observed.

4. Conclusions

The MARTINI CG force field was successfully used to investigate the binary component ion-exchange adsorption of HSA and bHb onto Q Sepharose FF with MD simulations. Considering the influence of the adsorption sequences, both simultaneous and sequential binary components adsorption were simulated.

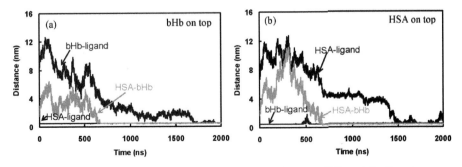

Figure 4. Minimum distance between HSA and the ligands, between bHb and the ligands, between HSA and bHb in simulations: (a) bHb on top of pre-adsorbed HSA and (b) HSA on top of pre-adsorbed bHb.

The competition and interaction between HSA and bHb in binary adsorption were observed in those simulations. However, the adsorption states and numbers of binding sites of adsorbed proteins were found to be similar in both single and binary adsorption. It verifies the use of experimental single adsorption parameters to predict binary adsorption (Liang et al., 2012a). The influence of adsorption sequence was derived by comparing the simultaneous and sequential binary simulation results. The multi-layer adsorption of bHb in experimental studies (Liang et al., 2012a; Höök et al., 1998) has been seen and analyzed in the sequential simulations.

References

C. Chang, A. M. Lenhoff, 1998, Comparison of protein adsorption isotherms and uptake rotes in preparative cation-exchange materials, Journal of Chromatography A, 827, 2, 281-293.

F. Höök, M. Rodahl, B. Kasemo, P. Brzezinski, 1998, Structural changes in hemoglobin during adsorption to solid surfaces: Effects of pH, ionic strength, and ligand binding, Proceedings of the NationalAcademy of Sciences of the United States of America, 95, 12271-12276.

J. Liang, G. Fieg, Q.H. Shi, Y. Sun, 2012a, Single and binary adsorption of proteins on ion-exchange adsorbent: The effectiveness of isothermal models, Journal of Separation Science, 35, 17, 2162-2173.

J. Liang, G. Fieg, F.J. Keil, S. Jakobtorweihen, 2012b, Adsorption of proteins onto ion-exchange chromatographic media: a molecular dynamics study, Industrial and Engineering Chemistry Research, 51, 49, 16049-16058.

S.J. Marrink, H.J. Risselada, S. Yefimov, D.P. Tieleman, A.H. de Vries, 2007, The MARTINI force field: Coarse grained model for biomolecular simulations, Journal of Physical Chemistry B, 111, 27, 7812-7824.

L. Monticelli, S.K. Kandasamy, X. Periole, R.G. Larson, D.P. Tieleman, S.J. Marrink, 2008, The MARTINI coarse-grained force field: Extension to proteins, Journal of Chemical Theory and Computation, 4, 5, 819-834.

S. Pronk, S. Páll, R. Schulz, P. Larsson, P. Bjelkmar, R. Apostolov, M.R. Shirts, J.C. Smith, P.M. Kasson, D. van der Spoel, B. Hess, E. Lindahl, 2013, GROMACS 4.5: a high-throughput and highly parallel open source molecular simulation toolkit, Bioinformatics, 29, 7, 845-854.

A.J. Rzepiela, D. Sengupta, N. Goga, S.J. Marrink, 2010, Membrane poration by antimicrobial peptides combining atomistic and coarse-grained descriptions, Faraday Discussions, 144, 431-443.

Q.H. Shi, Z.C. Shi, Y. Sun, 2012, Dynamic behavior of binary component ion-exchange displacement chromatography of proteins visualized by confocal laser scanning microscopy, Journal of Chromatography A, 1257, 48-57.

S.J. Traylor, X.K. Xu, A.M. Lenhoff, 2011, Shrinking-core modeling of binary chromatographic breakthrough, Journal of Chromatography A, 1218, 16, 2222-2231.

L. Zhang, Y. Sun, 2010, Molecular simulation of adsorption and its implications to protein chromatography: A review, Biochemical Engineering Journal, 48, 408-415.

Jiří Jaromír Klemeš, Petar Sabev Varbanov and Peng Yen Liew (Editors)
Proceedings of the 24th European Symposium on Computer Aided Process Engineering – ESCAPE 24
June 15-18, 2014, Budapest, Hungary.

Hybrid Modeling of Phase Transition for Evaporators and Condensers in Chillers

Jing Wu*, Christian Jallut, Emilie Gagnière, Françoise Couenne, Boussad Hamroun

Université de Lyon, Université Claude Bernard Lyon 1, Laboratoire d'Automatique et de Génie des Procédés, UMR CNRS/UCBL 5007, ESCPE, 43, Bd du 11 Novembre 1918, 69622 Villeurbanne Cedex, France.
jwu@lagep.univ-lyon1.fr

Abstract

A novel hybrid dynamic model for two-phase heat exchangers is described in this paper. This model is developed for dynamic modeling of chillers and heat pumps. It permits to represent over time the spatial distribution of the state variables such as the mass fraction, the mass density, the temperature and the pressure. A switching procedure between different regimes based on a phase stability test is applied to ensure the continuity of the system evolution. This switching is performed by matrix operations, which permit to achieve a global and very compact representation of the system. The manipulated matrices are analytically determined from a thermodynamic model of the refrigerant based on an equation of state. A simulation program is developed using the Matlab software. Simulation tests with step-type inputs are provided, which show the relevance of the model as well as its high flexibility since one can switch automatically from an evaporation situation to a condensation situation and vice-versa.

Keywords: two-phase, heat exchanger, hybrid dynamic model, thermodynamics.

1. Introduction

The main difficulty for heat exchangers dynamic modelling arises when a phase transition occurs, the state of the fluid (vapor, liquid or two-phase mixture) under consideration varying with position and time. This is the situation that occurs in condensers and evaporators of chillers and heat pumps. The solution of the mass and energy balance equations, which differs according to the single- or two-phase nature of the refrigerant, requires the consideration of discrete events associated with transitions between different situations at a given point: hence it refers to hybrid systems that are very well described in automatic control (Song et al., 2012).

As far as chillers evaporators and condensers are concerned, two approaches are mainly used in the literature (Rasmussen, 2012): the moving-boundary models and the 1-D models. These two approaches are based on an equivalent 1-D geometry for the heat exchanger. In 1-D models, partial differential equations are derived from mass and energy balances. The resulting PDEs have to be discretized in order to be numerically solved (Ndiaye et al., 2012). In order to get a lumped parameter model easier to solve, the moving-boundary method has been proposed (McKinley et al., 2008). It consists in defining single and two-phase zones and to calculate the time dependent position of the boundaries between these zones. This situation is also hybrid since in some circumstances, one boundary can disappear and switching between different sub-models is necessary (Willatzen et al., 1998). Most of the published articles using the two methods remain imprecise about the way the balance equations are solved and the thermodynamic tools that are used. Besides, they often rest on numerical evaluation or pre-determined tables to calculate the derivatives of thermodynamic properties with respect to thermodynamic state variables.

In this paper, a 1-D model is described, which permits to represent over time the spatial distribution of the state variables such as the mass or void fraction, the temperature and the pressure. The discretization of the equations system is accomplished by considering a cascade of CSTRs so that mass and energy balance equations are directly written for each of them. The discrete events of switching between different regimes are detected by phase stability tests. A switching procedure performed by matrix operations is proposed to ensure the continuity of the state variables evolution. Moreover, all the thermodynamic properties are analytically determined from a thermodynamic model of the refrigerant based on an equation of state.

2. Model description

2.1. Spatial discretization and balance equations

The condenser and evaporator are both handled in the same manner using a 1-D model of an equivalent tube. The geometric dimensions of the tube are determined from the real characteristics of the heat exchanger such as the heat transfer surface area, the mass of the heat exchanger wall, the refrigerant volume, etc. As shown in Figure 1, the total volume of refrigerant is divided into a serial arrangement of N identical CSTRs, each of them being associated with two elements at a uniform temperature, a piece of wall and an external fluid element (see Goma Bilongo et al., 2012 for a similar approach applied to extruders). The heat exchanger is supposed to be counter flow. The main assumptions of the model are: (a) the refrigerant pressure drop is neglected; (b) in two-phase zone of the refrigerant, the liquid and vapor are in thermodynamic equilibrium; (c) the axial conduction effects are neglected; (d) radial heat fluxes are accounted by using heat transfer coefficients; (e) the external fluid is assumed to remain as a single phase fluid.

The mass and energy balance equations for the refrigerant in the kth CSTR are:

$$\dot{m}_{k-1} = \dot{m}_k + V\dot{\rho}_k \tag{1}$$

$$h_{k-1}\dot{m}_{k-1} + \alpha_{iw}A_{iw}(T_{w_k} - T_k) = h_k\dot{m}_k + V(\dot{\rho}_k u_k + \rho_k \dot{u}_k) \tag{2}$$

where $\dot{m}$ is the refrigerant mass flow rate, V is the refrigerant volume of each element, ρ is the refrigerant mass density, h and u are respectively the specific enthalpy and specific internal energy of the refrigerant, T and T_w are the temperatures of the refrigerant and the wall, α_{iw} and A_{iw} are respectively the refrigerant side heat transfer coefficient and the corresponding surface area.

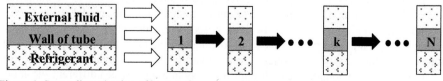

Figure 1. Space discretization of heat exchanger

The intermediate flow rates of the refrigerant can be algebraically eliminated through a recursive procedure from Eq.(1) (Bendapudi et al., 2008):

$$\dot{m}_k = \dot{m}_{in} - V \sum_{j=1}^{k} \dot{\rho}_k \tag{3}$$

$$\dot{m}_{out} = \dot{m}_{in} - V \sum_{j=1}^{N} \dot{\rho}_k \tag{4}$$

where $\dot{m}_{in}$ and $\dot{m}_{out}$ are the mass flow rate at the inlet and outlet of the heat exchanger. In order to include the heat exchanger model into the global chiller model, the mass flow rates $\dot{m}_{in}$ and $\dot{m}_{out}$ are chosen as boundary conditions for the mass balance equations. The energy balance equation for the tube wall and the external fluid are:

$$c_{P_w} \dot{T}_{w_k} = \alpha_{iw} A_{iw} (T_k - T_{w_k}) + \alpha_{ow} A_{ow} (T_{a_k} - T_{w_k}) \tag{5}$$

$$c_{P_a} \dot{T}_{a_k} = C_{P_a} \dot{m}_a (T_{a_{k+1}} - T_{a_k}) - \alpha_{ow} A_{ow} (T_{w_k} - T_{a_k}) \tag{6}$$

where c_{P_w} and c_{P_a} are the wall and external fluid heat capacities, T_a is the external fluid temperatures, α_{ow} is the heat transfer coefficient between the wall and the external fluid and A_{ow} the corresponding surface area and finally $\dot{m}_a$ is the external fluid mass flow rate.

2.2. Mathematical model structure

In single-phase zones, density and temperature are selected to describe the refrigerant thermodynamic state, which are also employed to express the time derivatives of the pressure P and the specific internal energy u :

$$\dot{P} = (\frac{\partial P}{\partial \rho_k})_T \dot{\rho}_k + (\frac{\partial P}{\partial T_k})_\rho \dot{T}_k \tag{7}$$

$$\dot{u}_k = (\frac{\partial u_k}{\partial \rho_k})_T \dot{\rho}_k + (\frac{\partial u_k}{\partial T_k})_\rho \dot{T}_k \tag{8}$$

In single-phase zones, the vapor mass fraction is constant (0 or 1), so we have:

$$\dot{x}_k = 0 \tag{9}$$

An equation of state developed for the refrigerant R410A is used (Lemmon, 2003) for the single phase zones. This equation permits to express the thermodynamic properties such as the specific enthalpy, the specific internal energy, the pressure and the partial derivatives appearing in Eq.(7 - 8) as functions of the density and temperature. Finally, Eqs.(2), (4), (5), (6), (7) and (9), applied to the N CSTRs, result in a closed dynamic system of 5N+1 ordinary differential equations:

$$A_m(X) \cdot \dot{X} = B_m \tag{10}$$

where $X^T = \begin{bmatrix} \rho_1 & T_1 & x_1 & T_{w_1} & T_{a_1} & \cdots & \rho_N & T_N & x_N & T_{w_N} & T_{a_N} & P \end{bmatrix}$.

In two-phase zones, the thermodynamic properties of each phase only depend on one state variable. Therefore, the overall refrigerant properties can be described using the temperature and the vapor mass fraction profile, as well as their time derivatives:

$$\dot{\rho}_k = (\frac{\partial \rho_k}{\partial x_k})_T \dot{x}_k + (\frac{\partial \rho_k}{\partial T_k})_x \dot{T}_k \tag{11}$$

$$\dot{u}_k = (\frac{\partial u_k}{\partial x_k})_T \dot{x}_k + (\frac{\partial u_k}{\partial T_k})_x \dot{T}_k \tag{12}$$

The time derivative of the pressure in these zones can be expressed as follows:

$$\dot{P} = (dP / dT_k) \dot{T}_k \tag{13}$$

An empirical model of polynomial equations as a function of the temperature, based on curve fitting of the ASHRAE data (2001), is used to calculate the saturated properties of each phase as well as the derivatives appearing in Eqs.(11) - (13). In the same way as the Eq.(10), the Eqs.(2), (4), (5), (6), (11) and (13) constitute also a closed dynamic system of 5N+1 ordinary differential equations:

$$A_d(X) \cdot \dot{X} = B_d \tag{14}$$

The state of the refrigerant of each control volume can actually be either single-phase or two-phase in the heat exchanger, thus a generic model permitting to describe both of the cases is proposed:

$$A(X) \cdot \dot{X} = B \tag{15}$$

with $A = E \cdot A_m + (I - E) \cdot A_d$, $B = E \cdot B_m + (I - E) \cdot B_d$, in which E is a (5N+1)-diagonal matrix with the diagonal constituted by 1 and 0 (1 if the refrigerant state of the corresponding CSTR is single-phase, 0 if it is two-phase), I is the 5N+1 identity matrix. After any phase transition process, A and B are updated once the states of all the refrigerant CSTRs is known.

2.3. Phase transition detection

The phase transition detection is based on stability tests. Such stability tests are commonly used for mixtures at given pressure and temperature (Michelsen, 1982). In our case, a phase stability test at given temperature and volume is more suitable (Souza et al., 2006) since it is based on the value of the refrigerant density as it is calculated from the balance equations. At a given temperature and a given density, if the tangent plane to the Helmoltz free energy is somewhere above the Helmoltz free energy curve in the phase diagram, the single phase under consideration is unstable. This formulation is equivalent to the fact that a single-phase system having a mass density located between the saturated liquid and vapor densities is less stable than a system made of the two phases. According to the initial situation, the vapor mass fraction or the mass density is used to apply this stability test to each CSTR and at each time.

From an initial two-phase situation, if the vapor mass fraction x that is the current state variable reaches a value close to 0 or 1, the refrigerant is considered as liquid or vapor phase. It is noted that a threshold should be set to ensure that the vapor mass fraction remains within [0, 1], since the time step of calculation cannot be infinitely small.

From an initial single-phase situation, the mass density is the current state variable and the refrigerant becomes two-phase when its mass density $\rho(t)$ becomes greater than the saturated vapor mass density $\rho_{vs}(T(t))$ or lesser than the saturated liquid mass density $\rho_{ls}(T(t))$.

3. Example of numerical simulation

A fourth-fifth order Runge-Kutta method with adaptive step size (ode45) is used within the framework of the Matlab software. In Figure 2, the dynamical responses of the heat exchanger to a step change of the external fluid inlet temperature are shown. We can observe that the heat exchanger works initially as an evaporator, but its evaporation capacity is lowered while the external fluid inlet temperature has decreased from 50 s. Finally it becomes even a condenser when the external fluid inlet temperature is continually reduced to be inferior to the refrigerant temperature beyond 250 s. This example has demonstrated that the model proposed in this paper is fully able to depict the phase transition as well as to automatically switch from one situation where the exchanger is used as an evaporator to another one where it is used as a condenser. This point is very important since, with the view of simulating a chiller, only one model is necessary, that is applied for both the two exchangers.

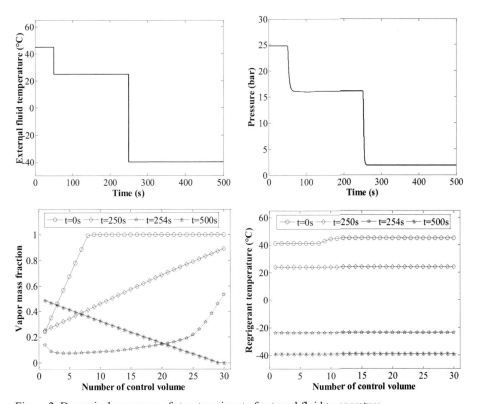

Figure 2. Dynamical responses of step-type input of external fluid temperature

4. Conclusions

A 1-D hybrid model for simulating the dynamic behaviour of two-phase heat exchangers is described. This model is able to represent the distribution of the state variables over time and space. The mechanism of phase transition is established, which has guaranteed the continuity of the state variables evolution. The main originalities of this model are as follows. The void fraction is calculated from the balance equations. As a consequence, no model for the void fraction is necessary since we do not assume the nature of the refrigerant fluid at a given point. A switching procedure between the single phase and two-phases situations is performed by matrix operations, which permit to achieve a global and very compact representation of the system that is true for all the situations. Such an approach is possible because all the thermodynamic properties and their partial derivatives are analytically calculated. A numerical simulation test with step-type input responses is executed, which show qualitatively the relevance of the model and its flexibility.

5. Acknowledgements

This work has been funded by the French National Research Agency (ANR) within the framework of the project ACLIRSYS (Advanced Control for Low Inertia Refrigeration Systems).

References

ASHRAE, 2001, Fundamentals Handbook, American Society of Heating Refrigerating and Air-Conditioning Engineers, Atlanta, USA.

T. Goma Bilongo, F. Couenne, C. Jallut, Y. Le Gorrec, A. Di Martino, 2012, Dynamic modeling of the reactive twin-screw co-rotating extrusion process: experimental validation by using inlet glass fibers injection response and application to polymers degassing, IEC Res., 51, 35, 11381-11388.

C. J. L. Hermes, C. Melo, 2008, A first-principles simulation model for the start-up and cycling transients of household refrigerators, International Journal of Refrigeration, 31,8, 1341-1357.

E. W. Lemmon., 2003, Pseudo-pure fluid equations of state for the refrigerant blends R-410A, R-404A, R-507A and R-407A, International Journal of Thermophysics, 24, 4, 991-1006.

T. L. McKinley and A.G. Alleyne, 2008, An advanced nonlinear switched heat exchanger model for vapor compression cycles using the moving-boundary method. International Journal of Refrigeration, 31, 7, 1253-1264.

M. L. Michelsen, 1982, The isothermal flash problem. Part I. Stability, Fluid Phase Equilibria, 9, 1-19.

D. Ndiaye, M. Bernier, 2012, Transient model of a geothermal heat pump in cycling conditions - Part A: The model, International Journal of Refrigeration, 35, 8, 2110-2123.

B. P. Rasmussen, 2012, Dynamic modelling for vapor vapor compression systems – Part I: Literature review, HVAC&R Research, 22, 5, 934-955.

C. Song, B. Wu, P. Li, 2012, A hybrid model-based optimal control method for nonlinear systems using simultaneous dynamic optimization strategies, Journal of Process Control, 22, 5, 852-60.

A. T. Souza, L. Cardozo-Filho, F. Wolff, R. Guirardello, 2006, Application of interval analysis for Gibbs and Helmoltz free energy global minimization in phase stability analysis, Brazilian Journal of Chemical Engineering, 23, 1, 117-124.

M. Willatzen, N.B.O.L. Pettit, L. Ploug-Sørensen, 1998, A general dynamic simulation model for evaporators and condensers in refrigeration. Part II: simulation and control of an evaporator, International Journal of Refrigeration, 21, 5, 404–414.

Jiří Jaromír Klemeš, Petar Sabev Varbanov and Peng Yen Liew (Editors)
Proceedings of the 24th European Symposium on Computer Aided Process Engineering – ESCAPE 24
June 15-18, 2014, Budapest, Hungary. Copyright © 2014 Elsevier B.V. All rights reserved.

Reformulation-linearization Method for Global Optimization of Mixed Integer Linear Fractional Programming Problems with Application on Sustainable Batch Scheduling

Dajun Yue, Fengqi You*

Northwestern University, 2145 Sheridan Rd., Evanston, IL, 60201, USA
you@northwestern.edu

Abstract

In this work, we propose a novel approach to the effective global optimization of mixed integer linear fractional programming (MILFP) problems: reformulation-linearization method. The proposed reformulation-linearization method is based on the integration of Charnes-Cooper transformation and Glover's linearization scheme. This method can provide the exact mixed integer linear programming (MILP) reformulation of a general MILFP problem, thus allowing the global optimization of MILFP problems by solving the equivalent MILP problems with the powerful MILP methods, only once. Reformulation and analysis are presented, along with a side-by-side comparison with the other MILFP solution methods. To illustrate its application, we address in this work a case study on sustainable batch scheduling modelled as MILFP problems. The results show that orders of magnitude reduction in CPU times can be achieved when using the proposed approach, compared to solving the problems with the general-purpose MINLP solvers. The proposed method is also shown to have comparable computational performance as the parametric algorithm.

Keywords: reformulation-linearization, mixed-integer linear fractional programming, MILFP, sustainable scheduling.

1. Introduction

Mixed-integer linear fractional program (MILFP) is a special class of mixed-integer nonlinear programs (MINLP) where the objective function is the ratio of two linear functions and all constraints are linear (Chu and You, 2013). MILFP problems can be coped with general-purpose MINLP methods and global optimizers, including but not limited to, standard branch-and-bound method, extended cutting plane method, branch-and-reduce method, the α-BB method, the spatial branch-and-bound search method and GloMIQO algorithm. However, global optimization of large-scale MILFPs can be computationally intractable due to the presence of discrete variables and the pseudoconvex/ pseudoconcave objective function (Yue et al., 2013). The tailored parametric algorithm was proved to be efficient for MILFP problems (You et al., 2009), but the gap information is not available during its solution (Zhong and You, 2014).

MILFP problems emerge in batch production scheduling. Maximizing the productivity is often considered as the economic objective. Productivity is defined as the total profit divided by the corresponding makespan, which accounts for both the absolute profit and the temporal aspect. To address the increasing environmental concerns, sustainability metrics originated from the life cycle assessment methodology can be employed (Yue et al., 2013). As suggested, the unit environmental impact, defined as the total impact divided by the produced quantity in terms of functional unit should be chosen as the environmental objective (Capón-García et al., 2011).

The major contributions of this work are summarized as follows.
- An efficient reformulation-linearization method for transforming MILFPs into their equivalent MILP problems, allowing the global optimization of large-scale MILFPs using efficient MILP methods within modest computational times.
- An application of the proposed method on optimal sustainable scheduling of flexible batch chemical processes.

2. Mixed-integer linear fractional program

An MILFP includes both continuous and discrete variables. All the constraints of an MILFP are linear, and the objective function is expressed as the ratio of two linear functions. Mathematically, a general MILFP can be formulated as the following problem (P0):

$$\textbf{(P0)} \quad \max \quad \frac{A_0 + \sum_{i \in I} A1_i x_i + \sum_{j \in J} A2_j y_j}{B_0 + \sum_{i \in I} B1_i x_i + \sum_{j \in J} B2_j y_j} \tag{1}$$

$$\text{s.t.} \quad C_{0k} + \sum_{i \in I} C1_{ik} x_i + \sum_{j \in J} C2_{jk} y_j = 0, \ \forall k \in K \tag{2}$$

$$x_i \geq 0, \ \forall i \in I \text{ and } y_j \in \{0,1\}, \ \forall j \in J \tag{3}$$

where x_i are continuous variables and y_j are discrete variables. For problem (P0), it is assumed that the denominator $B_0 + \sum_{i \in I} B1_i x_i + \sum_{j \in J} B2_j y_j > 0$ for all feasible solutions and all inequalities are converted into equalities through the use of slack variables (Dinkelbach, 1967).

3. Reformulation-linearization method

Charnes and Cooper (1962) proposed a method to reformulate a linear fractional program into an equivalent linear program by introducing an additional continuous variable and an additional constraint. This method is known as the Charnes-Cooper transformation, and has been shown to be very efficient for solving continuous linear fractional programs. However, Charnes-Cooper transformation cannot be directly applied to MILFP problems since it is restricted to the case where all the variables are continuous.

We propose a novel and generalized approach to reformulate MILFP problems into an equivalent MILP form. Our approach is based on the reformulation of Charnes-Cooper and the Glover's linearization scheme (Glover, 1975). The former allows converting the MILFP into an MINLP, while the latter transforms this MINLP into an equivalent MILP.

3.1. Equivalent MILP reformulation

The equivalent MILP reformulation of the original MILFP problem (P0) is given below and denoted as (PR). Considering to the length of the paper, detailed derivation is omitted and can be found in the work by Yue et al. (2013).

Table 1. Comparison in terms of problems sizes and iterations numbers between the proposed reformulation-linearization method and the parametric algorithm

	General MILFP problem (P0)	Reformulated MILP problem (PR)	MILP subproblem of parametric algorithm
# binary 0-1 variables	$\|J\|$	$\|J\|$	$\|J\|$
# continuous variables	$\|I\|$	$\|I\| + \|J\| + 1$	$\|I\|$
# constraints	$\|K\|$	$3 \cdot \|J\| + \|K\| + 1$	$\|K\|$
# iterations required	--	one	At least one

where $\|I\|$, $\|J\|$, $\|K\|$ are the numbers of continuous variables, binary variables and constraints of the original MILFP problem, respectively.

$$\textbf{(PR)} \qquad \max \quad A_0 \cdot u + \sum_{i \in I} A1_i z_i + \sum_{j \in J} A2_j \cdot w_j \tag{4}$$

$$\text{s.t.} \quad C_{0k} \cdot u + \sum_{i \in I} C1_{ik} \cdot z_i + \sum_{j \in J} C2_{jk} \cdot w_j = 0, \ \forall k \in K \tag{5}$$

$$B_0 \cdot u + \sum_{i \in I} B1_i \cdot z_i + \sum_{j \in J} B2_j \cdot w_j = 1 \tag{6}$$

$$w_j \le u, \ \forall j \in J \tag{7}$$

$$w_j \le M \cdot y_j, \ \forall j \in J \tag{8}$$

$$w_j \ge u - M \cdot (1 - y_j), \ \forall j \in J \tag{9}$$

$$u \ge 0, \ z_i \ge 0, \ \forall i \in I \ \text{and} \ w_j \ge 0, \ y_j \in \{0,1\}, \ \forall j \in J \tag{10}$$

where $u = \dfrac{1}{B_0 + \sum_{i \in I} B1_i x_i + \sum_{j \in J} B2_j y_j}$; $z_i = u \cdot x_i$; $w_j = y_j \cdot u$. M is a sufficiently large

number. Constraint (5) corresponds to constraint (2). Constraint (6) establishes the equivalence between problem (PR) and (P0). Constraint (7)-(9) are for the linearization of bilinear term $y_j \cdot u$.

3.2. Comparison with other approaches
The major advantages of the proposed reformulation-linearization approach include that we can globally optimize a nonconvex MILFP problem by solving a similar size MILP problem, only once and the gap information is available during the solution process. Similar to the parametric algorithm, the proposed reformulation-linearization method can take advantage of the state-of-the-art MILP solvers, which have become more and more efficient in the past decades (Cornuejols, 2008). Table 1 shows the problem sizes of the original MILFP problem (P0) and the reformulated MILP problem (PR), and the MILP subproblem of parametric algorithm. Extensive numerical case studies were presented in the work by Yue et al. (2013).

4. Sustainable scheduling application
The problem addressed in this case study is recently studied by (Capón-García et al., 2011). This multiproduct batch plant produces 3 acrylic fiber formulations through 14 processing stages. The time horizon is 100 h. For each product, the maximal demand is 3 batches and the minimal demand is 1 batch. The batch sizes, operation times associated with each processing stage are given in the production recipe. The economic

Table 2. Description of the cleaning methods

Cleaning method	Time	Cost	Env. Imp.	Method based on the use of
1	Very low	Medium	Medium	Steam
2	Very high	Very low	Very low	Water
3	Medium	High	High	Organic solvent

and environmental data related to each product are also given. We consider 3 cleaning methods as changeover options given in Table 2, which differ in time, cost and environmental impact. The goal is to determine the optimal batch sequence, start/finish timing, and changeover options under both economic and environmental concerns.

We adopt the time-slot-based continuous-time formulation for the scheduling problem (Erdirik-Dogan & Grossmann, 2008), and a brief formulation is presented as follows.

$$\min \quad productivity = \frac{profit}{makespan} \tag{11}$$

$$\min \quad unit\ impact = \frac{total\ environmental\ impact}{produced\ quantity} \tag{12}$$

s.t.   timing constraints, matching/assignment constraints, sequencing constraints, selection of changeover options, cost and environmental impact related constraints, etc.

We solve for 1,096 instances by taking values of the ε parameter evenly distributed in the interval [3.794, 4.889]. The MILFP problems related to each instance are solved using the parametric algorithm and the reformulation-linearization method. The relative optimality tolerance is set as 0% for all instances. Same solutions are returned by both methods. Totally 67 unique Pareto solutions are identified and plotted in Figure 3(a).

In Figure 1(a), the horizontal axis stands for the economic objective and the vertical axis stands for the environmental objective. As the productivity increases from 760 to 1,262 m.u./h, the relative environmental impact increases monotonically from 3.794 to 4.888 pts/mg. Each Pareto solution corresponds to a unique schedule. Schedule 2C2B2B2B2A2 on the lower-left corner has the lowest relative environmental impact. This schedule indicates producing maximal amount of product B. Hence, product B might be the most environmental friendly product. In addition, cleaning method 2 is selected for all changeover options, because it has the lowest environmental impact, though it is also the most time consuming one. Schedule 1A1A1A1C1B1B1B1C1C1 on the upper-right corner has the highest productivity. Each product is produced to its maximal demand. Cleaning method 1 is selected for all changeover options, due to its short operational time and reasonable economic cost. The Gantt chart of this schedule is given in Figure 1(b). It is interesting to note that, the second batch of product C is not processed immediately after the first batch, but after three batches of product B, because this sequence avoids the changeover between product A and product B, which is not economical. All the Pareto solutions constitute a Pareto frontier, solutions above which are suboptimal and below which are infeasible. One can choose among these Pareto solutions for industrial manufacturing according to the preference. Solutions on the left emphasize more on minimizing the relative environmental impact of the process, while solutions on the right tend to pursue higher productivity.

Reformulation-linearization Method for Global Optimization of Mixed Integer Linear
Fractional Programming Problems with Application on Sustainable Batch Scheduling

953

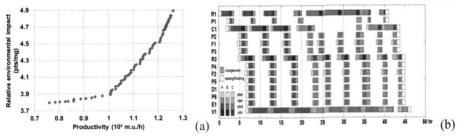

Figure 1. Optimal scheduling results: (a) Pareto curve (b) Gantt chart of schedule 1A1A1A1C1B1B1B1C1C1

The total CPU time for solving all 1,096 instances using the parametric algorithm is 7488.249 s that is about 2 h. The computational times for solving each instance range from 3.822 s to 51.247 s. The total CPU time for solving all 1,096 instances using the reformulation-linearization algorithm is 15,203.029 s that is about 4.5 h. The CPU times for solving each individual instance range from 3.136 s to 113.413 s. For a thorough comparison with general purpose MINLP solvers and global optimizer, we present the computational results in Table 3 for four instances where the ε parameter is set to 3.794, 4.006, 4.500 and 4.889, respectively.

The computation times for parametric algorithm to globally optimize instances 1-4 range from 3.885 s to 6.848 s. The computation times for the reformulation-linearization method to globally optimize instances 1-4 range from 3.213 s to 29.141 s. DICOPT requires comparable computation times as the parametric algorithm and the reformulation-linearization method, but it cannot guarantee the global optimality of its solutions (instances 2-4). This is because DICOPT is based on the outer-approximation method, which is unable to deal with MILFP problems with pseudo-convex/concave

Table 3. Comparison of computational performances of different solution methods

Inst.	ε	Productivity (10^3 m.u./h)	Relative environmental	CPUs	Solvers
1	3.794	0.760	3.794	3.885	Parametric
		0.760	3.794	3.213	R-L
		0.760	3.794	597.952	SBB
		0.760	3.794	8.346	DICOPT
		0.760	3.794	244.240	BARON 11
2	4.006	1.038	3.994	4.572	Parametric
		1.038	3.994	29.141	R-L
		1.038	3.994	3522.3155	SBB
		0.771	3.984	5.788	DICOPT
		1.038	3.994	501.010	BARON 11
3	4.500	1.184	4.491	6.848	Parametric
		1.184	4.491	9.048	R-L
		1.184-1.219	4.491	3600[b]	SBB
		0.982	4.481	21.216	DICOPT
		1.184	4.491	900.940	BARON 11
4	4.889	1.262	4.888	3.978	Parametric
		1.262	4.888	6.677	R-L
		1.262	4.888	2407.127	SBB
		1.157	4.862	19.625	DICOPT
		1.262	4.888	489.27	BARON 11

objective functions. SBB returns global optimal solutions for instance 1, 2 and 4, but not instance 3. Note that, although SBB is a local optimizer, it is able to guarantee global optimal solutions for MILFP problems. The global optimizer BARON is able to return global optimal solutions for all instances 1-4. The computation times are much longer than the parametric algorithm and the reformulation-linearization method. Overall, the parametric algorithm and the reformulation-linearization method are much more efficient than general-purpose MINLP solvers and global optimizer.

5. Conclusions

We introduced a novel global optimization approach for large-scale MILFP problems. The reformulation-linearization method provides exact MILP reformulation, thus allowing us to take advantage of the efficient MILP methods for solving MILFP problems. The equivalent MILP problem needs to be solved only once and gap information is available during solution. A case study on sustainable batch scheduling was addressed to illustrate the application of the proposed reformulation-linearization method. Both the economic and environmental objective functions were model as linear fractional functions, thus leading to MILFP problems. Various solution approaches were applied. The proposed reformulation-linearization method was proved to be much more efficient than the general-purpose MINLP methods and global optimizers, and exhibited comparable computation performance to the parametric algorithm.

References

E. Capon-Garcia, A. D.Bojarski, A. Espuna, L. Puigjaner, 2011, Multiobjective Optimization of Multiproduct Batch Plants Scheduling Under Environmental and Economic Concerns, AIChE Journal, 57, 2766-2782.

A. Charnes, W. W. Cooper, 1962, Programming with Linear Fractional Functionals, Naval Research Logistics Quarterly, 9, 181-186.

Y. Chu, F.You, 2013, Integration of production scheduling and dynamic optimization for multi-product CSTRs: Generalized Benders decomposition coupled with global mixed-integer fractional programming, Computers and Chemical Engineering, 58, 315-333.

G. Cornuejols, 2008, Valid inequalities for mixed integer linear programs, Mathematical Programming, 112, 3-44.

W. Dinkelbach, 1967, On Nonlinear Fractional Programming, Management Science, 13, 492-498.

M. Erdirik-Dogan, I. E. Grossmann, 2008, Slot-Based Formulation for the Short-Term Scheduling of Multistage, Multiproduct Batch Plants with Sequence-Dependent Changeovers, Industrial and Engineering Chemistry Research, 47, 1159-1183.

F. Glover, 1975, Improved Linear Integer Programming Formulations of Nonlinear Integer Problems, Management Science, 22, 455-460.

F. Q. You, P. M. Castro, I. E. Grossmann, 2009, Dinkelbach's Algorithm as An Efficient Method to Solve A Class of MINLP Models for Large-Scale Cyclic Scheduling Problems, Computers and Chemical Engineering, 33, 1879-1889.

D. Yue, G. Guillén-Gosálbez, F. You, 2013, Global optimization of large-scale mixed-integer linear fractional programming problems: A reformulation-linearization method and process scheduling applications, AIChE Journal, 59, 4255-4272.

D. Yue, M. A. Kim, F. You, 2013, Design of Sustainable Product Systems and Supply Chains with Life Cycle Optimization Based on Functional Unit: General Modeling Framework, Mixed-Integer Nonlinear Programming Algorithms and Case Study on Hydrocarbon Biofuels, ACS Sustainable Chemistry and Engineering, 1, 1003-1014.

Z. Zhong, F. You, 2014, Globally convergent exact and inexact parametric algorithms for solving large-scale mixed-integer fractional programs and applications in process systems engineering, Computers and Chemical Engineering, 61, 90-101.

Jiří Jaromír Klemeš, Petar Sabev Varbanov and Peng Yen Liew (Editors)
Proceedings of the 24th European Symposium on Computer Aided Process Engineering – ESCAPE 24
June 15-18, 2014, Budapest, Hungary. Copyright © 2014 Elsevier B.V. All rights reserved.

Product Quality Monitoring Using Extreme Learning Machines and Bat algorithms: A Case Study in Second-Generation Ethanol Production

Felix S. Farias Júnior[a,*], Renan A. Azevedo[a], Elmer C. Rivera[b], William E. Herrera[c], Rubens M. Filho[c], Luiz P. Lima Júnior[a]

[a]LLTECH Automation, Avenida Caxangá, 2474, SL103, CEP 50731-000, Recife-PE, Brazil
[b]Brazilian Bioethanol Science and Technology Laboratory,Brazilian Center for Research in Energy and Materials (CTBE/CNPEM), Caixa Postal 6170, CEP 13083-970 Campinas, SP, Brazil
[c]School of Chemical Engineering – University of Campinas (UNICAMP), CEP 13083-852 Campinas, SP, Brazil
felix.farias@lltech.com.br

Abstract

In this study, a new methodology for online monitoring of second-generation ethanol production is presented. The prediction of the concentration of ethanol, substrate and cells from secondary measurements (pH, turbidity, CO_2 and temperature) is compared with experimental data from the fermentation of a mixture of molasses and hydrolyzed sugarcane bagasse from the alkaline hydrogen peroxide pre-treatment at 25 % and 75 % of volume. The Extreme Learning Machine algorithm (ELM) provided a very good alternative to traditional Multilayer Perceptron neural networks (MLP) and the BAT optimization technique applied to ELM algorithm provided a fast parallel search for the best solution. This new methodology offered a good alternative to the standard soft-sensor approach based on MLP and fast and reliable product quality estimates for key process variables as in second-generation ethanol production.

Keywords: Extreme Learning Machine, Artificial Neural Networks, BAT algorithm, second generation ethanol.

1. Introduction

In the last decade, a lot of research has been conducted around the world in the development of cleaner and renewable alternatives to oil products, and specially in liquid fuels. Ethanol production technology from sugarcane has been in use extensively in Brazil's energy matrix since Proálcool program in the 1970s. However, low efficiency and high costs in the production from these first-generation plants (based on sugar cane molasses and broth) and heavy competition with the sugar market demanded, over the years, support from the government.

The second-generation ethanol production process aims to produce ethanol from sugar cane bagasse and straw (Dias et al., 2013). This new process uses raw materials already available and shares existing facilities with first-generation processes, potentially maximizing efficiency and reducing costs. However, the efficiency of fermentation of *Saccharomyces cerevisiae* using lignocellulosic feedstock depends on the fermentability of sugars from the hydrolysates and these reaction rates are affected by inhibitors in byproducts of the pre-treatment and hydrolysis processes. In order to accomplish higher efficiency and productivity in this process, it is necessary to achieve online monitoring and control of some important variables that are difficult to obtain in practice, such as compositions and reaction rates (Herrera, 2013). A possible and potentially suitable solution for better control and enhanced economic viability is to use an inference system or soft-sensor (Rivera, 2009).

Artificial Neural Networks (ANN) is a standard mathematical structure for the development of soft-sensors and Multilayer Perceptron neural networks (MLP) have been used in a number of systems in the industry (Salvatore, 2009). In recent years, a new algorithm has been proposed in the literature, the Extreme Learning Machine (ELM) (Huang, 2009). ELM is a training algorithm for ANN with only one input layer, one hidden layer and one output layer. This algorithm is noted for its training speed and few parameters, providing a faster alternative to conventional MLP networks.

ELM and MLP networks are sensitive to the choice of parameters (Oliveira, 2012). Thus, in this study, an optimization algorithm was also used to optimize topology. The BAT Algorithm (Yang, 2010) is used to perform this search procedure. This algorithm is an optimization technique bio-inspired by the echolocation of bats in flight. The echolocation consists of broadcasting ultrasonic waves and measuring the gap between send and return time to the source, after being reflected by the object or prey. These waves have their pulse rate and loudness increased when the bat is looking for a prey, and decreased when the prey is captured. In the algorithm, each bat is a possible solution for the proposed problem.

2. Experiments

A system operated in repeated-batch mode with cell recycling was carried out in bioreactor Bioflo III (New Brunswick Scientific Co., Inc., Edison, NJ) with 1 L of working volume, stirred by two flat blade turbines, with six blades each, at 5 Hz (300 rpm). The substrate is a mixture of molasses and hydrolyzed bagasse from the alkaline hydrogen peroxide pre-treatment at 25 % and 75 % of volume. It operated at temperatures of 30 °C, 32 °C, 34 °C, 36 °C and 38 °C where the initial substrate concentration was kept constant at 180 kg/m^3. For each temperature, cells were recycled for two (30 °C), four (32 °C), five (34 °C), four (36 °C) and three (38 °C) consecutive alcoholic fermentation. *Saccharomyces cerevisiae* grown in the Laboratory of Bioprocess Engineering, at School of Food Engineering, State University of Campinas were used in these experiments. Details of material and analytical methods for the determination of concentrations of ethanol, substrate and cells and online measurements (pH, turbidity, CO_2 and temperature) are described elsewhere (Herrera et al., 2012).

3. Extreme Learning Machines

The ELM is a training algorithm for ANN with only one input layer, one hidden layer and one output layer. This algorithm is noted for its training speed and few parameters (Huang, 2009; Oliveira, 2012). The ANN can modeled as follows.

$$\sum_{i}^{N_h} \beta_i g(w_i \cdot x_j + b_i) = t_j, \qquad j = 1, \cdots, N \qquad (1)$$

where x_j and t_j represent the jth input and output vector, b_i is the bias of the ith hidden neuron, w_i is the input weight vector connecting the ith hidden neuron to input layer, β_i

is the output weight vector connecting the ith hidden neuron to the output layer, and the neural network has N_h hidden neurons and activation function $g(\bullet)$. These elements are treated as a system of matrices.

$$H \cdot \beta = T \tag{2}$$

In this equation H is the matrix obtained by applying the activation function of the neuron to the product of the inputs and weights of the hidden layer, with bias added to the hidden layer, β is the matrix of weights of the output layer and T is the matrix of desired outputs of the network. The aim of the algorithm is to find the matrix of output weights β by solving the system matrices.

4. BAT Optimization

Optimization techniques aim to minimize or maximize particular function parameters. Among them, the bio-inspired algorithms have been widely used. They consist of optimization techniques inspired by the behaviour of animal groups. One of the most recent, the BAT Algorithm was inspired by the echolocation of bats in flight (Yang, 2010).

The BAT is an optimization technique bio-inspired in echolocation of bats in flight. The echo-location consists of broadcasting ultrasonic waves and measuring the gap between send and return time to the source, after being reflected by the object or prey. These waves have their pulse rate and loudness increased when the bat looking for a prey, and decreased when it is captured. In the algorithm BAT, each bat is a possible solution to the proposed problem. Each n solution has its frequency f_{it}, velocity v_{it} and position x_{it} updated at each iteration t in search of a better solution. The control exploration is performed by varying the loudness A_{it} and pulse rate r_{it}. When a solution better than the previous ones is found, the pulse rate r_i^t is increased and the loudness A_i^t is decreased. The algorithm can be summarized as follows.

Initialize x_i, v_i, f_i, A_i and r_i (i = 1, 2, ..., n)

While (t < Max number of iterations)

For $(i = 1, 2, ..., n)$

$$f_i = f_{min} + (f_{max} - f_{min})\beta, \beta \in [0,1]$$

$$v_i^t = v_i^{t-1} + (x_i^t - x_*)f_i$$

$$x_{temp}^t = x_i^{t-1} + v_i^t$$

if $(\beta > r_i, \beta \in [0,1])$

$$x_{temp}^t = x_* + \epsilon A_m, \epsilon \in [-1,1]$$

Generate a new solution by flying randomly

If $(\beta < A_i \ \& \ f(x_i^t) < f(x_*), \beta \in [0,1])$

$$x_i^t = x_{temp}^t$$

$$r_i^{t+1} = r_i^0[1 - e^{-\gamma t}]$$

$$A_i^{t+1} = \alpha A_i^t$$

Rank the bats and find the current best x_*

5. Results and Discussions

Neural Networks for predicting of the concentration of ethanol, substrate and cells from secondary measurements (pH, turbidity, CO_2 and temperature) were trained with ELM, MLP and BAT+ELM algorithms and compared with experimental data.

Figure 1 illustrates the performance of the three algorithms in forecasting of ethanol (normalized values) concentration under different batch temperature conditions and recycle numbers. Table 1 shows the operating conditions used for model training and validation.

The ELM algorithm proved to be very fast when compared to a standard MLP Levenberg–Marquardt (LM) training algorithm. Table 2 illustrates the time required and the Sum of Square Errors (SSE) index performance over all data points. The pure ELM algorithm provides a much faster training than LM at the same network size at the cost of SSE performance. However, it is possible to train a better ELM network with more neurons and still be much faster than 100 neurons performance, as illustrated in Table 2. This performance difference increased with network size as MLP's LM complexity is $O(N^3)$ and the pseudo inverse used in ELM algorithm is $O(MN)$.

Table 1. Operating conditions of experiments

Experiment	Temperature	Number of cells recycling
1	30 °C	2
2	32 °C	4
3	34 °C	5
4	36 °C	4
5	38 °C	3

Table 2. Neural Network training performance

Technique	time	SSE
ELM 10	0.59 s	73.4
ELM 100	0.70 s	8.5
MLP 10	35 s	14.7
MLP 100	598 s	4.3
BAT + ELM (288/10x1000)	398 s	5.4

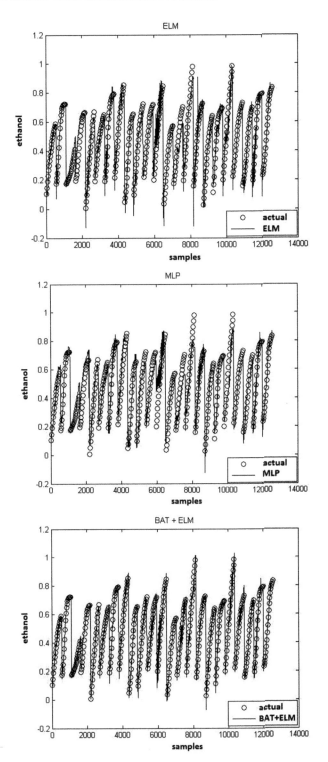

Figure 1. Performance of a) ELM b) MLP c) BAT+ELM algorithms

ELM and MLP networks are sensitive to the number of neurons parameter. Because of the fast training performance of the ELM algorithm the network size can be evaluated quickly under many configurations. Also, because of the random initialization nature of the ELM training algorithm, the results from different training instances of the same network size can differ. Thus, in this study the BAT algorithm was used to optimize the number of neurons. In this configuration, each bat is a solution to the problem. The number of neurons of each ELM varies in each time step and a new random initialization takes place. The varying loudness factor A determines if another evaluation with the same number of neurons should be estimated. The experimental data was divided in training and testing data, the SSE performance in Table 2 is related to testing data. The ten bat parallel search enabled the algorithm to find an optimal ELM network size (288 neurons) and adjustment at a lower cost than a similar performance LM MLP training algorithm of equivalent and guess-based network size.

6. Concluding remarks

In this work, a novel methodology for the online monitoring of second-generation ethanol production was presented. The ELM algorithm provided a very good alternative to traditional MLP networks. Additionally, the BAT optimization technique applied to the ELM algorithm provided a fast parallel search for the best solution. This novel methodology offered a good alternative to the standard soft-sensor approach and fast and reliable product quality estimates for key process variables in second-generation ethanol production.

Acknowledgement

The authors acknowledge the support from LLTECH, CTBE/CNPEM and LOPCA-UNICAMP.

References

M.O.S. Dias, T.L. Junqueira, O. Cavalett, L.G. Pavanello, M.P. Cunha, C.D.F. Jesus, R. Maciel Filho, A. Bonomia, 2013, Biorefineries for the production of first and second generation ethanol and electricity from sugarcane, Applied Energy, 109, 72–78.

J. F. L. Oiveira, T. B. Ludermir, 2012, A Modified Artificial Fish Swarm Algorithm for the Optimization of Extreme Learning Machines, Proceedings ICANN 2012. (Org.). Lecture Notes in Computer Science. 1ed.: Springer Berlin Heidelberg, 7553, 66-73.

L. Salvatore, M.B. Souza Júnior, M.C M.M. Campos, 2009, Design and Implementation of a Neural Network Based Soft Sensor to Infer Sulfur Content in a Brazilian Diesel Hydrotreating Unit, Chemical Engineering Transactions, 17, 1389-1394.

E.C. Rivera, F.S. Farias Jr, D.I.P. Atala, R.R. Andrade, A.C. Costa, R. Maciel Filho, 2009, Development and implementation of an automated monitoring system for improved bioethanol production, Chemical Engineering Transactions, 18, 451-456.

W.E. Herrera, R. Maciel Filho, 2013, Development of a monitoring hybrid system for bioethanol production, Chemical Engineering Transactions, 32, 943-948.

W.E. Herrera, 2012, Development and implementation of a software sensor for monitoring online of bioprocess, MSc dissertation, School of Chemical Engineering, State University of Campinas, Brazil.

X-S. Yang, 2010, A New Metaheuristic Bat Inspired Algorithm, Nature Inspired Cooperative Strategies for Optimization, 284, 65-74.

G-B. Huang, Q-Y. Zhu, C-K. Siew, 2009, Extreme Learning Machine: A New Learning Scheme of Feedforward Neural Networks, Proceedings of International Joint Conference on Neural Networks, 2, 985-990.

Jiří Jaromír Klemeš, Petar Sabev Varbanov and Peng Yen Liew (Editors)
Proceedings of the 24th European Symposium on Computer Aided Process Engineering – ESCAPE 24
June 15-18, 2014, Budapest, Hungary.

Multi-level Optimization Framework Applied to the Systematic Evaluation of Metabolic Objective Functions

Pavel Vaskan,[a] Gonzalo Guillén-Gosálbez,[a] Albert Sorribas,[b] Rui Alves,[b] Laureano Jiménez[a]

[a]*Department of Chemical Engineering, University Rovira i Virgili. Tarragona, 43007, Spain*
[b]*Departament de Ciències Mèdiques Bàsiques, Universitat de Lleida & IRBLleida, Lleida, 25008, Spain*
novbateki@gmail.com

Abstract

In this work we present a multi-level optimization method based on flux balance analysis models (FBA) for identifying meaningful biological objective functions that drive the cell's metabolic machinery under different conditions. Our approach identifies in a rigorous and systematic manner the most probable objective functions for a given set of experimental conditions. We benchmark the method by analyzing experimentally which combination of objective functions better explains a set of metabolic fluxes that were experimentally determined *in vivo*. Our analysis emphasizes that biomass maximization is a fundamental objective function under the experimental conditions of the benchmark. Furthermore, our method also identifies additional sets of functional criteria that, along with the growth rate, improve the model fitting to experimental data.

Keywords: flux balance analysis, metabolic objective functions, mixed-integer nonlinear programming, Karush–Kuhn–Tucker conditions.

1. Introduction

In industrial settings humans establish a clear objective function to be met, creating and optimizing designs to attain that objective efficiently under specific constraints and conditions. In contrast, the emergence of new designs in natural systems results from random mutation followed by natural selection. While one can argue that this process tends to optimize the structure and behaviour of natural systems, the objective(s) function(s) and constraints (i.e., the optimization-like problem we call natural selection) of the process are unclear. Determining such function and constraints would allow biologists to identify biological design principles, a central topic in systems biology (Barabási and Oltvai, 2004). The identification of such biological design principles can be posed as a reverse optimization problem for which the solution (the actual system) is known and the criteria (if any) that have been optimized to arrive to that solution need to be determined (Lewis, 2012).

Several in silico frameworks for determining a most likely objective function have been proposed (Feist and Palsson, 2010). For example, ObjFind, was built under the assumption that natural systems optimize a linear combination of biological objectives that are related to the fluxes of biological reactions (Burgard and Maranas, 2003). These approaches rely on single-objective models that assume existence of a unique universal biological objective function. However, a recent study by Sauer and co-workers (Schuetz et al., 2012) has shown that there might be more than one meaningful fitness function driving the metabolic machinery. Particularly, these authors suggested the existence of three main biological criteria that microorganisms might attempt to optimize simultaneously: maximum ATP yield, maximum biomass yield, and minimum sum of absolute fluxes.

If we expect to understand the evolution and functional properties of complex metabolic networks, it is important to develop a rigorous framework that can identify the criteria underlying design selection in biological systems. Here we report the development of a multi-level linear programming framework inspired on the work by Burgard and Maranas (2003). We extend their method to deal with several objective functions simultaneously and adapt it for its application to biological optimization problems. Particularly, given a set of experimental observations, our framework allows us to infer the form of the multi-objective optimization problem that shapes the adaptation of microorganisms to the environment. We pose this problem in mathematical terms as a multilevel linear program that includes an outer problem and a set of inner models. The outer problem optimizes the least square difference between the experimental observations and the optimal solution predicted in silico. The inner problems, which are defined for each experimental condition, optimize a linear combination of objectives subject to the weights imposed by the outer problem.

The overall multi-level model identifies those combinations of weights that make fitting of the model to each experimental condition optimal, considering several objectives simultaneously. A nonzero weight implies that the objective is biologically meaningful, while a zero weight implies the converse. Binary variables are added for controlling the number of plausible fitness functions. Efficient solution of the multi-level problem is achieved by reformulating it as a standard mixed-integer linear program (MILP).

We test the capabilities of our method through its application to the study of an in vivo flux distribution in Escherichia colis central metabolism using data derived from 13C isotopomer analysis (Fischer et al., 2004). We adapt a FBA model of that metabolism (Schuetz et al., 2007) to use the data and consider biomass growth rate and a set of reaction fluxes that determine production/consumption of ATP and redox potential as surrogates for cellular fitness functions. We confirm that biomass maximization is a fundamental objective function under the observed experimental conditions. In addition, we find that its combination with additional criteria improves the capacity of the FBA model to explain the experimental observations. Our results also show that the fitting of the model to the experimental data improves with the number of objectives considered in the analysis, first sharply and then marginally after a certain point. Finally, we show also that there are several groups of objectives that behave similarly, which suggests a certain degree of redundancy among diverse biological criteria. This may have significant implications in explaining the emergence of alternative and seemingly equally fit solutions in replicate experiments of long term evolution (Richards, 2011).

2. Summary of the method

Given a set of experimental observations, our framework allows us to infer the form of the multi-objective optimization problem that shapes the adaptation of microorganisms

to the environment. We aim to develop a systematic approach that will consecutively perform the following steps:
1. Propose weights for the different objectives functions;
2. Solve the minimization problem whose objective function is given by the corresponding weighted sum of objectives;
3. Obtain the optimal velocities for the given linear combination of weights;
4. Calculate the Euclidean distance between estimated and experimentally determined rates;
5. Minimize the distance calculated in Step (4) by iteratively varying the weights proposed in Step (1).
6. At the end of the optimization, identify the objectives with large weight values and tag them as biologically meaningful, while discarding objectives with low weight values.

Steps (1)-(6) can be automated using a multi-level linear program that includes an outer problem and a set of inner models. The outer problem seeks to optimize the least square difference between the experimental observations and the optimal solution predicted in silico. The inner problems, which are defined for each experimental condition, optimize a linear combination of objectives, subject to the weights imposed by the outer problem. The overall multi-linear problem termed BIMO can be expressed in compact form as follows:

$$(BIMO) \qquad \min_{w_j, x_j} \sum_{j \in EX} \left(v_j - v_j^{\exp} \right)^2$$

$$s.t.$$

$$\begin{pmatrix} \min_{v_j} \sum_{j=1}^{jup} v_j w_j \\ s.t. \qquad \sum_{j=1}^{M} S_{ij} v_j = 0 \qquad \forall i \in N \\ \underline{v_j} \le v_j \le \overline{v_j} \qquad \forall j \in M \end{pmatrix}$$

$$\sum_{j=1}^{jup} w_j = 1$$

$$0 \le w_j \le x_j \overline{w_j} \qquad \forall j \in M$$

Where S_{ij} is the stoichiometric coefficient of metabolite i in reaction j, v_j represents the flux of v_j reaction j, v_j^{exp} is the experimental flux, and w_j is the weight associated with objective j, which can be a reaction flux or a combination of fluxes v_j. Set N refers to the set of metabolites, EX contains the set of experimentally determined fluxes, and M is the set of reactions. The overall multi-level model seeks those combinations of weights that make each experimental condition optimal, considering several objectives simultaneously. A nonzero weight implies that the objective is biologically meaningful, while a zero weight implies the opposite.

To solve the bi-level program efficiently, we reformulate it into a standard mixed-integer nonlinear program (MINLP) by replacing the inner problems by their Karush-Kuhn-Tucker conditions. The multi-objective optimization problem (MOO) is therefore reformulated as a Mixed-Integer Quadratically Constrained Program (MIQCP) with linear constraints and a quadratic objective function. Binary variables are added for controlling the number of plausible fitness functions. This requires definition of auxiliary binary variables for each inequality present in the inner problems. Such binaries take a value of one if the constraint is active and zero otherwise. The MIQCP can be solved by standard branch and cut methods, which provides the set of meaningful objectives and associated weights under several experimental conditions.

3. Results and discussion

We first apply our approach to each experimental data set separately. We consider for the analysis the following four experiments: Experiment A: batch growth on glucose under aerobic conditions with fast grow (0.6 1/h); experiment B: chemostat growth 0.02 1/h ; experiment C: chemostat growth 0.4 1/h ; experiment D: chemostat growth (0.4 1/h) under ammonium limitation (Schuetz et al., 2007).

Each individual rate of the model is regarded as a potential objective function. Our method then automatically finds the optimal weights to be attached to a given maximum number of velocities such that the optimization of this weighted combination of objectives is as close as possible to the experimental results. We solve the reformulated MIQCP for each data set (obtained under a set of specific conditions) independently. We start by allowing any number of objectives in the MIQCP, and then constrain the maximum number of criteria to 4, 3, 2 and 1, respectively, imposing an upper bound on the binary variables that denote whether one objective is considered or not in the model. The summation of all of the weights must equal one. Hence, a weight close to one implies that the associated velocity/flux plays a role in the optimization (i.e., the microorganism attempts to optimize it) while a low weight value implies the opposite.

Figure 1 and Figure 2 summarize the results. In Figure 1 we show the Euclidean distance (ED) between the experimental fluxes and those predicted by the model for each experiment. This distance quantifies the extent to which predicted fluxes match their experimental values (lower distances imply more accurate predictions). As observed, the Euclidean distance decreases as we increase the maximum number of allowable objectives. Note, however, that in almost all of the cases the addition of more objectives leads to marginal reductions in the Euclidean distance, which suggests the existence of a small number of meaningful biological objectives. Figure 2 summarizes the weights determined by our method for each objective function in the individual experiments. In this figure we show only velocities with weights above 0.01 (the number of bars does not always match the number of objectives considered because objectives with small weights are not shown). As observed, in all of the experiments the MIQCP calculates a large weight for biomass growth (velocity 102). This is in agreement with previous works (Burgard and Maranas, 2003), in which biomass maximization was found to be a fundamental biological objective driving the evolution of cells machinery.

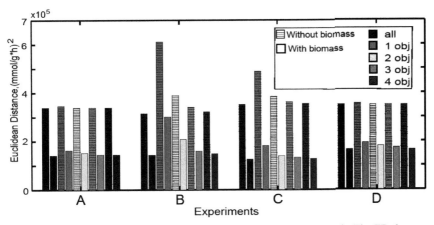

Figure 1. Results for four experiments with and without biomass growth. The ED decreases as we increase the number of objectives. The inclusion of biomass growth as a potential objective function leads to better ED values.

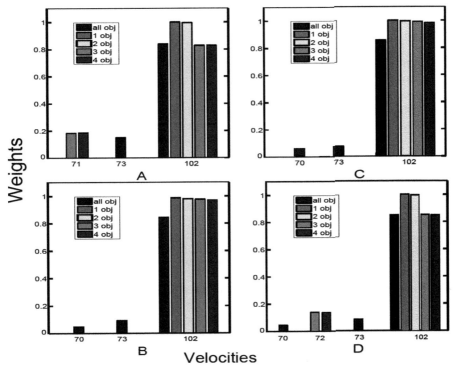

Figure 2. Weights calculated for all of the velocities with the MINLP for different limits on the total number of objectives considered in the analysis. In all of the cases the weight attached to biomass growth rate is above 0.8, which confirms its importance as a meaningful biological objective driving the cell's machinery. Velocity 70 is Acetaldehyde dehydrogenaseII R1, 71 is Acetaldehyde dehydrogenase R2, 72 is Ethanol dehydrogenase, 73 is Alcohol dehydrogenase class III, 102 is biomass production.

To investigate the importance of biomass maximization as a meaningful biological objective, we repeated the calculations but this time fixing a zero weight for biomass growth rate. Figure 1 shows the results obtained following the above commented procedure. Comparing the results between normal calculation and calculation without biomass growth, we can see that the ED drops drastically for all of the experiments when biomass is not considered as a meaningful objective.

4. Conclusions

We have presented a novel framework that integrates network stoichiometry and experimental flux data to determine the most likely set of objective functions for a given biological system. Our approach is based on a multi-level optimization problem that considers the existence of several plausible biological objective functions. We solve this problem by reformulating it into a single-level optimization model via the Karush-Kuhn-Tucker (KKT) conditions.

We illustrate the utility of our method on a model based on the E. coli central metabolism in which we identify the coefficients of importance for a variety of input conditions. We found that the maximization of the aggregate biomass flux is consistent with the observed experimental flux values. Thus, the maximization of cellular biomass appears to be an important descriptor, although not the unique one, in explaining the observed fluxes. We show that there is no single universal objective function for microorganisms; rather, there is a set of fitness functions that cells seek to optimize simultaneously. The relative importance of each of these functions depends on the external conditions. Under different conditions different criteria may emerge as predominantly controlling the optimization at the expense of worsening the remaining objectives. Numerical results show also that experimental observations can be well explained by a reduced number of objectives (i.e., 3), and that there are different combinations of objectives leading to similar errors.

References

A.L. Barabási, Z.N. Oltvai, 2004, Network biology: understanding the cell's functional organization, Nature Reviews Genetics, 5, 2, 101-113.

A.P. Burgard, C.D. Maranas, 2003, Optimization-based framework for inferring and testing hypothesized metabolic objective functions, Biotechnology and bioengineering, 82, 670–677.

A.M. Feist, B.O. Palsson, 2010, The biomass objective function, Current opinion in microbiology, 13, 344–349.

E. Fischer, N. Zamboni, U. Sauer, 2004, High-throughput metabolic flux analysis based on gas chromatography–mass spectrometry derived ^{13}C constraints, Analytical biochemistry, 325, 308–316.

N. E Lewis, H. Nagarajan, B.O. Palsson, 2012. Constraining the metabolic genotype–phenotype relationship using a phylogeny of in silico methods. Nature Reviews Microbiology, 10, 4, 291-305.

E. J. Richards, 2011, Natural epigenetic variation in plant species: a view from the field. Current opinion in plant biology, 14, 2, 204-209.

R. Schuetz, N. Zamboni, M. Zampieri, M. Heinemann, U. Sauer, 2012, Multidimensional optimality of microbial metabolism, Science, 336, 601–604.

Jiří Jaromír Klemeš, Petar Sabev Varbanov and Peng Yen Liew (Editors)
Proceedings of the 24ᵗʰ European Symposium on Computer Aided Process Engineering – ESCAPE 24

Reynolds Number Effects on Particle Agglomeration in Turbulent Channel Flow

Mohammad Afkhami*, Ali Hassanpour, Michael Fairweather, Derrick O. Njobuenwu

Institute of Particle Science and Engineering, School of Process, Environmental and Materials Engineering, University of Leeds, Leeds LS2 9JT, UK
M.Afkhami5@leeds.ac.uk

Abstract

The work described in this paper employs large eddy simulation and a discrete element method to study particle-laden flows, including particle dispersion and agglomeration, in a horizontal channel. The particle-particle interaction model is based on the Hertz-Mindlin approach with Johnson-Kendall-Roberts cohesion to allow the simulation of Van der Waals forces in a dry air flow. The influence of different flow Reynolds numbers, and therefore the impact of turbulence, on particle agglomeration is investigated. The agglomeration rate is found to be strongly influenced by the flow Reynolds number, with most of the particle-particle interactions taking place at locations close to the channel walls, aided by the higher turbulence and concentration of particles in these regions.

Keywords: LES, DEM, particle, agglomeration, channel flow

1. Introduction

In this work, an advanced predictive technique for describing fluid motion, namely large eddy simulation (LES), is coupled with the discrete element method (DEM) to provide further understanding of flows containing solid particles. In the context of two- and multiphase horizontal channel flows, the most recent studies using one- and two-way coupled approaches for dispersed particle regimes are mainly focused on the influence of complex flow structures on particle motion, and the study of non-spherical particle shapes. Recent work on four-way coupled flows, considered herein, includes that of Alletto and Breuer (2012) who studied LES predictions of a particle-laden turbulent flow at high mass loading downstream of a confined bluff body. Mallouppas and van Wachem (2013) similarly used LES to study a turbulent particle-laden channel flow. These works however, did not consider particle agglomeration in the flow. It is worthy of note that direct numerical simulation (DNS) continues to be used to study such flows, although this is generally for low Reynolds number cases. Therefore one of the main challenges for LES is to compute flows with high precision at sufficiently high Reynolds numbers to more closely replicate those conditions found in practical applications. Furthermore, the dynamics of particle-laden fluid flows include a number of important aspects that dictate whether particle agglomeration will occur, affecting in turn particle dispersion and deposition. These include properties such as the instantaneous particle velocity, collision frequency and surface properties. As a result, many complications arise when analysing the underlying mechanisms responsible for agglomeration, and solving practical problems. The coupling of LES and DEM is an effective approach that is capable of overcoming these issues, and providing insight as well as the potential to predict many practically-relevant flows, such as oil and gas flow assurance in pipes, powder dispersion in dry powder inhalers and particle re-suspension in nuclear waste ponds. The work described builds on previous findings presented at ESCAPE 23 (Afkhami et al., 2013) which used LES and DEM to demonstrate that a high particle mass loading is not required to promote particle agglomeration in turbulent channel flows.

2. Numerical Simulation

The LES employed a top-hat filter as this fits naturally into a finite-volume formulation. This decomposition is then applied to the Navier-Stokes equations for an incompressible Newtonian fluid with constant properties, bringing about terms which represent the effect of the sub-grid scale (SGS) motion on the resolved scale motions. The SGS stress model employed in this work was the dynamic model of Germano et al. (1996), applied using the approximate localisation procedure of Piomelli and Liu (1995). Computations were performed using the commercial CFD code ANSYS Fluent. The code implements an implicit finite-volume incompressible flow solver using a co-located variable storage arrangement. The simulation time taken for each run was approximately 7 days on a Dell Precision T5500 workstation utilising 12GB installed memory and 8 processors. The code is parallel and uses the message passing interface HP MPI. Further information on the mathematical model employed, and the numerical algorithm and its application, may be found in the ANSYS Fluent 13.0 theory guide.

A Lagrangian approach was used to model particle motion from the instantaneous fluid velocity field in which the particles are tracked along their trajectories through the unsteady, non-uniform flow field. The particle-laden flow was assumed to be dilute, and the method incorporated full coupling between the phases, i.e. interactions between particles were considered, and the flow and particles were two-way coupled. Particle-wall collisions were assumed to be inelastic. Particle-particle interactions were modelled using the discrete element method incorporating the contact model of Herz-Mindlin with Johnson-Kendall-Roberts cohesion (Johnson et al., 1971) to allow the simulation of the Van der Waals forces which influence particle behaviour. The particle surface attractive force was altered by specifying the surface energy. All particles were assumed to be soft spheres with equal diameter and density, and particles much heavier than the fluid were assumed. The effect of gravity was also neglected. Elghobashi and Truesdell (1993) have shown that the only significant forces in such systems are the Stokes drag and buoyancy forces, although buoyancy was also neglected in this work as the fluid was a gas. The shear induced Saffman lift force was taken into account as it assumes non-trivial magnitudes in the viscous sub-layer.

The flow is described by a three-dimensional Cartesian co-ordinate system (x, y and z) representing the streamwise, spanwise and wall-normal directions, respectively. The boundary conditions for the momentum equations were set to no-slip at the channel walls and the instantaneous flow field was considered to be periodic along the streamwise and spanwise directions, with a constant mass flux through the channel. The shear Reynolds numbers, $Re_\tau = hu_\tau/v$, used in the simulations were 150, 300 and 590 corresponding to bulk Reynolds numbers of $Re_b \sim 2,100$, 4,200 and 8,260, respectively, based on half the channel height, h. The rectangular channel considered was of dimensions $2h \times 2\pi h \times 4\pi h$. The length of the channel in the streamwise direction was sufficiently long to capture the streamwise-elongated, near-wall turbulent structures that exist in wall-bounded shear flows. The non-uniform Cartesian grid used 1 million computational nodes. The initial particle positions were distributed randomly throughout the channel, with their initial velocity set to zero and with the particles coming in-line with local flow velocities with time. Particles were assumed to interact with turbulent eddies over a certain period of time, that being the lesser of the eddy lifetime and the transition time. Particles that moved out of the channel were re-introduced into the computational domain using periodic boundary conditions. The total number of particles considered in the computational domain was 20,000 in all cases. Particle and fluid densities were set to $\rho_p = 1,000$ and $\rho_f = 1.3$ kg m^{-3}, respectively, with the kinematic viscosity $v = 15.7 \times 10^{-6}$ m^2 s^{-1}. The particle relaxation time is given by $\tau_p = \rho_p d_p^2/18\rho U$, and the non-dimensional particle response time is defined as the particle Stokes number, $St = \tau_p^+ = \tau_p/\tau_f$, where τ_f is a characteristic time scale of the flow (defined as $\tau_f = v/u_\tau^2$, where the shear velocity $u_\tau = 0.221$). The particle surface energy considered was 0.5 J m^{-2}.

3. Results and Discussion

The results generated by the LES for the fluid phase were verified using DNS predictions for the various shear Reynolds number flows considered. Overall, the LES showed good agreement with the DNS, with the mean velocities and rms of fluctuating velocity components matching those of the DNS in both magnitude and position. The particle phase behaviour was also compared with one-way coupled DNS predictions, with results again in reasonable agreement with those derived on the basis of the DNS.

Figure 1 shows results for the number of particle bonds in the channel. The results clearly show an increase in the number of bonds with time due to the effects of flow turbulence on the particles; furthermore, the rate at which the particles form bonds increases with the flow Reynolds number. For all three shear Reynolds numbers, initially the rate of bond formation increases roughly linearly with time but then changes to a more exponential profile. In the higher shear Reynolds case, however, the trend is highly exponential, indicating an ever increasing rate at which particle bonds form with time. Further scrutiny of the results shows that agglomeration first occurs at approximately $t = 0.001$ s for the 300 and 590 Reynolds number flows; here the particles have increased their velocity to an extent where the flow turbulence now causes significant particle-particle interactions. In the case of the 150 Reynolds number flow, agglomeration is first seen at around $t = 0.01$ s, indicating a slower acceleration of the particles. A linear increase in particle bond numbers then continues to about $t = 0.05$ s, after which an increasing divergence is seen between the highest and lower Reynolds number flows. This trends is again repeated at $t = 0.1$ s where the $Re_\tau = 300$ flow deviates at an increasing rate from the $Re_\tau = 150$ case. This behaviour suggests that there is a mechanism within the flow that advantages the particles exposed to higher Reynolds numbers in the formation of agglomerates, other than the bulk flow velocity alone. This occurs as a result of regions of high particle concentration and low particle mean velocity near the channel walls; in such regions the number of bonds formed is proportionally higher for particles of higher Reynolds number as the particles migrate to these regions at a faster rate. Moreover, the increased shear in the high Reynolds number flows increases the intensity of these turbulent regions, and therefore the particle fluctuations and hence their interactions. Further analysis is required to establish a relationship between the particle fluctuating velocity and its impact on the formation of successful bonds. The dispersing behaviour of the particles and the regions in which bonds are formed are, however, discussed further below. At the end of the simulation, and for the Re_τ = 150, 300 and 590 flows, respectively, there are 528, 635 and 1,524 particle bonds in the flow. These figures further indicate that increases in flow Reynolds number dramatically enhance turbulence, and as a results particle agglomeration. It is thus clear that the effects of turbulence are significant in creating successful particle-particle bonds, and that the flow Reynolds number is a key factor in determining particle agglomeration

Figure 2 shows the time evolution of the number of particles close to the wall. The results clearly show that particles initially accumulate at the wall at an approximately linear rate. For Re_τ = 150, 300 and 590 particles are first seen to be in contact with the wall at 0.072, 0.055 and 0.037s, respectively. This behaviour suggests that the increasingly turbulent flow with increasing Reynolds number accelerates the particles at a faster rate in all directions (including towards the walls). From previous work, it is known that for turbulent channel flows particle positions close to a wall correlate with instantaneous regions of low velocity along the streamwise direction, with particles avoiding regions of high velocity. The behaviour observed in Figure 2 is also consistent with previous LES and DNS results where turbophoresis is known to cause the accumulation of particles in near-wall regions, which in the present flow also enhances the rate of particle agglomeration in such regions.

Figure 3 shows the location of particles with bonds in the wall-normal direction for all three Reynolds numbers, and their number at each location at time $t = 0.2$ s. Results are shown for 15 equally spaced regions across the channel, with particle statistics combined within each of the slabs of fluid considered. The columns for the number of bonds are plotted in relation to the channel walls, with columns 1 and 15 adjacent to the lower and upper walls, respectively. These two regions extend over the viscous sub-layer and buffer layer within the near-wall region. The results show a general movement of agglomerates towards the walls, indicated by columns 1 and 15 accounting for approximately 60% of the total particle bond count at all Re_τ. For Re_τ = 150, 300 and 590, at the channel centre (column 8) the number of bonds is 20, 18 and 47, respectively, with these values increasing towards the walls, where for columns 1 and 15 they increase to an average of 129, 203 and 249, respectively. Particle agglomeration near to the wall can be attributed to the high particle concentration and the high turbulence levels in this region (Afkhami et al., 2013).

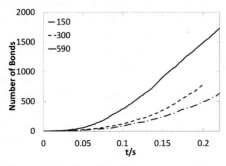

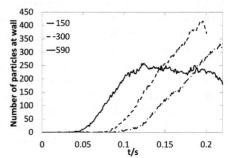

Figure 1. Number of bonds between particles with time for shear Reynolds numbers of 150, 300 and 590..

Figure 2. Particle number at the wall of the channel for shear Reynolds numbers of 150, 300 and 590.

Further scrutiny of the results shows that for the high Reynolds number flow, particle agglomeration is roughly double that of the other flows at the channel centre. This relationship also holds between the high and low Reynolds number flows at the channel walls, although the number of agglomerates at $Re_\tau = 300$ is relatively closer to that of the $Re_\tau = 590$ case. Such behaviour is indicative of higher turbulence in the $Re_\tau = 300$ and 590 flows, which drives the particles to regions of lower fluid velocity. Throughout the flow, particle agglomeration is enhanced through high fluctuating velocities which affect a high number of particle-particle interactions, with peak levels typically at 30 wall units away from the solid boundaries. This influence is therefore most evident in the results for columns 2 and 14, which contain the highest agglomerate number, bar those regions closest to the walls where particle concentrations are high.

Lastly, Figure 4 gives the relationship between the instantaneous particle position in the wall-normal direction for all three Reynolds numbers, plotted against the particle fluctuating velocity magnitude in the streamwise direction at time $t = 0.2$s. The loca-

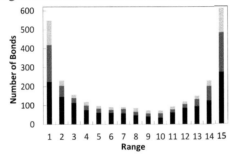

Figure 3. Agglomerate distribution across the channel (black – $Re_\tau = 590$, mid-grey $Re_\tau = 300$, light-grey $Re_\tau = 190$).

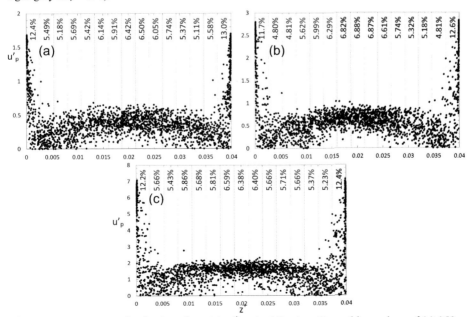

Figure 4. Instantaneous distribution of particle z^+ and u'_p for shear Reynolds numbers of (a) 150, (b) 300 and (c) 590 ($t = 0.20$s).

tions of the points are plotted relative to the lower wall. In general, the particles are well dispersed along the transverse direction, with more particles located close to the channel walls, as previously noted, where particle fluctuating velocities are higher than at other locations. In the regions closest to the walls, the particle velocity fluctuations show peak values of 1.7, 2.7 and 7.3 m s^{-1} with increasing Reynolds number, with particle proportion in these regions, on average, 12.7, 12.2 and 12.3 %. These results clearly illustrate the dramatic increase in fluctuating velocities with Reynolds number in regions where preferential agglomeration occurs. In the next zones moving away from the walls, the peak fluctuating velocities are 1.2, 1.7 and 4.6 m s^{-1}, with average proportions of 5.5 %, 4.8 % and 5.5 %, respectively. The range in particle velocity fluctuations in the highest Re_τ case demonstrates the significant influence of flow turbulence on particle agglomeration in both these regions. Relating the results of Figures 3 and 4, and the findings of Afkhami et al. (2013), the difference in particle agglomeration between the various Reynolds numbers in the latter zones can be attributed to a combination of both the particle mean velocity and the particle velocity fluctuation. Finally, at the channel centre, the particle velocity fluctuation peak values are 0.6, 1.1 and 2.1 ms^{-1}, for Re_τ = 150, 300 and 590. In this region the fluctuations are seen to be low, thereby explaining the lower levels of particle agglomeration.

4. Conclusions

Particles with identical physical parameters have been simulated in three channel flows with different levels of flow turbulence, achieved by increasing the Reynolds number of the flow, using a fully coupled LES-DEM approach. The particle size and surface energy selected were 150 µm and 0.5 Jm^{-2}. Results derived for the three flows show that the rate of agglomeration is strongly influenced, and increases, with the intensity of the flow turbulence, with most of the particle-particle interactions taking place at locations close to the channel walls and in regions of high turbulence, where their agglomeration is aided both by the high levels of turbulence and the high concentration of particles. It can be concluded that it is a combination of the effect of both the flow mean and fluctuating velocities that is most significant in determining successful particle agglomeration in the channel flows considered.

References

M. Afkhami, A. Hassanpour, M. Fairweather, D.O. Njobuenwu, 2013, Particle-Interaction Effects in Turbulent Channel Flow, Computer Aided Chemical Engineering, 32, 847-852.

M. Alletto, M. Breuer, 2012, One-way, Two-way and Four-way Coupled LES Predictions of a Particle-laden Turbulent Flow at High Mass Loading Downstream of a Confined Bluff Body, Int. J. Multiphase Flow, 45, 70-90.

S. Elghobashi, G.C. Truesdell, 1993, On the Two-Way Interaction Between Homogeneous Turbulence and Dispersed Solid Particles, I: Turbulence Modification, Phys. Fluids, A5, 1790-1801.

M. Germano, U. Piomelli, P. Moin, W.H. Cabot, 1996, Dynamic Subgrid-Scale Eddy Viscosity Model, In Summer Workshop, Center for Turbulence Research, Stanford, CA.

K.L. Johnson, K. Kendall, A.D. Roberts, 1971, Surface Energy and the Contact of Elastic Solids, Proc. R. Soc. A, 324, 301-313.

G. Mallouppas, B. van Wachem, 2013, Large Eddy Simulations of Turbulent Particle-Laden Channel Flow, Int. J. Multiphase Flow, 54, 65-75.

U. Piomelli, J. Liu, 1995, Large Eddy Simulation of Rotating Channel Flows Using a Localized Dynamic Model, Phys. Fluids, 7, 839-848.

Jiří Jaromír Klemeš, Petar Sabev Varbanov and Peng Yen Liew (Editors)
Proceedings of the 24th European Symposium on Computer Aided Process Engineering – ESCAPE 24
June 15-18, 2014, Budapest, Hungary. Copyright © 2014 Elsevier B.V. All rights reserved.

Optimal Design of a Bioethanol Supply Chain Considering Different Environmental Impact Assessment Methods

Gustavo Lucas[a], Fabrizio Bezzo[b], Ana Carvalho[a]*

[a]CEG-IST, Instituto Superior Técnico, Universidade de Lisboa, Av. Rovisco Pais, 1049-001, Lisboa, Portugal
[b]CAPE-Lab – Department of Industrial Engineering, University of Padova, Via Marzolo 9, 35131, Padova PD, Italy
anacarvalho@tecnico.ulisboa.pt

Abstract

Several studies have been conducted regarding the optimal design of bioethanol supply chains considering economic aspects. However, biofuels were targeted to be more sustainable than traditional fossil fuels. In order to achieve that goal a sustainable supply chain needs to be achieved and therefore environmental impacts should be considered as an optimization objective. The aim of this work is to analyze the influence of including different Life Cycle Assessment (LCA) methods in the optimization model, namely *Recipe*, *Eco-Indicator 99* and I*mpact2002+*. Conclusions will be drawn regarding the influence of the LCA methods in the final optimized network structure and in the correspondent economic results obtained for the final network structure of the bioethanol's supply chain.

Keywords: LCA methods, sustainability, bioethanol, supply chains

1. Introduction

In the past decades, industries have been urged to develop more environmental friendly processes, products and practices. The first proposals to reduce the supply chains environmental impacts were at process/plant level. The main drawback of these approaches is that reducing negative environmental impact somewhere in the supply chain might be done at the expense of increasing it elsewhere (Chaabane et al., 2012). Life Cycle Assessment (LCA) has been an accepted tool to quantify environmental burdens and their potential impacts over the whole life cycle of a product, process or activity (Pieragostini et al., 2012). However, researchers and the European Commission have not reached to a consensus on what is the best LCA method to use. Liu et al. (2010) used Eco-indicator 95 and Impact 2002+ to assess the environmental impacts of semiconductor industry production processes, while Suer and Andersson-Sköld (2011) applied ReCiPe to evaluate the environmental consequences of soil remediation. Since several methods can be applied to analyze the Life Cycle of a specific product (Carvalho et al., 2013), one question arises: Does the selected LCA method affect the optimized solution? Will this influence the decision-maker analysis?

Aiming to answer these questions, three different LCA methods, namely Eco-Indicator 99, Impact 2002+ and ReCiPe, were applied to a bioethanol supply chain optimization model. The model has been based on the one developed by Giarola et al. (2011) and addresses the design of a bioethanol supply chain structure in Northern Italy.

2. LCA methods

LCA quantifies energy and materials used, wastes released to the environment and performs the assessment of the impact of those inputs and outputs through the use of different impact categories. In the last decades several authors have proposed different LCA methods and most of them follow the methodology presented in Figure 1.

This methodology considers that a process/product has an inventory of impacts that can be further translated into diverse impact categories through the application of environmental impact factors (midpoint). These impact categories are then associated to a final endpoint, which represents a set of broader aspect, that correlates different impact categories. The type and number of midpoints and endpoints covered, varies depending on the LCA method. In this work *Eco-Indicator 99*, *Impact 2002+* and

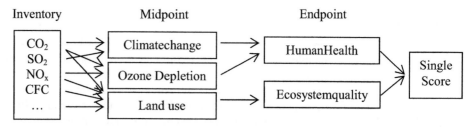

Figure 1. LCA methods midpoint/endpoint technique

Table 1. Key featuresof *Eco-Indicator 99*, *Impact 2002+* and *ReCiPe* approaches (EuropeanUnion, 2010).

	Eco-Indicator 99	Impact 2002+	ReCiPe
Purpose	Developing an endpoint method that can be used in any LCA.	Providing combined midpoint/damage approach	Combining midpoint and endpoint in a consistent way
Midpoint impacts covered	Climate change, Ozone layer depletion, Acidification / Eutrophication, Carcinogenic, Respiratory organic, Respiratory inorganic, Ionizing radiation, Ecotoxicity, Land-use, Mineral resources, Fossil Resources	Human toxicity, Respiratory effects, Ionizing radiation, Ozone depletion, Photochemical oxidant formation, Aquatic ecotoxicity, Terrestrial ecotoxicity, Aquatic eutrophication, Terrestrial eutrophication and acidification, Land occupation, Global warming, Non renewable energy, Mineral extraction	Climate change, Ozone depletion, Terrestrial acidification, Freshwater eutrophication, Marine eutrophication, Human toxicity, Photochemical oxidant formation, Particulate matter formation, Terrestrial ecotoxicity, Freshwater ecotoxicity, Marine ecotoxicity, Ionising radiation, Agricultural land occupation, urban land occupation, Natural land transformation, Depletion of fossil fuel resources, Depletion of mineral resources, Depletion of freshwater resources
Endpoint impacts covered	Human health, Ecosystem quality and Resource depletion	Human health, Ecosystem quality, Climate change and Resources	Human health, Ecosystem quality and Resources

ReCiPe are the environmental assessment methods selected to evaluate the bioethanol supply chain environmental impacts (European Union, 2010). Table 1 summarizes the purpose of the methods and the midpoints and endpoints covered by each method. To apply these methods in the optimization models, the parameters related to the environmental impact factors for each impact category need to be collected. The environmental impact parameters were collected from *Ecoinvent* database, available in *SimaPro* (commercial software for LCA analysis) and introduced in the model as single score values, calculated as Figure 2 illustrates.

In the inventory step data regarding all resources and emissions involved in the supply chain are collected. Then, characterization factors are applied to the inventory data in order to obtain the different contributions of the impact categories (mid- and end-points). Since the impact categories are not in the same unit it would not be possible to aggregate them into a single score, therefore a normalization process is required. After the normalization of the impact categories, the single score value can be obtained by simply adding all normalized impact categories or by first place giving weights to the different impact categories and then summing them into a final single score. The main differences between the different LCA methods are the characterization factors, the normalization factors and the weights considered.

3. Model overview

This paper applies a model that deals with the strategic design optimization of bioethanol supply chains. Since the goal of this study is to analyze different LCA methods the objective function was established as the environmental impact minimization. The model accounts a strategic decision over a15-year horizon. Northern Italy is the region chosen to a spatially explicit multi-period perspective. It was modeled a single objective Mixed Integer Linear Programming and implemented in GAMS ®. The general mathematical formulation was defined as in Giarola et al. (2011), while the environmental performance implementation was developed in this work. The objective function is the minimization of the overall environmental impacts, based on the single score values attributed by each method to each entity. The main variables to be optimized over the planning time horizon are: 1) Geographical location and production rate of biomass;2) Biomass transport from biomass fields to production facilities; 3) Bioethanol facilities technology selection, location and scale; 4) Bioethanol transport from production plants to blending terminals; 5) Environmental and economic performance of the supply chain. The demand scenario in this model considers that gasoline and diesel should reach separately the targets set by the European Commission (EC), starting from an insignificant ethanol production in 2012. Furthermore, the ethanol blending rate in 2013 is the one fixed by the Directive (2009/28/EC) as the starting point in 2010, i.e. 5.75 % in energy basis. As a consequence, the increasing trend in the substitution quota was extended until 2027, in order to anticipate further regulations and to consider the starting delay in achieving European targets. Bioethanol is assumed to be sent to blending terminals existing at given locations. Regarding biomass resources, the model only considers corn as possible biomass, since there was no environmental data available for other feedstock. The corn and bioethanol price

Figure 2. Single Score calculation

dynamics considered in this model are based on a Time Series Decomposition approach, which proved to have a very good fit with the historical data. The parameter values were obtained by a regression on historical USA average data from 2008 to 2012 and then adapted to Italian situation by Mazzetto et al. (2013). The model includes the biomass transport from the crops region to the production plants and the bioethanol distribution from the production plants to the demand terminals. Four different transportation means are considered in the model, namely truck, ship, rail and barge. Two bioethanol production technologies were available in the model, both based in the Dry Grind Process (DGP), which is the typical method to produce ethanol from corn. Both technologies produce Dried Distillers Grains with Soluble (DDGS) as by-product: one considers the DDGS sale and the other burns the DDGS to produce electricity. Regarding the environmental performance, the impact assessment was based on all life cycle stages, which is required in a LCA analysis. Therefore the considered stages were biomass growth, biomass transport, fuel production, fuel distribution and emission credits. Emission credits were given to by-products that can be recovered and therefore they are not emissions (DDGS and electricity).

3.1. Mathematical formulation of environmental impacts

Since the aim of this work is to present the implementation of LCA methods in mathematical models, the formulation regarding the implementation of the LCA methods is presented here. The total environmental impact of the bioethanol supply chain results from the sum of the environmental impacts of each life cycle stage, as it is presented in Eq.(1).

$$TI = \sum_s StageImpact_{s,t} , \quad \forall\, t \tag{1}$$

Where $StageImpact_{s,t}$[single score/time period] is the total single score per life cycle stage s per time period t. The StageImpact is generally defined as Eq.(2).

$$StageImpact_{s,t} = SS_s \cdot F_{s,t} \forall s,t \tag{2}$$

where the reference flow $F_{s,t}$[unit/time period], specific for each life cycle stage s and time t is multiplied by a global emission factor, SS_s [single score/unit], representing the single score impact at stage s per unit of reference flow, obtained through the methodology presented in Figure 2.

4. Results

Applying the different LCA methods two different supply chain structures were obtained, one achieved through the application of *Eco-Indicator 99* and *ReCiPe*, and another one applying *Impact 2002+*.

4.1. Impact 2002+

The first solution presented is the optimal environmental bioethanol supply chain using *Impact 2002+* to measure the environmental impacts. Figure 3 represents the final supply chain structure presented in the optimized solution. According to Figure 1, four bioethanol production plants of DGP with DDGS sale should be built, in order to minimize the total environmental impact. As expected (see Giarola et al., 2011), a negative Net Present Value (NPV) is obtained: - 890 M€.

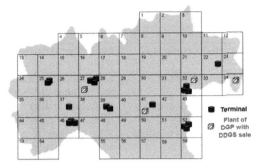

Figure 3. Bioethanol supply chain structure -*Impact 2002+*

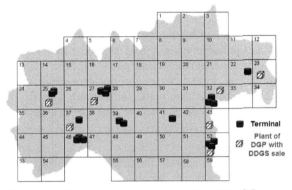

Figure 4. Bioethanol supply chain structure-*Eco-Indicator 99* and *ReCiPe*

4.2. Eco-Indicator 99 and ReCiPe

When the environmental impacts are assessed through *Eco-Indicator 99* and *ReCiPe*,
the supply chain structure obtained by the optimization model is the structure
represented in Figure 4.

From Figure 4, it is possible to verify that instead of four bioethanol production plants,
this solution suggests to build seven bioethanol production plants to minimize the total
impacts. The supply chain structure is the same applying Eco-Indicator 99 and ReCiPe
methods, however the expected profit is different. Assessing the environmental impacts
through Eco-Indicator 99 losses increase up to 990 M€, while using ReCiPe the
economic result is NPV = - 996 M€.

4.3. Comments

Table 2 compares the results achieved when applying the different LCA methods.
Since similar environmental impacts were attributed to each region, there are not
differences in the geographical location and production rate of biomass. The main
differences verified are related to transport distances, number of bioethanol production
plants to build and profitability of the overall supply chain. The differences obtained on
the transport distances and number of bioethanol production plants can be justified by
the allocation of the environmental impacts attributed by each LCA method to these
activities. The LCA methods that attribute a greater impact to bioethanol production
process than to transport system, suggest a reduced number of plants to build and a
greater distance between entities.

Table 2. Summary of results achieved applying different environmental assessment methods.

Optimization variables	Results applying the diverse methods
Geographical location and production rate of biomass	Similar between methods
Biomass transport from biomass fields to production facilities	Same transport means, but different networks and travelled distances
Bioethanol facilities selection, location and scale	Different numbers of facilities selected, location and capacities
Bioethanol transport from production facilities to blending terminals	Same transport means, but different networks and distances travelled
Profitability	Different from method to method

On the other hand, the LCA methods that consider transport system more pollutant than the bioethanol production process, recommend the construction of more plants, aiming to reduce the distance travelled by the transport network. Regarding the most influent impact categories it was possible to verify that the top 3 categories for the three methods were not consistent (*Eco-Indicator 99*: Land use; fossil fuels e Resp. inorganics; *Impact 2002+:* Resp. inorganics; global warming; non-renewable energy; *Recipe*: fossil depletion, climate change, particulate matter formation). This fact again reinforces the importance of selecting the method that will be used for the assessment.

5. Conclusion

This study shows that LCA methods influence the structure and consequently the economic performance of bioethanol supply chains (Impact 2002+: NPV= - 890 M€; Eco-Indicator 99: NPV= 990 M€; ReCiPe: NPV = - 996 M€). . In this sense, decision makers should carefully select the LCA method to apply in their projects, selecting them according to their features and final purpose. Moreover, this fact shows that decisions cannot be taken only based on environmental factors and that multi-objective approaches should be considered when assessing environmental concerns. This work also leads to an important future research path, where LCA methods should be studied in more detail so that some guidelines can be given in terms of the best method to apply.

References

A. Carvalho, A. F. Mimoso, A. N. Mendes, H. A. Matos, 2013, From a Literature Review to a Framework for Environmental Process Impact Assessment Index, Journal of Cleaner Production, 64, 36–62.

A. Chaabane, A. Ramudhin, M. Paquet, 2012, Design of sustainable supply chains under the emission trading scheme, International Journal of Production Economics, 135, 1, 37–49.

EuropeanUnion, 2010, Analysis of existing Environmental Assessment methodologies for use in LCA, ILCD Handbook, Italy.

C. H. Liu, S. J. Lin, C. Lewis, 2010, Life cycle assessment of DRAM in Taiwan's semiconductor industry. Journal of Cleaner Production, 18, 5, 419–425.

S. Giarola, A. Zamboni, F. Bezzo, 2011, Spatially explicit multi-objective optimisation for design and planning of hybrid first and second generation biorefineries, Computers and Chemical Engineering, 35, 9, 1782–1797.

F. Mazzetto, R. A. Ortiz-Gutierrez, D. Manca, F. Bezzo, 2013, Strategic design of bioethanol supply chains including commodity market dynamics, Ind. Eng. Chem. Res., 52, 10305–16.

C. Pieragostini, M. C. Mussati, P. Aguirre, 2012, On process optimization considering LCA methodology, Journal of environmental management, 96, 1, 43–54.

P. Suer, Y. Andersson-Sköld, 2011, Biofuel or excavation? - Life cycle assessment (LCA) of soil remediation options. Biomass and Bioenergy, 35, 2, 969–981.

Jiří Jaromír Klemeš, Petar Sabev Varbanov and Peng Yen Liew (Editors)
Proceedings of the 24th European Symposium on Computer Aided Process Engineering – ESCAPE 24
June 15-18, 2014, Budapest, Hungary.

Modeling Multi-period Operations using the P-graph Methodology

István Heckl[a], László Halász[a], Adrián Szlama[a], Heriberto Cabezas[a,b], Ferenc Friedler[a,*]

[a]*Department of Computer Science and Systems Technology, University of Pannonia, 10 Egyetem utca, Veszprém, 8200, Hungary*
[b]*Office of Research and Development, U.S. Environmental Protection Agency, 26 West Martin Luther King Drive, Cincinnati, OH 45268, USA*
friedler@dcs.uni-pannon.hu

Abstract

A new modeling technique is presented here for handling multi-period operations in process-network synthesis (PNS) problems by the P-graph (process graph) framework. Until now, the P-graph framework could only handle single-period operating units. It means that the operating conditions and the load of each unit remain unchanged throughout its operation. This assumption is usually true for the chemical industry but may be false in agriculture or in other areas where seasonal effects are important. Hence, the current work proposes the notion of multi-period operation wherein the load of an operating unit may vary from period to period. Subsequently, a modeling technique is proposed to represent operating units in the multi-period operation. The idea is to represent separately the physical body of an operating unit and the operations in each period. Surprisingly, to achieve these tasks, there is no need to dramatically change or augment the basic structure of the P-graph methodology, e.g. with a new type of multi-period unit, but the already available constituents are adequate.

Keywords: process-network synthesis, P-graph, multi-period, optimization

1. Introduction

A process system aims at producing certain products from a set of raw materials through a sequence of processing steps. The major developments in this area have been comprehensively reviewed by Sargent (2004). Usually, a multitude of alternative feasible network structures is capable of producing the desired products, because of the combinatorial nature of the problem. Normally, process synthesis seeks the optimal network structure in terms of some objective function. The determination of the optimal network structure is frequently referred to as process-network synthesis (PNS) or flowsheet design.

The significance of PNS is highlighted by numerous publications in the technical literature. The structural properties, especially the redundancy, of the super-structures of the processes of interest have been explored (Farkas et al., 2005). A novel representation, the state-task network, has been introduced originally for scheduling problems (Kondili et al., 1993). This representation includes explicitly both the states (feedstocks, intermediates, and final products) and the tasks (operations) as network nodes. The state-task network and state-equipment network has been applied to aid process synthesis (Yeomans and Grossmann, 1999).

The P-graph framework aims to solve the PNS problem rigorously (Bertok et al., 2013). The P-graphs are bipartite graphs, comprising one class of nodes for materials, and the other, for operating units, as well as arcs linking them. The framework constitutes three cornerstones: the representation of process-networks with P-graphs; the five axioms stating the underlying properties of the combinatorially feasible process-networks; and effective algorithms. These are: the algorithm for the maximum-structure generation, MSG (Friedler et al., 1993); the algorithm for solution-structure generation, SSG; and the algorithm for the optimal-structure determination, ABB (Friedler et al., 1995).

A MILP mathematical model is generated automatically from the structural model. It contains a continuous and a binary variable for each operating unit. The former signifies the capacity of the unit, the latter marks the existence of the same unit. The mathematical model is capable of determining the n-best optimal solution.

The P-graph framework was developed originally for chemical processes. Nevertheless, due to the versatility and flexibility of the P-graph framework, it has been deployed for a wide range of problems involving synthesis, e.g., separation-network synthesis (Heckl et al., 2010), steam supply system (Halasz et al., 2002), emission reduction (Klemeš and Pierucci, 2008), and the usage of renewable energy sources (Lam et al., 2010) among others.

The current work aims at PNS using the P-graph framework involving multi-period operations. It is presumed that steady-state operating conditions are strictly maintained within each period, which nevertheless vary from period to period to accommodate the change in demand and availability of the raw materials. The current work also proposes a modeling technique for representing operating units involved in multi-period operation.

2. Comparison of the single and multi-period operations

Multi-period operation is important on many areas, including economic portfolio selection (Wu et al., 2014), supply network synthesis (Čuček et al., 2013), and district energy systems (Fazlollahi et al., 2013). A motivational example is presented herein to illustrate the notion of multi-period operation in PNS problems. The example involves a single task, the peeling of 30 tons of apples. It is assumed that the weight of peels is negligible.

In single period operation, the feed is unchanging, 2.5 t in each month. In multi-period operation, there are three periods, October - February, March - July, and August - September, with 5, 10, and 15 t/period demands, respectively. Both the single and the multi-period operations produce 30 tons of peeled apples in a year. The cost data of this specific example are compactly expressed algebraically in the following equations;

$$cc = 140 + 20m \qquad [€] \qquad (1)$$

$$acc = 140 / 10 + (20 / 10)m \qquad [€/y] \qquad (2)$$

$$oci = (6 + 3a_i)pl_i, \text{ for all } i \qquad [€/y] \qquad (3)$$

$$a_i \leq m, \text{ for all } i \qquad [t/y] \qquad (4)$$

$$tc = acc + \Sigma oci \qquad [€/y] \qquad (5)$$

where cc, acc, oc_i, pl_i, and tc stand for the capital cost, the annualized capital cost, the operating cost in period i, the period length of period i, and the total cost, respectively. Moreover, a_i and m signify the actual deployed, or simply actual capacity, in period i, and the maximal capacity, respectively.

In the single-period operation the maximal structure contains only the feed, the peeler unit, and the peeled apple. The only question is the value of the capacity, x, of the peeling machine. During the single period the capacity of the apple peeler, is always fully utilized and matches the yearly demand 30 t/y. For the payback period of 10 years, the annualized capital cost, acc, the operating cost, oc_1, and the total cost, tc, are calculated from Eqs. (2), (3), and (5), respectively. The results are summarized in Table 1.

The multi-period operation involves 3 periods of 5, 5, and 2 months. Unlike the single period operation, the maximal capacity of the apple peeler, m, is not necessarily fully deployed in all periods. The actual capacity in each period, a_i, can be calculated by dividing the periodic feed, pf_i, by the length of the corresponding period, pl_i.

$$a_i = pf_i / pl_i \qquad [t/y] \qquad (6)$$

Obviously, m = a_3 = 90 t/y to accommodate the capacity needed in the peak period operation. Naturally, the capital cost, cc, is concomitant only with E, and

Table 1. Pertinent data for the single and multi-period operation.

	Single period	Multi-period		
	Period 1	Period 1	Period 2	Period 3
Period length, pl_i [y]	1	5/12	5/12	2/12
Monthly feed, mf_i [t/month]	2.5	1	2	7.5
Periodic feed, pf_i [t/period]	30	5	10	15
Actual capacity, a_i [t/y]	30	12	24	90
Maximal capacity, m [t/y]	30		90	
Ann. capital cost, acc [€/y]	74		194	
Operating cost, oc_i [€/period]	96	17.5	32.5	46
Total cost, tc [€/y]	170		290	

the operating cost, oc_i, needs to be computed for an individual period on the basis of the actual capacity, a_i.

The multi-period operation is more expensive than the single period one, 170 €/y vs. 290 €/y, because the capital cost of the latter is significantly greater. On the other hand single period operation requires larger storage capacity which would increase its cost.

3. The P-graph model of the multi-period operation

The multi-period operating unit can be modeled with traditional operating units. First, three distinct operating units, O_1, O_2, O_3, are needed to represent the operations in each period. The capacities of these units, x_1, x_2, and x_3, correspond to the actual capacities of the multi-period unit, a_1, a_2, and a_3. Second, an operating unit, E, is needed to represent the equipment, i.e., the physical body of the multi-period unit. Its capacity corresponds to the maximal capacity of the multi-period unit, m. New materials, M_1, M_2, and M_3 and the proposed structure ensures that the capacity of the equipment is the same as the largest of the capacities of the operations, see Figure 1.

Practically, the operations and the physical realization of a multi-period unit have been separated. The operating cost of the multi-period unit is associated with the operations; the capital cost is associated with the equipment.

Algorithm ABB can calculate the capacities and the costs for the suggested structure. The results are in accord with those obtained with the manual calculation as discernible in Table 1, thus indicating that the proposed method is indeed valid.

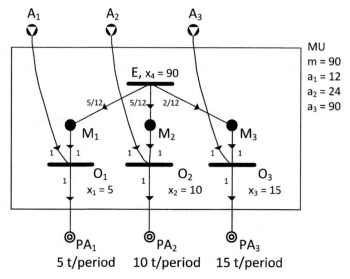

Figure 1. Representation of a multi-period unit, MU.

4. Case study: St. Margarethen

To explore these ideas with a practical case, we consider St. Margarethen, a small town in Burgenland, Austria. The town considers environmental protection seriously, thus, the use of alternative energy sources are carefully weighted (Gwehenberger and Narodoslawsky, 2008). Corn is a typical agricultural product of the area; consequently, the drying of corn and the use of corn cubs are important tasks. The aim is to design a process-network capable fulfilling these tasks, as well as produce heat for greenhouses. The available resources are biogas, forest wood, fast growing wood, heat, and corn. Processing units are present in this area such as biogas units, dryers, and so on. The dryer can be used for both corn and wood drying.

Corn cannot be stored for long because it spoils quickly. As a result, the demands changes within the year, and a design method is needed which can take this into account. The PNS framework with the proposed representation for multi-period operation is such a method.

Three time periods are defined, one for winter, one for summer, and one for the corn harvest (termed as corn period). The lengths of the first two periods are 3,600 h, and the length of the last period is 1,440 h. The P-graph model of the problem is too large to visualize here given the space limitations. The model contains 18 operating units and 21 materials. The biogas production and the drying work in multi-period operation. The details of the model and all results are available from the authors on request. The solution of the problem with algorithm ABB results in objective value of 366,195 €/y. Until now the P-graph framework could not be used in situations where a single unit, e.g., the dryer, could be used for two purposes, e.g., drying either corn or wood but now it can.

5. Conclusions

The concept of multi-period operation of an operating unit in the P-graph framework has been introduced. This is important because often in practice raw materials cannot be stored indefinitely or the majority of the product is required in a certain time period. A modeling technique has been proposed to represent multi-period units. The main idea is to differentiate the operations of a multi-period unit into a sequence of different time periods using the same equipment. The elegance in this modeling technique is that: (1) the multi-period units are represented by traditional operating units, and (2) the period length can be adjusted as needed. The main result of this work is, therefore, the major qualitative progress in the development of P-Graph theory rather than a quantitative improvement in any particular model.

Acknowledgments

We acknowledge the financial support of the Hungarian State and the European Union under the TAMOP-4.2.2.A-11/1/ KONV-2012-0072. This research was realized in the frames of TÁMOP 4.2.4. A/2-11-1-2012-0001 „National Excellence Program – Elaborating and operating an inland student and researcher personal support system" The project was subsidized by the European Union and co-financed by the European Social Fund.

References

R. W. Sargent, 2004, Introduction: 25 years of progress in process systems engineering, Computers and Chemical Engineering, 28, 437-439.

T. Farkas, E. Rev, Z. Lelkes, 2005, Process flowsheet superstructures: Structural multiplicity and redundancy: Part II: Ideal and binarily minimal MINLP representations, Computers and Chemical Engineering, 29, 2198-2214.

E. Kondili, C. C. Pantelides, R. H. Sargent, 1993, A general algorithm for short-term scheduling of batch operations - I. MILP formulation, Computers and Chemical Engineering, 17, 211-27.

H. Yeomans, I. E. Grossmann, 1999, A systematic modeling framework of superstructure optimization in process synthesis, Computers and Chemical Engineering, 23, 709-731.

B. Bertok, M. Barany, F. Friedler, 2013, Generating and Analyzing Mathematical Programming Models of Conceptual Process Design by P-graph, Software, Industrial and Engineering Chemistry Research, 52, 166-171.

F. Friedler, K. Tarjan, Y. W. Huang, L. T. Fan, 1993, Graph-Theoretic Approach to Process Synthesis: Polynomial Algorithm for Maximal Structure Generation, Computers and Chemical Engineering, 17, 929-942.

F. Friedler, J. B. Varga, L. T. Fan, 1995, Decision-Mapping: A Tool for Consistent and Complete Decisions in Process Synthesis, Chemical Engineering Scence, 50, 1755-1768.

I. Heckl, F. Friedler, L. T. Fan, 2010, Solution of separation network synthesis problems by the P-graph methodology, Computers and Chemical Engineering, 34, 700-706.

L. Halasz, A. B. Nagy, T. Ivicz, F. Friedler, L. T. Fan, 2002, Optimal Retrofit Design and Operation of the Steam-Supply System of a Chemical Complex, Applied Thermal Engineering, 22, 939-947.

J. Klemeš, S. Pierucci, 2008, Emission reduction by process intensification, integration, P-Graphs, micro CHP, heat pumps and advanced case studies, Applied Thermal Engineering, 28, 2005-2010.

H. L. Lam, P. Varbanov, J. Klemeš, 2010, Optimisation of regional energy supply chains utilising renewables: P-graph approach, Computers and Chemical Engineering, 34, 782-792.

H. Wu, Y. Zeng, H. Yao, 2014, Multi-period Markowitz's mean–variance portfolio selection with state-dependent exit probability, Economic Modelling, 36, 69-78.

L. Čuček, M. Martín, I. E. Grossmann, Z. Kravanja, 2013, Multi-period Synthesis of a Biorefinery's Supply Networks, Computer Aided Chemical Engineering, 32, 73-78.

S. Fazlollahi, G. Becker, F. Maréchal, 2013, Multi-objectives, multi-period optimization of district energy systems: II—Daily thermal storage, Computers and Chemical Engineering, DOI:10.1016/j.compchemeng.2013.10.016

Jiří Jaromír Klemeš, Petar Sabev Varbanov and Peng Yen Liew (Editors)
Proceedings of the 24th European Symposium on Computer Aided Process Engineering – ESCAPE 24
June 15-18, 2014, Budapest, Hungary. Copyright © 2014 Elsevier B.V. All rights reserved.

Life Cycle Modelling of Alternative Gas-fuelled Power Plants with CO_2 Capture and Storage

Zhenggang Nie, Anna Korre*, Sevket Durucan

Department of Earth Science and Engineering, Royal School of Mines, Imperial College London, London SW7 2BP, United Kingdom
a.korre@imperial.ac.uk

Abstract

This paper presents the Life Cycle Inventory models developed at unit process level for alternative gas-fuelled power plants with/without CO_2 capture and storage. The models for Auto-thermal Reforming power plant with Pressure Swing Adsorption CO_2 capture are demonstrated in detail. The models developed quantify flows of materials, natural resources, energy, intermediate products or emissions at component unit process level, based on fundamental physical/chemical principles or process simulations which, to a greater extent, account for the technological, spatial and temporal characteristics of the power generation systems in consideration.

Keywords: Life cycle assessment, gas power generation, CO_2 capture and storage

1. Introduction

The life cycle greenhouse gas (GHG) emissions of various gas fuelled power generation plant configurations with alternative CO_2 capture, transport, and storage scenarios have been investigated by a number of previous Life Cycle Assessment (LCA) studies (Fadeyi et al., 2013). However, the majority of these studies are based on a low resolution inventory analysis with plant level or gate-to-gate data (Viebahn et al., 2012), specific case studies (Skone et al., 2011) or inventory data based on engineering calculations (Singh et al., 2011).The use of low resolution inventory data implies that the energy production systems have been largely simplified with constants and linear coefficients used to assign inputs and outputs. In addition, the actual variability of process parameters and operating conditions are implicitly neglected. Process simulation method was used to eliminate these limitations by Korre et al. (2012) to evaluate the life cycle impacts of gas power plant systems with alternative CO_2 capture options. Fadeyi et al. (2013) simulated CO_2 chemical absorption processes for LCA of gas plant with post-combustion CO_2 capture. Process simulation method was also successfully used for other LCA applications such as methanol production (Li et al., 2012) and benzene production (Morales-Mendoza et al., 2012). On the other hand, most previous LCA studies focus on Combined Cycle Gas Turbine (CCGT) plants with post-combustion CO_2 capture. Steam Methane Reforming (SMR) plants and Autothermal Reforming (ATR) plants with CO_2 capture are not investigated in detail in the literature.

This paper presents the Life Cycle Inventory (LCI) models developed at unit process level for a CCGT plant, CCGT plant with post-combustion CO_2 capture, SMR with H_2 membrane reactor, and an ATR power plant with Pressure Swing Adsorption (PSA) CO_2 capture. The comprehensive and quantitative LCI database developed models inputs/outputs of processes at high level of detail, allowing to account for technical and geographic differences in the power generation value chain analysed.

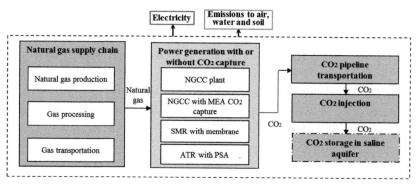

Figure 1. Generalised outline of the power generation with CCS LCA system and boundaries.

2. System boundaries

The system boundaries of LCA on gas fuelled power generation with Carbon Capture and storage (CCS) are presented in Figure 1. The LCI models developed for the subsystems include natural gas fuel supply chains, different natural gas based power generation with/without alternative CO_2 capture options, CO_2 transportation and CO_2 storage. This paper focuses on the power generation with/without CO_2 capture only. The LCA models of natural gas supply chain (Nie et al., 2013), CO_2 pipeline transportation and CO_2 storage in saline aquifers (Nie et al., 2011) developed by the authors are used to support the full value chain analysis presented. The functional unit was selected as 1 MWh of electricity generated.

3. Life cycle inventory modelling: level of detail, modelling approach and an example

The LCI analysis and modelling involves the data collection and implementation of calculation procedures to quantify relevant inputs and outputs of the product systems. Alternative types of approaches to conduct a life cycle inventory analysis (or modelling) are summarised and compared in Table 1.

The subsystems shown in Figure 1 were further broken down or modularised at component unit processes connected by flows of intermediate products or emissions. Engineering calculations or process simulation methods are used for the majority of processes including the ATR unit, SMR unit with hydrogen membrane reactor, the water gas shift reaction unit, etc. In the following paragraphs, an LCI model developed for the ATR unit is described as an example to demonstrate the capacity and strengths of the LCI models developed.

Table 1. Different approaches to life cycle inventory analysis (Modified from Shires et al., 2009).

Approach	Hierarchy
Published emission factors	
Equipment manufacturer emission factors	Improved accuracy
Engineering calculations	Additional data requirements
Process simulation or other computer modelling	
Emissions monitoring over a range of conditions	Higher cost
Periodic or continuous monitoring of emissions	

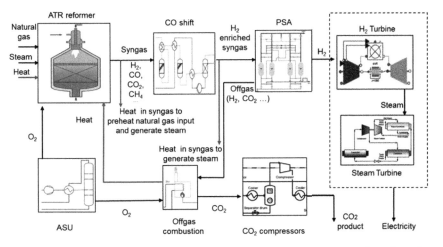

Figure 2. The configuration of the auto-thermal reforming plant with pressure swing adsorption CO₂ capture power plant.

In the auto-thermal reforming plant with pressure swing adsorption CO_2 capture (Figure 2), natural gas, steam and oxygen are consumed. The chemical reactions of natural gas in the ATR are a combination of partial combustion and steam reforming and water-gas shift reactions. The partial combustion of natural gas provides the heat for the steam reforming reactions; therefore, no or only a small amount of heat is required. The syngas generated from the reformer is transferred to the CO shift unit, where CO reacts with H_2O to generate more H_2. The syngas with mainly H_2 and CO_2 enters the PSA unit, where CO_2 is separated from H_2. The H_2 from PSA is used for power generation in a hydrogen turbine and steam turbine combined cycle power plant. PSA also releases offgas with CO_2 (85-90 %) and H_2 (10-15 %). Following the offgas H_2 combustion with pure oxygen, the offgas (which is mainly CO_2) is sent to the CO_2 compression unit. The heat generated by offgas combustion is used by the ATR unit. The high temperature syngas from the ATR is used to preheat input natural gas and generate steam.

The LCI model developed for ATR reformer unit is based on chemical equilibrium, mass and energy balances, considering process conditions, such as temperature and pressure. The chemical reactions and operational parameters considered by the model are demonstrated in Figure 3. Given the operational parameters, the inputs and outputs of the ATR LCI model are presented in Figure 4. The sensitivity analysis of outputs against different operational temperatures as an example is demonstrated in Figure 5 (a). As the model is based on chemical equilibrium, the ATR LCI model outputs are non-linear, which eliminates the limitations introduced by the linear input/output coefficients used by conventional LCI models. The other advantage of modelling power plant at component unit process level is that the emissions and outputs can be traced back to component unit processes, as demonstrated in Figure 5 (b).

4. Results and analysis

The performances of alternative gas fuelled power generation with or without CO_2 capture are compared in Figure 6. Compared to SMR membrane plant and CCGT with MEA CO_2 capture, the ATR with CO_2 PSA capture has the lowest plant efficiency and the highest GHG emissions per MW generated. This is due to the configuration of ATR plant, which requires O_2 from an air separation unit which consumes energy. Furthermore, a considerable amount of H_2 in the offgas exits from the PSA unit. The H_2 in the offgas is combusted, rather than being converted to electricity, which also reduces the whole plant energy efficiency. Compared to a conventional CCGT plant, the energy penalties for CO_2 capture in SMR with H_2 membrane plant, CCGT with MEA CO_2 capture plant and ATR with CO_2 PSA capture plant are 4.59 %, 6.14 % and 9.45 %. Figure 7 demonstrates the case of a Caribbean Sea gas production and LNG transportation to Japan with alternative power generation configurations. Figure 7 (a) shows that the majority life cycle GHG emissions are from the gas processing plant, the LNG plant, LNG shipping and the power plant. Other processes or activities account for insignificant GHG emissions in the life-cycle perspective. These results are in line with literature results (Skone et al., 2011). Figure 7 (b) illustrates that, in this case, the natural gas power plants with CO_2 capture and storage can reduce life cycle GHG emissions by 80 - 87 %, which is in good agreement literature results (Fadeyi et al., 2013) and at slightly higher level as a higher CO_2 capture rate (95 %) is applied here.

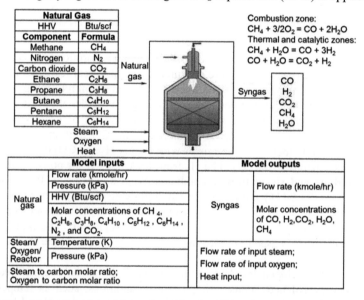

Figure 3. Life cycle inventory model developed for the ATR unit.

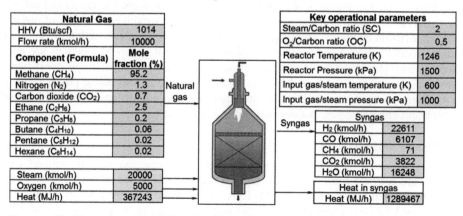

Figure 4. The illustration of the ATR unit LCI model results.

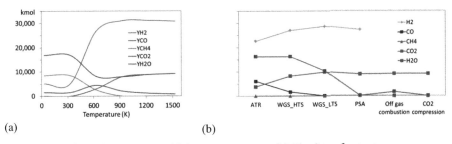

(a) (b)

Figure 5. (a) The ATR outputs sensitivity to temperature; (b) The fate of outputs across power plant component units.

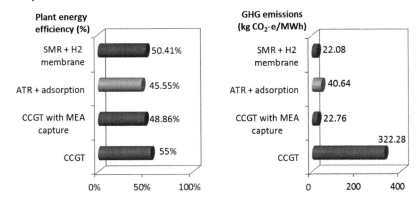

Figure 6. Performance comparison of alternative power generation configurations.

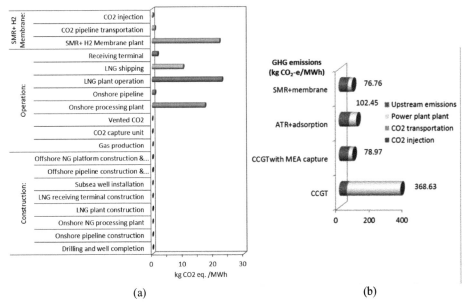

(a) (b)

Figure 7. The case of a Caribbean Sea natural gas production and LNG transportation to Japan MSR with alternative power generation configurations: (a) Life-cycle GHG emissions break-down for SMR with H₂ membrane plant; (b) Comparison of life cycle GHG emissions of alternative power generation configurations.

5. Conclusions

The LCI models developed quantify flows of materials, natural resources, energy, intermediate products or emissions at component unit process level, based on fundamental physical/chemical principles or process simulations which, to a greater extent, account for the technological, spatial and temporal characteristics of the power generation systems in consideration. This approach not only addresses the limitations of conventional LCI models that use linear input/output coefficients, but also facilitates the screening of technological options in order to improve the life cycle environmental performance of a power generation system with CCS. The models referred to in the literature address LCA needs of the existing power generation plants, however, they do not offer solutions for novel systems that are not commercially operated. The LCI methodology developed in this research provides an innovative and robust approach for conducting LCA for novel systems by configuring virtual systems at unit process level. The results of the case study conclude that gas-fired power generation with alternative CO_2 capture systems can reduce life-cycle GHG emissions by 80 - 87 %. For gas powered plant with alternative CO_2 capture routes, the majority life cycle GHG emissions are from the gas supply chain.

References

S. Fadeyi, H.A. Arafat, M.R.M. Abu-Zahra, 2013, Life cycle assessment of natural gas combined cycle integrated with CO2 post combustion capture using chemical solvent, International Journal of Greenhouse Gas Control, 19, 441–452

A. Korre, Z. Nie, S. Durucan, 2012, Life cycle assessment of the natural gas supply chain and power generation options with CO2 capture and storage: Assessment of Qatar natural gas production, LNG transport and power generation in the UK, Sustainable Technologies, Systems and Policies 2012, CCS Workshop:11, DOI:10.5339/stsp.2012.ccs.11.

H. Li, S. Yang, Y. Qian, 2012, Life cycle assessment of coal-based methanol, Computer Aided Chemical Engineering, 31, 530-534.

L.F. Morales-Mendoza , C. Azzaro-Pantel, J.-P. Belaud , L. Pibouleau, S. Domenech, 2012, An integrated approach combining process simulation and life cycle assessment for eco-efficient process design, Computer Aided Chemical Engineering, 30, 142-146.

Z. Nie, A. Korre, S. Durucan, 2011, Life cycle modelling and comparative assessment of the environmental impacts of oxy-fuel and post-combustion CO2 capture, transport and injection processes, Energy Procedia, 4, 2510–2517.

Z. Nie, A. Korre, S. Durucan, 2013, Full chain analysis and comparison of gas-fired power plants with CO2 capture and storage with clean coal alternatives, Energy Procedia, 37, 2840–2847.

T.M. Shires, C.J. Loughran, S. Jones, E. Hopkins, 2009, Compendium of greenhouse gas emissions methodologies for the oil and gas industry, American Petroleum Institute, Z00109, Washington, USA.

B. Singh, A.H. Strømman, E. Hertwich, 2011, Life cycle assessment of natural gas combined cycle power plant with post-combustion carbon capture, transport and storage, International Journal of Greenhouse Gas Control, 5, 3, 457-466.

T.J. Skone, J. Littlefield, J. Marriott, 2011, Life cycle greenhouse gas inventory of natural gas extraction, delivery and electricity production, National Energy Technology Laboratory, DOE/NETL-2011/1522, Pittsburgh, Pennsylvania, USA.

P. Viebahn, V. Daniel, H. Samuel, 2012, Integrated assessment of carbon capture and storage (CCS) in the German power sector and comparison with the deployment of renewable energies, Applied Energy, 97, 238–248.

Jiří Jaromír Klemeš, Petar Sabev Varbanov and Peng Yen Liew (Editors)
Proceedings of the 24th European Symposium on Computer Aided Process Engineering – ESCAPE 24
June 15-18, 2014, Budapest, Hungary.

Investigation on Life-cycle Cost of Coal-based Synthetic Natural Gas (SNG)

Jun Zhang, Hengchong Li, Siyu Yang*, Xiuxi Li, Yu Qian

School of Chemical Engineering, State Key Lab of Pulp and Paper Engineering
South China University of Technology, Guangzhou, 510640, P.R. China
cesyyang@scut.edu.cn

Abstract

Coal-based synthetic natural gas (SNG) is considered to be a promising alternative of clean energy, especially for urban uses, to response to the insufficient supply of natural gas in China, In this paper, life cycle costing is conducted for SNG in three main urban applications: heating boiler use, residential use, and transit bus use, respectively. The results show that the SNG is competitive for residential use, while it is not as cost-effective as expected when used for heating boiler use or transit bus use. Major shortcoming of SNG is from the large environmental emissions in the production stage.

Keywords: synthetic natural gas (SNG); life cycle costing; environmental emission.

1. Introduction

Accompanied by the booming of China's economy, the total energy consumption in China reached up to 3.62 billion tonnes of standard coal equivalent (tce) in 2012 (National Bureau of Statistics of China (NBSC), 2013). Coal is the dominant energy resource, supplying 67.4 % of the national energy demand (NBSC, 2013). Because of this coal-dominant structure, serious air pollution becomes one of the biggest threats to residents' health. To relieve the pollution problem, the Chinese government calls for the movement of shifting from coal to cleaner energy resources such as natural gas, solar energy, wind energy, hydro energy, etc. Natural gas is the most promising cleaner energy alternatives for coal. Its production increases by 6.7 % year on year, to 107.2 billion m^3 in 2012 China (NBSC, 2013), however, current natural gas production volume still could not feed the big appetite. Spurred by the huge demand, China has signed many long-term LNG sales and purchase agreements (SPAs) and pipeline gas import contracts with Kazakhstan, Turkmenistan, Burma, Indonesia, Malaysia, Iran, Australia and Russia (Wang et al., 2013).

Besides domestic and imported natural gas, another important way for increasing the natural gas supply is to convert coal to natural gas. In China, Inner Mongolia and Xinjiang areas are rich in coal, while far away from the eastern coastal areas, major natural gas consuming areas. In situ coal conversion to SNG also makes the energy transportation easily since the SNG could be transported and distributed by the existing or newly built pipeline systems. In recent years, the coal-based SNG plants are quickly sprouted in these areas. As of October 2013, the Chinese government has approved ten large SNG projects with a total capacity of 67.1 billion m^3/y (Yang and Jackson, 2013; Xinhua News, 2013). Besides, there are about 54 SNG projects in planning with a total capacity of 163.8 billion m^3/y of SNG (ICIS, 2013).

However, there have been quite a few controversial opinions whether large-scale development of SNG is really cost-effective and to what applications this SNG should be better applied. With regards to the use stage, SNG is commonly considered as much cleaner than coal. However, with the current coal-based SNG technology, there is a great risk in large-scale investment (Huo et al., 2013). Ding et al. (2013) argued that the coal-based SNG will not accomplish the tasks of both energy conservation and CO_2 reduction from the life cycle perspective. Yang and Jackson (2013) argued that the CO_2 emissions, water needs, and wider environment impacts associated coal-based SNG are mostly neglected, which could mislead China into an unsustainable development path.

In this paper, we aim to investigate the economic performances of the coal-based SNG applied in urban gas sector which is very likely to be extended by the government. Life cycle costing method is employed. Environmental emissions from each life cycle stage of the SNG are estimated by the external cost. According to the results from this work, appropriate suggestions are proposed to policymakers on application of the SNG.

2. Life cycle modeling of SNG in urban gas sector

There are three major end-use applications in the urban gas sector: residential and commercial use, transit bus use, and heating boiler use. To conduct life cycle costing of the coal-based SNG, the life cycle boundaries of the fuels in each application is determined, and then the model for the life cycle costing is developed. Data used in the current work were collected through literature search, field survey, interviews, and private communication.

2.1. Life cycle boundaries of the SNG and conventional fuels

The purpose of developing the coal-based SNG in China is to complement the shortage of NG. The first task in this paper is to compare the life cycle cost for SNG and NG. For each of the three applications, there are conventional fuels and other alternatives. The life cycle boundary for each fuel is different to those of others. These boundaries as well as the function units for the applications are described as follows. The SNG is compared to coal and NG in heating boiler use, to LPG in residential use, and to diesel and coal-based methanol in transit bus use. Their life cycle boundaries and corresponding function units are shown in Figure 1.

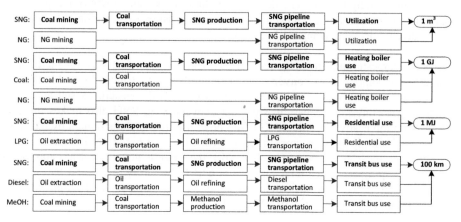

Figure 1. Life cycle boundaries of the SNG and it alternatives for different applications

2.2. Life cycle costing modeling

Life cycle costing methodology is for cost accounting of a product over its lifetime. Life cycle cost (C_{LC}) consists of internal cost (C_{In}) and external cost (C_{Ex}). C_{In} is the conventional cost related to manufacturing, labor, overheads, etc. CEx is the potential cost for environmental, health, and societal impacts (Fthenakis and Alsema, 2006).

CIn in each life cycle stage could be formulated as Eq. (1), where i represents life cycle stages, Cf the cost of raw materials, C_{lb} labor cost, I_a annual fixed asset investment, S_b sales income of by-products, and C_O other cost.

$$C_{In,i} = \sum C_{f,i} + C_{lb,i} + I_{a,i} + C_{O,i} - \sum S_{b,i} \tag{1}$$

C_{Ex} is the marginal damage costs based on willingness to pay to avoid the damage caused by environmental emissions (Fahlén and Ahlgren, 2010). In fossil fuel based processes, it is associated with the potential costs for emissions, including CO2, CO, CH4, VOC, SO2, NOX, PM, etc. Reported by different researchers and institutes, there are diverse values of C_{Ex} of a certain kind of emission depending on the environmental carrying capacity of each region (CAFE, 2008; NEEDS, 2009). In this paper, we will not include the variation of C_{Ex}. We simply fix the unit C_{Ex} of a kind of emission according to Pa's work (Pa et al., 2013), which gave the comprehensive C_{Ex} of the emissions as shown in Table 1. C_{Ex} could be calculated by using Eq. (2), where j represents environmental emission, E_j the unit C_{Ex} for j, and e_j the emission quantity of j.

$$C_{Ex} = \sum_i C_{Ex,i} = \sum_i \sum_j E_{j,i} e_{j,i} \tag{2}$$

3. Results and discussion

3.1. Compared to natural gas

The selling price of NG is subject to government pricing in China. Taking the NG used for heating boiler use for example, its selling price is 0.44 $/m3 (Beijing Municipal Commission of Development & Reform, 2013). The C_{LC} comparison between the SNG and NG is made and shown in Figure 2. From the life cycle point of view, the SNG is not as cost-effective as NG. The high C_{Ex} of the SNG is a shortcoming. Essentially, using coal to produce SNG is to transfer the environmental emissions from urban areas to rural areas near to the coal mines. However, the rural areas like Xinjiang and Inner Mongolia suffer from fragile environment due to the arid nature of temperate continental climate. This transfer will lead to costly damaging outcome sooner or later if the Chinese government persists in expanding the SNG industry in the current pace.

3.2. Compared to coal and NG in heating boiler use

The C_{LC} comparison among of SNG, coal, and NG in heating boiler use for generating 1 GJ heat is conducted and shown in Figure 3. The SNG features higher C_{LC} than that of coal. Using the SNG is not cost-effective compared to using coal for boilers. When NG is used for heating boilers, although its C_{In} is much higher than that of coal and SNG, its C_{Ex} is much lower than that of the other two fuels. From the life cycle perspective, NG is the most cost-effective fuel for heating boiler use.

Table 1. Unit C_{Ex} for environmental emissions (Pa et al., 2013).

Emissions	CO_2	CO	CH_4	VOC	SO_2	NO_X	PM
E_j ($/kg)	0.032	0.68	0.24	3.58	4.01	5.23	11.84

Boiler fuel is dominated by coal for long, especially in most northern cities of China. NG is regarded as one alternative fuel for coal. Because of the much higher price of NG than that of coal, huge energy costs would be spent every year for heating generation. In terms of C_{In}, using SNG seems to be cheaper than NG. However, the SNG does not show economically as we expected through the above analysis. The SNG is favored by policymakers because of its less environmental emissions in use stage. This advantage could relieve the environmental burden of urban areas. However, potential C_{Ex} of the emissions transfer is usually neglected by policymakers. Thus, we have to consider the source for producing NG. If it is derived from coal, the environmental cost for using it is even more than using coal directly. Thus, NG should be the preferred alternative for boilers. It reduces both emissions and the C_{LC} spent from root cause.

3.3. Compared to LPG in residential use

The C_{LC} comparison between the SNG and LPG for generating 1 MJ effective heat is shown in Figure 4. The C_{LC} of the SNG is lower than that for LPG. Using the SNG is better than using LPG in residential use. Most LPG is derived from oil, so the C_{In} of LPG is highly dependent on oil price. The high dependence on imported oil of China leads to high oil price and high C_{In} of LPG. In order to explore the chemical potential of LPG for more profits, the Chinese government encourages the development of LPG-based chemical processes. Thus, replacing LPG gradually by SNG should be encouraged because this could procure dual advantages on saving C_{LC} and reserving LPG for chemical conversion.

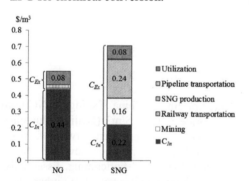

Figure 2. C_{LC} comparison of the SNG and NG

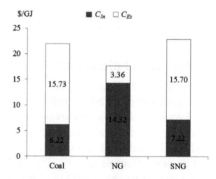

Figure 3. C_{LC} comparison of the SNG, coal and NG in heating boiler use

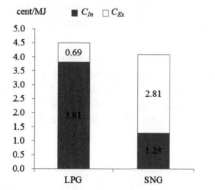

Figure 4. C_{LC} comparison of the SNG and LPG in residential use

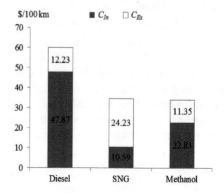

Figure 5. C_{LC} comparison of the SNG, diesel, and methanol in transit bus use

3.4. Compared to diesel and methanol in transit bus use

In this application, we compare the C_{LC} for the SNG, diesel, and methanol on the basis of the transit buses running 100 km (Figure 5). The C_{In} of the SNG is 10.59 \$, less than a quarter of that for diesel. However, the C_{Ex} of the SNG is \$24.23, nearly twice of that for diesel. The C_{Ex} of the SNG and diesel in the use stages are 4.75 \$ and 8.56 \$. SNG is much cleaner than diesel. By life cycle costing, it is concluded that the C_{LC} of the SNG is much less than that for diesel. Compared to the C_{In} of the SNG, the C_{In} of coal-based methanol is 12.24 \$ higher. In contrast, the C_{Ex} of the methanol is 12.88 \$ lower than that for the SNG. In consequence, the C_{LC} of the coal-based methanol and the SNG are roughly the same, with the former slightly lower than the latter.

Vehicle exhaust is a major source of air pollution in China. The government is increasingly aware of the importance of vehicle emissions reduction. Transit buses are placed on the very top of the list, according to the "bus priority" policy (Guang, 2013). NG (including SNG) and methanol are alternatives for diesel because of their hydrogen-rich composition. On the other hand, the production capacity for methanol is 51.5 Mt much more than the actual production 31.3 Mt in 2012 (China Nitrogen Fertilizer Industry Association, 2013). This is a long-standing problem for China's methanol industry. Consuming methanol for transit bus use could to some extent relieve the problem of its overcapacity and decrease the environmental cost. For conclusion, we suggest that methanol transit buses should be encouraged in China rather than SNG transit buses.

4. Conclusions

To avoid the unexpected cost and environmental impact aroused from inappropriate applications of the SNG, life cycle costing has been conducted in assessing the three applications of the SNG in urban gas sector. The results brought several conclusions:

(1) When SNG is used for heating boiler, the C_{In} of the SNG and coal are 7.22 \$/GJ and 6.22 \$/GJ, while the C_{Ex} of them are roughly the same, which is about 15.70 \$/GJ. The SNG is not as cost-effective as coal. NG has a higher priority than the synthetic NG.
(2) The C_{LC} of SNG and LPG are 4.50 \$/GJ and 4.09 \$/GJ. Therefore, SNG has a better economic performance than LPG for residential use. Replacing LPG gradually by the SNG should be encouraged because this could bring dual advantages on saving C_{LC} and reserving LPG for chemical conversion.
(3) SNG is better than diesel in transit bus use, but it is worse than methanol. The cost of methanol, SNG and diesel are 34.18 \$/GJ, 34.82 \$/GJ, and 60.10 \$/GJ , respectively. Developing methanol for transit bus use could cut more environmental impacts and meanwhile make use of the spare production capacity of methanol in China.

To conclude, SNG is not so lucrative in most applications compared to other alternatives from the life cycle costing perspective. The main consequence of developing the SNG is to transfer the environmental emissions from urban areas to rural areas near to the coal mines. If the development of SNG is without restriction, the transfer of pollution emissions will lead to costly damages sooner or later. At present, there is not any policy relevant to environmental penalty policy in China. However, from the view of sustainable development, levying external cost is a reasonable way to penalize the transfer of environmental emissions. The Chinese government could make multiple gas price mechanism so that the end-users of the SNG could compensate the environmental losses in the SNG-producing regions. Only then could the SNG industry in China be developed healthily and sustainably.

Acknowledgements

We would like to express our appreciations to financial supports from the Natural Science Foundation of China (No. 21306056, 21176089, 21376091), the National Science & Technology Support Plan (2012BAK13B02), Guangdong Natural Science Foundation Team Project (S2011030001366), and the Fundamental Research Funds for the Central Universities (No. 2013ZP0010).

References

Beijing Municipal Commission of Development & Reform, 2013, Prices of natural gas and LPG, < www.bjpc.gov.cn/ywpd/wjgl/cx/jz/201208/t3884350.htm>, accessed on 24/10/2013.

CAFE, 2008, Clean Air for Europe, <www.cafe-cba.org> accessed on 02/07/2013.

China Nitrogen Fertilizer Industry Association, 2013, Methanol Industry Statistics of 2012, China Nitrogen Fertilizer Industry Association, Beijing, China.

Y. Ding, W. Han, Q. Chai, S. Yang, W. Shen, 2013, Coal-based synthetic natural gas (SNG): A solution to China's energy security and CO_2 reduction?, Energy Policy, 55, 445-453.

E. Fahlén, E.O. Ahlgren, 2010, Accounting for external costs in a study of a Swedish district-heating system – An assessment of environmental policies, Energy Policy, 38, 4909-4920.

V. Fthenakis, E. Alsema, 2006, Photovoltaics energy payback times, greenhouse gas emissions and external costs: 2004–early 2005 status, Progress in Photovoltaics: Research and Applications, 14, 275-280.

H. Guang, 2013, The selection of clean fuel transit buses in cities, Gas Technology, 6, 4-7.

J. Huo, D. Yang, F. Xia, H. Tang, W. Zhang, 2013, Feasibility analysis and policy recommendations for the development of the coal based SNG industry in Xinjiang, Energy Policy, 61, 3-11.

ICIS, 2013, The development of coal-bsed SNG may be faster in China, <www.icis-china.com/detail/4806734.html>, accessed on 05/08/2013 (in Chinese).

NBSC, 2013, Statistical Bulletin of National Economy and Social Development of China in 2012. Beijing (in Chinese).

NEEDS, 2009, New Energy Externalities Development for Sustainability, <www.needs-project.org>, accessed on 02/07/2013.

A. Pa, X.T. Bi, S. Sokhansanj, 2013, Evaluation of wood pellet application for residential heating in British Columbia based on a streamlined life cycle analysis, Biomass and Bioenergy, 49, 109-122.

J. Wang, L. Feng, L. Zhao, S. Snowden, 2013, China's natural gas: Resources, production and its impacts. Energy Policy, 55, 690-698.

Xinhua News, 2013. The biggest coal-based SNG project of China will be esthaleshed in Zhundong, Xinjiang, <news.xinhuanet.com/energy/2013-10/08/c_125494523.htm>, accessed on 21/10/2013 (in Chinese).

C. Yang, R.B. Jackson, 2013, China's synthetic natural gas revolution, Nature Climate Change, 3, 852-854.

W. Zhou, 2011, The Application of Uncertainty Analysis Method into Assessing Indirect Coal-to-Liquids (ICL), Ph.D. Dissertation, Tsinghua University, Beijing (in Chinese).